SPEECH AND HEARING SCIENCE

PRENTICE-HALL INTERNATIONAL, INC., London
PRENTICE-HALL OF AUSTRALIA, PTY. LTD., Sydney
PRENTICE-HALL OF CANADA, LTD., Toronto
PRENTICE-HALL OF INDIA PRIVATE LTD., New Delhi
PRENTICE-HALL OF JAPAN, INC., Tokyo

SPEECH AND HEARING SCIENCE
Anatomy and Physiology

WILLARD R. ZEMLIN
Professor of Speech
University of Illinois

PRENTICE-HALL, INC., Englewood Cliffs, New Jersey

TO

MARNA AND WILLIAM WAYNE FLETCHER

Preface

No doubt one of the most distinctive features of human behavior is speech and language, and indeed the processes of communication, regardless of medium, deserve careful study. Some communication is direct—from talker to listener—while some takes place by means of an interposed transmission system (telephone microphone, transmission line, and receiver, for example). Regardless of their complexity, however, most communication systems are initially dependent upon a speech generating mechanism, and ultimately dependent upon a hearing mechanism. In other words, communication can almost always be resolved into talkers and listeners. The purpose of this book is to describe the normal anatomical structures involved, and the consequences of their actions, during the production and reception of speech sounds. A second purpose is to provide a basic working knowledge with which the student might assess the clinical implications of structural and/or functional deviations of the speech and hearing mechanisms.

Although a great deal of time has been devoted to the preparation of the manuscript and illustrations for this book, it is by no means complete. A comprehensive description of the speech and hearing mechanisms, and the way in which they function, might easily require several volumes, provided, of course, all the data were in. Hopefully, this book will stimulate students of speech and hearing to pursue their unanswered questions, to fill in gaps of information where they exist, and to integrate disjointed data. We have a way to go. This textbook, if successful, will serve as a starting point.

A book such as this one, which crosses so many areas of academic and professional interests, could not have been written without help. The author wishes to acknowledge: Professor William Castle, for his critical review of the original manuscript; Mrs. Maria Ikenberg, of the Eye and Ear Infirmary, Chicago, for her valuable criticism and contributions in the preparation of illustrative materials; Dr. Francis Lederer, Head of the Department of Otolaryngology, University of Illinois College of Medicine, Chicago, for his encouragement and contributions of illustrative materials; Dr. Samuel Prusansky and Professor Robert Mason, of the Cleft Palate Clinic, University of Illinois, Chicago, for their criticism and valuable contributions of illustrative materials; Mr. Mel Allen, also of the Cleft Palate Clinic, for his generous help in preparing illustration materials; Professor John J. O'Neill, Chairman, Speech and Hearing Science, and Director, Speech and Hearing Clinic,

University of Illinois, for his criticism of the original and revised manuscripts; Mrs. Helene Levin, for her generous contributions of histological specimens; Professor A. J. Derbyshire, Director of Research, Eye and Ear Infirmary, Chicago, for his review of manuscript material; Professor Stan Stolpe, Department of Anatomy and Biophysics, University of Illinois, for his cooperation and very generous contributions of specimen materials.

A very special thanks to Professor Elaine Paden, of the Department of Speech and Theatre, University of Illinois, for her untiring efforts and valuable contributions in her editing of the entire revised manuscript.

The author wishes to acknowledge the patient understanding and tolerance of his wife during the preparation of the book, her critical review of manuscript, and her preparation of glossary material. The author also wishes to acknowledge his children, Therese and Karl, who relinquished a father while the book was being written.

W. R. Zemlin

Contents

SPEECH AND HEARING SCIENCE

1

Introduction and Orientation

INTRODUCTION

Definition of Anatomy
Definition of Physiology
Basel Nomenclature System
Anatomical Position
Planes of Reference and Some General Terms
Cells and Tissues

ELEMENTARY TISSUES

Epithelial Tissues

Epithelial tissue proper
Endothelial tissue
Mesothelial tissue

Connective Tissues

Areolar tissue
Adipose tissue
Dense fibrous tissue

Tendon
Aponeurosis
Ligament
Fascia

Reticular tissue
Cartilage

Hyaline
Elastic
Fibrous

Bone

    Compact
    Spongy

    Classification of Joints
        Synarthrodial
        Amphiarthrodial
        Diarthrodial

Muscle Tissues

Striated
Smooth
Cardiac
Muscle architecture
Muscle action

Nervous Tissue

The motor unit

Vascular Tissue (Blood and Lymph)

ORGANS

SYSTEMS

THE SPEECH MECHANISM

SELECTIVE READING LIST

INTRODUCTION

At the present time, man occupies the space at the top of the phylogenetic ladder. He is of the

PHYLUM — Chordata
SUBPHYLUM — Vertebrata
CLASS — Mammalia
ORDER — Primate
SUBORDER — Anthropoid
FAMILY — Hominidae
GENUS — Homo
SPECIES — Sapiens

A dictionary definition of man is: An individual of the highest type of animal existing or known to have existed, different from other high types of animals, especially in his extraordinary mental development. Man alone has the power of articulate speech, and largely by virtue of this power, the ability to reason. We might paraphrase this definition by saying: "Man is the only animal so highly developed he is able to tell himself he is superior to all other animals."

In the pages to follow, the speech and hearing mechanisms unique to man will be presented for study in an attempt to account for speech and hearing on anatomical, physiological, and neurological bases. The purpose of this chapter is to define anatomy and physiology and to familiarize the reader with some appropriate terminology used in anatomical and physiological descriptions.

Two of the primary tasks for the student of anatomy and physiology are to acquire the proper vocabulary and, having once acquired the vocabulary, to use it appropriately. Anatomy and physiology are very old sciences, and the language often stems from Latin or Greek roots. The student will be greatly aided in his learning if he will turn to the glossary at the back of this book or to a dictionary for the meaning of each new word he encounters. A valuable hint to the student in using the glossary is that anatomy is a descriptive science in which many of the names given to the structures are descriptive terms relating to the shape or function of the structure. Some structures in the body bear the name of the person who discovered or extensively studied them, while others (primarily muscles and ligaments) are named for their points of attachment. In the names of muscles, the origin (or the more immobile point of attachment) is given first, and the insertion (the more mobile point of attachment) is given second.

In a few instances, however, it is not known with certainty which is the more mobile point, and the terms may be used interchangeably. For example, the thyrohyoid muscle may be called the hyothyroid muscle.

Examples of descriptive names are those for the familiar ossicles in the middle ear, the malleus (hammer), incus (anvil), and stapes (stirrup); an example of a structure named after its discoverer is Poupart's ligament, also called the inguinal ligament.

Definition of Anatomy

Anatomy is the study of the structure of organisms and the relations of their parts. The field of anatomy has grown, and consequently a number of subdivisions has come to be recognized. The names of the subdivisions imply a specialized interest within the field of anatomy. The subdivisions are:

1. Descriptive, or systematic (systemic), anatomy, in which the body is considered as being composed of a number of systems. Each system is composed of rather homogenous tissues which exhibit some peculiar functional unity. The systems in the body will be considered in greater detail toward the end of the chapter.

2. Regional, or topographical, anatomy, which deals primarily with the structural relationships of the various parts of the body. Thus, we have head and neck anatomy, anatomy of the extremities, and so forth.

3. Applied, or practical, anatomy, which is concerned with the application of anatomy to a specialized field, such as surgery or anthropology.

4. Microscopic anatomy, which is concerned with the details of structure as revealed through the microscope.

5. Developmental anatomy which specializes in the growth of the organism, from the single cell to birth.

6. Comparative anatomy, which deals with the structure and the comparative structure of all living organisms.

Definition of Physiology

Physiology may be defined as a science dealing with the functions of living organisms or their parts, as distinguished from morphology, which is concerned with their form or structure. Some subdivisions of physiology are:

1. Animal physiology, which deals with the functions of the living animal as a whole.

2. Applied physiology, in which physiologic knowledge is applied to problems in medicine, industry, etc.

3. Cellular physiology, in which the physiology of individual cells or small groups of cells are studied.

4. Experimental physiology, in which experiments are carried on in a laboratory environment with experimental animals or human subjects.

5. Pathologic physiology, which is the study of functions that have been modified by disease.

Basel Nomenclature System

Anatomy, like many other sciences, has its own language. In order to identify all the structures in the body. something in excess of five thousand terms are required. In 1895, a series of international meetings of anatomists was begun in Basel, Switzerland. The purpose of these meetings was to adopt a system of anatomical terminology. The terminology adopted is called the BNA system (Basle Nomina Anatomica). The BNA gives all the terms in Latin, which in 1895 was almost a universal language. In 1935 the Germans revised the BNA to form the JNA (Jena Nomina Anatomica). The British also revised the BNA, and their revision is known as the BR (British Revision). In spite of the revisions of the BNA, rather good agreement still exists in the nomenclature employed by the various countries. A liberal Anglicized version of the BNA will be used in the text, and wherever possible, descriptive terms will be defined in the glossary. The terms used in this text refer most often to the human body in the anatomical position.

Anatomical Position

Conventionally, all descriptive accounts in anatomy are made with reference to what is known as the anatomical position. This is the position shown in Figure 1–1 of the living body standing erect, facing the observer, with arms at the sides and palms forward. (Anatomy is a study of the living body, and not of the dead.) Confusion

Fig. 1–1. The anatomical position.

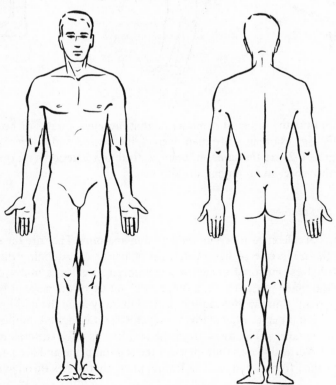

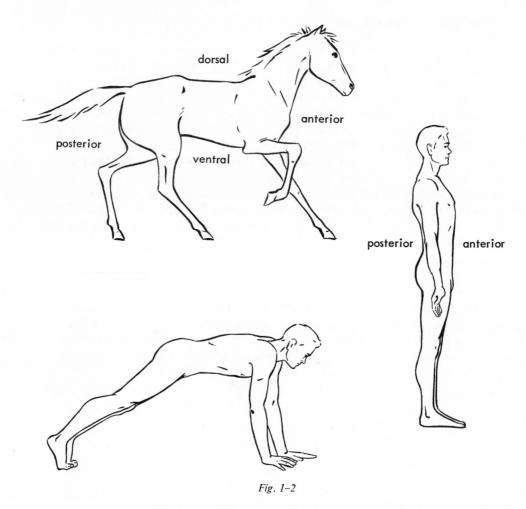

Fig. 1–2

arises at times over the usage of some terms that are appropriate for both man and lower animals. For example, since man is erect, the ventral and anterior surfaces, as shown in Figure 1–2, are the same, whereas ventral and anterior have quite different meanings with respect to an animal on all fours.

Planes of Reference

Three planes of reference are commonly used in anatomy. They are the sagittal, the frontal, and the transverse planes. A vertical plane, or cut, dividing the body into right and left halves (mirrored images in the embryo) is called a mid-sagittal plane. The mid-sagittal plane passes through the sagittal suture of the parietal bones of the skull. A plane parallel to the mid-sagittal plane, but away from the mid-line is usually called a para-sagittal plane. Frequently, however, the term sagittal implies a mid-line plane, and any parallel plane, away from the mid-line, is referred to as para-sagittal or longitudinal. Vertical planes that intersect the sagittal plane and are parallel to the forehead are called frontal planes. The frontal plane that passes through the coronal

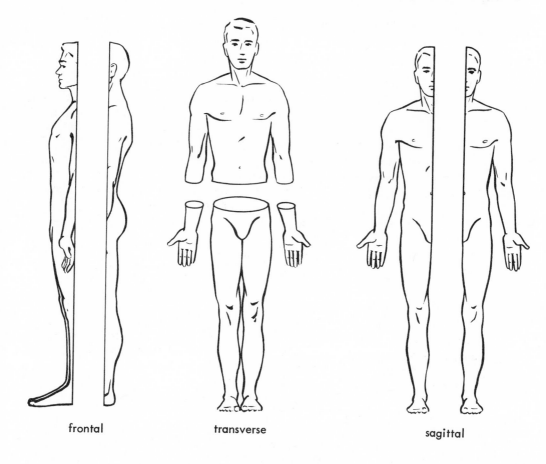

frontal   transverse   sagittal

Fig. 1–3. Planes of reference.

suture of the skull is called the coronal plane. A plane which divides the body into upper and lower parts, at any level, is called a transverse plane. These planes are shown in Figure 1–3.

Some General Terms

Some general terms for location and for anatomical surfaces are:

1. Ventral, away from the backbone, or toward the front of the body.
2. Dorsal, toward the backbone, or away from the front of the body.
3. Anterior, toward the front, or away from the back. This term is usually used with reference to the free extremities or the head but is sometimes used interchangeably with ventral.
4. Posterior, toward the back, or away from the front. This term is also used with reference to the free extremities or the head, but may be used interchangeably with dorsal.
5. Cranial, toward the head. The term rostral is sometimes used.

6. Caudal, toward the tail, away from the head.
7. Superior, upper.
8. Inferior, lower.
9. Superficial, toward the surface.
10. Deep, away from the surface.
11. External, toward the outer surface. This term is most often used to describe body cavities or the body wall but is sometimes used interchangeably with superficial.
12. Internal, toward the inner surface. This term is also used to describe body cavities or the body wall but is sometimes used interchangeably with deep.
13. Medial (mesial), toward the axis, or near the mid-line.
14. Lateral, away from the axis or mid-line.
15. Peripheral, used with reference to the external surface or parts of a structure.
16. Proximal, toward the body or the root of a free extremity.
17. Distal, away from the body or the root of a free extremity.

No description of the anatomy of the human body would be complete without at least referring to cells, the basic building blocks in the formation of all animal tissue.

Cells and Tissues

Cells are highly organized masses of protoplasm, or cytoplasm, which possess the peculiar property we have come to call life. The following criteria determine the category of the living:

1. Irritability, the ability to be stimulated or affected by (to react to) a change in the environment.
2. Growth.
3. Spontaneous movement, or movement which originates from within the organism.
4. Metabolism, which is the use of food and oxygen to build or repair tissue, to produce heat and energy.
5. Reproduction, or the ability to produce new protoplasm.

Cells are unusually small and are measured in microns. A micron is one-thousandth of a millimeter, or 1/25,400 of an inch. A single cell would need to be about one hundred microns in diameter in order to be just visible to the unarmed eye. Red blood cells are about seven to eight microns in diameter.

The basic material that enters into the composition of all living cells is called protoplasm. The protoplasm of a living cell is divided into two principal parts, a nucleus and an enveloping mass of cytoplasm; i.e., cell-plasma.

The nucleus is usually spheroidal or slightly elongated and conforms to the general shape of the cell. The nucleus is invested by a nuclear membrane, and contains a ground substance in which chromosomes are suspended. Most cells contain a single nucleus, but certain specialized cells may be multinucleated. The nucleus usually contains a well-demarcated body known as the nucleolus.

The cytoplasm of a living cell appears rather homogenous when viewed under the bright field microscope. It is surrounded by a semipermeable membrane that controls the exchange of materials between the cell and its environment. A central body, or centrosome, lies at one side near the nucleus. The centrosome has been clearly asso-

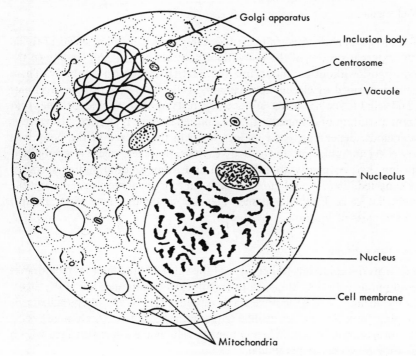

Fig. 1–4. *Schematic representation of a cell.*

ciated with the process of mitotic cell division. Other intracellular structures seem to be arranged around the centrosome. They include the Golgi bodies and mitochondria. In addition, many cells are characterized by fat droplets, fluid-filled vacuoles, and certain inert substances. A schematic cell is shown in Figure 1–4.

Since cells are individual units of living matter, they are subject to a limited life span. Some cells, such as those in nervous tissue, may live throughout the life of the organism which houses them, while others, such as the red blood cells, have a life span of about four months. Other cells, such as those of the skin, are continuously dying and being replaced by new cells.

When colonies of cells and their intercellular products combine in such a manner as to exhibit functional unity, we have what is commonly called tissue, a word derived from the Latin word *texere*—a texture or fabric. The branch of anatomy dealing with the microscopic structure of tissue is called histology.

ELEMENTARY TISSUES

Long before the development of precision optics and the microscope, anatomists were convinced there was more than one type of tissue in the body. Today it is generally agreed that there are but five basic types of tissues, called the elementary tissues. They are the epithelial, the connective, the muscular, the nervous, and the vascular tissues. The human body is made up solely of these five types of tissue.

Epithelial Tissues

Epithelial tissues are characteristically arranged in mosaics, forming sheets of tissue that cover the external surface of the body, line the tubes or passages leading to the exterior, and almost without exception line the internal cavities in the body. These tissues, which are formed by closely approximated cells, have very little intercellular substance. Epithelial tissue has a free surface and rests upon a basement tissue; that is, it rests upon a stratum of connective tissue. Epithelial tissue is subjected to various functional demands, depending upon its location. On the surface of the body it is subjected to drying and abrasion. In the body cavities, however, where it is subjected to little abrasion, it is covered with a fluid film and forms smooth gliding surfaces. As might be expected, there is a relationship between functional requirements and the shape of epithelial cells. Epithelial tissues may be subdivided into three groups, primarily on the basis of location.

Epithelial tissue proper

This tissue forms the epidermis (outer layer of the skin) and the internal membranes which are continuous with the skin, such as the mucous membranes lining the digestive, respiratory, urinary, and generative tracts or tubes. The shape of epithelial cells is varied, ranging from flat, pavement-like (squamous) to rod-like (columnar) cells. Intermediate forms are cuboidal. When columnar cells line a curved surface with a small radius they may appear pyramidal.

In addition, epithelial tissue may be composed of a single layer of cells (simple) or of several layers of cells (stratified). Some epithelial cells are specialized to serve as sensory cells for exteroceptors. They are usually columnar cells, often characterized by numerous cilia on their free surface.

An important variation of simple columnar epithelium may be seen in the form of goblet cells. These cells are found in the intestinal and respiratory tracts, and are actually single-cell mucous glands, which secrete mucin.

Endothelial tissue

This tissue is confined almost exclusively to the inner lining of the walls of the blood and lymph vessels, and, unlike internal epithelial tissue, it has no continuity anywhere with the epidermis. Endothelial tissues are composed of but a single layer of rather flat cells (simple squamous), and thus present an extremely smooth, almost slimy surface. Such structure reduces the possibility of fragmenting blood cells which might cause blood clots.

Mesothelial tissue

This is a specialized form of epithelial tissue which lines the primary body cavities. There are four primary body cavities in the human: the peritoneal cavity, which is located in the abdomen; the two pleural cavities, which house the lungs; and the pericardial cavity, which houses the heart. Mesothelium is sometimes referred to as serous membrane. Serous membrane consists of a sheet of areolar tissue (connective) whose free surface is covered by a single layer of flat cells not at all unlike those of endothelium. The free surface of serous membrane is extremely smooth and slippery.

The three serous membranes in the body cavities are called the peritoneal, pleural, and pericardial membranes, after the respective cavities which they line.

Connective Tissues

Connective tissues might best be described as those tissues which serve to connect or bind structures together, to support the body, and to aid in bodily maintenance. The various types of connective tissue, in contrast to epithelium, have relatively few cells and a proportionately large amount of intercellular substance. Interestingly enough, connective tissue is subdivided, not on the basis of the characteristics of the living cells in the tissue, but rather on the basis of the nonliving intercellular substances. For example, areolar tissue is characterized by soft intercellular substance, while the intercellular substance in cartilage is firm, yet flexible. In bone, the intercellular substance consists of deposits of inorganic salts and is hard and rigid.

Areolar tissue

This is a very loose tissue, in which the cells lie in an irregular network of fibers. It is a very primitive form of tissue, and due to its rather irregular structure is sometimes referred to as loose connective tissue. Areolar tissue is commonly found just beneath the skin. Indeed, it forms the "bed" for skin and mucous membrane.

Adipose tissue

Adipose tissue is simply a form of areolar tissue that is composed of cells which have absorbed and are impregnated with fat. Adipose tissue differs from areolar tissue in that the cells make up the bulk of the tissue. The cells are large and have an ovoid or spherical shape. The cytoplasm is displaced to the periphery of the cell and the nucleus, usually flattened, is pressed against the cell wall. When seen in fixed preparations, fat cells assume the shape of a signet ring.

Dense fibrous tissue

This tissue is unique in that intercellular substance predominates in its structure. In addition, it is characterized by closely packed fibers. Usually, collagenous fibers predominate, but in some ligaments elastic fibers predominate. It is on the basis of the intercellular fibers that the tissue is designated as either white and unyielding (white fibrous tissue) or yellow and elastic (yellow fibro-elastic tissue). Dense fibrous tissues are found in:

TENDONS — tough, nonelastic cords, largely composed of closely packed white fibers. A tendon is always associated with a muscle, and usually forms the attachment of the muscle to bone.

APONEUROSES — In general terms an aponeurosis is simply an expanded tendon that takes the form of a broad sheet to form the attachment of a muscle to bone. Aponeuroses also serve to form the connecting link between two muscles.

LIGAMENTS — very much like tendons, except that whereas tendons are nonelastic, ligaments possess varying amounts of elastic fibers. Ligaments serve to join bone to bone, bone to cartilage, or cartilage to cartilage. Many, if not most, of the bones in the body are held in position by ligamentous bonds.

FASCIAE — dense fibrous tissues, arranged in sheets which often form sheaths around bundles of muscles. They also function to separate groups of muscles one from the other.

Reticular connective tissue

Reticular connective tissue is a very delicate matrix of cells which have processes that extend in all directions to join the processes of neighboring cells. It often provides the supporting framework for the parenchyma of such organs as the thymus and spleen.

Cartilage

As is the case with other connective tissues, cartilage is composed of cells, intercellular fibers, and ground substance. The peculiar properties of the ground substance give cartilage a certain firmness and elasticity. It is capable of withstanding a considerable amount of pressure and tension. Cartilage covers the articular surfaces of most of the bones, and it forms the entire skeletal framework for such structures as the larynx, trachea, and bronchi. According to the nature and concentration of fibrous substance, cartilage may be subdivided into three types, hyaline, elastic, and fibrous.

Hyaline Cartilage.   Hyaline cartilage appears as a bluish-white translucent substance in the fresh state. It covers the articular surfaces of the joints and forms the framework for the larynx, trachea, and bronchi. Hyaline cartilage appears to be composed of cartilage cells and a rather homogenous intercellular matrix. The cells are located in irregular spaces called lacunae. The apparently homogenous intercellular substance actually contains a fine network of collagenous fibers. The ground substance seems to be concentrated in the areas immediately surrounding the lacunae, and is almost absent in the matrix between the cell areas.

Cartilage is devoid of vascular tissue, and nutrition is provided primarily through diffusion. Poor nutrition may be responsible for the dramatic changes that occur with age. Hyaline cartilage loses its translucency and appears yellowish and cloudy. In addition, a certain amount of calcification may occur.

Except for the articular cartilages, all cartilage is invested by a fibrous membrane called perichondrium. When muscles or tendons impinge upon cartilage, the union is made possible by virtue of the perichondrium. A similar fibrous membrane invests bone, and it is called periostium.

Elastic Cartilage.   Because of the large numbers of elastic fibers in its matrix, elastic cartilage appears yellow and opaque. It is flexible and elastic. As in hyaline cartilage, the ground substance contains collagenous fibers. Elastic cartilage occurs in the external auditory meatus, in the epiglottis, and in some small laryngeal cartilages. Calcification of elastic cartilage rarely, if ever, occurs.

Fibrous Cartilage.   Fibrous cartilage is composed of a dense network of collagenous fibers and cartilage cells. Variable amounts of hyaline matrix may be found in fibrous cartilage, particularly in the cell territories. Fibrous cartilage may be found in some joints in the body and in some ligaments, particularly in the spinal column.

Bone

By far the most dense of the connective tissues is bone. Like the other forms of connective tissues, bone is composed of cells, collagenous fibers, and ground substance. The rigidity of bone is due to the rather large amounts of inorganic salts that are deposited in its matrix. These salts constitute about two-thirds of bone weight.

Grossly, two kinds of bone may be identified, dense or compact bone, and spongy or cancellous bone. The histological character of the cells and intercellular substance, however, is the same in both compact and spongy bone. They differ only in the degree of porosity.

Compact bone, if inspected with the unarmed eye, appears white, homogenous, and without any particular structure. Spongy bone, on the other hand, appears porous. It consists of delicate spicules of bone which intersect each other to form a very complicated meshwork. Compact bone forms the outer shell or cortex of most bones, while the remainder is composed of spongy bone. The demarcation between compact and spongy bone is ill defined. Rather, a gradual transition between the two takes place. A longitudinal section of a long bone reveals both the compact and spongy bone. This is illustrated in Figure 1–5.

The primary characteristic of bone is its lamellar structure; that is, the fibers and ground substance are laid down in thin layers, or lamellae. When a cross section of compact bone is examined microscopically, it is seen to be pierced by longitudinal canals called the Haversian canals. These canals anastomose with each other to form an elaborate canal system, which accommodates blood vessels and nerves. The Haversian canals are surrounded by concentric lamellae, not unlike the growth rings of a tree. The bone cells are located within oval-shaped lacunae, which are situated within

Fig. 1–5. Longitudinal section through a femur showing spongy and compact bone.

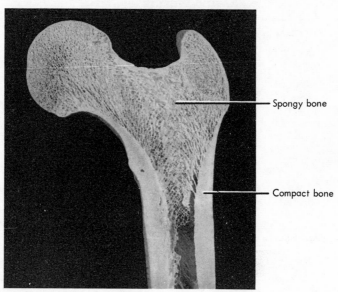

Spongy bone

Compact bone

the lamellae. Small canals (canaliculi) extend out from the lacunae to communicate with the canaliculi of adjacent lacunae.

The spaces within the meshwork of spongy bone are occupied by bone marrow. Two types of bone marrow are recognized, the red marrow, which manufactures red blood cells, and the yellow marrow, which is pure adipose tissue. In the very young, red marrow predominates, but with increasing age more and more red marrow is transformed into yellow marrow. In the very old, the yellow marrow is transformed into gelatinous marrow.

There is a tough, fibrous membrane covering the outside of bone. This membrane is known as periosteum or mucoperiosteum, and although it is closely adherent to the bone, it can be stripped off. The inner layer of periosteum contains osteoblasts, which are the cells for bone growth, while the superficial layer of the tissue is richly supplied with the capillaries that are responsible for the food supply to the bone. This is why bones in the fresh state have a characteristic pink hue.

On the basis of their shape, bones may be classified into three groups: long bones, short bones, and flat bones. Several bones are not amenable to classification, however, and are referred to as mixed or irregular bones. In addition, certain bones, particularly those adjacent to the nasal cavities, are hollow and are known as air-containing bones. Bones may also be classified as axial or appendicular. The axial skeleton is made of the vertebrae, the skull, the mandible, and the rib cage. The appendicular skeleton includes those bones that belong to the limbs of the body; that is, the bones of the pectoral (upper limb) girdle and the pelvic (lower limb) girdle. The axial and appendicular skeletons are shown in Figure 1–6.

Fig. 1–6. The axial and appendicular skeletons.

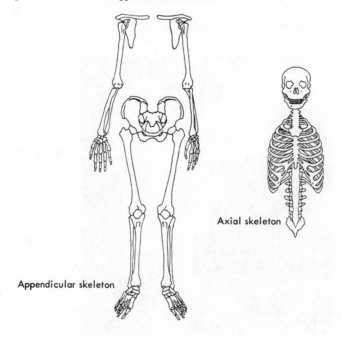

Axial skeleton

Appendicular skeleton

Frequently used anatomical terms for describing skeletal structures are defined as follows:

CONDYLE — a rounded or knuckle-like process
CREST — a prominent ridge
FORAMEN — an opening or perforation in a bone
FOSSA — a pit or hollow
GROOVE — a furrow
HEAD — an enlargement at one end of the bone, beyond its neck
MEATUS — a tube or passage
NECK — a constriction near the head of the bone
PROCESS — a bony prominence
SINUS — a cavity within a bone
SPINE — a sharp projection
TROCHANTER — a very large bony projection
TUBERCLE — a small round projection
TUBEROSITY — a large round projection

Classification of Joints.   Joints are conventionally categorized either on a functional basis or an anatomical basis. Either way there are three broad categories of joints. On a functional basis there are the synarthrodial or immovable, amphiarthrodial or yielding, and the diarthrodial or movable joints. On an anatomical basis there are fibrous (immovable), cartilaginous (yielding), and synovial (movable) joints.

Synarthrodial (fibrous, immovable) joints.   In a synarthrodial joint, the bones are firmly united by fibrous tissue. There are four varieties of synarthrodial joints: the suture, the schindylesis, the gomphosis, and the synchondrosis.

The suture is commonly found between the bones of the skull and is illustrated in Figure 1–7. The bone ends are serrated (or beveled and overlapped) and joined by

Fig. 1–7. Three major types of joints.

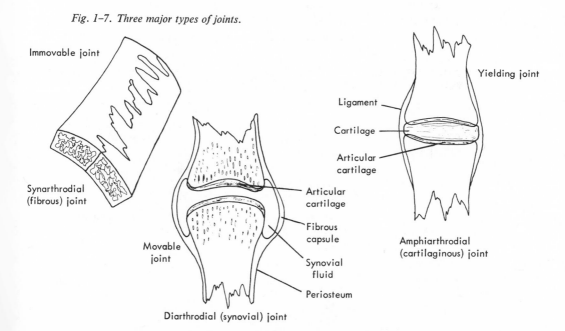

Immovable joint

Yielding joint

Ligament

Cartilage

Articular cartilage

Synarthrodial (fibrous) joint

Articular cartilage

Fibrous capsule

Amphiarthrodial (cartilaginous) joint

Movable joint

Synovial fluid

Periosteum

Diarthrodial (synovial) joint

fibrous tissue. A suture allows very little, or indeed, no movement. Sometimes two originally separate bones become united by an osseous union, and the joint becomes obliterated. Such a joint is called a synostosis.

The schindylesis is a type of joint in which a single plate of bone is inserted into a cleft which has been formed by the separation of two laminae in another bone. This joint, which is not well represented in the body, is probably best exemplified by the articulation of the sphenoid bone and perpendicular plate of the ethmoid bone with the vomer bone.

The gomphosis is found in instances where a conical process is inserted into a socket (alveolus), rigidly, as in the articulation of the roots of the teeth with the alveolar ridge of the mandible and maxillae.

The synchondrosis is broadly represented in the skeleton. It is a rather rigid cartilaginous joint that usually ossifies with increasing age. As such, it is often regarded as a temporary joint. Such joints are frequent in the skull at birth and for some years after birth. This type of joint is not to be confused with the amphiarthrodial type of joint.

Amphiarthrodial (cartilaginous, yielding) joints. This type of articulation is quite commonly found in the body. The amphiarthrodial joint permits a certain amount of movement, or give. If the joint is the type where the bone surfaces are connected by a fibrous cartilage, as in the pelvis and spinal column, it is usually called a symphysis. If a rather rigid joint is formed between two bones, due to an interosseus ligament, it is said to be a syndesmosis.

Diarthrodial (synovial, movable) joints. These joints have variable degrees and directions of free movement. The bones are joined by a band of fibrous tissue, called the articular capsule, within which is a joint cavity. An articular capsule is shown in Figure 1-7. The internal layer of the articular capsule secretes a small amount of synovial fluid, which lubricates the joint cavity. The opposed ends of bones in a diarthrodial joint are covered by a layer of hyaline cartilage. Various forms of movement are permitted in diarthrodial joints, among which are gliding, rotation, and circumduction. Diarthrodial joints, which are illustrated in Figure 1-8, are classified according to their types of movement. There are six classes of diarthrodial joints.

1. Ginglymus, or hinge joint. A ginglymoid joint permits movement in one plane, usually backward and forward.

2. Trochoid, or pivot joint. The trochoid joint restricts movement to rotation.

3. Condyloid joint. In the condyloid joint an oval-shaped articular facet fits into an elliptical-shaped cavity. Such an arrangement permits all types of movement, with the exception of rotation.

4. Enarthrosis, or ball and socket joint. The enarthrodial joint consists of a rounded, ball-like end of one bone that fits into a cup-like cavity in another in such a manner as to permit motion around a great number of axes.

5. Arthrodia, or gliding joint. Arthrodial joints are those in which plane surfaces are alternately slightly concave and convex. They only permit gliding movements.

6. Saddle joint. In this unique joint both articulating surfaces present a concave-convex appearance. This type of joint permits all types of movement, with the exception of rotation.

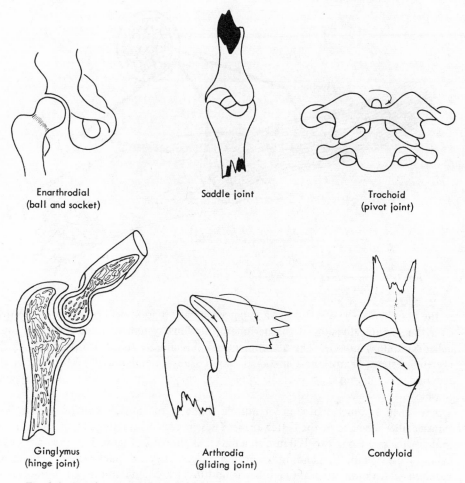

Enarthrodial
(ball and socket)

Saddle joint

Trochoid
(pivot joint)

Ginglymus
(hinge joint)

Arthrodia
(gliding joint)

Condyloid

Fig. 1–8. Six classes of diarthrodial joints.

Muscle Tissues

Muscle tissue is the mediator of all movement and by its contraction is responsible for all of our voluntary action and a good share of our involuntary behavior. This tissue, which accounts for about 40 per cent of our body weight, is popularly referred to as flesh.

Muscle tissue may be classified on either a histological or an anatomical basis; in both classifications, three types of muscle tissue may be identified: striated, smooth, and cardiac.

Striated muscle

Striated muscle consists of long fibers, which, when viewed under a microscope, are seen to be crossed quite regularly by evenly spaced transverse bands; hence the term striated. Striated muscle is innervated by nervous tissue from the somatic division

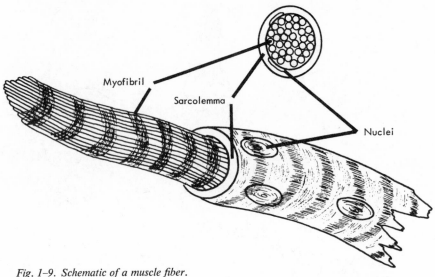

Fig. 1–9. Schematic of a muscle fiber.

of the peripheral nervous system, and since we have a good deal of voluntary control over the somatic division of the peripheral nervous system, striated muscle is often called voluntary muscle. The attachments of this muscle tissue are primarily to the skeletal system; many anatomists call this tissue skeletal muscle. Throughout the remainder of this text, we shall be concerned chiefly with the action of this type of muscle.

The smallest functional unit of muscle tissue is the muscle cell or muscle fiber (muscle fiber seems to be the better term). These muscle fibers range from .01 to .1 mm in diameter and from 1 to 120 mm in length. As shown in Figure 1–9, they are rather cylindrical in shape (depending upon how tightly they are packed) with somewhat blunt ends. An individual muscle fiber is multinucleated and composed of many long filament-like myofibrillae which are imbedded in a form of specialized protoplasm called sarcoplasm. The sarcoplasm of a muscle fiber is enclosed by a delicate cross-striated membrane called sarcolemma. Irregularly spaced nuclei lie imbedded within the sarcolemma. It is the structure of the sarcolemma which is responsible for the characteristic appearance of a skeletal muscle. The sarcoplasm of a muscle fiber is impregnated with numerous fat droplets, which may be more or less abundant, depending upon the extent to which the individual is nourished. Too, the relative concentration of sarcoplasm or myofibrillae varies in individual fibers. Those fibers with a low concentration of myofibrillae (rich in sarcoplasm) appear dark, while fibers with a high concentration of myofibrillae (poor in sarcoplasm) appear pale. These light and dark fibers, which are responsible for the light and dark meat in the Thanksgiving turkey, are not nearly as sharply demarcated in man.

Each muscle fiber is terminated rather bluntly, and is covered by a fibrous tissue called endomysium, which serves to bind the muscle fibers and to separate them from adjacent muscle fibers. Where an individual fiber terminates within a given muscle, the endomysium becomes continuous with the endomysium of the neighboring muscle fibers. It is in this manner, then, that individual muscle fibers are bundled together to form a functional muscle. At places where the muscle fibers attach to either bone or cartilage, the endomysium becomes continuous with the periostium or perichondrium.

Groups of muscle fibers (more properly called fasciculi) are similarly ensheathed and separated from other groups by a fibrous tissue more coarse and more pronounced than endomysium. It is called perimysium. Whereas fasciculi are ensheathed by perimysium, an entire muscle is encased by a still coarser fibrous envelope called epimysium. A fibrous intermuscular septum separates, and serves to compartmentalize, muscle groups.

At the ends of a muscle, the fibers are attached either to tendon, periostium, or perichondrium. Until recently there was some question as to whether the fibrillae of muscle and tendon are continuous, one with the other, or discontinuous and separated

Fig. 1–10. Two types of muscle tissue.

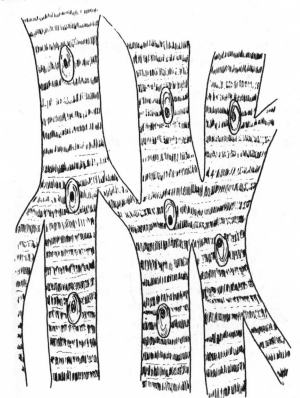

Striated (voluntary, skeletal)

Smooth (involuntary, visceral)

by sarcolemma. Electron microscopy has revealed that connective tissue fibrils insert into the sarcolemma and that muscle fibrillae are not continuous with the fibrillae of the connective tissue. For comparative purposes, skeletal and smooth muscles are shown in Figure 1–10.

Smooth muscle

Smooth muscle is a more primitive type of tissue than skeletal is, and it is found wherever movement is relatively independent of voluntary control. Smooth muscle is innervated by the autonomic division of the peripheral nervous system; because of the independent role it seems to play, it is sometimes referred to as involuntary muscle. This muscle is found in such organs as the stomach and intestines, blood vessels, and bronchial tubes. Because of the location of smooth muscle, some anatomists refer to it as visceral muscle. There are no transverse bands on the muscle cells, which accounts for its being referred to as smooth or unstriated.

Smooth muscle consists of spindle-shaped (fusiform) cells, which contain a single nucleus within the central portion of the cytoplasm. The cells bear faint longitudinal striations. Depending upon their location, the cells may appear long and slender, short and blunt, or irregular and twisted. The cells are small. They range from three to eight microns in diameter, and from fifteen to two hundred microns in length. The external surface of the cytoplasm functions as a very definite cell wall, but it does not serve as a well-defined sarcolemma. Contraction of smooth muscle is slow and sustained, testimony as to its primitive nature.

Cardiac muscle

Cardiac muscle, which is found only in the heart, seems to have some of the properties of both smooth and striated muscle. It is involuntary, but striated. The cells contain myofibrils that are essentially the same as those of striated muscle, but the muscle fibers do not seem to possess a definite sarcolemma. Fibrous connective tissue is particularly abundant in cardiac muscle. Albeit important, we shall not concern ourselves with the contributions of cardiac muscle.

The physiology and anatomy of muscle tissue is an extremely complex and challenging area of science. So much so, that it commands the attention of an entire discipline known as kinesiology, which by definition is the science of movement. It may prove beneficial to devote a little attention, at this time, to the architecture and actions of muscles.

Muscle architecture

The arrangement of muscle fasciculi and the manner in which they attach to tendons are varied. For example, in many muscles the course of the fasciculi is parallel to the long axis of the muscle. The fasciculi terminate at either end by means of a flat tendon as illustrated in Figure 1–11 (A). These muscles, often called parallel muscles, have a great range of motion, and may shorten by as much as one-half their total length. Other muscle arrangements sacrifice a range of motion for an increase in power. Certain muscles, for example, present a fan-shaped appearance. The fasciculi diverge or converge as they approach their attachments. They are called radiating muscles, and an example is shown in Figure 1–11 (B). Penniform muscles, as shown in Figure

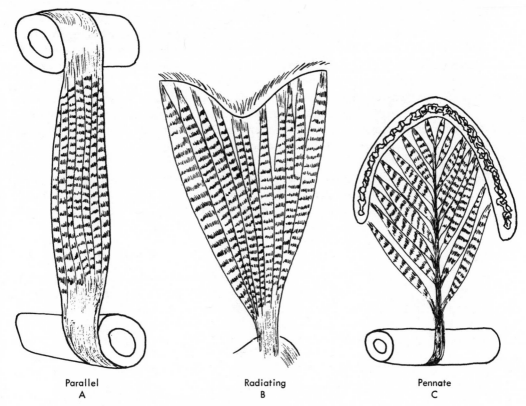

| Parallel | Radiating | Pennate |
| A | B | C |

Fig. 1–11. Various forms of muscle architecture.

1–11 (C), are composed of fasciculi which converge onto a tendon like the plumes of a feather onto the quill. In such muscles the power is the combined power of all the contracting fibers, while the change in length is simply equal to the amount of contraction executed by any given fasciculus. In parallel muscles, on the other hand, the power of the muscle is provided by the contraction of only the fibers contained in any transverse section, while the degree of shortening is equal to the sum total of the contraction of many fasciculi in series. Thus, architecture dictates the power of a muscle. In summary, the muscles composed of fasciculi running the length of the muscle have a great range of motion but little power, while the radiating and penniform muscles have less range of motion but a great deal more power.

When a muscle contracts, it usually acts upon movable structures to produce movement. In most instances the characteristics of the resultant movement are determined by the mechanical arrangements of the structures to which a muscle is attached.

Muscle action

Muscle contractions, almost without exception, produce movements. Skeletal muscles generally produce movement by acting on a joint that lies between the origin and insertion of the muscle. Contraction of muscle tissue decreases the distance between the origin and insertion, with rotational action occurring about the joint. Thus, with some knowledge of the anatomy of a given muscle and the type of joint it bridges, a student is in a position to predict the type of movement produced by its contraction. It is essential, however, that the student guard against assuming that the action in a living body is exactly the same as the action inferred from observations of attachments in a nonliving specimen. This is because muscles usually act in functional groups, and the laboratory is unable to demonstrate the effects of contraction of an opposing or complementary muscle in the muscle group. Knowledge of the nervous system is often helpful in the study of muscle actions; that is, there is often a correlation between the innervation of muscles and their functions. For example, opposing muscles are rarely innervated by the same nerve.

Skeletal muscles are, more often than not, the source of a force that is applied to a lever system which produces bodily movements. In such a "biological lever," the bones act as lever arms, and the joint functions as the fulcrum. There are three classes of lever systems, and all three are represented in the body.

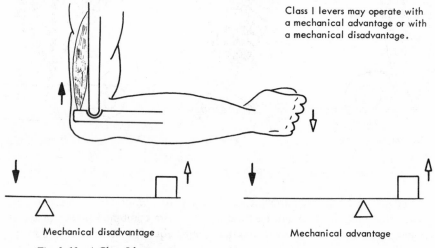

Class I levers may operate with a mechanical advantage or with a mechanical disadvantage.

Mechanical disadvantage

Mechanical advantage

Fig. 1–12. A Class I lever system.

A Class I lever is shown in Figure 1–12. There is an applied force at one end of the lever and a resisting force at the other end. The fulcrum, about which the lever rotates, is placed at some point between the two ends of the lever. If the force arm is longer than the resistance arm, the lever will operate with a mechanical advantage, and a small applied force will displace a large resistance force. If the force arm is shorter than the resistance arm, however, the system will operate with a mechanical disadvantage, and a large applied force will be required to displace a small resistance force. It must be noted, however, that where power is gained in a lever, the degree of excursion of the resistance arm is diminished by a proportional amount. It is even more important to realize that when power is lost in a Class I lever system, the degree of excursion of the resistance arm is increased. Many muscles in the body are part of Class I lever systems with a mechanical disadvantage. Power is sacrificed for speed of movement.

Class II levers are not well represented in the body. They consist of a lever arm with the fulcrum at one end and an applied force at the other. The resistance force lies

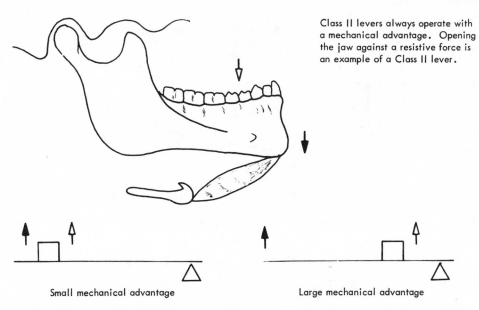

Class II levers always operate with a mechanical advantage. Opening the jaw against a resistive force is an example of a Class II lever.

Small mechanical advantage   Large mechanical advantage

Fig. 1-13. A Class II lever system.

somewhere between the fulcrum and the end of the lever arm. This is illustrated in Figure 1-13. Class II levers must operate with a mechanical advantage; that is, the force required to displace a weight when a lever is used is always less than the force required if no lever were used. There is good evidence that a Class II lever system is found in the ossicular chain of the middle ear. The ossicular chain will be discussed at some length in Chapter 6.

Whereas Class II levers always operate with a mechanical advantage, Class III levers always operate with a mechanical disadvantage. This is because the fulcrum is at one end of the lever arm, the resistance force at the other end, with an applied force at a point somewhere between the two ends. A Class III lever is illustrated in Figure 1-14. They are well represented in the body. Although power is lost in such a system, speed of movement is gained. As a result, rapid movements are possible with very little muscle contraction.

Throughout most of this text we shall be concerned with individual muscles and individual muscle actions. To some extent this is an unfortunate but conventional approach, for our brain does not mediate or monitor individual muscle actions; rather, it mediates and monitors skeletal and muscle group movements.

A muscle can exert a force in just one direction. It is incapable of exerting any force in the opposite direction. That is to say, muscles which act upon a joint to produce movement usually come in pairs, one to produce movements in one direction and another to produce movements in the opposite direction. Thus, either muscle in a functional pair may be the antagonist of the other. Those muscles directly responsible for producing desired movements are called prime movers; those which act to maintain the body in an appropriate posture are called fixation muscles. When a muscle contracts to suppress or negate some undesired movement that might normally be caused by a prime mover, it is said to be a synergist.

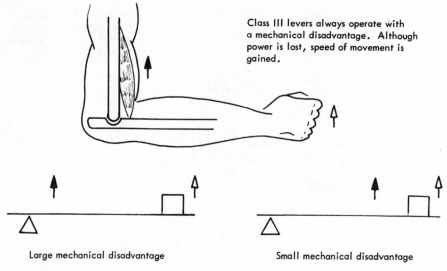

Class III levers always operate with a mechanical disadvantage. Although power is lost, speed of movement is gained.

Large mechanical disadvantage   Small mechanical disadvantage

Fig. 1–14. A Class III lever system.

Nerve impulses are the agents directly responsible for producing muscle contractions, and muscle actions are determined in large part by the characteristics of the nerve supply to the muscles.

Nervous Tissue

Nervous tissue is made of a large group of highly specialized cells that possess the unique property of being extremely irritable. They respond to abrupt environmental changes by modifying their electro-chemical composition. The contributions of the nervous system to speech production cannot be underestimated. Consequently, the nervous system will be treated separately and at some length in Chapter 7. For purposes of reference, however, the means by which a muscle is innervated may be found in Appendix A. Some muscles are well supplied with nervous tissue, others less so. Sarcoplasm, of which muscles are largely composed, is a unique form of protoplasm that is capable of contraction in response to chemical, electrical, or electro-chemical stimuli. Under normal circumstances sarcoplasm contracts in response to the electro-chemical stimuli provided by the nervous system. The relation between nerve supply and muscle action is outlined in the following brief discussion of the motor unit.

The motor unit

The functional unit for producing muscle action is called a motor unit. As shown in Figure 1–15, it consists of a nerve cell body and its process and the muscle fibers served by the nerve cell. The nerve cell process, called an axon, divides into a number of axon fibrils just prior to terminating by means of muscle end plates, which are in direct contact with the muscle fibers. A single motor unit may include anywhere from a few to over a hundred muscle fibers. Muscle end plates are not unlike electrodes, for they transmit nerve impulses to the sarcoplasm of muscle fiber, which in turn responds by short duration twitches, one twitch for each nerve impulse. A single

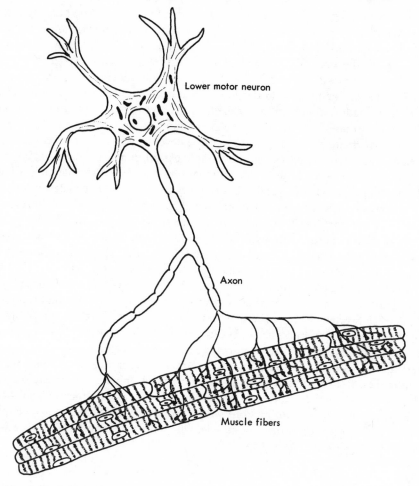

Fig. 1–15. Schematic of a motor unit.

muscle fiber is capable of "following" up to about fifty nerve impulses per second. It is interesting to note that all of the muscle fibers in a single motor unit contract as a whole, with one brief twitch for every impulse. Smooth, prolonged muscle contractions are accounted for by the mechanics of many motor units firing in volleys, repeatedly, so that their combined effects produce a seemingly constant contraction.

A critical inspection of a single motor unit muscle contraction reveals three distinct phases, the latent period, the contraction period, and the relaxation period. The interval between the onset of the stimulus and the onset of contraction is known as the latent period. The latent period is about 0.01 second in duration. Although no actual change in the length of the muscle fibers occurs during the latent period, the chemical status of the fibers is changing rapidly. The latent period is followed by the contraction period which lasts about 0.04 second. It is during the contraction period that work is done by the muscle. The relaxation period is about 0.05 second in duration, during which there is a return to the previous relaxed state. It is important to realize that relaxation is purely passive, caused by the elasticity of the muscle fibers and by external forces exerted upon the ends of muscle fibers. A fourth phase, known as the refractory phase, is sometimes recognized. During this phase, which lasts only about 0.005 second, chemical processes are occurring which restore the muscle to its normal resting state. Muscle fibers will not respond readily to a stimulus during the refractory phase.

During the contraction period the active portion of a muscle fiber becomes electrically negative with respect to adjacent tissue or inactive muscle. The electric potentials generated by an active muscle are known as muscle action potentials. These action potentials, which are similar in nature to those developed by nerves, may be detected by means of electrodes and, with suitable amplification, can be displayed on an appropriate recording device. The technique of recording muscle action potentials is known as electromyography (EMG), and it has recently become an important research tool.

Voluntary muscle contractions can be graded from a just perceptible shortening to a maximum contraction. The degree of muscle contraction is dependent upon the number of active motor units within a muscle, as well as the rate of firing of the active motor units. There is strong supportive evidence that single motor units behave in an all-or-none fashion; that is, once a stimulus has reached a certain critical level, all the muscle fibers of a motor unit contract. Within limits, the force exerted by the muscle fibers of a motor unit is directly related to the frequency of stimulus impulses, and the force exerted by an entire muscle is directly related to the number of active motor units. A weak stimulus activates fewer motor units; a strong stimulus activates more. In addition, there is a relation between the extent of nerve supply to a muscle (innervation) and the precision of muscle contraction. A muscle with a high innervation ratio, i.e., ratio of muscle fibers to nerve cell, will only be able to execute rather crude movements with large muscle contractions, while a low innervation ratio in a muscle will allow smaller contractions with finer control. We can predict, simply by means of the innervation ratio of a muscle, whether it is capable of fine, precise, or rather crude degrees of contraction.

Vascular Tissue

Vascular tissue might be thought of as the "fluid tissues" of the body. It is composed of blood and lymph. Blood consists of plasma, red and white corpuscles, blood platelets, and dissolved gases. Lymph, which is the immediate nutrient plasma of the tissues, appears to be a colorless watery-looking liquid. It contains numerous white corpuscles which resemble those of the blood. The fluid tissues have many important functions. For example, they convey food and oxygen to all the living cells in the body and take on the waste materials generated by cell activity. They distribute heat uniformly over the body and are instrumental in getting rid of the excess. In addition, they defend the body against disease-producing micro-organisms.

ORGANS

When two or more tissues combine in such a manner as to exhibit functional unity, they form an organ. The lungs, larynx, and tongue are some examples. Most organs are composed of various types of tissue, with one type predominating. The cells that compose the essential structure of an organ are known as the parenchyma. Other cells may be supportive, vascular, or nervous.

SYSTEMS

When two or more organs combine in such a manner as to exhibit functional unity, we have what is commonly called a system. There are at least nine recognized systems in the body, and very often eleven systems are listed. They are:

1. The skeletal system, which is composed of the bones and their related cartilages. The study of the skeletal system is known as osteology.
2. The articular system, which is composed of the joints and ligaments. The study of the articular system is known as arthrology.
3. The muscular system, which forms the fleshy parts of the body. Acting on 1 and 2, the muscular system produces movement and locomotion. The study of muscles is called myology.
4. The digestive system, which is composed of the digestive tract and its associated digestive glands. The study of the internal organs of the thorax and abdomen is known as splanchnology.
5. The vascular system, the study of which is angiology, is composed of the heart and blood vessels and the lymphatic system.
6. The nervous system, which is composed of the brain and spinal cord and all associated nerves, ganglia, and sense organs. The study of the nervous system is known as neurology.
7. The respiratory system, which is composed of the air passageways and the lungs.
8. The urinary system, which includes the kidneys and urinary passages.
9. The generative or reproductive system, which is closely associated with the urinary system and is sometimes included with it under the term urogenital system. The generative system is composed of the organs of reproduction.
10. The endocrine system, which is composed of the ductless glands in the body.
11. The integumentary system, which includes the skin, nails, and hair. The study of the integumentary system is called dermatology.

With just a moment of thought it becomes apparent that no one of these systems is independent of the others. The speech mechanism draws heavily on some systems and less heavily on others, but either directly or indirectly it is dependent upon all the systems in the body. We shall be directing our attention to a good share of the skeletal, muscular, nervous, and respiratory systems. We shall be less concerned with the circulatory and endocrine systems, and probably will mention the reproductive and digestive systems only in passing.

The Speech Mechanism

Speech production is sometimes described as consisting of four phases: respiration, phonation, resonation, and articulation. Those parts of the body most closely associated with speech production include the lungs, the trachea, the larynx, the pharynx,

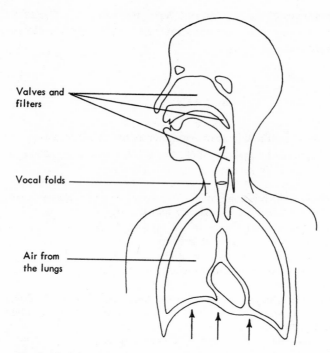

Fig. 1–16. Schematic of the speech mechanism.

the nasal cavities, and the mouth or oral cavity. These structures, which are shown schematically in Figure 1–16, form a versatile and intricate sound production system.

Two absolute requirements for the production of sounds of any kind are a source of energy and a vibrating element. The primary source of energy for speech production, of course, is air provided by the breathing apparatus, in particular, the lungs. They supply the sound vibrators with power in the form of a rather smooth flow of air. The conversion of a smooth flow of air into sound may take place almost anywhere along the vocal tract, which is that portion of the speech mechanism lying above the vocal folds. Usually we think of the vibrating vocal folds as the primary source of sound for speech production, but there are others. By constricting the vocal tract somewhere along its length, the air stream may become turbulent to produce fricative noise. Such turbulence may be generated with or without vibration of the vocal folds. Sound may also be generated by momentarily blocking the flow of air through the vocal tract. A sudden release of the air pressure may produce a mild explosion or a plosive sound. The vocal folds, the lips, the tongue, or the soft palate may act as valves to block the flow of air and to release it.

The quality of most speech sounds may be greatly modified by changes in the configuration and thus the acoustical properties of the vocal tract. These changes are brought about mainly by modifications in the shape of the oral cavity.

A physical analog of the speech mechanism might consist of a power supply, vibrating elements, a system of valves, and a filtering device. In the study of the speech mechanism, our first consideration ought to be the power supply, and so Chapter 2 deals with the breathing mechanism.

SELECTIVE READING LIST

Cates, H. A. and J. V. Basmajian, *Primary Anatomy*, 3rd ed. Baltimore: The Williams and Wilkins Co., 1955.

Cunningham, D. J., *Text-book of Anatomy*. 9th ed. New York: Oxford University Press, Inc., 1951.

Gray's *Anatomy* (C. M. Goss, ed.), 28th ed. Philadelphia: Lea and Febiger, 1966.

Henderson, I. F. and J. H. Kenneth, *A Dictionary of Scientific Terms*. 7th ed. Princeton, N. J.: D. Van Nostrand Co., Inc., 1960.

Judson, L. Y. and A. T. Weaver, *Voice Science*. New York: Appleton-Century-Crofts, 1965.

2

The Breathing Mechanism

DEFINITION OF BREATHING

The Physics of Breathing

THE RESPIRATORY PASSAGE

Introduction
The Trachea

The main stem bronchi
The Bronchioles
The Air Sacs

The Lungs

The shape of the lungs
The Apex
The Base
The Surfaces
The Borders
The Lobes

Weight
Capacity

The Pleurae

THE FRAMEWORK FOR THE BREATHING MECHANISM

Introduction
The Spinal Column
The Rib Cage

The sternum
The ribs (costae)
Movements of the ribs in breathing

The Scalenus Anterior
The Scalenus Medius
The Scalenus Posterior

Muscles of the Back

The latissimus dorsi
The sacrospinalis muscles

The Medial Spinalis Group
The Medial Longissimus Group (Intermediate Longissimus)
The Lateral Iliocostalis Group

The Muscles of Exhalation

Introduction

Abdominal Muscles of Exhalation

The abdominal aponeurosis
The lumbar fascia
The external oblique
The internal oblique
The transversus abdominis
The rectus abdominis

Thoracic Muscles of Exhalation

The transversus thoracis
The subcostals
The internal intercostals

The Back Muscles of Exhalation

The iliocostalis dorsi
The quadratus lumborum

THE FUNCTIONS OF THE MUSCLES OF RESPIRATION

Introduction and Terminology

Terminology

The Functions of the Muscles of Inhalation

Introduction
The diaphragm
The pectoralis major and minor muscles
The subclavius
The serratus anterior
The intercostal muscles
The levator costalis muscles
The serratus posterior superior muscles
The serratus posterior inferior muscles
The sternocleidomastoid muscles
The scalene muscles
The latissimus dorsi muscles
The sacrospinalis muscles

The Functions of the Muscles of Exhalation

The transversus thoracis muscles
The subcostal muscles
The internal intercostals
The quadratus lumborum muscles.
The abdominal musculature
Forces of exhalation other than muscular

The Mechanics and Physiology of Breathing

Pressure Changes in the chest cavity
Breathing behavior and the voice
Variations in breathing patterns

A Descriptive Account of a Cycle of Breathing

SELECTIVE READING LIST

DEFINITION OF BREATHING

Respiration is usually defined as a process of gas exchange between an organism and its environment. Perhaps it is more accurately defined as the oxidation of food to produce water, carbon dioxide, and heat, a process illustrated by the following formula:

$$C_6H_{12}O_6 + 6O_2 \longrightarrow 6CO_2 + 6H_2O + \text{heat}$$

For speech purposes, however, the above definitions do not adequately define respiration. Speech seems to require a primarily "nonrespiratory" function of the breathing mechanism for, in speech, the exhaled air serves to power the sound-producing mechanism and, of course, air also propagates the speech signal once it has been generated. The purpose of this chapter is to examine the means by which air is brought into the lungs and forced out again.

The Physics of Breathing

One of the best-established laws in physics is Boyle's Law, which states that if a gas is kept at constant temperature, pressure and volume are inversely proportional to one another and have a constant product. For an explanation of this law, we must turn to the kinetic theory of gases. The basis of kinetic theory is that gases are composed of large numbers of individual molecules that are engaged in unceasing motion. As shown in Figure 2–1 (A), when these molecules are confined in a vessel they move about randomly and at high speeds, colliding with one another and with the walls of the vessel. This bombardment exerts force on the walls of the vessel. Provided volume

Fig. 2–1. Illustration of pressure-gas-density relationship.

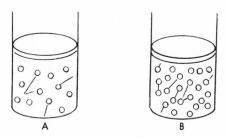

A   B

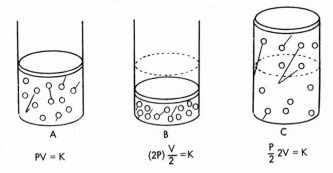

Fig. 2–2. Illustration of Boyle's Law.

and temperature are held constant, the force exerted on the walls of the containing vessel is a function of the number of gas molecules within the vessel. In Figure 2–1 (B) a greater number of gas molecules exerts a larger force on the walls than in (A).

Figure 2–2 (A) shows a volume of gas (V) in a cylinder which is under pressure (P). At the same time, a force (F) is being exerted on a piston. When the piston is pushed in until the volume is halved, as in (B), there is twice the number of gas molecules per unit volume (the density of the gas is doubled), and, consequently, twice as many collisions with other molecules and with the walls of the vessel will occur per unit time. The force on the piston and walls is doubled, and the pressure is doubled, but the product of pressure and volume remains the same; that is, $(2P)\frac{V}{2}$ is a constant. On the other hand, if the piston is raised to double the volume, as in (C), the pressure exerted on the walls of the vessel is cut in half. Symbolically this means that $P/2\ (2V)$ is the constant.

When air at atmospheric pressure is confined in an airtight container, equal amounts of pressure act on the outside and inside walls of the container, and the differential pressure is zero. A decrease in the volume of the container increases the pressure inside with respect to the outside, and an increase in the volume of the container decreases the pressure with respect to the outside. Pressures greater than atmospheric are often called positive pressures; pressures less than atmospheric are called negative pressures.

In man, the lungs lie inside an airtight (thoracic) cavity and communicate with the outside air by way of the trachea, larynx, pharynx, and the oral and nasal cavities. The structure of the thoracic cavity is such that its volume can be increased or decreased. An increase in the volume results in a negative pressure in the lungs with respect to the outside. Consequently, air rushes into the lungs until the outside and inside pressures are equalized. This phase of breathing is known as inspiration or inhalation. Both terms mean the same thing, and may be used interchangeably. A decrease in the volume of the thoracic cavity results in a positive pressure in the lungs, and air rushes out until the outside and inside pressures are equalized. This phase of breathing is called expiration or exhalation, terms that are synonymous. In the pages that follow we shall be concerned with the mechanisms by which the dimensions of the thoracic (or chest) cavity are increased and decreased during breathing, but only after we have accounted for the anatomy and properties of some of the structures that make up the respiratory passage.

THE RESPIRATORY PASSAGE

Introduction

The respiratory passage, which is shown schematically in Figure 2–3, includes, in descending order, the nasal and oral cavities, the pharynx, larynx, trachea, bronchi, and lungs. These structures form a continuous open passage leading from the exterior to the lungs. The lungs, of course, are the essential organs of respiration, and it is in the lungs that the actual exchange of gas takes place. Here the red blood cells give up their carbon dioxide to the air and take on new oxygen. Although the nasal, oral, and pharyngeal cavities are definitely intrinsic parts of the breathing mechanism, they are also important organs of articulation and resonance. In the present context then, suffice it to say these cavities filter, moisten, and warm the air prior to its entering the larnyx.

The larynx is a modification of the uppermost tracheal cartilages. It forms a highly specialized valvular mechanism that may open or close the air passageway. The larynx serves as a protective device. A sudden release of compressed air by the valvular mechanism will produce an explosive exhalation that will clear the air passage of threatening mucus or foreign objects. This, of course, is known as coughing. The valvular action also permits thoracic fixation for such activities as defecation, emesis, micturition, and heavy lifting. Thus, the larynx may serve as a basic biological organ as well as a specialized organ capable of utilizing expired air for the generation of voice. Because the larynx is so complex, and so important for speech production, a detailed description of the larynx will be found in Chapter 3.

Fig. 2–3. Schematic of the respiratory passage.

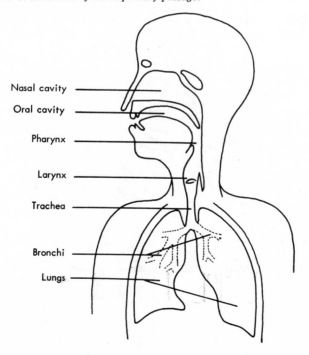

Nasal cavity

Oral cavity

Pharynx

Larynx

Trachea

Bronchi

Lungs

The Trachea

The trachea is composed of from sixteen to twenty horseshoe-shaped rings of hyaline cartilage, placed one above the other and separated by a small space that is occupied by a fibroelastic membrane. Each tracheal ring is interrupted in back where the trachea lies in direct contact with the esophagus. Two, and sometimes three, individual cartilages may be united either partially or completely. The intervening space between the ends of the tracheal rings is occupied by fibrous tissue and smooth muscle. Such an architecture permits the trachea to be stretched, as it might well be when the head is thrown back. The first tracheal cartilage is larger than the rest, and is connected with the inferior border of the cricoid cartilage of the larynx by means of the cricotracheal ligament. The last cartilage of the trachea bifurcates, giving rise to the main stem bronchi. The gross structure of the trachea is shown in Figure 2–4, and the detailed structure is shown in Figure 2–5.

Fig. 2–4. Schematic of the trachea and bronchial tree.

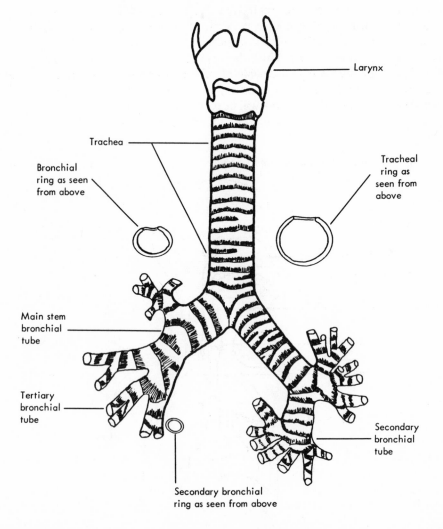

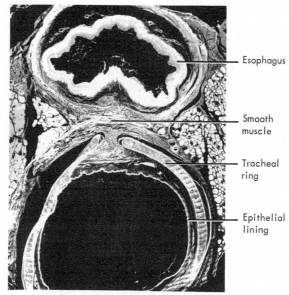

— Esophagus

— Smooth
  muscle

— Tracheal
  ring

— Epithelial
  lining

*Fig. 2–5. Photomacrograph of a transverse section of
a trachea.*

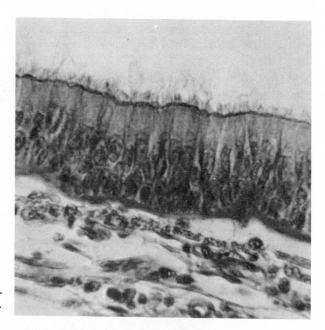

*Fig. 2–6. Photomicrograph of cil-
iated epithelial lining of the trachea.*

The fibrous membrane of the trachea consists of two layers, one of which passes
over the outer surface of the cartilaginous rings, while the other passes over the inner
surface. In the spaces between the rings, however, the two layers blend to form a
single intratracheal membrane which connects the tracheal rings one with another.
The smooth muscle which is found in the space between the ends of the tracheal
rings consists of an outer longitudinal layer and an inner transverse layer. These

muscles are normally in a state of sustained contraction. When oxygen requirements dictate, however, they may relax and thus allow the trachea to dilate. Since tracheal (and bronchial) cartilages have an inherent elasticity, these muscle fibers require no antagonists when they are relaxed. The mucous membrane which lines the trachea is continuous above with that of the larynx and below with that of the bronchi. The surface layer of membrane is composed of ciliated columnar epithelium. The cilia, which may be seen in the photomicrograph of Figure 2–6, perform an important function. They are continuously in motion, beating at first rapidly downward, and then slowly upward about ten times per second. This beating action has a tendency to rid the trachea of dust particles and accumulating mucus. The ciliated columnar epithelium rests upon a basement membrane beneath which is a submucous layer of connective tissue, blood vessels, and mucous glands.

The main stem bronchi

Each bronchus is slightly more than half the diameter of the trachea; however, the right bronchus is larger in diameter, shorter in length, and more in direct line with the trachea than is the left. The right bronchus is larger in diameter because it supplies the larger lung. The significance of the less abrupt divergence of the right bronchus lies in the fact that foreign bodies which may fall into the trachea are more liable to enter the right bronchus than the left. The construction of the bronchi is similar to that of the trachea. The bronchi are composed of imperfect cartilaginous rings, which are bound together by fibroelastic tissue. They are, however, more com-

Fig. 2–7. Photograph of partially dissected lungs and bronchial tree.

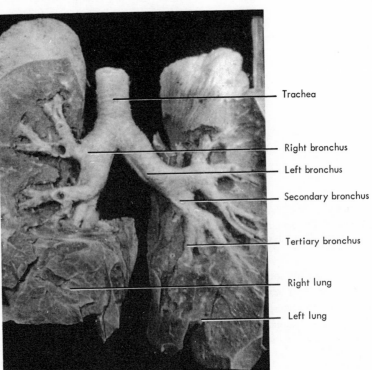

Trachea

Right bronchus

Left bronchus

Secondary bronchus

Tertiary bronchus

Right lung

Left lung

pletely invested by smooth muscle fibers than is the trachea. The right bronchus divides into three secondary bronchi, one for each lobe of the right lung. The secondary bronchi subdivide into ten tertiary bronchi, each of which supplies a lung segment. The left bronchus, on the other hand, divides into two secondary bronchi, from which issue eight tertiary bronchi, each of which supplies an individual lung segment. The bronchi and partially dissected lungs are shown in Figure 2–7.

The Bronchioles. The tertiary bronchi divide repeatedly, becoming progressively smaller, until they verge on the microscopic. It is interesting to note that although the bronchial tree may divide and subdivide, the combined cross-sectional area of any given subdivision is greater than the cross-sectional area of the parent division. The final division of the tertiary bronchi gives rise to the bronchioles, and repeated divisions of the bronchioles ultimately give rise to the terminal bronchioles, which communicate directly with the alveolar ducts that open into the minute air sacs of the lung. As the bronchioles divide, their cartilaginous framework becomes less and less prominent, while the amount of bronchial muscle tissue increases proportionately.

The Air Sacs. The air sacs are pitted with small depressions called alveoli. An elaborate network of capillaries invests each alveolus, and it is here that the red blood cells, separated from the alveoli by just a single-celled wall, exchange their carbon dioxide for oxygen. A photomicrograph of a segment of a terminal bronchiole and adjacent alveoli may be seen in Figure 2–8.

Fig. 2–8. Photomicrograph of a segment of a terminal bronchiole and adjacent alveoli.

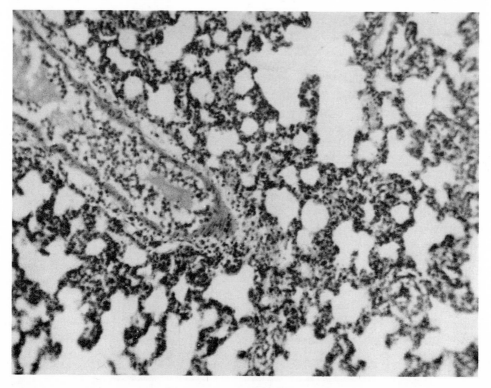

The Lungs

The thoracic cavity is largely occupied by the lungs and trachea. In addition, it houses the heart, the great blood vessels, the esophagus, and lesser lymph and blood vessels. These structures are accommodated in a space in the central region of the thorax known as the mediastinum. As shown in Figure 2–9, the mediastinum is bounded on each side by a lung and by a pleural sac (to be described later). The mediastinum is divided by imaginary lines into an anterior, middle, posterior, and superior mediastinum. The unimportant anterior mediastinum contains a few mammary vessels and lymph nodes, while the middle mediastinum contains the heart, which is surrounded by a closed membranous sac known as the pericardium. The posterior mediastinum, behind the heart, contains part of the esophagus and the greater blood vessels, while the superior mediastinum contains the blood vessels which supply the head, part of the esophagus and trachea, and some important nerves.

The lungs are probably best described as two irregularly cone-shaped structures. They are composed of spongy, porous, but highly elastic material, which contains but a few smooth muscle fibers. Thus, lung tissue is passive and cannot exert any force other than that provided by tissue elasticity. When handled, fresh lungs make a sound similar to the rustling of leaves. This is due to the presence of residual air within the countless minute air sacs of the lungs.

Fig. 2–9. Schematic transverse section of thorax.

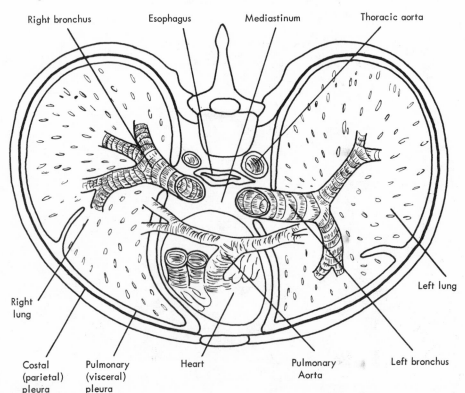

Right bronchus   Esophagus   Mediastinum   Thoracic aorta

Left lung

Right lung

Costal (parietal) pleura   Pulmonary (visceral) pleura   Heart   Pulmonary Aorta   Left bronchus

At birth the lungs are white in color or faintly pink. Pigmentation becomes more definite with age, and in the adult the lungs may appear grayish and mottled in black patches due to prolonged inhalation of smoky, dusty atmosphere.

The shape of the lungs

The paired lungs are not exactly the same in size, form, capacity, or weight. The right lung, slightly larger than the left, is also somewhat shorter and broader, due to

Fig. 2–10. Illustration of shape, lobes, and segments of the lungs.

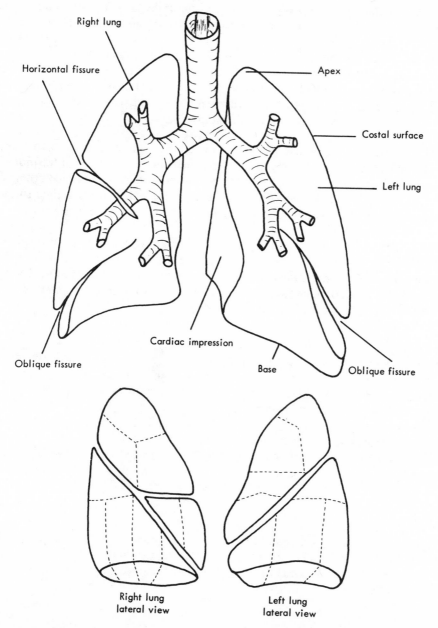

the raised arch of the diaphragm on the right side. The right lung is about 270 mm in length in males, and 260 mm in females. Each lung presents for examination an apex and a base, as well as three borders and two surfaces. The shape, lobes, and segments of the lungs are shown schematically in Figure 2–10.

The Apex.   The apex, shown in Figures 2–10 and 2–12, actually extends beyond the limits of the thorax and, indeed, into the root of the neck to about two to four cm above the superior border of the first rib.

The Base.   The base is concave and conforms to the thoracic surface of the diaphragm. The diaphragm separates the base of the right lung from the bulk of the liver and the base of the left lung from the stomach, the spleen, and part of the liver.

The Surfaces.   As shown in Figures 2–9 and 2–10, the costal or thoracic surface is convex and conforms to the shape of the thoracic walls. This surface lies in direct contact with the costal or parietal pleura. The mediastinal or medial surfaces of the lungs lie in direct contact with the mediastinal pleura and present "cardiac impressions" which accommodate the pericardium of the heart.

The Borders.   Each lung has an inferior, an anterior, and a posterior or vertebral border. The inferior border forms the dividing line between the base and the thoracic and mediastinal surfaces. In front, the mediastinal surface is separated from the costal surface by a sharply defined anterior border. Behind, the mediastinal surface is separated from the costal surface by an ill-defined posterior or vertebral border.

The Lobes.   As may be seen in Figure 2–10, the right lung is partially divided into three lobes by two fissures. The oblique fissure separates the superior from the inferior lobe, while a horizontal fissure gives rise to a small middle lobe. The left lung is divided by an oblique fissure into a superior and an inferior lobe, but it has no horizontal fissure and, therefore, no middle lobe.

Weight

Before respiration has occurred, the lungs have a specific gravity slightly greater than water, and they will sink. Once respiration has occurred, however, the lungs become partially filled with air, and their specific gravity may become as low as 0.3. Researchers have found it difficult to determine the exact weight of the lungs. This is because of various quantities of blood and other fluids that may be present in the lungs. As a consequence, values range from 1,300 grams to 267 grams for male lungs. Female lungs have somewhat smaller values. Spector (1958) lists the average weight of fresh lungs, determined as quickly as possible after removal, as 953 grams for young adult males and 793 grams for young adult females.

Capacity

A pair of well-developed young adult male lungs has a capacity in excess of 5,000 cu cm of air; in a female somewhat less. Due to the imperfect elasticity of the tissue, collapsed lungs (excised) will not be entirely exhausted, but will contain about 500 cu cm of air.

Occasional reference has been made to the pleurae and their significance with respect to breathing. Before we proceed any further, the structure and role of the pleurae ought to be elaborated upon.

The Pleurae

The inner surface of the thoracic cavity, the thoracic surface of the diaphragm, and the mediastinum are lined with an airtight membrane called the parietal or costal pleura. It is a thin, delicate, serous membrane that is almost identical to the peritoneum of the abdominal cavity. As shown in Figure 2–9, it is continuous with the visceral pleura by means of reflexions at the root of the lung (hilum), where a sleeve of pleura encloses the bronchi and pulmonary blood vessels. The visceral pleura is a serous membrane that invests the lungs and closely follows their contours. The parietal and visceral pleurae lie in almost direct contact with one another. They are separated by a thin film of watery serous fluid, which is secreted by the pleurae. Throughout every breathing cycle the lung surfaces are held in contact with the inner surface of the thoracic cavity by virtue of the surface tension of the serous fluids.

It is important to note that the right and left pleural sacs are completely separate, one from the other, and that the intervening space (the mediastinum) is occupied by the heart, blood vessels, and esophagus. One function of the pleurae is to provide friction-free lung and thoracic surfaces. The two moist surfaces glide on one another with every cycle of breathing. Rough or inflamed pleurae, as in pleurisy, and the accompanying friction account for the pain which occurs with each inhalation. The pleurae also seem to serve in a protective capacity. Since one lung is separated from

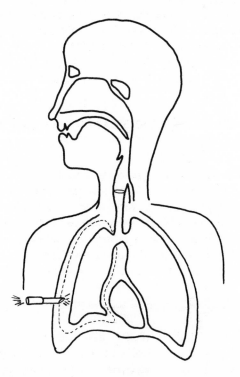

Fig. 2–11. Schematic of a pneumothorax.

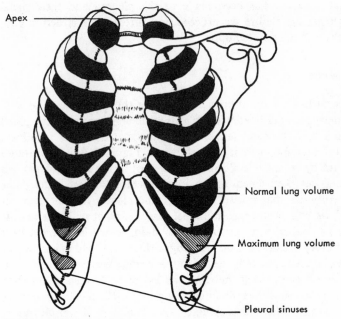

Fig. 2–12. Schematic of pleural sinuses.

the other by means of the airtight pleural sacs, a puncture of the thoracic wall results in the collapse of the lung just on the side of the puncture. If both lungs were enclosed within one airtight system (as is the case with some lower mammals), such a puncture would result in the collapse of both lungs and death by respiratory failure. Medically, a puncture which results in the collapse of lung is called a pneumothorax, and it is shown schematically in Figure 2–11.

In the adult, the lung tissue does not quite fill the thoracic cavity and so, in some areas as shown in Figure 2–12, pleural recesses or sinuses exist.

THE FRAMEWORK FOR THE BREATHING MECHANISM

Introduction

The framework for the breathing mechanism consists of the skeletal framework of the torso. The torso is divided into an upper cavity (thorax) and a lower cavity (abdomen) by a thin but very strong musculo-tendinous septum called the diaphragm. The thorax is almost completely filled with the lungs and heart, while the abdomen is filled with the digestive tract, various glands, and other organs. Although the most important musculature for breathing is located in the thorax and abdomen, some supplementary musculature is found in the neck and back.

The Spinal Column

As shown in Figure 2–13, the spinal column consists of 32 or 33 individual vertebrae. These vertebrae are joined together by a complex system of ligaments and intervertebral cartilages. There are seven cervical, twelve thoracic, five lumbar, five

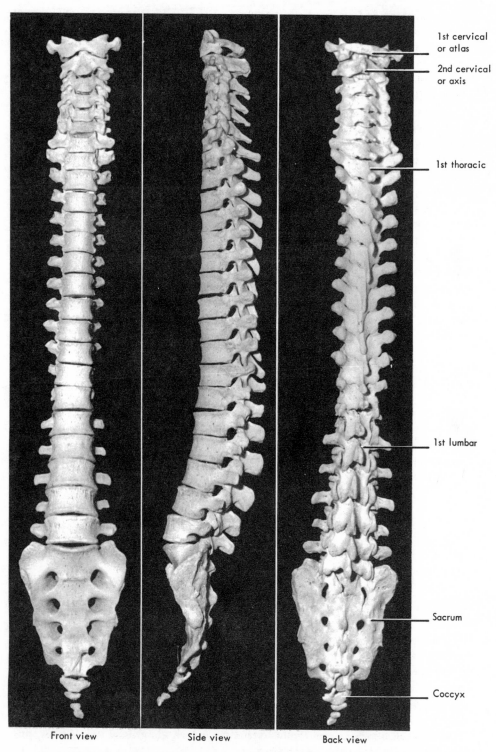

1st cervical or atlas

2nd cervical or axis

1st thoracic

1st lumbar

Sacrum

Coccyx

Front view   Side view   Back view

*Fig. 2–13. Various views of the articulated osseous compo-
nents that comprise the vertebral column.*

sacral, and three or four coccygeal vertebrae. The sacral vertebrae are solidly fused together and appear to be one bone, which is referred to as the sacrum. The coccygeal vertebrae are vestigial (not rudimentary) structures, which may vary in number from three to four, and occasionally, five. The individual coccygeal vertebrae are usually thought of as composing a single structure called the coccyx (pronounced kok-siks).

The bulk of an individual vertebra consists of a body or corpus, which is an unpaired and anteriorly directed cylindrical projection. As shown schematically in Figure 2–14, a pair of legs or pedicles arise from the corpus and are directed posteriorly. Two plate-like structures project backward from these pedicles to fuse in the midline, thus completing an arch which encloses a space called the vertebral foramen. This arch, the neural arch, protects the spinal cord which is contained within. A projection, directed dorsally and more or less inferiorly from the neural arch, is called the spinous process. It serves for the attachment of muscles and ligaments and, in addition, provides protection for the spinal column. Paired transverse processes project out laterally on either side of the vertebrae. These transverse processes form the points of attachment for muscles and ligaments and, in the case of thoracic vertebrae, points of articulation for ribs. There are, in addition, two superior and two inferior articular processes which articulate with adjacent vertebrae to form freely movable diarthrodial joints. The degree of movement at these joints is restricted by the nature of the ligamentous system and the amphiarthrodial joints between the vertebral bodies.

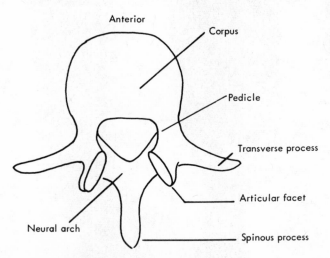

Fig. 2–14. Schematic lumbar vertebra as seen from above.

An intervertebral disc, made of fibrous cartilage, is found between each pair of vertebrae. Its shape conforms to that of the bodies of the vertebrae. The intervertebral fibrous cartilages are joined, by their surfaces, to thin layers of hyaline cartilage which cover the upper and lower surfaces of the bodies of the vertebrae. The result is an amphiarthrodial or yielding joint. The vertebrae are also joined by an extremely complex system of ligaments which run the entire length of the vertebral column.

The cervical, thoracic, and lumbar vertebrae, which are grossly very similar, present certain distinguishable characteristics.

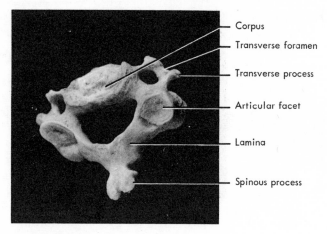

Corpus

Transverse foramen

Transverse process

Articular facet

Lamina

Spinous process

Fig. 2–15. A typical cervical vertebra.

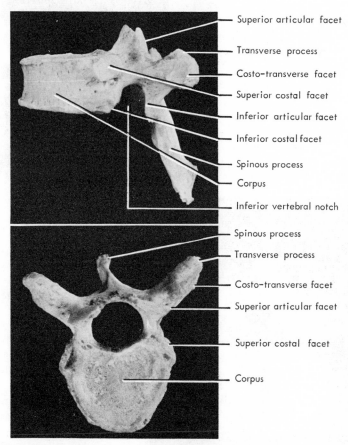

Superior articular facet

Transverse process

Costo-transverse facet

Superior costal facet

Inferior articular facet

Inferior costal facet

Spinous process

Corpus

Inferior vertebral notch

Spinous process

Transverse process

Costo-transverse facet

Superior articular facet

Superior costal facet

Corpus

Fig. 2–16. A typical thoracic vertebra as seen from above and from the side.

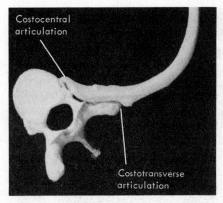

Fig. 2-17. A thoracic vertebra and rib attachments as seen from above.

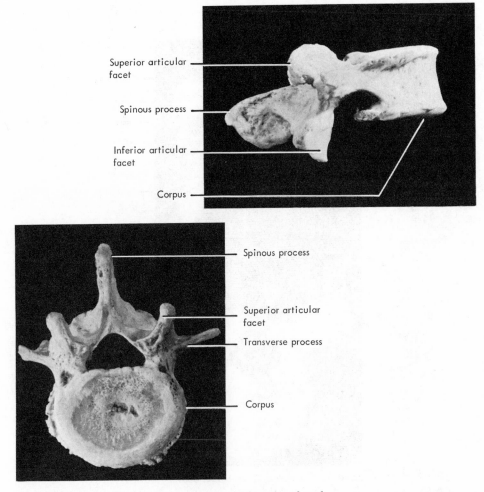

Fig. 2-18. A typical lumbar vertebra as seen from the side and from above.

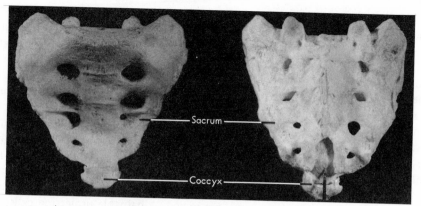

As seen from the front

As seen from behind

Fig. 2–19. A sacrum as seen from the front and from behind.

The seven cervical vertebrae have a distinguishing feature which sets them apart from the other vertebrae: transverse foramina, through which course the vertebral arteries. A fourth cervical vertebra, as viewed from above, is shown schematically in Figure 2–15.

The thoracic vertebrae are twelve in number and are distinctive because of the articular facets on their transverse processes and vertebral bodies. These facets provide points of attachment for the ribs. A typical thoracic vertebra as seen from above and from the side is shown in Figure 2–16. Another thoracic vertebra and its attachments with a rib are shown in Figure 2–17.

The lumbar vertebrae, five in number, are very large. Their massive bodies make them particularly suitable for their weight-bearing functions. These vertebrae are distinctive, not only because of their size but because of their lack of transverse foramina characteristic of the cervical vertebrae. They also lack the articular facets on their transverse processes and vertebral bodies, a characteristic of the thoracic vertebrae. A typical lumbar vertebra, as seen from above and from the side, is shown in Figure 2–18.

The sacrum is composed of five vertebral bodies that, in the adult, are united by four ossified intervertebral discs. This is most easily observed on its concave anterior surface. The body of the first sacral vertebra has a prominent oval upper surface, and an especially thick intervertebral disc unites it with the body of the fifth lumbar vertebra.

The coccyx, an inferiorly directed projection from the bottom of the sacrum, derives its name from a fancied resemblance to the beak of a cuckoo. The coccyx is composed of three or four fused vestigial vertebrae that articulate with the sacrum by means of a small intervertebral disc. A sacrum and a coccyx are shown in Figure 2–19.

The Rib Cage

The skeletal framework of the thorax consists of twelve thoracic vertebrae posteriorly, the sternum anteriorly, and the twelve pairs of ribs laterally. It is called the rib cage.

The sternum

The sternum, shown in Figures 2–20 and 2–21, is a prominent mid-line structure located on the superior, anterior thoracic wall. It is often referred to as the breastbone. The sternum, an oblong structure, consists of three parts, the manubrium, the corpus, and the ensiform or xiphoid process.

The uppermost segment of the sternum is known as the manubrium. It is a quadrilateral plate that is somewhat wider above than below. A principal landmark is found on its superior border in the form of a depression called the jugular or suprasternal notch. Lateral to this notch, on either side, is an oval articulatory facet, which forms the point of articulation for the manubrium with the medial end of the clavicle, or collar bone. On each lateral border of the manubrium is a depression for articulation with the first costal cartilage. The second costal cartilage joins the sternum at the level where the manubrium and corpus are joined. A palpable projection called the sternal angle indicates the junction of the manubrium and the corpus of the sternum. Palpation of this anteriorly directed prominence will also locate the level of articulation between the sternum and the second costal cartilage.

The corpus or body of the sternum is long and narrow, and is directed upward and somewhat backward. Its anterior surface is marked by indistinct ridges at the level of the third, fourth, and fifth ribs. These ridges are also found on the posterior surface in some specimens. The lateral borders of the body of the sternum are marked by the articulatory facets for the cartilages of ribs two through seven (true ribs).

Fig. 2–20. A sternum as seen from the front.

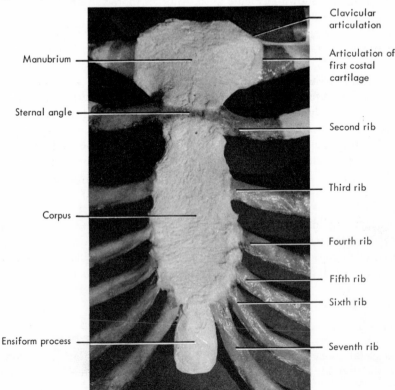

Manubrium

Sternal angle

Corpus

Ensiform process

Clavicular articulation

Articulation of first costal cartilage

Second rib

Third rib

Fourth rib

Fifth rib

Sixth rib

Seventh rib

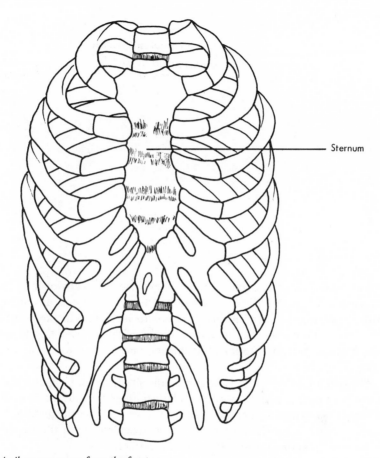

Fig. 2–21. A rib cage as seen from the front.

The inferior border of the corpus articulates with an elastic cartilaginous structure called the ensiform or xiphoid process.

The ribs (costae)

All twelve pairs of ribs articulate with the vertebral column by means of arthrodial or gliding joints that are effected typically by two demiarticulations. That is to say, with the exception of the first and the last three pairs of ribs, the head of every rib articulates with the bodies of two adjacent vertebrae and their intervertebral discs. The first, tenth, eleventh, and twelfth ribs join only with their numerically corresponding vertebrae. The scheme of vertebrocostal articulations is shown in Table 2–1. Anteriorly, the costal cartilages of the superior seven pairs of ribs join directly with the sternum. These ribs are known as the true ribs, or vertebrosternal ribs. With the exception of the first rib, the articulations of the true ribs with the sternum are arthrodial joints. The cartilage of the first rib is directly united with the sternum. A complex system of radiating ligaments at the costosternal joint limits the movements of the ribs. In old age, however, the cartilages of the ribs become continuous with the sternum, and the joint cavities disappear. The next three pairs of ribs (ribs eight, nine,

Table 2-1
Vertebrocostal Articulations

Rib No.	*Articulates with Transverse Process No.*	*and Vertebral Body No.*
1	1	1
2	2	1–2
3	3	2–3
4	4	3–4
5	5	4–5
6	6	5–6
7	7	6–7
8	8	7–8
9	9	8–9
10	10	10
11	none	11
12	none	12

and ten) are indirectly connected to the sternum by means of long costal cartilages. As shown in Figure 2–21, the cartilages of these ribs course upward where they join with the cartilage of the rib just superior to it. These ribs are called false ribs, or vertebrochondral ribs. The lowest two pairs of ribs (eleven and twelve) have dorsal attachments, but no anterior attachments, and are known as floating or vertebral ribs.

The bulk of a typical rib is known as the shaft, and since it is somewhat flattened, it exhibits upper and lower borders and inner and outer surfaces. Posteriorly, the head of the rib is separated from the shaft by a short neck. At the junction of the neck and shaft, a tubercle on the posterior surface articulates with the tip of the transverse process of the numerically corresponding vertebra.

Beginning at the head, the course of the rib is at first posteriorly downward and lateral until the rib abuts against the transverse process. A short distance from the tubercle, the shaft begins to course rather sharply in an anterior direction. The point where the rib abruptly changes course is known as the angle of the rib. As the rib approaches the sternum, it reaches its lowest point. At this point there is a sharp demarcation between the bone and the cartilage of the rib. Some anatomists consider the costal cartilage to be a separate hyaline structure that is joined to the rib, while others regard it as an unossified portion of the rib. In old age, however, the costal cartilages tend to undergo superficial ossification. A rib cage, as seen from behind, is shown in Figure 2–22.

The lower border of the shaft of a rib has a costal groove which accommodates and protects the intercostal blood vessels and nerves that course along each rib. As shown in Figure 2–22, a rib cage becomes progressively larger from the first rib to the seventh rib, and progressively smaller from the eighth to the twelfth rib, thus presenting a barrel-like appearance to the thoracic framework.

The posterior end of each rib is higher than the anterior end. This is not so true, however, in infants as it is in adults; in infants the course of the rib tends to be more horizontal.

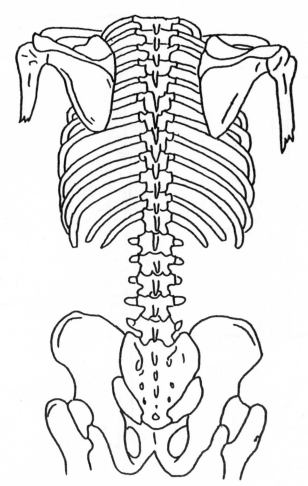

Fig. 2–22. A rib cage as seen from behind.

Movements of the ribs in breathing

During the inhalation phase of breathing, the dimensions of the thoracic cavity increase in three planes. The vertical dimension is increased by contraction of the dome-shaped diaphragm, an important muscle of inhalation that will be considered in more detail later. The transverse diameter of the thoracic cavity is increased by virtue of the raising of the curved ribs, while the antero-posterior diameter is increased by simultaneous forward and upward movement of the sternum. The movements of the rib cage are illustrated schematically in Figure 2–23. Although the analogy is not quite accurate, the raising of the ribs to increase the transverse dimensions of the thoracic cavity is sometimes likened to the raising of a bucket handle. This analogy is also illustrated in Figure 2–23. As this figure demonstrates, an upward movement of the ribs sharpens the angle which the ribs make with the vertebral column. It also shows that, as the sternum moves upward and forward, its angle with the vertebral column is maintained.

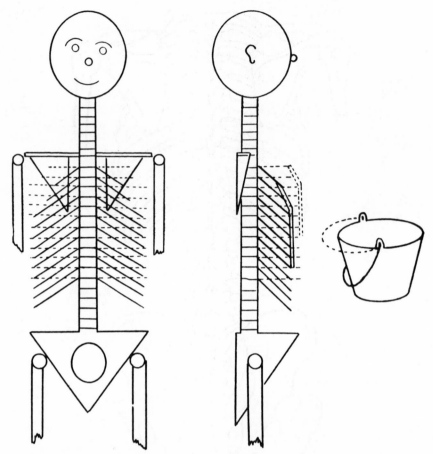

Fig. 2–23. Schematic of the movements of the rib cage.

The Pectoral Girdle

Two other important associated structures, the clavicle and the scapula, complete the thoracic framework for breathing. These two bones also form the pectoral girdle.

The clavicle

The clavicle, or collar bone, is essentially a strut of bone which serves to project the scapula (shoulder blade) sufficiently laterally to clear the barrel-shaped chest wall. If a clavicle is broken the entire shoulder may collapse medially. The head of the clavicle rides on the upper and lateral margin of the manubrium of the sternum and articulates with it by means of an arthrodial joint. The clavicle projects laterally and somewhat posteriorly, crossing over the first rib. The lateral end of the clavicle never reaches the point of the shoulder. Rather, it articulates by means of an arthrodial joint with the acromion, a hook-like projection of the scapula. This joint, the acromioclavicular joint, is easily palpated by placing the fingers on the anterior shoulder about an inch from the lateral-most point and rotating the arm. Medially the clavicle is somewhat enlarged and "rides" on the upper and lateral surfaces of the manubrium.

The space between the two medial ends of the clavicle may be seen as a notch that is readily palpable and easily visible at the root of the neck anteriorly. Earlier, this notch was identified as the suprasternal or jugular notch.

The scapula

The scapula, shown in Figure 2–24, is a thin, flat, triangular plate of bone situated dorsal to the upper seven or eight ribs, and is covered on both surfaces by muscles. It has a skeletal attachment only by virtue of its articulation with the clavicle. The scapula lies, freely movable, on the posterior-superior wall of the rib cage, just lateral to the vertebral column. With the body in the anatomical position, the longest side

Fig. 2–24. A scapula as seen from behind and from the front.

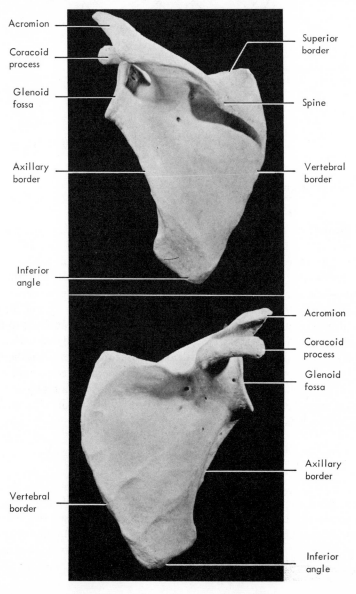

Acromion

Coracoid process

Glenoid fossa

Axillary border

Inferior angle

Superior border

Spine

Vertebral border

Acromion

Coracoid process

Glenoid fossa

Axillary border

Vertebral border

Inferior angle

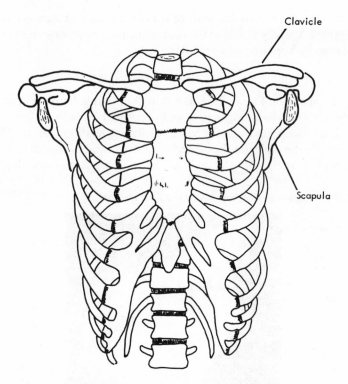

Clavicle

Scapula

Fig. 2–25. A rib cage and pectoral girdle as seen from the front.

(vertebral border) of the scapula lies parallel to and about six cm away from the vertebral spines. The scapula *in situ* is shown in Figures 2–22 and 2–25, along with the clavicle. The lower end of the scapula presents an inferior angle from which a dorsal projection, the axillary border, runs upward and laterally to terminate at the lateral angle, where the articular facet (glenoid fossa) for the upper arm bone is situated. The superior border runs almost horizontally from the glenoid fossa to meet the vertebral border at the superior angle of the scapula. Just anterior to the glenoid fossa is a prominent landmark of the scapula. It is a hooked projection that is directed somewhat laterally and anteriorly; it is called the coracoid process. Another prominent landmark of the scapula is the spine, a ledge of bone directed dorsally, beginning about a third of the way down the vertebral border, passing laterally and increasing in size until it terminates as a free projection called the acromion. The acromion, you will recall, has been associated with the lateral articulation of the clavicle.

The Pelvic Girdle

The coxal bone

The coxal bone, or os innominatum, which is shown in Figures 2–26 and 2–27, forms the pelvic girdle. This bone, which is composed of three lesser bones, is often referred to as the haunch or hip bone. Together with the sacrum and coccyx, the hip bones form the bony pelvis. The hip bone is an extremely complex structure, very difficult to visualize. It will be profitable for the student to rely heavily upon illustra-

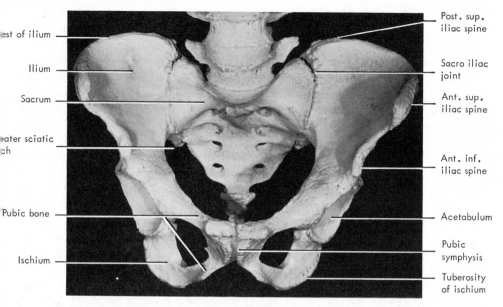

est of ilium

Ilium

Sacrum

ater sciatic
ch

Pubic bone

Ischium

Post. sup.
iliac spine

Sacro iliac
joint

Ant. sup.
iliac spine

Ant. inf.
iliac spine

Acetabulum

Pubic
symphysis

Tuberosity
of ischium

Fig. 2–26. The coxal bones and adjacent structures (which comprise the pelvis) as viewed from the front.

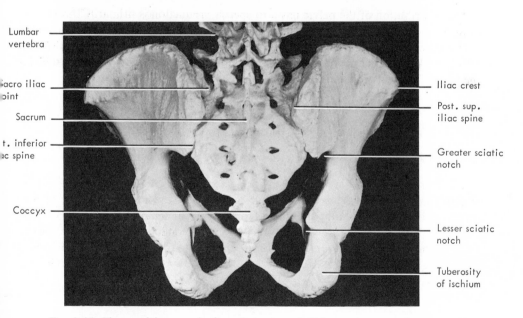

Lumbar
vertebra

acro iliac
oint

Sacrum

t. inferior
ic spine

Coccyx

Iliac crest

Post. sup.
iliac spine

Greater sciatic
notch

Lesser sciatic
notch

Tuberosity
of ischium

Fig. 2–27. The coxal bones and adjacent structures (which comprise the pelvis) as viewed from behind.

tive material and sketches of the bone. Probably the most distinctive landmark of the hip bone is the acetabulum, or "vinegar cup," which forms the socket for the reception of the head of the femur. The three individual bones that constitute the coxal bone meet at this point. These bones are the ilium, the ischium, and the pubis.

The great bulk of the hip bone is composed of the ilium, a roughly fan-shaped plate. Its upper margin forms the iliac crest, which is easily palpable from its anterior-superior spine to its posterior-superior spine. Just beneath each of these iliac spines is a corresponding inferior spine. The posterior part of the inner surface of each ilium is articulated, by means of an amphiarthrodial joint (yielding), with the lateral border of the sacrum and is firmly united with it over a wide expanse by a complex ligamentous system. This union is known as the sacroiliac joint. Just beneath the sacroiliac joint there is a very prominent notch, the greater sciatic notch, through which passes the sciatic nerve. Just below the angle of the notch, the ilium articulates with the ischium. The lower lateral portion of the acetabulum and a stout, triangular-shaped column of bone make up the ischium. The ischium descends in a vertical direction to terminate as a rough and large ischial tuberosity. The ischial tuberosity absorbs the weight of the body when one sits up straight. The large muscle of the buttock (the gluteus maximus muscle) conceals the ischial tuberosity, which nevertheless is easily palpated. The antero-medial portion of the acetabulum belongs to the pubis, which is continued in a horizontal direction as a bony bar called the superior ramus. It expands to form the body of the pubis. The body meets its fellow from the opposite side at the mid-line to form the pubic symphysis.

Extending from the anterior-superior iliac spine to the pubic symphysis is the inguinal ligament of Poupart, which marks the division between the lower abdomen and the leg. Between the palpable posterior iliac spines lies the rough posterior surface of the sacrum.

The contribution of the pelvic basin to speech production is primarily through the muscles of exhalation, which in general have attachments on the anterior iliac crest.

Having examined, in some detail, the framework for the breathing mechanism, the next logical step might be to examine the musculature that is responsible for producing the forces for inhalation and for exhalation.

THE MUSCULATURE FOR THE BREATHING MECHANISM

Introduction

The muscles of breathing may be divided on a functional basis into those responsible for inhalation and those responsible for exhalation. They may also be divided on an anatomical basis into muscles of the thorax and muscles of the abdomen. Interestingly enough, the muscles of inhalation are confined largely to the thorax, while the muscles of exhalation are confined primarily to the abdomen. Since breathing consists of an inhalation phase followed by an exhalation phase, the muscles of inhalation will be considered first.

The Muscles of Inhalation

The diaphragm

The diaphragm is without a doubt the most important single muscle of breathing. It is a thin, arched, musculo-tendinous partition, located between the thoracic and abdominal cavities. Some anatomists consider the diaphragm to be the most important muscle in the body—next after the heart.

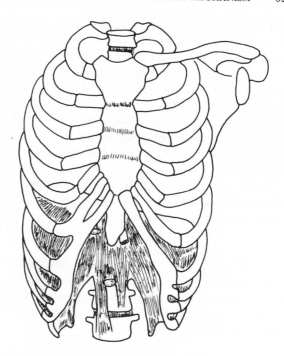

Fig. 2–28. A diaphragm in situ.

Fig. 2–29. Diagphram in situ. *The anterior portion of the rib cage has been removed.*

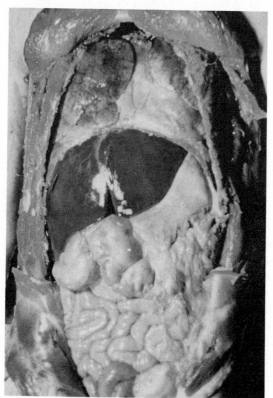

The diaphragm is dome shaped, slightly higher on the right side than on the left. It is often said to resemble an inverted bowl. The diaphragm *in situ* is shown in Figures 2–28 and 2–29. From the illustrations it can be seen that because of the pronounced dome shape of the diaphragm, many important abdominal organs in contact with its lower surface enjoy the protection of the lower ribs. This is particularly true of the liver, spleen, and kidneys.

The periphery of the diaphragm consists of muscular fibers, which take their origin from the margins at the outlet of the thorax. They course upward and inward and insert into the edges of the central tendon.

Central Tendon.   Centrally, the diaphragm consists of an aponeurosis, which is thin but extremely strong. This aponeurosis, usually referred to as the central tendon, is located somewhat closer to the front than to the back of the thorax. In outline it is uneven, and is said to bear a resemblance to a trifoliate leaf.   Structurally, the central tendon is composed of several layers of fibers which intersect at different angles. Such an arrangement gives it great strength with very little elasticity.

Because of the particular location of the central tendon within the diaphragm, the posterior muscle fibers are somewhat longer than the anterior fibers. The muscular portion of the diaphragm is usually described as having three parts: sternal, costal, and vertebral.

The Muscular Portion.   The sternal portion takes its origin from the lower border and back of the ensiform process. The fibers pass somewhat upward and medially to insert into the front of the middle leaflet of the central tendon. The sternal fibers are the shortest in the diaphragm.

The costal portion takes its origin, in the form of fleshy slips, from the lower borders and inner surfaces of the cartilages of ribs seven through twelve. Some fibers may originate from the portion of the ribs adjacent to the costal cartilages. These bundles of muscle fibers interdigitate with those of the transversus abdominis muscle. The fibers of the costal portion course at first sharply upward, and then medially, to insert into the central tendon.

The vertebral portion takes its origin from the upper lumbar vertebrae by means of two stout pillars of muscle fibers known as crura. As shown in Figure 2–28, the right crus is thicker and longer than the left. It arises from the upper three or four lumbar vertebrae and their intervertebral discs. Its fibers fan out as they course upward and medially. They decussate and encircle the esophagus before inserting into the central tendon. The left crus arises from the upper two lumbar vertebrae and their intervertebral disc. Its fibers course steeply upward and medially to insert into the central tendon. Figures 2–28 and 2–30 also indicate that the diaphragm is pierced by three large apertures and several smaller ones.

Openings in the Diaphragm.   The aortic hiatus, formed largely by the union of the crura, is located just at the level of the last thoracic vertebra. It permits the descending aorta to pass from the thorax to the abdomen.

The esophageal hiatus is located just posterior to the middle leaflet of the central tendon. It is nearly oval shaped, and is surrounded by a sphincter of muscle fibers. The esophagus and several small arteries pass through it.

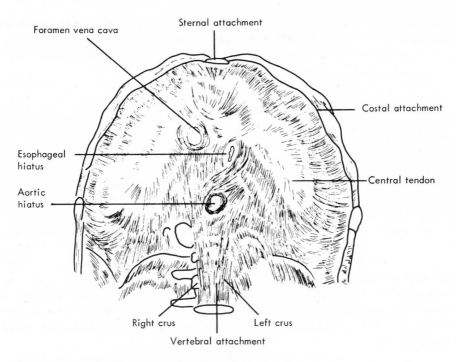

Fig. 2–30. A diaphragm as seen from beneath.

The foramen vena cava is located at the level of the eighth thoracic vertebra, and it pierces the central tendon at the junction of the right and middle leaflets. The inferior vena cava, several nerve bundles, and lymph vessels pass through it.

The Action of the Diaphragm. By virtue of their attachments to the rib cage, the abdominal, back, and thoracic muscles maintain the points of origin of the diaphragm relatively fixed in position. Contraction of the diaphragm pulls the central tendon downward and forward, thus increasing the vertical diameter of the thorax. This action results in an increase in volume and a decrease in pressure within the thoracic cavity. In addition, there is a decrease in volume and an increase in pressure within the abdominal cavity. That is, the descending diaphragm compresses the abdominal viscera, causing them to be displaced downward and forward against the passive resistance of the abdominal muscles. As a result, the abdominal wall may be distended slightly during the inhalation phase of breathing. The role of the diaphragm in breathing and in speech production will be treated more thoroughly later in the chapter.

Whereas the diaphragm is regarded by some anatomists as a muscle of the thorax, it is regarded by others as a part of the abdominal musculature. Since muscles of inhalation are confined largely to the thorax, there seems to be some merit in considering the diaphragm as a muscle of the thorax. Other muscles of the thorax are involved in inhalation but to a lesser extent than the diaphragm, and, as will be shown later, the contributions of the accessory muscles of inhalation are open to some question.

The diaphragm is unique in that it is the only unpaired muscle of respiration. In fact, with very few exceptions, all of the muscles in the body are paired. Therefore, unless otherwise stated, all muscles described in the remainder of the text are to be regarded as paired muscles.

Accessory Thoracic Muscles of Inhalation

The pectoralis major

The pectoralis major, shown schematically in Figure 2–31, is a prominent, fan-shaped muscle located on the superficial surface of the anterior thoracic wall. Some anatomists consider its extensive origin to be in five parts, other anatomists in just two, the sternal head and the clavicular head. We shall follow the two-part school of thought. Anatomically, the clavicular head seems to be set apart from the rest of the pectoralis major. It takes its origin from the anterior surface of the medial half of the clavicle and forms a thick band of muscle fibers that insert into the greater tubercle of the humerus. The sternal head is much more extensive. It arises from the entire length of the sternum, from the costal cartilages of ribs one through six or seven, and from the aponeurosis of the external oblique muscle. Its fibers rapidly converge as they course across the chest to insert into the greater tubercle of the humerus. The sternal head comprises the anterior muscular mass that forms the front wall of the axilla, or armpit.

The primary function of the pectoralis major is as an adductor of the arm. It also rotates the arm medially. The sternal and clavicular heads are capable of acting somewhat independently. Note in Figure 2–31 that the fibers decussate so that those with

Fig. 2–31. Schematic of pectoralis major.

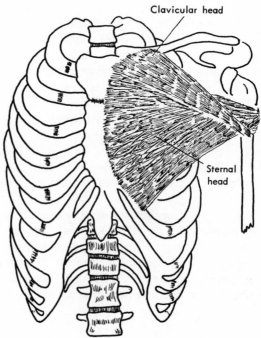

Clavicular head

Sternal head

the lowest origin have the highest insertion on the humerus. This accounts for the fact that the pectoralis major can aid in rotation of the arm. With the pectoral girdle in a fixed position, contraction of the pectoralis major may raise the ribs and sternum and thus contribute to expansion of the upper rib cage.

The pectoralis minor

Removal of the pectoralis major, as shown in Figure 2–32, reveals the pectoralis minor as well as the subclavius muscle. The pectoralis minor lies deep to the pectoralis major and is also fan shaped. The fibers take their origin from the anterior ends of ribs two through four or five. They course laterally upward and insert into the coracoid process of the scapula. This muscle functions as a shoulder extensor when you try for something just a little out of reach. When the pectoral girdle is fixed, however, this muscle may lift ribs two through four and thus facilitate expansion of the rib cage during inhalation.

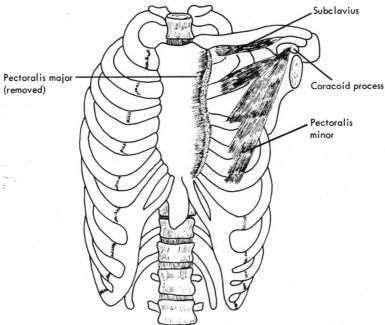

Fig. 2–32. Schematic of pectoralis minor and subclavius.

The subclavius

This tiny muscle originates at the junction of the first rib and its costal cartilage. It courses laterally to insert on the inferior surface of the clavicle near the point where the clavicle articulates with the acromion of the scapula. Upon contraction this muscle is said to exert an upward force on the first rib and thus to contribute to expansion of the upper rib cage.

The serratus anterior

The serratus anterior is an extremely powerful muscle of the shoulder girdle. It is a little more complex and difficult to visualize than the muscles described thus far. It is shown schematically in Figure 2–33. This muscle is sometimes called the ser-

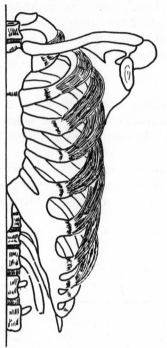

Fig. 2–33. Schematic of serratus anterior (serratus magnus).

ratus magnus, which is simply a descriptive term meaning a large serrated muscle. The fibers take their origin from ribs one through eight or nine, at the side, in the form of digitations or fingers, which, because of their saw-like appearance, give the muscle its name. The fibers course backward in close contact with the chest wall until they reach their insertion along the entire length of the vertebral border of the scapula; that is, the fibers course between the posterior surface of the ribs and the anterior surface of the scapula. The primary function of the serratus anterior is to fixate and protract the scapula. With the shoulder in a fixed position, however, contraction of this muscle may raise ribs one through eight or nine to assist in expansion of the rib cage during inhalation.

The intercostal muscles

As the name suggests, the intercostal muscle fibers are situated between the ribs. They are generally considered to be in two groups, the external intercostal and the internal intercostal muscles.

The external intercostals, shown in Figure 2–34, are a more prominent and stronger group of muscles than are the internal intercostals. They are eleven in number and occupy the space between the ribs in an area extending from the tubercle posteriorly to the anterior extremity of the rib. They are deficient in the cartilaginous (chondral) portion of the ribs. Each muscle takes its origin from the lower border of a rib, and is inserted into the upper border of the rib immediately below. The course of the fibers is obliquely downward and forward in front and downward and outward in back.

The internal intercostal muscles, shown in Figure 2–34, lie just deep to the external intercostals and are also eleven in number. They occupy an area extending from the

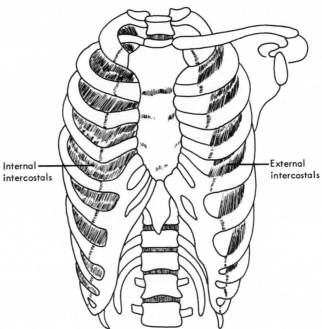

Fig. 2–34. The intercostal muscles, shown schematically.

anterior limits of the intercostal spaces to the angle of the rib posteriorly. They are continued to the vertebral column as thin aponeuroses, the posterior intercostal membranes. Thus, the area just lateral to the vertebral column contains muscle fibers of the external intercostal muscles only, while the area just lateral to the sternum contains muscle fibers of just the internal intercostal muscles. The significance of such muscle distribution will become apparent when we discuss electromyographic recording of breathing musculature. The internal intercostals take their origin from the lower borders of the upper eleven ribs and course from above downward to insert into the inner aspect of the ribs immediately below. In front, the course of the fibers is downward and outward, and in back the course is down and inward.

The function of the intercostal muscles is not free from debate. There is general agreement, however, that as a group, both the external and internal intercostal muscles contribute to the rigidity of the thoracic wall by preventing the intercostal spaces from bulging in and out during breathing. These muscles presumably help control the amount of space between the ribs. In addition, they couple the ribs, one to the other, so that movement of any given rib will influence the position of adjacent ribs.

Some fairly recent electromyographic studies of the intercostal muscles have shown that both the internal and external intercostals are active during inhalation as well as exhalation. The intercostals have also been shown to function in flexion of the trunk, and thus are classified as postural muscles. In addition, the intercostal muscles are said to play an active role in lifting the ribs during inhalation. This is particularly true if the muscles that insert into the uppermost ribs are contracted at the same time as the intercostals become active. Another viewpoint is that the external intercostals are active during inhalation and that the internal intercostals are active during exhalation. There is some supportive evidence for this latter viewpoint, particularly from studies employing electromyography. It seems very likely that the action of the intercostal muscles contributes to sequential muscular control of the breath stream during speech production. Some of these conflicting points of view will be examined in greater detail in a section of this chapter that deals with the physiology of the breathing mechanism.

The intercostals are unquestionably very important muscles of respiration. Some authorities (Campbell, 1958; Basmajian, 1962) regard them, along with the diaphragm, as the regular muscles of inhalation.

The levator costalis muscles

The levator costalis muscles, or costal elevators, presumably play an active role as elevators of the ribs during inhalation. There are twelve costal elevators on each side of the vertebral column. As illustrated in Figure 2–35, they take their origin from the transverse processes of the lowest cervical and upper eleven thoracic vertebrae. The fibers course downward and somewhat laterally, diverging slightly. The costal elevators are often divided into two groups, the levatores costarum brevis muscles, which insert into the outer surface of the ribs immediately beneath their points of origin, and the levatores costarum longus muscles, which pass over the ribs immediately beneath their origin and continue to the outer surface of the second rib below

Fig. 2–35. Costal elevators, serratus posterior superior, and the serratus posterior inferior.

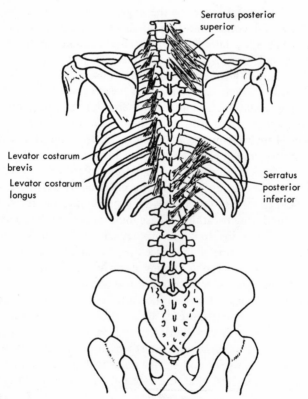

their points of origin. Upon contraction these muscles are said to elevate and abduct the ribs, thereby assisting in inhalation.

The serratus posterior—superior and inferior

The serratus posterior superior and the serratus posterior inferior muscles are often regarded as muscles of the back. The serratus posterior superior, located on the dorsal aspect of the upper thoracic wall, probably functions in inhalation, while the serratus posterior inferior, which is located at the junction of the lumbar and thoracic regions, probably functions during exhalation. Operationally, it will simplify matters to think of the former as part of the thoracic musculature and the latter as part of the back musculature.

The Serratus Posterior Superior.   The serratus posterior superior is shown schematically in Figure 2–35. It originates by means of a broad tendon from the spinous processes of cervical vertebrae six and seven and of thoracic vertebrae one and two. The fibers course downward and laterally to insert, lateral to the angles, on ribs two through five. Upon contraction, this muscle may assist in raising the ribs into which it inserts.

The Serratus Posterior Inferior.   This muscle, shown in Figure 2–35, is an irregularly shaped, quadrilateral sheet of tissue which originates by means of an aponeurosis from the spinous processes of thoracic vertebrae ten, eleven, and twelve and from lumbar vertebrae one, two, and three. The fibers course upward and laterally to insert, just beyond the angles, into the inferior border of ribs eight through twelve.

This muscle may contribute to deep or forced inhalation; that is, during forced inhalation it may anchor the lower four ribs and prevent them from being lifted as the diaphragm exerts pressure downward upon the abdominal viscera. With the lower ribs free to move, such a compression might simply retain the diaphragm in the same position while the ribs move upward. Such action would result in little or no increase in the vertical diameter of the thoracic cavity. Thus, the serratus posterior inferior may act as a muscle of either inhalation or of exhalation. During exhalation, contraction of this muscle might depress the lower four ribs into which it inserts.

Muscles of the Neck

With the head in a fixed position, contraction of two neck muscles, the sternocleidomastoid and the scalenes, may lift the sternum and the two uppermost ribs.

The sternocleidomastoid

This muscle, so-named because of its attachments, is located on the antero-lateral aspect of the neck. As shown in Figure 2–36, it is a prominent muscle that takes its origin in the form of a sternal and a clavicular head. The sternal head arises from the anterior surface of the manubrium of the sternum. It courses upward, backward, and somewhat laterally. The clavicular head originates from the superior surface of the sternal end of the clavicle. These fibers course almost vertically upward. As indicated

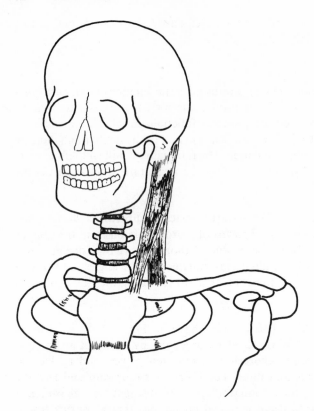

Fig. 2–36. Schematic of sterno-cleidomastoid muscle.

in Figure 2–36, the clavicular and sternal heads unite, course upward and laterally across the side of the neck, and insert as a single muscle into the mastoid process of the temporal bone. A few fibers insert into an adjacent portion of the occipital bone known as the superior nuchal line (nape of the neck).

Upon unilateral contraction, this muscle may draw the side of the head toward the shoulder and, at the same time, rotate it. Contraction of both sternocleidomastoid muscles tends to flex the head toward the thorax. When the head is held in a fixed position, this muscle may raise the sternum and clavicle to assist in inhalation. Elevation of the sternum increases the antero-posterior diameter of the thorax. In certain individuals, particularly those with chronic lung disease, this type of breathing activity may be most prominent. Pronounced use of the upper thoracic and neck muscles during inhalation is sometimes called clavicular breathing, and it is usually regarded as undesirable. In addition, clavicular breathing may be seen as compensatory behavior in persons with paralysis of the regular breathing muscles.

The scalene muscles

The deep muscles of the antero-lateral region of the neck are sometimes divided into an inner and an outer group, with the anterior tubercles of the cervical vertebrae forming the boundary line. The outer group (lateral vertebral muscles) may at times serve as supplementary muscles of inhalation. This group, shown in Figure 2–37, consists of the scaleni, which course from their insertion on the transverse processes of the cervical vertebrae to their insertion on the uppermost two ribs. (In some

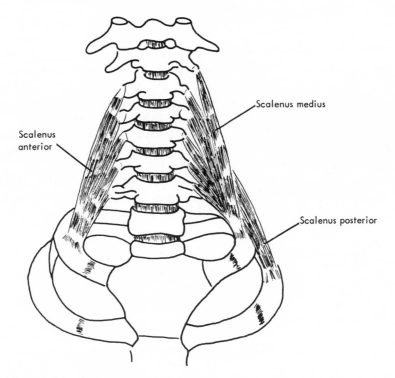

Fig. 2–37. The scaleni.

anatomy textbooks the ribs are given as the origin of the scaleni, and the cervical vertebrae are given as the points of insertion.)

The Scalenus Anterior.   The scalenus anterior muscle takes its origin, by means of four tendinous slips, from the transverse processes of cervical vertebrae three through six. The fibers course almost vertically downward to insert into the scalene tubercle, which is located on the inner border of the upper surface of the first rib. This muscle appears to have two functions. It may act from above to elevate the first rib and assist in inhalation, or it may act from below to flex and rotate the cervical vertebrae.

The Scalenus Medius.   As the name implies, the scalenus medius is located deep to the scalanus anterior. It takes its origin, by means of five tendinous slips, from the transverse processes of cervical vertebrae two through seven. The fibers course vertically downward and insert into the upper surface of the first rib by means of a broad tendon. The scalenus medius may act from above to elevate the first rib, or it may act from below to flex the cervical column.

The Scalenus Posterior.   This muscle is the smallest of the scaleni, and the deepest. It takes its origin from the posterior tubercles of the transverse processes of the lowest two or three cervical vertebrae. The fibers course downward and laterally to insert into the outer surface of the second rib. When the second rib is held fixed, this muscle may flex the neck, or, acting from above, it may raise the second rib during inhalation.

Muscles of the Back

The latissimus dorsi

Certain muscles of the back are capable of contributing to rib movement during inhalation. One such muscle is the latissimus dorsi. It is a superficial muscle that forms part of the second muscle layer of the back. (The first layer is formed by the trapezius muscle.) As illustrated in Figure 2–38, it is a very complex muscle covering the lower half of the back. Its primary function is to extend the arm and to rotate it. It arises from the spines of thoracic vertebrae seven through twelve, from the spines of the lumbar vertebrae and the sacrum (by means of an aponeurosis), from the posterior third of the crest of the ilium, and from the outer surface of ribs ten, eleven, and twelve, lateral to their angles. The fibers course upward and laterally and converge rapidly before inserting, by means of a stout tendon, into the humerus. Because of the costal attachments, contraction of the latissimus dorsi may raise the lower three or four ribs.

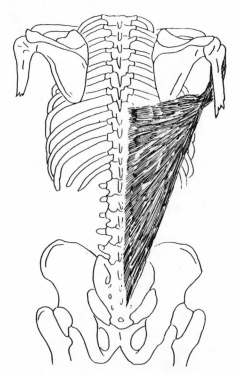

Fig. 2–38. Schematic of a latissimus dorsi.

The sacrospinalis

The deepest layer of back muscle is formed by the sacrospinalis group, a complex, vertically directed mass which flanks the vertebral column on either side. It extends from the occipital bone above to the sacrum below. This muscle is usually considered as being composed of three primary groups, the medial spinalis group, the medial longissimus group, and the lateral iliocostalis group. Each of these three groups is in turn further divided into three subgroups. Apparently, only the muscles in the lateral iliocostalis group may influence rib movement during respiration.

The Medial Spinalis Group.   The medial spinalis column of muscle is responsible for extension, lateral flexion, and rotation of the vertebral column and lateral movement of the pelvis. It is the deepest group of the sacrospinalis muscles, and is composed of the spinalis dorsi, the spinalis cervicis, and the spinalis capitis. These muscles take their origin from the spines of the vertebrae all along the extent of the vertebral column. They course vertically to insert into the spines of vertebrae above. The uppermost fibers insert into the occipital bone at the base of the skull.

The Medial Longissimus Group (*Intermediate Longissimus*).   The medial longissimus group is composed of three muscles, the longissimus dorsi, the longissimus cervicis, and the longissimus capitis. The fibers of the longissimus dorsi and longissimus cervicis take their origin from the transverse processes of the lumbar and thoracic vertebrae and course vertically upward to insert into the lower nine or ten ribs proximal to their angles and to adjacent transverse processes. The fibers of the longissimus capitis originate from the transverse processes of the upper four or five thoracic vertebrae and the lower three or four cervical vertebrae. They insert into the mastoid process of the temporal bone. The function of this latter muscle is to flex the head.

The Lateral Iliocostalis Group.   The lateral iliocostalis group is composed of the iliocostalis lumborum, the iliocostalis dorsi, and the iliocostalis cervicis.

Thus far in our account of the breathing mechanism we have directed our attention primarily to the musculature of inhalation. The iliocostalis lumborum, however, may be considered as a muscle of exhalation. It is composed of long fibers, which take their origin from the posterior iliac crest and from the sacrum. The fibers course vertically upward to insert into the lower nine ribs at their angles. Contraction of this muscle may depress the ribs during inhalation.

The iliocostalis dorsi consists of a series of fleshy bundles, which arise from the angles of ribs seven through twelve. They insert by eight tendons into ribs one through seven, at their angles, and into the transverse process of the seventh cervical vertebra. These muscles bind the ribs so that they tend to move together as a unit. With the lower ribs anchored in position by other back muscles, however, the iliocostalis dorsi may depress the upper seven ribs during forced exhalation.

The iliocostalis cervicis group consists of from four to six fleshy slips, which take their origin from the heads of ribs one through six. The fibers course upward to be inserted into the transverse processes of cervical vertebrae four through six. Contraction of this muscle may help elevate the first six ribs during inhalation.

The sacrospinalis muscles and their functions, as outlined above, may be summarized as follows:

SACROSPINALIS

A. Medial Spinalis
   1. Spinalis Dorsi ⎫
   2. Spinalis Cervicis ⎬ Flexion, extension, rotation of
   3. Spinalis Capitis ⎭ vertebral column or pelvis

SACROSPINALIS   (Continued)

B. Medial Longissimus
    1. Longissimus Dorsi ⎫ Flexion, extension, rotation
    2. Longissimus Cervicis⎬ of vertebral column or
    3. Longissimus Capitis ⎭ pelvis

C. Lateral Iliocostalis
    1. Iliocostalis Lumborum....depress ribs
    2. Iliocostalis Dorsi ....fixate or depress ribs 1-6
    3. Iliocostalis Cervicis ......elevate ribs

The Muscles of Exhalation

Introduction

The musculature responsible for a decrease in the dimensions of the thoracic cavity is confined largely to the abdomen. You will recall that contraction of the diaphragm during inhalation exerts a force on the contents of the abdominal cavity and in addition, raises the intra-abdominal pressure. Conversely, a force inward, exerted by contraction of the abdominal musculature, further increases the intra-abdominal pressure and causes the abdominal contents to push inward and upward against the diaphragm and return it to its relaxed position. At the same time, associated musculature, which courses from below upward to insert into the ribs, exerts a force downward to augment the decrease in the lateral dimensions of the thorax. This lateral decrease, together with a decrease in the vertical dimension caused by the return of the diaphragm to its uncontracted state, reduces the total volume of the thorax. The result, of course, is an increase in air pressure with respect to the exterior, and air flows out of the lungs in what is known as the exhalation phase of breathing. Forces other than muscular, such as tissue elasticity and gravity, contribute to exhalation, and will be considered later in the chapter. The purpose of the following section is to examine the muscles which may provide the forces of exhalation.

Abdominal Muscles of Exhalation

The abdominal muscles form a wall in the region between the pelvic girdle and the lower margin of the rib cage. There are four muscles which contribute to this muscular wall, the internal and external obliques, the transversus abdominis, and the rectus abdominis. These muscles attach to the skeleton by means of two large, complex, tendinous sheets called the abdominal aponeurosis and the lumbar fascia.

The abdominal aponeurosis

The abdominal aponeurosis is a broad, flat sheet of tendinous tissue situated in the ventral abdominal wall, and it extends from the sternum to the pubis. At the mid-line anteriorly it is seen as a dense, fibrous band, the linea alba, which extends from the ensiform process of the sternum, above, to the pubic symphysis, below. On either side of the linea alba, the aponeurosis divides into two layers, one of which passes deep to, while the other passes superficial to, the rectus abdominis muscle. Thus, the rectus abdominis is enclosed by an aponeurosis which is appropriately called the sheath of

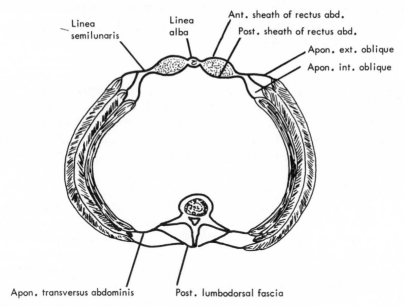

Fig. 2–39. Schematic of fasciae and aponeuroses of abdominal wall as seen from above.

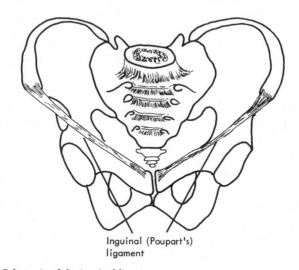

Fig. 2–40. Schematic of the inguinal ligament.

the rectus abdominis. Just lateral to the rectus abdominis the two layers of apo-neourosis meet to form a second vertical ribbon, the linea semilunaris, a landmark less identifiable than is the linea alba. As shown in Figure 2–39, the linea semilunaris divides, giving rise to three layers of aponeurosis into which the lateral abdominal muscles insert. The most superficial layer of the abdominal aponeurosis attaches superiorly to the lowermost fibers of the pectoralis major, to the ensiform process of the sternum, and to adjacent costal cartilages. Inferiorly it attaches to the pubic symphysis and to the anterior iliac spine. A prominent strand of thickened aponeurosis joins these two points, and is called the inguinal ligament, or Poupart's ligament, which is shown in Figure 2–40.

The lumbar fascia

A broad, two-layered tendinous sheet situated on the dorsal aspect of the lower part of the vertebral column is called the lumbar fascia. It has attachments on the spines of the lumbar vertebrae and on the posterior portion of the iliac crest. The fascia divides, as shown in Figure 2–39, giving rise to two layers of aponeurosis into which the fibers of the internal oblique and transversus abdominis attach.

The external oblique

The external obliques are the strongest and most superficial of the abdominal muscles. They are broad, thin, and roughly quadrilateral in shape. As shown in Figure 2–41, they take their origin by fleshy slips from the exterior surfaces and lower borders of ribs seven through twelve. Some of the fibers course downward and medially, where they insert into the anterior half of the iliac crest, while the remainder of the muscle fibers terminate in the broad abdominal aponeurosis.

The internal oblique

These muscles, also located on the lateral and anterior aspect of the abdominal wall, lie just deep to the external oblique muscles. As shown in Figure 2–42, their course is just opposite to that of the external obliques, and for this reason they are sometimes called the ascending oblique muscles. They take their origin from the lateral half of the inguinal ligament and from the anterior half of the iliac crest. The fibers which arise from the iliac crest course upward and medially to insert into the abdominal aponeurosis and the inferior borders of the chondral portion of ribs eight through twelve. The fibers which arise from the inguinal ligament course downward and medially to terminate in a tendinous sheet which inserts into the pubis as a slip called the falx inguinalis.

The transversus abdominis

The transversus abdominis muscles are the deepest of the abdominal muscles. As the name implies, the course of their fibers is horizontal. As illustrated in Figure 2–43, they originate from the inner surfaces of ribs six through twelve by means of fleshy slips. These slips interdigitate with the fibers of the diaphragm and triangularis sterni. Fibers also arise from the lumbar fascia, from the inner edge of the anterior half of the iliac crest, and from the lateral half of the inguinal ligament. The fibers course in a horizontal direction and insert into the deepest layer of the abdominal aponeurosis. A few of the inferior-most fibers course somewhat downward to insert into the pubis.

The rectus abdominis

As mentioned earlier, the rectus abdominis muscles are almost completely enclosed by an aponeurotic sheath, which holds the muscles in position without restricting their movement. They lie parallel to the mid-line, just lateral to the linea alba. They

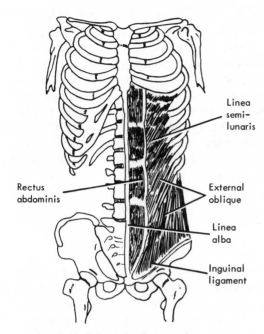

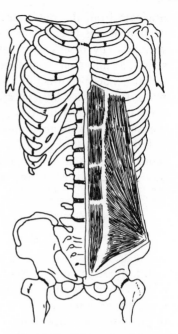

Fig. 2–41. Schematic of external oblique and rectus abdominis.

Fig. 2–42. Schematic of internal oblique muscle.

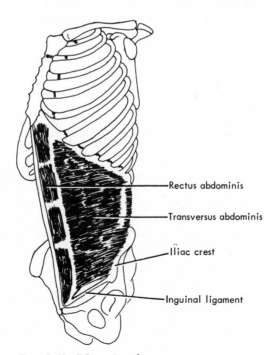

Fig. 2–43. Schematic of transversus abdominis.

originate from the outer surface of the ensiform process and from the chondral portion of ribs five, six, and seven. They course vertically to insert into the pubic symphysis by means of a flat tendon. These muscles are divided by tendinous inscriptions into four, sometimes five, segments, each of which is somewhat capable of independent contraction. At a distance about halfway between the umbilicus and pubis, the anterior layer of aponeurosis which forms the sheath of the muscle suddenly ceases, and from this point below, abdominal aponeurosis only runs deep to the muscle. A rectus abdominis muscle is shown in Figures 2–41, 2–42, and 2–43.

Although most of the muscles of exhalation are abdominal, two and possibly three thoracic muscles may be involved in the process of exhalation. They are the transversus thoracis, the subcostals, and the internal intercostals.

Thoracic Muscles of Exhalation

The transversus thoracis

The transversus thoracis, or triangularis sterni muscles, as they are sometimes called, are irregular muscles that vary in their attachments, sometimes even on opposite sides of the same specimen. They are thin, fan-shaped muscles, which originate from the posterior surface of the corpus of the sternum, from the posterior surface of the ensiform process, and from the posterior surfaces of the chondral portion of ribs five through seven. Their fibers course upward and outward to insert into the lower borders and inner surfaces of ribs two through six. As shown in Figure 2–44, the uppermost fibers course almost vertically, while the lower fibers course horizontally. The lowermost fibers are continuous with those of the transversus abdominis. Contraction of the transversus thoracis muscles may depress the ribs and thereby assist in exhalation.

Fig. 2–44. The rib cage as seen from within, showing transversus thoracis and the internal intercostals.

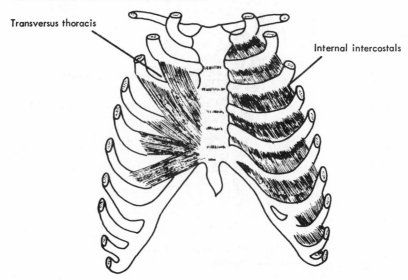

Transversus thoracis

Internal intercostals

The subcostals

The subcostals, sometimes called the infracostals, are scarcely distinguishable from the internal intercostals. They are well developed on the lower aspect of the ventral surface of the posterior thoracic wall. Their fibers originate from the lower part of the inner surface of the ribs, near the rib angles; they course down and medially, pass over one, sometimes two ribs, and insert into the second or third rib below. Upon contraction these muscles may depress the ribs, thus assisting in active exhalation.

It is noteworthy that these muscles course parallel to the internal intercostals, are highly variable in their form, and may be difficult to identify. They are sometimes considered to be simply the dorsal part of the triangularis sterni.

The internal intercostals

Although the internal intercostal muscles were described with the thoracic muscles of inhalation, they are often considered to be thoracic muscles of exhalation. There are differences of opinion regarding the action of these muscles; however, some recent research seems to support the viewpoint that the internal intercostals are active during exhalation. For a description of the internal intercostals, see page 68.

The Back Muscles of Exhalation

From the standpoint of mechanics, two back muscles are capable of influencing rib position, particularly in depressing the ribs. They are the iliocostalis dorsi and the quadratus lumborum.

The iliocostalis dorsi

The iliocostalis dorsi muscles were considered as a subgroup of the lateral iliocostalis group of the sacrospinalis muscles. They are described on page 75. The iliocostalis dorsi are said to bind the ribs so that they tend to move as a unit; with the lower ribs anchored in position by other back muscles, contraction of the iliocostalis dorsi depresses the upper seven ribs during forced exhalation.

The quadratus lumborum

The quadratus lumborum muscles are flat sheets of muscle located in the laterodorsal aspect of the abdominal wall. They are shown in Figure 2–45. The fibers take their origin, by means of an aponeurosis, from the iliac crest and from a prominent ligament, the iliolumborum ligament, which attaches to the transverse processes of the fifth lumbar vertebra medially and the crest of the ilium laterally. The fibers course almost vertically upward, converge slightly, and insert by slips into the transverse processes of lumbar vertebrae one through four and into the medial half and lower border of the last rib. From the standpoint of mechanics, two functions may be attributed to these muscles. Because of their costal attachments they may be regarded as active muscles of exhalation. In addition, the quadratus lumborum, along with the serratus posterior inferiors, may anchor the lower ribs against the lifting force of the diaphragm when it presses downward on the viscera. Inasmuch as fixation of the lower ribs may be complementary to diaphragm action, the quadratus lumborum might

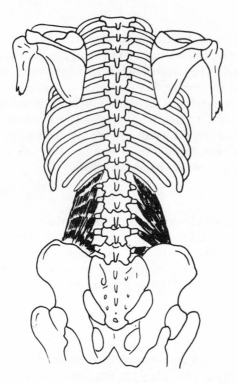

Fig. 2–45. Schematic of the quadratus lumborum muscles.

well be considered as accessory muscles in inhalation. There is very little supportive evidence for this viewpoint, however.

THE FUNCTIONS OF THE MUSCLES OF RESPIRATION

Introduction and Terminology

Many of the early experiments in breathing physiology attempted to demonstrate the relationship between the degree of muscle activity and the quantity of air that may be inhaled or exhaled. As a result, a rather well-established body of knowledge exists concerning the quantities of air that may be inhaled, exhaled, or exchanged during various breathing tasks. In addition, a standardized nomenclature has evolved for respiration physiology. The terms in current usage have very specific applications, and it is crucial that they be used appropriately.

Terminology

The volume of air inhaled and exhaled by an adult male, during a quiet cycle of breathing, amounts to about 750 cu cm, and is known as tidal volume. The air that is exchanged is known as tidal air. Wide variability in clinically normal individuals reduces the significance of this figure, however, and complicates its interpretation. For example, the 95 per cent range of tidal volume for adult males is from 675 to 895 cu cm, with a mean of 750 cu cm. The 95 per cent range for adult females is from 285 to 393 cu cm, with a mean of 339 cu cm.

The air which can be taken in, beyond that normally inspired in quiet breathing, amounts to about 1,500 cu cm, and has been called complemental air. In recent years, however, the term complemental air has been supplanted by the term inspiratory reserve volume. Unfortunately, physiologists are not in complete agreement as to the use of the term. Some investigators consider the total volume of air, from the beginning of quiet inhalation to the end of forced inhalation, to be the inspiratory reserve volume, while others measure from the conclusion of quiet inhalation. That is, some investigators include tidal volume as part of inspiratory reserve volume, while others consider tidal volume to be a separate quantity. The term as used in this text refers to the quantity of air inhaled beyond that inhaled during a quiet inhalation.

The amount of air that can be forcibly exhaled, following a quiet exhalation, is known as expiratory reserve volume. In the past this quantity has been known as reserve air, or supplemental air. It usually amounts to about 1,500 cu cm. The sum of the tidal and expiratory and inspiratory reserve volumes ought to represent the quantity of air that can be exhaled after as deep an inhalation as possible. This quantity is known as vital capacity, and in adult males it ranges from 3,500 to 5,000 cu cm. It is reasonable to expect a relationship between the relative size of individuals and vital capacity. In practice, vital capacity measurements are reduced to well-established standards which are based upon height and weight or on body surface area. An approximate normative value for vital capacity is 2,500 cu cm per square meter of surface area for adult males and about 2,000 cu cm per square meter of surface area for adult females.

Because of the negative intrathoracic pressure which envelops the lungs, a considerable quantity of air cannot be expelled, even with maximum effort. This air, called residual air, ranges in value from 1,000 to 1,500 cu cm in adult males. It remains in the lungs, even after death. We cannot speak on residual air, and it is unfortunate that some textbooks make reference to residual breathers or residual speakers. If the lungs are removed from the thorax immediately after death, almost all the residual air is expelled, but a small quantity of minimal residual air remains. For this reason lungs have a specific gravity less than water, and will float. Minimal residual air amounts to about 500 cu cm.

Regardless of the depth of inhalation, approximately 150 cu cm of air does not contribute oxygen to the blood or receive carbon dioxide from it. This air is called dead air. It remains in the nasal cavity, larynx, trachea, bronchi, and bronchioles. This air, which was the very last to be inhaled, is, of course, the first to be exhaled during the next cycle of respiration. On the other hand, the very last 150 cu cm of air which is forced from the alveoli during expiration is not expelled, but remains in the dead-air spaces. Although it is laden with carbon dioxide, it is the first air to be drawn back into the alveoli at the beginning of the next inspiration. Thus, about 150 cu cm of the tidal air ought to be considered as "nonfunctional" for purposes of internal respiration.

During quiet breathing, air is exchanged about twelve times a minute. At rest, there is no significant difference in breathing rate between males and females, but during heavy work the rate may increase to twenty-one breaths per minute for males and to thirty breaths per minute for females. (It is of interest to note that the breathing rate for sleeping newborn babies ranges from 24 to 116, with a mean of 43 breaths per minute.)

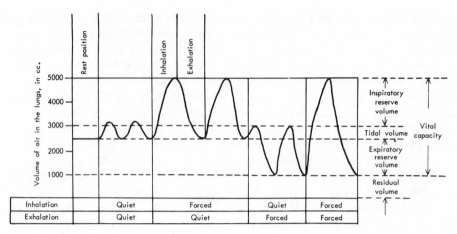

Fig. 2–46. Schematic recording of breathing movements and various lung volumes.

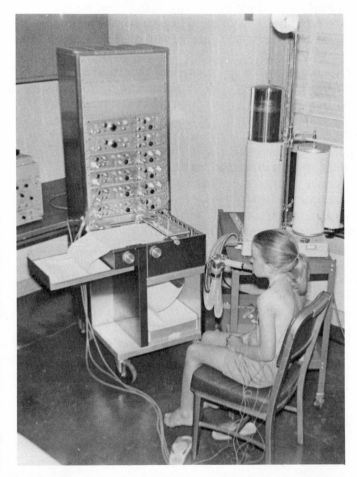

Fig. 2–47. Subject exhaling into a wet spirometer (recording type).

The total quantity of air exchanged in a minute is known as minute volume. It is expressed in liters per minute, and is simply the product of respiration frequency and tidal volume. Maximum minute ventilation is the quantity of air that can be exchanged in a minute under conditions of forced breathing. This quantity is also known as maximum minute volume. The relationships of some of the above volumes are illustrated schematically in Figure 2–46.

Most of the above volume measures may be obtained by means of a wet spirometer, which is a simple device, consisting of a vessel, inverted in a second vessel, which is filled with water. The inverted vessel is balanced by counterweights so that its weight is essentially zero. Air blown into the inverted vessel causes it to rise in the column of water, the ascent being dependent upon the quantity of air exhaled by the subject. A young subject exhaling into a spirometer is shown in Figure 2–47. The other apparatus is for an electromyographic experiment. A recent development is the dry spirometer, which operates on the same principle as the aneroid barometer.

The Functions of the Muscles of Inhalation

Introduction

Traditionally, the muscles we have described thus far have been regarded as contributors to respiration. To a certain extent the functions attributed to many of these muscles have been presumptive, based upon their physical arrangements and attachments. It seems logical, for example, to expect the pectoral muscles to exert an upward force on the anterior thoracic wall and thereby assist in inhalation. The same is true regarding the anterior serratus, the sternocleidomastoid, and the scalene muscles. We can reasonably expect these muscles, on the basis of their physical arrangements, to be accessory muscles of inhalation. If we are to appreciate fully the mechanisms involved in breathing, we ought to examine some of the available data regarding the contributions of the muscles of respiration.

A complete description of the functions of a muscle is an arduous task. In addition to an anatomical description, the effects of contraction and the circumstances in which contraction occurs must be determined. Until recently, physiologists were limited to radiography (X-ray), palpation, and various mechanical recording techniques. Although electromyography has been used as a research technique since about 1937, its use in breathing physiology did not begin until about 1952. Since that time electromyography (EMG) has contributed much toward an understanding of the functions of the breathing musculature. The following discussion is not meant to be exhaustive, but, rather, representative of research findings concerning functions of the muscles of breathing.

The diaphragm

Although the diaphragm is usually considered the most important muscle in breathing, it is very difficult to study, and information regarding its behavior is limited. Most of what is known about the diaphragm has been learned through X-ray. Wade and Gilson (1951), using X-ray, measured the vertical movements of the diaphragm and found that it amounted to 1.5 cm during quiet breathing, and 6-7 cm during deep breathing. In a replication of the experiment, Wade (1954) found that vertical movement of the diaphragm was about 10 cm in very deep breathing. In addition, he found little difference between the vertical excursions of the right and left domes. On the basis of diaphragm movement and assumed diaphragm area, Wade (1951) calculated its contribution to respiration. He found that each centimeter of vertical diaphragm movement would account for an inhalation of about 350 cu cm of air. Inasmuch as diaphragm movement is about 1.5 cm during quiet breathing, it alone ought to be responsible for an inhalation of about 525 cu cm of air. The mean tidal volume in an adult population (both male and female) amounts to about 615 cu cm. Although the figures of Wade ought to be interpreted with some caution, it is not unreasonable to regard the diaphragm as the principal muscle of respiration. Indeed, for some persons it may be the only truly active muscle during quiet breathing.

A pioneer in the use of X-ray for the study of the speech mechanism was Bloomer, who in 1936 obtained X-ray photographs of antero-posterior and lateral views of the thorax during the various phases of maximum inhalation and maximum exhalation. Bloomer was able to assess the degree of movement of the ribs with respect to the vertebral column and with respect to each other, as well as movements of the sternum and diaphragm. He was also able to determine the contributions of some other muscles of breathing. Some of the conclusions drawn by Bloomer are:

1. The first ribs have been found to undergo movement similar in character to that of the other ribs during respiration.

2. The average degree of costal mobility has been shown to decrease from the second or third rib downward.

3. The movement of the twelfth ribs was found to be of the same character as that of the other ribs.

4. The plane of the sternum remains at virtually the same angle with the vertical axis of the thorax at the extremes of inspiration and expiration.

5. The scaleni are active in elevating the first ribs.

6. Evidence indicates that the quadratus lumborum acts as a muscle of expiration drawing the twelfth ribs downward.

7. The excursion of the diaphragm is significant in volumetric changes of the thorax. The volume changes attributable to the diaphragm in ten cases ranged from 29 to 63 per cent of the vital capacity.

In addition, Bloomer found that the diaphragm movement was primarily in a downward and forward direction.

Electromyographic studies of diaphragm activity in man are few. Because of its location in the body, exploration by means of surface electrodes has not been successful, and as Campbell (1958) has pointed out, "There are obvious ethical objections to the exploration of the diaphragm with needle electrodes in conscious human subjects." The present author has obtained electromyographic recordings from a number of anesthetized dogs and cats. In each instance muscular activity was found throughout the inhalation phase, and in most cases it extended into the beginnings of the exhalation phase. Because of the uncertain effects of the surgically opened abdomen, however, the results must be interpreted with a great deal of caution.

Draper, Ladefoged, and Whitteridge (1959) seem to have been successful in obtaining electromyographic recordings from conscious human subjects. Their subjects swallowed a thin tube which contained electrodes and electrode leads. The tube was adjusted until the electrodes were at the point where the esophagus passes through the diaphragm. Thus, in effect, the electrodes were placed directly on the diaphragm. These subjects showed diaphragm activity throughout the inhalation phase, and in most cases the activity extended only slightly into the expiratory phase. Two of their subjects showed diaphragm activity all during inhalation, during the initial phase of exhalation, and, in addition, toward the end of exhalation when the expiratory reserve volume was small.

The mechanics of diaphragm action are complex. Earlier in the chapter we saw how contraction of the diaphragm pulls the central tendon downward and forward. The result is an increase in the vertical diameter of the thorax and a decrease in intra-thoracic pressure. In addition there is a simultaneous decrease in the volume of the abdominal cavity and an increase in intra-abdominal pressure. The costal margin of the diaphragm is usually regarded as relatively fixed, both in position and transverse dimensions. Under these conditions, contraction of the diaphragm may compress the abdominal viscera and raise intra-abdominal pressure to the extent that there is an expansion of the lower abdominal walls. This is sometimes known as abdominal or diaphragmatic breathing.

A rather common result of contraction of the costal fibers of the diaphragm is an expansion at the base of the thorax. The diaphragm expands the base of the thorax by thrusting the ribs upward and rotating them outward. The mechanism is as follows: When the diaphragm is in its normal, uncontracted state, it has a pronounced dome shape, and the course of the costal fibers is almost vertical. With the abdominal viscera in their normal spatial relation with the diaphragm they may act as a fulcrum when the costal fibers contract. The result is a downward force against the viscera and an upward force against the costal margin of the diaphragm. This action, illustrated in Figure 2–48, is presumably what takes place during "costal breathing." The base of the thorax expands with each inhalation, and the abdominal viscera may simply fill the space created in the upper abdomen. Very little protrusion of the lower abdominal walls occurs, and, in fact, the abdomen may actually be drawn in with each inhalation.

With progressively deeper breathing, however, expansion of the base of the thorax may decrease and protrusion of the abdominal wall increase proportionately. Near the very end of maximum inhalation the situation may be reversed; that is, the thorax may expand rapidly to the extent the abdominal walls may actually be drawn in.

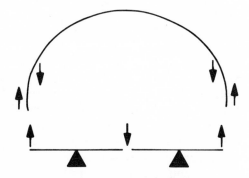

Fig. 2–48. Schematic of the way in which a downward movement of the diaphragm is resolved into an upward movement of the costal margin.

Although we seemingly have considerable voluntary control over the rate and depth of breathing, there appears to be little if any voluntary control over diaphragmatic action. Wade (1951; 1954) and Campbell and Jellife (1951, unpublished) examined diaphragmatic movements in physiotherapists and singing teachers who believed they had voluntary control of their diaphragms. Although these subjects were able to control rib movements during breathing, there was no evidence of voluntary control over the regular muscles of inhalation, particularly the diaphragm.

In summary, contraction of the diaphragm causes descent of the dome in a downward and forward direction and, very often, expansion at the base of the thorax. The majority of the movement takes place in the posterior portion of the diaphragm. This activity is responsible for the majority of tidal volume in quiet breathing. Finally, we have little or no voluntary control over the diaphragm.

These statements might lead to the erroneous conclusion that the accessory muscles of inhalation are not capable of, or do not contribute to, expansion of the thorax. Quite the contrary. In conditions of diaphragmatic paralysis, for example, very little reduction in breathing capacity has been noted (Little, 1956). Thus, there is evidence of a great "functional reserve" supplied by the accessory muscles of inhalation. The contributions of some of the specific accessory muscles, under normal conditions, are open to some question.

The pectoralis major and minor muscles

With the shoulder and upper arm fixed, the pectoralis major and minor muscles may draw the upper ribs outward and upward, and they are usually regarded as accessory muscles of inhalation. Campbell (1954) found that the only activity in normal subjects occurred at the end of maximum inhalation. Peterson (1964, unpublished) employed surface electrodes in an EMG study of the accessory muscles of inhalation. She expressed the point at which muscular activity occurred in terms of percentage of vital capacity. Twelve females and eight males served as subjects. The sternal head of the pectoralis major showed no activity until 96 per cent of the vital capacity had been inhaled. In addition, 50 per cent of the subjects showed no activity in the clavicular head of the pectoralis major, even at the point of maximum inhalation. Activity did occur, however, when the breath was held after maximum inhalation.

The subclavius

On the basis of its attachments, the subclavius would appear to be a muscle of inhalation. There are no data on this muscle, and even if it were active, its contributions to inhalation would probably be inconsequential because it is so small.

The serratus anterior

Presumably the serratus anterior muscle can raise the ribs if the shoulder is fixed. Catton and Gray (1951) and Campbell (1954) examined this muscle electromyographically and failed to detect activity, even during very deep breathing. Zemlin examined the serratus anterior electromyographically on a small number of subjects and was unable to detect activity, except when the breath was held after a maximum inhalation. Electrical contamination from adjacent muscles, however, may have contributed to the activity that was detected. In summary, there is no evidence that the serratus anterior muscle contributes to breathing activity.

The intercostal muscles

The intercostal muscles have been studied extensively, and much controversial data regarding their contributions to breathing have been accumulated. The various functions attributed to them have been summarized by Campbell (1958) as follows:

1. Both the external and internal intercostals are inspiratory in function.

2. Both groups are expiratory in function.

3. The external intercostals are inspiratory in function, and the internal are expiratory, with the exception of the intercartilaginous portion of the internal intercostals, which is inspiratory.

4. The external intercostals are expiratory, and the internal are inspiratory.

5. Both groups are inspiratory and expiratory at the same time.

6. Both groups act together, but their functions vary in different parts of the chest.

7. They are not concerned with either inspiration or expiration, but regulate the tension in the intercostal spaces.

The complicated nature of the arrangements of these muscles probably contributes to the controversy that exists even today. It may be of value to examine the attachments and courses of the intercostals and to speculate as to the probable mechanical effects produced by their contraction.

Fig. 2–49. Schematic of the action of the external intercostal muscles.

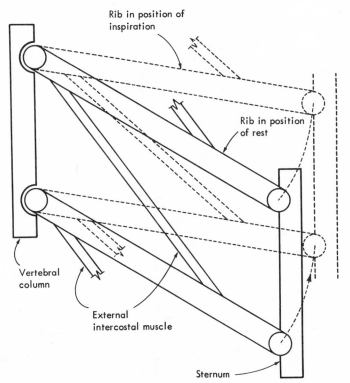

Rib in position of
inspiration

Rib in position
of rest

Vertebral
column

External
intercostal muscle

Sternum

You will vividly recall that the external intercostal muscles occupy the space between the ribs in an area extending from the tubercle posteriorly to the anterior extremity of the osseous portion of the rib. They are deficient in the chondral portion of
the ribs. The fibers originate from the lower border of a rib and insert into the upper
border of the rib immediately below. Anteriorly the fibers course obliquely down and
forward (medially), and posteriorly they course downward and outward (laterally).
The course and probable effects of contraction of the external intercostals are shown
schematically in Figure 2–49. The arrangement of the fibers is such that a Class III
lever is formed with both the upper and lower rib. Note, however, that the lever
system of the lower rib is considerably more efficient than that for the upper rib; that
is, the elevating force applied to the lower rib greatly exceeds the depressing force
applied to the upper rib. Consequently, contraction of each external intercostal muscle
ought to elevate the lower rib to which it attaches. This elevating effect would be
minimized, or indeed negated, were the external intercostals to occupy the intercostal
spaces in the chondral portion of the ribs. Fortunately for our mechanical model,
this is not the case. Thus, on a mechanical basis, the external intercostals ought to
act as muscles of inhalation.

The internal intercostal muscles occupy an area extending from the anterior limits
of the intercostal spaces to the angle of the ribs posteriorly. In front, the course of the
fibers is downward and outward, while in back, the course is downward and inward.
The course and probable effects of contraction of the intercartilaginous portion of
the internal intercostals are shown schematically in Figure 2–50. Note that the arrangement of the fibers is such that a Class III lever is formed with both the upper and
lower rib, and, as is the case with the external intercostals, the elevating force applied

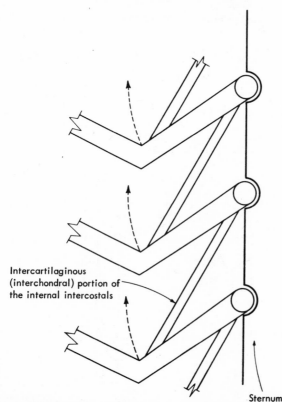

Intercartilaginous
(interchondral) portion of
the internal intercostals

*Fig. 2–50. Schematic of the action
of the intercartilaginous portion
of the internal intercostal muscles.*

Sternum

to the lower rib exceeds the depressing force applied to the upper rib. On the basis of mechanics, the intercartilaginous portion of the internal intercostals ought to be inspiratory in function.

The interosseous portion of the internal intercostals probably decreases the intercostal spaces and, through the abdominal muscles, depresses the ribs to aid in exhalation.

Probably the most widely accepted theory of intercostal function is Hamberger's (Campbell, 1958), which states that as the external intercostals and the intercartilaginous portion of the internal intercostals contract they elevate the ribs and as the interosseous portion of the internal intercostals contract they depress the ribs.

There seems little doubt that the intercostal muscles elevate the ribs during normal and moderately deep breathing. Electromyographic recordings taken from the intercostals have, to a large extent, offered supportive evidence for Hamberger's theory. Campbell (1955) examined the intercostals in young male subjects and detected activity in the lower intercostal spaces (5th-9th) during inspiration. He also found that the muscular activity increased with progressively deeper inspiratory efforts. These same muscles were found to be inactive throughout expiration during quiet and rapid breathing. Draper *et al.* (1959), using needle electrodes, detected activity in the interosseous portion of the internal intercostals during speech production with a low expiratory reserve.

After a deep inspiration, preparatory to speech, the elastic recoil of the thorax may provide air pressure in excess of that required by the larynx for voice production. Draper *et al.* found that under such circumstances inspiratory muscles may continue to be active and thus counteract the elastic recoil of the inflated thorax. During speech production, as the volume of air in the lungs decreases, the "relaxation pressure" becomes less, and the checking action of the inspiratory muscles ceases; at that point, in order to maintain the necessary air pressure for speech, the expiratory muscles begin to contract. Draper *et al.* found that the external intercostals were largely responsible for providing a checking action. This activity continued as long as relaxation pressure was in excess of that required by the larynx for speech.

In a subsequent EMG study of the respiratory muscles, Eblen (1963) also noted a checking action. He placed electrodes over the pectoralis major, the internal intercostals, the rectus abdominis, the serratus anterior, and the external intercostal muscles and detected checking action at some time from all electrode locations. In other words, he detected checking activity from the muscles of inspiration and the muscles of expiration as well. The main purpose of Eblen's study was to investigate the limitations of surface electromyography, and he cautions that the checking activity detected at any electrode location may have been due to action-potential contamination of adjacent muscles. Other findings by Eblen are beyond the scope of this introduction to the functions of respiratory musculature.

The intercostal muscles are very powerful and are probably major contributors to inspiratory efforts. Campbell (1958) has shown that high levels of pulmonary ventilation can be produced with just the intercostal muscles. In addition to producing rib movements during inhalation, the intercostal muscles contribute to the rigidity of the thoracic wall by preventing the intercostal spaces from bulging in and out during breathing. These muscles also help control the amount of space between the ribs and, in addition, couple the ribs, one to the other, so that movements of any given rib influence the position of adjacent ribs. This latter activity may be seen during expiratory efforts. When the lower ribs are drawn downward by contraction of the abdominal muscles, contraction of the intercostals tends to draw the upper ribs downward as well.

In summary, it can be stated with reasonable certainty that the external intercostals and the intercartilaginous portion of the internal intercostals are major contributors to inspiratory efforts. These muscles are inactive during expiration in quiet breathing but become active during forced expiratory efforts. They also remain in a contracted state after maximum inhalation and provide a checking action to counteract the relaxation pressure of the inflated thorax. And finally, the interosseous portion of the internal intercostals is probably active during speech production, particularly on low expiratory reserve air.

The levator costalis muscles

Because of their attachments and probable action, the levator costalis muscles are often described as contributors to inhalation. Data, however, are very limited, and there is no adequate evidence to support an inspiratory function. They are probably best described as postural muscles.

The serratus posterior superior muscles

The respiratory function of the serratus posterior superior muscles has not been examined. Anatomically, however, they could elevate the ribs and assist in inhalation.

The serratus posterior inferior muscles

On the basis of mechanics the serratus posterior inferior muscles could depress the lower ribs, and are therefore often regarded as muscles of expiration. In addition, they may assist inspiration by fixing the lower four ribs and preventing them from being lifted by the lever action of the contracting diaphragm. There seems to be no adequate supportive evidence for either viewpoint.

The sternocleidomastoid muscles

Because of their sternal and clavicular origins, the sternocleidomastoid muscles may exert an upward force on the sternum and thereby increase the antero-posterior diameter of the thorax. Campbell (1955) examined these muscles on young male subjects and found limited activity during quiet breathing. They were very active, however, during maximum inspiratory efforts. Campbell regards the sternocleidomastoids as the most important accessory muscles of inspiration. He found that his subjects were able to reach a tidal volume of 2,500 cu cm before activity was detected. Peterson (1964, unpublished) examined the clavicular and sternal heads electromyographically and found that the subjects inhaled about 83.4 per cent of their vital capacity before activity was detected in the clavicular head, and they inhaled about 88 per cent of their vital capacity before activity was detected in the sternal head. The mean quantity of air inhaled before activity was detected was 3,611 cu cm for the clavicular head and 3,425 cu cm for the sternal head. In addition, three subjects showed no activity on the sternal head, even for maximum inspiration.

The scalene muscles

These neck muscles act on the upper two ribs and appear to be important accessory muscles of inhalation. Some authorities regard the scalene muscles at least as important as the intercostals. They appear to be active during quiet breathing, and their activity increases with increased inspiratory effort. They do not appear to be active during exhalation, however. Peterson (1964, unpublished) examined the anterior scalene muscles on twenty seated subjects and noted muscle activity when the subjects had inhaled about 69 per cent of their vital capacity. Values ranged from 28 per cent to 95 per cent of vital capacity.

The latissimus dorsi muscles

The latissimus dorsi muscles, which insert into the upper humerus, contain fibers that originate from the lower three or four ribs. With the shoulder girdle fixed, they may be able to elevate these ribs and assist in inspiration. In addition, contraction of the muscle as a whole may pull downward on the lower thorax and facilitate exhalation. These muscles have not been studied extensively, and the limited data fail to support an expiratory function. Tokizane, Kawamata, and Tokizane (1952) reported muscular activity during deep breathing. Zemlin (unpublished) has noted activity during severe expiratory efforts such as coughing.

The sacrospinalis muscles

The sacrospinalis muscles are largely fixation muscles, and their respiratory function is not well understood. Because of electrical contamination effects produced by adjacent active muscles, their activity in respiration has been difficult to assess.

The Functions of the Muscles of Exhalation

The transversus thoracis muscles

The transversus thoracis muscles are almost always described as expiratory in function. There is no supportive evidence for this viewpoint, and an expiratory function has apparently been assigned them on the basis of their probable mechanics. If the sternum can be assumed to be fixed in position, relative to the ribs, contraction of the transversus thoracis muscles ought to exert a downward pull on the ribs and decrease the transverse diameter of the thorax. On the other hand, if the ribs can be assumed to be fixed in position, contraction of the transversus thoracis muscles would tend either to lift the sternum and thrust it outward or evert the ribs and thus assist during inhalation. It seems that these muscles may be inspiratory or expiratory in function, depending upon the action of other muscles.

The subcostal muscles

Although it can be reasoned, on a mechanical basis, that the subcostal muscles are expiratory in function, there is no evidence to offer in support of this viewpoint. These muscles probably function in much the same way as the intercostals.

The internal intercostals

These muscles and their functions were discussed at some length on pp. 89–92.

The quadratus lumborum muscles

On anatomical grounds, the quadratus lumborum muscles seem to be potential muscles of either inspiration or expiration. During deep breathing they may fix the lowest ribs and facilitate diaphragmatic action, and during expiration they may depress the lowest ribs. Bloomer (1936), in an X-ray study of the mechanics of respiration, found evidence to indicate that the quadratus lumborum acts as a muscle of expiration, drawing the twelfth ribs downward.

The abdominal musculature

The actions of the abdominal musculature are many and varied. One quite obvious function is simply to enclose and lend support to the abdominal contents. This supportive function is facilitated by virtue of the varied courses of the three layers of the lateral abdominal muscles. By analogy, the abdominal wall is not unlike plywood, with the various layers coursing in different directions thus adding greatly to its strength. Assuming that the muscles which act upon the vertebral column are in an uncontracted state, let us examine the effects which the abdominal muscles may produce.

If the muscles on both sides are contracted simultaneously, the body is bent forward. If the muscles on just one side are contracted, the body is bent laterally. Contraction of the external oblique on one side with simultaneous contraction of the internal oblique on the contralateral side produces a rotating movement of the body. With the vertebral column held in a rigid state, contraction of the abdominal muscles compresses the abdominal contents, and, since these muscles have attachments on the rib cage, contraction also tends to draw the ribs downward, thus assisting in decreasing the size of the thoracic cavity. Because of their attachments and courses, the abdominal muscles probably do not contribute to expiratory activity to the same degree. On mechanical grounds the oblique muscles are probably the more effective depressors of the ribs, while the transverse muscles probably are more effective in compressing the abdominal contents.

With the laryngeal muscles contracted so as to prevent expulsion of air (thoracic fixation), the abdominal muscles function in those activities that require high intraabdominal pressure. They include micturition (urination), defecation (evacuation of the bowels), emesis (vomiting), parturition (child birth), and heavy lifting.

The external oblique and rectus abdominis muscles are superficial, and they are the only abdominal muscles that have been studied rather extensively. For this reason the abdominal muscles will be discussed as a group, and only the respiratory activity of the external oblique and rectus abdominis muscles will be cited.

In one of his early studies Campbell (1952) reported that there was no activity in the external oblique and rectus abdominis muscles of supine subjects breathing quietly. Activity was easily detected, however, during maximum expiratory efforts. In addition, activity was detected at the height of maximum inspiration. On the basis of his data, Campbell concluded that contraction of the abdominal muscles was a factor which limited the depth of inspiration. This limiting action was not detected in very rapid and deep breathing due to oxygen deprivation.

These muscles are never active during the initial stages of the expiratory phase of breathing, but, rather, they become active toward the end of maximum expiration. Davis and Zemlin (1965, unpublished) examined the external obliques and the rectus abdominis muscles in a group of young adults and always detected activity during rapid forced expiration and during such activities as coughing. The external oblique was invariably found to be the more active of the two, and many subjects exhibited very little activity of the rectus abdominis, even at the end point of maximum expiration.

Forces of exhalation other than muscular

Although it has been well established that the thoracic dimensions may decrease as the result of muscle contraction, certain other important factors contribute to exhalation. They include torque, tissue elasticity, and gravity. For this reason, exhalation ought to be thought of as combining both active and passive forces. The passive forces play a predominant role in the initial stages of exhalation, and they are followed by the active muscular forces.

As was shown earlier, the muscles of inhalation act to raise the ribs. In doing so, they must overcome the effect of gravity upon the heavy skeleton, the effect of tissue elasticity, and the effect of torque. The effect of torque occurs when the ribs are raised. The ribs' cartilaginous attachments to the sternum are twisted and placed under a rotational stress. This effect is schematized in Figure 2–51. When the muscles of inhalation relax, the force exerted by the torque causes the ribs to resume their normal position. Of course, the forces of tissue elasticity supplement the torque, as does the sheer weight of the bony skeleton. The lungs are liberally supplied with elastic tissue.

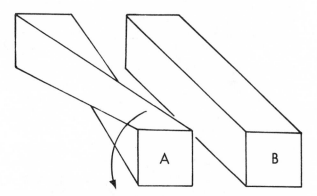

Fig. 2–51. Schematic illustration of torque.

An elastic rod, twisted as in A, will exert a rotational restoration force that is called torque.

Due to an increase in the dimensions of the thoracic cavity they are subjected to an increasing stretching force throughout the inhalation phase of breathing. They may also be maintained in a distended state by thoracic fixation. When the muscles of inhalation relax, the forces of exhalation decrease the size of the thoracic cavity, and the lungs contract elastically, as rapidly as the diminishing thorax permits.

The Mechanics and Physiology of Breathing

Microscopic examination reveals that the lungs are liberally supplied with elastic connective tissue. This gives them an extraordinary degree of elasticity, a feature that is of considerable importance in the mechanics of breathing. We have seen how the lungs are separated from the thoracic wall by a thin layer of serous fluid. The surface tension of this fluid causes the lung surfaces to adhere to the thoracic wall with considerable force, and the lungs follow, faithfully, any movements of the thorax. The space between the visceral and parietal pleurae is known as intrathoracic space. In actuality, however, it is a nonexistent but potential space between the pleurae.

At birth, the lungs completely fill the thoracic cavity, and are not placed under tension in the position of respiratory rest. That is, at the beginning of inspiration or at the end of expiration, the intrathoracic pressure is very nearly the same as atmospheric. Thus, infant lungs contain very little residual air. During inspiration, the lung surfaces follow the enlarging thoracic cavity, and the lung tissue is subjected to a stretching force. This force, however, is resisted by the inherent elastic properties of the lung, and they tend to pull away from the thoracic wall. They are bound, however, by surface tension; as a result, the intrathoracic pressure becomes negative with respect to the intrapulmonic pressure (pressure within the lungs). That is, resistance to the stretching force accounts for negative intrathoracic pressure. As the individual matures, the rate of growth of the thoracic cavity exceeds that of the lungs; nevertheless the lung surfaces and chest wall always remain in contact (through the fluid). Thus, in the adult, the lungs are continuously subjected to a stretching force, to the extent that intrathoracic pressure is always below intrapulmonic pressure, even at the position of respiratory rest. Because of the ever-present negative intrathoracic pressure, the lungs cannot be completely evacuated. The air that cannot be exhaled from the lungs is known as the residual air we have already referred to.

During inspiration the lungs are stretched, and the intrapulmonic pressure begins to fall below atmospheric. This pressure drop is, of course, responsible for a flow of air into the lungs. When the forces of inhalation are removed and the forces of exhalation decrease the dimensions of the thoracic cavity, the stretching force on the lungs is reduced, and by virtue of their elasticity they resume their normal shape and dimensions, insofar as negative intrathoracic pressure permits.

Under normal circumstances expulsion of air from the lungs is accomplished solely by the elastic contraction of the lung tissue, and not by actual compression of the lungs. Compression of the lungs would only be possible were intrathoracic pressure to exceed intrapulmonic pressure, and it never does! During exhalation then, the decrease in size of the thorax simply reduces the magnitude of negative intrathoracic pressure, making it possible for the elasticity of the lung tissue to assert itself, and air is expelled until the intrapulmonic pressure is equal to atmospheric.

By now it ought to be plainly (or painfully) evident that the pressure relationship between the chest cavity and outside air continuously changes during breathing.

Pressure changes in the chest cavity

With the laryngeal valve open and the muscles of respiration completely relaxed, there is free communication from the lungs to the outside air, and the pressure within the lungs (intrapulmonic pressure) is the same as atmospheric. This pressure relationship is shown in Figure 2–52. From what we know about the behavior of gases it is obvious that if intrapulmonic pressure were anything but atmospheric, air would be either entering or leaving the lungs. The moment inspiration begins, intrapulmonic pressure begins to fall below atmospheric, and at the height of inspiration the intrapulmonic pressure is lowest, amounting to −1 to −2 mm Hg (millimeters of mer-

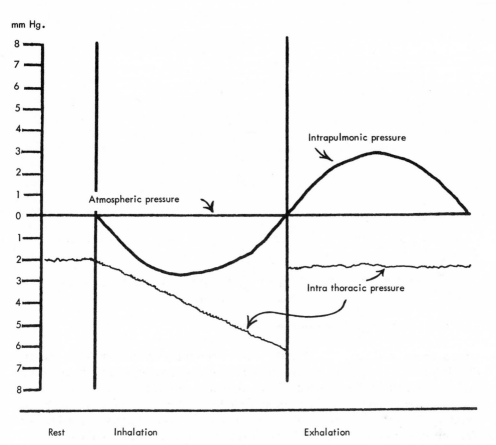

mm Hg.

Rest   Inhalation   Exhalation

*Fig. 2–52. Simultaneous recording of intrapulmonic and intra-
thoracic pressures showing their relationships.*

cury). As the inspiration phase comes to an end, the intrapulmonic pressure begins
to rise, and at the very end of inspiration (with the laryngeal valve open) it is the same
as atmospheric. As expiration movement begins, the lungs contract elastically as
rapidly as the diminishing chest cavity permits, and the air within the lungs is compressed. Intrapulmonic pressure exceeds atmospheric by about 2-3 mm Hg, and the
air rushes out of the lungs until once again the intrapulmonic pressure reaches atmospheric.

Intrathoracic pressure also changes during breathing. As shown in Figure 2–52,
the pressure is 2-4 mm Hg below atmospheric in the position of respiratory rest.
During inspiration the intrathoracic pressure continues to fall and reaches a value of
−6 to −8 mm Hg below atmospheric at the height of inspiration. It is at this point of
course that the lungs are subjected to maximum stretching force.

From the previous discussion of the passive forces of exhalation and of the pressure
changes in the chest, we ought to suspect that the elastic and muscular forces and the
volume of air in the lungs are somehow closely related. The relationships between
these factors were first shown graphically by Rohrer and Jaquet in 1916. The graph,
shown in Figure 2–53, is known as the pressure-volume diagram. The curves represent

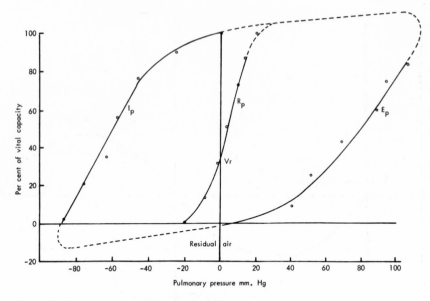

Fig. 2–53. Pressure-volume diagram of breathing.

three different conditions: (1) when the muscles of respiration are completely relaxed, (2) when all the inspiratory muscles are maximally contracted, and (3) when all the expiratory muscles are contracted. The potentialities and significance of the pressure-volume diagram might never have been made known were it not for subsequent respiratory physiologists such as Rahn (1946), Fenn (1951), and, later, Campbell (1958). The curves, shown in Figure 2–53, when examined critically, describe the forces and mechanical limits of the respiratory apparatus.

The relaxation-pressure curve (R_p) represents the pressure in the lung terminals at any lung volume when all the respiratory muscles are completely relaxed. In other words, this curve represents the elastic forces of exhalation supplied by the lungs and

Table 2-2
Relaxation Pressures at Various Lung Volumes

Relaxation Pressure

Number of Subjects	Volume % VC	Pressure mm Hg
14	0	−19.2 (−31.8 to −6.6)
14	13.9	−8.5 (−15.5 to −1.5)
14	31.0	−1.3 (−9.9 to 7.3)
14	51.0	4.1 (−1.9 to 10.1)
14	72.0	10.5 (1.9 to 19.1)
14	87.0	14.9 (0.3 to 29.5)
14	100.0	20.6 (10.2 to 31.0)

From: Rahn, H., A. B. Otis, L. E. Chadwick, and W. O. Fenn, "The Pressure-volume Diagram of the Thorax and Lung," *American Journal of Physiology*, CLXVI 1946, 161–178.

Table 2-3
Inspiratory Pressures at Various Lung Volumes

Inspiratory Pressure

Number of Subjects	Volume % VC	Pressure mm Hg
11	3.9	−86.0 (47.0 to 125.0)
11	21.7	−74.6 (46.4 to 102.8)
11	34.8	−63.3 (25.9 to 100.7)
11	55.6	−56.8 (25.6 to 88.0)
11	75.7	−44.8 (16.8 to 72.8)
11	91.0	−23.6 (2.2 to 49.4)

From: Rahn, *et al.*, 161–178.

thorax. These passive forces are usually measured in millimeters of mercury, above or below atmospheric pressure. The data, represented by curve R_p, may be obtained by (1) inflating the lungs (by pressure) of a subject whose respiratory muscles are completely relaxed or (2) having a subject inspire or expire a given volume of air and then relax his respiratory musculature. In either method, the pressure in the respiratory tract is measured by means of a manometer. It stands to reason if the lungs of a relaxed subject are inflated, the expiratory forces exerted will be a true measure of the passive forces of exhalation. Representative values of relaxation pressures at various lung volumes are shown in Table 2-2, and they are shown graphically as the relaxation-pressure curve in Figure 2-53. Note that the curve crosses the zero axis at V_r, which is often referred to as the relaxation volume or functional reserve volume (FRV) of the lungs. Some of the implications of this curve may be easily overlooked. For example, the area between the relaxation-pressure curve and the zero axis above V_r represents the force which the muscles of inspiration must exert in order to overcome the elastic forces of resistance. On the other hand, the area below V_r represents the force which must be exerted by the muscles of expiration during a maximum expiration. In other words, these areas represent the combined elastic forces of the lungs and thorax. The implications of the relaxation-pressure curve are discussed in much greater detail by Rahn, Otis, Chadwick, and Fenn (1946) and by Campbell (1958).

Additional pressure curves may be obtained by measuring the active inspiratory and expiratory forces. To obtain inspiratory pressure curves the lungs are first voluntarily inflated to a given percentage of the vital capacity, after which the subject inhales through a closed manometer. On mechanical grounds, the inspiratory pressure ought to be maximal with the lungs deflated, and it ought to be minimal with the lungs completely inflated. Values obtained by Rahn, *et al.* (1946), are shown in Table 2-3, and they are shown graphically, as the I_p curve in Figure 2-53. To obtain expiratory pressure curves, the subject completely deflates his lungs voluntarily. When this has been accomplished, the only air in the lungs is residual. The subject then inhales a given percentage of his vital capacity, after which he exhales maximally into a closed manometer. Expiration forces ought to be minimal with almost deflated lungs, and maximal with completely inflated lungs. This is borne out by the data of Rahn, *et al.* (1946), which are shown in Table 2-4. The expiratory pressure curve E_p is shown in Figure 2-53.

Table 2-4
Expiratory Pressures at Various Lung Volumes
Expiratory Pressure

Number of Subjects	Volume % VC	Pressure mm Hg
12	9.7	41.5 (14.7 to 68.3)
12	25.0	52.5 (10.9 to 94.1)
12	43.8	69.9 (30.5 to 109.3)
12	60.0	90.0 (47.0 to 133.0)
12	75.0	93.3 (58.1 to 128.5)
12	83.0	107.0 (74.4 to 139.6)
100	100.0	119.0 (86.0 to 145.0)

From: Rahn, *et al.*, 161–178.

Pressures greater or less than atmospheric may be measured by means of a manometer. Wet manometers are simply U-shaped tubes containing mercury or some other liquid. Physiologic measurements are usually made with an open manometer, an example of which is shown schematically in Figure 2–54. The difference in height of the two mercury columns indicates the amount by which the pressure in column A differs from atmospheric. This difference is conventionally read directly in centimeters of mercury (cm Hg). A manometer frequently used for clinical purposes is the dry manometer. Although it is not as accurate as the mercury manometer, it is much more convenient. Dry manometers operate on the principle of the Bourdon gauge, which is simply a curved hollow tube that straightens out or curls up with changes in pressure. The tube operates a pointer on a scale. Some sensitive dry manometers operate on the principle of the dry or aneroid barometer. It consists of a metal capsule, one end of which is closed off by a thin elastic diaphragm (usually brass). Pressure introduced into the other end causes the diaphragm to move a pointer indicator. These manometers must be checked frequently against a mercury manometer.

Fig. 2–54. Schematic of mercury manometer.

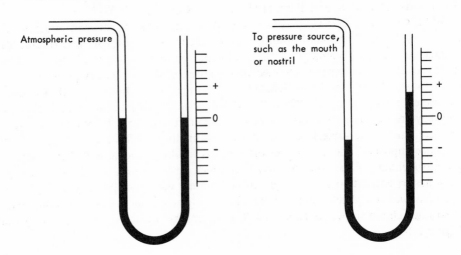

Atmospheric pressure

To pressure source, such as the mouth or nostril

Breathing behavior and the voice

The breathing apparatus has been likened to a power supply for the sound-producing mechanism. Although the power requirements for the larynx and the rest of the speech mechanism have not been specified, it may prove fruitful to discuss briefly the relation between breathing behavior and the quality and strength of the voice.

In the past, a great deal of attention has been given to the relationship between the capacity of the lungs, depth of inhalation, and the quality of the voice.

In an early study, Idol (1936) found a negligible positive correlation between vital capacity and loudness of the voice and a slightly negative correlation between vital capacity and quality (pleasantness) of the voice. In other words, there is a slight tendency for quality to vary inversely with vital capacity. Results such as those obtained by Idol and others (Barnes, 1926; Lindsley, 1929; Gray, 1936; Sallee, 1936; Wiksell, 1936) raise a question about the efficacy of breathing exercises as a means of improving voice.

Rahn et al. (1946) found that resting lung volume was equal to about 38 per cent of vital capacity and that tidal volume equaled about 15 per cent of the vital capacity. In other words, about 53 per cent of vital capacity is inhaled during quiet breathing. The results of at least two studies have indicated that breath requirements for speech production are not very different (if at all) from those required for life purposes. Idol (1936) found that more than half of her 140 subjects breathed more deeply for life purposes than for normal speech. Hoshiko (1964, unpublished) determined that approximately 50 per cent of vital capacity is inhaled for speech purposes. From these studies, and others, it seems reasonable to conclude that if the breathing behavior of an individual is within normal broad limits and is sufficiently deep for life purposes, it ought to be perfectly adequate for speech purposes. And therein lies the clinker, for we ought to add: provided the breath is used to proper advantage by the larynx and articulators. Improper laryngeal behavior, for example, may result in a significant waste of breath. Inadequate loudness may be the result, not of insufficient breath support, but rather of improper use of the larynx and the articulators and resonators. Studies have shown that not everyone requires more breath for loud speech than for normal. Idol (1936) found that air expenditure for loud speech was less than for normal speech in about one-third of her 140 subjects. These results have been supported in a subsequent study by Ptacek and Sander (1963). This seemingly paradoxical state of affairs will be discussed again in the chapter that deals with the mechanics of phonation.

Variations in breathing patterns

It is well known that there are variations in breathing patterns. Some individuals exhibit a marked protrusion of the anterior abdominal wall with each inhalation, while others exhibit a lateral expansion of the thorax with little protrusion of the abdominal wall. In a few individuals the expansion is predominantly in the extreme upper chest. These individuals seem to be "lifting" their rib cage by elevating their shoulders. These differences have led to the use of popular descriptive terms such as diaphragmatic (or abdominal), thoracic, and clavicular breathing.

Campbell (1954) and Wade (1954) have shown that diaphragmatic breathing does not necessarily mean that an individual is selectively using the diaphragm as the principal muscle of inspiration. They also have shown that thoracic breathers do not demonstrate a marked increase over diaphragmatic breathers in the activity of the intercostals.

It probably makes little or no difference in normal speech whether an individual uses diaphragmatic or thoracic breathing. Lindsley (1929) found a natural tendency for diaphragmatic breathing in both males and females, and, in addition, he noted that females tended toward thoracic breathing. These results have been supported by those of Sallee (1936) and Gray (1936). In most persons, the abdomen and lower and upper thorax all expand during inspiration, but there is not much question that the region of predominant expansion may vary from individual to individual. Gray (1936) found that about 65 per cent of men and women breathe diaphragmatically. He also found evidence that voice quality or audibility is unlikely to be affected by regional predominance.

Gray (1936) stresses that because clavicular breathing may result in excessive tension in the throat and an inadequate breath supply, it ought to be avoided. Pure clavicular breathers, however, are not encountered frequently. In fact, there is some question as to whether clavicular breathing ever occurs in isolation; that is, set apart from thoracic breathing.

Occasionally, however, a peculiar breathing pattern is encountered that seems to interfere with speech production. It is known as oppositional breathing, and seems to be the result of a lack of control over the sequential pattern of muscular contraction. Persons who use oppositional breathing may simultaneously contract the muscles of inspiration and expiration.

A recent approach to the study of breathing patterns has been through multiple-channel electromyographic recording. Early application of EMG was made by Stetson (1951), who attempted to describe the sequence of muscle activity that occurred while breathing for speech. Stetson found that a discrete monosyllabic word "ah" would be released by the internal intercostals and arrested by the external intercostals, while a syllable with a consonant, vowel, consonant (CVC word) composition would be released and arrested by auxiliary consonant movements, with some aid from the external intercostal muscles. Some of Stetson's findings have not been supported by subsequent studies.

Hoshiko (1960) investigated the sequence of activity of the internal intercostals, the rectus abdominis, and the external intercostals, as derived from action potential patterns during the preparation for utterance and the utterances of syllables at varying rates, and during the utterance of short samples of connected discourse at normal rate. The purpose of the study was to test some of the earlier findings by Stetson. Hoshiko found the order of onset for both the vowel "a" and the syllable "pup" to be: internal intercostals, rectus abdominis, and external intercostals. The order of termination for the vowel was as follows: rectus abdominis, external intercostals, and internal intercostals. The order of termination for the syllable "pup" was rectus abdominis, internal intercostals, and external intercostals. These findings were contradictory to those of Stetson.

Draper *et al.* (1959) also investigated the sequential activity of breathing muscula-ture. Four muscles or groups of muscles were studied: the external intercostals; the internal intercostals; the latissimus dorsi; rectus abdominis, internal and external obliques, and the diaphragm. These investigators employed both needle electrodes, which were placed directly into the muscles, and surface electrodes. In addition to EMG, a plethysomograph was used simultaneously to record changes in the volume of air in the lungs. Kymographic recordings were also made of air pressure in the trachea, measured indirectly by changes in intraesophageal pressure. A typical recording, demonstrating the relation between volume of air in the lungs, the indirect measure of intratracheal pressure, and the muscular activity which accompanied the pressure and volume changes, is shown in Figure 2–55. The upper part of the figure is a reproduction of a record of the variations in the volume of air in the lungs and the esophageal pressure during respiration and speech (counting 1 to 32 at conversational intensity). The lower part of the figure is a diagrammatic representation of the muscular activity which was observed to accompany such pressure and volume changes. The dashed line superimposed on the pressure record indicates the relaxation pressure

Fig. 2–55. Diagram illustrating sequence of muscle activity during speech production and during passive breathing. (After Draper et al., 1959)

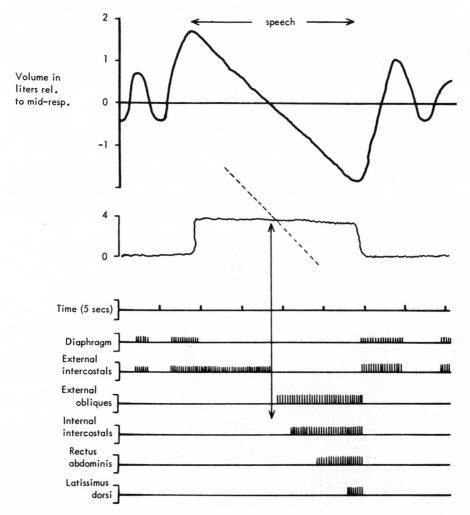

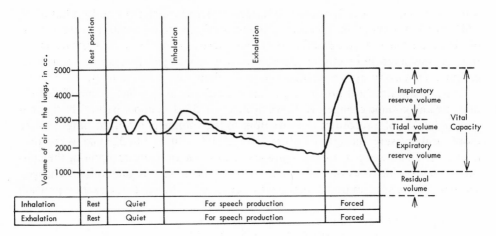

Fig. 2–56. Illustration of inhalation-exhalation durations during quiet breathing, breathing for speech purposes, and for forced breathing.

associated with the corresponding volume of air in the lungs. It is equal to zero when the amount of air in the lungs is the same as that at the end of a normal breath. The vertical arrow indicates when the relaxation pressure is no longer greater than the mean pressure below the vocal folds. At this moment the external intercostal activity ceases, and that of the internal intercostals begins. Note that the activity of the external intercostals is continued into the exhalation phase of the breathing cycle. From such records, it would appear that they are providing checking action.

The lung-volume diagram at the upper part of the figure is not typical. Speech is not usually carried so far into the exhalation phase before inhalation occurs. Lung-volume curves, similar to those in Figure 2–55, may be obtained by indirect measures, and although they have certain serious limitations, they do give indications of thoracic

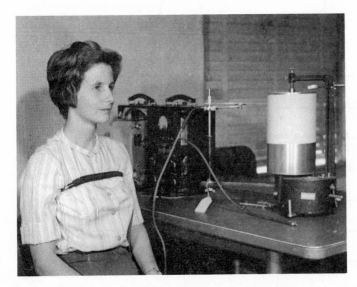

Fig. 2–57. Subject fitted with pneumographic apparatus.

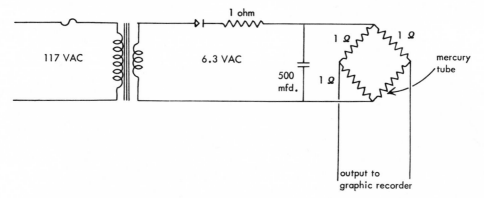

Fig. 2–58. Schematic of electronic pneumograph.

expansion and compression during breathing. A record like the one shown in Figure 2–56 may be obtained by means of a pneumograph, which is a very simple device, consisting of a closed collapsible rubber tube that is placed around the upper thorax, as shown in Figure 2–57. As the thorax expands, the tube is stretched slightly, and a negative pressure is developed. The pneumograph is coupled to a suitable pressure recorder, which yields a graphic recording of the expansion and contraction of the thorax and, indirectly, the changes in lung volume. A rather complete account of instrumentation for speech pathology is given by Steer (1957).

The pneumograph shown in Figure 2–58 is an electronic modification of the pneumatic type. The "pneumograph" is a thin rubber tube filled with mercury. A constant electric current (six volts) is passed through it. When the subject inhales or exhales, the electrical resistance of the mercury is changed. This change is registered graphically by a sensitive recording device. The electronic pneumograph is more sensitive than its pneumatic predecessor, but the curves are nevertheless an indirect index of lung volume. They do yield some very useful information, however, such as the absolute duration of the inhalation and exhalation phases of breathing. As shown in Figure 2–56, these phases are almost of equal duration during quiet breathing. This figure also shows an inhalation and exhalation curve during speech. Note the relatively long exhalation phase. These curves, plus other findings, suggest that fine control over speech utterances may be dependent upon a subtle balance between the forces of exhalation and those of inhalation.

Breathing is no simple process. Indeed, a complete and comprehensive integration of the vast body of knowledge accumulated to date would be, to say the least, a monumental task. The following paragraphs are by no means intended to represent such an integration of information. Rather, they are intended to be a schematic account of a cycle of breathing, a form of summary.

A Descriptive Account of a Cycle of Breathing

At rest, the pressure within the lungs is the same as atmospheric, and the diaphragm, which is the principal muscle of inspiration, presents the appearance of an inverted bowl. Upon initiation of inspiration, contraction of the posterior muscle fibers and,

Table 2-5

A Summary of the Forces of Breathing (Tentative)

| CONDITION | | CONDITION | | CONDITION | CONDITION | |
Quiet inhalation	Action	Forced inhalation	Action	Quiet exhalation	Forced exhalation	Action
Diaphragm	Increases vertical dimension of thorax	Includes all the muscles active during quiet inhalation plus:		Passive forces include:	Includes all passive forces plus:	
External intercostals	Elevate all ribs but rib 1			Tissue elasticity		
Scaleni				Gravity		
Anterior	Elevate rib 1					
Medius	Elevate rib 1			Torque		
Posterior	Elevate rib 2					
		Quadratus Lumborum	Anchor or depress rib 12		External Oblique	Depress ribs 8–12
		Pectoralis Major	Elevate sternum		Internal Oblique	Depress ribs 7–12
		Pectoralis Minor	Elevate ribs 2–5		Transversus Abdominis	Compress abdomen
		Sternocleido-mastoid	Elevate sternum		Rectus Abdominis	Compress abdomen
		Latissimus Dorsi	Elevate ribs 9–12		Quadratus Lumborum	Depress rib 12
					Triangularis Sterni	Depress ribs 2–6
					Subcostals	Depress ribs 3–12
					Internal Intercostals	Depress ribs 3–12

to a lesser extent, the anterior fibers draws the central tendon downward and forward to increase the vertical diameter of the thorax. The diaphragm is apparently active in everyone, and its action is almost always assisted by the intercostals which evert the ribs and enlarge the antero-posterior and the lateral diameters of the thorax. The scaleni may become active toward the end of a quiet inhalation and help raise the uppermost ribs. An increase in the size of the thorax results in a negative pressure in the lungs with respect to the outside, and air rushes in until the intrapulmonic pressure is the same as atmospheric. During quiet inhalation about 600–750 cu cm of air may be drawn into the lungs.

The downward and forward movement of the diaphragm exerts a pressure on the abdominal contents and raises the intra-abdominal pressure. As the lungs approach inflation, the activity of the muscles of inspiration ceases, but during speech activity may persist into the exhalation phase. Muscles of inspiration seem to provide a checking action for the expiratory forces, which for quiet breathing are torque, gravity, and tissue elasticity. These forces tend to return the thorax to its resting position and, as a result, raise the intrapulmonic pressure. Air is expelled from the lungs until intrapulmonic pressure is once again the same as atmospheric. If conditions warrant, additional air may be expelled by the action of the abdominal muscles, which increase the intra-abdominal pressure and force the abdominal contents upward against the diaphragm and return it to its uncontracted state.

During quiet breathing, air is exchanged about twelve times a minute, and may be increased to twenty or more times per minute during heavy work. The volume of air inhaled for speech purposes does not vary significantly from tidal volume.

There seems to be little or no relation between breathing patterns and voice production. And finally, breathing that is adequate for life purposes ought to suffice for normal speaking. Table 2–5 summarizes the forces acting upon the breathing mechanism during quiet and forced breathing.

SELECTIVE READING LIST

Barnes, J., "Vital Capacity and Ability in Oral Reading," *Quarterly Journal of Speech Education,* XII, 1926, 176–81.

Basmajian, J. V., *Muscles Alive.* Baltimore: The Williams & Wilkins Co., 1962.

Bloomer, H. H., "A Roentgenographic Study of the Mechanics of Respiration," *Speech Monographs,* III, 1936, 118–24.

——— and H. Shohara, "The Study of Respiratory Movements by Roentgen Kymography," *Speech Monographs,* VIII, 1940, 91–102.

Campbell, E. J., "An Electromyographic Study of the Role of the Abdominal Muscles in Breathing," *Journal of Physiology* (London), CXVII, 1952, 222–33.

———, "The Muscular Control of Breathing in Man." Ph. D. Thesis, University of London, 1954.

———, "An Electromyographic Examination of the Role of the Intercostal Muscles in Breathing in Man," *Journal of Physiology,* CXXIX, 1955, 12–16.

———, *The Respiratory Muscles and the Mechanics of Breathing.* London: Lloyd-Luke Ltd., 1958.

Catton, W. T. and J. E. Gray, "Electromyographic Study of the Action of the Serratus Anterior Muscle in Respiration," *Journal of Anatomy* (London), LXXXV, 1951, 412.

Draper, M. H., P. Ladefoged, and D. Whitteridge, "Respiratory Muscles in Speech," *Journal of Speech and Hearing Research*, II, 1959, 16–27.

Eblen, R. E., "Limitations on Use of Surface Electromyography in Studies of Speech Breathing," *Journal of Speech and Hearing Research*, VI, 1963, 3–18.

Fenn, W. O., "Mechanics of Respiration," *American Journal of Medicine*, X, 1951, 77–91.

Gray, G. W., "Regional Predominance in Respiration in Relation to Certain Aspects of Voice," in *Studies in Experimental Phonetics*, ed. G. W. Gray, Louisiana University Studies No. 27, pp. 59–78. Baton Rouge: State University Press, 1936.

Haldane, J. S., *Respiration*. New Haven: Yale University Press, 1935.

Hoshiko, M. S., "Sequence of Action of Breathing Muscles During Speech," *Journal of Speech and Hearing Research*, III, 1960, 291–97.

Idol, H. R., "A Statistical Study of Respiration in Relation to Speech Characteristics," in *Studies in Experimental Phonetics*, ed. G. W. Gray, Louisiana State University Studies, No. 27, pp. 79–98. Baton Rouge: State University Press, 1936.

Lindsley, C. F., "Objective Study of the Respiratory Processes Accompanying Speech," *Quarterly Journal of Speech*, XV, 1929, 42–48.

Little, G. M., "Loss of Ventilatory Function after Surgical Procedures for Pulmonary Tuberculosis," *Tubercle* (London), XXXVII, 1956, 172–76.

Ptacek, P. H. and E. K. Sander, "Maximum Duration of Phonation," *Journal of Speech and Hearing Disorders*, XXVIII, 1963, 171–82.

Rahn, H., A. B. Otis, L. E. Chadwick, and W. O. Fenn, "The Pressure-volume Diagram of the Thorax and Lung," *American Journal of Physiology*, CLXVI, 1946, 161–78.

Sallee, W. H., "An Objective Study of Respiration in Relation to Audibility in Connected Speech," in *Studies in Experimental Phonetics*, ed. G. W. Gray, Louisiana University Studies No. 27, pp. 52–58. Baton Rouge: State University Press, 1936.

Spector, W. S., *Handbook of Biological Data*. WADE Technical Report 56–273, ASTIA Document No. AD 110501, Aerospace Medical Research Laboratories, Wright-Patterson Air Force Base, Ohio. October, 1956.

Steer, M. D., "Instruments in Speech Pathology," in *Handbook of Speech Pathology*, ed. L. E. Travis. New York: Appleton-Century-Crofts, 1957.

Stetson, R. H., *Motor Phonetics*, 2nd ed. Amsterdam: North-Holland Publishing Co., 1951.

Tokizane, T., K. Kawamata, and H. Tokizane, "Electromyographic Studies on the Human Respiratory Muscles," *Japanese Journal of Physiology*, II, 1952, 232–47.

Wade, O. L., "The Chest and Diaphragm in Respiration." M. D. Thesis, University of Cambridge, 1951.

———, "Movements of the Thoracic Cage and Diaphragm in Respiration," *Journal of Physiology* (London), CXXIV, 1954, 193–212.

——— and J. C. Gilson, "The Effect of Posture on Diaphragmatic Movement and Vital Capacity in Normal Subjects with a Note on Spirometry as an Aid in Determining Radiological Chest Volumes," *Thorax*, VI, 1951, 103–26.

Wiksell, W. A., "An Experimental Analysis of Respiration in Relation to the Intensity of Vocal Tones in Speech," in Studies in Experimental Phonetics, ed. G. W. Gray, Louisiana University Studies No. 27, pp. 37–51. Baton Rouge: State University Press, 1936.

Zemlin, W. R., "An Electromyographic Investigation of Certain Muscles of Respiration," (unpublished).

3

The Structure for Phonation

INTRODUCTION

BIOLOGICAL FUNCTIONS OF THE LARYNX

NONBIOLOGICAL FUNCTIONS OF THE LARYNX

The Mechanics of the Sound Generator

Glottal stops and attacks

The Supportive Framework for the Larynx

The hyoid bone

The Cartilaginous Framework of the Larynx

The thyroid cartilage
The cricoid cartilages
The arytenoid cartilages

The Surfaces
The Angles
The Apexes (Corniculate Cartilages of Santorini)
The Cricoarytenoid Joint

The epiglottis

The Anterior Surface
The Posterior Surface
The Function of the Epiglottis

The cuneiform cartilages of Wrisberg

Membranes of the Larynx

Introduction
Extrinsic laryngeal membranes

111

Supplementary laryngeal elevators

The Hyoglossus Muscle
The Genioglossus Muscle

The infrahyoid muscles

The Sternohyoid Muscle
The Omohyoid Muscle
The Thyrohyoid Muscle
The Sternohyoid Muscle

The Intrinsic Muscles of the Larynx

Introduction

The Thyroarytenoid Muscle

THE THYROMUSCULARIS
THE THYROVOCALIS

Abductor musculature

The Posterior Cricoarytenoid Muscle

Adductor musculature

The Lateral Cricoarytenoid Muscle
The Interarytenoid Muscle (Arytenoid Muscle)

The transverse arytenoid muscle
The oblique arytenoid muscle

Glottal tensor musculature

The Cricothyroid Muscle

SELECTIVE READING LIST

INTRODUCTION

Earlier in the text, the speech mechanism was likened to a mechanical system consisting of a power supply, vibrating elements, and a system of valves and filters. Having accounted for the power supply, the next step in the chain of events should be to examine the means by which vocal tones are produced.

Energy, in the form of an unmodulated stream of air from the lungs, passes into the trachea and, finally, into the larynx. The larynx is the principal structure for producing a vibrating air stream, and the vocal folds, which are part of the larynx, constitute the vibrating elements. Rapid opening and closing of the vocal folds periodically interrupt the air stream to produce a vocal or glottal tone within the pharyngeal, oral, and nasal cavities. Modifications of the acoustic properties of these cavities, which are known collectively as the vocal tract, transform the relatively undifferentiated glottal tone into meaningful speech sounds.

The larynx, which forms the superior terminal of the trachea, is an unpaired, mid-line, musculo-cartilaginous structure, located in the anterior neck. Its location is shown in Figure 3–1. An anteriorly directed prominence of the larynx, located mid-

Fig. 3–1. Lateral X-ray of the neck showing the location of the larynx and hyoid bone.

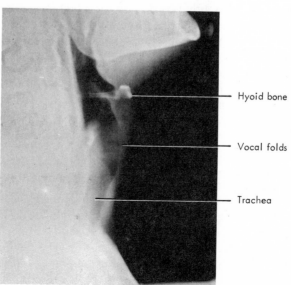

Hyoid bone

Vocal folds

Trachea

way on the vertical axis, is easily palpated by placing the fingers on the mid-line of the neck, just beneath the chin. By exploring and pressing lightly, a rather definite notch may be detected. This is the thyroid notch, and it indicates the approximate anterior attachment of the vocal folds. By placing the index finger lightly in the thyroid notch, the fingernail will press upward against the hyoid bone, the structure from which the larynx is suspended. Thus, the larynx is located between the trachea inferiorly and the hyoid bone superiorly. Vertically, it is located about on a level with the third, fourth, fifth, and sixth cervical vertebrae, but as we shall see, this position may vary with age, sex, head position, and laryngeal activity.

Production of an air stream for speech purposes has been referred to as a "non-respiratory" function of the breathing mechanism; the production of sound by the larynx may be thought of as a nonbiological function. That is to say, we have seen how the breathing mechanism has biological and nonbiological functions; by the same token, the larynx has biological and nonbiological functions.

BIOLOGICAL FUNCTIONS OF THE LARYNX

The principal biological function of the larynx is to act as a valve by (1) preventing air from escaping the lungs; (2) preventing foreign substances from entering the larynx; and (3) forcefully expelling foreign substances which threaten to enter the trachea.

In many lower forms of animals, particularly aquatic animals, water must be prevented from entering the lungs where it would cause death by asphyxiation. Animals such as the lung fishes and other air-breathing fishes are thus equipped with a primitive larynx, which consists simply of a sphincter-like orifice at the floor of the pharynx. This sphincter is in a contracted state while the animal is in the water and in a relaxed state when the animal begins breathing air, Lung fishes have no mechanism for opening the valve, however, but merely a sphincter which relaxes to permit air to enter the lungs. Such primitive larynxes contain no cartilaginous framework or abducting mechanism. Thus, these lower animals are perfectly able to "inhale" air and to prevent air from escaping once it has been "inhaled," but they do not possess a mechanism for dilating the sphincter. Animals slightly more developed than the lung fishes begin to demonstrate a laryngeal dilating mechanism. Certain salamanders, birds, and reptiles, for example, are equipped with rudimentary laryngeal cartilages and with muscles, which contract laterally to dilate actively the laryngeal opening. Higher animals, including man, utilize their elaborate larynxes in a manner not very different from the lower animals, such as the lung fishes. The student who is interested in the comparative anatomy and physiology of the larynx is urged to refer to the monumental work of Negus (1949).

Threatening substances and foreign bodies are prevented from entering the larynx by active closure of the laryngeal valve. Active closure also accompanies thoracic fixation, which was referred to in Chapter 2. Closure of the laryngeal valve prevents air escape and facilitates those activities demanding abdominal pressures, such as bowel and bladder evacuation and heavy lifting. The same mechanism responsible for thoracic fixation is active in forceful expulsion of foreign substances from the respiratory tract. Once intrathoracic pressure has been developed, a sudden, active dilation of the laryngeal valve results in a violent explosive emission of air to expel the foreign substance from the respiratory tract. This behavior, of course, is what we refer to as coughing.

NONBIOLOGICAL FUNCTIONS OF THE LARYNX

The principal nonbiological function of the larynx is sound production. Because speech is such an integral part of human behavior, however, the notion that it is nonbiological may be open to criticism. It is largely through speech that we are able to communicate with others and to make known our wants and needs. Indeed, speech is so much a part of human behavior, it might well be considered a "second-order" biological function. Regardless of the stand one may take, there is no debating that the larynx functions as a sound generator only when it is not fulfilling the biological functions listed above.

The human larynx is well equipped for sound production. The vocal folds are long, smoothly rounded bands of muscle tissue, which may be lengthened and shortened, tensed and relaxed, as well as abducted and adducted. In addition, there is good evidence that the tension of the vocal folds may be varied segmentally as well as grossly. Compared with animals less well-developed than man, the human arytenoid cartilages are quite small with respect to the total length of the valvular mechanism. Thus, the muscular, vibrating portion of the vocal fold is quite long and well suited for sound production.

The Mechanics of the Sound Generator

During normal breathing, the vocal folds are spaced rather widely apart—somewhat less for exhalation than for inhalation—and the air stream is unimpeded as it flows in and out of the lungs. Later, when the structural and behavioral characteristics of the larynx have been discussed, we will be in a position to examine closely how the unimpeded air stream may be set into vibration to produce the glottal tone. Very briefly, the larynx produces glottal tones by generating a rapid series of short-duration air pulses, which excite the supralaryngeal air column so as to produce a complex tone. Generation of the air pulses may be initiated as follows:

The vocal folds are adducted, either slightly less than completely, or completely but rather loosely, to restrict the flow of air from the lungs. At the same time, the forces of exhalation produce an increasing amount of air pressure beneath the folds, and when it becomes sufficient, they are literally blown apart, thus releasing a puff of air into the vocal tract. This release of air results in an immediate decrease of pressure beneath the vocal folds, and the elasticity of the tissue, plus the reduction of air pressure, simply allows them to snap back into their adducted position, ready to be blown apart again, once the air pressure has again built up. What has just been described is one cycle of vocal-fold vibration. In normal vowel production such vibration occurs at a rate of about 135 complete vibrations per second for men, about 235 vibrations per second for women, and even higher for children.

Glottal stops and attacks

Abrupt contraction of the adductor muscles in the larynx forcibly approximates the vocal folds to arrest their vibration. Such action is usually referred to as a glottal stop. Abrupt release of the adductor mechanism may also initiate vocal-fold vibration suddenly in what is known as a glottal attack or glottal stroke, whereas a less abrupt release by the adductor mechanism may allow vocal-fold vibration to be initiated gradually. Glottal attacks and stops occur with great frequency in some languages other than English. In parts of Germany, for example, glottal attacks and stops are used with great regularity, but they do not enjoy phonemic significance. In Turkey, on the other hand, glottal attacks are used phonemically. In the English languages glottal arrests and releases are used far more often than one might suppose.

We will want to examine the release and stop mechanisms of the larynx much more closely, but only after the structural characteristics of the larynx have been examined.

The Supportive Framework for the Larynx

The hyoid bone

The hyoid bone is actually a supportive structure for the root of the tongue rather than an integral part of the laryngeal framework. The larynx is, nevertheless, suspended from the hyoid bone, which also serves as the superior attachment for some extrinsic laryngeal muscles. In addition to serving as the point of attachment for laryngeal muscles, the hyoid bone forms the inferior attachment for the bulk of the tongue musculature. In all, there are about thirty muscles which either take their origin from, or insert into, the hyoid bone. Many of these muscles are important for the production of speech. Because of the intimate relationship of the hyoid bone to speech production, and in particular, phonation, it seems appropriate to discuss it with the laryngeal mechanism.

The hyoid bone is unique in that it is not directly attached to any other bone in the skeleton; rather, it is bound in position by a complex system of muscles and ligaments which render it a highly mobile structure. Muscles from the tongue and chin approach the hyoid bone from above and in front, while muscles and ligaments from the temporal bone approach from above and behind. Extrinsic muscles from the larynx approach from below, as do muscles from the sternum and clavicle. The muscles which attach to the hyoid bone and suspend it in position are sometimes called the hyoid sling muscles. Very briefly, the hyoid sling muscles include:

Muscle	Origin	Insertion
1. Stylohyoid	styloid process	hyoid bone
2. Digastricus (posterior)	mastoid process	hyoid bone
3. Digastricus (anterior)	hyoid bone	mandible
*4. Geniohyoid	mandible	hyoid bone
*5. Thyrohyoid	thyroid cartilage	hyoid bone
*6. Sternohyoid	manubrium sterni	hyoid bone
*7. Sternothyroid	manubrium sterni	thyroid cartilage
*8. Omohyoid	superior border scapula	hyoid bone

*These muscles are often known as the "strap muscles" of the neck. They are shown schematically in Figure 3–2.

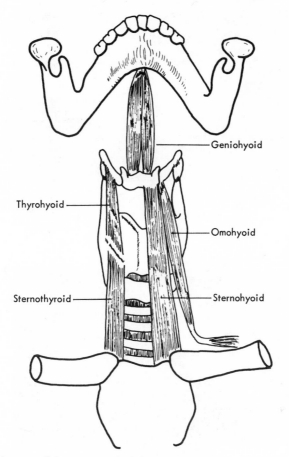

Fig. 3–2. Schematic of the strap muscles of the neck.

As shown in Fig. 3–3, the hyoid bone is somewhat horseshoe shaped. It is located in the neck horizontally, at the level of the third cervical vertebra, with the limbs of the U directed backward and slightly upward. The bulk of the hyoid bone consists of an unpaired ventral body, or corpus. It is roughly quadrilateral in shape, presenting a convex anterior surface and a pronounced concave posterior surface. A vertical medial ridge divides the anterior surface into right and left halves, while a well-defined transverse ridge courses through the upper half. Posteriorly directed limbs, one on either side of the corpus, are known as the greater horns, or greater cornua. They are somewhat more flattened than the corpus, and diminish in size from the corpus backward to terminate as tubercles, which articulate indirectly with the superior cornua of the thyroid cartilage of the larynx.

The junction of a greater cornu with the corpus is characterized by a superiorly directed, cone-shaped prominence known as a lesser cornu. The lesser cornua are usually in line with the transverse ridge of the corpus, and may be directed somewhat posteriorly as well as superiorly. They are capped by small, cone-shaped elastic cartilages. The lesser cornua are not prominences in the usual sense, because they are

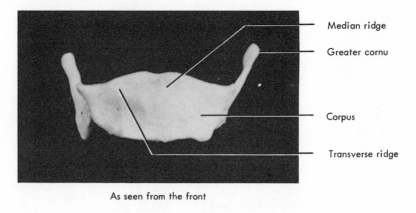

Median ridge

Greater cornu

Corpus

Transverse ridge

As seen from the front

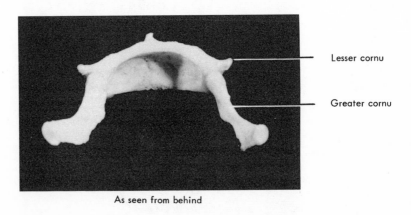

Lesser cornu

Greater cornu

As seen from behind

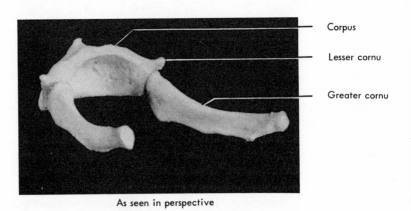

Corpus

Lesser cornu

Greater cornu

As seen in perspective

Fig. 3–3. Photographs of the hyoid bone from various angles.

actually separate bones, connected to the corpus by a synovial articulation, which tends to disappear with age. They also may be cartilaginous in some young specimens.

The Cartilaginous Framework of the Larynx

The structural framework of the larynx consists of nine cartilages and their connecting membranes. Of the nine, three are unpaired, large cartilages, and three are paired, smaller cartilages, as follows:

1 Thyroid	2 Arytenoid
1 Cricoid	2 Corniculate
1 Epiglottis	2 Cuneiform

The thyroid cartilage

The thyroid, illustrated in Figure 3–4, is the largest cartilage of the larynx. It forms most of the anterior and lateral walls of the larynx, and is composed essentially of two somewhat quadrilateral plates of hyaline cartilage, called the thyroid laminae.

Fig. 3–4. Various views of the thyroid cartilage.

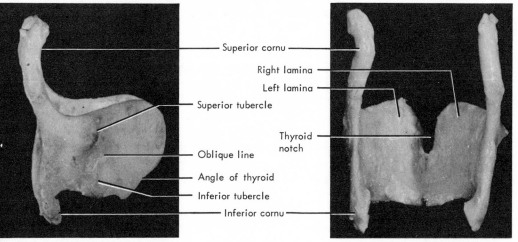

Superior cornu

Right lamina

Left lamina

Superior tubercle

Thyroid notch

Oblique line

Angle of thyroid

Inferior tubercle

Inferior cornu

A. As seen from the side

B. As seen from behind

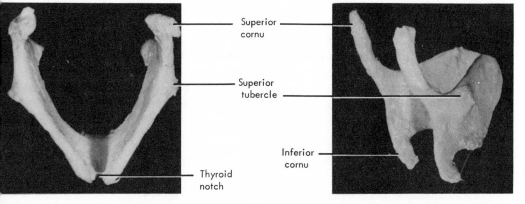

Superior cornu

Superior tubercle

Inferior cornu

Thyroid notch

C. As seen from above

D. As seen in perspective

These laminae are fused, one with the other at the mid-line, anteriorly. The point of junction is known as the angle of the thyroid. This junction is incomplete superiorly and results in a prominent, V-shaped notch called the superior thyroid notch. This notch was identified earlier as a palpable depression just above the anterior projection of the larynx known as the laryngeal prominence, or Adam's apple. When viewed from behind, as in Figure 3–4B, the thyroid laminae may be seen to diverge to enclose a wide, wedge-shaped space. The union of the laminae forms an angle of about 90 degrees in male larynxes, and 120 degrees in female larynxes. The posterior border of each thyroid lamina is prolonged upward and downward as cornua, known as the superior and inferior thyroid cornua, respectively. As shown in Figure 3–4, the superior cornua are directed upward, backward, and medially. They are attached, by means of a ligament, to the corresponding major cornua of the hyoid bone.

The inferior cornua, shorter and somewhat thicker than the superior, are directed down, slightly medially, and articulate with the cricoid cartilage laterally by means of an articular facet on the medial surface of each horn tip.

A prominent landmark of the thyroid cartilage is the oblique line, shown in Figure 3–4A, which runs down and forward from the superior to the inferior thyroid tubercle. This oblique line forms the point of attachment for some important extrinsic laryngeal musculature to be considered in detail later.

The cricoid cartilage

The cricoid cartilage is a hyaline structure that derives its name from a fancied resemblance to a signet ring. It is located immediately superior to the uppermost tracheal ring. It is smaller but stouter than the thyroid and forms the lower portion of the laryngeal framework. The cricoid cartilage consists of two parts: an anterior arch and a posterior quadrate lamina. As shown in Figure 3–5, the cricoid lamina is a hexagonal plate (the signet). It extends upward to occupy the space between the posterior borders of the thyroid cartilage. A prominent vertical ridge on the mid-line of the cricoid lamina separates two shallow depressions. The ridge serves as the point of attachment for the longitudinal muscle fibers of the upper esophagus, while the shallow depressions are the sites of origin for the posterior cricoarytenoid muscles. Laterally, on either side, the arch of the cricoid presents small oval articular facets (for articulation with the inferior cornua of the thyroid). The result is a diarthrodial pivot joint, which permits either the thyroid or the cricoid to rotate about an axis through the joint, as indicated by the dotted line in Figure 3–6. This rotational movement is an important part of the pitch-changing mechanism, which will be elaborated on in Chapter 4. The inferior border of the cricoid cartilage is smooth and contains no important landmarks. It attaches to the first tracheal ring by means of the cricotracheal membrane (or ligament). The upper border, however, runs backward and upward to the lamina, which presents, on its superior border, a posterior cricoid notch. This notch is located at the mid-line, between two smooth, convex, articular facets, which receive the bases of the arytenoid cartilages.

The arytenoid cartilages

As shown in Figure 3–6, the paired arytenoid cartilages, which are mainly hyaline, are located on the sloping superior border of the cricoid lamina. They are tetrahedral in form and so offer four surfaces and an apex for examination.

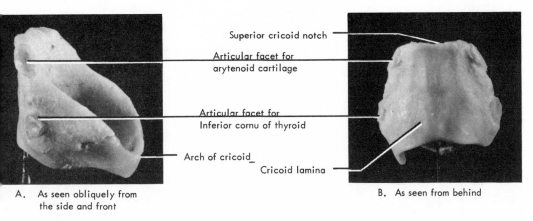

Superior cricoid notch

Articular facet for
arytenoid cartilage

Articular facet for
Inferior cornu of thyroid

Arch of cricoid

Cricoid lamina

A. As seen obliquely from
the side and front

B. As seen from behind

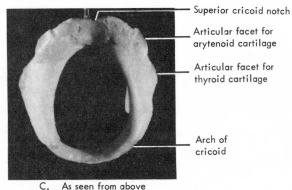

Superior cricoid notch

Articular facet for
arytenoid cartilage

Articular facet for
thyroid cartilage

Arch of
cricoid

C. As seen from above

Fig. 3–5. *Various views of the cricoid cartilage.*

Fig. 3–6. *Articulated laryngeal cartilages illustrating rotational axis at cricothyroid joint.*

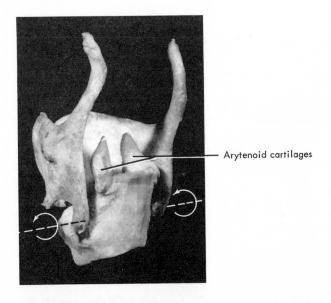

Arytenoid cartilages

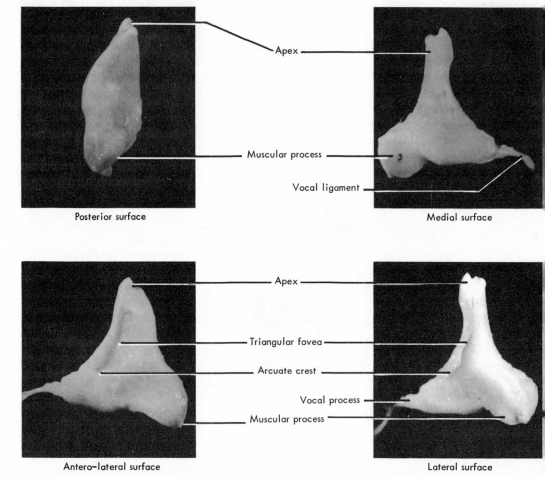

Fig. 3–7. *Various views of a left arytenoid cartilage.*

The Surfaces.   The posterior surface is smooth and somewhat concave, while the medial surface is smooth, flat, and covered with mucous membrane. The medial surfaces of the arytenoid cartilages form a part of the intercartilaginous border of the glottis (the glottis being the space between the vocal folds). The antero-lateral surface, shown in Figure 3–7, is the most extensive. It presents two pits for examination, a triangular-shaped fovea near the apex and an elongated fovea near the base, which receives the vocalis muscle (to be described later). The two foveae are separated by a horizontally directed ridge called the arcuate crest. The antero-lateral surface, near the apex, has an eminence called the colliculus. The base of the arytenoid cartilage is broad and somewhat concave for articulation with the cricoid cartilage.

The Angles.   The posterior-lateral angle of the arytenoid cartilage, near the base, is thick and somewhat projecting, and is known as the muscular process. The muscular process is the point of attachment for the posterior and lateral cricoarytenoid muscles.

The anterior angle, near the base, is prolonged anteriorly as a rather pointed projection known as the vocal process. It forms the point of insertion for the vocal ligament. The median angle is sharply rounded, but aside from that is rather nondescript.

The Apexes (Corniculate Cartilages of Santorini).   The apexes of the arytenoid cartilages curve upward, backward, and slightly medially, and are capped by a pair of conical elastic cartilages, the corniculate cartilages of Santorini, which are also directed backward and medially. They are probably vestigial structures which once served an important protective function.

The Cricoarytenoid Joint.   Since many of the biological and nonbiological functions of the larynx are mediated, to a large degree, through movements of the arytenoid cartilages, it is important to appreciate the nature of the cricoarytenoid joint. It is usually described as a synovial (diarthrodial) joint, which allows rocking and lateral gliding movements of the arytenoid cartilages. Some anatomists, however, describe the joint as one which permits rotary movements and gliding movements in both the medial and lateral directions as well as forward and backward. A prominent posterior cricoarytenoid ligament limits front and back movements of the arytenoid cartilage. Although there are various descriptions of the cricoarytenoid joint, there seems to be general agreement that it is of the synovial type; that is, it consists of a fibrous articular capsule lined by a synovial membrane. The cricoid articular facet is located, laterally, on the sloping surface of the superior border of the cricoid lamina. It is oval shaped, convex, and placed obliquely with its long axis directed from behind, laterally and slightly anteriorly. This is illustrated in Figure 3–8. The articular surface of the arytenoid cartilage, on the other hand, is also oval, but concave and with its long axis directed in an anterior-posterior direction. Such an arrangement dictates the movements of the arytenoid cartilages. Thus, they are able to glide medially and laterally and to rotate slightly. They may also slide forward and backward, but with restricted movements. Almost any combination of the above movements may occur simultaneously. For example, the arytenoids may rock forward, thus approximating the vocal processes, and at the same time they may slide medially.

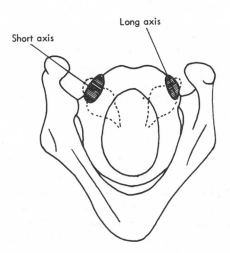

Long axis

Short axis

Fig. 3–8. Schematic of thyroid and cricoid cartilages as seen from above illustrating the axes of the cricoarytenoid joint.

The epiglottis

The epiglottis is a leaf-like structure which takes its origin, in the form of a long stalk, from the angle of the thyroid cartilage just beneath the thyroid notch. The epiglottis is shown in Figure 3–9. It is composed of yellow elastic cartilage and is attached to the thyroid cartilage by means of the thyroepiglottic ligament. The

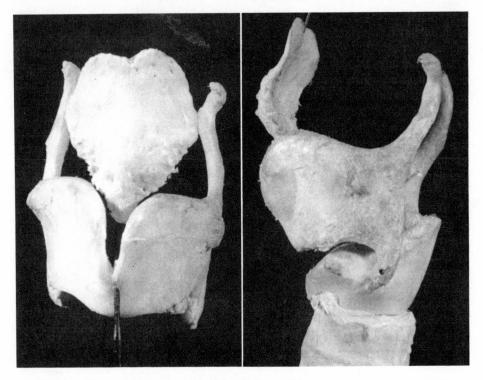

Fig. 3–9. The epiglottis in situ *as seen from the front and from the side.*

anterior surface of the epiglottis is connected, at the level where the leaf-like portion is broadest, to the body of the hyoid bone by an elastic, hyoepiglottic ligament. The upper free extremity, which is broad and rounded, lies just posterior to the root of the tongue, and indeed may actually be in contact with the tongue. This portion of the epiglottis is easily observed in dogs and children. Since the epiglottis is a thin lamella of cartilage, it presents an anterior and a posterior surface for examination.

The Anterior Surface. The anterior or lingual surface is curved forward when viewed from the side, and is convex when viewed from above. It is invested by mucous membrane, which is continuous with the sides and root of the tongue, giving rise to three glossoepiglottic folds. The lateral glossoepiglottic folds are continuous with the lateral pharyngeal wall, as well as with the sides of the tongue. The median glossoepiglottic fold is directed anteriorly to the root of the tongue at the mid-line. When viewed from above, as in Figure 3–10, two rather deep pits may be seen between

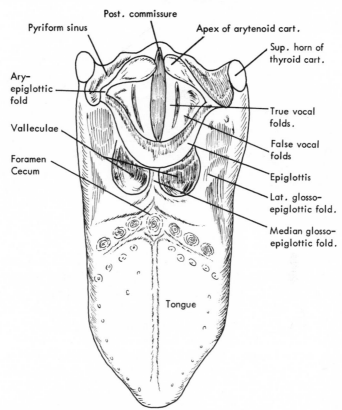

Post. commissure

Pyriform sinus

Apex of arytenoid cart.

Sup. horn of
thyroid cart.

Ary-
epiglottic
fold

True vocal
folds.

Valleculae

False vocal
folds

Foramen
Cecum

Epiglottis

Lat. glosso-
epiglottic fold.

Median glosso-
epiglottic fold.

Tongue

*Fig. 3–10. Schematic of epiglottis in situ, as seen from above,
and its relation to adjacent structures.*

the epiglottis and the root of the tongue, one on either side of the median glossoepiglottic fold. They are bounded laterally by the lateral glossoepiglottic folds. These pits are called the valleculae, and they are highly variable in their dimensions, depending upon the relation of the epiglottis to the tongue. A fat pad, extending from the hyoid bone to the level of the thyroid notch, separates the lower half of the anterior surface of the epiglottis from the hyoid bone, the thyrohyoid ligament, and the thyroid cartilage.

The Posterior Surface. The posterior or laryngeal surface is concave when viewed from above and slightly S-shaped when viewed from the side. The lower portion of the posterior surface is characterized by a prominent tubercle which is easily seen by indirect laryngoscopy. The posterior surface is invested by mucous membrane in which are contained numerous mucous glands. Removal of the mucous membrane reveals a number of small pits, which indicate the location of the mucous glands.

The Function of the Epiglottis. The epiglottis is often regarded as a vestigial structure in man and as a structure that has important biological functions in lower forms of life. It is not a vital organ in man.

Negus (1949), in his classical work, noted that all mammals have an epiglottis, and those with a keen sense of smell have a particularly well-developed epiglottis.

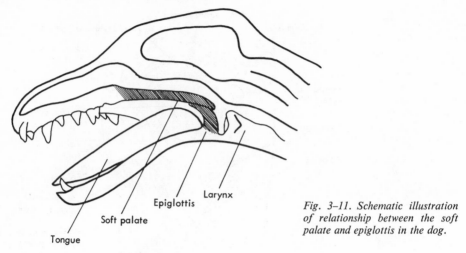

Fig. 3–11. Schematic illustration of relationship between the soft palate and epiglottis in the dog.

In Figure 3–11, note how the epiglottis rests upon the soft palate. Negus supposed that the function of the epiglottis in lower animals is to isolate the oral cavity from the remainder of the respiratory tract, especially when the animals are feeding. Inhaled air must, of course, pass through the nasal cavities and past the olfactory sense organs. Thus, the smell of food in the mouth is not able to contaminate the smell of inhaled air, and furthermore, the animal is in possession of maximum olfactation, even when the mouth is opened. The olfactory sense is crucial to lower animals, giving warning of the presence of enemy and informing a hunting animal of the presence of prey.

In man, the shape of the epiglottis is markedly altered, probably as the result of degeneration, and there is an unfilled gap between the epiglottis and the soft palate. The human epiglottis is often said to function in preventing food from entering the larynx during deglutition. The exact mechanism by which this protective, valve-like action occurs, however, is open to some question.

A fairly simple explanation is that the epiglottis acts as a sort of trapdoor, which, by reflex, snaps down over the entrance to the larynx while the bolus of food slides past on its way to the esophagus. The depression of the epiglottis is mediated through contraction of muscle fibers within the aryepiglottic fold (to be described later).

Another slightly more complicated viewpoint is that the tongue, in initiating deglutition, is pressed against the epiglottis while it simultaneously moves the bolus of food into the pharynx. The action of the epiglottis is seen to be purely passive. In fact, it is something that just happens to be in the way during swallowing, and so it is pushed aside. The protective action is still maintained, but the base of the tongue is actually responsible for its execution.

We can safely say that the epiglottis contributes very little to the production of speech. It may modify the laryngeal tone, however, by producing changes in the size and shape of the laryngeal cavity. Some singers claim the epiglottis is capable of modifying tone quality by partially covering the laryngeal opening during the production of the "covered tone." It may be of interest to point out that while engaged in high-speed photography of the larynx, the author has witnessed changes in the concavity of the posterior surface of the epiglottis as the subject for photography underwent changes in the pitch of phonation. Thus, it seems as if the aryepiglottic muscle fibers actively engage in modification of the shape of the epiglottis during phonation at various pitches. The concavity was seen to increase with increases in pitch in some subjects, usually untrained singers.

The Cuneiform Cartilages of Wrisberg.   Folds of mucous membrane, which enclose ligamentous and muscular fibers, extend from the sides of the epiglottis to the apexes of the arytenoid cartilages. They are called the aryepiglottic folds, and they form the entrance to the larynx. They are shown in Figure 3–15. Imbedded within the aryepiglottic folds, just anterior and lateral to the corniculate cartilages, are paired, elongated rods of elastic cartilage. They are the cuneiform cartilages of Wrisberg, which appear as highlighted elevations when the larynx is viewed from above. These cartilages may be absent in some specimens, however, for they are vestigial structures,

Fig. 3–12. Photographs of major laryngeal cartilages and trachea.

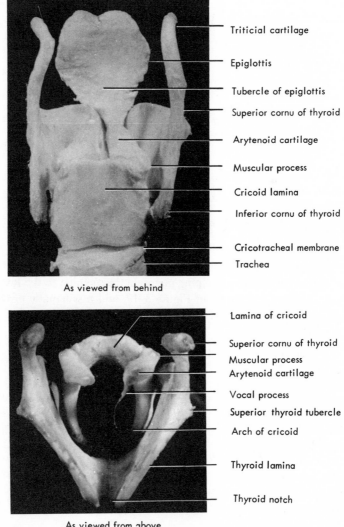

Triticial cartilage

Epiglottis

Tubercle of epiglottis
Superior cornu of thyroid

Arytenoid cartilage

Muscular process

Cricoid lamina

Inferior cornu of thyroid

Cricotracheal membrane
Trachea

As viewed from behind

Lamina of cricoid

Superior cornu of thyroid
Muscular process
Arytenoid cartilage

Vocal process

Superior thyroid tubercle

Arch of cricoid

Thyroid lamina

Thyroid notch

As viewed from above

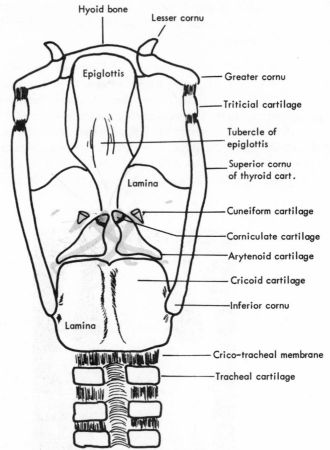

Fig. 3–13. Schematic of laryngeal cartilages and associated structures.

much more prominent in lower forms of animals. They seem to lend support to the aryepiglottic folds, thus helping maintain the opening to the larynx. The major laryngeal cartilages are shown in Figure 3–12, and a schematic of the laryngeal cartilages and associated structures as viewed from behind is shown in Figure 3–13.

Membranes of the Larynx

Introduction

A group of ligamentous membranes connects the laryngeal cartilages with adjacent structures. They are called extrinsic laryngeal membranes, and include the hyothyroid membrane (thyrohyoid), the paired lateral hyothyroid ligaments, the hyoepiglottic ligament, and the cricotracheal membrane. Another group of membranes interconnects the various laryngeal cartilages and helps regulate the extent and direction of their movements. They are the intrinsic laryngeal membranes, one of which (the conus elasticus) actually contributes to the composition of the vibrating portion of the vocal folds.

Extrinsic laryngeal membranes

The Hyothyroid Membrane.   The hyothyroid membrane is an unpaired, fibroelastic sheet, which arises along the whole of the superior border of the thyroid cartilage. The fibers are directed vertically upward to attach on the posterior surface of the body and major horns of the hyoid bone near the superior border.

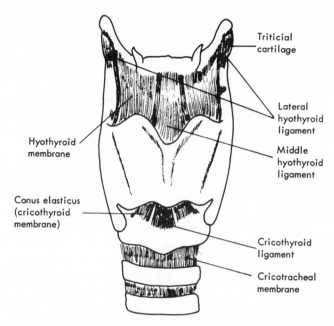

Fig. 3–14. Ligaments and membranes of the larynx as seen from the front.

A thickened medial portion of the hyothyroid membrane is known as the middle hyothyroid ligament. It is shown in Figure 3–14. Thus, the larynx is suspended from the hyoid bone by a continuous sheet of fibroelastic membrane.

The Lateral Hyothyroid Ligament.   The suspension of the larynx from the hyoid bone is facilitated laterally by a round, cord-like elastic ligament, which is continuous with the postero-lateral border of the hyothyroid membrane. This ligament, known as the lateral hyothyroid ligament, extends from the tip of the superior horn of the thyroid cartilage to the posterior tip of the major horn of the hyoid bone. A frequently noted peculiarity of the lateral hyothyroid ligament is the presence of a small, bony or cartilaginous nodule that may be found imbedded within the substance of the ligament. This structure, shown in Figures 3–12 and 3–14, is known as the triticial (grain of wheat) cartilage.

The Hyoepiglottic Ligament.   The hyoepiglottic ligament was described earlier in the discussion of the epiglottis as an unpaired, mid-line, elastic ligament extending from the anterior surface of the epiglottis to the upper border of the body of the hyoid bone.

The Cricotracheal Membrane.   The previously mentioned cricotracheal membrane connects the lower border of the cricoid cartilage with the upper border of the first tracheal ring. It is slightly more extensive than the membranes which connect the tracheal rings with each other.

Intrinsic laryngeal membranes

With the exception of the ligaments at the points of articulation of the laryngeal cartilages, the intrinsic laryngeal membranes stem from one broad sheet of tissue called the elastic membrane of the larynx. This membrane, which is covered on its inner surface by mucous membrane, may be thought of as a continuous fibroelastic sheet that, except for a small interval between the vocal and ventricular ligaments (to be described later), lines the entire larynx. The lower portion of the elastic membrane is the most extensive and is well defined. It consists of paired lateral sections, which together form the conus elasticus. The upper portion, less well defined, is usually called the quadrangular membrane, which roughly describes its shape.

The Conus Elasticus (*Cricovocal Membrane*).   The conus elasticus connects the thyroid, cricoid, and arytenoid cartilages with one another. Conventionally, it is divided into an anterior ligament and two lateral membranes. The anterior ligament, shown in Figure 3–14, is better known as the cricothyroid ligament, while the lateral portions are known as cricothyroid membranes.

The cricothyroid ligament.   This is a well-defined band of yellow elastic tissue. As shown in Figure 3–14, it is a midline structure, extending from the superior border of the cricoid arch to the inferior border of the thyroid cartilage, at the angle. It is broader below than above.

The cricothyroid membranes.   These membranes, which form the lateral portions of the conus elasticus, are much thinner than the midline, ligamentous portion just discussed. They originate from the superior border of the cricoid cartilage, course superiorly and medially, and terminate as free margins extending from the vocal processes of the arytenoid cartilages to the angle of the thyroid cartilage. The free borders of the cricothyroid membranes are often referred to as separate structures called the true vocal ligaments. Each vocal ligament lies within the body of the corresponding vocal fold, and it forms the medial portion of the fold. The cricothyroid membranes, shown in Figure 3–14, are often referred to collectively as the conus elasticus.

The Quadrangular Membranes.   The paired quadrangular membranes arise from the lateral margins of the epiglottis and adjacent thyroid cartilage near the angle. The fibers course posteriorly downward and attach to the corniculate cartilages and to the medial surfaces of the arytenoids. Each membrane appears roughly as a vertically directed sheet of membranous tissue. The membranes are widely separated superiorly, and converge slightly as they descend. Inferiorly, they terminate as free thickened borders called the ventricular ligaments. The inferior borders of the quadrangular membranes may be thought of as the counterparts of the free thickened borders of the cricothyroid membranes. Anteriorly, the ventricular ligaments attach to the thyroid cartilage near the notch. Posteriorly, where they are more highly developed, they attach to the triangular foveae of the arytenoids. A schematic of a frontal section of

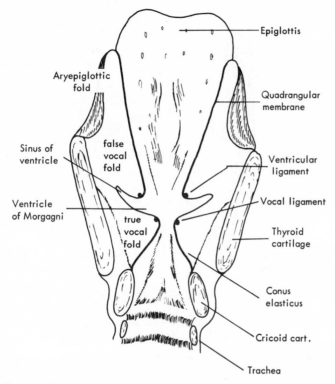

Fig. 3–15. *Frontal section of larynx illustrating the relationship of quadrangular membrane with conus elasticus.*

the larynx is shown in Figure 3–15. This figure shows the quadrangular membrane and its relationship with the conus elasticus and other laryngeal structures.

The Aryepiglottic Folds.   The superior margins of the quadrangular membranes are modified by submucous muscle tissue (the aryepiglottic muscles) to form the paired aryepiglottic folds. They extend from the sides of the epiglottis near the rounded superior border to the apexes of the arytenoids, where the fibers seem to be continuous with other laryngeal musculature. In fact, some anatomists believe the aryepiglottic muscles to be simply an extension of the oblique interarytenoid muscles (to be described later). The cuneiform cartilages, when present, are imbedded within the aryepiglottic folds.

There is supportive evidence that the aryepiglottic folds form a sphincter-like superior aperture for the larynx. Contraction of the aryepiglottic muscles, during swallowing or gagging, may close the laryngeal aperture, either by drawing the sides medially, or by depressing the epiglottis. Quite probably both mechanisms are involved.

The Cricoarytenoid Ligaments.   The anterior and posterior cricoarytenoid ligaments restrict and, to a certain extent, dictate the movements of the arytenoid cartilages. The anterior cricoarytenoid ligament extends from the cricoid cartilage to the antero-lateral base of the arytenoid. It limits backward movement of the arytenoid cartilage.

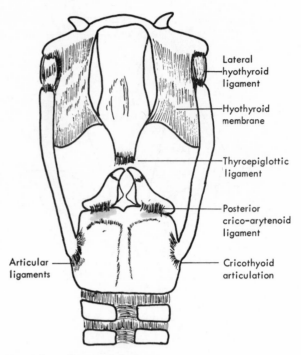

Fig. 3–16. Ligaments and membranes of the larynx as seen from behind.

The prominent posterior cricoarytenoid ligament, described earlier, extends from the posterior surface of the cricoid lamina near the superior border upward to the base of the posterior surface of the arytenoid cartilage. It is shown in Figure 3–16. This ligament restricts the extent of the forward movement of the arytenoid.

Mucous membrane of the larynx

The distribution of the quadrangular membrane and the conus elasticus is such that the entire cavity of the larynx is reinforced by a submucous fibroelastic membrane. A small area between the vocal and ventricular ligaments is excepted. A mucous membrane, continuous above with the lining of the mouth and pharynx and below with the lining of the trachea, lines the whole of the cavity of the larynx. This

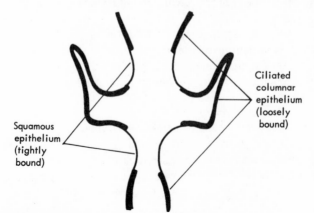

Fig. 3–17. Schematic of laryngeal mucous membrane.

membrane is particularly rich in mucous glands in the area between the vocal and ventricular ligaments. It is closely adherent to the epiglottis, the aryepiglottic folds, and the vocal folds. Elsewhere in the larynx it is loosely attached to a submucous basement tissue. The mucous membrane on the anterior surface and upper half of the posterior surface of the epiglottis, the upper portion of the aryepiglottic folds, and the medial surface of the ventricular and vocal folds is covered by stratified squamous epithelium. The remainder of the laryngeal mucous membrane is covered by columnar epithelium. This is shown schematically in Figure 3–17.

The Cavity of the Larynx

The cavity of the larynx extends from the laryngeal entrance above to the inferior border of the cricoid cartilage below. It is divided into supraglottal and infraglottal portions by the medial projection of the true vocal folds. The portion above the vocal folds is known as the vestibule. The entrance to the vestibule, or, more properly, the aditus laryngis, is a triangular opening, wider in front than behind, which slopes obliquely downward and backward. The boundaries of this opening include the epiglottis in front, the aryepiglottic folds laterally, and the apexes of the arytenoid cartilages behind. The cavity of the vestibule is wide above, becoming narrower toward the vocal folds. This is depicted in Figure 3–18.

A deep depression, lateral to the aditus laryngis, is known as the pyriform sinus. As shown in Figure 3–19, it is bounded laterally by the thyroid cartilage (and thyrohyoid membrane) and medially by the aryepiglottic fold.

Some anatomists place the lower boundary of the vestibule at the level of the ventricular folds, whereas others place it at the level of the vocal folds. That is, some anatomists include the ventricle of the larynx as part of the vestibule while others refer to

Fig. 3–18. Frontal section showing divisions of the larynx.

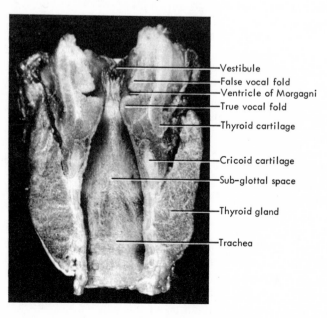

Vestibule
False vocal fold
Ventricle of Morgagni
True vocal fold

Thyroid cartilage

Cricoid cartilage

Sub-glottal space

Thyroid gland

Trachea

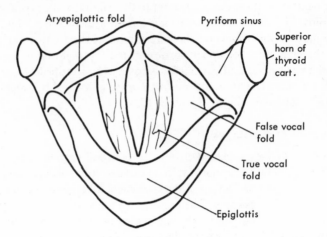

Fig. 3–19. Schematic of larynx as viewed from above showing relationship of pyriform sinus to thyroid cartilage and aryepiglottic fold.

the ventricle as a separate division of the laryngeal cavity. Designating the ventricle as a separate division of the cavity seems to facilitate description without necessarily complicating matters, and so we shall refer to the ventricle as the middle division.

The ventricle of the larynx (laryngeal sinus)

The ventricle of the larynx, first described by Galen, an early Greek physician (A.D. 130–200), was described in detail by Morgagni in 1741, and so it is very often referred to as the ventricle of Morgagni. As shown in Figure 3–18, it is bounded above by the ventricular or false vocal folds and below by the true vocal folds. Laterally, it is bounded by the thyroarytenoid muscle. The ventricle extends almost the entire length of the true vocal folds, and anteriorly it is continued upward as the laryngeal saccule. The paired ventricular folds are sometimes referred to as the superior vocal folds. They consist of thick folds of mucous membrane, which enclose a few muscle fibers and the ventricular ligaments. The ventricular ligaments, you will recall, were described earlier in this chapter as the free inferior margins of the quadrangular membrane. They are attached anteriorly to the angle of the thyroid cartilage and posteriorly to the antero-lateral surface of the arytenoid cartilages, in the area of the triangular foveae. The lower margin of the ventricular ligament, enclosed in mucous membrane, forms the free, crescent-shaped upper boundary of the ventricle of Morgagni. Although the ventricular folds contain a few fibers of the thyroarytenoid muscle, they present a soft and flaccid appearance and are unable to become completely tense. They are most prominent anteriorly, where they attach to the angle of the thyroid immediately below the attachment of the epiglottis. Posteriorly, they attach to the antero-lateral surfaces of the arytenoids. The ventricular folds move with the arytenoid cartilages but stand farther apart than the true vocal folds; under normal circumstances they do not contract or vibrate during phonation. The space between the medial boundaries of the ventricular folds is called, appropriately, the false glottis, or glottis spuria.

Negus (1949) ascribed a valvular function to the ventricular folds. He stated that they may function, along with the true vocal folds, in preventing the escape of air from the lungs.

Sphincteric action of certain laryngeal muscles may approximate the ventricular folds. In such cases, voice is either produced or significantly modified by the vibration of the ventricular folds. Every now and again a person is described clinically as having ventricular dysphonia (hyperkinesia of the false folds). The chief symptom is roughness of the voice, which varies in severity. The ventricular folds, which are normally separated widely, are adducted, and may partially or completely cover the true vocal folds. This condition may be psychogenic, or it may be secondary to organic disease of the larynx. On the basis of conventional laryngoscopic examination it is often difficult, if not impossible, to determine if the false vocal folds are actually the vibrating elements or if the adducted false vocal folds are simply being set into vibration by the modulated air stream emitted by the vibrating true vocal folds beneath. Stroboscopic or high-speed cinematographic laryngoscopy is the only way in which the actual mechanism may be viewed objectively. In normal circumstances, the ventricle and ventricular folds may contribute to a modification of the laryngeal tone produced by the vibrating true folds. Van den Berg (1955), in observing X-ray films of a well-trained singer, found evidence that the ventricle, by damping high-frequency components, may act as a low-pass filter. He also found evidence that the medial projection of the false vocal folds was more pronounced in the well-trained than in the untrained singer.

The Appendix of the Laryngeal Ventricle (Laryngeal Saccule). As stated earlier, the laryngeal ventricle is continued upward anteriorly as the saccule. It is shown schematically in Figure 3–15. At its anterior extremity the saccule extends almost to the upper border of the thyroid cartilage. It is liberally supplied with mucous glands, which are imbedded within submucous fatty tissue. The saccule is contained by a delicate capsule of fibrous tissue, which is continuous with the ventricular ligament. Muscle fibers adjacent to the saccule, sometimes known as Hilton's muscle, compress the mucous glands and express mucus which apparently lubricates the vocal folds. These muscle fibers originate at the apex of the arytenoid cartilage and become ill-defined and finally lost in the aryepiglottic fold. The fibers seem to be continuous with those in the oblique interarytenoid muscles (to be described later).

The laryngeal saccule is quite large in apes and other anthropoids, and it is said to function as an accessory phonatory organ. Negus (1949) questioned this viewpoint, however. Kaplan (1960) stated that the sacculus represents an atavistic (throwback) structure in man.

The vocal folds (plicae vocales)

The inferior or true vocal folds lie parallel to, but just beneath the false vocal folds, and are separated from them by the space comprising the laryngeal ventricle. The paired folds take their origin from the posterior surface of the thyroid laminae, near the angle, and below the thyroid notch. The anterior attachment (anterior commissure) of the folds is common, but they diverge as they course posteriorly toward their attachments on the antero-lateral surface of the arytenoid cartilages. The medial border of the vocal folds is free. Thus, the vocal folds project shelf-like into the cavity of the larynx. This is illustrated in Figure 3–18.

Each fold consists of two primary bundles of muscle tissue bounded medially by the vocal ligament and covered by a tightly adherent mucous membrane. The muscle fibers apparently do not enter into the vocal ligament. These muscle bundles, which will be discussed in some detail later, are the thyrovocalis portion (sometimes called the vocalis muscle) and the thyromuscularis portion of the thyroarytenoid muscle.

Depending upon their contractile state, the vocal folds may present anywhere from a sharp, well-defined medial border, as in a tense fold, to a round, rather ill-defined medial border, as in the relaxed vocal fold.

As stated earlier, the vocal folds are covered by a tightly adherent mucous membrane, which is comparatively nonvascular in nature. Although the vocal folds are actually slightly pink, when viewed by conventional laryngoscopic techniques they appear glossy white. Due to the presence of elastic cartilage, they may appear yellowish at the anterior commissure. The folds may appear as pale red or pink in heavy smokers or persons with laryngitis.

The inferior division

The inferior or infraglottal portion of the laryngeal cavity is bounded above by the vocal folds and below by the inferior margin of the cricoid cartilage. A conspicuous feature of this division of the larynx is the lack of landmarks. When seen in a frontal section, as in Figure 3–18, the inferior division of the larynx appears narrowest at the level of the vocal folds, becoming wider below. This portion of the larynx is lined with ciliated columnar epithelium, which extends into the trachea and bronchi. The cilia beat toward the pharynx and thus help remove accumulations of mucus and foreign matter from the larynx.

The rima glottidis

The rima glottidis is a variable opening between the vocal folds anteriorly and the vocal processes and bases of the arytenoids behind. Conventionally, it is referred to as the glottal chink, or simply, the glottis. It is shown schematically in Figure 3–20. The anterior portion, which is bounded laterally by the vocal ligaments and muscular portion of the vocal folds, is known as the vocal or membranous glottis. It comprises about three-fifths the total length of the glottis and extends from the anterior commissure of the vocal folds to the vocal processes of the arytenoid cartilages. During quiet breathing the length of the membranous glottis is about 15 mm in males and 12 mm in females. The posterior portion is bounded by the vocal processes and medial surfaces of the arytenoid cartilages and is, therefore, referred to as the cartilaginous glottis. The extent to which the vocal processes extend into the vocal folds is shown in Figure 3–21. The length of the cartilaginous glottis is about 8 mm in males, slightly less in females.

As shown in Figure 3–22, the dimensions and configurations of the glottis are highly variable, depending upon laryngeal activity and the adjustment of the arytenoid cartilages. The various glottal configurations are shown schematically in Figure 3–23.

When studied by means of ultra high-speed motion-picture photography, the membranous portion of the vibrating vocal folds appears to be the most active, and the term vocal glottis seems appropriate. Unfortunately, the term may imply that the remainder of the glottis, that is, the cartilaginous glottis, ought to be called the non-

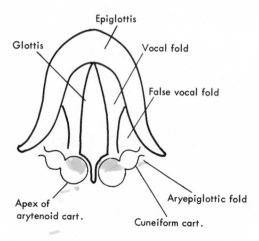

Fig. 3–20. Schematic of larynx as seen from above.

Fig. 3–21. Transverse section of adult larynx at level of glottis illustrating the extent to which the vocal process projects into the vocal fold. (Courtesy F. L. Lederer, Diseases of the Ear, Nose, and Throat. *F. A. Davis Company, 1938.)*

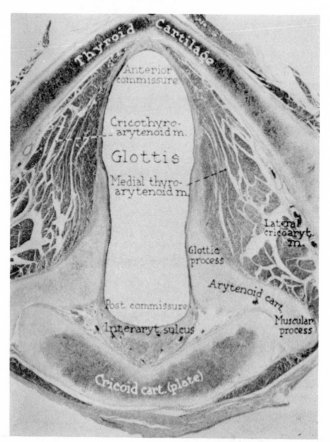

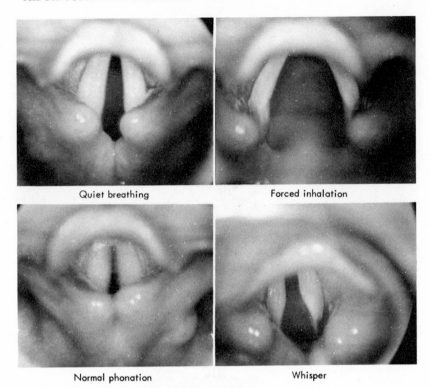

Fig. 3–22. Photographs of various glottal configurations.

Fig. 3–23. Schematic of various glottal configurations.

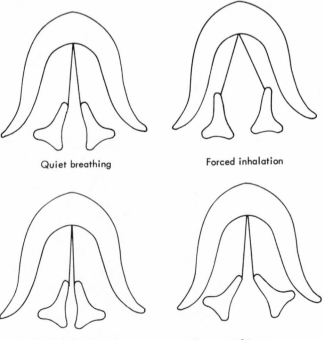

Start

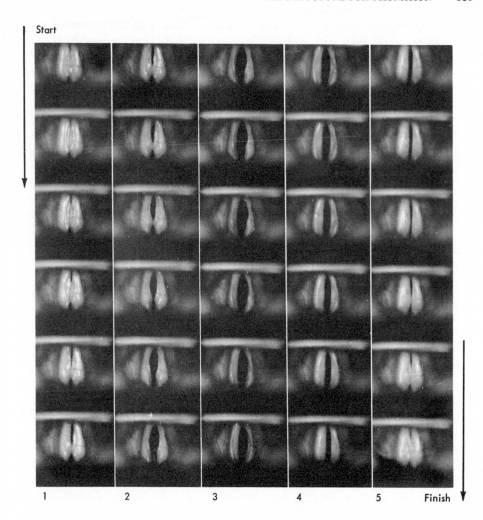

1   2   3   4   5   Finish

*Fig. 3–24. A single cycle of vocal fold vibration taken from a
high-speed film exposed at 4,000 frames per second.*

vibrating or nonvocal glottis. Again, evidence obtained from high-speed photography demonstrates that the anterior portion of the cartilaginous glottis does enter into the vibration and does contribute to voice production. The configurations of the glottis during a single cycle of vocal-fold vibration are shown in Figure 3–24. These motion pictures were taken at an exposure rate of 4,000 frames per second, and the entire vibratory cycle represents glottal activity during 1/140 seconds.

On the basis of what has been said thus far, it ought to be evident that the length, width, and shape of the glottis is subject to extreme variability, not only from individual to individual, but within a given individual.

Hollien and Moore (1960) found, for example, that the total length of the glottis ranged from 19.1 to 23.0 mm in six adult males with the folds in the abducted position (at rest). Measurements obtained from the same population during phonation at various pitches ranged from 8.7 mm for low tones to 20.5 mm for high-pitched tones (within the "natural register"). Hollien and Moore noted a rather systematic increase in the length of the vocal folds with increases in vocal pitch. Zemlin (unpublished) found the length of the glottis for eleven males to range from 11.6 mm to 16.7 mm, with a mean of 14.5 mm, during phonation at conversational pitch and intensity and from 13.0 to 19.6 mm, with a mean of 16.0 mm, during phonation at a pitch one octave above conversational pitch.

At rest, the width of the glottis, measured at the vocal processes, is about 8 mm in the male. During forced inhalation this value may almost double. In addition, the configuration of the glottis may vary anywhere from a thin slit to a lozenge-shaped opening.

Factors contributing to changes in the size and shape of the glottis will be discussed in considerable detail in the following chapter, where the mechanism of voice production is treated more thoroughly. For the present, suffice it to say that the shape and size of the glottis can be altered by the abduction or adduction, rotation or tilting of the arytenoid cartilages, by the air stream that is directed against the vocal folds, and by contraction of the laryngeal muscles.

The Muscles of the Larynx

Introduction

The muscles of the larynx are generally considered in two groups, the extrinsic and the intrinsic muscles. The extrinsic muscles are those which have at least one attachment to structures outside the larynx, while the intrinsic muscles are those which have both attachments within the larynx. Although both the extrinsic and intrinsic muscles may influence laryngeal function, the intrinsic muscles are largely responsible for control of sound production. The extrinsic muscles are largely responsible for support of the larynx and for fixing it in position. They also elevate and depress the larynx. The extrinsic muscles may be divided into two groups on either an anatomical or a functional basis. Anatomically, they may be divided into suprahyoid and infrahyoid muscles; functionally they may be divided into the laryngeal elevators and laryngeal depressors. There are four suprahyoid muscles, the digastric, the stylohyoid, the mylohyoid, and the geniohyoid muscles. The suprahyoid muscles are also laryngeal elevators.

The Extrinsic Muscles of the Larynx

The suprahyoid muscles (laryngeal elevators)

The Digastric Muscle.   The digastric is a paired muscle, rather complex in structure, and very difficult to visualize. It will profit the student to rely upon the illustrative material. As the name suggests, the digastric muscle consists of two fleshy bellies. They are actually two distinct muscles, but are hardly ever considered as such. As shown in Figure 3–25, the anterior belly takes its origin from the inside surface of the lower border of the mandible near the symphysis. The fibers course down and back. The posterior belly, which is considerably longer than the anterior, takes its origin from the mastoid process of the temporal bone. The fibers course down and forward. The two bellies meet, and are joined at an intermediate tendon. This tendon, which

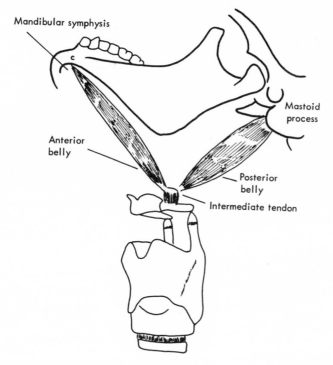

Mandibular symphysis

Mastoid process

Anterior belly

Posterior belly

Intermediate tendon

Fig. 3–25. Schematic of digastric muscle.

perforates the stylohyoid muscle, is attached to the junction of the corpus and greater cornu of the hyoid bone by a fibrous loop, which is part of a more extensive suprahyoid aponeurosis.

As might be supposed, contraction of the digastric muscle raises the hyoid bone, or, if the hyoid is in a fixed position, it may assist in depressing the lower jaw. Contraction of the anterior belly draws the hyoid up and forward, while contraction of the posterior belly draws the hyoid up and backward. Both actions are important to the early stages of deglutition. For example, when both bellies are contracted, the hyoid bone is drawn directly upward, thus elevating the base of the tongue, which during the initial stage of deglutition is pressed against the hard palate. During the second stage of deglutition, contraction of the posterior belly elevates the larynx and draws it under the base of the tongue. This action helps prevent food from entering the larynx.

The Stylohyoid Muscle. The stylohyoid, shown in Figure 3–26, is a long, slender muscle placed just superficially to the posterior belly of the digastric muscle. It takes its origin from the styloid process of the temporal bone. The fibers course down and forward, roughly parallel to the fibers of the posterior belly of the digastric muscle. Just above the hyoid bone the muscle splits into two slips which pass, one on either side of the intermediate tendon of the digastric, to insert into the body of the hyoid at its junction with the greater cornu. Contraction of this muscle draws the hyoid bone up and backward.

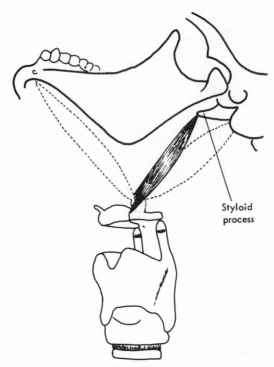

Fig. 3–26. Schematic of stylo-hyoid muscle.

The Mylohyoid Muscle.   The mylohyoid is a thin, unpaired, trough-like sheet of muscle fibers which form the floor of the mouth. The fibers take their origin along the mylohyoid line, which runs along the inner surface of the mandible and extends from the mandibular symphysis (mental symphysis) to the last molar. As shown in Figure 3–27, the fibers course medially and downward to join their fellows from the opposite side at a tendinous mid-line raphe. This raphe extends from the mental symphysis to the hyoid bone. The posterior-most fibers attach directly to the corpus of the hyoid bone. With the mandible fixed, contraction of the mylohyoid muscle elevates the hyoid bone, the floor of the mouth, and the tongue. This muscle is an important contributor to deglutition. With the hyoid bone in fixed position, it may assist in depressing the mandible.

Fig. 3–27. Schematic of mylohyoid and geniohyoid muscles.

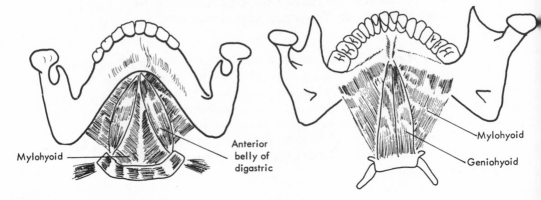

The Geniohyoid Muscle. The geniohyoid is a paired cylindrical muscle, located above the superior (buccal) surface of the mylohyoid muscle. It is shown in Figure 3–27. The muscles lie in direct contact with each other but on opposite sides of the mid-line. The fibers take their origin, by means of a short tendon, from the lower mental spine at the mandibular symphysis. They diverge slightly as they course backward and downward to insert on the anterior surface of the body of the hyoid bone. With the mandible in a fixed position, the geniohyoid muscles pull the hyoid bone up and forward.

The four suprahyoid muscles just described perform some very important functions during deglutition. During the first phase of swallowing the bolus of food is swept into the oropharynx by the tongue. This action is facilitated by the anterior belly of the digastric, the mylohyoid, and the geniohyoid muscles, which as a group carry the hyoid bone and the tongue upward and forward. During the second stage of swallowing, the hyoid bone, the tongue, and the larynx are elevated directly. When the bolus has passed through the pharynx, the posterior belly of the digastric and the stylohyoid muscles elevate and retract the hyoid bone and the base of the tongue to complete the third or pharyngeal phase of swallowing.

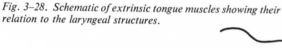

Supplementary laryngeal elevators

The Hyoglossus Muscle. Although the hyoglossus is usually considered to be an extrinsic muscle of the tongue, it may influence the position of the larynx. As shown in Figure 3–28, it arises from the upper border of the corpus and greater

Fig. 3–28. Schematic of extrinsic tongue muscles showing their relation to the laryngeal structures.

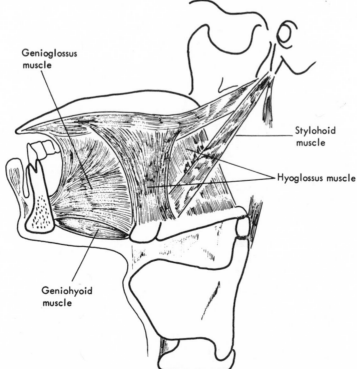

Genioglossus muscle

Stylohoid muscle

Hyoglossus muscle

Geniohyoid muscle

cornua of the hyoid and courses directly upward to insert into the posterior and lateral regions of the tongue.

The Genioglossus Muscle.   The genioglossus is also an extrinsic tongue muscle that may influence the position of the larynx. It is a complex muscle that originates at the genial tubercle of the mandible. The fibers diverge as they course toward their insertion. The inferior fibers are inserted into the body of the hyoid bone, while the upper fibers are inserted into the whole of the under surface of the tongue. Contraction of the genioglossus may elevate the hyoid bone and draw it forward. This muscle, along with the hyoglossus, will be considered in detail in Chapter 5 when the tongue is discussed at greater length. The extrinsic tongue muscles and their relation to the laryngeal structures are shown in Figure 3–28.

The infrahyoid muscles

Two paired extrinsic laryngeal muscles support the hyoid bone from below. They are the sternohyoid and the omohyoid muscles, both of which are "strap muscles of the neck."

The Sternohyoid Muscle.   The sternohyoid is a flat muscle, lying on the anterior surface of the neck. It is shown schematically in Figure 3–29. It originates from the posterior surface of the manubrium of the sternum, from the medial end of the clavicle, and from adjacent ligamentous tissue. The fibers course vertically and insert on the lower border of the body of the hyoid bone. The muscles on either side come very near one another as they course upward toward their insertion. In fact, they sometimes lie in direct contact with each other. If the sternum is in a fixed position, the ster-

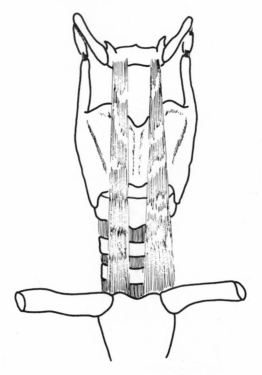

Fig. 3–29. Schematic of sternohyoid muscle.

nohyoid muscles draw the hyoid downward, and if the hyoid is fixed in position, the muscles may aid in elevating the sternum. There is no supportive evidence for this latter function, however.

The Omohyoid Muscle.   The omohyoids are long, narrow, two-bellied muscles, which are situated on the antero-lateral surface of the neck. They are difficult to visualize. The inferior (posterior) belly takes its origin from the upper border of the scapula. As shown in Figure 3–30, the fibers course almost horizontally forward to terminate at an intermediate tendon, which is held in position, just above the sternum, by tendinous fibers which run to the sternum and to the cartilage of the first rib. The superior (anterior) belly originates from the intermediate tendon and courses vertically and slightly medially to insert along the lower border of the greater cornu of the hyoid bone, just lateral to the insertion of the sternohyoid muscle. Contraction of the omohyoid depresses the hyoid bone.

In addition to the muscles just described, two other extrinsic laryngeal muscles support the larynx. They are the thyrohyoid (sometimes called the hyothyroid) and the

Fig. 3–30. Schematic of omohyoid muscle.

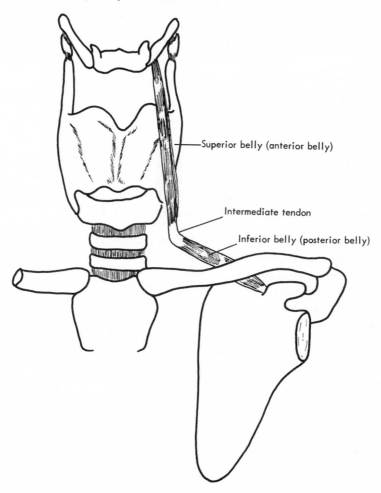

Superior belly (anterior belly)

Intermediate tendon

Inferior belly (posterior belly)

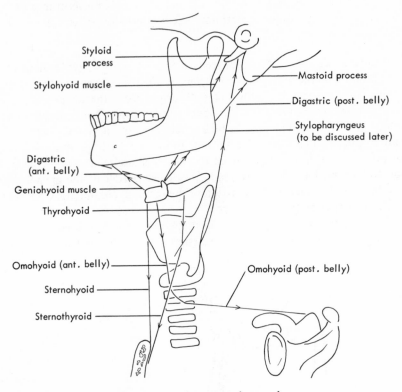

Fig. 3–31. Schematic of the actions of the extrinsic laryngeal muscles.

sternothyroid muscles. The first supports the larynx from above and is, therefore, a laryngeal elevator, while the second courses to the larynx from below and is a laryngeal depressor. Thus, there are, in all, five laryngeal elevators and three laryngeal depressors. Their action is shown schematically in Figure 3–31.

The Thyrohyoid Muscle.   The thyrohyoid, which seems to be a superiorly directed extension of the sternothyroid, is a broad, thin muscle located beneath the omohyoid and the sternohyoid muscles, on the antero-lateral surface of the neck. As shown in Figure 3–32, it originates from the oblique line of the thyroid lamina. The fibers course vertically upward and insert into the lower border of the greater cornu of the hyoid bone. Contraction of this muscle lessens the distance between the thyroid cartilage and the hyoid bone. With the thyroid cartilage fixed, it depresses the hyoid bone, and with the hyoid fixed, it elevates the thyroid cartilage. The thyrohyoid muscle is also shown schematically in Figure 3-33.

The Sternothyroid Muscle.   The sternothyroid, shown schematically in Figure 3–33, is a long, thin muscle located in the anterior neck just beneath the omohyoid and sternohyoid muscles. It originates from the posterior surface of the manubrium of the sternum and from the first costal cartilage. The fibers course upward and slightly laterally and insert along the oblique line of the thyroid lamina, as shown in

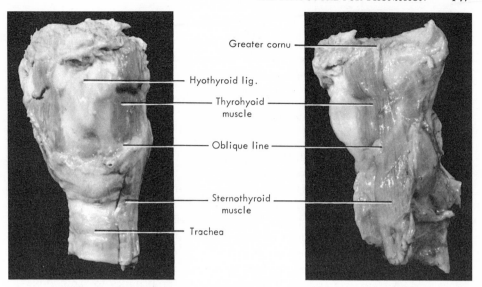

Greater cornu

Hyothyroid lig.

Thyrohyoid
muscle

Oblique line

Sternothyroid
muscle

Trachea

As seen from the front

As seen from the side

Fig. 3–32. Photographs of a larynx showing the origin and insertion of the thyrohyoid muscle and the insertion of the sternothyroid muscle.

Fig. 3–33. Sternothyroid muscle and thyrohyoid muscle shown schematically.

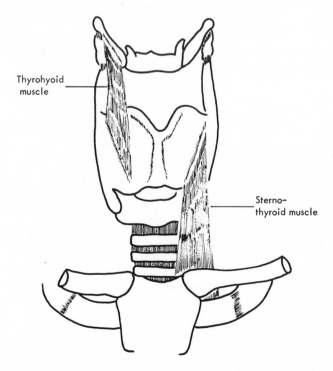

Thyrohyoid
muscle

Sterno-
thyroid muscle

Figure 3–32. Some fibers may continue into the thyrohyoid muscle and into the inferior pharyngeal constrictor (to be described later). Its principal action is to draw the thyroid cartilage downward. Some investigators claim the sternothyroid muscle may enlarge the pharynx by drawing the larynx down and forward.

The Intrinsic Muscles of the Larynx

Introduction

Socially adequate voice production, with appropriate pitch inflections and proper intensity changes, is a rather common event. Most of us are unimpressed by such things as voice quality in the speech of persons around us. Indeed, it usually is not until we are in the presence of someone with a voice disorder that we might become aware of quality. Students of speech and voice pathology are painfully aware of the complexities of the speech mechanism and of the rapid sequences of subtle changes required of it during the production of everyday speech.

The larynx is one of the most complex structures in the entire speech and hearing mechanism. An intricate system of intrinsic muscles contributes to the complexity of the larynx. These muscles, by virtue of their unique structure and architecture, are able to accomplish the many and varied rapid changes that are required during speech production. The intrinsic laryngeal muscles may be categorized according to their effects on the shape of the glottis and on the vibratory behavior of the vocal folds. There are abductor, adductor, tensor, and relaxer muscles in the larynx. The abductor muscles, which separate the arytenoids and vocal folds for respiratory activities, are opposed by the adductors, which approximate the arytenoids and vocal folds for phonation and for protective purposes. The glottal tensors elongate and tighten the vocal folds. They are opposed by the relaxers, which shorten them. The main mass of the vibrating vocal folds is composed of the thyrovocalis, or simply the vocalis muscles. They form the medial portion of the more extensive thyroarytenoid muscles, and so are sometimes referred to as the internal thyroarytenoids.

The Thyroarytenoid Muscle. As stated in an earlier discussion of the vocal folds, the thyroarytenoid muscle is very complex, and is composed of two primary bundles, often referred to as the thyromuscularis and the thyrovocalis portions.

The thyromuscularis. The thyromuscularis (external thyroarytenoid muscle) is a thin bundle of muscle fibers that runs roughly parallel to, and is bounded medially by, the thyrovocalis. It is bounded laterally by the thyroid lamina to which it attaches. The fibers originate anteriorly from the lower half of the thyroid angle, course posteriorly, and diverge slightly before inserting into the antero-lateral surface and muscular process of the arytenoid cartilage. Some fibers continue around the lateral border of the arytenoid and continue on as part of the oblique arytenoid muscle (to be described later). Other fibers, which course almost vertically upward from the angle of the thyroid to insert into the lateral margin of the epiglottis, are often referred to as a distinct muscle, the thyroepiglottic muscle. A few fibers course along the lateral margin of the ventricle and insert into the lateral margin of the epiglottis. These fibers constitute the ventricular, or Hilton's muscle.

The exact function of the thyromuscularis is not known with certainty, but it appears to be a glottal relaxer. It may affect the mode of vibration of the vocal folds by varying the tension of the tissue into which the thyrovocalis fibers attach. That is, by drawing the arytenoid closer to the thyroid cartilage, the thyrovocalis muscles may be rendered more flaccid. This point of view is contested by Greene (1957), who says that the thyroarytenoid (thyromuscularis) shortens but does not relax the vocal folds. She states that thickening of the opposing surfaces of the vocal folds is assisted by the contraction of the main bulk of the thyroarytenoid muscle and, in addition, the tension of the vocal folds is not determined by their length, but by contraction of the thyroarytenoid muscle. Thus, Greene refers to the thyroarytenoid not as a glottal relaxer, but rather as the internal tensor of the larynx. This interesting point of view may have to be taken into account when the mechanics of phonation are discussed in Chapter 4.

The thyromuscularis, which is shown schematically in Figure 3-34, may contribute to the formation of a sphincter ring around the superior portion of the larynx. This ring is completed by the adductor muscles of the larynx and by muscles that depress the epiglottis.

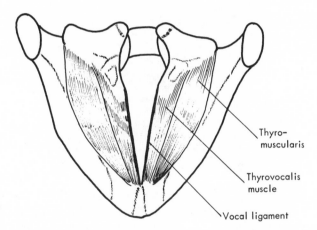

Thyro-
muscularis

Thyrovocalis
muscle

*Fig. 3–34. Schematic of the thyro-
arytenoid muscle.*

Vocal ligament

The thyrovocalis.   The thyrovocalis, also shown in Figure 3–34, is more extensive than the thyromuscularis. Bounded laterally by the thyromuscularis and medially by the conus elasticus, it forms the main mass of the vibrating vocal folds. When seen in cross section, as in Figure 3–35, it appears roughly triangular in shape. The thyrovocalis originates from the posterior surface of the angle of the thyroid and courses posteriorly to insert into the vocal process and lateral surface of the arytenoid cartilage. Its primary function seems to be as a tensor of the vocal folds, and, by partial or segmental contraction, it may alter the frequency and mode of vocal-fold vibration.

Some investigators report that a few fiber bundles, located in the medial-most portion of the vocal fold, enter the vocal ligament and function to execute subtle adjustments of the vocal ligament during phonation. This small bundle of muscle tissue is often designated as the aryvocalis muscle. Von Leden and Konig (1961), however, in investigation of three thousand histological sections from normal vocal folds were unable to locate muscle fibers that enter into the vocal ligament. There seems to be very little anatomical evidence to support the existence of an aryvocalis muscle. On the other hand, all dissections indicated strong muscular attachments

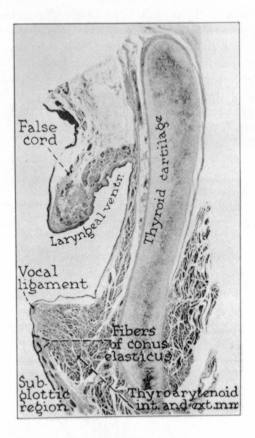

Fig. 3–35. Frontal section, stained for elastic fibers, through the true and false vocal folds. (Courtesy F. L. Lederer, Diseases of the Ear, Nose, and Throat.)

between the fibers of the thyromuscularis and the conus elasticus. These findings support the contention by Negus (1929) that the thyromuscularis fibers adjust vocal-fold mass and tension during changes in vocal register. These findings have serious theoretical implications, and will be discussed in the following chapter.

Abductor musculature

The Posterior Cricoarytenoid Muscle. There is just one abductor muscle in the larynx. It is the paired, posterior cricoarytenoid, a broad, fan-shaped muscle which originates from a shallow depression on the posterior surface of the cricoid lamina. The fibers course upward and laterally and converge upon the posterior surface of the muscular process of the corresponding arytenoid cartilage. The posterior cricoarytenoid muscle is illustrated photographically and schematically in Figure 3–36, and its action is shown schematically in Figure 3–37. The uppermost fibers are chiefly responsible for rotation of the arytenoids, while the lower fibers produce a medial gliding movement of the arytenoids. Because of its important adductor action, the posterior cricoarytenoid muscle is sometimes known as the laryngeal dilator. Laryngeal dilation is easily observed during forced inhalation. A photograph of abducted vocal folds was shown in Figure 3–22. The photograph was made while the subject was taking a deep breath.

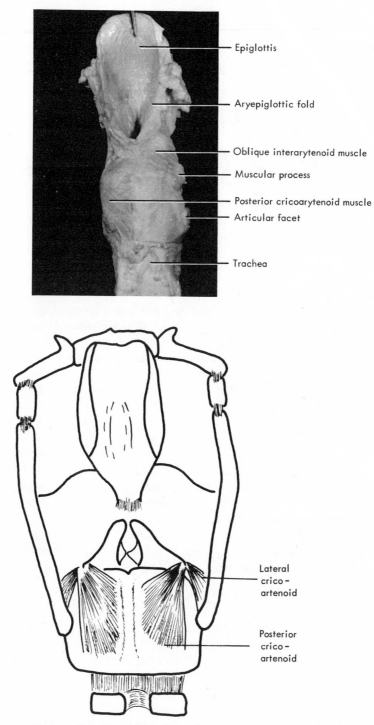

Fig. 3–36. Photograph and schematic of posterior crico-arytenoid muscle.

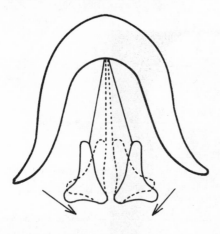

Fig. 3–37. Schematic of the action of the posterior cricoarytenoid muscles.

Adductor musculature

Two muscles act as antagonists to the posterior cricoarytenoid muscle. They are the lateral cricoarytenoid and the interarytenoid muscles. Upon contraction they close the glottis.

The Lateral Cricoarytenoid Muscle.   The lateral cricoarytenoid muscle is an important glottal adductor that may also function as a glottal relaxer. As we shall see later, both functions are very important for phonatory activity. It is a fan-shaped muscle, located deep to the thyroid cartilage in the antero-lateral wall of the larynx. The medial surface of this muscle lies in direct contact with the conus elasticus. As shown in Figure 3–38, the muscle fibers take their origin from the upper border of the arch of the cricoid cartilage. They course upward and back and rapidly converge before inserting into the anterior surface of the muscular process of the corresponding arytenoid cartilage. Its action upon the glottis is shown schematically in Figure 3–39. Upon contraction, this muscle rotates the arytenoid, drawing the muscular process forward and the vocal process medialward. The lateral cricoarytenoid muscle may draw the arytenoid cartilage forward somewhat, and, as shown in Figure 3–39, it may also shape the glottis for the production of a whisper. A photograph of the glottis during the production of a whisper was shown in Figure 3–22. Thus, depending upon its action, the lateral cricoarytenoid muscle may be classified as an adductor (its primary function), a relaxer, or as an abductor (as in the whisper). When acting as an abductor, the lateral cricoarytenoid functions in direct antagonism to the interarytenoid muscle.

The Interarytenoid Muscle (Arytenoid Muscle).   The interarytenoid is an unpaired muscle located on the posterior surfaces of the arytenoid cartilages. It arises from the posterior surface and lateral border of one arytenoid cartilage and inserts into the corresponding parts of the opposite arytenoid cartilage. It is a rather complex muscle, usually considered in two parts, often designated as the transverse arytenoid and the oblique arytenoid muscles.

The transverse arytenoid muscle.   The transverse arytenoid muscle is more extensive than the oblique arytenoid. As shown schematically in Figure 3–40, the fibers originate from the lateral margin and posterior surface of one arytenoid cartilage, course in a horizontal direction, and insert into the lateral margin and posterior surface of the

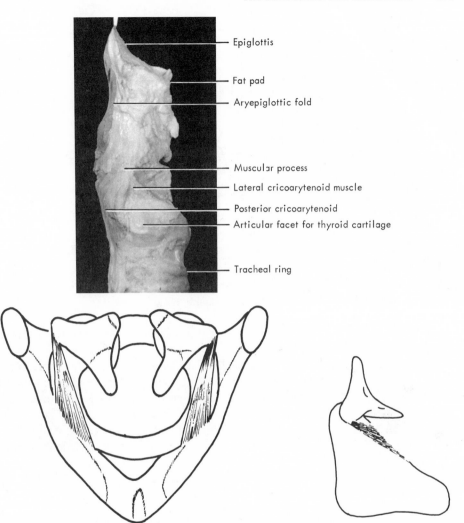

— Epiglottis

— Fat pad
— Aryepiglottic fold

— Muscular process
— Lateral cricoarytenoid muscle
— Posterior cricoarytenoid
— Articular facet for thyroid cartilage

— Tracheal ring

Fig. 3–38. Photograph and schematic of the lateral crico-arytenoid muscle and some adjacent structures.

Fig. 3–39. Schematic of the action of the lateral cricoarytenoid muscles.

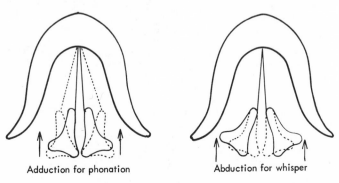

Adduction for phonation

Abduction for whisper

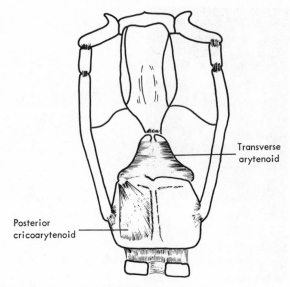

Fig. 3–40. *Schematic of transverse arytenoid muscle.*

opposite arytenoid cartilage. Contraction of this muscle approximates the arytenoid cartilages, especially their median angles.

The oblique arytenoid muscle.   The oblique arytenoid muscle is the more superficial of the two parts. It consists of two fasciculi, each of which originates from the posterior surface of the muscular process of one arytenoid cartilage and inserts into the apex of the opposite cartilage. When viewed from behind, as in Figure 3–36, the fasciculi appear to cross each other, like the limbs of the letter X. As shown in Figure 3–41, a few muscle fibers continue around the apex of the arytenoids laterally

Fig. 3–41. *Schematic of oblique and aryepiglottic fibers of the interarytenoid muscle.*

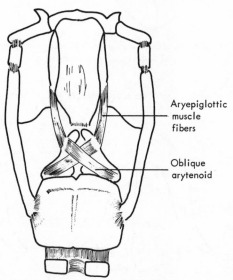

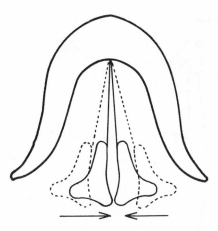

Fig. 3–42. Schematic of the action of the interarytenoid muscles.

and angle upward and forward to insert into the lateral borders of the epiglottis. These muscle fibers constitute the aryepiglottic muscles, which enter into the aryepiglottic folds. A few fibers insert into the quadrangular membrane. The aryepiglottic and oblique arytenoid muscles comprise sphincteric structures which serve in a protective function. In addition, the oblique arytenoid muscle approximates the arytenoid cartilages, as illustrated in Figure 3–42.

Glottal tensor musculature

Aside from the thyrovocalis muscle, there is but one other muscle that can actively tense or elongate the vocal folds. It is the cricothyroid muscle. It is important to note, however, that elongation of the vocal folds does not necessarily result in an increase in tension. This apparently holds true, however, only within certain limits.

The Cricothyroid Muscle. As shown in Figure 3–43, the cricothyroid is a fan-shaped muscle, broader above than below. It originates from the antero-lateral arch of the cricoid cartilage. The fibers diverge and insert into the thyroid cartilage as two distinct parts. The lower or oblique fibers (pars oblique) course upward and back to insert into the anterior margin of the inferior cornu of the thyroid cartilage. The upper or anterior fibers (pars recta) course nearly vertically upward and insert along the inner aspect of the lower margin of the thyroid lamina. From the standpoint of the mechanics of phonation, this muscle is extremely important. Upon contraction of the anterior fibers, the distance between the cricoid arch and the thyroid laminae is diminished. This means that the distance between the thyroid cartilage, at the angle, and the vocal processes of the arytenoid cartilages is increased by a proportional amount. This action is illustrated in Figure 3–44. If the thyroid cartilage is fixed in position (by the extrinsic laryngeal muscles), contraction of the cricothyroid muscle raises the cricoid; if the cricoid is fixed, the thyroid tilts downward. Either action provides the modifications in tension or length of the vocal folds that are necessary for pitch changes. Contraction of the oblique fibers pulls the thyroid cartilage forward on the cricothyroid joint, and this action, also shown in Figure 3–44, further increases the distance between the arytenoid and thyroid cartilages.

Having become familiar with some of the intricate structure of the larynx, our next immediate task ought to be to examine the manner in which the laryngeal mecha-

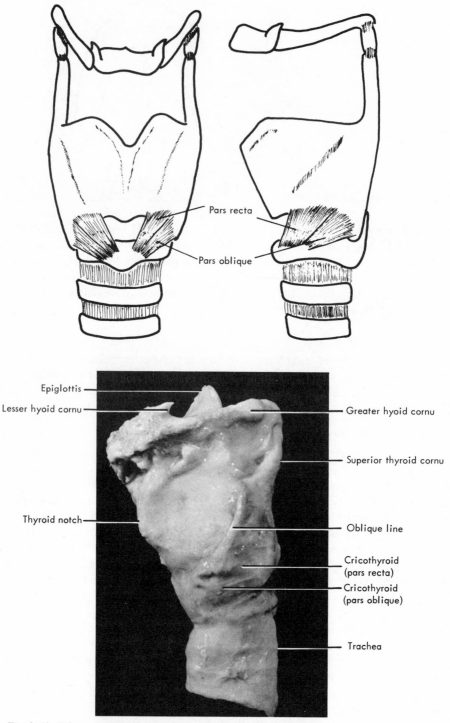

Fig. 3–43. Schematic and photograph of cricothyroid muscle
and associated laryngeal structures.

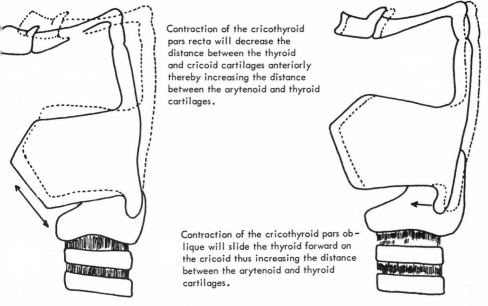

Contraction of the cricothyroid pars recta will decrease the distance between the thyroid and cricoid cartilages anteriorly thereby increasing the distance between the arytenoid and thyroid cartilages.

Contraction of the cricothyroid pars oblique will slide the thyroid forward on the cricoid thus increasing the distance between the arytenoid and thyroid cartilages.

Fig. 3–44. Means by which the cricothyroid may function to tense the vocal folds.

nism functions during voice production. In an earlier discussion of the nonbiological functions of the larynx, it was shown, rather grossly, how the vibrating vocal folds function as a sound generator. A more elaborate discussion of the mechanics of phonation will be found in the following chapter.

SELECTIVE READING LIST

Berg, Jw., van den, "On the Role of the Laryngeal Ventricle in Voice Production," *Folia Phoniatrica*, VII, 1955, 57–69.

Greene, M. C. L., *The Voice and its Disorders*. New York: The Macmillan Company, 1957.

Hollien, H. and P. Moore, "Measurements of the Vocal Folds During Changes in Pitch," *Journal of Speech and Hearing Research*, III, 1960, 157–65.

Judson, L. S. and A. T. Weaver, *Voice Science*, 2nd ed. New York: Appleton-Century-Crofts, 1965.

Kaplan, H. L., *Anatomy and Physiology of Speech*. New York: McGraw-Hill Book Company, 1960.

Leden, H. von, "The Mechanism of Phonation," *Archives of Otolaryngology*, LXXIV, 1961, 660–66.

Lederer, F. L., *Diseases of the Ear, Nose, and Throat*, 1st ed. Philadelphia: F. A. Davis Company, 1938.

Myerson, M. C., *The Human Larynx*. Springfield, Ill.: Charles C. Thomas, Publisher, 1965.

Negus, V. E., *The Mechanism of the Larynx*. London: William Heinemann, Limited, 1929.

———, *The Comparative Anatomy and Physiology of the Larynx*. New York: Grune & Stratton, Inc., 1949.

Saunders, W. H., "The Larynx," *Clinical Symposia*, XVI, 1964, 67–99. Published by the Ciba Pharmaceutical Products, Inc. (Summit, N. J.).

4

The Mechanics of Phonation

INTRODUCTION

THE HISTORY OF LARYNGOSCOPY

Introduction
Transillumination
Photography of the Larynx
Stroboscopy
Motion-picture Photography
High-Speed Cinematography
Transillumination-photoconduction
Recent Developments

THE PITCH AND INTENSITY MECHANISMS

Introduction
The Onset of Phonation

Characteristics of a vibratory cycle

The Pitch-changing Mechanism

Introduction
The pitch-raising mechanism

Subglottal Air Pressure and Pitch

The pitch-lowering mechanism

The Extrinsic Muscles and the Pitch-changing Mechanism
Voice Registers
The Limits of the Pitch Range
The Intensity Changing Mechanism
The Vibrato

VOCAL QUALITIES

    Breathiness
    Harshness
    Hoarseness
    Nasality
    Whisper

AGE AND SEX DIFFERENCES IN THE LARYNX

THEORIES OF VOICE PRODUCTION

    Myoelastic-aerodynamic Theory
    Neuro-chronaxic Theory
    Cavity-tone Theory
    Harmonic Theory

SELECTIVE READING LIST

INTRODUCTION

Researchers have been actively investigating the laryngeal mechanism for over a century and a half. There is evidence, however, that men speculated on the function of the larynx long before any actual observations were made. Galen was one of the first to recognize the glottis as the source of vocal sounds. He supposed that vocal intensity was dependent upon the adjustment of the soft palate and uvula. In the early 1700's, Dodart described the relationship between the glottal air stream and vocal intensity. He concluded that vocal sounds were produced by the impact of glottal air upon the relatively dormant supraglottal air column.

Since the first attempts at laryngoscopy in 1807, many variations of several devices have been employed in an attempt to gain a better understanding of the functions of internal laryngeal activity during voice production. Much has been learned regarding the nature of internal laryngeal activity during voice production. A major element contributing to the accumulating body of knowledge has been the development of increasingly better techniques for examination of the larynx and for recording laryngeal activity. But in spite of significant technical advances, different opinions exist today on some very fundamental concepts of laryngeal physiology.

A brief review of the development of laryngoscopic techniques might put us in a better position to appraise some of the more prominent observations and conjectures regarding vocal-fold adjustments and action during the production of vocal sounds. The following survey is not meant to be exhaustive but, rather, representative of events that have led to the current status of laryngoscopy.

THE HISTORY OF LARYNGOSCOPY

Introduction

Laryngoscopy for research purposes poses three very real problems which must be overcome before any success can be realized. (1) The larynx is located out of view deep in the neck; (2) the larynx is dark, and must be adequately illuminated to permit viewing; and (3) the movements of the vocal folds during phonation are much too rapid to see by any conventional optical system or by the unaided eye.

These problems make successful laryngoscopy a formidable task indeed. Small wonder then that the development of satisfactory laryngoscopic techniques was 150 years in coming.

The Development of Indirect Laryngoscopy

One of the first devices for laryngoscopy was a speculum designed by Bozzini of Frankfort-am-Main (see Moore, 1937) in 1807. His invention consisted of a metal tube, divided by a partition into two sections, one for light transmission, the other for passage of the reflected image. Bozzini's belief that reflected and incident light could not travel through the same passage accounted for the divided speculum. A small mirror, tilted in such a way as to allow the investigator to look downward toward the larynx, was placed at the end of one partition, and a mirror to reflect light into the larynx was placed at the end of the other. A candle, reinforced by a reflection mirror, served as a light source. The results obtained by Bozzini's speculum apparently were not significant, and he was criticized severely by the medical profession. The invention was forgotten.

Twenty years later, in 1827, Dr. Senn of Geneva (see Moore, 1937) used a specially constructed mirror in an attempt to examine the larynx of a small girl. Although Senn attributed his failure to the small mirror used, he probably was unsuccessful because of inadequate illumination.

Two years later, in England, Dr. Benjamin Babington reported in the *London Medical Gazette*, "a newly designed 'glottiscope' for the examination of parts within the fauces not admitting of inspection by unaided sight." The instrument consisted simply of an oblong piece of "looking-glass" set in silver wire and provided with a long shank for a handle. During this same year M. Gagniard de la Tour placed a mirror in the back of his throat and, with sunlight for illumination and the aid of a second mirror, tried to view his own larynx. Although he was only partially successful, his experiment represents the first attempt at autolaryngology.

In 1837, Robert Liston, a London surgeon, published a book entitled *Practical Surgery*, in which he stated: "A view of the parts may be sometimes obtained by means of a speculum, such a glass as is used by dentists, on a long stalk, previously dipped in hot water, introduced with the reflecting surface downward and carried well into the fauces" (reported by Wright, 1902).

The next major contribution seems to have been in 1839, when Baumes demonstrated to the medical profession in Lyons a mirror the size of a two-franc piece for use in examination of the posterior nares and larynx.

As stated earlier, one of the primary difficulties in laryngology is inadequate illumination. Investigators during this period were restricted to the use of candle light and reflecting mirrors. Adam Warden, in 1844, suggested the use of a refracting prism to direct light to the larynx and the reflected image back to the investigator. During the same year, Avery, of London, utilized a head band to which was fastened a small semispherical mirror. A hole in the center of the reflector permitted the examiner to place the mirror over one eye. This device was similar to the mirror used by present-day physicians. The modern head mirror, however, was designed by Czermak in 1857, but that is part of another story.

Probably the most significant contribution to laryngoscopy was made in 1855, when Manuel Garcia, a singing teacher in France, described observations made on the interior of the larynx during the act of singing. A little mirror on a long handle (suitably bent) was placed in the throat of the person being examined. Sunlight was directed against the mirror by means of a second, hand-held mirror. By means of his technique, Garcia discovered several new and important facts concerning internal laryngeal behavior during singing. Garcia is often given credit for the development of laryngoscopy.

As late as 1832 there was considerable speculation on the part of the medical profession as to whether an examination of the larynx was possible. Although the report of Garcia's method and findings was received apathetically by the British, it apparently created some interest in Austria. In 1857, Turck of Vienna read Garcia's article and became interested. He had some mirrors made and tried them in the wards of the General Hospital in Vienna. His laryngeal mirrors were bulky, his illumination was inadequate, and his attempts at laryngoscopy were unsatisfactory. That same year, Czermak, a professor of physiology at the University of Pesth, borrowed some mirrors from Turck and improved them by removing the bulky hinges attaching the mirror to the handle. By the introduction of the ophthalmoscope mirror for concentration of artificial light, Czermak was very successful in viewing the larynx. Probably Czermak, more than anyone else, was responsible for laryngoscopy's becoming a clinical tool. The results obtained by Turck and Czermak stirred a great deal of interest within the medical profession in France and undoubtedly were responsible for the rapid growth of laryngology in America. Shortly after Czermak published his results, Krackwizer and Stagenwald in New York obtained laryngoscopic apparatus from Czermak and began making laryngological examinations.

Transillumination

In 1858, Czermak described a new technique for examination of the larynx. He called it transillumination of the larynx. Rather than direct light down the throat, as in the Garcia technique, Czermak directed a concentrated spot of light on the anterior surface of the neck. The light passed through the tissue to illuminate the interior of the larynx. Inspection of the transilluminated larynx, by means of a guttural mirror, revealed it in "delicate shades of red." Czermak suggested that transillumination might be a useful technique for measuring the vertical dimensions of the vocal folds.

In 1888, Voltolini described an apparatus for transillumination of the larynx which used the newly invented Edison glow-lamp for a light source. Voltolini suggested that because tissue matter must obey the laws of optics, transillumination might be useful for defining the contours of a tumor.

Transillumination apparently was not received with enthusiasm, and the technique was subjected to considerable criticism. In 1889, Gottstein published an article on transillumination of the larynx, in which be referred to a statement made by Serrater, a Britisher, who called transillumination an "elegant sport." Gottstein defended transillumination as an excellent technique for examination of the pyriform sinuses.

Benedict, in 1911, referred to the work of Voltolini and called attention to the fact that light can, in some cases, be just as effective in diagnoses as X-ray. In 1917, Freudenthal defended Voltolini's method of transillumination as a technique for examination of both the larynx and sinus maxillaris.

Horst Wullstein, in 1936, obtained electrical recordings of glottal variation as a function of infraglottal air pressure on an excised calf larynx, using the response of a cesium photocell to subglottal transillumination.

Photography of the Larynx

During the early phases of laryngoscopy, investigators were limited to indirect methods of gathering data on the larynx. There was as yet no technique for obtaining accounts of laryngeal function other than descriptive methods. In 1884, however, Dr. Thomas R. French published a report of a technique for laryngeal photography, and for the first time recorded data were available.

French used an ingenious hand-held camera fastened to a guttural mirror. A second mirror, similar to the ophthalmoscope mirror of Czermak, concentrated sunlight for illumination. With such an apparatus, Dr. French was able to take remarkably high-quality photographs of the larynx. While French and others were working on perfecting the photography process, however, other researchers were devoting their attention to improvements of the indirect laryngoscopic techniques.

Wertheim, of Vienna, using concave laryngeal mirrors, attempted to view a magnified image of the larynx. Voltolini sought the same result using a modified Galilean telescope. Binocular viewing was attempted in an effort to gain a more accurate image of the larynx, but the results seem to have been somewhat less than satisfactory.

While French is usually given credit for perfecting the process of laryngeal photography, a survey of the German literature reveals that Czermak published the results of his attempted laryngeal photography in 1861, some twenty-three years before French. Czermak's negatives were very small, and he projected them onto a screen. Other researchers working on photography of the larynx had relatively little success. Lennox-Browne and Behnke, for example, in 1883, used a 10,000-candle-power light source and an apparatus that required two photographers, two medical doctors, and electricians in attendance to produce poor-quality photographs that were only one and a half millimeters in diameter (reported by Moore, 1937).

Although several variations of French's technique were attempted during the period shortly after 1884, not much real gain was obtained until 1919, when Garel, a Frenchman, developed a practical technique for taking stereoscopic photographs of the larynx. Clerf, in 1925, using the apparatus of Garel, was also successful in taking high-quality photographs of the larynx.

Stroboscopy

Coincident with the development of motion-picture photography was the development of strobolaryngoscopy, in which the principles of stroboscopy were utilized in the investigation of the larynx.

The stroboscope is an instrument which permits an observer to view moving objects in such a manner that they appear to be stationary. A primitive form of stroboscope, such as the one built by Faraday, consists of a revolving disc, with holes or slots equally spaced around the periphery. Thus, a beam of light directed through the revolving disc will be interrupted periodically, and a moving object below will be illuminated for short, regular intervals. A cyclic movement, therefore, can be made to appear stationary if the speed of the disc is adjusted so that a hole is opposite the beam of light only when the moving object reaches the same point in each cycle; during the remainder of the cycle the disc blocks out the light. Since the moving object is always viewed when it is in exactly the same position, the persistence of vision makes it appear to be standing still.

Contemporary stroboscopes utilize a flashing light to illuminate the moving object periodically. Because a flash of light can be made to have an extremely short duration by the use of gaseous-discharge lamps, the object being viewed moves a negligible distance while it is being illuminated and appears to be sharp and well defined. If the light is just a little out of synchrony with the cyclic rate of the moving object, the object will seem to be moving very slowly, either in one direction or the other, depending upon whether the flashing light is slightly fast or slightly slow.

Although Michael Faraday developed a practical stroboscope as early as 1825, Töpler, in 1866, was the first to suggest that stroboscopic principles might be useful in examination of the vocal folds. It remained for Oertel, in 1878, to make the first attempt at strobolaryngoscopy. He tried various types of stroboscopes, but they were found to be unreliable and cumbersome. It was not until glow-lamp stroboscopy was developed that the technique became suitable for research purposes.

In 1930, Tiffin and Metfessel, at the University of Iowa, utilized an ingenious technique for firing a glow-lamp stroboscope. Their device used the output from a vacuum-tube amplifier for the discharge voltage. The input of the amplifier was coupled to a microphone. As the subject phonated during strobolaryngoscopy, the rate of firing of the glow-lamp was in response to the basic rate of vibration of the vocal folds. When the firing rate of the glow-lamp was in synchrony with the vibratory frequency of the vocal folds, the folds appeared motionless. By adjusting the firing rate of the lamp slightly out of synchrony with their vibratory frequency, the vocal folds would have an apparent rate of vibration in the order of only one or two cycles per second. Examination of the vocal folds was accomplished, as in the past, by directing the flashing light to a guttural mirror. West, Kallen and Polin, Hegener and Musehold, and Moore are but some of the names associated with the development of strobolaryngoscopic techniques. For an excellent review of strobolaryngoscopy, the reader is referred to Moore (1937).

Motion-Picture Photography

In 1913, when cinematography was just beginning to be a reality, Chevroton and Vles made the first motion pictures of the larynx. Their films revealed information regarding gross laryngeal action, such as the approximation of the vocal folds prior to vocalization and the separation of the folds during inhalation.

Combining the principles of stroboscopy and those of photography enabled Hegener and Panconcelli-Calzia to take stroboscopic motion pictures in 1913. By 1929 experimenters had become rather sophisticated in the use of stroboscopic motion-picture photography, and in the following year, G. O. Russell and G. H. Tuttle, using an incandescent light source, reported good-quality color movies of vocal-fold activity. Light was directed into the pharynx by means of a quartz rod.

Numerous investigators modified and improved the cinematographic techniques, and although considerable improvement in the quality of the results was realized, the motion-picture films revealed little more information than could be obtained by conventional, indirect laryngoscopy.

High-Speed Cinematography

The development of high-speed cinematography was the next important achievement to yield information regarding the characteristics of vocal-fold movements. In 1940, Farnsworth, at Bell Telephone Laboratories, developed a high-speed motion-picture camera and a technique for taking high-speed motion pictures of the larynx at an exposure rate of 4,000 frames per second. The gratifying results stimulated considerable research, and much information regarding laryngeal function has been obtained in subsequent high-speed motion-picture studies of the larynx.

In order to illuminate the larynx safely, the light emitted by a 5,000-watt lamp was directed through a water-filled tank. The water absorbed the energy in the red-infrared portion of the light spectrum, thereby removing the heat. When the light had passed through the water, it struck an eight-inch condenser lens with a focal length of twelve inches (the effective focal length was about 28 inches). The lens formed one side of the light-cooling tank. The light was then directed to a seven-by-nine-inch first-surfaced plane mirror, set forty-five degrees to the optical axis of the light and forty-five degrees to the optical axis of the camera. Because the optical axis of the light was perpendicular to that of the camera, an elliptical hole was cut in the plane mirror to accommodate the optical field of the camera. Light reflected from the plane mirror was then directed to a one-inch laryngeal mirror. In later experiments the laryngeal mirror was also first-surfaced.

Figure 4–1 shows a top-view schematic drawing of an optical system very similar to that used by Bell Telephone Laboratories; Figure 4–2A shows a subject in position for laryngeal photography. The electrodes on the neck of the subject are for electro-

Fig. 4–1. Top view schematic of high-speed photographic apparatus.

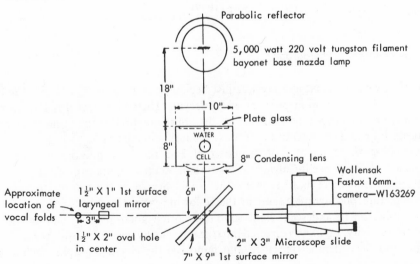

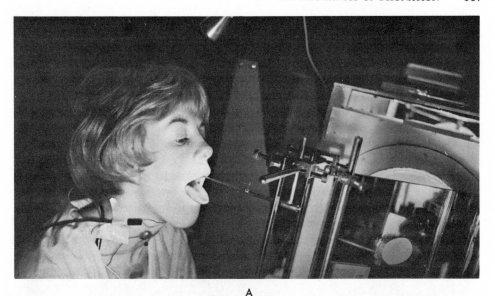

A

B

Fig. 4–2. (A) Subject in position for laryngeal photography and (B) experimenter prepared to photograph.

myographic recording of some extrinsic laryngeal muscles. Figure 4–2B shows an experimenter prepared to fire a high-speed camera. This installation, at the University of Illinois Speech and Hearing Research Laboratory, is essentially the same as the Bell Telephone installation, with the exception that the camera is located inside a sound-treated room. The purpose of the sound treatment is to help squelch the high-pitched whine of the camera, which often tends to affect the performance of the subject being photographed. Figure 4–3 shows one complete cycle of vocal-fold vibration taken out of a high-speed film exposed at a rate of 4,000 frames per second.

Start

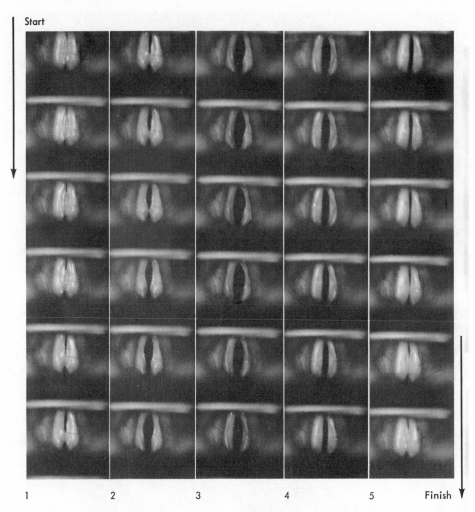

| 1 | 2 | 3 | 4 | 5 | Finish |

*Fig. 4–3. A single cycle of vocal fold vibration taken from a
high-speed film exposed at 4,000 frames per second.*

A great deal of credit can be given to Paul Moore for developing high-speed laryngeal photography to the extent that it is a practical research tool. Moore and von Leden; William Fletcher; Moore and Hollien; and Rubin, using high-speed laryngeal photography, have made important contributions to an understanding of laryngeal physiology. Some of these contributions will be discussed in some detail later in the chapter.

Transillumination-Photoconduction

Because of the elaborate apparatus and quantities of film required and because of difficulty in obtaining suitably trained subjects, high-speed motion-picture photography is expensive and often quite time-consuming. In 1959 Zemlin attempted to develop a less expensive and less time-consuming technique for investigation of the glottis during voice production. The technique is similar to that used by Wullstein in 1936.

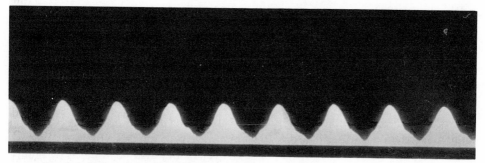

Fig. 4–4. Enlarged variable area movie sound track from a
transillumination-photoconductive recording.

Zemlin subglottally transilluminated the larynx of a subject; as the vocal folds
opened and closed, during phonation, they acted as a valve, permitting varying
amounts of light to pass between them. The light struck a photocell, which responded
by passing electrical energy in amounts proportional to the amount of light striking it.
This energy was fed into a high-quality magnetic recorder. Voltage change was
expressed on the magnetic tape in varying degrees of magnetic flux density. This
magnetic recording was represented graphically by transferring the data to a unilateral, variable-area movie sound track. For illustrative purposes, an enlargement
of such a sound track is shown in Figure 4–4. Although the technique is still in the
initial stages of development, the results suggest that transillumination offers great
potential as a supplemental technique for laryngeal examination.

Recent Developments

Recently, a number of X-ray laminagraphic studies of laryngeal activity during
phonation has been reported. Among them are studies by Sonninen and Vaheri
(1958), Zaliouk and Izkovitch (1958), Luchsinger and Dubois (1956), van den
Berg (1955), and Hollien and Curtis (1960; 1962). Hollien recently modified standard
X-ray laminagraphy by combining the principles of stroboscopy and laminagraphy.
The results obtained thus far have been gratifying, and the "strobolaminagraphic"
technique may well prove to be very rewarding.

THE PITCH AND INTENSITY MECHANISMS

Introduction

The purpose of the remainder of this chapter is to elaborate on some of the basics
laid down earlier. That is, in the discussion of the nonbiological functions of the
larynx, it was shown, rather grossly, how the vibrating vocal folds act as a sound
generator. We are now in a position to examine in some detail the way in which the
normal laryngeal mechanism generates vocal sounds.

In 1886, Stoker suggested that the larynx operated in a manner similar to a simple
stringed instrument. He proposed that the pitch of the voice was controlled by the
tension of the vocal folds and that loudness of the voice was dependent upon the
volume and force of air flow through the glottis.

Woods, in 1892, suggested a formula which related the forces involved to the frequency of the tone produced by the larynx:

$$n = \left(\sqrt{\frac{T}{M}} \right)(2L)^{-1}$$

where n = frequency of vibration, L = length of the vocal folds, T = tension of the folds, and M = mass per unit length. According to the above formula, the primary factors which determine the vibratory rate of a string or the vocal folds are mass and tension in relation to length. Thus, the frequency of a string's vibration may be doubled by simply halving its length. The frequency may also be doubled by multiplying the tension or dividing the mass by four. The above formula expresses a lawful relationship between the length, tension, and mass and the frequency of vibration of a string when these factors are known. For example, tension of a string in a musical instrument may be increased or decreased without appreciably affecting either its mass or length. On the other hand, the length may be increased, and although the mass of the string is also increased, its tension remains essentially the same.

Matters become a little more complex, however, when length, tension, and mass are related to the frequency of vibration of the vocal folds. For example, it appears from studies of the larynx that an increase in the tension of the vocal folds is almost always accompanied by an increase in their length and a decrease in mass per unit length. Further complications arise in understanding the behavior of the vocal folds because of their relative inaccessibility. To date there is no successful technique for accurately assessing the tension of the vocal folds, and although the cross-sectional area of the folds can be measured by special X-ray techniques (Hollien and Curtis, 1962), their mass per unit length cannot be determined. These problems have been recognized by Sonninen (1956), who stated that the relationship between the factors influencing the pitch of the voice can be represented by the following equation:

$$f = C\frac{K}{M}$$

where f = frequency of vocal fold vibration, C = constant, $K = K^1 + K^2$, where K^1 represents the inner passive tension of the vocal fold (related to tissue elasticity) and K^2 represents an inner active tension (related to muscular contraction and changes in length of the vocal fold), and M = mass of the vocal fold. There is an interesting similarity between Sonninen's equation and Woods's. With mass, length, and tension of a string held at a constant, the individual vibrations will recur with moderately precise regularity. The vocal folds, however, are not quite the steady-state sound generators that a vibrating string is.

Zemlin (1962) investigated the variations that occurred in the periods of vocal-fold vibration during the production of prolonged vowel sounds. In a population of thirty-three subjects, he found that the cycle-to-cycle differences in period ranged from .2 to .9 milliseconds, with a mean of .41 milliseconds for the [a] vowel. While these variations are not large, they suggest that very slight changes in length, tension, or mass of the vocal folds occur during the course of normal vibration.

Table 4–1 gives the duration of fifty consecutive cycles of vocal-fold vibration (expressed in milliseconds) of a normal subject while producing an [i] vowel. This particular subject had a range in the vibratory period of from 8.1 to 8.5 milliseconds,

Table 4–1, Duration, in milliseconds, of 50 consecutive
cycles of vocal fold vibration during the
production of the vowel [i].

Cycle					
1.	8.3	18.	8.4	35.	8.3
2.	8.3	19.	8.3	36.	8.4
3.	8.3	20.	8.5	37.	8.4
4.	8.2	21.	8.2	38.	8.4
5.	8.2	22.	8.3	39.	8.4
6.	8.2	23.	8.2	40.	8.5
7.	8.2	24.	8.1	41.	8.4
8.	8.3	25.	8.2	42.	8.5
9.	8.4	26.	8.4	43.	8.3
10.	8.5	27.	8.3	44.	8.4
11.	8.3	28.	8.3	45.	8.3
12.	8.5	29.	8.4	46.	8.4
13.	8.1	30.	8.4	47.	8.4
14.	8.5	31.	8.5	48.	8.5
15.	8.2	32.	8.3	49.	8.5
16.	8.2	33.	8.3	50.	8.4
17.	8.3	34.	8.4		

Mean = 8.34 Milliseconds
Range = 8.1–8.5 Milliseconds
Fund. Freq. = 118 cps.

with a range of variation of .4 milliseconds. As long as the variations fall within certain critical limits, slight cycle-to-cycle variations in vibratory period apparently do not produce adverse effects in vocal quality. The normal limits of vibratory regularity will be discussed in greater detail later in the chapter.

Both the pitch and spectral characteristics of the voice (voice quality) are dependent upon (1) the frequency of vocal-fold vibration, (2) the pattern or mode of vocal-fold vibration, and (3) the resonant characteristics of the vocal tract. Our tasks during the remainder of the chapter will include an examination of the mechanisms by which the frequency and mode of vocal-fold vibration are controlled. These topics, however, will be preceded by a short discussion of the manner in which phonation is initiated.

The Onset of Phonation

For descriptive purposes, the onset of phonation may be divided into two phases: the prephonation phase and the attack phase. Together they comprise the onset of phonation.

The prephonation phase may be defined as the period during which the vocal folds move, more or less abruptly, from an abducted to either an adducted or a partially adducted position. When the folds are observed prior to the onset of phonation, they are usually seen to be in an abducted position; that is, the subject is in the inhalation phase of breathing. During quiet breathing the adult male glottis is about 13 mm wide at its broadest point (Negus, 1929), and during forced inhalation this value may almost double. In addition, the glottis is usually somewhat wider during inhalation

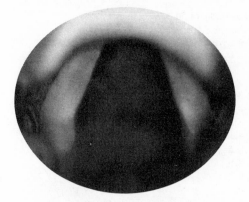

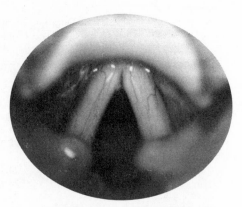

Forced inhalation. This subject is demonstrating very nearly maximum abduction
of the vocal folds.

Forced exhalation. In this condition the
glottis does not appear grossly different
from the glottis during quiet breathing.

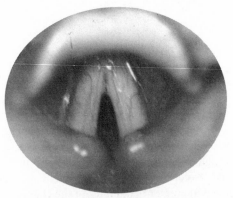

Normal inhalation. During quiet breathing
the glottis may remain essentially unchanged
from inhalation to exhalation.

*Fig. 4–5. Glottal configurations for forced inhalation and
exhalation and during quiet breathing.*

than during exhalation. In Figure 4–5, the larynx is shown during forced inhalation,
forced exhalation, and quiet breathing. Although these views are representative of
what occurs in the larynx during breathing, many persons maintain a rather constant
glottal aperture during inhalation and exhalation. This is particularly true during
quiet breathing.

The duration of the prephonation phase and the extent to which the vocal folds
approximate are highly variable, depending largely upon the utterance to be emitted.
As the folds approximate or near approximation, they begin to obstruct the outward
flow of air from the lower respiratory tract, and the pressure beneath the folds, the
intratracheal or subglottal pressure, begins to increase. In addition, the velocity of the
air as it flows through the glottal constriction is raised sharply, which is a most
important point to remember.

Photographs of a larynx during various stages of a prephonation phase are shown
in Figure 4–6. These photographs are single-frame excerpts from a high-speed motion-

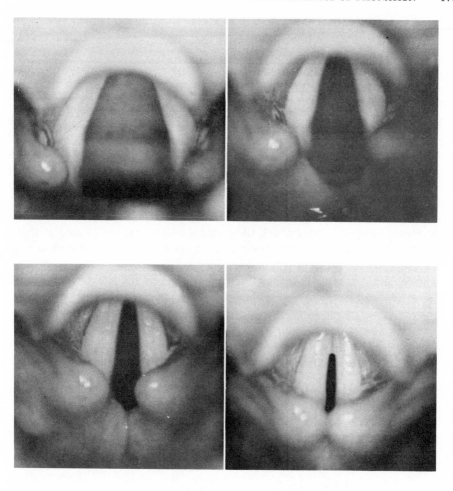

Fig. 4–6. Four stages of pre-phonation phase.

picture film of the onset of phonation. The entire prephonation phase extended over 700 frames, which represents about .160 seconds. Figure 4–6A shows the folds abducted, and B and C show the folds as they have moved toward the mid-line. Figure 4–6D shows the folds completely adducted. The extent to which the folds are approximated is sometimes referred to as being produced by "medial compression," which is brought about by the action of the adductor muscles.

It may be profitable at this point to examine the muscular activity responsible for approximation of the vocal folds. The exact relationship between muscular contraction and laryngeal behavior is not known with absolute certainty, and is a subject for some speculation. Accumulated data from mechanical analogs of the larynx, as well as data from high-speed photography, afford us some insight into the mechanics of internal laryngeal activity. Information regarding gross muscle function may also be gained from knowledge of the muscle attachments and from the general architecture of the structures involved. It is crucial, however, to weigh such information very carefully before any generalizations are made or conclusions drawn. This is because rarely, if ever, do individual muscles act to execute a movement. Rather, they work in pairs and groups, and contraction of any one particular muscle is usually accompanied by contraction of companion muscles. A subtle, delicate interplay of the various muscle actions produces the appropriate movement, and that is also a most important point to remember.

A case in point is adduction of the vocal folds. We have called the lateral cricoarytenoid and the interarytenoid muscles adductors. The schematic in Figure 4–7 demonstrates what might happen if just one or the other of these muscles should contract independently of the other. Note in A that contraction of the interarytenoid muscles may draw the muscular processes posteriorly, thus toeing out the vocal processes. Although the arytenoid muscles are classified as adductors, in this case they are actually abducting the vocal folds. On the other hand, when the lateral cricoarytenoid muscle is contracted, the arytenoid cartilages are rotated so that the muscular processes are pulled anteriorly and the vocal processes toed inward to produce the glottal configuration required for the production of a whisper as in B. In C, simultaneous contraction of the lateral cricoarytenoid and the interarytenoid muscles approximate the arytenoid cartilages and the vocal folds so that their medial borders

Fig. 4–7. Schematic of the action of some intrinsic laryngeal muscles.

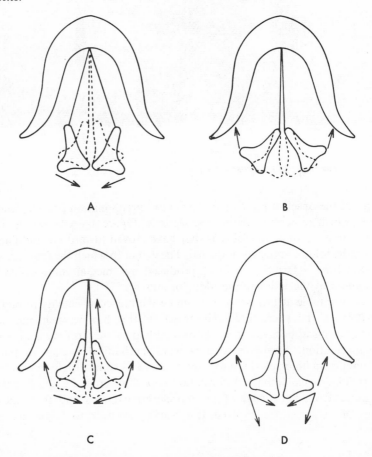

A

B

C

D

are parallel. Such muscle action, however, may also draw the arytenoid cartilages forward, a movement that is restricted by the antagonistic action of the posterior cricoarytenoid muscle, as illustrated in D. The result of the activity of the three muscles is such that the vocal folds are rather tightly approximated, and if exhalation is initiated while the vocal folds are adducted, they are set into vibration to produce a laryngeal tone. Needless to say, there is a direct relationship between the extent of adduction, or medial compression, and the amount of air pressure required to force the vocal folds apart.

The attack phase begins with the vocal folds adducted, or nearly so, and extends through the initial vibratory cycles. This phase is also highly variable in its duration, depending primarily upon the extent to which the vocal folds are adducted during the prephonation phase and the manner in which the air stream is released.

Usually the folds are not completely adducted during the prephonation phase; that is, they may be adducted, but not to the extent they approximate. It is extremely important to note that complete obstruction of the air passageway is not necessary to initiate phonation. If the glottal chink is narrowed to about 3 mm, a minimal amount of air flow will set the folds into vibration. According to von Leden (1961), a subglottic pressure equal to 20–40 mm of water is sufficient. The experiment was carried out on freshly excised human larynxes.

High-speed laryngeal photography shows that the initial movement in incompletely adducted vocal folds is medialward. This medial movement can be adequately accounted for by the Bernoulli effect. Bernoulli, who was an eighteenth-century mathematician, formulated an aerodynamic law which states that the sum of the density (d), multiplied by one-half the square of the velocity (v) and pressure (p) is a constant: $d \times 1/2(v^2p) = c$. Or, to put the Bernoulli effect another way, in the case of an ideal fluid, as velocity of fluid flow increases, pressure must decrease, so long as total energy remains at a constant. Pressure is perpendicular to the direction of fluid flow. Thus, if volume fluid flow is constant, velocity will increase at an area of constriction, with a corresponding decrease in pressure at the constriction. To apply the Bernoulli effect to phonation, assume the vocal folds are nearly approximated at the instant the air stream is released by the forces of exhalation. The air stream will have a constant velocity until it reaches the glottal constriction. Velocity will increase, however, as the air passes through the glottal chink. The result is a negative pressure between the medial edges of the vocal folds, and they will be literally sucked toward one another. The Bernoulli effect is of major importance in understanding the vocal mechanism, especially as it applies to ordinary phonation. For illustrative purposes, the movements of the vocal folds during the onset of vibration are shown graphically in Figure 4–8. As glottal area reaches a certain critical value, the folds begin to execute vibratory movement, before they have actually approximated; that is, the initial movement results in a decrease in glottal area. Note further that the folds undergo a number of vibrations before they meet to obstruct the air stream completely.

As long as subglottal pressure is sufficient, the medial compression of the folds will be overcome, and they will be blown apart to release a puff of air into the supraglottal area. This somewhat explosive release of air results in an immediate decrease in subglottal pressure, and the elasticity of the vocal-fold tissue, plus the Bernoulli effect, causes the vocal folds to snap back again into an adducted position. The nature

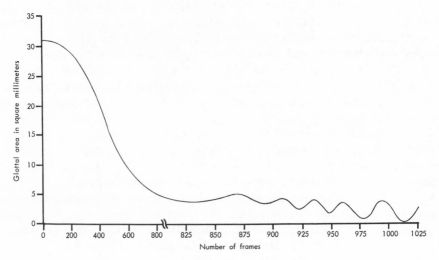

Fig. 4–8. Changes in glottal area during prephonation and attack phases.

of the initial vibratory cycles may be influenced by a host of variables, including the intensity of phonation, the linguistic environment of the sound to be emitted, the pitch of the voice, and voice habits. The problem of the manner in which phonation may be initiated was recognized by Moore in 1938. He suggested there may be three ways in which phonation may be initiated: the simultaneous, the breathy, or the glottal attack.

In the simultaneous attack there is a healthy balance between the respiratory and laryngeal mechanisms, and the air stream is released just prior to the activity of the laryngeal musculature. For practical purposes, the respiratory and laryngeal activity occur simultaneously, or very nearly so. Buchthal and Faaborg-Anderson (1964) found that the interval between activity of the respiratory and laryngeal muscles was between about 100 and 200 milliseconds for phonating an isolated [e] vowel. In the phonation of "ma," however, activity of the respiratory musculature preceded activity of the laryngeal musculature by approximately 50 milliseconds.

In the breathy attack the air stream is released before vocal-fold adduction is completed, and a considerable quantity of air may be exhaled while the folds are being set into periodic vibration.

If phonation is not initiated at the beginning of the expiratory phase of breathing, the vocal folds may move completely to the mid-line to prevent exhalation until such time as phonation is initiated. This is the sort of thing we do when we "hold our breath" until the appropriate moment to speak arrives. It is very common behavior, and we ought to be aware of it, because when phonation is initiated while the folds are subjected to considerable medial compression, the voice exhibits an onset rather more sudden than during either the simultaneous or the breathy attack. Under such circumstances the vocal tone is explosive in nature, and the initiation of phonation is often called a glottal attack, glottal shock, or stroke of the glottis.

It is generally agreed by voice therapists and laryngologists alike that the simultaneous attack is less abusive to the vocal mechanism than is the glottal attack, and ought to be advocated. Most often, however, the glottal attack is produced in such a manner as to be hardly, if at all, discernible from a simultaneous attack, and indeed, it may be surprising, when all the data are in, to find how frequently the glottal attack is used in everyday speech. Habitual use of the breathy attack is considered to be an ineffective method of voice production. Because of the unmodulated air that escapes from between the vocal folds, a fricative noise is often superimposed upon the vocal tone to produce what is actually known as "breathy quality." Breathiness is a troublesome vocal quality disorder that is frequently encountered by the speech therapist.

Characteristics of a vibratory cycle

A complete vibratory cycle is usually considered in three phases: an opening phase, a closing phase, and a closed phase, and, as we shall see later in the chapter, the relative durations of these phases is variable, depending upon the circumstances of phonation. A film of a typical cycle of vocal-fold vibration is shown in Figure 4–9; in Figure 4–10, the glottal area has been extracted from each frame and plotted

Fig. 4–9. A typical cycle of normal vocal fold vibration taken from a high-speed motion picture film of the larynx.

Start

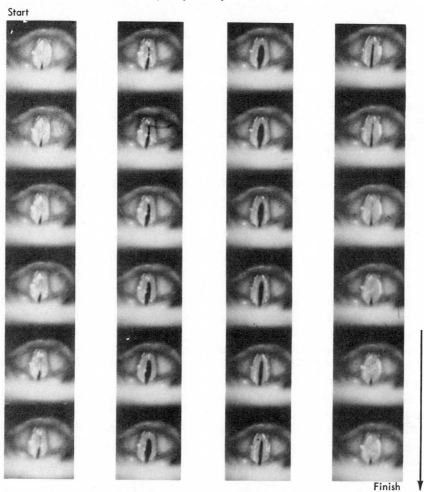

Finish

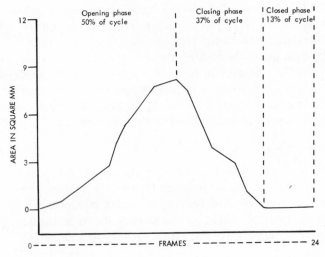

Fig. 4–10. Curve of glottal area plotted against the number of frames in the cycle.

against time. The vibratory rate for this particular subject was about 168 cycles per second, and the film was exposed at a rate of about 4,000 frames per second. The opening phase extended through the first twelve frames. In other words, it occupied one-half or 50 per cent of the vibratory cycle. The closing phase extended through the next nine frames and occupied about 37 per cent of the cycle. The closed phase extended through the final three frames and occupied about 13 per cent of the total cycle. These values are typical for phonation at conversational pitch and intensity.

Timcke, von Leden, and Moore (1958) have made extensive measures of the glottal wave. They illuminated the larynx by means of an advanced "synchrostroboscopic" technique. They expressed the relative durations of the phases of the vibratory cycle in terms of quotients. Thus, the ratio of the fraction of the cycle during which the glottis is open, compared with the total duration of the cycle, is referred to as the open quotient (OQ). Later, the investigators employed high-speed photography of the larynx. They were interested in measuring the difference in duration between the opening and closing phases, and selected the ratio between the two phases which they termed the speed quotient (SQ). Thus,

$$SQ = \frac{\text{Time of abduction or lateral excursion}}{\text{Time of adduction or medial excursion}}$$

The advantage of using the speed quotient is simply that in many instances the glottis never actually closes, and the open quotient is therefore 1.0. The speed quotient provides additional descriptive information about the vibratory characteristics. For Figure 4–10, the open quotient = .85, and the speed quotient = 1.17.

The mode of vocal-fold vibration has also been investigated. Note in Figure 4–9 that the vocal folds begin to open at first posteriorly, with the glottal chink moving anteriorly. Closure begins with the entire medial edge of the folds moving toward the mid-line, and the posterior portion is the last to close. The vibratory cycle shown in Figure 4–9 is rather typical, normal, internal laryngeal behavior. Sometimes, however, the folds may separate at first anteriorly, with the glottal chink moving posteriorly, as shown in Figure 4–11.

Start

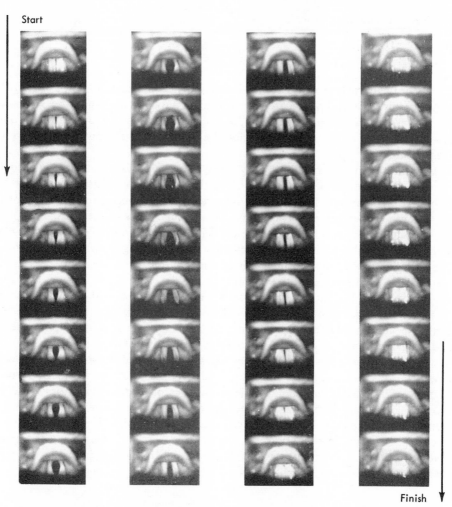

Finish

Fig. 4–11. A cycle of normal vocal fold vibration demonstrating
a mode of vibration that is different from that in Fig. 4–9.

High-speed laryngeal photography reveals the vocal folds to be approximated rather tightly along their entire length during the closed phase of the vibratory cycle, especially at high intensity. Many subjects, however, exhibit a small glottal chink posteriorly, and this chink persists during the course of the vibratory cycle. The laryngeal valve is never quite closed, and there is continuous air leakage from between the vocal folds throughout the various phases of the vibratory cycle. Air leakage may result in a frictional noise being generated which, when prominent, may result in a breathy or aspirate voice quality. The size of the glottal chink necessary to produce a breathy voice quality is not known. The mechanism of conversion of air flow into random acoustic noise has been discussed by Stevens (1965), who made use of the theory of fluid flow through constricted tubes and around obstacles and who states, "Of basic importance in this theory is a dimensionless constant called the 'Reynold's number,' given by

$$Re = \frac{vh}{V}$$

where v is the particle velocity, h is the length dimension, and V is the viscosity coefficient for air." According to Stevens, turbulent flow results when the Reynold's number exceeds a critical value of about 1,800. On the basis of such data, it is quite possible that the critical value of a glottal chink may be computed, at least on a theoretical level.

At conversational pitch and intensity levels, the vocal folds vibrate in their entirety, and the vibration of the rounded edge of the folds is transmitted in a wave-like fashion to the main mass of the folds. As a result, there appears to be a slight phase lag between the leading edges and the main muscular mass of the folds. This phase lag seems to disappear at higher pitch levels. The presence or absence of this phase lag seems to be a relatively satisfactory technique for estimating the tension of the folds. The vibration of the folds is primarily horizontal, but there is a slight vertical displacement amounting to about 0.2 to 0.5 mm.

From critical observations of high-speed motion pictures of the larynx, it seems that the vocal folds begin to be forced open from beneath, with an upward progression of the opening in an undulating fashion. Thus, the lower edges of the folds are the first, and the upper edges the last, to be blown apart. During the closing phase, however, the lower edges lead the upper edges. This mode of vibration produces what is known as a vertical phase difference, and it is illustrated in schematic form in Figure 4–12. In addition, some single-frame excerpts from a vibratory cycle are shown enlarged in Figure 4–13. Evidence of a vertical phase difference may be clearly seen. The mode and rate of vocal-fold vibration may vary with different conditions of pitch and intensity of phonation, as well as from person to person, to the extent that generalization may not always be well founded. Indeed, probably the most striking feature of laryngeal behavior is the variability from person to person.

Fig. 4–12. Schematic of vertical phase difference during a cycle of vocal fold vibration.

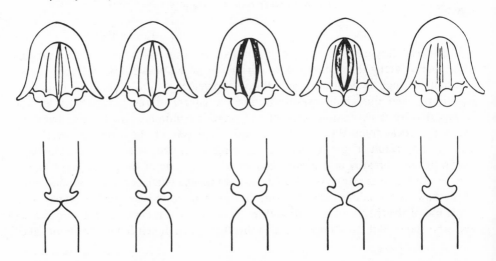

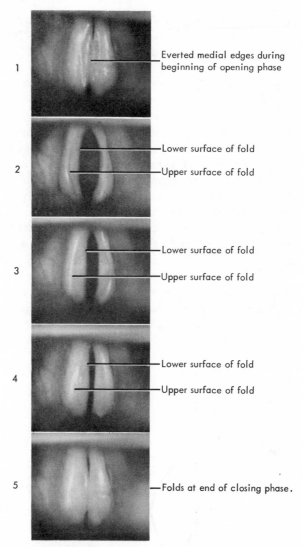

1 — Everted medial edges during beginning of opening phase

2 — Lower surface of fold
— Upper surface of fold

3 — Lower surface of fold
— Upper surface of fold

4 — Lower surface of fold
— Upper surface of fold

5 — Folds at end of closing phase.

Fig. 4–13. Single-frame excerpts from high-speed film showing vertical phase difference.

We have been directing our attention to phonation at a specific pitch level or, at best, a narrow range of pitches. If we but take a minute or two to listen to the speech of those around us, it becomes apparent that the larynx is a very versatile instrument. It is capable of producing tones at any one of a vast number of pitches and intensities. The mechanism responsible for the pitch and intensity changes is remarkable and worthy of very careful study.

The Pitch-Changing Mechanism

Introduction

According to Fairbanks (1959), a person engaged in relaxed, normal phonatory activity is liable to produce laryngeal tones that vary in pitch over a range of almost two octaves. Usually, however, the pitches produced are distributed in such a manner that a mode or central tendency is very evident. This mode, when expressed in terms of musical notes, is usually called the pitch level. When the mode is expressed in cycles per second, it is more properly referred to as the fundamental frequency of the sample. There is a one-to-one relationship between fundamental frequency and rate of vocal-fold vibration. The vocal pitch of young adult males is about C_3 and of females about an octave higher, or C_4 (based on the international standard that $A_4 = 440$ cps). In other words, males have a fundamental frequency of about 130 cps, and females about 260 cps. A schematic distribution of pitch ranges for males and females is shown in Figure 4–14. Note that the distribution of pitch extends somewhat further below than above the mode; that is, the distribution is negatively skewed. And, as Fairbanks has pointed out, occasionally a pitch is used that is lower than any sustainable pitch; "these very low pitches almost always occur at the ends of periods of phonation, when the intensity is decreasing rapidly." That is, a pitch is used that is not within the pitch range as the term is ordinarily used. The pitch ranges of males and females overlap considerably.

There is good reason to believe that there is a particularly suitable pitch level for each individual. This level, which is sometimes called the "natural level," is largely determined by the physical characteristics of the individual vocal mechanism. According to Fairbanks, in his excellent discussion of pitch and pitch variability, the

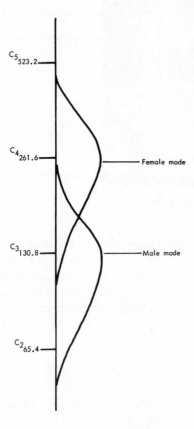

Fig. 4–14. Schematic distribution of ranges of males and females (adults).

natural pitch is located about one-fourth up the total singing range (including falsetto), when the range is expressed in musical notes. The fraction one-fourth was derived from the work of Pronovost (1942), who intensively studied superior male speakers. There is no evidence, however, that the "one-fourth technique" will locate the natural pitch in persons with voice disorders or restricted pitch ranges. The pitch mode actually used by an individual is called the "habitual level"; optimally it is the same as the natural level.

From the graph in Figure 4–14, we see that pitch may be shifted down or up from the habitual level. Although we want to avoid delineating laryngeal functions, it seems prudent, at this point, and certainly expedient, to approach the pitch-changing mechanism as one that produces either a lowering or a raising of pitch. Let us proceed to the pitch-raising mechanism.

The pitch-raising mechanism

The two avenues of approach to the study of the pitch-raising mechanism are the physiological accompaniments of increases in pitch and the mechanics of pitch increases.

When measured in their abducted position, the vocal folds range in length from approximately 15 to 20 mm for males, and from 9 to 13 mm for females. Although the evidence is not absolutely conclusive, in all likelihood the vocal folds are very near maximum length in the abducted position and, contrary to popular opinion, are considerably shorter when adducted for purposes of phonation. Support for such a viewpoint has been obtained by means of motion-picture photographs of the larynx. The data in Table 4–2, cited from Hollien and Moore (1960), illustrate the magnitude of length change that accompanies change in pitch. Note that the length

Table 4–2, Length change in vocal folds that accompany increases in pitch

Condition	Subjects					
	A	B	C	D	E	F
65 cps	?*					
82 cps	13.8	9.4	?*			
110 cps	15.2	9.8	12.7	11.8	8.7	8.9
130 cps	16.0	10.0	14.1	13.1	11.9	10.0
170 cps	17.9	11.9	17.3	13.4	13.0	11.9
220 cps	16.4†	12.0†	19.4	14.4	14.0	12.6
260 cps	17.2	13.0	20.5	15.6	14.9	13.0
330 cps	17.3	13.0	16.9†	14.2	12.2†	14.3†
440 cps	17.8	13.5	16.6	?*	11.3	10.2
520 cps	?*	12.2	14.8		?*	9.6
660 cps		10.6**	14.7**		?*	?*
880 cps			?*			
Abduction	23.0	17.3	22.3	20.3	19.1	19.8

* No measurable frames.

† First falsetto frequency.   (After Hollien and Moore, 1960)

** Interpolated measures.

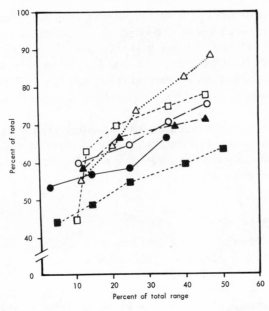

Fig. 4–15. Variation in vocal fold length with change in vocal pitch. (After Hollien and Moore, 1960).

of the vocal folds at various pitches never exceeds the length given for the abducted position. These same data are presented in graphic form in Figure 4–15, where vocal-fold length during phonation is plotted by subject as percentages of the abducted length. If we refer back to the formula by Woods (1892) that $n = (\sqrt{T/M})(2L)^{-1}$, we note that the frequency of vibration may be increased by simply reducing the length of the vibrator (while maintaining the other variables at a constant). Herein lies a paradox, for in the larynx, as pitch is increased, we find a concomitant increase in the length of the folds rather than a decrease as dictated by the above formula. Since length is not being held constant during pitch changes, we must conclude that changes in mass or tension play a role in the pitch-changing mechanism.

Increases in length of the folds seem to result in a decrease in cross-sectional area (mass), which, according to Woods's formula, will result in an increase in pitch. Hollien and Curtis (1962), for example, found in a laminagraphic study that mean thickness of the vocal folds decreased systematically as pitch was raised. The same observation was made for cross-sectional area. Thus, research data seem to support the contention that vocal-fold thickness plays an important role in determining fundamental frequency.

According to Woods's formula, mass per unit length must be decreased by a factor of four in order to increase frequency by one-half. According to the data of Hollien and Curtis, however, vocal-fold thickness (an index of mass) was never reduced below one-half that during the lowest pitch of phonation. Thus, increases in pitch cannot be accounted for solely by a reduction in mass. We must conclude that the tension factor also plays an important role in the pitch-changing mechanism. In fact, it is not at all unreasonable to suppose that an increase in tension of the vocal folds is the sole agent responsible for pitch increases and that the accompanying length and thickness change is simply the result of the elastic tissue of the vocal folds yielding to the marked increase in tension. This is pure speculation (armchair research), of course, and a fit subject for study.

Modifications in the length and tension of the vocal folds necessary to produce an increase in pitch are mediated primarily through the interplay of three intrinsic laryngeal muscles, the cricothyroid, the thyroarytenoid, and the posterior cricoarytenoid.

The cricothyroid (described on page 155), you will recall, originates on the antero-lateral arch of the cricoid cartilage and inserts into the thyroid cartilage as two distinct muscle bundles. The lower bundle (pars oblique) courses upward and back to insert into the anterior margin of the inferior horn of the thyroid cartilage, and the upper or anterior bundle (parts recta) courses vertically to insert into the lower border of the thyroid lamina. Contraction of the anterior fibers causes either the cricoid or the thyroid cartilage to rotate about the cricothyroid joint, with a resultant decrease in distance between the cricoid and thyroid cartilages anteriorly. Most often, the thyroid cartilage rotates about the cricoid cartilage on a rotational axis as indicated in Figure 4–16. The result of this rotation is an increase in distance between the vocal processes of the arytenoid cartilages and the thyroid cartilage, at the angle. Since the vocal folds extend from the vocal processes of the arytenoids to the thyroid cartilage, it follows that contraction of the anterior bundle of the cricothyroid muscle elongates the vocal folds and makes them thinner. Contraction of the oblique fibers of the cricothyroid muscle slides the thyroid cartilage forward on the cricothyroid joint, as illustrated in Figure 4–16, and this action also elongates the vocal folds. According to Greene (1957), the action of the cricothyroid muscle need not result in an increase in tension of the vocal folds.

We have seen that lengthening a vibrating element normally results in a decrease in frequency of vibration and that, contrariwise, the vocal folds exhibit an increase in length with increases in pitch. With no opposing muscular forces acting upon the vocal folds, contraction of the cricothyroid muscle may simply elongate them and make them thinner, or it may slide the arytenoid cartilages forward on the cricoid. In either case, little or no increase in pitch results.

Fig. 4–16. Illustration of the mechanism by which the crico-thyroid may function to tense the vocal folds.

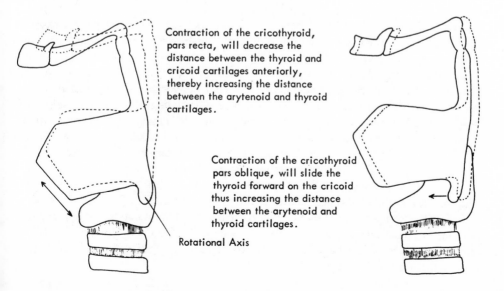

Contraction of the cricothyroid, pars recta, will decrease the distance between the thyroid and cricoid cartilages anteriorly, thereby increasing the distance between the arytenoid and thyroid cartilages.

Contraction of the cricothyroid pars oblique, will slide the thyroid forward on the cricoid thus increasing the distance between the arytenoid and thyroid cartilages.

Rotational Axis

Start

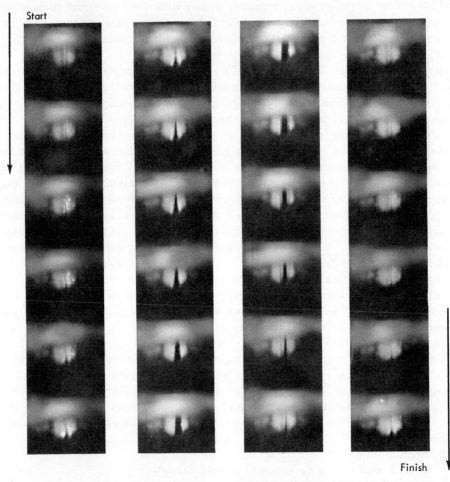

Finish

Fig. 4–17. A cycle of normal vocal fold vibration (F = 168 cps).

Clearly then, some additional mechanism is necessary to cause an increase in tension of the vocal folds. Anterior sliding movements of the arytenoid cartilages may be restricted by the cricoarytenoid ligament and by contraction of the posterior cricoarytenoid muscle. In our earlier discussion of the onset of phonation we saw how the posterior cricoarytenoid muscle abducted the vocal folds. Thus, it becomes evident that this very important muscle is active in initiating phonation as well as in producing pitch changes. The thyroarytenoid muscle, acting without opposition, would simply decrease the distance between the arytenoid cartilages and the thyroid cartilage to produce a shortening of the vocal folds. Pitch increases, therefore, are probably brought about by the antagonistic action of two vocal tensors and the laryngeal dilator muscle. The vocal tensors are the thyroarytenoid and the cricothyroid muscles, and the laryngeal dilator is the posterior cricoarytenoid muscle. Differential contraction of muscle bundles within the thyroarytenoid may result in increased tension, or, by a subtle balance of muscle forces, the folds may be tensed with no appreciable increase in length. This seems to be particularly true for trained singers and for the upper limits of the pitch range (falsetto).

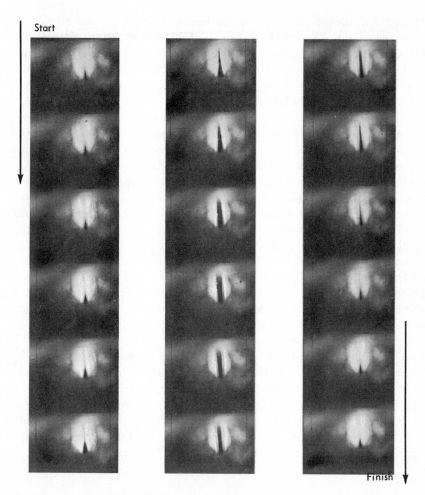

Fig. 4–18. A cycle of high pitch phonation (F = 250 cps).

As the vocal folds are tensed and elongated for the production of higher-pitched tones, some rather predictable changes occur. These changes are easily observed by means of strobolaryngoscopy or by high-speed laryngeal photography. As pitch is increased, the folds lengthen and change from round, thick lips to narrow bands, and whereas the vocal folds seem relaxed and almost flaccid during phonation at the natural pitch level, they appear stiff and rigid at higher pitches. The glottis appears as more of a variable slit, and only the medial edges of the folds undergo vibration. A single cycle, from a high-speed film of phonation at the natural pitch level, is shown in Figure 4–17; for comparative purposes, a cycle of phonation at a pitch approximately one octave higher is shown in Figure 4–18. Note the difference in length of the folds and in the general shape of the glottis. The relative durations of the opening, closing, and closed phases of the vibratory cycle remain about the same within the normal pitch range (Timcke, *et al.*, 1958). At extremely high pitches, however, there is an increased tendency for failure of the vocal folds to approximate completely in the area of the vocal processes. This may explain why voice quality tends toward breathiness at the higher pitches.

Hollien and Moore have studied, by means of laryngeal motion-picture photography, the relation between changes in vocal-fold length and the pitch of phonation. This relationship was illustrated in Table 4-2. From such data it seems evident that the length of the vocal folds increases systematically with increases in vocal pitch and that degree of length increase is not significantly greater in any one portion of the pitch range (excluding falsetto). Hollien (1960) also found a relationship between general vocal-fold length and the natural frequency of phonation. That is, persons with large larynxes and long vocal folds tend to phonate at a lower pitch level than do persons with smaller larynxes and shorter vocal folds. This relationship seems to hold equally well for both adult males and females.

Hollien and Curtis (1960) employed X-ray laminagraphy in a study of the larynx during changes in vocal pitch. Four groups of subjects were used. The groups were composed of (1) six males with very low-pitched voices, (2) six males with very high-pitched voices, (3) six females with very low-pitched voices, and (4) six females with very high-pitched voices. Each subject was required to phonate at four pitch levels, representing the 10, 25, 50, and 85 per cent points in relation to the total pitch range, including falsetto. During each task, frontal cross-sectional views of the subject's vocal folds were made with X-ray laminagraphy. Measurements were made of vocal-fold cross-sectional area and thickness. Results indicated that the folds became less massive and thinner as frequency was raised, with larger changes occurring in the low-frequency portion of the subjects' ranges.

In a subsequent study, Hollien and Curtis (1962) reported the results of an X-ray laminagraphic study that was designed to investigate the relationship between elevation of the vocal folds and increases in pitch and the relationship between upward tilting of the vocal folds and increases in pitch. The authors were able to report a tendency for the vocal folds to become progressively elevated and a tendency for vocal-fold tilt (the superior borders slope upward toward the mid-line) to become progressively greater with increases in vocal pitch. These trends did not hold for falsetto, however.

Subglottal Air Pressure and Pitch.   The characteristics of air supply to the larynx have long been recognized as a factor that may influence pitch. The deeper one probes into the literature dealing with the relation between subglottal air pressure and pitch, the more liable he is to emerge with a picture that is unclear. This is largely due to the diversity in approaches. Experiments have been conducted with excised human and animal larynxes, mechanical models made from the leg muscles of frogs, rubber, and plaster casts of the larynx. Various theoretical approaches have been offered by physicists and mathematicians, and some limited experiments have been conducted on living human subjects. A number of experiments has also been performed on the larynxes of living dogs.

Experimental models and nonliving specimens have a single inherent weakness: they are not able to generate intrinsic tensions characteristic of living specimens. Disadvantages in using living animals include the facts that the larynx is not human, making extrapolation somewhat hazardous, and that phonation is *elicited* while the animal is under anesthesia. A distinct advantage, however, is that many of the obvious ethical objections that apply to human subjects can be cast aside, so long as well-recognized humane principles are adhered to in the use of experimental animals.

In evaluating many of the experiments relating subglottal pressure to pitch, the reader ought to be mindful of a rather important point. Although rises in pitch may be accompanied by increases in subglottal pressure, increases in subglottal pressure need not produce rises in pitch. Brodnitz (1959), for example, has noted that in singing an upward scale, the subglottic air pressure increases because the greater stiffness of the stretched vocal folds offers increased resistance.

In 1846, Liskovius (see also Rubin, 1963) stated that pitch was elevated as the glottic chink narrowed and subglottic pressure increased. In addition, he noted that with a constant glottal opening, pitch rose in response to increased air pressure alone. The famous physiologist Johannes Müller, in 1843, working with human cadaver larynxes and models, noted that an increase in vocal intensity without an increase in pitch had to be accompanied by a decrease in tension of the vocal folds. He also suggested that pitch rose in response to increasing air flow.

Negus (1929), using living human subjects and excised human larynxes, concluded that an increase in pitch can be obtained either by an increase in the elasticity of the glottic margin or by an increase in tracheal air pressure. He also noted that in actual phonation, elastic tension and air pressure are associated in such a way that a slight increase in air pressure causes a considerable rise in pitch.

In 1936, Wullstein, experimenting on freshly excised larynxes, found that frequency rose from 85 to 125 cps when air pressure was doubled.

In the early twentieth century, experimenters, utilizing electrical stimulation of the laryngeal musculature of dogs, attempted to relate muscle tension to air supply. Early experiments by Katzenstein and Dubois-Reymond and later by Dunker and Schlosshauer (1958) led to the conclusions that (1) pitch rose in response to increasing voltage applied to the nerves supplying the cricothyroid muscles, but not to increasing frequency of stimulation impulses and (2) increasing air flow with muscle tension held constant did not raise pitch. One year after Dunker and Schlosshauer, Isshiki (1959) noted in electrical stimulation experiments on dogs that pitch was increased by increasing air flow alone and that pitch elevation was accompanied by increasing subglottic pressure if air flow remained constant. Pitch increases were based on qualitative judgments.

Ladefoged and McKinney (1963) experimented with a single living human subject. They measured intratracheal pressure indirectly by inserting a rubber catheter (with a small latex balloon fastened to the end) into the nose and down into the esophagus, so that the balloon was positioned just above the bifurcation of the trachea. The authors note: "In this position, the balloon pressed against the thin membrane at the back of the trachea, and was affected by any variation in the pressure below the vocal cords." As part of their experiment the subject attempted thirty-two utterances of the vowel [a] at various loudness levels, making no effort to control pitch. Subglottal pressures were recorded, and vocal frequency was analyzed. Ladefoged and McKinney found "fairly good correlation between subglottal pressure and the logarithm of the frequency of vibration of the vocal cords for the sounds in this group. If the subject made no changes in the tension of the vocal cords, then it appears that an increase of subglottal pressure of about 6 or 7 cm aq produced a half-octave increase in the fundamental frequency."

Rubin (1963) reported a carefully controlled experiment on thirty-eight dogs, in which he provided independent electrical stimulation of each of the four nerves supplying the intrinsic muscles of the larynx. He also controlled air flow to the larynx and measured subglottal air pressure. He found that variations of air flow, within physiological limits, did not alter pitch. His results support those of Piquet, Decroix, Libersa, and Dujardin (1956), Dunker and Schlosshauer (1958), and Fessard and Vallencien (1957). Rubin did note, however, that the complexity of the vocal tone (which may lead to a subjective impression of increased pitch) and the intensity increased with increases in air flow.

Timcke, *et al.* (1958), von Leden (1961), and van den Berg report a simple experiment that may demonstrate the effect of subglottic pressure on pitch. A sudden push on the abdomen of a subject during the production of a sustained sound not only raises the intensity of the voice but also produces an increase in pitch. Rubin (1963) notes, however: "If during sustained phonation at constant pitch, a sharp push is given another part of the body. . . where applied pressure has no direct influence on the diaphragm or rib cage and cannot directly affect air flow, the pitch also rises in the same manner." Rubin attributes the pitch increase to a laryngeal reflex.

Thus, in spite of the many apparently well-controlled and often similar experiments, the results are often contradictory. Indeed, there is no assurance that a crucial experiment has as yet been conducted. In light of the recent and instrumentally sophisticated experimentation, however, a tentative working hypothesis might possibly be justified.

An increase in subglottal pressure, with laryngeal tension held constant, will produce a negligible rise in pitch. In addition, pitch changes are mediated primarily through modifications in glottic tension and mass. This viewpoint is supported by Pressman and Kelemen (1955), who state: "Actually the variation produced in tone by pressure changes is relatively small, and if this were the primary mechanism involved, enormously impractical elevations of pressure would be required to cover the range of the human voice."

The pitch-lowering mechanism

The pitch-lowering mechanism may be approached either on a descriptive or on a physiological level. A person with a habitual pitch of about C_3 (131 cps) can be expected to encompass a singing range that extends from D_2 (73.4 cps) to about C_5 (523 cps), not including falsetto, which may extend the range as high as C_6 (1,047 cps). In other words, the habitual pitch is very near the lower limits of the pitch range.

From the now familiar formula of Woods, that

$$n = \left(\sqrt{\frac{T}{M}}\right)(2L)^{-1}$$

it is apparent that a decrease in pitch might be produced either by a decrease in tension (and an increase in mass) or by an increase in the length of the vocal folds. Data, such as those provided by Hollien and Moore (1960) demonstrate quite conclusively that lengthening of the folds only accompanies *increases* in pitch. Thus, a decrease in vibratory frequency must be accounted for either by a decrease in tension or by an increase in the mass per unit length of the folds. Data on laryngeal behavior suggest that reciprocity exists between vocal-fold mass and tension; that is, one cannot be affected without influencing the other. The glottic margins can be relaxed by two mechanisms. The first is tissue elasticity. Once the folds have been placed under tension, they tend to resume their relaxation state solely by virtue of their inherent elasticity. A further decrease in tension, however, must be produced by active forces that shorten the vocal folds, thus relaxing and thickening them. The thyromuscularis portion of the thyroarytenoid muscle has one main action, and that is to draw the arytenoid cartilage forward, toward the thyroid, and thus shorten and relax the folds. The lateral-most portions, because of their attachments on the base and muscular process of the arytenoid cartilage, rotate the arytenoids inward and help maintain medial compression during phonation at low pitches. This action may be facilitated by the lateral cricoarytenoids, but supportive evidence is scarce.

The role of the extrinsic musculature ought not be overlooked, however, in producing changes in pitch.

The Extrinsic Muscles and the Pitch-Changing Mechanism

In order to produce tones at the extreme ends of the pitch range, some extrinsic laryngeal musculature may be called into play. It is a rather common occurrence for the larynx to rise during the production of high-pitched tones and to lower during production of low tones. This raising and lowering of the larynx is brought about by the laryngeal elevators and depressors and by the middle and inferior pharyngeal constrictor muscles (to be discussed later). For example, the tensing action of the cricothyroid muscle may be augmented by simultaneous contraction of the sternothyroid muscle, which tends to tilt the thyroid cartilage forward. This tilting action may be assisted by contraction of the inferior constrictor muscles of the pharynx, which insert into the thyroid cartilage along the posterior border. On the other hand, contraction of the thyrohyoid muscle and the geniohyoid and anterior belly of the digastric muscles tilts the thyroid cartilage upward to diminish the distance between the anchor points of the vocal folds and cause them to relax for a decrease in pitch.

From what has been presented thus far, it ought to be evident that the laryngeal structures are complex and that muscles may complement each other's activities one moment and counteract them the next. It is of utmost importance to realize that any changes brought about in the larynx are the result of the algebraic sum of the various forces in action.

Voice Registers

By convention, the rate of vocal-fold vibration is described either in terms of musical notes (pitch), or in terms of fundamental frequency (cycles per second). In either case the scale is on a continuum ranging from less than 60 cps (B_1 on the musical scale) in the basso voice to over 1,568 cps (G_6 on the musical scale) in the soprano voice. Singers often describe phonation not in terms of cycles per second or in musical notes, but rather in registers.

In 1841, Manuel Garcia defined the voice register as follows:

> By the word register we mean a series of succeeding sounds of equal quality on a scale from low to high, produced by the application of the same mechanical principle, the nature of which differs basically from another series of succeeding sounds of equal quality produced by another mechanical principle.

This definition is not very different from that given by Webster:

A particular series of tones, especially of the human voice, produced in the same way and having the same quality: the head register.

The terminology with regard to voice registers suffers from the existence of a fantastic abundance of terms (over a hundred) and little agreement as to their use.

In his excellent little book *Traits Complet de l'Art du Chant* (1841), Garcia recognized three voice registers, which in English might be described as the chest register, the middle or mixed register, and the head register. Very often, just the chest and head registers are used. Other voice-register systems recognize as many as five registers. It is important to note, however, that no one singer is expected to encompass all five registers.

Mörner, Fransson, and Fant (1964) have recognized the problems of voice-register terminology and state that music and voice specialists appear to agree reasonably well as to the average pitch of the boundaries between registers; i.e., the breaks or voice transitions. They have noted, for example, that the average boundary between the middle- and high-pitch levels varies rather little within the particular kind of voice. It is located at C_4 (278 cps) for a bass voice and at F_4 (349 cps) for a soprano voice. The transition from low to mid level occurs at D_3 (147 cps) for a bass voice and at E_3 (165 cps) for a tenor. Mörner, *et al.* suggest: "The only secure common denominator for defining a register is by means of its range on the musical scale." They suggest five basic registers, which are referred to as the deepest range, deep level, mid level, high level, and highest range. The approximate ranges and boundary limits of these registers are shown in Figure 4–19. In addition, some synonyms are listed.

Fig. 4–19. The physiological ranges of the singing voice according to Nadoleszny (1923), terms used to describe voice registers, and the approximate boundaries and terms for voice registers as suggested by Mörner.

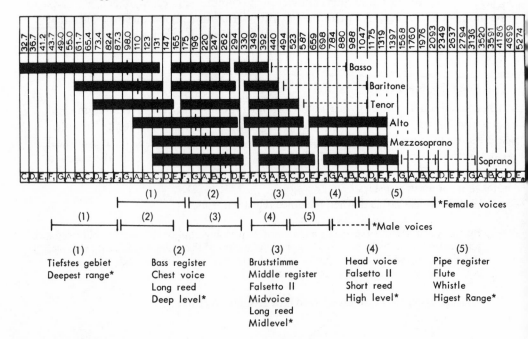

A particular mode or pattern of vocal-fold vibration is usually confined within a given pitch range, and when phonation is attempted outside the limits of this range, the mode of vibration will be altered appropriately to accommodate the succeeding range. This modification of the mode of vocal-fold vibration may be regarded as an operational definition of voice register. Thus, as a person transcends the limits of a particular vocal register, the voice may undergo an abrupt modification of quality. This vocal quality is often the primary characteristic of voice register. Voice specialists, and singing teachers in particular, seem to be in common agreement that one of the primary tasks in training for singing is to blend the registers (however many there may be) into a single unit of function that makes it difficult for even a trained listener to detect points of transition. In fact, this is considered ideal (Brodnitz, 1959).

Depending upon the extent of a singer's talent and his particular kind of voice, he may appear to have a "single register" that encompasses two or three "registers" of another singer. In fact, certain well-trained individuals are able to produce a gliding pitch throughout their entire pitch range (which may be over three octaves) without a perceptible voice break or transition. Operationally, it is reasonable to regard such a person as having but a single voice register, but according to Mörner, *et al.*, such a singer would have produced vocal tones within a specified number of registers solely on the basis of the range of musical tones encompassed.

In other words, much of the difficulty encountered in terminology stems from the fact that there are as yet no common grounds upon which to establish vocal-register criteria. Ideally, if we are to adhere to the definitions advanced by Garcia and others, registers ought to be defined from a physiological point of view. Our knowledge of the larynx, however, is far from complete, and the boundaries that have been established from a subjective evaluation of the singing voice are probably just as valuable to singers as "objective boundaries," based on meager data, might be. Brodnitz (1959) has noted that the conventional classification of singing voices as bassos, baritones, tenors, contraltos, mezzo-sopranos, and sopranos has a practical value for the assignment of musical parts but does not stand up to anatomic-physiologic criteria.

As an individual approaches the limits of his normal pitch range, some very interesting laryngeal adjustments may suddenly occur. These adjustments, which apparently facilitate voice production at extreme pitches, often result in easily identifiable voice-quality modifications, notably the falsetto, laryngeal whistle, and glottal fry.

The Limits of the Pitch Range

When a person reaches the upper limits of his normal pitch range, the mode of vocal-fold vibration may be suddenly modified to produce a range of tones that is called falsetto. It is extremely important to realize that although falsetto is confined to the extreme upper portion of the pitch range, it is also a peculiar vocal quality that is a function of the mode, and not just the rate, of vocal-fold vibration. That is, there is a certain amount of overlap between the upper limits of the normal pitch range and the lower limits of the falsetto range. Most singers (and many of us who are nonsingers) are quite capable of producing a high note that is recognized as being within the middle register and of producing a note with the same pitch that is recognized as being within the lower portion of the falsetto range or register.

High-speed motion pictures of the larynx during falsetto production reveal that the folds vibrate and come into contact only at the free borders and that the remainder of the folds remains relatively firm and nonvibratory. Furthermore, the folds appear long, stiff, very thin along the edges, and often somewhat bow-shaped. For illustrative purposes, a cycle of falsetto, taken from a high-speed film, is shown in Figure 4–20. This is the same subject that appears in Figures 4–17 and 4–18. The vibratory behavior suggests that the thyrovocalis muscle is tensed while the thyromuscularis remains relaxed. This is purely speculative, however, and is a suitable subject for research. Indeed, the mechanism of falsetto is not entirely free from debate. An early description by Aikin (1902) seems to have withstood the test of time.

> The (vocal) ligaments are pressed together so firmly by the strong contraction of the lateral crico-arytaenoid muscles, as well as the other muscles of approximation, that their edges are in contact for a short distance in front of the vocal processes, leaving only a shortened length of ligament free to vibrate. It is possible to relax the arytaenoid muscles a very little, and allow a slight opening of the valve, without disturbing the pitch.

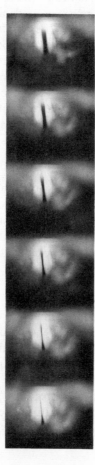

Fig. 4–20. A cycle of falsetto (F = 400 cps) by the same subject as in Fig. 4–18.

Brodnitz (1959), Pressman (1942), and Pressman and Kelemen (1955) attribute falsetto to a similar mechanism. That is, when the folds have been tensed and lengthened as much as possible, further increases in pitch must be accomplished by a different mechanism, namely, damping. The posterior portions of the folds are very firmly approximated, and do not enter into vibration. As a result, the length of the vibrating glottis is shortened considerably.

We see from our now familiar formula,

$$n = \left(\sqrt{\frac{T}{M}}\right)(2L)^{-1},$$

that decreasing the length of a vibrating element increases the frequency of vibration, and that (plus tension) is precisely what happens in the case of a damped larynx. You will recognize this as the same means of pitch change employed by musicians playing stringed instruments. We have all seen a guitarist finger the strings of his guitar in order to modify the length of the vibrating element.

Farnsworth (1940) based a description of the falsetto mechanism upon high-speed films of the larynx. He stated that at extremely high pitches only the medial edges of the folds seem to vibrate, with slight changes in glottal width. He also noted that the vibration tends to be confined more and more toward the forward portions of the vocal folds as pitch is increased.

Judson and Weaver (1965) attribute falsetto production to a mechanism not grossly different from that suggested by Aikin. They state that the external fibers of the thyroarytenoid muscles relax while the internal fibers contract strongly. In addition, the contraction of the posterior cricoarytenoid and cricothyroid muscles slightly increases the antero-posterior diameter of the glottis. Thus the vocal folds are placed under a considerable tension. They also suggest that vibration is confined primarily to the middle and anterior third of the glottis.

For comparative purposes, glottal configurations during phonation at normal pitch, high pitch, and falsetto are shown in Figure 4–21. Note the elliptical glottis, suggesting that vibration is confined to the anterior position. The quality of a tone produced by falsetto is almost flute-like in nature. This is due partly to the rather simple form of vibration executed by the vocal folds and partly to the high rate of vibration. As shown in Figure 4–22, when the fundamental frequency is very high, harmonically related overtones are widely separated in frequency; consequently, in any given frequency range there are fewer components in the sound than in a sound (or voice) with a lower fundamental frequency. This partly accounts for the rich quality of the bass voice when compared with the relatively thin quality of the tenor voice. Very often the configuration of the glottis is such that the folds never quite approximate during the closed phase of the vibratory cycle, and breathiness is often evident. A rather large glottal chink may be seen in Figure 4–18 and in the high pitch and falsetto of Figure 4–21.

According to Brodnitz (1959), the falsetto lies above the head register (in accordance with the definition of register by Garcia). High female voices do not exhibit a falsetto, however, but a laryngeal whistle, which is not produced by vibration of the vocal folds, but by the whistling escape of air from between them. The laryngeal whistle is regarded as a true vocal register of soprano voices. Many children are able to produce a very clear, flute-like, laryngeal whistle. The vocal folds are extremely tense and

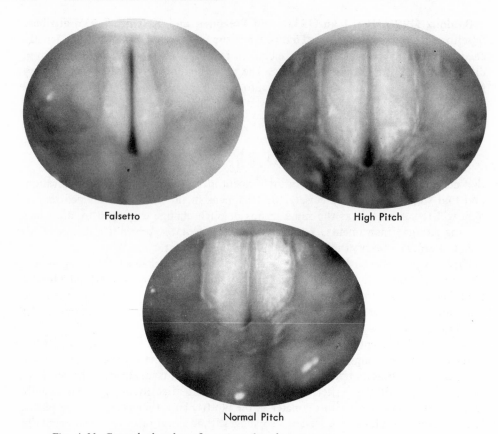

Falsetto   High Pitch

Normal Pitch

Fig. 4–21. General glottal configurations for phonation at normal pitch, high pitch and falsetto.

Fig. 4–22. Schematic spectrum of laryngeal wave.

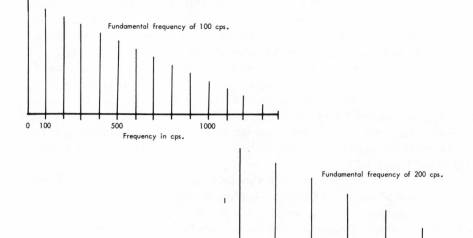

Fundamental frequency of 100 cps.

Frequency in cps.

Fundamental frequency of 200 cps.

Frequency in cps.

highly damped to the extent that only a small chink appears in the anterior third of the glottis.

The position of the falsetto and laryngeal whistle is shown in Figure 4–19. The range of the various singing voices is also shown. In the figure, the interruptions of the black columns mark the points of transition from chest, to mixed, to head registers. The dotted areas above the columns of the male voices indicate the falsetto range; above the soprano, the whistle register. The horizontal black lines indicate the approximate average or habitual pitch of the speaking voice for each type. The musical scale is based on the international standard that $A_4 = 440$ cps.

Laryngeal adjustment at the lower limits of the pitch range may result in what is called a glottal fry, or creaky voice. Moser (1942) says of glottal fry: "It is very easy to demonstrate, but very difficult to describe. You may recognize it as the sound produced by many youngsters in imitating a motor boat, but to me it more nearly resembles the sound of vigorously popping corn." Glottal fry is often equated with, or accompanies, harsh voice quality. It may be produced by simply phonating quietly at the lowest possible pitch, so that the sound feels as if it is bubbling out of the larynx in discrete bursts. Indeed, that is precisely what is happening. High-speed photography by the author has revealed that the folds are approximated tightly, but at the same time they appear flaccid along their free borders, and subglottal air simply bubbles up between them at about the junction of the anterior two-thirds of the glottis. The frequency of vocal-fold vibration has been found to range from about thirty to eighty per second, with a mean of approximately sixty per second. The closed phase occupies about 90 per cent of the vibratory cycle, and the opening and closing phases combined occupy about 10 per cent of the cycle.

Fig. 4–23. Schematic representation of the vibratory cycle, during glottal fry, as noted by Moore and von Leden (1958), above, and as seen by the present author, below.

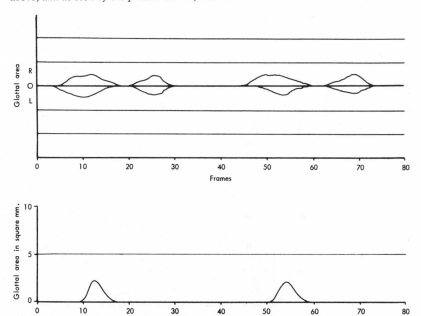

Moore and von Leden (1958) described vocal-fold vibration during production of glottal fry. They found that the vocal folds opened and closed twice in rapid succession and then remained closed for a long period of time. They termed this double vibration pattern "syncopated rhythm." They found the vocal folds to be open for about 27–30 per cent of the cycle, to close for an instant, and to open again for approximately 18–20 per cent of the cycle, and then close again for a period nearly equal to the duration of the other three events combined. Figure 4–23 illustrates the vibratory cycle as noted by the author and as described by Moore and von Leden. Oscillographic analysis of glottal fry has confirmed that both single and double vibratory patterns may occur. The mechanism of glottal fry is not at all well understood, and is a fit topic for research. The behavior of vocal folds suggests that they are tightly approximated by virtue of the lateral cricoarytenoid and interarytenoid muscles and that they are held relaxed by contraction of the thyroarytenoid muscle. Supportive evidence, however, is lacking.

The Intensity-Changing Mechanism

Surprisingly little attention has been devoted to the mechanisms responsible for changes in vocal intensity. What little research there is has been conducted on small populations and has been largely devoted to changes in the larynx that occur with variations in intensity. Intensity changes are an important part of our everyday verbal behavior, and it ought to come as no surprise to learn that the extremes in intensity of vocal tones occupy a considerable range, even during conversational speech. Figure 4–24 shows an intensity curve of a sentence spoken by the author. The nonsense sentence, devised by Fairbanks, samples each phoneme of the general American dialect just once. From the curve it is evident that the range in intensity is something in excess of thirty decibels. This represents a ratio of intensity in the order of a thou-

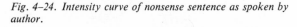

Fig. 4–24. Intensity curve of nonsense sentence as spoken by author.

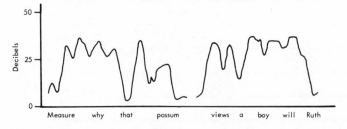

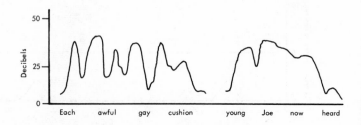

sand to one. The difference between the least and most intense sounds a person can produce, from a faint sound to a genuine rebel yell, amounts to over seventy decibels, a considerable range indeed.

One of the earliest attempts to account for variations in intensity was that of Dodart in 1700. In 1741, Ferrein examined glottal adjustments on living dog larynxes, and concluded, according to Grutzner (1879), that loudness of phonation is greatest when the glottis is narrowest. Ferrein also observed that an increase in breath pressure tended to increase the amplitude of vocal-fold movement. Magendie, in 1824, stated that the intensity of the voice was proportional to the force of air expelled from the chest and depended upon the extent of amplitude of vocal-fold vibration. A few years later Müller concluded, from studies on cadaver, dog, and artificial larynxes, that vocal intensity, with a given pitch, was dependent upon the relationship between subglottal air pressure and vocal-fold tension, "the latter varying inversely with the former."

In 1873, Merkel reported that changes in intensity are accompanied by a proper balance between the force of subglottal air and the tension of the glottic muscles but that there is a direct relationship between the quantity of air passing through the larynx and increased vocal intensity. He also noted that increased intensity was accompanied by greater excursion of the vocal folds. Ewald (1898), using frog leg muscles in a model of the larynx, found an inverse relation between muscle tension and air pressure for changes in intensity at a constant pitch.

Aikin (1902) concluded from observations of the vocal folds in living humans that vocal intensity was higher when there was a small glottal opening because, "When the valve is closed, the whole pressure of the breath is acting upon the reed, and the sound is more intense. When it is open, the subglottic pressure escapes and the intensity is diminished." Curry (1940) stated that increases in air pressure above the minimal value necessary to initiate vibration at a given frequency determine the amplitude of the vibration and hence the intensity of phonation.

On the basis of this brief survey of the literature, it seems evident that considerable disagreement existed regarding vocal-intensity mechanisms well into the twentieth century. A very rewarding approach to the investigation of internal laryngeal activity has been high-speed motion-picture photography. In an early study of this sort, Farnsworth (1940) noted that as intensity is increased, the folds remain closed for a proportionately longer time during each vibratory cycle. He also noted that the maximum displacement of the folds increased with intensity, but not proportionately. Pressman (1942) was in essential agreement with Farnsworth. He stated that the amplitude of vibratory movement becomes greater as subglottal pressure is increased; the added excursion to the mid-line is more complete.

In another high-speed photographic study, Fletcher (1950) compared the modes of vocal-fold vibration of three subjects during phonation at moderate intensity and at five and ten decibels above the moderate level. He also obtained high-speed films of the larynx during a crescendo. From the information obtained by this technique, one fact seems to stand out: the duration of the closed phase of the vibratory cycle increases with intensity. Figure 4–25 shows glottal area as a function of time with an intensity difference between phonations of five decibels. The dotted line is the high intensity curve. Note the increase in duration of the closed phase. This curve is

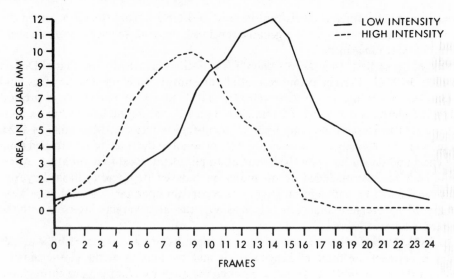

Fig. 4–25. Glottal area as a function of time (time interval per frame = .25 millisecond) Low pitch (168 cps) Intensity difference = 5 db.

representative of the modifications that take place in the mode of vocal-fold vibration with intensity changes. These changes are also evident in high-speed films of crescendo. Figure 4–26 shows glottal area as a function of time for typical vibratory cycles, selected at ten-foot intervals from a film of crescendo. The total intensity change amounted to about twelve decibels at a frequency of 212 cps. Two features are apparent: the duration of the closed phase increases with intensity, and the maximum glottal area remains essentially constant. These films do not support the notion that maximum lateral excursion of the folds increases with vocal intensity.

Within recent years, measurements have been made of the relation of subglottal pressure to vocal intensity. Researchers, such as van den Berg (1956) and Ladefoged (1960), have demonstrated a relation between subglottal pressure and intensity; that is, sound pressure level of the voice is proportional to the square of subglottal pressure. In a rather intensive study of intensity and subglottic pressure during speech, Ladefoged and McKinney (1963) found that peak subglottal pressure was proportional to the peak value of the effective sound pressure ($Sp^{0.6}$); that is, glottic pressure was proportional to the 0.6 power of subglottic pressure.

Rubin (1963), in a study partially reported earlier, found that at any given pitch level, an increase in air flow is accompanied by greater vocal loudness. He quickly pointed out: "This does not imply, however, that vocal intensity is a function of air flow alone." He was able to conclude that vocal intensity may be raised by increasing air flow with constant vocal-fold resistance, and/or by increasing vocal-fold resistance at constant air flow. Rubin also pointed out that the mechanisms of vocal pitch and intensity are so interrelated that to attempt to isolate one from the other, except for the most elementary considerations, is virtually impossible. This is a most important point to remember.

In 1964, Isshiki investigated the relationship between vocal intensity (sound pressure level), subglottal pressure, air-flow rate, and glottal resistance. He made simultaneous

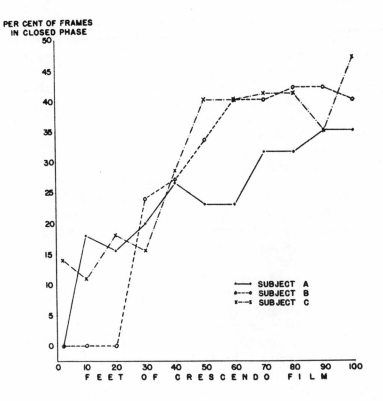

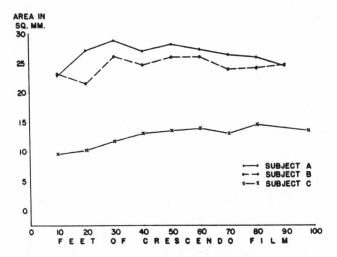

Fig. 4–26. Percentage of frames in closed phase (top), and maximum glottal openings (bottom) of typical cycles at selected intervals from a high speed film of crescendo From W. Fletcher, 1950).

recordings of sound pressure level of the voice, subglottal pressure, air-flow rate, and the volume of air expenditure during phonation at various pitches and intensities. He used a single human subject and found that at low-pitch phonation, the intensity of the voice was raised by an increase in glottal resistance. That is to say, the medial compression of the folds and their tension are increased to provide increasing resistance to air flow. At high pitch, however, glottal resistance is already so high, very nearly maximum, that resistance cannot be easily increased without affecting vocal pitch. As a result, Isshiki concluded that intensity at high pitch is probably controlled, not by changes in glottal resistance, but by rate of air flow through the glottis. This air flow is mediated, of course, by the forces of exhalation.

From the results obtained by Isshiki, it might be supposed that internal laryngeal behavior ought to vary markedly as intensity is increased during phonation at low pitch and that it ought to vary less as intensity is increased during high-pitch phonation. On the other hand, differences in the activity of the muscles of exhalation might be expected to be greater during intensity increases at high-pitch phonation than at low-pitch phonation.

In 1965, Charron attempted to put Isshiki's conclusions to test by investigating glottal and breathing activity during phonation at various pitches and intensities. He used four young adult subjects and photographed their glottal activity during low- and high-pitch phonation at low and at high intensities. He also employed electromyography to detect the relative activity of the musculture of exhalation under the same conditions of phonation. A sample from his photographic measurements is shown in Figure 4–27, and a schematic representation of his EMG data is shown in Figure 4–28. The glottal-area variations during phonation at low pitch and low intensity are typical of normal laryngeal activity, and the glottal-area curves for phonation at low pitch and high intensity exhibit the characteristic increase in

Fig. 4–27. Glottal area variations during phonation at low pitch and at high and low intensities and at high pitch at high and low intensities for a single subject.

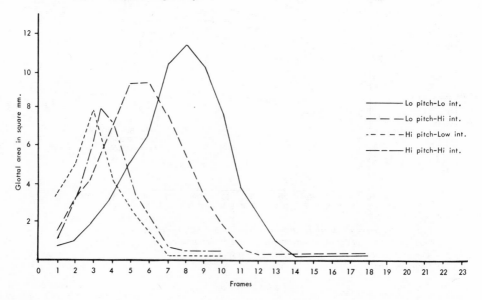

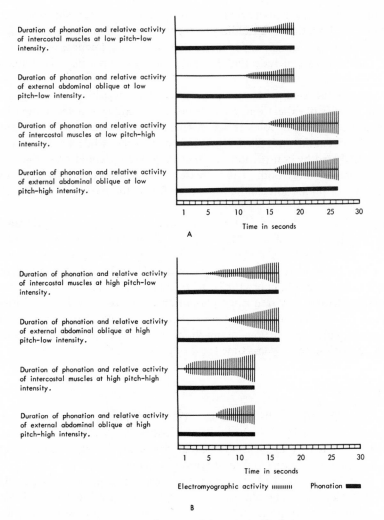

Fig. 4–28. Schematic of the duration of phonation and relative
activity of the muscles of exhalation at low pitch at low and
at high intensity (A) and at high pitch at low and high
intensity (B).

duration of the closed phase, suggesting that glottal resistance has increased. Glottal
area for phonation at high pitch, low intensity was found to be considerably reduced
from the low-pitch conditions. Note in Figure 4–28 that during phonation at high
pitch, low intensity, the vibratory cycle includes a closed phase. Note further, however,
that the relative duration of the closed phase remains the same during the high-pitch,
high-intensity condition, suggesting a rather constant glottal resistance at low- and
high-intensity phonation at high pitch. The increase in glottal area might well have
been due to an increase in subglottal pressure, but this is only an inference supported
by the data from the EMG recordings. Relative muscle activity at high- and low-
intensity phonation at low pitch is shown in Figure 4–28A, and the relative muscle
activity at high and low intensity at high pitch is shown in B. These data indicate
heightened activity and rapid growth patterns during high-pitch, high-intensity

phonation, as opposed to less activity and less abrupt growth patterns during high-pitch, low-intensity phonation. In addition, they suggest that low-pitch, high-intensity phonation requires less air expenditure than low-pitch, low-intensity phonation. Charron was able to conclude that his data strongly supported the findings of Isshiki.

Although it cannot be said with certainty, three, and possibly four, laryngeal muscles, plus the muscles of exhalation, are responsible for changes in vocal intensity. Forceful adduction of the vocal folds is accomplished by simultaneous contraction of the lateral cricoarytenoid and the interarytenoid muscles, while an increase in glottic tension is mediated by contraction of either the thyroarytenoid muscles or the cricothyroid, or quite probably both. The increases in pitch that usually accompany increases in intensity of phonation can be accounted for by the greater tension of the vocal folds.

It need not be supposed that an increase in vocal intensity should significantly affect the rate of expenditure of air. Although the amount of subglottal pressure required for phonation is higher, the resistance of the larynx is also greater, and volume flow per unit time may actually be decreased. This viewpoint is supported by Isshiki and by Ptacek and Sander (1963), who found that some of their subjects were able to maintain loud, low-frequency phonation for considerably longer durations than soft or moderately loud phonations. Because the vocal folds are in the closed phase for a greater proportion of the vibratory cycle in high-intensity than in low-intensity phonation, there is less time for air flow to occur.

The Vibrato

Thus far, we have limited our discussion to rather gross pitch changes that might occur with discrete vocal tasks. A large body of literature is directed toward small and rapid pitch and intensity changes that occur primarily during singing. These pitch and intensity changes are most often referred to as vibrato.

The vibrato is a curious vocal phenomenon that, when present, adds a peculiar "rich color" to the voice. Although almost anyone is capable of producing a vibrato, proper pitch and intensity variations are usually acquired only after some training. If the pitch and intensity changes are quite extensive, the term trill is usually used.

It is curious that although considerable research has been directed toward vibrato, very little is known regarding the physiological mechanism responsible for its production. This is primarily because the researchers have directed their efforts toward a description of the acoustic product and not the physiology. Names such as Seashore (1923), Kwalwasser (1926), Metfessel (1932), Gray (1926), Tiffin (1932), and Schoen (1922) are frequently encountered in the literature describing and defining vibrato, but it remained for Schoen in 1922 to attempt a physiological account of its production. His account may be found in the University of Iowa Studies, *The Vibrato* (1932):

> Summarizing these facts in their bearing upon vibrato of the singer it is evident that the vibrato is a phenomenon in every respect similar to the tremor here described. The tremor is a constant rate but varies in amplitude, so is the vibrato: the tremor is beyond the control of the patient, so is the vibrato; it only occurs when the muscle is under slight strain, so does the vibrato: it is about half the rate of normal muscular discharge, so is the vibrato.

We may then summarize the foregoing facts in their bearing upon the vibrato as follows:

Singing is essentially an emotional act involving the neuro-muscular mechanism or muscles functionally connected with this specific type of emotional expression, the whole act involving the usual type of muscular response to stimulation characteristic of skeletal muscle. Further, that the neuro-muscular apparatus of the singing organism is peculiar in kind, in that to a certain extent it manifests those phenomena of muscle pathology found in the tremor, in that the vocal muscle, under tension, brought about as a result of the emotional excitement involved in singing, responds with a rhythm of muscular discharge at a rate half of that found in the normal state, and that this tremor is manifested particularly in that organ which is functionally connected with vocal emotional expression, the larynx.

Its (the vibrato) specific seat is the muscle or muscles controlling the movements of the larynx in phonation.

Using the indirect technique, Schoen examined the larynxes of fourteen subjects during vibrato production. He noted that in no case was the vibrato confined entirely within the larynx. All subjects had some definite muscle oscillation which could be felt either in "the region of the diaphragm" or just above the larynx. He noted further that in some cases the back of the tongue could be seen in oscillation at the vibrato rate. According to Schoen, the diaphragm and internal intercostals may be the antagonists used in producing the fluctuations felt in the breathing muscles. He felt that the diaphragm, likewise, can act in antagonism to the abdominal muscles. Schoen further supposed that possibly the inferior pharyngeal constrictor muscle or the hyoglossus, which attaches to the root of the tongue, are in antagonism with the cricothyroid or the thyroarytenoid muscles in certain types of vibrato production. Schoen called these "supra-laryngeal vibratos." He remarked upon the possibility of the vocal folds acting as a valve by opening and closing recurrently, checking the column of air from the lungs and thereby inducing a fluctuation in the breathing musculature.

In 1932, Tiffin and Seashore commented upon the physiology of the vocal vibrato:

The physiology of the vibrato presents two fundamental issues: first, what particular musculature, or muscle-group, controls the change in rate and extent of pitch, intensity and timbre? Second, what is the neurological timing device which controls these changes: Neither of these questions has been answered adequately. It has been shown that through control of the muscles of the diaphragm, vibrato changes may be produced, and that these muscles ordinarily function in the normal production of the vibrato; but the probability is that there are several kinds of control of the vibrato involving different sets or series of muscles.

Much light has been thrown on the neurological problem by means of action current and related techniques. It seems probable that the vibrato is but one of the normal periodicities which occur in all the large musculatures in animal life. It also seems probable that a certain type of tension or instability favors the emergence of the periodicity in the voice analogous to a tremor.

Some of the questions raised by Tiffin and Seashore might be answered with contemporary laboratory instrumentation. In 1965, Mason studied the vibrato mechanism by means of simultaneous electromyography and high-speed photography. Laryngeal elevators, depressors, and some musculature of the tongue and of exhalation were studied by means of electromyography, while simultaneous high-speed motion

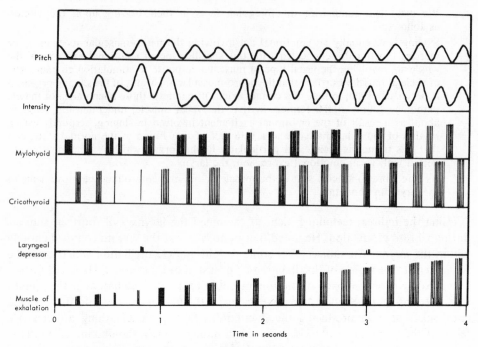

Fig. 4–29. Schematic reproduction of acoustic and electro-myographic recordings during the production of vibrato.

pictures of the larynx producing a vibrato were made. Two highly trained singers and two untrained persons were used as subjects.

A summary of some typical data found by Mason is shown schematically in Figure 4–29. The upper two tracings are from voice recordings made simultaneously with electromyographic recordings. Data indicate heightened activity of the cricothyroid muscle and, in some cases, increased activity of the muscles of exhalation during increases in pitch and intensity, and heightened activity of the mylohyoid muscle during decreases in pitch and intensity. Such an inverse phase relationship suggests that the muscles in the mylohyoid region act to check the pitch-raising effects of the cricothyroid muscle. The data further suggest that additional subglottal pressure may be provided in some subjects by increased activity of the muscles of exhalation. This activity is also dependent upon the functional air reserve of the subject. The additional subglottal air pressure may account for the increases in intensity during vibrato.

The high-speed laryngeal photographs revealed little to differentiate vibrato from ordinary phonation. Apparently the changes in internal laryngeal behavior during vibrato are too subtle to be detected by visual means. Very slight modifications in vocal-fold tension need not be accompanied by a change in length.

VOCAL QUALITIES

For most individuals, under normal circumstances, the vocal folds behave in such a manner as to generate a tone that is auditorially acceptable, if not actually pleasant.

Occasionally, however, vocal behavior is such that the tone is unbecoming or unacceptable. It is not the place of this text to enter into a discussion of voice and speech disorders, but it may be of some value to attempt a description of some variations in vocal-fold behavior that may result in unacceptable voice quality.

Voice quality is a controversial issue, far from resolved, and, as might be expected, terminology is the basis for much of the disagreement. Without entering into the argument, it can be rather safely asserted that there are four voice-quality disorders: breathiness, hoarseness, harshness, and nasality. For matters of clarity, we ought to make a distinction between voice quality and vocal-quality disorders. Vocal-quality disorders are due to abnormal patterns of vocal-fold behavior, which in turn produce unpleasant variations in vocal tone. As such, there are three vocal-quality disorders: breathiness, harshness, and hoarseness. The fourth disorder, nasality, is not a vocal disorder but rather a voice disorder. That is, nasality is a disorder probably resulting not from faulty vocal -fold behavior, but from faulty articulation.

Breathiness

In an earlier description of normal vocal-fold vibration we saw how the folds approximate at the mid-line during the closed phase of the cycle. Under normal circumstances the result is a complete, or very nearly complete, blockage of the air passage. In the case of breathy voice, however, incomplete blockage during the closed phase results in a continuous flow of air during the entire vibratory cycle. Acoustic analysis of breathy vocal quality reveals a rather broad-band noise superimposed on the periodic vocal tone. The implication is that air leakage is generating a strong frictional noise component which accompanies the tone generated by the vibrating vocal folds. The resultant vocal quality is referred to as breathy or asthenic. Spectograms of the vowel [æ] produced deliberately with different vocal qualities are shown in Figure 4–30. The spectograms are short segments taken from sustained samples.

As can well be imagined, breathiness is an inefficient form of phonation and usually results in a very limited intensity range. The degree of breathiness may vary during the breathing cycle in some persons. It is usually most prominent at the begin-

Fig. 4–30. Spectrograms of various voice qualities.

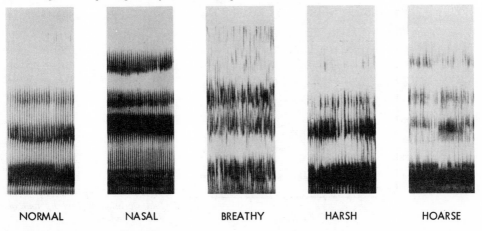

NORMAL   NASAL   BREATHY   HARSH   HOARSE

ning of the expiratory cycle. Breathiness may be the result of poor vocal habits, or it may be organic in nature; that is, it may be the result of a structural peculiarity in the larynx. Its severity may also be dependent upon phonetic environment. The vowel [æ] from the isolated word "apple," for example, is not likely to be nearly as breathy as the [æ] from the word "happy," where the vowel is preceded by an aspirate sound.

On the basis of the very limited data accumulated thus far on the topic, there seem to be two physiological correlates of breathiness. Whether the acoustic end-products are different or not is a fit subject for research and has real implications with respect to the therapeutic approach to treatment of breathy vocal quality. The most commonly cited correlate of breathiness is a persistent glottal chink in the posterior-most portion of the glottis. This chink is undoubtedly the result of insufficient medial compression of the arytenoid cartilages. Critical examination of high-speed motion pictures of a large number of larynxes reveals that a good many persons with apparently healthy laryngeal structures and normal-sounding voices display a sizable glottal chink in the posterior portion of the glottis. We can suppose that there is a critical value in the magnitude of glottal chink that will result in a breathy voice. The exact relationship between size of glottal chink and vocal quality is not well understood.

From a high-speed motion-picture study (at 1,400 frames per second) of glottal function in deliberate breathiness (and other vocal qualities), Fletcher (1947) concluded that the distinctive difference between normal and breathy phonation was in the extent of lateral excursion of the vocal folds. He also pointed out that the glottal closure may be complete, even during the production of an extremely breathy quality. As shown in figure 4–31, glottal area during maximum lateral excursion was equal to more than 130 per cent of the normal area. Fletcher attributed the abnormal lateral excursion of the folds to a relaxed thyroarytenoid muscle.

In order to obtain absolute measurements of glottal dimensions, Fletcher devised a simple but ingenious technique to determine the optical magnification due to the photography and projection. He placed a grid, calibrated in millimeters, at the same location as had been occupied by the vocal folds during photography. While maintaining all optical conditions (his depth of field was practically zero), the scale was photographed, projected, and compared with the original scale. He was thus able to

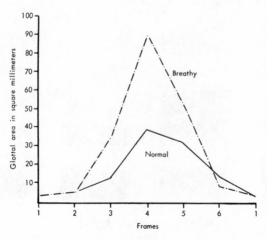

Fig. 4–31. Comparison of vocal fold vibration in breathy and in normal qualities.

determine, within reasonable limits, the extent to which the laryngeal image was magnified.

Harshness

The peculiar behavior of the vocal folds during the production of a harsh voice is relatively unknown and is a suitable topic for research. The acoustic product, however, has managed to come under the scrutiny of some recent researchers, and, on the basis of the accumulated information, we might at least speculate on laryngeal behavior during the production of harsh or rough vocal quality. Examination of the spectograms in Figure 4–30 reveals that the feature which differentiates the normal from the harsh voice is aperiodic noise, or irregular vocal-fold vibration, which is often due to excessive tension of the folds. Persons with harsh voices tend to initiate phonation with glottal attack. Some evidence also suggests that these people are phonating at an inappropriate pitch level, usually slightly low for their vocal mechanisms.

The irregularities in vocal-fold vibration that may lead to the perception of harshness or roughness of the voice may be so slight as to escape detection when studied by means of high-speed photography. In 1963, Wendahl employed an electronic laryngeal analog to generate stimuli which varied in the magnitude of frequency differences between successive cycles. He used two median fundamental frequencies, which had frequency variations about the median of 10 cps, 8 cps, 6 cps, 4 cps, 2 cps, and 1 cps. Listeners rated the stimuli for roughness. Wendahl found that very slight frequency variations, as little as one cycle per second around the median, sounded rough, and the magnitude of roughness judgments was directly related to the frequency differences between successive cycles. He also found evidence to suggest that the degree of perceived roughness was related to the median frequency, with frequency variation held constant. Thus, in the case of a male and a female voice, with equal frequency variations, the male would be judged to have the rougher voice.

Hoarseness

Hoarseness is easily identified in persons with acute laryngitis. Fairbanks (1959) stated that hoarseness combines the features of harshness and breathiness. He also pointed out that the harsh element may predominate in some hoarse voices, the breathy element in others, and variations of predominance may be heard within a given hoarse voice. These variations and differences in predominance probably contribute to the problem of identification or classification of deviant vocal qualities and give rise to terms such as husky, throaty, and so forth.

Chronic hoarseness is usually a symptom of laryngeal pathology, and anyone troubled by such vocal problems ought to seek prompt and appropriate medical advice. A very common cause of hoarseness is simple acute laryngitis, with its associated swelling and thickening of the vocal folds. As a result, vibration may be aperiodic and may occur with phase differences and incomplete glottal closure. The result is hoarseness. Vocal abuse, allergy, or neoplasms may also produce hoarse voices.

Nasality

Nasal voice quality, or hypernasality, is not necessarily objectionable; in fact, a certain amount of it may be pleasant. Nasality is usually attributed to a coupling of the nasal passages to the oral and pharyngeal cavities in such a manner that the quality of the emitted sound is noticeably affected by the added resonating cavity. Thus, a voice may sound slightly nasal or very nasal, depending upon the amount of coupling between the resonating cavities. Nasality may be the result of insufficient palatal tissue to insure proper isolation of the pharyngeal and nasal cavities, or it may be the result of insufficient palatal closure due to poor speaking habits, or it may be the result of an inability to control the palate. The contributions of the nasal cavities to speech production will be discussed in some detail in the following chapter.

While nasality is almost always regarded as a defect of transmission and not a true vocal problem, Fletcher (1947) has shown that vocal-fold behavior is different from normal during the production of a nasalized vowel. He noted a peculiarity of vocal-fold conformation that was consistent in three filmings. As shown in Figure 4–32, the opening phase in hypernasality is quite different from the normal quality. Fletcher also noted that the degree of lateral movement was much greater for the right than for the left fold. Asymmetrical vocal-fold vibration was found only in the nasal quality.

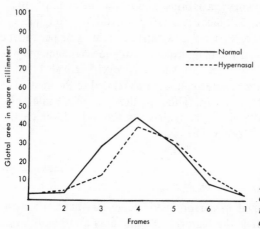

Fig. 4–32. Schematic of the modes of vocal fold vibration during normal and hypernasal voice production (From W. Fletcher, 1947).

Earlier authors had also suggested that nasality may have its seat, at least in part, in the larynx. Curry (1910), for example, postulated that nasality could be caused by insufficient velo-pharyngeal closure, by pharyngeal constriction, or by excessive tension in the larynx, or by a combination of all of these. Paget (1930), Russell and Tuttle (1930), Russell (1931), Travis, Bender, and Buchanan (1934), Warren (1936), and Curry (1940) have all suggested that nasality may be due in part to the vibratory pattern of the vocal folds. There is no assurance, however, that changes in the acoustic resistance of the vocal tract (due to articulation) will not produce slight changes in the vibratory pattern of the vocal folds. The question of laryngeal contribution to nasality remains unresolved and is a suitable topic for research.

Whisper

Most of us, at one time or another, have had occasion temporarily to supplant phonation by whispering, which is nonvocal sound production. The essential difference between vocalization and whispering lies in the configuration of the glottis during exhalation, and the resultant acoustic product. During conventional phonation the arytenoid cartilages are approximated so that their medial surfaces are in direct contact. The vocal folds lie parallel to one another. In whispering, however, the arytenoids are slightly abducted and "toed in" so that there is a small triangular chink in the region of the cartilaginous glottis. When the breath stream is released, turbulence occurs in the chink, and frictional sounds are generated. As shown in Figure 4–33, the glottis assumes a shape not unlike that of an inverted Y. Note, however, that the vocal folds are not adducted.

Pressman and Kelemen (1955) assert that in a low-volume whisper the folds assume a position a little more closely approximated than that for quiet respiration. They go on to state that when the vowel [ɑ] is produced, the margins of the glottis are straight, and that upon producing an [i], there is a "toeing-in" movement of the vocal processes of the arytenoids, but without a medial shift of the mass of their bodies. They account for such a glottal configuration by positing that the interarytenoid muscles fail to contract during the production of an [i] vowel. It would be interesting to be able to view the glottis during the production of an [i] vowel, either whispered or phonated. If it were possible to lower the arch of the tongue so that a guttural mirror might be inserted into the pharynx, we would be in a position either to confirm or refute these claims.

In order to approximate the vocal folds with any force at all, the interarytenoids and posterior cricoarytenoid muscles must contract. In all probability the toeing in of the arytenoid cartilages is the result of the failure of the posterior cricoarytenoids to contract. Thus, when the lateral cricoarytenoid muscles become active, they simply pull forward on the muscular processes of the arytenoids.

When the larynx is viewed by means of either strobolaryngoscopy or high-speed photography during a whisper, the vocal folds may be seen to move very slightly in

Fig. 4–33. Glottal configuration for whisper and for breathy phonation.

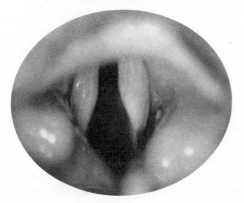
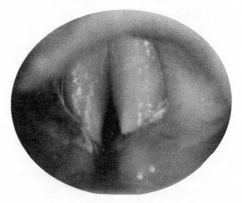

Whisper   Breathy

some subjects and not at all in others, but in no case do they vibrate to any great extent, or periodically as in conventional phonation. In the stage or forced whisper, however, the folds vibrate very much as they do during deliberate breathiness.

Although whispering places few demands upon the vocal mechanism, as a form of sound production it is, at best, second best. For example, a loud whisper is 20 db less in intensity than conversational speech. Whispering is also a very uneconomical way to use the breath supply. Whereas a person can phonate for as long as thirty seconds during vocalization, only about ten seconds of sound can be produced by whispering before another breath must be taken.

Frictional noises, such as those produced by whispering, are composed largely of aperiodic sounds which at any point in time have an unspecifiable spectrum. They possess no fundamental frequency. For this reason, whispered speech cannot easily be inflected. Only the band width of the noise can be altered by slight changes in the vocal tract. These alterations may produce a subjective impression of an increase in pitch. Only slight modifications in the intensity of whispered sounds are possible.

AGE AND SEX DIFFERENCES IN THE LARYNX

The infant larynx is not simply a miniature model of the adult larynx. It differs in shape, relative size, and position. At birth the lowest level of the larynx is opposite the middle of the sixth cervical vertebra. In the adult it is about at the level of the lower border of the same vertebra. The cartilages of the infant larynx are much softer and more pliable than the adult. The thyroid laminae form somewhat of a semicircle, which during growth becomes more and more angulated, until it approaches 90° in the mature male, and about 120° in the female.

According to Nauck (1942), the infant larynx is not only smaller than the adult, but proportionately so in relation to the size of other structures. At birth, the vocal folds are only about three millimeters in length. The rate of growth is very rapid during the first year (the folds almost double in length), and throughout childhood the rate is gradual. The folds are about 5.5 mm long at the end of the first year, 7.5 mm at the end of the fifth year, 8.0 mm at the end of the sixth year, and at fifteen years, they are about 9.5 mm long. In infancy the growth rate of the vocal folds exceeds the antero-posterior growth of the laryngeal cartilages. According to Negus (1929), the proportion is 1 to 2.3. By the end of the first year the proportion has decreased to 1 to 1.5. This proportion remains essentially constant throughout childhood, and in the female it continues through puberty, which for the male marks the onset of a period of rapid change in growth rate. The growth of the male larynx is accelerated due to influences of sex hormones. The cartilaginous structures grow particularly rapidly in the antero-posterior direction, which accounts for the reduction in the ratio cited by Negus (1929). The vocal folds grow about 10.0 mm in a very short period of time, thicken, and the lower range of the voice drops by about a full octave. This change in the larynx is known as mutation.

The female larynx also grows during puberty, but at about the same rate as it did throughout childhood. The vocal folds increase by about 4.0 mm, and the lower range of the voice drops by about two or three musical tones. Prior to the onset of puberty there is very little difference in the pitch or pitch range between boys and girls (Fairbanks, Herbert, and Hammond, 1949; Fairbanks, Wiley, and Lassman, 1949).

The voice range of infants is very limited and, according to Brodnitz (1959), extends only over a few notes. The range increases, however, until it reaches about two octaves at the time of puberty. On the other hand, Fairbanks (1942), found a pitch range of almost five octaves in infant hunger wails.

Research has suggested that changes in pitch level and pitch range accompany growth and the aging process. Results obtained by Fairbanks (1942), Fairbanks, Wiley, and Lassman (1949), and Mysak (1959) suggest that vocal pitch lowers at a rate roughly corresponding to laryngeal growth, and at middle age the pitch level begins to rise slightly. Changes in pitch range that may accompany increasing age are not well documented, but there seems to be a trend toward a decrease in range with increasing age. With increasing age, ossification and calcification of the laryngeal cartilages begin to occur. Bone is usually seen first in the thyroid cartilage, often by twenty-five years of age. The cricoid also ossifies at an early age, and by sixty-five the entire laryngeal framework, except for the elastic cartilages, is totally calcified or ossified. These structural changes are almost without exception accompanied by a decrease in general mobility and control.

THEORIES OF VOICE PRODUCTION

Two broad categories of theories have dominated much of the literature dealing with voice production. One theoretical issue revolves around the manner in which the vocal tone is generated by the vibrating vocal folds, and the other deals with the way in which the vocal folds are set into vibration. It is not the purpose of this text to weigh and attempt to pass judgment on the various theories of voice production. Throughout most of the discussion of the function of the laryngeal structures, however, the author has been alluding to a particular theory of voice production at the expense of another currently prominent theory. That is, the author has been guilty of presenting a biased viewpoint without first airing the various theories. The classical theory of voice production is usually called the myoelastic-aerodynamic theory. It is in direct opposition to the more recent neurochronaxic theory.

Myoelastic-Aerodynamic Theory

Briefly stated, the myoelastic-aerodynamic theory postulates that the vocal folds are subject to well-established aerodynamic principles. The vocal folds are set into vibration by the air stream from the lungs and trachea, and the frequency of vibration is dependent upon their length in relation to their tension and mass. These factors are regulated primarily by the delicate interplay of the intrinsic laryngeal muscles. The myoelastic-aerodynamic theory was first advanced by Johannes Müller in 1843, and has enjoyed popular acceptance ever since. Minor modifications of the theory have been suggested by Tonndorf (1925) and by Smith (1954), but its salient features have remained unchanged through the years. Then, in 1950, a well-known physicist and voice scientist, Raoul Husson, introduced a new theory that differs radically from the classical theory.

Neurochronaxic Theory

The neurochronaxic theory, advanced by Husson, postulates that each new vibratory cycle is initiated by a nerve impulse transmitted from the brain to the vocalis muscle by way of the recurrent branch of the vagus nerve. The frequency of vocal-fold vibration is dependent upon the rate of impulses delivered to the laryngeal muscles.

The myoelastic-aerodynamic and the neurochronaxic theories are divergent to the extent that they probably cannot be united into a single working theory. Rather, the accumulating body of information derived from research will probably someday enable us to evaluate the two theories and to settle upon either the myoelastic-aerodynamic or the neurochronaxic theory as being the least tenuous.

Some limited data have been obtained and are currently available. Models and analogs of the vocal tract, direct observations and photography of laryngeal functions in normal and abnormal larynxes, anatomical and histologic evidence, information from electromyographic recordings of laryngeal muscles, as well as physical and theoretical data, all have contributed to the accumulating body of knowledge regarding laryngeal function. The following review is intended not to be exhaustive, but simply representative of the various types of experiments that have been conducted in an attempt to resolve the controversy between the myoelastic-aerodynamic and neurochronaxic theories of voice production.

Görttler in 1951 and Behringer in 1955 reported that histological studies of the vocalis muscle revealed two bundles of tissue, each of which inserted obliquely into the vocal ligament. These results offered strong supportive evidence for the neurochronaxic theory, since contraction of the vocalis muscle would result in a lateral movement of the vocal folds. Contradictory results, however, have been obtained by van den Berg and Moll (1955), by Konig and von Leden, and others. These investigators found that the course of the vocalis muscle was primarily antero-posterior, with few or, indeed, no muscle fibers inserting into the vocal ligament. Muscle fibers were found to be inserted into the conus elasticus, however.

Supportive evidence for the myoelastic-aerodynamic theory may be obtained from high-speed motion pictures of a normal and breathy attack. If the fibers of the vocalis muscle course obliquely and insert into the vocal ligament, as proposed by Husson, the initial movements of the vocal folds ought to be lateral. Repeated experiments by various investigators have shown that during breathy and normal attacks the initial vibratory activity begins with a medial or inward movement of the folds.

The neuroanatomy of the larynx offers further support for the myoelastic-aerodynamic theory. It is well established that the left branch of the recurrent laryngeal nerve is about ten centimeters longer than the right. The left fold is supplied by the left branch, and the right fold by the right branch. If we can assume that the neural impulses are generated or initiated at the level of the brain, they would arrive at the left vocal fold somewhat later than the impulses to the right vocal fold. The highest velocity a nerve impulse can attain (in type A fibers) is in the vicinity of 100 meters per second. At a firing rate of 500 cycles per second (to produce a vibratory rate of 500 cycles per second), the nerve impulse would arrive at the left vocal fold approximately one millisecond behind the impulse to the right fold. One millisecond amounts to half the duration of the vibratory cycle at 500 vibrations per second. In other words, the right and left vocal folds would be completely out of phase. One fold would be in the open position, while the other would be in the closed or mid-line position. This condition is sometimes seen but only for short periods of time in voice breaks or in cases of laryngeal pathology.

As stated earlier, according to the neurochronaxic theory, the vibratory rate of the vocal folds is determined by the frequency of nerve impulses to the vocalis muscles. Husson, the most vigorous proponent of the neurochronaxic theory, has asserted that the upper frequency limit of phonation is limited by the refractory period of the nervous tissue innervating the vocalis muscle. The refractory period cited by Husson is about two milliseconds. Physiologists tell us that the absolutely refractory period of a nerve fiber is in the order of about two milliseconds and that for about an additional millisecond, or millisecond and a half, the nerve fiber is in a state of recovery called the relatively refractory period. That is, a nerve, having fired, ought to have returned to a state of equilibrium in about three to three and a half milliseconds. Nerve fibers do not conduct for very long periods at such high rates as 300–500 impulses per second, however, for they soon fatigue.

It is important to realize that during the relatively refractory period, the threshold for excitation of a nerve fiber is raised. If we can assume that the impulses are sufficiently strong to overcome the subexcitability of the nerve during the relatively refractory period, the upper frequency limits of vibration could possibly reach 500 per second, but only if the muscle fiber is capable of 500 contractions per second. There is also an absolutely and relatively refractory period in muscle tissue, however, which is in the order of five milliseconds. Therefore, regardless of the frequency of stimulation, the maximum contraction rate must be set at about 200 per second, and that is unreasonably high, for the muscle would fatigue and tetanize in just a small part of a second. For vocal-fold vibration at rates higher than those possible by single contractions of muscle groups, Husson has claimed that the individual muscle fibers within a group receive nerve impulses, and contract, in volleys. With just some muscle fibers contracting while others are in a refractory state, an extremely high rate of vocal-fold vibration is said to be possible.

In 1957, Piquet *et al.* offered support for the neurochronaxic theory in the form of a high-speed film which showed vibrating vocal folds, even though the air stream had been diverted from its usual course through the larynx out of the neck anteriorly through a tracheastoma. They stopped the trachea just beneath the larynx so that life air of the patient entered and left the air passage via the tracheastoma, and presumably no air coursed through the larynx. When the patient was asked to phonate, the vocal folds seemed to vibrate at what appeared to be a normal rate. The results would imply that the vibrations were due to repetitive nerve impulses and not to activation by a stream of air. It is interesting to note that the experimenters not only saw the vocal folds vibrating, they also heard sound, in spite of the absence of an air stream to modulate, which is a highly improbable state of affairs. Experiments of exactly the same sort have been performed by van den Berg (1957), Rubin (1960), and others. Repeated high-speed photographic and stroboscopic experiments on tracheostomized subjects with normal larynxes revealed the vibration of the vocal folds to be interrupted and initiated alternately as the stoma was opened and closed. These results support the classical viewpoint that vocal-fold vibration is an aerodynamic phenomenon.

Electromyographic recordings of the vocal folds by Moulonguet, Laget, and Husson (1953) and by Portmann, Humbert, Robin, Laget, and Husson (1955) seem to offer support for the neurochronaxic theory. These researchers demonstrated synchrony between impulses obtained from the recurrent laryngeal nerve and the rate of vocal-fold vibration. The recordings, however, were very probably what physiologists call passive electromyograms. These passive electromyograms are the result of a microphonic effect, produced by the vibrations of the muscle fibers and the needle electrodes inserted into them. Such recordings lack the characteristic muscle-spike potential that is seen in active electromyograms, are the result of experimental artifacts, and in fact may often be a bothersome nuisance.

Whereas most normal laryngeal functions may be accounted for quite easily by the myoelastic-aerodynamic theory, very little conclusive evidence may be found to support the neurochronaxic theory of vocal fold vibration. Many experimenters have had little difficulty in rejecting the neurochronaxic theory in favor of the myoelastic-aerodynamic theory. However, there is no evidence that a crucial test of either theory has yet been performed.

Cavity-Tone Theory

Vocal tones and the way they are generated seem to have occupied men's minds for hundreds of years. One of the earliest major publications on the topic of vowel tones was by Willis (1830). Willis mentioned Friar Bacon as one of the first to attempt to create vowel sounds by artificial means. Friar Bacon lived during the latter part of the thirteenth and early part of the fourteenth centuries. Albertus Magnus, who published in 1651, was also credited by Willis as being an early experimenter in the development of artificial speech sounds. Shortly after the founding of the French Academy of Science, Abbe Mical is said to have produced several "talking machines," and he presented them to the Academy in 1783. Not much is known about the details of the machines except that they were in the shape of enormous heads. According to Willis, Mical destroyed the machines when the government refused to grant him a reward. Having left no record of the workings of the machines, we do not know how they were constructed. Willis credited Kranzenstein (1770) with one of the earlier attempts to produce vowel sounds by scientific means. Kranzenstein's attempts were limited to the production of the vowels *a, e, o, u, i* by means of a reed of a novel and ingenious construction connected to various pipes, some of them of a most grotesque and complicated figure. No reason was given for the unique shape of the pipes, save that experience had shown these forms to be the best adapted for the production of the sounds in question.

In 1791, Kempelen attempted to produce speech sounds by techniques very reminiscent of those of Mical. He constructed a device for the production of speech sounds, based on a system that made use of a wind supply, a reed, a resonator, and a cover. His artificial vowel machine formed the basis for a more refined version that Willis was to use in his experiments forty years later. Kempelen considered the production of the vowel to be a function of the manipulation and modification of the voice by the lips and tongue. His view might best be summarized by saying that the vowels are formed by the vocal organ, modified, but not interrupted, by the varied positions of the tongue and lips. The differences between the various vowels depend upon the proportions between the aperture of the lips and the internal cavity of the mouth, which is altered by the different elevations and positions of the tongue.

By closely following the design of the experimental work by Kempelen, Willis conducted a series of experiments with cavity resonators in order to determine the responsible agents for the production of vowel sounds. Willis thought the apparatus of Kempelen was faulty in design and, on the basis of his own theory, constructed a series of resonating cavities that were coupled to a vibrating-reed sound source. The diameter of the resonating tubes was constant, but the length was made variable by a series of extension tubes. Willis concluded that the vowel was a cavity tone, the form of which was dependent upon the length of the resonating tube. He further supposed that the cavity tone had no relationship to the composition of the reed tone or to the fundamental frequency of the vibrating-reed sound source. Willis presented his theory to the French Academy of Science in 1829. The theory of Willis is now considered to be the original "cavity-tone" theory of vowel production, although it may be referred to variously as the puff, inharmonic, or transient theory. The basis of the theory was that the sound identified as a vowel was dependent only upon the length of the resonating tube and that the vowel tone was completely independent of the reed tone. In his experimentation he discovered that the vowels were heard in the following order as the length of the resonating tube was increased: *i, e, a, o,* and *u*. As the length of the tube reached multiples of the length of the wave of the reed tone, the pattern was repeated, but in reverse order. Willis felt that the larynx functioned simply to provide puffs of air that might excite the supraglottal resonating cavities.

Harmonic Theory

In 1837, Charles Wheatstone attempted to replicate the experiments of Willis and concluded that the theory, while not incorrect, was not the real answer to the question of vowel production. Wheatstone noted that the reed tone was not simple, but rather complex, containing many harmonics of the fundamental frequency. He supposed that the vowel heard was the result of an augmentation of certain of the harmonic components of the reed tone. Because of this relationship the theory advanced by Wheatstone is called the "harmonic theory." It is also known as the overtone, or steady-state theory. According to Wheatstone, the larynx functioned to generate a complex tone that would be acted upon by the supraglottal cavities.

It is evident that in either theory the vowel quality is dependent upon the natural frequencies (resonant frequencies) and the damping of the vocal tract.

In the years to follow, scientists were divided into two camps, one advocating the harmonic and the other advocating the inharmonic theory.

In 1862, Helmholtz, a brilliant German scholar, repeated the experiments of Wheatstone and conducted several other experiments of a similar nature and, on the basis of his evidence, concluded that Wheatstone had the right idea of the production of vowel sounds but that he had not carried the experiments to the appropriate conclusions. Helmholtz noted that the cavities of resonance acted upon all of the reed tone's harmonics that coincided or even closely approximated their natural frequencies. With the aid of a resonating device, since called a "Helmholtz resonator," he claimed to have been able to hear the various strong frequencies within the complex structure of the vowel tone. He also studied the structure of the inner ear and on the basis of his observations advanced what is now referred to as the "resonance theory of hearing." Although the vowel theory of Helmholtz was only a refinement of that proposed earlier by Wheatstone, he is sometimes given credit for originating the harmonic theory of vowel production. It seems, however, that Helmholtz was not a particular advocate of either theory, because he concluded that the two theories were different only in point of view and were simply different methods of representing the same mechanisms.

In 1890, Hermann attempted to reinforce the conclusions arrived at by Willis. He illustrated the improbability of the harmonic theory on the basis of the overtone structure of a sound sung at G_{-1} (49 cps on the International scale), in which the frequency characteristics of a vowel were comparable to the twenty-eighth harmonic of the fundamental tone. According to Hermann, such a harmonic in a tone would be too feeble to be heard, even if reinforced by a cavity resonator. He failed to find any necessary relationship between the structure of a complex tone and the structure of the vowel tone and concluded that the two tones were independent, one from the other. Hermann called the regions of prominent energy in vowels "formant bands," a term that has persisted ever since.

In 1896, Rayliegh and Trendelenburg made extensive analyses of vowel sounds and on the basis of their observations concluded that the controversy between the two theories need not be unreconcilable. These men felt that both the harmonic and inharmonic theories had points of merit and that both could be considered as contributors without causing confusion.

In 1904, however, Scripture, on the basis of a very thorough review of the various experiments conducted on vowel production, claimed that the evidence was overwhelmingly in favor of the cavity-tone theory advanced by Willis and those who supported him. Scripture concluded on the basis of his own experiments that the vowel is not a function of the overtone structure of the reed tone, but rather a function of the natural resonance of the head cavities.

In 1929, Fletcher reinforced the notion that the two theories have merit. He stated:

> The difference in the two theories is not, as some suppose, a difference in the conception of what is going on while the vowel sounds are being produced, but in the method of representing or describing the motions in definite physical terms.[1]

Fletcher pointed out that the inharmonic theory enables one to visualize in a more direct way what is taking place and is of value to the phonetician interested in the mechanism of speech production. The harmonic theory, on the other hand, is of use to the engineer who is interested in separating speech into its component frequencies.

In this text we are concerned with the mechanism of speech production, and, having provided the mechanism with an air stream and vibrating larynx, we might turn to the structures responsible for modifying the laryngeal tone and for adding additional speech sounds. These structures are referred to as the articulators.

---

[1] H. Fletcher, *Speech and Hearing* (Princeton, N.J.: D. Van Nostrand Co., Inc., 1929).

SELECTIVE READING LIST

Aikin, W. A., "The Separate Functions of Different Parts of the Rima Glottidis," *Journal of Anatomy and Physiology*, XVI, 1902, 253–56.

Babington, Benjamin, "Proceedings of the Humanitarian Society," *London Medical Gazette*, X, 1829, 555.

Behringer, S., "Die Anordnung der Muskultur in der menschlichen Stimmlippe und im Gebiet des Connus elasticus," *Zeitschrift für Anatomie und Entwicklungsgeschichte*, CXVIII, 1955, 324–42.

Benedict, A. L., "Transillumination," *Medical Record*, LXXX, 1911, 1277–78.

Berg, Jw. van den, "Direct and Indirect Determination of the Mean Subglottic Pressure," *Folia Phoniatrica*, VIII, 1956, 1–24.

———, "On the Role of the Laryngeal Ventricle in Voice Production," *Folia Phoniatrica*, VII, 1955, 57–69.

———, "Subglottic Pressures and Vibrations of Vocal Folds," *Folia Phoniatrica*, IX, 1957, 65–71.

———, and J. Moll, "Zur Anatomie des menschlichen Musculus vocalis," *Zeitschrift für Anatomie und Entwicklungsgeschichte*, CXVIII, 1955, 465–70.

Brodnitz, F. S., *Vocal Rehabilitation*. Rochester, Minnesota: Whiting Press, Inc., 1959.

Buchthal, F. and K. Faaborg-Anderson, "Electromyography of Laryngeal and Respiratory Muscles: Correlation with Phonation and Respiration," *Annals of Otology, Rhinology and Laryngology*, LXXIII, 1964, 118.

Charron, R., "An Instrumental Study of the Mechanisms of Vocal Intensity." Unpublished Master's thesis, University of Illinois, 1965.

Chevroton, L. and F. Vles, "Cinematographie des Cordes Vocales et de Leurs Annexes Laryngienne," *Comptes Rendus Academie Science*, CLVI, 1913, 949–52.

Clerf, Louis, "Photography of the Larynx," *Annals of Otology, Rhinology and Laryngology*, XXXIV, 1925, 101–21.

Curry, R., *The Mechanism of the Human Voice*. New York: David McKay Co., Inc., 1940.

Curry, S. S., *Mind and Voice*. Boston: Expression Company, 1910.

Czermak, Johann, "Application de la Photographie à la Laryngoscopie et à la Rhinoscopie," *Comptes Rendus Academie Science*, 1861.

———, "Bemurkungen zur Lehr von Mechanismus des Larynx Verschlusses," *Wien Medizinische Wochenschrift*, X, 1860, 745–47.

———, *Der Kehlkopfspiegel*, Leipzig: Englemann, 1860.

Dodart, M., "Supplément au Mémoire sur la Voix et les Tons," *Mémoires de l'Academie Royale des Sciences*, 1707, 73.

———, "Sur les Causes de la Voix de l'Homme, et de ses Differens Tons," *Mémoires de l'Academie Royale des Sciences*, 1700, 256–66.

Dunker, E. and B. Schlosshauer, "Klinische und experimentelle studien über Stimmlippenschwingungen," *Archiv für Ohren-Nasen und Kehlkopfheilkunde*, CLXXII, 1958, 363.

Ewald, J. R., "Die physiologie des Kehlkopfes und der Luftrohre," in *Handbuch der Laryngologie und Rhinologie*, ed. Paul Heymann, Vienna, 1898.

Fairbanks, G., "An Acoustical Study of the Pitch of Infant Hunger Wails," *Child Development*, XIII, 1942, 227–32.

———, *Voice and Articulation Drillbook*, 2nd ed. New York: Harper and Row, Publishers, 1959.

———, E. L. Herbert, and J. M. Hammond, "An Acoustical Study of Vocal Pitch in Seven- and Eight-year-old Girls," *Child Development*, XX, 1949, 71–78.

———, J. H. Wiley, and F. M. Lassman, "An Acoustical Study of Vocal Pitch in Seven- and Eight-year-old Boys," *Child Development*, XX, 1949, 63-69.

Farnsworth, D. W., "High-Speed Motion Pictures of the Human Vocal Cords," *Bell Laboratories Records*, XVIII, 1940, 203–08.

Ferrein, A., "De la Formation de la Voix de l'Homme," *Histoire de l'academie royale des sciences de Paris*, Tome 51, 1741, 409.

Fessard, A. and B. Vallancien "Données Electrophysiologiques sur le Fonctionnement de l'Appareil Phonatoire du Chien," *Folia Phoniatrica*, IX, 1957, 152–63.

Fletcher, H., *Speech and Hearing*. Princeton, N.J.: D. Van Nostrand Co., Inc., 1929.

——, *Speech and Hearing in Communication*. Princeton, N.J.: D. Van Nostrand Co., Inc., 1953.

Fletcher, W. W., "A High-speed Motion Picture Study of Vocal Fold Action in Certain Voice Qualities." Master's thesis, University of Washington, 1947.

——, "A Study of Internal Laryngeal Activity in Relation to Vocal Intensity." Doctor's thesis, Northwestern University, 1950.

French, Thomas R., "On a Perfected Method of Photographing the Larynx," *New York Medical Journal*, 1884, 653.

——, "The Laryngeal Image Photographed During the Production of Tones in the Singing Voice," *Transactions of the American Laryngological Association*. VIII, 1886, 107.

Freudenthal, Wolff, "On Transillumination of the Larynx and of the Sinus Maxillaris, with Special Reference to Voltolini's Work," *American Journal of Medicine*, XXIII, 1917, 511–13.

Garcia, Manuel, "Observations on the Human Voice," *London, Edinborough and Dublin Philosophical Magazine and Journal of Science*, X, 1855, 511–13.

Garel, J., "Nouvel Appareil Perfectionné pour la Photographie Stéréoscopique du Larynx sur le Vivant," *Review de Laryngologie*, XL, 1919, 249.

Görttler, K., "Die Anordnung, Histologie, und Histogenese der quergestrieften Muskulatur im menschlichen Stimmband," *Zeitschrift für Anatomie*, CXV, 1951, 352–401.

Gottstein, J., "Die Durchleutung des Kehlkopfs," *Deutsche Medizinishe Wochenschrift*, XV, Oct., 1889, 140–41.

Gray, G. W., "An Experimental Study of the Vibrato in Speech," *Quarterly Journal of Speech Education*, XII, 1926, 296–333.

Greene, M. C. L., *The Voice and its Disorders*. New York: The Macmillan Company, 1957.

Grutzner, P., "Physiologie der Stimme und Sprache," *Handbuch der Physiologie*, I, Berlin, 1879.

Hegener, J. and G. Panconcelli-Calzia, "Eine einfache Kinematographie und die Strobokinematographie der Stimmlippenbewegungen beim lebenden," *Vox*, XXIII, 1913, 81–82.

Helmholtz, H., von, *On the Sensations of Tone*, trans. A.J. Ellis. New York: David McKay Co., Inc., 1912.

Hermann, J., "Phonophotographische Untersuchungen," *Pflüger's Archiv für die Geschichte Physiologie*, LXXIV, 1890, 380.

Hollien, H., "Laryngeal Research by Means of Laminography," *Archives of Otolaryngology*, LXXX, 1964, 303–08.

——, "Some Laryngeal Correlates of Vocal Pitch," *Journal of Speech and Hearing Research*, III, 1930, 52–58.

—— and J. Curtis, "Elevation and Tilting of Vocal Folds as a Function of Vocal Pitch," *Folia Phoniatrica*, XIV, 1962, 23–36.

—— and J. Curtis, "A Laminagraphic Study of Vocal Pitch," *Journal of Speech and Hearing Research*, III, 1960, 361–71.

—— and P. Moore, "Measurements of the Vocal Folds During Changes in Pitch," *Journal of Speech and Hearing Research*, III, 1960, 157–165.

Husson, R., "Étude des Phénomèmes Physiologiques et Acoustiques Fondamentaux de la voix chantée," Thesis, Paris, 1950.

Isshiki, N., "Regulatory Mechanism of the Pitch and Volume of Voice," *Otorhinolaryngology Clinic*, Kyoto, LII, 1959, 1065.

————, "Regulatory Mechanism of Vocal Intensity Variation," *Journal of Speech and Hearing Research*, VII, 1964, 17–30.

Judson, L. S. and A. T. Weaver, *Voice Science*, 2nd ed. New York: Appleton-Century-Crofts, 1965.

Kempelen, W., von, *Mechanismus der menschlichen Sprache*. Wien: 1791.

Kwalwasser, J., "The Vibrato," *Psychological Monographs*, XXXVI, 1926, 84–108.

Ladefoged, P., "The Regulation of Sub-glottal Pressure," *Folia Phoniatrica*, XII, 1960, 169–175.

———— and N. McKinney, "Loudness, Sound Pressure, and Subglottal Pressure in Speech," *Journal of the Acoustical Society of America*, XXXV, 1963, 454–60.

Leden, H., von., "The Mechanism of Phonation," *Archives of Otolaryngology*. LXXIV, 1961, 660–76.

Lennox-Browne, "On Photography of the Larynx and Soft Palate," *British Medical Journal*, II, 1883, 811–14.

Liskovius, K. F., *Physiologie der menschlichen Stimme*. Leipzig: 1846.

Luchsinger, V. R. and C. Dubois, "Phonetische und Stroboskopische Untersuchungen an einem Stimmphenomen," *Folia Phoniatrica*, VIII, 1956, 201–10.

Magendie, F., *An Elementary Compendium of Physiology*, trans. E. Milligan. Philadelphia: 1824.

Mason, R. M., "A Study of the Physiological Mechanisms of Vocal Vibrato," Doctor's thesis, University of Illinois, 1965.

Merkel, C. L., *Der Kehlkopf*. Leipzig: 1873.

Metfessel, M., "The Vibrato in Artistic Voices," *University of Iowa Studies in the Psychology of Music*, I, 1932, 14–117.

Moore, P., "A Short History of Laryngeal Investigation," *Quarterly Journal of Speech*, XXIII, 1937, 531–54.

————, "Motion Picture Studies of the Vocal Folds and Vocal Attach," *Journal of Speech Disorders*, III, 1938, 235–38.

———— and H. von Leden, "Dynamic Variations of the Vibratory Pattern in the Normal Larynx," *Folia Phoniatrica*, X, 1958, 205–38.

Mörner, M., F. Fransson, and G. Fant, "Voice Registers," *Speech Transmission Laboratory, Quarterly Progress and Status Report*, IV, 1964, 18–20.

Moser, H. M., "Symposium on Unique Cases of Speech Disorders: Presentation of a Case," *Journal of Speech Disorders*, VII, 1942, 102–114.

Moulonguet, A., P. Laget, and R. Husson," Démonstration, chez l'homme, de l'existence dans le nerf récurrent de potentiels d'action moteurs synchrones avec les vibrations des cordes vocalles," *Bulletin de l'Academie Nationale Medicine*, CXXXVII, 1953, 475–82.

Mysak, E. D., "Pitch and Duration Characteristics of Older Males," *Journal of Speech and Hearing Research*, II, 1959, 46–54.

Nadoleczny, Max, *Untersuchungen über den Kunstgesang*. Berlin: Springer, 1923.

Nauck, E., *Morphologisches Jahrbuch*, LXXXVII, 1942, 536.

Negus, V. E., *The Mechanism of the Larynx*. St. Louis: C. V. Mosby Co., 1929.

————, *The Comparative Anatomy and Physiology of the Larynx*. New York: Grune and Stratton, Inc., 1949.

————, "The Mechanism of the Larynx," *Laryngoscope*, LXVII, 1957, 961–86.

Oertel, M., "Uber eine neue Laryngostroboskipische Untersuchungsmethode," *Zentralbl. f.d. med. Wissensch*. XVI, 1878, 81–82.

Paget, R., *Human Speech*. New York: Harcourt, Brace and World, Inc., 1930.

————, "Artificial Vowels," *Proc. Roy. Soc. A.*, CII, 1923, 755.

Piquet, J. and G. Decroix, "Les Vibrations des Cordes Vocales," *Annals of Otology, Rhinology, and Laryngology*, LXIV, 1957, 337–40.

————, G. Decroix, C. Libersa, and J. Dujardin, "Die Stimmlippenschwingungen. Experimentelle Studien," *Archiv für Ohren-Nasen-Kehlkopfheilkunde*, CLXIX, 1956, 297.

————, G. Decroix, C. Libersa, and J. Dujardin, "Etude Experimentale Peroperatoire, chez l'Homme, des Vibrations des Cordes Vocales sans Courant d'Air Sousglottique," *Revue de Laryngologie*, LXXVIII, 1957, 510–14.

Portmann, G., R. Humbert, J. Robin, P. Laget, and R. Husson, "Etude Electromyographique des Cordes Vocales chez l'Homme," *Comptes rend., Soc. Biol.*, CXLIX, 1955, 296–300.

Pressman, Joel, "Physiology of the Vocal Cords in Phonation and Respiration," *Archives of Otolaryngology*, XXXV, 1942, 355–98.

———— and G. Kelemen, "Physiology of the Larynx," *Physiological Reviews*, XXXV, 1955, 506–54.

Pronovost, W., "An Experimental Study of Methods for Determining Natural and Habitual Pitch," *Speech Monographs*, IX, 1942, 111–23.

Ptacek, P. H. and E. K. Sander, "Breathiness and Phonation Length," *Journal of Speech and Hearing Disorders*, XXVIII, 1963, 267–72.

————, "Maximum Duration of Phonation," *Journal of Speech and Hearing Disorders*, XXVIII, 1963, 171–82.

Rubin, H. J., "The Neurochronaxic Theory of Voice Production: A Refutation," *AMA Archives of Otolaryngology*, LXXI, 1960, 913–20.

————, "Vocal Pitch and Intensity," *Laryngoscope*, LXXIII, 1963, 973–1015.

Russell, G. O., *Speech and Voice.* New York: The Macmillan Company, 1931.

———— and C. H. Tuttle, "Some Experiments in Motion Photography of the Vocal Cords," *Journal of the Society of Motion Picture Engineers*, XV, 1930, 171–80.

Schoen, M., "The Pitch Factor in Artistic Singing," *Psychological Monographs*, XXXI, 1922, 230–59.

Scripture, E. W., *Elements of Experimental Phonetics.* New York: Charles Scribner's Sons, 1904.

Seashore, C., "Measurements on the Expression of Emotion in Music," *Proceedings of the National Academy of Science*, 1923, 323–25.

Smith, S., "Remarks on the Physiology of the Vibration of the Vocal Cords," *Folia Phoniatrica*, VI, 1954, 166–78.

Sonninen, A., "The Role of the External Laryngeal Muscles in Length-adjustment of the Vocal Cords in Singing," *Acta Oto-Laryngologica Supplementum* CXXX, 1956.

———— and E. Vaheri, "A Case of Voice Disorder Due to Laryngeal Asymmetry and Treated by Surgical Medioposition of the Vocal Cords," *Folia Phoniatrica*, X, 1958, 193–99.

Stevens, K., "Acoustical Aspects of Speech Production," Chap. 9, *Handbook of Physiology, Section 3, Respiration*, eds. W. Fenn and O. Rahn. Baltimore: The Williams and Wilkins Co., 1965.

Stoker, G., "The Voice as a Stringed Instrument," *British Medical Journal*, I, 1886, 641–42.

Tiffin, J., "The Role of Pitch and Intensity in the Vocal Vibrato of Students and Artists," *University of Iowa Studies in the Psychology of Music*, I, 1932, 134–65.

———— and M. Metfessel, "Use of the Neon Lamp in Phonophotography," *American Journal of Psychology*, XLII, 1930, 638–39.

———— and H. Seashore, "Summary of the Established Facts in Experimental Studies in the Vibrato up to 1932," *University of Iowa Studies in the Psychology of Music*, I, 1932, 344–76.

Timcke, R., H. von Leden, and P. Moore, "Laryngeal Vibrations: Measurements of the Glottic Wave. Part I, The Normal Vibratory Cycle," *Archives of Otolaryngology*, LXVIII, 1958, 1–19.

Timcke, R., H. von Leden, and P. Moore, "Laryngeal Vibrations: Measurements of the Glottic Wave. Part II, Physiologic Variations," *Archives of Otolaryngology*, LXIX, 1959, 438–44.

Tonndorf, W., "Die mechanik bei Stimmlippenschwingungen und beim Schnarchen," *Zeitschrift für Hals-Nasen und Ohrenheilkunde*, XII, 1925, 241–45.

Töpler, A., "Das princip der Stroboskopischen scheiben," *Annals d. Physik*, CXXVIII, 1866, 108–25.

Travis, E. W., R. G. Bender, and A. R. Buchanan, "Research Contributions to Vowel Theory," *Speech Monographs*, I, 1934, 65–71.

Voltolini, Rudolph, *Die Krankheiten der Nase*. Breslau: E. Morgenstern, 1888.

Warden, Adam, "New Application of the Reflecting Prism," *London Medical Gazette*, II, 1844, 256.

Warren, N., "Vocal Cord Activity and Vowel Theory," *Quarterly Journal of Speech*, 1936, 651–55.

Wendahl, R. W., Laryngeal Analog Synthesis of Harsh Voice Quality," *Folia Phoniatrica*, XV, 1963, 241–50.

Wheatstone, C., *Westminister Review*, 1837, 27.

Willis, W., "On Vowel Sounds, and on Reed-organ Pipes," *Transactions of the Cambridge Philosophical Society*, III, 1830, 231.

Woods, R. H., "Law of Transverse Vibrations of Strings Applied to the Human Larynx," *Journal of Anatomy and Physiology*, XXVII, 1892–93, 431–35.

Wright, J., "The Nose and Throat in Medical History," *Laryngoscope*, XII, 1902, 271–72.

Wullstein, Horst, "Der Bewegungsvorgang und den Stimmlippen während der Stimmgebung," *Archiv für Ohren-Nasen-und Kehlkopfheilkunde*, CXLII, 1936, 124.

Zaliouk, A. and I. Izkovitch, "Some Tomographic Aspects in Functional Voice Disorders," *Folia Phoniatrica*, X, 1958, 34–40.

Zemlin, W. R., "A Comparison of a High Speed Cinematographic and a Transillumination Photo-conductive Technique in the Study of the Glottis During Voice Production," unpublished Master's thesis, University of Minnesota, 1959.

———, "A Comparison of the Periodic Function of Vocal Fold Vibration in a Multiple Sclerosis and a Normal Population," unpublished Doctor's thesis, University of Minnesota, 1962.

5

The Articulators

INTRODUCTION

Resonance

THE BONES OF THE SKULL

Introduction

Bones of the facial skeleton

The Mandible
The Maxillae
The Nasal Bones
The Palatine Bones
The Lacrimal Bones
The Zygomatic Bones
The Inferior Nasal Conchae (Inferior Turbinated Bones)
The Vomer Bone

Bones of the cranium

The Ethmoid Bone
The Frontal Bone
The Parietal Bones
The Occipital Bone
The Temporal Bones
The Sphenoid Bone

THE SINUSES

Introduction

The frontal sinuses
The maxillary sinuses
The ethmoid sinuses or air cells
The mastoid air cells

Functions of the Sinuses

THE CAVITIES OF THE VOCAL TRACT

Introduction

The buccal cavity
The oral cavity
The fauces
The pharyngeal cavity

The Nasopharynx
The Oropharynx
The Laryngopharynx

The nasal cavities

THE ARTICULATORS AND ASSOCIATED STRUCTURES

The Mouth

Introduction
The lips
The cheeks (buccae)

Muscles of the Face and Mouth

Introduction
The orbicularis oris muscle
The transverse facial muscles

The Buccinator (Bugler's) Muscle
The Risorius Muscle

The angular facial muscles

The Quadratus Labii Superior Muscle
The Zygomatic Muscle
The Quadratus Labii Inferior Muscle

225

The mandibular elevators

The Masseter Muscle
The Temporalis Muscle
The Internal Pterygoid Muscle

The Palate

Introduction
The hard palate
The palatal vault
The soft palate

The Levator Palatine Muscle
The Tensor Palatine Muscle
The Uvular Muscle
The Glossopalatine (Palatoglossus) Muscle
The Pharyngopalatine (Palatopharyngeus) Muscle

The tonsils

The Pharynx

The nasopharynx
The oropharynx
The laryngopharynx
The muscles of the pharynx

The Inferior Constrictor Muscle
The Middle Constrictor Muscle
The Superior Constrictor Muscle
The Stylopharyngeal Muscle
The Salpingopharyngeal Muscle

Passavant's pad and velopharyngeal closure

DEVELOPMENT AND GROWTH OF THE FACIAL REGION

Introduction and Early Embryonic Development
Development of the Facial Region and Palate
Development of the Primary and Secondary Palates
Postnatal Growth of the Head

SELECTIVE READING LIST

227

INTRODUCTION

Thus far in our account of the speech mechanism, we have described the power source and the vibrating elements. The power source, which consists of the lungs and associated skeletal and muscular structures, provides energy in the form of an inaudible steady stream of air. The vibrating vocal folds convert this steady breath stream into a rapid series of puffs. If it were somehow possible to isolate the larynx from the vocal tract, the output of the larynx would consist simply of an unintelligible buzz that varied in frequency as the vocal folds vibrated at different rates. An acoustic analysis of the characteristics of the laryngeal buzz would reveal that it was composed not of a single component, but rather of a vast number of components that were, for the most part, multiples of the rate of vocal-fold vibration. Thus, with the vocal folds vibrating at a rate of 100 times per second, the composition of the laryngeal buzz would include a 100-cycle-per-second component and components that were integral multiples of 100. That is, 100, 200, 300, 400. . . cycle-per-second components would be found in the tone. We call this a complex tone. The laryngeal tone, in all its complexity, is the raw material of which speech is mostly made.

The laryngeal buzz carries very little meaning, and in order to produce speech as we know it, the character of the laryngeal tone must be modified by the structures that lie between the vocal folds and the mouth opening. To a large extent, modifications of the laryngeal buzz can be accounted for by the principle of resonance and its antithesis, damping.

Resonance

Almost all matter, under appropriate conditions, will, when energized by an outside force, vibrate at its own natural frequency. We have seen how the frequency of the vibrating vocal folds, energized by an air stream, is a direct function of tension and an inverse function of mass. A swing in the back yard or the limbs on a tree, when driven by gusts of wind, will tend to swing at a rate that is most appropriate. It is a common experience to anyone who has had the pleasure of sitting on a swing that no matter how hard the effort, no matter how hard one "pumps" the rate or frequency of each successive round trip remains the same. The extent of the excursion of the swing may vary with effort, but not the rate! The swing has a "natural period, or frequency," and it takes an unreasonable amount of effort to cause it to travel at an "unnatural period"; that is, we would have to force it into vibration. The term for such vibration is "forced vibration." If the outside force is removed from a system vibrating at its natural frequency, it will continue to vibrate for some considerable length of time. The damping forces are slight. The vibrations of something vibrating at an unnatural frequency, or executing forced vibration, will, when the outside driving force is removed, cease quite abruptly. Such a system is said to be highly damped.

The tines of a tuning fork vibrate with maximum force and for a maximum length of time at their natural frequency, and at no other. Thus, if the natural period of a tuning fork is 200 cps and if it is driven by a vibratory force that contains 100, 200, 300, 400, and 500 cps components (a complex tone, that is), the fork will vibrate at the 200 cps rate, even if the 200 cps component is not the most intense in the series. The tuning fork absorbs the energy of the 200 cps component, and we say it resonates to 200 cps. By the same token, anything that absorbs energy at a specific frequency radiates energy best at that same frequency. Vibrating systems always resonate at their natural frequencies when they can! They do not absorb energy well at frequencies other than their natural frequencies.

Air columns also have their own natural frequencies, just like swings and trees. This is probably best exemplified in the pipes of an organ or, better yet, in the vocal tract of a speech mechanism. A simple experiment will demonstrate how an air column may be set into vibration.

Almost everyone has blown across the top of a narrow-necked bottle to produce a deep, mellow tone, called an edge tone. No matter how intense the air stream (within certain limits) the bottle resonates at just one frequency. The air particles in the bottle may vibrate with greater excursions due to increased breath force, but they vibrate no faster. In other words, the sound may become louder, but never higher in pitch. The vibrating air column has a natural frequency, or to put it another way, the bottle will resonate at a specific frequency. If water is added, however, the air column is shortened and the resonant frequency increases. Thus, the resonant frequencies of vibrating air columns may be manipulated by modifying the size and configuration of the cavities.

An edge tone is one way to set an air column into vibration, but there are other ways. If a bottle (the same one as in the previous experiment) is held an inch or so from the lips and a puff of air is released into it (call them bilabial puffs, for want of a better term), a short-duration note is emitted from the mouth of the bottle. The pitch of the note, although it is of short duration, is the same as when the air column is set into vibration by means of an edge tone. Adding water to the bottle raises the pitch, just as in the previous experiment. If we could now place our bottle over the isolated vibrating vocal folds mentioned earlier, we should not be surprised to find that the air column in the bottle is set into vibration at the same rate as before, and not at the vibratory rate of the vocal folds. The implication, of course, is that although the vocal folds may vibrate and release puffs of air at some particular frequency, the rate of vibration of the air column in the bottle is determined solely by its length and configuration. The resonating cavity in the bottle absorbs energy, contained in the puffs of air, only at the natural frequency of the bottle, and that is a most important point to remember.

An even more important point, however, is that the air column is set into vibration for a short duration with each discrete puff of air that is emitted by the vocal folds. The rate at which the air column is driven into vibration determines the pitch, while the frequency or frequencies at which the air column resonates determines the quality of the tone. This is the reason, for example, that the speech mechanism is capable of producing a given vowel quality over the entire pitch range while a static vocal-cavity configuration is maintained.

The part of the speech mechanism above the vocal folds is called the vocal tract and is composed of the pharyngeal, nasal, and mouth cavities. Adjustments of the shape and acoustical properties of the vocal tract are known as articulation, and the structures which mediate the adjustments are called articulators. The articulators may also generate speech sounds. When the air stream passes through a constriction somewhere along the vocal tract, friction causes the air to become turbulent, and noise called fricative noise is generated. This is the sort of thing we do when we admonish someone to be quiet by producing a "sh-sh-sh-sh" sound. Other speech sounds may be generated by blocking the outward flow of air through the vocal tract. In order to accomplish this, articulators such as the lips and tongue function as valves to block the vocal tract, and the sudden release of a valve produces an audible puff of air. Sounds generated by such manipulations are called "stops," examples of which are the [p] and [t] sounds. It is important to keep in mind that fricatives and stops may be generated rather independently of vocal-fold vibration. If the vocal folds are active while plosives or fricatives are being generated, the resultant acoustic product consists of a noise superimposed upon the vocal tone. Speech elements that are produced with vocal-fold vibration are referred to appropriately as voiced sounds, while those that are produced without vocal-fold vibration are known as unvoiced sounds. Thus, fricatives and plosives (which fall into the broad classification of consonants) may be voiced, as in [ð], or unvoiced, as in [θ], while vowels are always voiced.

The purpose of this chapter is to describe the articulatory mechanism and to relate the articulatory structures to speech production. As is the case with both the breathing and laryngeal mechanisms, the articulatory mechanism consists of a supportive framework and a muscular system. The supportive framework consists primarily of the facial skeleton and the lower jaw or mandible.

THE BONES OF THE SKULL

Introduction

The skull is composed of almost two dozen irregularly shaped bones that, excepting the lower jaw, are rigidly joined together. It is usually considered in two major parts: (1) the cranium, which houses and protects the brain, and (2) the facial skeleton, which forms the framework for much of the articulatory mechanism. The division of the skull bones into facial and cranial skeletons is as follows:

Bones of the Facial Skeleton		Bones of the Cranial Skeleton	
Mandible	1	Ethmoid bone	1
Maxillae	2	Frontal bone	1
Nasal bones	2	Parietal bones	2
Palatine bones	2	Occipital bone	1
Lacrimal bones	2	Temporal bones	2
Zygomatic bones	2	Sphenoid bone	1
Inferior conchae	2		
Vomer	1		
Total	14	Total	8

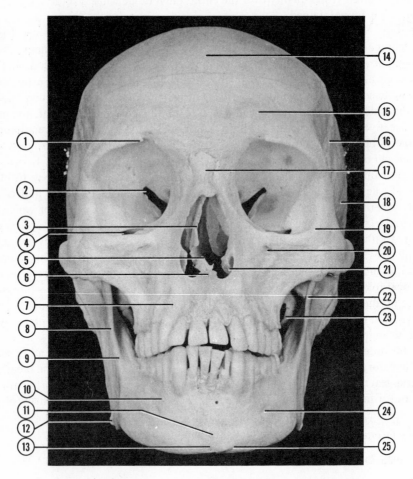

1. Supra-orbital margin
2. Superior orbital fissure
3. Bony septum (ethmoid)
4. Inferior orbital fissure
5. Bony septum (vomer)
6. Anterior nasal spine
7. Canine eminence
8. Ramus of mandible
9. Oblique line
10. Corpus of mandible
11. Mental protuberance
12. Angle of mandible
13. Mental symphysis
14. Frontal bone
15. Superciliary ridge
16. Sphenoid bone (greater wing)
17. Nasal bone
18. Temporal bone
19. Zygomatic bone
20. Infra-orbital foramen
21. Inferior nasal concha
22. Coronoid process of mandible
23. Styloid process of temporal bone
24. Mental foramen
25. Mental tubercle

Fig. 5–1. The skull as seen from the front.

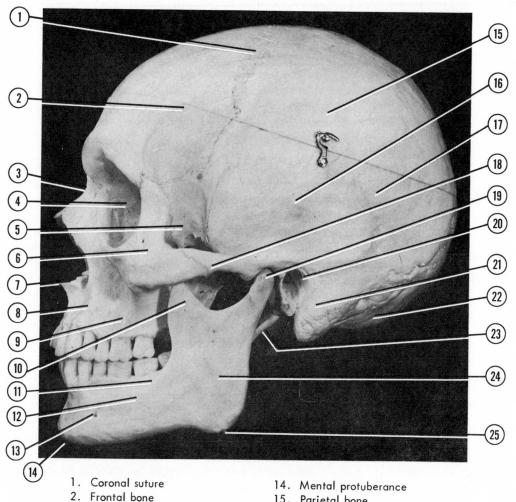

1. Coronal suture
2. Frontal bone
3. Nasal bone
4. Lacrimal bone
5. Sphenoid bone (greater wing)
6. Zygomatic bone
7. Anterior nasal spine
8. Canine eminence
9. Maxillary bone
10. Coronoid process
11. Oblique line
12. Mandible (corpus)
13. Mental foramen
14. Mental protuberance
15. Parietal bone
16. Temporal bone
17. Squamosal suture
18. Zygomatic arch
19. Condyloid process of mandible
20. External auditory meatus
21. Mastoid process of temporal bone
22. Occipital bone
23. Styloid process of temporal bone
24. Ramus of mandible
25. Angle of mandible

Fig. 5–2. The skull as seen from the side.

We shall be concerned primarily with the facial skeleton, which will be discussed at some length. A less detailed description of the cranium will suffice. Various views of an articulated skull are shown in Figures 5–1, 5–2, and 5–3.

A word of encouragement: At first glance the skull may seem unreasonably complex, and it is not unusual for a student to become hopelessly lost and confused during the first exposure. And therein lies the secret to understanding the amazing architecture of the bones of the skull. That is, it will take two, three, or perhaps more exposures before an integrated picture begins to emerge. Although words and pictures are valuable in themselves, nothing is quite so useful as an actual skull to study. With a skull at hand (or preferably in hand), the following pages will simply point the way for study, and that is best. One additional hint: It is very often useful to learn the general shape, the processes, and finally the worthwhile landmarks of a bone before attempting to learn its articulations with other bones.

Bones of the facial skeleton

The Mandible.   The adult mandible, shown in Figure 5–4, is usually regarded as a single bone. At birth, however, its mirrored halves are joined by a fibrous symphysis, which usually ossifies during the first year of life, and only then can the mandible be considered a single bone. When viewed from beneath, as in Figure 5–4A, the mandible appears to be U shaped. That portion making up the arch is called the body or corpus, and the point where the two halves are joined is called the mental symphysis. When the mandible is viewed from in front, as in Figure 5–4B, the mental symphysis appears as a vertically directed mid-line ridge that bifurcates near the lower border to form a triangular projection called the mental protuberance (point of the chin). It is usually depressed somewhat in the center, thus giving rise to two anterior projections called mental tubercles. The inner surface of the mandible, near the symphysis, presents two small posteriorly directed ridges, one placed just above the other. These ridges, called mental spines, vary considerably from specimen to specimen, to the extent that some simply appear rough or irregular while others appear as obvious ridges. The mental spines are shown in Figure 5–4C.

The upper surface of a tooth-bearing mandible is called the alveolar process. It is hollowed into numerous cavities (alveoli) for the reception of teeth.

The arch of the mandible is continued in a posterior and somewhat lateral direction until it joins the mandibular ramus, at which point the two halves of the jaw have become widely separated. When viewed from the side, as in Figure 5–4D, the posterior border of the ramus meets the inferior border of the corpus to form the angle of the mandible. Each ramus is a quadrilateral and perpendicularly directed plate extending upward from the posterior portion of the body of the mandible. The superior border of a ramus contains two prominent and important landmarks, the coronoid and condyloid processes. They are separated by the mandibular or semilunar notch. The coronoid process, the anterior of the two, is a beak-like projection directed somewhat posteriorly, and is, therefore, convex forward and concave behind. It serves as the point of attachment for the temporalis muscle (to be described later). The condyloid process forms the mandibular head and fits into the mandibular fossa of the temporal bone. The condyle presents a surface which articulates with the meniscus (articular disc) of the temporomandibular joint. The medial surface of the ramus

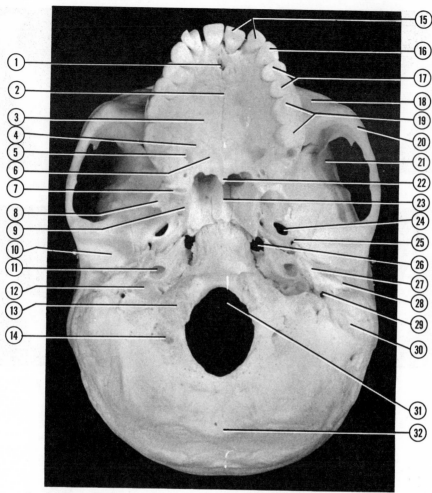

Fig. 5–3. The skull as seen from beneath.

1. Incisive foramen
2. Inter-maxillary suture
3. Palatine process of maxilla
4. Transverse maxillo-palatine suture
5. Major palatine foramen
6. Horizontal lamina of palatine bone
7. Hamulus of medial pterygoid plate
8. Lateral pterygoid plate
9. Medial pterygoid plate
10. Mandibular fossa
11. Carotid canal
12. Jugular fossa
13. Occipital condyle
14. Condyloid fossa
15. Incisor teeth
16. Cuspid (canine) tooth

17. Bicuspid (pre-molars)
18. Maxillary bone
19. Molar teeth
20. Zygomatic bone
21. Greater wing of sphenoid bone
22. Posterior nasal spine
23. Posterior border of vomer bone
24. Foramen ovale
25. Foramen spinosum
26. Foramen lacerum
27. Styloid process of temporal bone
28. External auditory meatus
29. Stylo-mastoid foramen
30. Mastoid process of temporal bone
31. Foramen magnum of occipital bone
32. Inferior nuchal line

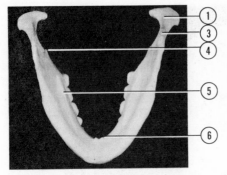

A. As seen from beneath

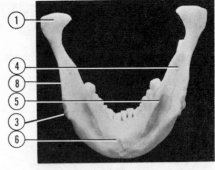

C. As seen from behind and beneath

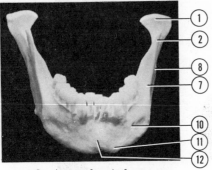

B. As seen from in front

D. As seen from the left and above

1. Mandibular condyle
2. Coronoid process
3. Angle of mandible
4. Mandibular foramen
5. Mylohyoid line
6. Mental spines

7. Oblique line
8. Ramus of mandible
9. Semilunar notch
10. Mental foramen
11. Mental tubercle
12. Mental protuberance

Fig. 5–4. Various views of a mandible.

contains an easily identifiable landmark, the mandibular foramen, which permits entrance of nerves and blood vessels.

The corpus of the mandible also presents some worthwhile landmarks. Beginning from each mental tubercle, running posteriorly and upward, is an indistinct ridge called the oblique line. As shown in Figure 5–4D, it is continuous with the anterior surface of the ramus. A prominent landmark may be seen just above the oblique line, lateral to the symphysis. It is the mental foramen, a perforation in the bone that permits the mental nerve and blood vessels to pass from within the bone to the external surface. An easily identified landmark on the medial surface of the corpus is called the mylohyoid line. It begins in the region of the mental spines and runs diagonally backward and upward to terminate near the alveolar ridge in the region of the last molar. Its course is roughly parallel to that of the oblique line. The mylohyoid line is the site of attachment for some important muscles of speech production to be considered later in the chapter.

The mandible is a large bone, very dense, and extremely strong. Its major contribution to speech production is probably that it houses the lower teeth and forms the points of attachment for much of the tongue and other musculature. Movements of the mandible and its contained tongue result in modifications of the size and acoustic characteristics of the oral cavity. The extent of jaw movement during normal speech production is surprisingly small, amounting to a few millimeters when measured at the incisors. In fact, the jaw need not move at all during speech production. Testimony to this may be seen in the cigar and pipe smokers who seem to have no trouble at all producing perfectly adequate speech with their oral pacifiers clenched firmly between their teeth.

The Maxillae. Except for the mandible, the maxillae are the largest bones in the face. They are also the most important as far as speech production is concerned. They are paired bones which form the entire upper jaw and contribute to the formation of the roof of the mouth, the floor and lateral walls of the nasal cavity, and the floor of the orbital cavity.

Each bone consists of a body, roughly pyramidal in shape, and the zygomatic, frontal, alveolar, and palatine processes. Since the body of the maxilla is tetrahedral, it presents four surfaces for inspection, the anterior, posterior (infratemporal), superior (orbital), and medial (nasal) surfaces.

The anterior surface presents a number of landmarks, some of which are shown in Figures 5–1 and 5–5. Those worth noting include the canine eminence, the infraorbital

Fig. 5–5. *Juxtaposed maxillae as seen from the front (top figure) and a maxilla as seen from the side (bottom).*

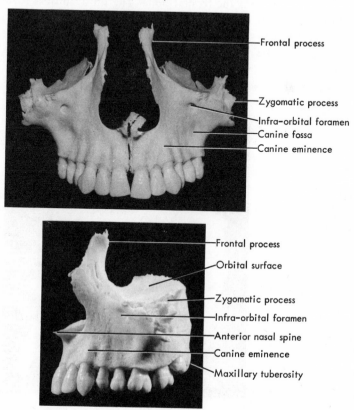

foramen, and the anterior nasal spine. The significance of some of these landmarks may become apparent as we progress through the chapter. The posterior surface forms part of the infratemporal fossa. The anterior and posterior surfaces would be continuous were it not for the zygomatic process, which forms a dividing boundary. The posterior surface contains two landmarks: (1) the alveolar canals, which carry the posterior-superior blood vessels and nerves, and (2) the maxillary tuberosity, which articulates with the palatine bone. The superior surface of the maxilla is triangular in shape, and it forms most of the floor of the orbital cavity. The medial border articulates with the lacrimal, ethmoid, and palatine bones. The outstanding landmark of the superior surface is the infraorbital groove, which carries infraorbital blood vessels and nerves. The medial surface is broken by an opening into the maxillary sinus. As shown in Figure 5–6, this opening is best seen in a disarticulated skull. In the articulated specimen, the medial surfaces are all but hidden by the nasal conchae.

The maxillae are not the massive heavy bones their size might indicate. This is because they are not solid masses, but, rather, each contains an extensive maxillary sinus, or antrum of Highmore. Thus, the maxillae in the adult skull are but hollow shells that might easily yield to the pressures of biting and chewing, were it not for three buttresses of bone which course upward obliquely from the alveolar arch. These buttresses are shown in schematic form in Figure 5–7. One runs up the medial side of the orbit, while another runs up the lateral side and divides into an upper and lower limb, one of which courses horizontally back as the zygoma, to be discussed later. The other (upper limb) forms the lateral boundary and wall of the orbital cavity and ultimately reaches the frontal bone. The third buttress is formed by the pterygoid processes of the sphenoid bone (also to be discussed later). It extends from the last upper molar to the base of the skull, as shown in Figure 5–7. It is apparent that the processes of the maxillae contribute to the strength of the facial skeleton.

Fig. 5–6. A left maxilla as seen in medial view showing opening of antrum.

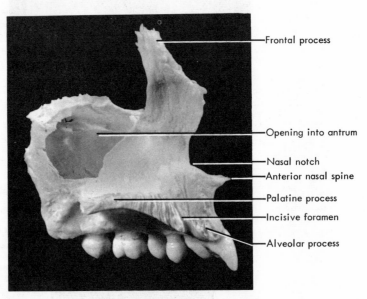

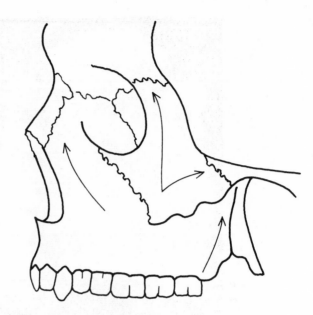

Fig. 5–7. Schematic of buttresses which lend support to the maxillae.

The triangular-shaped zygomatic process is directed superiorly and laterally. It articulates with the zygomatic bone. The frontal process is a very strong bony plate that is directed upward, medially, and slightly posteriorly. It forms the lateral bony framework of the nose, while its medial surface contributes to the lateral wall of the nasal cavity. The alveolar process is the thick, spongy part of the maxilla that houses the teeth. The adult alveolar process is divided into eight cavities, each of which contains a tooth. In some specimens the canine tooth may perforate the alveolar process and extend into the antrum of Highmore. In the articulated, tooth-bearing skull, the alveolar processes of the maxillae form the alveolar arch or ridge.

The palatine process is a thick, horizontal, medially directed projection, which articulates with its fellow from the opposite side at the mid-line to form most (three-fourths) of the floor of the nasal cavity and bony roof of the mouth. As shown in Figure 5–6, it is considerably thicker in front than behind. When viewed from beneath, as in Figure 5–8B, the concave, rough surface presents some noteworthy landmarks. A mid-line suture courses anteriorly and terminates at the incisive foramen. In the very young, and in lower animals, a fine suture may be seen extending from the incisive foramen to the space between the lateral incisors and the canine or cuspid teeth. The small triangular-shaped part in front of this fine suture forms the premaxilla, which in most vertebrates is a separate bone known as the premaxilla, or intermaxillary bone. The fine sutures which form the boundary lines of the premaxilla disappear at a very early age, and very often no trace of them can be found in the adult skull. A photograph of the bony roof of the mouth (palate) of an ape is shown in Figure 5–8A, and for comparative purposes, the bony palate of an adult is shown in Figure 5–8B. Note the fine sutures extending laterally from the incisive foramen in the ape palate and the absence of such sutures in the human palate.

When seen in a frontal section, as in Figure 5–9, the medial border of the palatine process presents a raised ridge known as the nasal crest, which, together with the crest

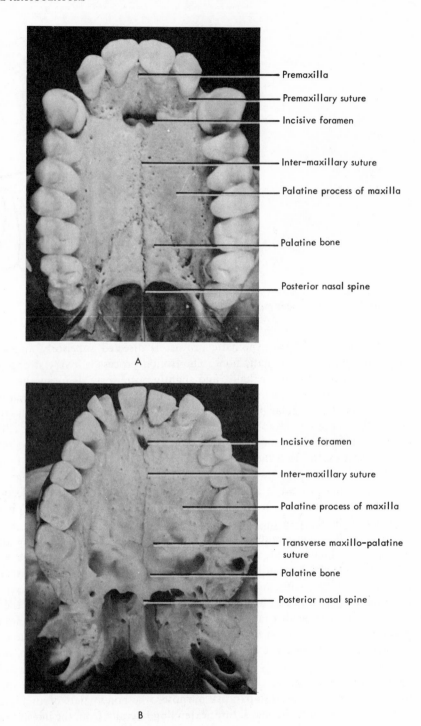

Premaxilla

Premaxillary suture

Incisive foramen

Inter-maxillary suture

Palatine process of maxilla

Palatine bone

Posterior nasal spine

A

Incisive foramen

Inter-maxillary suture

Palatine process of maxilla

Transverse maxillo-palatine suture

Palatine bone

Posterior nasal spine

B

Fig. 5–8. Photograph of the palate of an ape (A) and of an adult human (B).

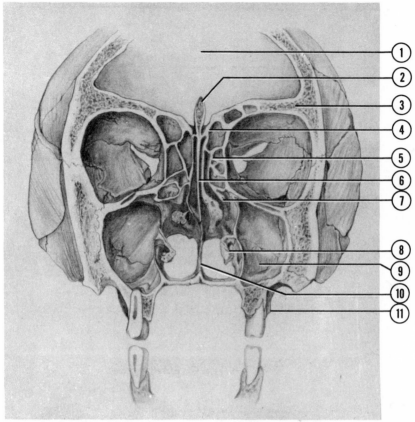

1. Anterior cranial cavity
2. Crista galli of the ethmoid
3. Frontal sinus
4. Cribriform plate of ethmoid
5. Ethmoid sinus
6. Perpendicular plate of ethmoid
7. Middle nasal concha
8. Inferior nasal concha
9. Antrum of maxilla
10. Vomer bone
11. Alveolar process of maxilla

Fig. 5-9. A frontal section of the skull. (Drawing by Adrienne Warren.)

from the opposite side, forms a longitudinal groove that accommodates the perpendicular vomer bone. Anteriorly, the nasal crest is continued forward as a sharp process called the anterior nasal spine, an important landmark in X-ray studies of the skull.

Each maxilla articulates with nine bones: the frontal and ethmoid bones of the cranium; the nasal, lacrimal, zygomatic, palatine, vomer, and inferior nasal concha of the facial skeleton; and the maxilla from the opposite side.

The Nasal Bones. Two small oblong plates of bone, placed side by side, form the bridge of the nose. They are the nasal bones, shown in Figures 5-1 and 5-2. Situated medial to the frontal processes of the maxillae, they articulate with the frontal bone

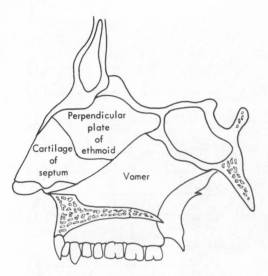

Fig. 5–10. Schematic of medial wall of nasal cavity showing vomer bone, perpendicular plate of the ethmoid, and the articulation of the nasal bone with the septum.

above, with the perpendicular plate of the ethmoid bone, and with the nasal bone from the opposite side. They also articulate with the septal cartilage of the nose, as in Figure 5–10.

The Palatine Bones. Although the palatine bone shown in Figure 5–11 is relatively small, it is extremely important and equally complex. As shown schematically in

Fig. 5–11. Articulated palatine bones as seen from beneath (top figure) and as seen in perspective from behind (bottom figure).

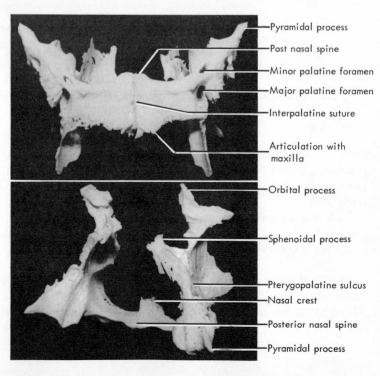

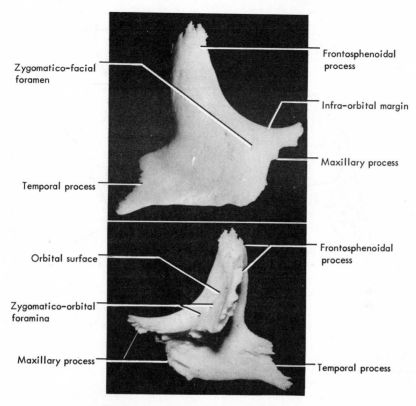

Frontosphenoidal process

Infra-orbital margin

Maxillary process

Zygomatico-facial foramen

Temporal process

Frontosphenoidal process

Orbital surface

Zygomatico-orbital foramina

Maxillary process

Temporal process

Fig. 5–12. The malar (top figure) and temporal (bottom figure) surfaces of a zygomatic bone.

Figure 5–13, it is located at the back of the nasal cavity and, like the maxilla with which it is so closely associated, contributes to the formation of three cavities: the floor and lateral wall of the nasal cavity, the roof of the mouth, and the floor of the orbital cavity. Of particular interest to us is the horizontal part of the palatine bone. It is quadrilateral in shape and has two surfaces, a concave superior surface, which forms part of the floor of the nasal cavity, and a concave inferior surface, which forms part of the roof of the mouth. The palatine bone forms the posterior one-fourth of the bony palate. Its anterior border is serrated for articulation with the palatine process of the maxilla, while the posterior border is free. Medially, the bone is continued posteriorly and, when it is united with its fellow from the opposite side, forms the posterior nasal spine, an important landmark for X-ray study of the skull. Laterally, the palatine bone turns abruptly upward to form a vertically directed plate. Thus, when viewed from behind, the palatine bone resembles a letter L. The palatine bone articulates with six bones: its fellow from the opposite side, the sphenoid, ethmoid, maxilla, inferior nasal concha, and the vomer.

The Lacrimal Bones.   The lacrimal bone is the smallest of the facial bones. It forms part of the medial wall of the orbital cavity. It has an orbital and a nasal surface and articulates with four bones: the frontal, ethmoid, maxilla, and inferior nasal concha. The lacrimal bone was shown in Figure 5–2.

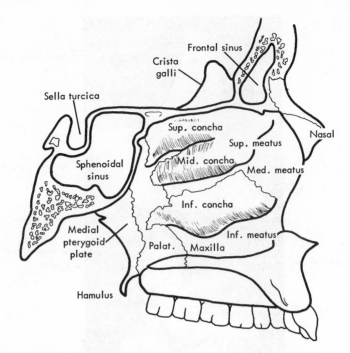

Fig. 5–13. Lateral wall of nasal cavity showing relationship of inferior nasal concha to adjacent structures.

The Zygomatic Bones.   The zygomatic or malar bone, shown in Figure 5–12, consists of a body that is roughly quadrilateral in shape, and four processes: the fronto-sphenoidal, orbital, maxillary, and temporal. It is a rather small bone, which, with the zygomatic process of the maxilla and of the temporal bone, forms the prominent zygomatic arch or cheekbone. The zygomatic articulates with the frontal, sphenoid, maxillary, and temporal bones. It contributes to the lateral wall and floor of the orbital cavity. As shown in Figure 5–3, the zygomatic arch is elevated from the side of the skull, and for this reason the zygomatic bone presents a malar (outer) surface and a temporal (inner) surface. Some important muscles of articulation and mastication attach to the zygomatic bone. These muscles will be considered in some detail later in the chapter.

The Inferior Nasal Conchae (*Inferior Turbinated Bones*).   The inferior nasal concha makes up the inferior-most part of the lateral nasal wall. In its general configurations the inferior nasal concha is much like the scroll-like, lateral extensions of the ethmoid bone (to be considered later). The inferior nasal concha articulates anteriorly with the maxilla and posteriorly with the palatine bone, while the inferior border is free. The inferior border forms the lateral and superior boundaries of the inferior nasal meatus. The inferior nasal concha and its relationship to adjacent structures are shown in Figures 5–1, 5–9, and 5–13.

The Vomer Bone.   The inferior half of the bony nasal septum consists of the vomer bone, a thin quadrilateral plate that articulates with the maxillae and palatine bones inferiorly and the perpendicular plate of the ethmoid bone and the rostrum of the sphenoid bone superiorly. The posterior border is free, whereas the anterior border articulates with the cartilaginous septum of the nose. The vomer and adjacent bones are shown schematically in Figure 5–10.

Bones of the cranium

The Ethmoid Bone. The anterior base of the cranium, shown in Figure 5–9, is made of a very delicate and complex bone, the ethmoid. It is projected down from between the orbital plates of the frontal bone, and contributes to the walls of the orbital and nasal cavities. It consists of four parts: the horizontal or cribriform plate, two lateral masses collectively called the superior and middle nasal conchae, and a perpendicular plate or mesethmoid. When viewed from above, the ethmoid is roughly cuboidal in shape; when viewed from behind, as in Figure 5–14, it appears to be T shaped. The horizontal plate serves as a partition between the cranium and nasal cavities. The lateral masses of the cribriform plate appear to be a labyrinth, made up of scroll-like cavities that can be grouped into the superior and middle turbinates. As shown in Figure 5–13, this labyrinth forms part of the lateral wall of the corresponding nasal cavity, and, as was shown in Figure 5–10, the perpendicular plate of

Fig. 5–14. Various views of the ethmoid bone.

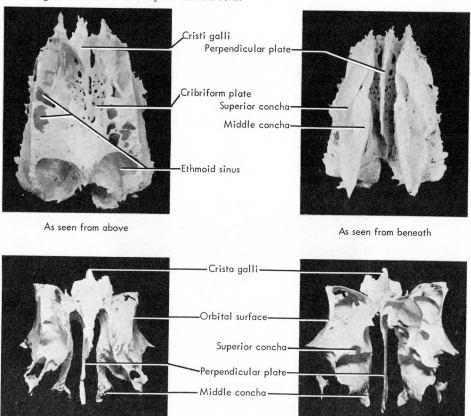

Cristi galli
Perpendicular plate—

Cribriform plate
Superior concha—
Middle concha—

Ethmoid sinus

As seen from above

As seen from beneath

Crista galli

Orbital surface

Superior concha—

Perpendicular plate—

Middle concha

As seen from in front

As seen from behind

the ethmoid forms the upper third of the bony nasal septum. The perpendicular plate is nearly quadrilateral in shape, with the anterior surface joining with the anterior margin of the vomer behind. The posterior margin is thin and articulates with the rostrum of the sphenoid bone. The perpendicular plate is more often than not deflected slightly to one side (deviated).

The Frontal Bone. The frontal bone shown in Figure 5–15 is an unpaired structure forming the anterior brain case as well as the roof of the orbital and nasal cavities. The frontal bone, shown in Figures 5–1 and 5–2, consists of two portions: a vertically directed squamous portion and a horizontal portion. The external surface of the vertical portion is convex in shape, and is very often marked by a mid-line frontal, or metopic, suture. The horizontal portion is composed of two thin plates that are separated one from the other by the cribriform plate of the ethmoid bone. Because these two thin plates of the frontal bone form the vaults of the orbital cavity, they are sometimes called the orbital plates, while the space between them (occupied by the cribriform plate) is called the ethmoid notch.

The Parietal Bones. The paired parietal bones form the bulk of the brain case. They are very large bones, forming the greater part of the sides and a large portion of the roof of the cranium. As may be seen in Figure 5–16, they are roughly quadrilateral

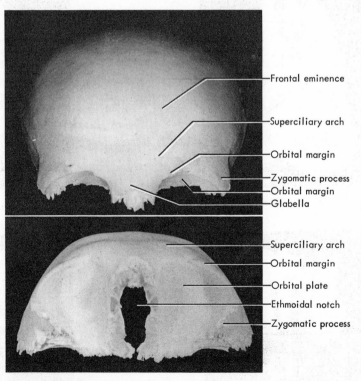

Fig. 5–15. The frontal bone as seen from the front (top figure) and as seen from beneath (bottom figure).

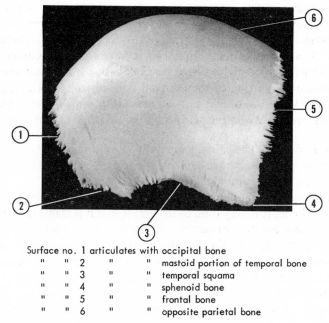

Surface no. 1 articulates with occipital bone
" " 2 " " mastoid portion of temporal bone
" " 3 " " temporal squama
" " 4 " " sphenoid bone
" " 5 " " frontal bone
" " 6 " " opposite parietal bone

Fig. 5–16. Right parietal bone, outer surface.

in shape. Each bone articulates with five bones: its fellow from the opposite side, the occipital, frontal, temporal, and sphenoid bones.

The Occipital Bone. The occipital bone, shown in Figure 5–17, forms the back and lower brain case. The most prominent landmark of the occipital bone is the foramen magnum, an oval aperture through which the spinal cord passes. The major portion of the occipital bone is composed of a thin convex plate called the squamous portion.

Fig. 5–17. The occipital bone as seen in perspective from beneath.

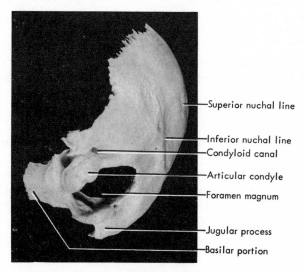

Superior nuchal line

Inferior nuchal line
Condyloid canal

Articular condyle

Foramen magnum

Jugular process

Basilar portion

A small rectangular section, anterior to the foramen magnum, is called the basilar portion. The squama is seen to be rough and uneven, particularly in the lower portion near the mid-line. It is marked by two transverse ridges called the superior and inferior nuchal lines. Small parts of the occipital bone lateral to the foramen magnum are marked by the articular condyles where the skull joins with the superior facets of the atlas. The squamous portion of the occipital bone articulates with the parietal and temporal bones, while the basilar portion articulates with the sphenoid bone. The lateral portions articulate with the petrous portion of the temporal bone.

The Temporal Bones.   The paired temporal bones form most of the lateral base and sides of the brain case. Each bone consists of five parts: the squamous, mastoid, petrous, and tympanic parts, and the styloid process.

As shown in Figure 5–18, the squamous portion forms the anterior and upper part of the temporal bone. It is very thin, to the extent that it is translucent in some specimens. A prominent anterior projection of the squamous portion is the zygomatic process, which articulates with the temporal process of the zygomatic bone.

The mastoid portion forms the posterior-most part of the temporal bone. It is continued in an inferior direction to form the conical mastoid process of the temporal bone. The mastoid process is hollowed into a great number of spaces called the mastoid air cells. They are irregular in shape and in number, varying extensively among specimens. They are filled with air and collectively are sometimes called the mastoid sinus. Another cavity, located superior and anterior to the mastoid portion, is called the tympanic antrum. Although it is continuous with the mastoid air cells, it must be distinguished from them. The tympanic antrum communicates with the middle-ear cavity or tympanum, which will be discussed in detail in the following chapter. The antrum is bounded above by the tegmen tympanum, a paper-thin sheet of bone; below by the mastoid process; laterally by the squamous portion; and medially by the lateral semicircular canal. The tympanic antrum is important to hearing, and will also be discussed in greater detail in the following chapter.

The petrous portion of the temporal bone is located at the base of the skull between the sphenoid and occipital bones. It is extremely important because it houses the essential parts of the organs of equilibrium and hearing. The petrous portion of the temporal bone will be considered in some detail in the following chapter.

The tympanic part of the temporal bone lies just below the squamous portion and just anterior to the mastoid process. Its posterior and superior surfaces are concave, forming the anterior wall, floor, and part of the posterior wall of the bony external auditory meatus. Its anterior and inferior surface forms the posterior surface of the mandibular fossa. The relationship between the external auditory meatus and the mandibular joint has many important implications with respect to hearing. The external meatus, which is about two centimeters in length, is directed medially and somewhat anteriorly, and its medial end is closed off by the tympanic membrane or ear drum.

The styloid process is a slender projection of the temporal bone that is directed tooth-like in a downward direction from the underside of the temporal bone. It is a significant process with respect to speech, since it forms attachments for the stylohyoid and stylomandibular ligaments and for the stylohyoid, styloglossal, and stylopharyngeal muscles. The styloid process lies at a point medial to and halfway between

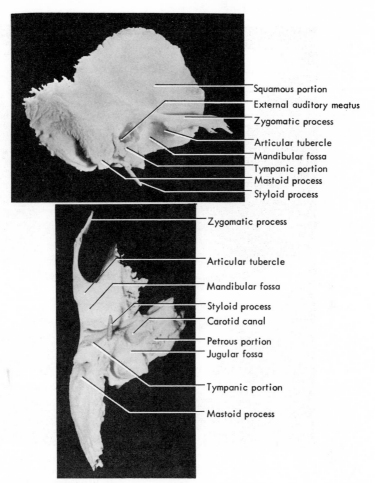

Squamous portion
External auditory meatus
Zygomatic process

Articular tubercle
Mandibular fossa
Tympanic portion
Mastoid process
Styloid process

Zygomatic process

Articular tubercle

Mandibular fossa

Styloid process
Carotid canal

Petrous portion
Jugular fossa

Tympanic portion

Mastoid process

Fig. 5–18. A right temporal bone as seen from the side (top figure) and as seen from beneath (bottom figure).

the orifice of the external auditory meatus and the mastoid process. The temporal bone articulates with five bones: the occipital, parietal, sphenoid, and zygomatic bones, and the mandible. It is shown in Figures 5–1, 5–3, and 5–18.

The Sphenoid Bone.   The sphenoid is probably the most complex bone in the skull: It is certainly the most difficult to understand. This is unfortunate, because it is so very important with respect to the speech mechanism. The sphenoid bone, shown in Figure 5–19, is at the base of the skull, just anterior to the foramen magnum of the occipital bone. It is often likened to a bat with extended wings or to a butterfly. It consists of a body, two greater wings and two lesser wings, extending in a lateral direction, and two pterygoid plates extending from the body vertically downward. Because of its complexity, the interested student is urged to find a well-prepared skull, and perhaps a well-prepared instructor, for supplementary information.

The body of the sphenoid, roughly cuboidal in shape, contains two sphenoid air sinuses, separated one from the other by a mid-line septum. The superior surface of

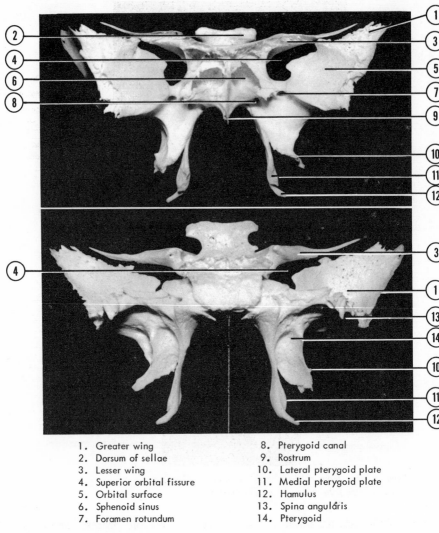

1. Greater wing	8. Pterygoid canal
2. Dorsum of sellae	9. Rostrum
3. Lesser wing	10. Lateral pterygoid plate
4. Superior orbital fissure	11. Medial pterygoid plate
5. Orbital surface	12. Hamulus
6. Sphenoid sinus	13. Spina anguláris
7. Foramen rotundum	14. Pterygoid

Fig. 5–19. A sphenoid bone as seen from the front (top) and from behind (bottom figure).

the body is characterized by a deep depression, the sella turcica (Turkish saddle), which houses the hypophysis cerebri or pituitary gland. The lateral surfaces of the body give rise to the greater wings and the medial pterygoid plates. The posterior surface of the sphenoid articulates with the basilar portion of the occipital bone. The greater wings are paired processes that course upward and lateralward to form the posterior wall of the orbital cavity and the medial fossa of the skull. The superior surface of the greater wing forms a part of the medial brain case. It lies in contact with the temporal lobe of the brain. The inferior surface of the greater wing forms much of the orbital wall. The lesser wings originate from the anterior-superior aspect of the body and are directed laterally and anteriorly. The lower surface contributes to the orbital cavity, while the anterior surface articulates with the frontal bone. The pterygoid processes, or plates, are paired structures, one on either side of the body, directed downward from the region where the greater wing joins with the body of the sphenoid. Each pterygoid process is divided into a medial and a lateral pterygoid plate. These plates are fused anteriorly, but diverge as they course posteriorly. They are shown in Figure 5–19. The V-shaped space between the two pterygoid plates is known as the pterygoid fossa, which houses some important muscles for speech production. The internal pterygoid plate has a small, hook-like projection inferiorly, which is referred to as the hamulus. This important little slip of bone acts as an intermediary for the attachment of the tensor palatine muscle.

The sphenoid bone articulates with all the bones of the cranium: the occipital, parietal, frontal, ethmoid, and temporal. It also articulates with the palatine bones, the vomer, and occasionally with the tuberosity of the maxilla. Thus it might be regarded as the topographical center of the skull.

THE SINUSES

Introduction

From outward appearances the bones of the skull may appear to be solid and massive. As may be seen in Figure 5–9, however, many of the skull bones are but hollow shells. That is, they contain sinuses. Four pairs of accessory sinuses drain into the nasal cavities. They are called the paranasal sinuses, and include the frontal, maxillary, ethmoid, and sphenoid sinuses.

The frontal sinuses

The frontal sinuses were shown in Figures 5–9 and 5–13. They are located directly behind the superciliary arches or ridges, shown in Figure 5–1. The frontal sinuses are paired, separated one from the other by a mid-line bony septum. These sinuses, practically absent at birth, attain their full size only after puberty. They drain into the medial meatus of the nasal cavity.

The maxillary sinuses

The maxillary sinuses, which were described with the maxillary bones, are the largest of the paranasal sinuses. The extent of the sinus cavity may be seen in Figure 5–9. Each sinus, often referred to as the antrum of Highmore, drains into the medial meatus of the nasal cavity.

The ethmoid sinuses or air cells

These sinuses, also shown in Figure 5–9, consist of a labyrinth of thin-walled cavities, which are usually divided into an anterior, middle, and posterior group.

The mastoid air cells

The air cells of the mastoid portion of the temporal bone are regarded as diverticula of the tympanic antrum rather than true sinuses. The mastoid air cells do, however,

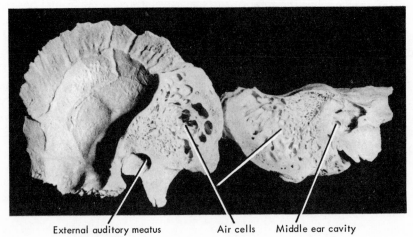

External auditory meatus   Air cells   Middle ear cavity

Fig. 5–20. Photograph of the mastoid air cells of a right temporal bone.

significantly decrease the mass of the temporal bone. The cells, shown in Figure 5–20, are filled with air and are lined with mucous membrane that is continuous with that of the tympanic cavity.

Functions of the Sinuses

The sinuses have no real significance with respect to speech production, except perhaps for contributions of a minimal sort to the resonant characteristics of the skull bones. There is some difference of opinion regarding the functions of the sinuses. One line of thought, for example, is that the differential growth of the facial bones away from the cranial bones results in the development of cavity spaces within the bone tissue. One thing is certain, the sinuses do reduce the weight of the skull.

It is frequently claimed that sinus infections affect voice quality, and on that basis a resonance function is sometimes assigned to the sinuses. It may be true that voice quality is affected when the sinuses are infected, but it is unlikely that infections of the sinuses affect voice quality. That is to say, there is probably a simultaneous infection of the sinus cavities and the nasal cavities proper, and the combined effects result in changes in voice quality. Since the mucous membrane lining the paranasal sinuses is continuous with that of the nasal cavity, very likely any inflammation of mucous membrane of the nasal cavity is communicated to the mucous membrane of the sinuses.

THE CAVITIES OF THE VOCAL TRACT

Introduction

We are all well aware that the laryngeal tone is complex. It contains many overtones, or harmonics of the fundamental frequency. In accordance with the resonant characteristics of the vocal tract, certain of the overtones are reinforced at the expense of others. Information contributing to the intelligibility of speech is not conveyed so much by the frequencies of the energy in the voice or by the amount of power or energy in the voice, but, rather, it is conveyed by the distribution of energy within the speech sounds. Changes in the gross configurations of the vocal tract result in modifications of the resonant characteristics to produce sounds with various energy distributions. Thus the vocal tract acts as a modifier of speech sounds. It also acts as a generator of speech sounds. By placing the lower lip against the upper teeth and releasing a puff of air, we are able to produce the [f] sound, and by phonating with the same articulation we generate its voiced counterpart [v]. By placing the tongue to the edge of the upper teeth and releasing a puff of air, we generate a [θ] sound as in "thin." Or, by phonating with the same articulation we produce the [ð] as in "these." And so on.

The vocal tract may be divided, on an anatomical basis, into four cavities: the buccal, oral, pharyngeal, and paired nasal cavities. In an attempt to preserve a sense of continuity in this section of the chapter, the various cavities will be described briefly, followed by a detailed description of the structures and musculature associated with them. Thus, while the teeth and tongue may be mentioned in the description of the oral cavity, a detailed description will follow, in a section titled "The Articulators and Associated Structures."

The buccal cavity

The buccal cavity is highly variable in its shape and dimensions, depending upon the status of lips and cheeks. It is the small space that is limited by the lips and cheeks externally and by the gums (gingivae) and teeth internally. It communicates with the mouth or oral cavity, with the jaws closed, by the small spaces between the teeth, and by space on either side behind the last molars or "wisdom teeth."

The oral cavity

The oral cavity proper is bounded anteriorly and laterally by the teeth and alveolar processes, superiorly by the hard and soft palates, posteriorly by the anterior faucial pillars, and inferiorly by the muscular floor consisting primarily of the tongue. The oral cavity and some associated structures are shown schematically in Figure 5–21, and a photograph of an oral cavity is shown in Figure 5–22.

The fauces

The port through which the oral cavity communicates with the pharyngeal and nasal cavities is called the fauces, or isthmus of fauces (isthmus of fauces is sometimes considered archaic). The fauces are bounded laterally by the palatine arches or faucial pillars, above by the soft palate, and below by the dorsum of the tongue.

The pharyngeal cavity

The pharynx is a musculo-membranous tube extending from the base of the skull to the level of the sixth cervical vertebra behind and the cricoid cartilage in front. It is about 12 centimeters in length and is oval shaped in cross section, being somewhat wider in the transverse than in the antero-posterior dimension. The cavity of the pharynx is often divided into a nasopharynx, an oropharynx, and a laryngopharynx.

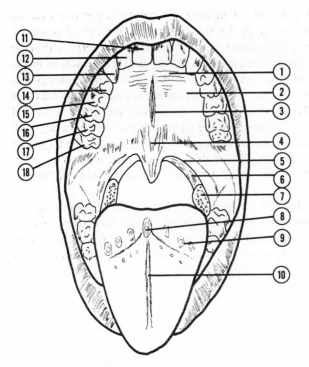

1. Rugae
2. Hard palate
3. Median raphe
4. Soft palate
5. Anterior faucial pillar
6. Posterior faucial pillar
7. Palatine tonsil
8. Sulcus terminalis
9. Papillae vallatae
10. Median sulcus
11. Central incisor
12. Lateral incisor
13. Cuspid
14. 1st bicuspid
15. 2nd biscuspid
16. 1st molar
17. 2nd molar
18. 3rd molar

Fig. 5–21. Schematic of oral cavity and adjacent structures.

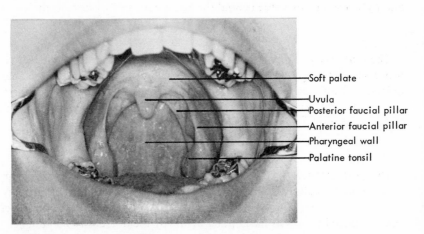

Soft palate
Uvula
Posterior faucial pillar
Anterior faucial pillar
Pharyngeal wall
Palatine tonsil

Fig. 5–22. Photograph of an oral cavity.

The Nasopharynx. The nasopharynx is bounded above by the rostrum of the sphenoid bone and the pharyngeal protuberance of the occipital bone. Inferiorly it is limited at the level of the soft palate. The nasopharynx communicates anteriorly with the posterior nares or the choanae of the nasal cavities and laterally with the pharyngeal orifice of the auditory (Eustachian) tube (to be described later).

The Oropharynx.   The superior limit to the oropharynx is at the level of the soft palate, while the lower boundary is at the level of the hyoid bone. Anteriorly, it communicates with the oral cavities by way of the fauces.

The Laryngopharynx.   The laryngopharynx is bounded above at the level of the hyoid bone; inferiorly it is continuous with the esophagus. Anteriorly, it communicates with the opening of the larynx which is formed anteriorly by the epiglottis and laterally by the aryepiglottic folds. Thus, the pharynx communicates with the tympanic, oral, laryngeal, and nasal cavities, as well as the esophagus.

The nasal cavities

The nasal cavities consist of two narrow, approximately symmetrical chambers, separated by the nasal septum. They communicate with the exterior by way of the nostrils or nares and with the nasopharynx by way of the choanae. The nasal cavities are extremely complex in their gross configuration and demand a little more detailed description. The nasal septum is a medially placed, vertically directed plate of bone and cartilage, which, more often than not, is deviated (buckled) to one side, usually the right. The anterior portion of the septum, shown in Figure 5–10, is cartilaginous, while the posterior portion is formed by the vomer bone below and the perpendicular plate of the ethmoid above. The lateral walls of the nasal cavities are composed of the superior, middle, and inferior nasal conchae and their corresponding nasal passages or meati. The conchae are liberally covered by mucous membrane. The labyrinthine structure of the conchae greatly increases the surface area within the nasal cavities. Most of this surface filters and moistens the air as it is inhaled through the nares. The channels for air passage formed by the conchae are referred to as the superior, medial, and inferior meati. The lateral walls also contain orifices through which the nasal cavities communicate with the paranasal sinuses. A frontal section

Fig. 5–23. Frontal section through the nasal cavities of a fetal head.

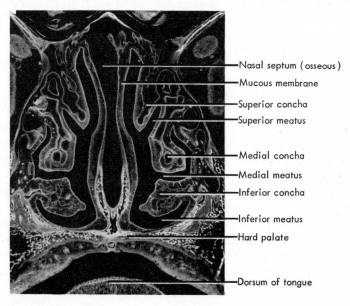

Nasal septum (osseous)
Mucous membrane
Superior concha
Superior meatus
Medial concha
Medial meatus
Inferior concha
Inferior meatus
Hard palate
Dorsum of tongue

of the nasal cavities is shown in Figure 5–23, while the lateral and medial walls of the cavities are shown in Figures 5–10 and 5–13 respectively. The floor of the nasal cavities is concave, and is formed by the maxillae and palatine bones. The roof is very narrow from side to side, and is pierced by the many minute foramina in the cribriform plate of the ethmoid bone. The perforations permit the entrance of the branches of the olfactory nerves, which terminate on the upper septum and adjacent lateral walls, and occupy an area no larger than two square centimeters. (Cates and Basmajian, 1955)

THE ARTICULATORS AND ASSOCIATED STRUCTURES

The Mouth

Introduction

The mouth, like other parts of the speech production mechanism, has biological as well as nonbiological functions. An important biological function is to establish communication between the digestive and respiratory tracts and the exterior. The mouth communicates with the pharyngeal cavity by way of the fauces and with the exterior by way of the buccal orifice or mouth slit. A second biological function of the mouth is as the initiator of the digestive process. A content of saliva that has to do with food breakdown is ptyalin. It acts directly on starches, converting them to maltose, or disaccaride (double sugar). Ptyalin is an extremely powerful enzyme, but the way most people eat, it has but a moment to act before the food departs for the stomach.

Because of the extremely mobile lips and tongue, the mouth is certainly the most movable and adjustable of the cavities in the vocal tract. Other mouth structures associated with articulation of speech sounds are the teeth, hard palate, soft palate, cheeks, and lower jaw. The relative mobility of the various structures has been a subject for research. In an early experiment dealing with the mobility of the articulators, Hudgins and Stetson (1937) found a high degree of consistency between nine subjects who were asked to repeat various syllables as rapidly as possible. They were repeated in such a manner as to represent repetitions of singular movements. The tip of the tongue was found to be the most mobile of the articulators. It could move 8.2 times per second, in the production of "ta ta ta." Values for other articulators were 7.3 per second for the jaw, 7.1 per second for the back of the tongue, 6.7 for the lips, and 6.7 for the soft palate. These values are in essential agreement with subsequent studies.

As stated earlier, the structures in the mouth have two important nonbiological functions. First, they act as a modifier of the resonant characteristics of the vocal tract, and secondly, they may act as generators of speech sounds. There are other nonbiological functions of the mouth that perhaps play a less important role in speech and communication. For example, the lips are not only important articulators of speech sounds, they are also mediators of facial expression. In addition, the movements of the lips and face provide visible secondary cues which facilitate communication far more than most people realize. Lip reading is something most of us do quite unconsciously, and it is surprising how expert we are!

In a very real sense, separation of the activities of the structures comprising the speech mechanism into biological and nonbiological functions is somewhat artificial, and can be justified only from a strictly operational point of view. This problem has been recognized by Martone (1963), who has outlined an area extending from the sternum to the tip of the nose and on to the outer orifices of the ears. This area has been termed a pyramid of polyfunction, since it contains the organs and structures responsible solely or in part for functions of facial expression, mastication, deglutition, breathing, and speech. This is a truly functional approach, which is worthy of some thought. Such an approach, however, demands some prior knowledge of the descriptive and functional anatomy of the mouth and related structures.

The lips

The lips, which form the orifice of the mouth and part of the external boundary of the buccal cavity, are covered externally by integument (skin) and internally by mucous membrane. Between the skin and mucous membrane are muscle, a considerable amount of fat, and glandular tissues. The lips are often described as being composed of four layers of tissue, which, in order of increasing depth, are cutaneous, muscular, glandular, and mucous.

The mucous membrane lining the lips and cheeks is continuous with the integument of the lips and with the mucous lining of the pharynx. It is covered by stratified, squamous epithelium. The integument of the lips terminates as a well-defined line (Cupid's bow on the upper lip) and a transitional area, the vermilion zone, exists between the integument and the mucous membrane (Orban, 1957). The epithelium in the vermilion zone is very thin and has a high content of eleidin, which increases the transparancy of the tissue to the extent that the red hue of the underlying vascular tissue may be seen. In the mid-line of the vermilion zone of the upper lip is a slight projection called the tubercle. A vertical groove connecting this area to the septum of the nose is called the philtrum, which is bounded on either side by a ridge. On the inner, or lingual, surface, the upper lip connects to the alveolar process at the mid-line by a fold of tissue called the labial frenulum (frenum). A similar but weaker structure joins the lower lip with the alveolar process of the mandible.

Labial glands, which lie just beneath the mucous membrane, are located on the inner surface of the lip (the labial surface of the buccal cavity) around the orifice of the mouth. Spherical in shape and resembling small peas, they open into the cavity by numerous small orifices. Structurally, they are similar to the salivary glands.

The cheeks (buccae)

The cheeks, like the lips with which they are continuous, are composed externally of skin and internally of mucous membrane, between which may be found a rather prominent subcutaneous pad of fat, facial muscles, the muscles of mastication, and glandular tissue. The mucous membrane of the cheek blends into the gingivae of the mandible and maxillae and is continuous with the mucosa of the soft palate. This membrane is firmly bound to the fascia of the musculature of the cheek, and closely follows muscular movements. Glands similar to the labial glands, but smaller, are found between the mucous membrane and the musculature of the cheek. Five or six of these glands, larger than the others, open by ducts into the buccal cavity just opposite the last molars. They are called, quite appropriately, the molar glands. The cheek also contains the duct of the parotid salivary gland (Stensen's duct). It opens into the buccal cavity just opposite the second upper molar. The status of the mucous membrane is maintained by the emollient (softening) action of the mucin content of saliva. Mucin is a mixture of glycoproteins that makes the basis of mucus. The emollient action allows free movement of the membranes without the damaging effects of friction. Saliva also functions as a demulscent; that is, it allays irritation of the mucous membrane within the mouth. A rather constant flow of saliva is essential to normal speech production. We all, at one time or another, have experienced "dry mouth" (possibly from nervousness in a tense speech situation) and the sluggish, ill-controlled movements of the tongue as it contacts the various surfaces of the mouth cavity.

The mouth also receives secretion from the submaxillary (submandibular) salivary glands by way of Wharton's ducts, which open into the underside of the tongue on either side of the lingual frenulum, a vertical fold of tissue that extends from the lingual surface of the gum to the inferior surface of the tongue. It also receives secretions from the sublingual salivary glands by way of the ducts of Rivinus, which open into the cavity medial to Wharton's ducts.

As stated earlier, the deep surface of the cheek musculature is covered by mucous membrane. The superficial surface, however, lies in direct contact with a prominent deposit of fatty tissue. This pad of fat is usually referred to as the buccal fat pad, or pad of Bichat. It is particularly well developed in infants and is said to play a role in the suckling activity of nursing babies. It is sometimes called the suckling pad. Supportive evidence of its function is inconclusive.

Muscles of the Face and Mouth

Introduction

The facial muscles, and in particular those of facial expression, are unique in that they are devoid of fascial sheaths characteristic of skeletal muscles. Their size, shape, and extent of development are dependent, among other things, upon age, dentition, and sex, as well as intrinsic individual variations. Also, many of their fibers insert directly into the skin. These characteristics make possible the numerous combinations of facial expression we witness in our day-to-day living. The lips are the most mobile part of the face by virtue of the many facial muscles which act upon them. In fact, the muscles of the face and lips are so intrinsically related they exhibit functional unity.

The orbicularis oris muscle

The principal muscle that acts upon the lips is the orbicularis oris, an unpaired oval ring of muscle fibers located within the lips and which completely encircle the mouth slit. It is a complex muscle that may be thought of as being composed of intrinsic as well as extrinsic muscle fibers. That is, it is composed of fibers from other facial muscles that insert into the lips and of fibers that are exclusive to the lips. The muscles of the lips may also be divided into two layers, a deep layer in which the fibers are arranged in concentric rings and a series of superficial fibers into which the other muscles of the face converge. The orbicularis oris is a sphincter muscle which, when it contracts, closes the mouth and puckers the lips. It is shown in Figure 5–24. The extrinsic muscles may be grouped into three sets: transverse muscles, which course

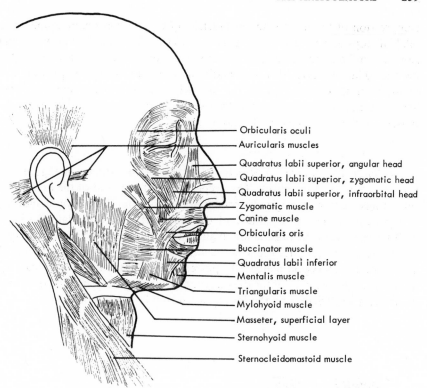

Orbicularis oculi
Auricularis muscles
Quadratus labii superior, angular head
Quadratus labii superior, zygomatic head
Quadratus labii superior, infraorbital head
Zygomatic muscle
Canine muscle
Orbicularis oris
Buccinator muscle
Quadratus labii inferior
Mentalis muscle
Triangularis muscle
Mylohyoid muscle
Masseter, superficial layer
Sternohyoid muscle
Sternocleidomastoid muscle

Fig. 5–24. Some of the muscles of the face and lips.

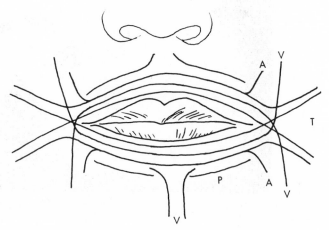

Fig. 5–25. Schematic of facial muscle fibers that insert into the lips.

horizontally from their origin and insert into the orbicularis oris; angular muscles, which approach the corners of the mouth obliquely from above and below; and the labial or vertical muscles, which enter the corners of the mouth directly from above and below. The way in which these muscles insert into the lips is shown schematically in Figure 5–25. The transverse muscles pull the lips against the teeth and facilitate compression of the lips for the production of certain consonant sounds, such as the bilabial stops and nasals. The angular muscles are instrumental in producing expressions of smiling, frowning, etc. The labial or vertical muscles are also important in producing facial expression and in addition are important in compressing the corners of the mouth. A fourth group, the parallel muscles, is also shown in Figure 5–25. They are not lip muscles in the true sense of the word but rather are superficial muscles of the integument in the mouth region.

The transverse facial muscles

The Buccinator (Bugler's) Muscle. The buccinator, shown in Figure 5–24, is the principal muscle of the cheek. The deepest of the facial and of the extrinsic musculature, it has a complex origin. Its primary origin is from the pterygomandibular raphe or ligament, while the remainder of the fibers arise from the lateral surface of the alveolar process of the maxilla and mandible in the region of the last molars.

The pterygomandibular raphe is a tendinous structure which runs from the hamulus of the internal pterygoid plate to the posterior limit of the mylohyoid line. It is shown in Figure 5–26. Were it not for the pterygomandibular raphe, the fibers of the superior pharyngeal constrictor and the buccinator would be continuous.

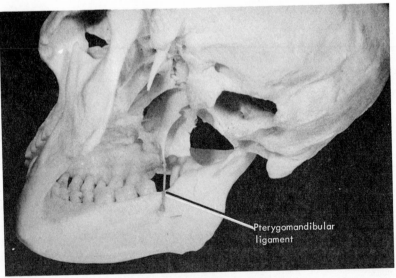

Fig. 5–26. *The skull as seen in perspective from beneath showing a reconstruction of the pterygomandibular ligament.*

The fibers of the buccinator course horizontally forward and medialward to enter and blend with the muscle fibers of both the upper and lower lip. The fibers of the central portion converge toward the corner of the mouth and decussate before inserting. The superior-most fibers do not decussate but, rather, enter the upper lip, while the inferior-most fibers enter the lower lip. Upon contraction the buccinator compresses the lips and cheeks against the teeth and draws the corners of the mouth laterally. Posteriorly, the buccinator is covered by the masseter muscle (to be described later), while anteriorly it is covered by other facial muscles which enter the lips. Some of these muscles are shown in Figure 5–24.

The Risorius Muscle. The risorius is a highly variable muscle which originates from a fascia covering the masseter muscle. Its course is horizontal, with the fibers running parallel with and superficial to the buccinator muscle. Most fibers insert into the skin and mucosa at the corner of the mouth, while a few fibers continue, to blend with the muscle fibers of the lower lip. Upon contraction the risorius helps draw the mouth angle lateralward.

The angular facial muscles

The angular facial muscles include the quadratus labii superior, the zygomatic, and the quadratus labii inferior.

The Quadratus Labii Superior Muscle. The quadratus labii superior is a flat, broad, triangular muscle, located above the upper lip and lateral to the mid-line. It is composed of three heads, each of which has a distinct origin.

The angular head takes its origin from the frontal process and infraorbital margin of the maxilla. As shown in Figure 5–24, the fibers course downward and slightly laterally to insert into the lateral cartilaginous framework of the nostril and into the orbicularis oris. The angular head acts as a dilator of the nostrils and raises the upper lip.

The infraorbital head, as the name implies, originates from the infraorbital margin. As shown in Figure 5–24, the fibers converge as they course downward. They insert into the orbicularis oris, lateral to the fibers of the angular head.

The zygomatic head originates from the facial (malar) surface of the zygomatic bone in the region of the zygomaticomaxillary suture. The fibers course downward and medially to insert into the orbicularis oris, as in Figure 5–24.

When contracting as a whole, the quadratus labii superior is the principal elevator of the upper lip. It may also evert the lip slightly or, with assistance from the canine muscle (to be described later), raise the angle of the mouth, as in smiling.

The Zygomatic Muscle. The zygomatic muscle (not to be confused with the zygomatic head of the quadratus labii superior) is a rather long, slender muscle that arises from the malar surface of the zygomatic bone just lateral to the origin of the zygomatic head of the quadratus labii superior. As shown in Figure 5–24, the fibers course downward and medialward to insert into the orbicularis oris and into the integument at the corner of the mouth. Upon contraction this muscle draws the angle of the mouth upward and lateralward, as in grinning or smiling broadly.

The Quadratus Labii Inferior Muscle. The quadratus labii inferior is a small, flat, quadrangular muscle, located beneath the lower lip, lateral to the mid-line. It arises from the oblique line of the mandible near the mental foramen. Upon contraction this muscle draws the lower lip downward and lateralward. It is shown in Figure 5–24.

The vertical facial muscles

There are three pairs of vertical muscles which insert into the orbicularis oris: the mentalis, the triangularis, and the canine muscles. They compress and assist in elevating and lowering the lips.

The Mentalis Muscle. The mentalis is a small bundle of fibers which originates from the mandible in the region of the mental tuberosity. It courses vertically upward, with some fibers blending with those of the contralateral muscle. Others insert into the integument of the chin, and some continue, to insert into the orbicularis oris. Upon contraction, the mentalis muscle, which is shown in Figure 5–24, wrinkles the chin or everts the lower lip.

The Triangularis Muscle. The triangularis is a flat, triangular sheet of muscle, located superficially and laterally to the fibers of the quadratis labii inferior. It arises from the oblique line of the mandible, its fibers interdigitating with those of the platysma. The fibers converge as they course vertically upward, and they insert for the most part into the orbicularis oris at the angle of the mouth. Some fibers, however, insert into the upper lip, and upon contraction, this muscle may either depress the angle of the lip or assist in compressing the lips by drawing the upper lip downward against the lower lip. The triangularis is shown in Figure 5–24.

The Canine Muscle. The canine, part of which may be seen in Figure 5–24, seems to be the superior counterpart of the triangularis. It is a flat, triangular muscle, located above the angle of the mouth but deep to the quadratus labii superior. Its origin, lateral to the ala nasi, is at the canine fossa on the superficial surface of the maxilla. The fibers converge as they course toward the angle of the mouth, where some fibers insert into the upper lip. Others cross over to insert into the lower lip at the angle. Upon contraction, the canine muscle draws the corner of the mouth upward and also assists in closing the mouth by drawing the lower lip upward. Upon dissection, the fibers of the canine and triangularis seem to be common; that is, it appears that the two are actually but one vertically directed muscle originating at the canine fossa of the maxilla and inserting into the mandible.

The parallel facial muscles

The Incisivis Labii Superior Muscle. The incisivis labii superior is a flat, narrow muscle, located deep to the superior quadratus labii. Its course is parallel to the transverse fibers of the orbicularis oris of the upper lip. The fibers originate on the maxilla at a point just above the upper canine teeth. They run lateralward to the angle of the mouth where they blend with other fibers of the region. Upon contraction, the incisivis labii superior draws the corner of the mouth medially and upward.

The Incisivis Labii Inferior Muscle. This is the inferior counterpart of the incisivis labii superior. It is a small narrow muscle located inferior to the angle of the mouth and deep to the inferior quadratus muscle. The muscle arises from the mandible in the region of the lateral incisors. Its fibers course parallel with those of the transverse fibers of the orbicularis oris of the lower lip. They continue to the angle of the mouth and insert by interdigitating with those of the orbicularis oris. Upon contraction, the muscle draws the corner of the mouth medially and downward.

The platysma muscle

Although the platysma may act upon the lower lip, it is actually a superficial muscle of the neck region. It is an indistinct muscle, extremely variable, and seems to be rather independent of other neck and facial muscles. As the name implies, it is a flat, thin sheet of muscle. It arises from a broad cervical fascia in the pectoral region and from the fascia covering the sternocleidomastoid muscle. The fibers course upward to insert into the lower portion of the mandible and the deep surface of the skin in an area extending from the corner of the mouth to the anterior limits of the masseter muscle. Contraction of the platysma draws the lips outward and downward.

The platysma is easily seen when an effort is made to depress the angles of the mouth with the teeth firmly clenched and the mouth tightly closed. It is the muscle used to relieve the pressures of a tight collar.

The muscles of the nose

In the normal organism, the muscles of the nose, shown in Figure 5–27, contribute very little to speech production. They may be rather significant mediators of secondary cues and facial expression, however. Five muscles act directly upon the nose.

The procerus is a small triangular muscle that arises by tendinous slips from the fascia of the lower nasal bone and upper lateral nasal cartilages. It inserts into the integument on the lower forehead between the eyebrows. Some fibers interdigitate with those of the scalp muscles. Upon contraction the procerus depresses the medial angle of the eyebrows, as in frowning. It also wrinkles the skin over the bridge of the nose.

The nasalis muscle originates in an area above and lateral to the incisive fossa of the maxilla. The fibers course upward and medially and blend into an aponeurosis

Fig. 5–27. Schematic of the muscles of the nose.

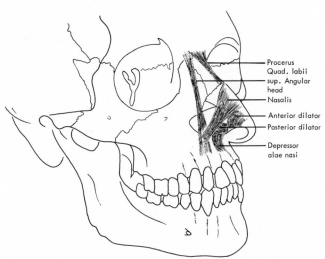

that is continuous with its fellow from the opposite side and with the aponeurosis of the procerus muscle. Upon contraction the nasalis muscle depresses the cartilages of the nose, thereby narrowing the nostrils, a compensatory action sometimes seen in persons with hypernasality, especially when it is due to a cleft palate.

The depressor septi, or depressor alae nasi, arises from the incisive fossa of the maxilla and inserts into the lower border of the cartilagenous nasal septum and adjacent alae of the nose. As the name implies, this muscle depresses the alae of the nose and constricts the nostrils.

Two muscles dilate the nostrils, the anterior and posterior nasal dilators. The first of these muscles arises from the lower edge of the lateral cartilage of the nose and inserts into the deep surface of the skin covering the alae of the nose. The second arises from the edge of the nasal aperture of the maxilla and adjacent sesamoid cartilages of the nose and inserts into the skin over the posterior and lower part of the alar cartilages.

The angular head of the quadratus labii superior also dilates the nostrils. It was described with the muscles of the face.

The Teeth

Introduction

We are all aware of the biological as well as some of the nonbiological functions of the teeth. As is the case with so many other structures in the body, specific functions may be ascertained from the name given a tooth. Thus, incisors (incisive or cutting teeth) are chisel shaped with a sharp cutting edge suited for biting or shearing food, while the pointed tusk-like canine teeth are best suited for ripping or tearing. The molar teeth, with their flat, broad surfaces are well adapted for crushing and grinding. Biologically, therefore, the teeth are seen to be the precursors of the digestive process.

The nonbiological functions of the teeth play a vital role in the day-to-day life of a person. The contribution of dental structure to the appearance of the entire face is a much discussed one, and for good reason. Aside from his personality, a person's face is probably his most individual characteristic. The jaws and teeth, which comprise almost two-thirds of the face, are important determinants of the characteristics of facial structure (Martone, 1963). The teeth and their supporting structures are important for normal speech production. They are directly involved during the production of some consonants, particularly the [f], [v], [θ] and [ð] sounds. By means of palatography, and other recording techniques, it is quite evident that the tongue makes contact with the teeth during the production of many other sounds, notably those often classified, quite appropriately, lingua-velar, lingua-palatal, and lingua-alveolar sounds. The point, however, is that the teeth play an important role in the production of almost all the sounds we emit, including most of the vowels.

Higher-order mammals, including man, are provided with two sets of teeth. The first set of teeth is well developed *in utero* and makes its appearance in infancy and early childhood. They are milk or deciduous teeth. As the word deciduous implies, they are temporary. The second set, however, is permanent. They erupt at an early age and, unless disease intervenes, remain for life.

At first appearance a tooth may seem to be nothing more than a bony tusk protruding from the alveolar ridge. A closer look, however, reveals it to be a dynamic living organ, composed of connective tissue, blood vessels, and nerves, as well as inorganic materials. As such, a tooth is subject to disease, infection, and damage, just as is any other part of the body. Before discussing the deciduous and permanent dental arches, it might be of some value to take a critical look at the general structure of a tooth.

The structure of a tooth

A tooth may be divided into three sections, the crown, neck, and root. The crown is the portion that is visible; that is, the portion of a healthy tooth that projects above the gums. It comprises about a third of the tooth. The root is the portion that is firmly imbedded within the alveolar process of the jaw. It comprises about two-thirds of the tooth. The root is invested by the same periosteum that lines the depressions (alveoli) of the jaw. A thin layer of bone, deposited on the root of the tooth, is called cementum. It is invested by the periosteum (usually called periodontal fibers), and serves to hold the tooth firmly within its socket. The neck is a small, ill-defined region of transition between the crown and root. Identification of the neck is facilitated by a characteristic constriction between the crown and root. The remainder of the tooth consists of the dentin and enamel. A schematic section is shown in Figure 5–28.

Fig. 5–28. Schematic section of an incisor tooth.

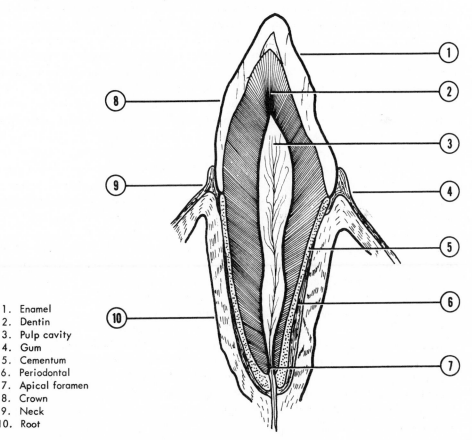

1. Enamel
2. Dentin
3. Pulp cavity
4. Gum
5. Cementum
6. Periodontal
7. Apical foramen
8. Crown
9. Neck
10. Root

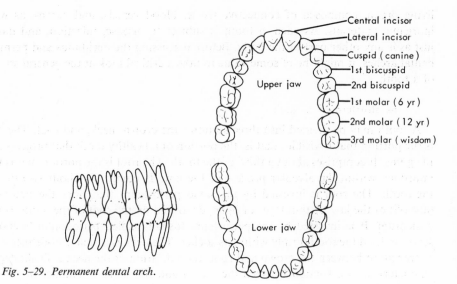

Fig. 5–29. Permanent dental arch.

Dentin (sometimes called the ivory of the tooth) makes up the bulk of the solid portion of the tooth. It is calcified tissue, and is closely related to bone, but differs in microscopic structure. Dentin consists of about one-third animal and two-thirds inorganic salts. The animal matter consists of tubules of protoplasmic substance (dental canaliculi) which are placed parallel to one another, and course the length of the tooth. These tubules are instrumental in conveying the sensation of pain to the nerves of the dental pulp when they are disturbed by such agencies as bacteria, mechanical pressure, or chemical action. Enamel is the most dense portion of the tooth. It covers the exposed portion of the crown as far as the root. Enamel is the hardest substance in the human body, and is composed almost exclusively of inorganic salts. It has one function, to resist abrasion. It is thickest on the grinding surfaces of the teeth and becomes progressively thinner toward the neck.

There are four general types of teeth: incisors, canines, premolars, and molars. They are shown in Figure 5–29. The upper central incisors are chisel shaped, and bear a single root. They are directed somewhat obliquely downward and forward. The upper lateral incisors are smaller than the upper central incisors and have a shorter root. The lower central incisors are similar in shape to the upper incisors, except that they are considerably smaller. In fact, the lower central incisors are even smaller than the lower lateral incisors. Because the diameter of the maxillary arch is larger than that of the mandible, the lower incisors are overlapped by the upper incisors. The lower incisors are directed more vertically than are the upper incisors.

The cuspids, or canine teeth (sometimes called the eye teeth), are located laterally to the lateral incisors. They are large teeth, with a single pointed crown and an especially well-developed root. The upper canine teeth are larger than the lowers.

The premolars or bicuspids are located posterior to the canines. There are eight bicuspids in the permanent dental arch and none in the deciduous arch. The crown of a premolar is characterized by two cusps or points, which accounts for the name bicuspid. The bicuspid usually has a single flat root; however, the upper bicuspids have a tendency to bear two.

The molars are the largest teeth in the mouth. There are twelve in the permanent arch, six in each jaw. Each deciduous arch contains four molars. As shown in Figure 5–29, the molars have large, broad, almost rectangular-shaped crowns, well adapted to their function. Most often the first molar in both the upper and lower jaws is the largest, while the third molar (wisdom tooth) is the smallest. Usually the upper molars have three roots while the lower molars have but two. Interestingly enough, however, the upper molars are in general slightly smaller than the lowers. The grinding surface of molars is distinctive. The first molar usually has four cusps, the second has three or four, and the third has but three.

The development of teeth

The developmental sequence is essentially the same for deciduous and permanent teeth, and the life cycle of a tooth, whether it be deciduous or permanent, may be considered in four periods: growth, calcification, eruption, and attrition.

The growth period includes the beginning formation of the tooth bud, specialization and arrangement of cells to outline the future tooth, and deposition of the enamel and dentin matrix. Calcification consists of hardening of the enamel and dentin matrix by deposition of inorganic salts, largely calcium. Eruption consists of the migration of the rather fully developed tooth into the oral cavity, while attrition is the wearing away of the enamel on the contact surfaces of the erupted tooth.

Growth.   The teeth, which are modifications of ectoderm and mesoderm, begin to show the first signs of development during the fifth or sixth week of embryonic life (11 mm embryo). The initial stage of tooth growth is the formation of the tooth bud from the epithelial tissue contained in what will eventually become the jaws and associated connective tissue. During the fifth or sixth week, the oral epithelium is separated from the subadjacent connective tissue (mesoderm) by a thin basement membrane. Certain cells in the basal layer of the epithelium begin to proliferate at an accelerated rate, which results in a thickening of epithelium along the whole of the future dental arch. This growing epithelium extends into the mesoderm (from which bone and other connective tissues will develop) to form a thin strand of tissue called the dental lamina. During about the seventh week, oval swellings begin to develop in the dental lamina. These swellings are known as tooth buds, and their positions correspond to the future locations of the primary teeth. Once the development of a tooth bud is initiated, its cells begin to proliferate faster than adjacent cells. The proliferation is differential, however, and the unequal growth results in an invagination of the deeper surface of the tooth bud. This is illustrated in Figure 5–30. The developing tooth is now said to have entered the cap stage.

As proliferation continues, the dental cap begins to surround and engulf mesoderm. This mesoderm, which will eventually be located inside the tooth, is known as the dental papilla. Thus, the dental cap is surrounded by mesoderm (which ultimately forms the cementum of the tooth and the periodontal tissue), and it also surrounds mesoderm (which gives rise to dental pulp and contributes to the formation of dentin).

While papillae are being formed, certain changes are occurring in the cells of the special dental germ or cap. The cells become differentiated into three distinct layers. Those in contact with the papillae undergo modifications and acquire the ability to form enamel; they are identified as ameloblasts, or enamel cells. The cells in the outer

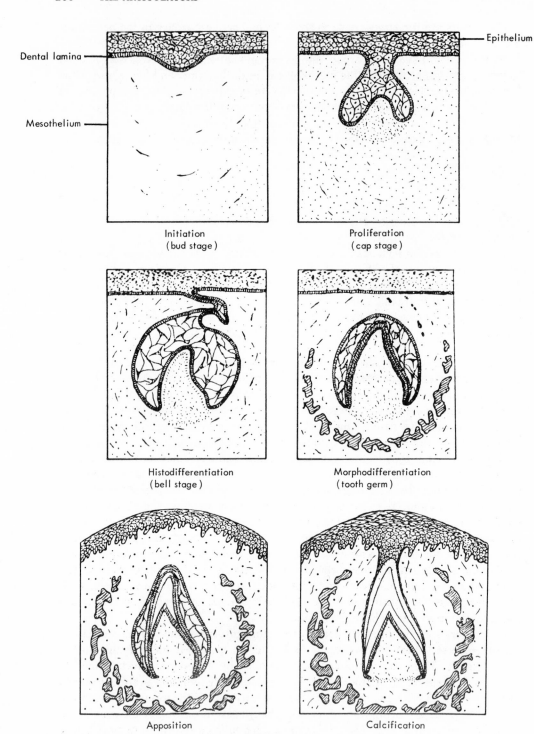

Fig. 5–30. Schematic representation of the growth of a tooth. (*From* Atlas of the Mouth. *Courtesy American Dental Association.*)

layer of the cap are called external enamel epithelium. These cells, plus the cells in the intermediate layer, become modified to form enamel pulp. When these changes have been completed, the special dental germ, or dental cap, is spoken of as the enamel organ. At this stage of development the enamel organ has assumed a bell shape. Thus the tooth has transcended the cap stage and has entered the bell stage. A tooth in the advanced bell stage is shown in Figure 5-30.

Concomitant with the development of the dental organ and papilla, there is a modification of the mesoderm immediately surrounding the developing tooth. The cells become extremely dense and give rise to a fibrous layer of tissue known as the dental sac. The dental organ and its contained dental papilla, plus the dental sac, constitute the formative tissues for the tooth and its periodontal tissue. These structures collectively are called the tooth germ.

The cells of the inner dental epithelium become arranged to form a complex matrix for the deposition of enamel. When these cells have become fully developed they are known as ameloblasts, and form the enamel matrix which is structurally the same as the mature enamel in the erupted tooth but has a consistency of cartilage. The process whereby the enamel matrix is transformed into enamel is called, appropriately, maturation of the enamel, during which mineral salts are deposited and crystallized. The formation and maturation of the enamel matrix are inordinately complex, and the interested reader is referred to Orban (1957).

All the while enamel is being formed in the enamel organ, certain changes are taking place in the mesoderm cells of the papillae. The cells in contact with the inner layer of special dental germ become modified to form odontoblasts. These cells are responsible for the formation of the dentin of the crown of the tooth. The odontoblasts form a layer of dentin, move toward the center of the papilla and produce a second layer of dentin, move again and produce a third layer, and so forth. Thus, upon close examination, a tooth may be seen to contain growth rings, not unlike growth rings in the trunk of a tree. The growth pattern and general health of an individual may be ascertained by the calcification pattern and the incremental growth rings of a tooth. The very center of the papilla, however, does not undergo differentiation, but rather remains as the pulp of the tooth. The root of the tooth, which is a downgrowth of the dental germ, begins to be formed just before clinical eruption occurs. Growth of the root, however, continues for some time after eruption.

Eruption. The usual concept of eruption of teeth is their migration into the oral cavity. Thus, when the tooth is sufficiently well developed so that it may withstand the stresses to which it will be subjected, it makes its way through the gum, as in Figure 5-31. This stage of eruption is called clinical eruption (the observable eruption). Some time prior to clinical eruption, however, the tooth erupts through the alveolar ridge in a phase known as intraosseous eruption. It is interesting to note that calcification of the papilla and development of the tooth are still in progress during intraosseous eruption. Shortly after intraosseous eruption occurs, the bony tissue between the teeth, which separates them, begins to ossify. This tissue forms the alveoli, which are responsible for providing a solid footing for the teeth.

Attrition. Once a tooth has erupted into the oral cavity it is immediately subjected to wear, pressure, and strain. Eventually, even though enamel is the hardest substance in the body, the teeth begin to wear. This process of wear is called attrition and is

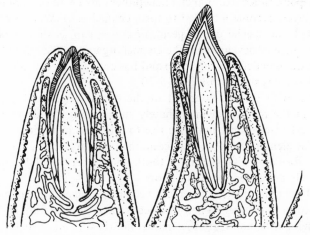

Schematic of clinical eruption

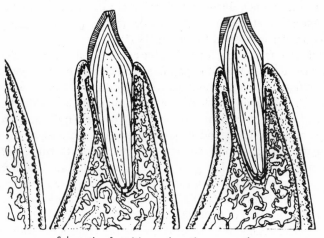

Schematic of attrition and continuous eruption

Fig. 5–31. Schematic of attrition and continuous eruption.
(*From* Atlas of the Month.)

shown in Figure 5–31. By definition, attrition means an abrasion or wearing away of the enamel of the teeth by use. Abnormal, or premature attrition may be seen in the clasping teeth of pipe smokers. The usual sites for normal attrition are the occlusal surfaces, those which make contact during normal function, and the interproximal surfaces, the contacting surfaces of two adjacent teeth. Usually, while attrition occurs, continuous eruption of the teeth helps maintain the spatial relationships.

The deciduous dental arch

The deciduous, temporary, primary, or milk teeth are smaller and fewer in number than the permanent teeth. In general form, however, they closely resemble their permanent successors. The complete deciduous dental arches contain twenty teeth, ten in the maxillary and ten in the mandibular arch. Each half of a dental arch contains a central and lateral incisor, a canine tooth, and two molars. The distribution of deciduous teeth may be expressed by the following formula:

$$I\frac{2}{2}\,C\frac{1}{1}\,M\frac{2}{2} \times 2 = 20.$$

The symbol I represents incisor, C represents canine, and M represents molar. Thus in each half dental arch there are two incisors, one canine or cuspid, and two molars. A deciduous dental arch is shown schematically in Figure 5–32, and a photograph of deciduous teeth is shown in Figure 5–33.

Eruption of the temporary teeth usually begins during the second half of the first year and continues until the end of the second year. It is crucial to be ever-mindful of the variations in eruption times; that is to say, normative data are based on relatively large samples of the population, and may not necessarily represent the actual sequence of eruption for any single child. Approximate ages of eruption and shedding, as well

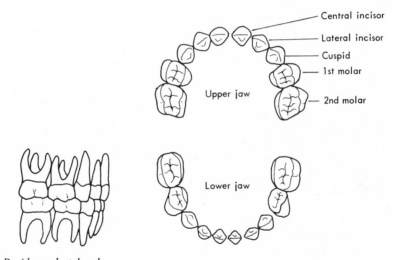

Fig. 5–32. Deciduous dental arch.

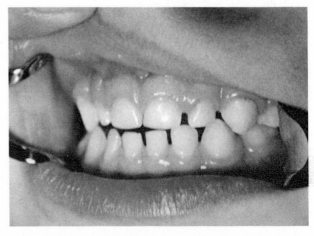

Fig. 5–33. Deciduous dentition.

Table 5-1.
Sequence of Eruption and Shedding of the Deciduous Teeth

	Eruption	*Shedding*	
Lower Central Incisors	6 to 9 mo.	6	to 8 years
Upper Central Incisors	8 to 10 mo.	7	to 8 years
Upper Lateral Incisors	8 to 10 mo.	7 1/2 to 8 1/2 years	
Lower Lateral Incisors	15 to 20 mo.	6 1/2 to 7 1/2 years	
First Molars	15 to 21 mo.	9 1/2 to 11 years	
Canines	15 to 20 mo.	9	to 12 years
Second Molars	20 to 24 mo.	10	to 11 1/2 years

Eruption of the lower teeth usually precedes eruption of the upper teeth by a short interval.

as variations in eruption and shedding times, are shown in Table 5–1. Toward the end of the fifth or during the sixth year, the first of the permanent teeth may erupt in the deciduous arch. Thus, a child of six years may have anywhere from 20 to 24 teeth, provided the central incisors have not been shed.

From what has been said thus far regarding the growth of teeth and the development of the alveolar ridge, it ought to be apparent that the dental arch is not simply an inorganic static structure but rather a dynamic, living organ. Proper growth and the health of the entire dental apparatus is dependent upon the balance of forces acting upon the teeth and their supportive structures. The deciduous teeth are often neglected because they are "only temporary" and are soon to be replaced by permanent teeth. It is important to realize, however, that the health of deciduous teeth is crucial in maintaining the proper spatial relationships for the permanent teeth. Although the early loss of a deciduous incisor is not particularly serious, premature loss of a cuspid or molar may produce such disastrous results as malocclusion of the entire permanent dental arch. In *Atlas of the Mouth*, published by the American Dental Association (1958) the following statement is made regarding premature loss of teeth:

> The first permanent molar is the keystone of the dental arch. The extraction of a lower first molar, without immediate replacement, especially after eruption of the second permanent molar, may result in shifting of the teeth, malocclusion, periodontal injury and caries.

The permanent dental arch

There are two groups of permanent teeth: those which replace the deciduous teeth, and those which have no deciduous predecessors. The first of these are called successional permanent teeth; the latter are called superadded permanent teeth. The development of permanent teeth is essentially the same as that of deciduous teeth. Formation of the successional teeth begins approximately during the tenth week of embryonic life. They first appear as swellings in the same dental lamina that gives rise to the deciduous teeth, and by the time clinical eruption of the deciduous teeth has taken place, the successional permanent teeth are well on their way to maturity. The pattern of development of the superadded permanent teeth is slightly different from that of the successional teeth. By the fifth month of embryonic life, the dental lamina from which the deciduous teeth arise has extended posteriorly beyond the growing second deciduous molar teeth and has become modified into a special dental germ that will

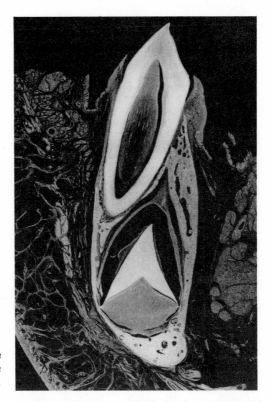

Fig. 5–34. A histological section through an erupted deciduous tooth and a developing permanent tooth.

become the first permanent molar. Simultaneously, the mesoderm subadjacent to the special dental germ undergoes modification to become a papilla for the same tooth. Thus, the development of the permanent teeth is well under way, even before the first deciduous teeth make their appearance. The formation of the special dental germ and the papilla for the second permanent molar takes place about the same time the first deciduous teeth erupt. The special dental germ and the papillae for the third molars begin to form about the time that the first permanent molars erupt.

During their development, the permanent teeth migrate to the lingual side of the deciduous teeth, and are separated by bony partitions. A histological section through an erupted deciduous tooth and a developing permanent tooth is shown in Figure 5–34. As the crown of the permanent tooth reaches maturity, an interesting modification of the corresponding deciduous tooth and bony partition takes place. Osteoclasts, which are large multinuclear cells that have the peculiar property of being able to resorb bone, appear. Gradually, the bony partitions separating the permanent from the deciduous teeth, as well as the roots of the deciduous teeth, are resorbed, until all that remains of the deciduous teeth is the crown. This crown is shed when clinical eruption of the permanent teeth is imminent. The deciduous teeth are not simply pushed from their corresponding socket by the erupting permanent teeth, and that is a most important point to remember. The sequence of eruption for the permanent teeth is shown in Table 5–2. Again, a word of caution: These are normative data, compiled from information on a large population. The ideal or so-called normal sequence may not be representative of an actual individual sequence of eruption.

Table 5-2.
Sequence of Eruption of the Permanent Teeth

Upper Central Incisors	7– 8	Age in Years
Lower Central Incisors	6– 7	
Upper Lateral Incisors	8– 9	
Lower Lateral Incisors	7– 8	
Upper Cuspids	11–12	
Lower Cuspids	9–10	
Upper First Bicuspids	10–11	
Lower First Bicuspids	10–12	
Upper Second Bicuspids	10–12	
Lower Second Bicuspids	11–12	
Upper First Molars	6– 7	
Lower First Molars	6– 7	
Upper Second Molars	12–13	
Lower Second Molars	11–13	
Upper Third Molars	17–25	
Lower Third Molars	17–25	

The teeth usually erupt earlier in girls than they do in boys.

Occasionally an additional tooth may be found in the region of the upper central incisors. These are called supernumerary teeth.

Spacial relationships of the teeth

In the normal skull the maxillary arch has a slightly larger diameter than the mandibular arch. This being the case, the normal relationship between the upper and lower teeth is such that there is a maxillary overbite. That is, the upper arch overlaps and confines the lower arch in such a manner that the upper incisors and canines, and to a lesser extent the bicuspids, bite labial to (outside) the lower teeth. The upper bicuspids and the upper molars are shifted buccally. The normal relationship between the teeth of the upper and lower arches is such that (excepting the upper third molars and the lower central incisors) each tooth is opposed by two teeth of the opposite arch. This was illustrated schematically in Figure 5–29, and a photograph of healthy, mature, permanent dentition is shown in Figure 5–35. During the process of eruption of the permanent teeth, spaces may develop between them. This condition, called diastema, is considered normal, and is usually self-correcting. It is illustrated in Figure 5–36.

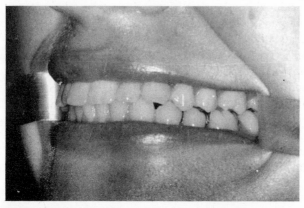

Fig. 5–35. Healthy, permanent dentition.

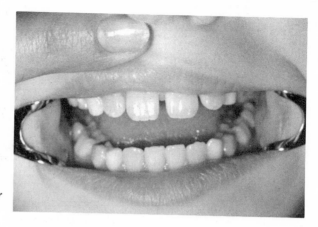

Fig. 5–36. Diastema in a nine-year old child.

Occlusion

By definition, occlusion means the full meeting or contact, in a position of rest, of the masticating surfaces of the upper and lower teeth. In actual practice, however, the term has come to include the alignment of the teeth in the opposing dental arches, the relationship of the upper and lower arches to each other, as well as the positioning of individual teeth. Thus, abnormal occlusion may result from abnormal positioning of the jaws or from abnormality in the position of the teeth. A description of occlusion must of necessity include terms to describe the positioning of the jaws as well as terms to describe the positions of individual teeth.

In 1899, Angle first proposed a system for classification of malocclusions. Classic examples of occlusion are shown in Figure 5–37. It is important to note that Angle's classification refers to the relationship of the upper to the lower jaw. It is not intended to describe the relationship of the upper and lower teeth. Angle's classification follows:

Class I: Abnormal positioning of the teeth, with a normal jaw relationship. The malocclusion is due to the teeth and alveolar processes. The term neutrocclusion is sometimes used in reference to Class I malocclusion.

Class II: A retruded mandible, with respect to the maxillae. The term distocclusion (when the mandibular teeth are more posterior than normal) is often used in reference to Class II malocclusion.

Class III: A protruded mandible in relationship to the maxillae (a prognathous mandible). The term mesiocclusion is sometimes used in reference to a Class III malocclusion.

Certain terms have come into general use in describing the positions of individual teeth.

1. AXIVERSION — Improper axial inclination

2. DISTOVERSION — A tilting backward of the posterior teeth or a tilting away from the mid-line of the anterior teeth

3. INFRAVERSION — A tooth that has not erupted sufficiently to reach the line of occlusion

4. LABIOVERSION — A tilting of a tooth toward the lips or cheek

5. LINGUOVERSION — A tilting of a tooth toward the tongue

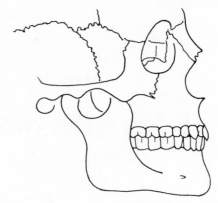

Normal occlusion

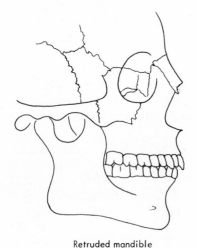

Retruded mandible
(class II)

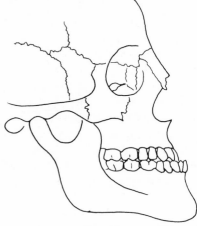

Prognathous mandible
(class III)

Fig. 5–37. Examples of types of occlusions.

6. MESIOVERSION — A forward tilting of the posterior teeth or a tilting toward the
   mid-line of the anterior teeth

7. SUPRAVERSION — A tooth that has grown past the normal line of occlusion. It
   extends too far into the oral cavity

8. TORSIVERSION — A tooth that is rotated on its long axis

Occasionally, in the course of dental development, the anterior teeth fail to erupt
sufficiently to reach the line of occlusion (infraversion), or the posterior teeth have
erupted past the normal line of occlusion (supraversion). In either case a condition
known as open bite results; that is, the anterior teeth are unable to approximate, and
a persistent space exists between them. Conversely, either due to infraversion of the
posterior teeth or supraversion of the anterior teeth, the posterior teeth fail to meet,
a condition known as closed bite. These conditions of open and closed bite need not
necessarily occur bilaterally but may occur only on one side of the dental arch. In

that case, a condition known as a lateral open bite exists. An open bite may be detrimental to the general health of an individual and may contribute to the production of defective speech.

The Tongue

Introduction

The primary biological function of the tongue is in taste, mastication, and deglutition. It moves food into position to be crushed by the teeth, helps mix food with saliva, and later sweeps the place clean before forming the food into a bolus. It finishes the job by shoving the bolus into the pharynx. The tongue is without doubt the most important and the most active of the articulators. It functions to modify the shape of the oral cavity and thus the resonance characteristics of the oral and associated cavities. The tongue also acts as a valve either to inhibit or stop the flow of air, and, in conjunction with the teeth, alveolar processes, and palate, may act as a noise generator. At times, it functions both as a noise generator and a modifier of the laryngeal tone, as in the production of voiced consonants. Indeed, the tongue is a very remarkable structure, able to assume many different configurations and positions in amazingly rapid sequences. It is primarily due to high innervation and to the complex arrangements of the muscle fibers making up the bulk of the tongue that such rapid and subtle sequences of movement are possible. Perhaps a more intimate look at the structure of the tongue will put us in a better position to appreciate its attributes.

On an anatomical basis the tongue may be divided into a blade and a root. It may also be divided on a functional basis into regions or areas. Phoneticians, linguists, and speech pathologists, for example, have divided the dorsum of the tongue into

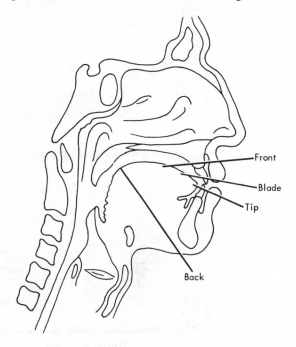

Fig. 5–38. Divisions of the dorsum of the tongue.

four regions. This division is based upon the relationship of the tongue to the roof of the mouth. As shown in Figure 5–38, the portion of the tongue nearest the front teeth is called the tip, the portion just below the upper alveolar ridge is called the blade, the portion just below the hard palate is called the front, and the portion beneath the soft palate is called the back of the tongue.

The tongue is fastened posteriorly to the hyoid bone, the epiglottis, the soft palate, and the pharynx. It is free anteriorly, laterally, and dorsally. The dorsum of the tongue is divided by a longitudinal median sulcus, which runs back to a pit called the foramen cecum. A groove, the sulcus terminalis, courses anteriorly and laterally, from the foramen cecum to the lateral margins. It separates the anterior two-thirds of the dorsum from the posterior one-third. The dorsum contains many punctiform projections or papillae, which are specialized sense organs that contain taste buds. The pharyngeal surface of the root of the tongue contains lymphatic masses that vary considerably in extent from individual to individual. These masses are sometimes referred to as the lingual tonsil.

There are eight, sometimes nine, muscles of the tongue, which may be divided into intrinsic and extrinsic muscle groups. With the exception of the superior longitudinal muscle, they are all paired. The significance of this becomes apparent in hemiplegia and some other forms of brain injury, where the tongue, when protruded, may deviate to one side.

Fig. 5–39. Frontal sections through the tongue of a five-month fetus.

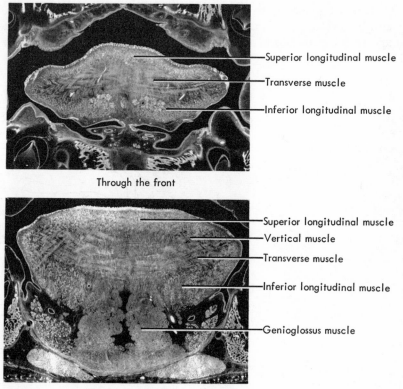

Superior longitudinal muscle

Transverse muscle

Inferior longitudinal muscle

Through the front

Superior longitudinal muscle

Vertical muscle

Transverse muscle

Inferior longitudinal muscle

Genioglossus muscle

Through the blade

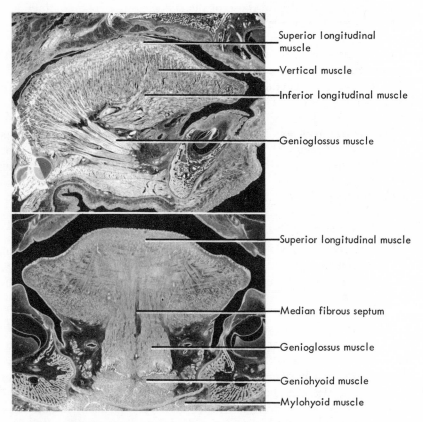

Superior longitudinal muscle

Vertical muscle

Inferior longitudinal muscle

Genioglossus muscle

Superior longitudinal muscle

Median fibrous septum

Genioglossus muscle

Geniohyoid muscle

Mylohyoid muscle

Fig. 5–40. A parasagittal section (top) and a frontal section (bottom) through the tongue of a five-month fetus.

The intrinsic muscles of the tongue

There are four intrinsic tongue muscles, the superior longitudinal, the inferior longitudinal, the transverse, and the vertical muscles. They are shown in Figures 5–39, and 5–40.

The Superior Longitudinal Muscle.   The superior longitudinal consists of a thin layer of oblique and longitudinal muscle fibers lying just deep to the mucous membrane of the dorsum of the tongue. The fibers from submucous fibrous tissue close to the root and from the median fibrous septum, which may be seen in the frontal section of Figure 5–40, course anteriorly and terminate at the edges of the tongue. Upon contraction, the muscle shortens the tongue or it may turn the tip and lateral margins upward, giving the dorsum a concave appearance.

The Inferior Longitudinal Muscle.   The inferior longitudinal consists of a bundle of muscle fibers located on the under surface of the tongue, somewhat laterally. The fibers blend with those of the genioglossus and the hyoglossus muscles (to be described later). Muscle fibers of the inferior longitudinal muscle extend from the root to the apex of the tongue. Some muscle fibers arise from the hyoid bone, while anteriorly a few fibers may blend with those of the styloglossus. Upon contraction this muscle either shortens the tongue or it may pull the tip downward.

The Transverse Muscle.   The transverse muscle fibers arise from the median fibrous septum and course directly in a lateral direction to terminate in the submucous fibrous tissue at the lateral margins of the tongue. This muscle narrows and elongates the tongue.

The Vertical Muscle.   The vertical muscle fibers originate from the mucous membrane of the dorsum of the tongue. They course vertically down and somewhat laterally to terminate at the inferior surface of the tongue. These fibers are confined primarily to the anterior and lateral portions of the tongue. Upon contraction they flatten the tongue.

The extrinsic muscles of the tongue

Four muscles originate from adjacent structures and insert into the tongue. They are the genioglossus, the styloglossus, the palatoglossus, and the hyoglossus. The extrinsic tongue muscles and associated structures are shown schematically in Figure 5–41.

The Genioglossus Muscle.   The genioglossus, which forms the bulk of the tongue tissue, is the strongest and largest of the extrinsic muscles. It is a flat, triangular muscle, located close to the median plane. Part of the genioglossus may be seen in Figure 5–39, and it is shown schematically in Figure 5–41. It originates from the mental tubercle on the posterior surface of the mandibular symphysis. The lowermost fibers course to the hyoid bone, while the remainder radiate fan-like to the dorsum of the tongue and insert into submucous tissue on either side of the mid-line in an area extending from the root to the tip. A few muscle fibers blend into the sides of the pharynx. The muscles of the opposite sides are separated by the median fibrous septum of the tongue, which can be seen in Figure 5–40. In front, however, they blend. This muscle accounts for many tongue positions. The posterior fibers draw the whole of the tongue anteriorly to protrude the tip from the mouth. Certain states of emotion are sometimes expressed by the use of the posterior muscle fibers. Contraction of the anterior fibers is responsible for retraction of the tongue, while contraction of the entire muscle draws the tongue downward, thus rendering the dorsum trough-like.

The Styloglossus Muscle.   The styloglossus begins as a short slip of muscle that arises from the anterior surface of the styloid process and from the stylomandibular ligament. It begins to radiate just anteriorly to its origin and rapidly develops into a flat, fan-shaped sheet of muscle as it courses downward and anteriorly. As shown in Figure 5–41, some fibers enter the side of the tongue near the dorsum and interdigitate with those of the inferior longitudinal muscle, while the remainder overlap and blend with fibers of the hyoglossus muscle. Upon contraction the styloglossus draws the tongue upward and backward, and thus may be considered as a true antagonist of the genioglossus muscle. It also may draw the sides of the tongue upward, thus assisting the intrinsic muscles in making the dorsum concave or trough-like.

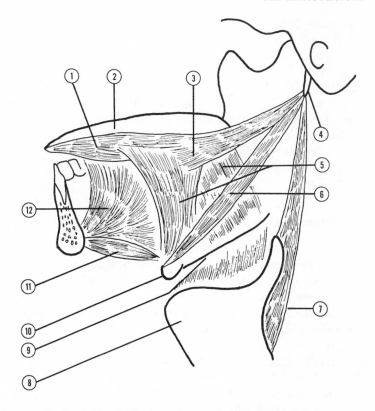

Fig. 5–41. *Schematic of extrinsic tongue musculature and some associated structures.*

1. Inferior longitudinal	7. Stylopharyngeus
2. Dorsum of tongue	8. Thyroid cartilage
3. Styloglossus	9. Greater cornu
4. Styloid process	10. Hyoid bone
5. Hyoglossus	11. Geniohyoid
6. Stylohyoid	12. Genioglossus

The Glossopalatine Muscle. The glossopalatine may be considered either as a muscle of the tongue or of the palate. When considered as a muscle of the palate it is sometimes referred to as the palatoglossus muscle. It originates from the anterior surface of the soft palate, where it is continuous with its fellow from the opposite side. The fibers course downward and somewhat laterally to insert into the sides of the tongue, where they blend and become continuous with those of the transverse and with the superficial fibers of the styloglossus and hyoglossus muscles. Upon contraction it may either lower the soft palate or raise the back of the tongue. This muscle, which forms the anterior faucial pillars, will be referred to again in the section dealing with the fauces and soft palate.

The Hyoglossus Muscle. The hyoglossus, a thin, quadrilateral sheet of muscle, originates from the upper border of the greater cornu and from the corpus of the hyoid bone. The fibers course vertically, diverging slightly before inserting into the lateral submucous tissue of the posterior half of the tongue. These fibers interdigitate and become continuous with those of the palatoglossus. A small bundle of muscle fibers that originates from the corpus and lesser cornu of the hyoid bone follows a parallel course with the hyoglossus muscle and inserts into the intrinsic muscles at the sides of the tongue. This bundle of muscle fibers is sometimes considered to be a part of the hyoglossus, or it may be known as a separate muscle, the chondroglossus. The fibers of the chondroglossus form a layer of muscle that separates the fibers of the hyoglossus from those of the genioglossus. Besides functioning to retract and depress the tongue, the hyoglossus and chondroglossus may elevate the hyoid bone. Thus, it may be seen that there is an implicit relationship between the muscles of the tongue and those of phonation.

The Dynamics of Tongue Movement

The modifications of the vocal tract that are necessary to produce the speech sounds in our repertory are reasonably well documented or classified. For example, phoneticians learned long ago that rather specific tongue positions are associated with production of certain vowel sounds. Because the tongue is so highly variable and makes contact with so many structures in the mouth, adequate descriptions of tongue positions are very difficult. In practice, the configuration of the tongue is described by specifying its gross position during the production of certain vowels.

We have come to regard the position of the highest point of the mass of the tongue as its position. It is difficult, however, to describe tongue positions as being high, low, front, back, and so forth, without some sort of reference. Denes and Pinson (1963) state that tongue positions are usually described by comparing them with positions used for making the cardinal vowels, which are a set of vowels whose perceptual quality is substantially the same regardless of language used. Within reasonable limits a vowel produced with the tongue high up and in front, as in Figure

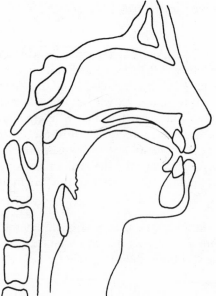

Fig. 5–42. Schematic of tongue position for the production of an [i] vowel.

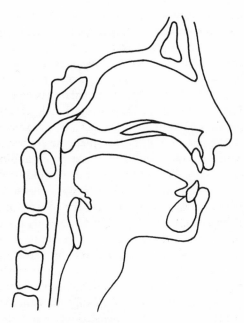

Fig. 5–43. Schematic of tongue position for the production of an IPA [a] vowel (Ah).

5–42 (without the tip touching the palate), will be recognized as an [i]. On the other hand, if the tongue is moved to the opposite extremes of the oral cavity, that is, low and back, as in Figure 5–43, the vowel will probably be recognized as an [ɑ]. In all there are eight such cardinal vowels, and their relative physiologic positions are shown in the form of a cardinal-vowel diagram in Figure 5–44.

The cardinal vowels are useful because they describe the physiologic limits of tongue position for the production of vowel sounds; all the vowels we produce fall within the boundaries of the cardinal-vowel diagram. The traditional vowel triangle, or perhaps better, the vowel quadrilateral, is shown in Figure 5–45. It indicates the articulatory positions of the commonly recognized vowels, relative to the cardinal vowels. Another group of sounds, similar to vowels, is called the diphthongs. They are sometimes described as blends of two separate vowels, spoken within the same syllable. A syllable is initiated with the articulators in the position for one vowel;

Fig. 5–44. Schematic representation of tongue positions for cardinal vowel articulation.

Fig. 5–45. Tongue positions for English vowels as represented by a vowel quadrilateral.

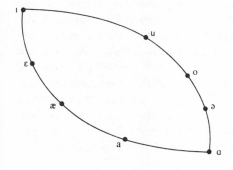

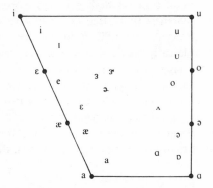

they then shift with a smooth transition movement toward the position for another vowel. The transition movement may bridge two, three, or even more vowels.

The consonants, which are characterized physiologically by an obstruction of the vocal tract, are usually described by place-and-manner of articulation, and whether they are voiced or unvoiced. The places of articulation include the lips (labial or bilabial), the gums (alveolar), the hard palate (palatal), the soft palate (velar), and the glottis (glottal). The manner of articulation describes the degree of closure as the consonants initiate or terminate a syllable. For example, if closure is complete, the consonant is called a stop; if it is incomplete the consonant is called a fricative. Sometimes, when complete blockage is followed by an audible release of the impounded air, the consonant is called a stop-plosive, or simply a plosive. In other instances complete closure is followed by a rather slow release of the impounded air as the tongue sweeps the palate backward; here the consonant is called an affricate. Carrell and Tiffany (1960) stress that an affricate depends upon the shift or change for its basic nature and is not to be thought of as a simple stop-plus-fricative combination. Other sounds, called glides, are produced by rapid movements of an articulator, and the noise element is not as prominent as it is in stops (plosives) and fricatives. Examples are [r], [w], [j], and [hw] (which is sometimes considered a fricative rather than a glide). Some sounds seem to qualify for either a vowel or a consonant classification, and they are designated semivowels. That is, in certain phonetic contexts they may be syllabic and consequently serve as vowels, while in other contexts these same sounds either initiate or terminate syllables and therefore function as consonants. Three semivowels, [m], [n], and [ŋ], are classified as nasal consonants (when they function as consonants) because of their nasal quality. Liquids, including laterals, are distinctive consonants because of the unique manner in which they are articulated. In production of the liquid [l] for example, the tongue blocks the center of the alveolar ridge, while the breath stream flows freely around the sides of the tongue. The place-and-manner of articulation of English consonants is summarized in the consonant classification chart (Table 5–3).

For many years the place-and-manner of articulation of speech sounds has been studied by means of repeated careful introspection and critical observation of the speech mechanism. The classifications that have evolved usually represent idealized articulations during the production of idealized sounds, often produced in isolation. Variations may occur due to individual speech habits and to the influences of immediately adjacent sounds during continuous speech.

In an attempt to obtain quantifiable descriptions of the articulation of speech sounds, phoneticians and linguists have resorted to various instrumental techniques. In spite of a rather high degree of sophistication in the use of instrumentation, the rapid changes that often occur during speech production, even for a single, simple speech event, are difficult to measure. Very precise measurements are particularly valuable to researchers interested in speech synthesis and to linguists. As Fujimura (1961) has pointed out, when an experimenter tries to produce a syllable by means of an electrical analog, he may find he is unable to give in advance a detailed specification of the rates at which the component parts of the speech mechanism must move. Although information regarding the behavior of the articulators may be derived from detailed acoustic analysis of speech, the analysis often turns out to be postdictive rather than predictive. In other words, the specific changes in the states of the articu-

Table 5-3.
Classification of English Consonants by Place-and-Manner of Articulation

Place of Articulation	Stops		Fricatives		Nasals		Glides and Laterals	
	Voiceless	Voiced	Voiceless	Voiced	Voiceless	Voiced	Voiceless	Voiced
Labial	[p]	[b]				[m]	[hw]	[w]
Labiodental			[f]	[v]				
Dental			[θ]	[ð]				
Alveolar	[t]	[d]	[s]	[z]		[n]		[l]
Palatal	[tʃ]	[dʒ]	[ʃ]	[ʒ]				[j] [r]
Velar	[k]	[g]				[ŋ]		
Glottal			[h]					

lators necessary to produce a given modification of the acoustic event are not known until after the analysis, and even then certain assumptions often must be made. Simultaneous acoustic and physiological measures are vital to an understanding of the dynamics of the speech processes, but they are often difficult to obtain.

The dynamics of tongue placement and movements during speech production have been the subject of a number of instrumental investigations, and at present there are at least three techniques in use. They are palatography, X-ray, and electromyography. The earliest and probably the most thoroughly exploited technique is palatography. It is used by descriptive phoneticians and speech scientists to record areas of lingua-dental and lingua-palatal contact during the production of various sounds. There are two traditional palatography techniques, one a direct and the other an indirect process. Indirect palatography requires the construction of a thin artificial palate from dental wax or dental metal. A conventional dental cast is usually used as the mold for the artificial palate. To obtain a palatogram, the artificial palate is dusted with corn starch prior to placement in the mouth. The subject then produces the sound in question and carefully removes the artificial palate, which is then examined to determine where the corn starch has been wiped away by contact with the wet tongue. Some palatograms of various speech sounds are shown in Figure 5–46. By carefully selecting representative speech sounds, in appropriate phonetic environments, a thorough description of the tongue positions for any given individual can be determined. Indirect palatography is time consuming, and as a result, palatographic descriptions of tongue positions have been restricted to intensive studies of small populations. Also, best results are usually obtained from sounds produced in isolation, a factor that poses serious limitations on the technique.

A second, more recent method is known as direct palatography. A schematic of a direct palatography apparatus is shown in Figure 5–47, and the simple steps in obtaining a palatogram are shown in Figure 5–48. In this technique the hard palate, the lingual surfaces of the teeth, and the soft palate are all dusted, by means of an atomizer, with a dark powder (as in Figure 5–48A) prior to the production of the sound in question. A mixture of one part charcoal to two parts of powdered sweetened chocolate has been found to be most satisfactory. It adheres to the palate very well,

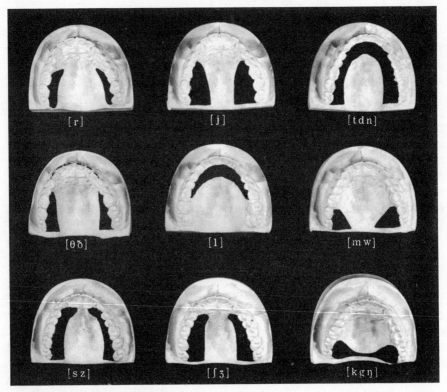

Fig. 5–46. Palatograms of some selected speech sounds.

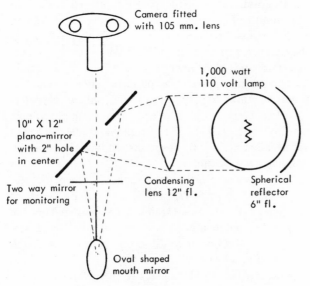

Fig. 5–47. Top view schematic of direct palatography apparatus.

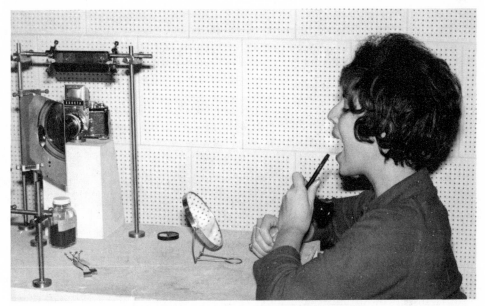

(A)   Subject dusting her palate with an atomizer

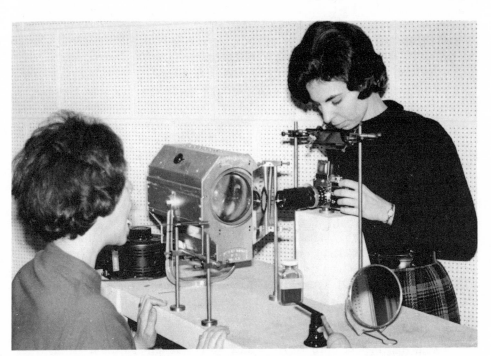

(B)   Photography of the palate

Fig. 5–48. Steps in making a direct palatograph.

tastes surprisingly pleasant, and is easily rinsed away when the experiment has been completed. Admittedly it is a bit messy. Once the sound has been produced, a small oval mirror is inserted into the oral cavity, and the entire roof of the mouth is either examined directly or photographed as in Figure 5–48B. No cast of the dental structures is necessary, and the data are recorded in the form of photographs of the roof of the mouth. An additional advantage of direct palatography is that the tongue contact with the soft palate and the teeth may be determined. Also, the articulation of speech sounds is not subject to the influence of an artificial palate. An undusted palate is shown in Figure 5–49A, while the dusted palate is shown in B. The palate, as it appears just after the production of an isolated [d] sound is shown in Figure 5–49C. The primary advantage of direct palatography is its speed, but both the indirect and direct techniques are limited by the fact that only isolated speech sounds can be adequately sampled and studied.

Recently Palmer (paper delivered at the 1964 convention of the American Speech and Hearing Association, San Francisco) reported a palatographic technique that permits continuous recording of lingua-palatal contacts. A series of transducers, imbedded in a thin artificial palate, operate on contact with the tongue. Tongue contacts are measured visually by means of a series of miniature lamps mounted on a pictorial display of the upper dental arch. Permanent recordings may be obtained by means of motion pictures with a synchronized sound track. The chief advantage of the system is that it permits prolonged continuous recordings of tongue-palate contact. It suffers, however, from the fact that contact area must be extrapolated from a series of fixed points. Nevertheless, continuous palatography provides heretofore unavailable data on the dynamics of tongue movement during the production of continuous speech.

Lateral and frontal head X-rays provide an additional method of obtaining information regarding the relationships of the articulators during the production of isolated speech sounds. Russell (1928) made early use of lateral head X-rays in an effort to study articulation during vowel production. His data formed the basis for a very interesting book, *The Vowel,* in which the significance of jaw-lip relationships and the influence of the resonant characteristics of the hard and soft palates were stressed. Russell concluded that vowels have no constant characteristics with respect to resonant cavities or tongue positions and that the traditional vowel triangle was fallacious. In subsequent works, Trevino and Parmenter (1932) questioned the conclusions of Russell, basing their criticism on inadequate control of head positions during the X-ray exposures, thus rendering serial X-rays unsuitable for comparision, one with the other. These works provided impetus to the use of X-ray in the study of speech production, and in 1934 Kelly and Higley analyzed forty radiograms, pictures taken during the production of vowels [u], [o], [a], and [e] on each of ten subjects. They used a specially designed head holder to eliminate the posture artifact and concluded that the traditional vowel triangle is valid, except for the vowel [o].

Holbrook and Carmody (1937) made use of over five hundred lateral head X-rays of subjects producing vowel and consonants in English and several other languages. They found that the standard vowels tended to fall at rather definite points, thus supporting the general notion of a vowel triangle or vowel quadrilateral.

Recently, the development of motion-picture radiography combined with image intensification has provided researchers with a technique (usually called cinefluoro-

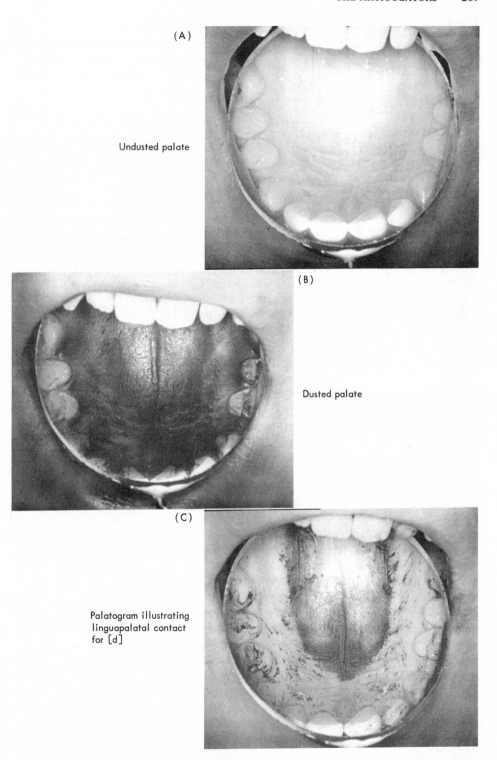

(A)

Undusted palate

(B)

Dusted palate

(C)

Palatogram illustrating
linguapalatal contact
for [d]

Fig. 5–49. An example of a direct palatogram.

graphy or cineradiography) for observing tongue, jaw, and palatal movements during the production of continuous speech and during such otherwise unobservable events as swallowing. The value of information as provided by radiography is dependent to a large extent upon control measures employed during filming. Certain factors, which have been discussed by Moll (1965), should be taken into account. For example, the methods used should place as few restrictions as possible on the normal activity of the speech mechanism. Head stabilizers, abnormal positioning of the head and neck, sedation, or topical anesthesia should not be used unless their effects are taken into consideration.

A third technique, more recent than the others, is electromyography. Although electromyography is a well established clinical tool, its use in the research laboratory has only recently come into being. By inserting needle (usually hypodermic) electrodes directly into the tongue musculature or by the use of small surface electrodes, the relative activity of the various tongue muscles can be determined. For example, MacNeilage and Sholes (1964), using small surface electrodes, recorded muscle activity from thirteen locations of the tongue of a single subject during phonation of seventeen different types of [p]-vowel-[p] monosyllables. In addition, X-ray data and anatomical information were utilized in an attempt to describe the action of specific tongue muscles during vowel production. They found that the posterior portion of the genioglossus muscle contracts to move the tongue anteriorly, thus increasing the depth of the oropharynx, particularly for those vowels which exhibit a high tongue position. They also found that the anterior portion acted in antagonism to back and upward movements of the tongue. The authors were able to assign specific functions to many of the extrinsic tongue muscles, but discrete activity of certain intrinsic muscles was not easily detected or specifiable. As a result of this study, the over-all picture of the motor control of the tongue which emerges is one which might be expected from knowledge of the complexity of the tongue musculature and the speed and accuracy with which it functions. The impression is not one of ballistic movements which are seen in simple musculature (those which result from sudden contractions of single muscles which cease abruptly before the movement ceases), but rather it is of a complex pattern of finely graded changes in activity in which one or two of the muscles produce most of the movement, and others cooperate in movement, stabilize adjacent structures, or actively oppose the movement.

Mandibular Movement

Introduction

The principal function of the mandible is in mastication, and its contribution to speech production is in modifications of the resonant characteristics of the oral cavity. It also houses the lower teeth, which are important articulatory structures. Although jaw movement is very slight during the production of normal speech, inadequate, inappropriate, or sluggish movements may result in severe articulatory defects. The rapidity of jaw movement is surprising, and although it is a rather massive structure, it is exceeded in mobility only by the tip of the tongue. That is, the maximum rate of movement of the jaw is about 7.5 per second (producing "pa pa pa"), while the maximum rate of movement for the tip of the tongue is approximately 8.2 per second (producing "ta ta ta").

The primary movements of the jaw are elevation and depression. It may also be protruded or retracted, as well as moved laterally in a grinding motion. Normal mobility of the lower jaw is dependent upon the integrity of the temporomandibular joint. The anatomy of this joint is noteworthy because improper temporomandibular articulation may result in malocclusion, and conversely, such disturbances as over-closure may occur due to improper dentition.

The temporomandibular joint

The mandible, which is the only truly movable bone in the face, articulates with the temporal bone by means of a gynglymoarthrodial joint. Attachment to the temporal bone is by means of a system of ligaments. The condyle of the mandible rests in the glenoid (mandibular) fossa of the temporal bone, and is separated from it by the articular disc, or meniscus. The articular capsule is a thin envelope which surrounds the joint completely and is attached to the articulatory surfaces of the mandibular fossa and to the neck of the condyle of the mandible.

The ligaments of the temporomandibular joint are three in number. They are the temporomandibular, the sphenomandibular, and the stylomandibular ligaments, and are shown schematically in Figure 5–50. The temporomandibular or lateral ligament is composed of two short bundles or fasciculi which extend from the malar surface of the zygomatic arch to the lateral surface and posterior edge of the neck of the mandible. The sphenomandibular ligament, located on the inner surface of the joint, is a flat, thin band attached to the inner surface of the ramus of the mandible in the region of the mandibular foramen below and to the spina angularis of the sphenoid bone above. The stylomandibular ligament extends from the styloid process above to the posterior border of the ramus near the angle.

Fig. 5–50. Schematic of the temporomandibular ligaments.

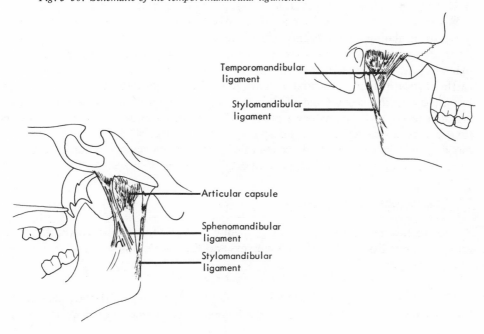

Temporomandibular ligament

Stylomandibular ligament

Articular capsule

Sphenomandibular ligament

Stylomandibular ligament

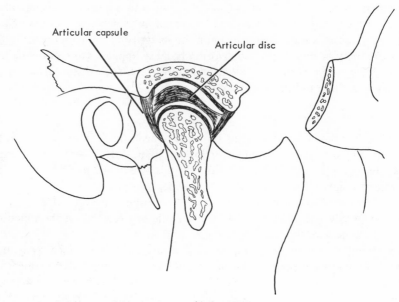

Articular capsule

Articular disc

Fig. 5–51. Schematic of the temporomandibular joint.

The hinge and gliding movements of the jaw are made possible by the peculiar nature of the articular capsule, in particular the unique articular disc. As shown schematically in Figure 5–51, its structure is such that there are actually two articulations, one between the condyle and the articular disc and another between the articular disc and the mandibular fossa.

During the first phase of mouth opening, the action is that of a simple hinge, and only the lower half of the articular joint is used, with the head of the condyle rotating about an area on the inferior surface of the disc. As the mandible is dropped further, however, a gliding action begins which moves the ramus forward and somewhat downward so that hinge action can continue. Gliding action occurs beween the articular disc and the mandibular fossa, and as a result, the condyle of the mandible is carried forward. During maximum opening of the jaw, anterior gliding action may bring the articular capsule out of the mandibular fossa so that it moves under the articular tubercle of the zygomatic process of the temporal bone. When this (subluxation) occurs, a very definite sharp snap may be felt, and heard! During protraction of the jaw, only the gliding action occurs, and in grinding movements, gliding occurs in one articular capsule to produce a lateral displacement in the other.

The Muscles of Mastication

The muscles responsible for opening, closing, and grinding action may be grouped on a functional basis into the jaw depressors and the jaw elevators.

The mandibular depressors (inframandibular muscles)

Three of the four muscles responsible for depressing the mandible have previously been described as elevator muscles of the larynx. They are the digastricus, the mylohyoid, and the geniohyoid muscles. The fourth muscle is the external pterygoid. It probably ought to be classified as a mandibular protractor, although it is very instrumental in depressing the lower jaw.

To review quickly the depressors of the mandible, or the elevator muscles of the larynx, the digastricus consists of an anterior and a posterior belly, united by a central or intermediate tendon. The posterior belly arises from the mastoid process of the temporal bone and then courses anteriorly and inferiorly to the corpus of the hyoid bone. The anterior belly arises from the inner surface of the lower border of the mandibular symphysis and courses posteriorly and inferiorly to the intermediate tendon which is held in position at the side of the corpus and greater cornu of the hyoid bone by a tendinous loop. Contraction of this muscle raises the hyoid bone or lowers the jaw. The anterior belly draws the hyoid forward, while the posterior belly draws the hyoid backward and upward. The mylohyoid forms the muscular floor of the mouth. It originates from the mylohyoid line of the mandible, which extends from the last molar to the symphysis. The fibers course inferiorly and medially to join with their fellows from the opposite side at the mid-line raphe. The posterior-most fibers, however, insert into the corpus of the hyoid bone. Upon contraction, this muscle depresses the jaw. It may also raise the hyoid bone and, consequently, the base of the tongue and the larynx. The geniohyoid is located just superior to the medial border of the mylohyoid muscle. It arises from the inferior mental spine on the posterior surface of the mental symphysis. The fibers course posteriorly and inferiorly to be inserted into the anterior surface of the hyoid bone and upon contraction may assist in elevating the larynx or depressing the lower jaw.

The External Pterygoid Muscle. The external pterygoid muscle originates from two heads, one from the lateral portion of the greater wing of the sphenoid bone and the other from the lateral surface of the lateral pterygoid plate. The fibers converge as they course horizontally backward to insert into the condyloid process of the mandible and into the articular capsule of the temporomandibular joint. Upon contraction, the external pterygoid muscle protracts the mandible and is instrumental in moving it in a grinding fashion. This muscle also contributes to depressing the jaw by pulling the condyle forward, causing the jaw to rotate about an axis located near the angle. Depression is assisted by the digastric, mylohyoid, and the geniohyoid muscles. The external pterygoid muscle is shown in Figure 5–52.

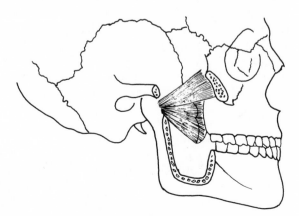

Fig. 5–52. Schematic of external pterygoid muscle.

The mandibular elevators

The jaws are approximated by those muscles which draw the mandible upward. There are three mandibular elevators; the masseter, the temporalis, and the internal pterygoid muscles.

The Masseter Muscle.   The masseter is the most powerful of the muscles of mastication. It is a thick, flat, quadrilateral muscle that covers the lateral surface of the mandibular ramus, and is composed of an external and an internal layer. The external fibers arise from the zygomatic arch by means of a long aponeurosis. The fibers course inferiorly and somewhat posteriorly to be inserted into the angle and lateral surface of the ramus of the mandible. The internal or deep fibers are much less extensive.

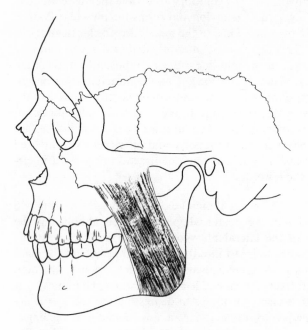

Fig. 5–53. Schematic of the masseter muscle (external layer).

They originate from the posterior surface of the lower border and from the full length of the medial surface of the zygomatic arch. The fibers course downward and forward to be inserted into the upper half of the ramus and the lateral surface of the coronoid process of the mandible. Upon contraction, this muscle closes the jaws. The external layer of the masseter is shown in Figure 5–53. The masseter is a muscle adapted for power. Its fibers contract slowly but powerfully and are specially suitable for the grinding action of the molars. It is well developed in the herbivores, which grind their food before swallowing.

The Temporalis Muscle.   The temporalis is a broad, thin, fan-shaped muscle that arises from the entire temporal fossa. As shown in Figure 5–54, its fibers converge rapidly as they course under the zygomatic arch to insert at the anterior border of the ramus. Upon contraction this muscle closes the jaws and retracts the mandible. It is a snapping muscle, built for speed, and is particularly well developed in carnivores which tear their food but do not grind it before swallowing.

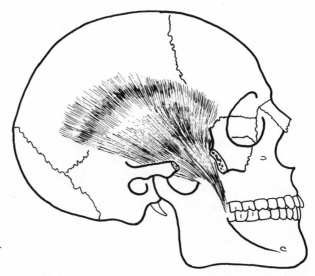

Fig. 5–54. Schematic of the temporalis muscle.

The Internal Pterygoid Muscle. The internal pterygoid is a thick, quadrilateral muscle that originates from the lateral pterygoid plate and from the perpendicular plate of the palatine bone. A few fibers also originate in the region of the tuberosity of the maxilla. The fibers course downward, laterally, and backward, to be inserted into the medial surface of the ramus and angle. It is shown in Figure 5–55. The internal pterygoid is sometimes called the internal masseter, a term that is operationally descriptive. The internal pterygoid and the masseter form a muscular sling in which the angle of the mandible rests and which straps the ramus to the skull. Acting together they impart an important rotary, grinding action to the molar teeth (trituration).

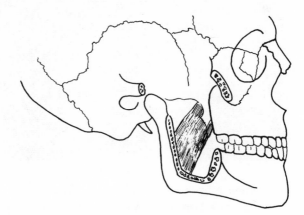

Fig. 5–55. Schematic of internal pterygoid muscle.

The Palate

Introduction

The contribution of the palate to speech production may be stated quite simply. It modifies the degree of coupling between the nasopharynx and the remainder of the vocal tract. It consists of a fixed bony plate in front and a muscular valve behind, although it is often described as consisting of three parts, the alveolar arch, the bony hard palate, and the muscular soft palate. A side-view schematic of the palate was shown in Figure 5–6, while the hard palate as seen from beneath was shown in Figure 5–8 and in frontal section in Figure 5–23. The alveolar arch, you will recall, consists of the bony, tooth-bearing processes of the maxillae and its mucous membrane covering.

The hard palate

The hard palate is formed by the medial projections of the palatine processes of the maxillae, which articulate at the mid-line and contribute to about the anterior three-fourths of the bony roof of the mouth and floor of the nasal cavity. As may be seen in Figure 5–6, the palatine processes are thicker in front, where they blend with the alveolar arch, than they are behind. Posteriorly, the palatine processes articulate with the horizontal plates of the paired palatine bones. They comprise the posterior one-fourth of the hard palate. The posterior borders of the horizontal plates are free, and

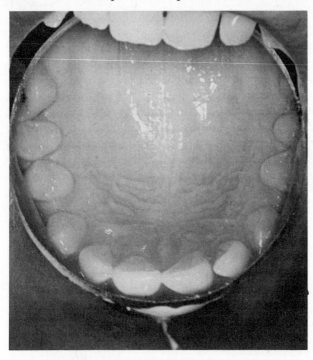

Fig. 5–56. Photograph of the roof of a mouth showing the rugae and a middle raphe.

are continued back at the mid-line to form the posterior nasal spine. The hard palate is covered by a mucous membrane that is tightly bound to subadjacent mucoperiosteum. This membrane is particularly well developed on the posterior slope of the alveolar arch, where it presents a series of transverse ridges or wrinkles called rugae. The palatal rugae, which become less prominent with age, probably facilitate linguapalatal articulation. Posterior to the rugae and continued back throughout the length of the palate may be seen a mid-line raphe, which is subject to individual variation. Rugae and a mid-line raphe may be seen in Figure 5–56

The palatal vault

As shown in Figures 5–6 and 5–23, the hard palate is thick at its anterior and lateral margins, becoming progressively thinner toward the mid-line. As a result, the inferior surface is arched transversely as well as antero-posteriorly. The extent of the palatal arch, or vault, varies considerably from individual to individual and is dependent to a large extent upon the status of dentition. Edentulous jaws have a tendency to atrophy, with a resultant flattened appearance of the palate. The height of the palatal vault has direct bearing on the acoustic properties of the oral cavity and may well contribute to individual voice characteristics. Topographical descriptions of the palatal vault are possible by means of a palatopograph, a measuring instrument that provides contour lines of an individual palatal vault. Early descriptions of palatal vaults were provided by Bloomer (1943); they included the height of the vault, the angle of the slope, and the palatal area at various planes. Palatal vaults also have been classified in terms of their geometric configurations. Crane and Ramstrum (1943) have described three basic palatal shapes: trapezoid, triangular, and ovoid. The significance of palatal configurations has yet to be determined quantitatively.

The soft palate

The soft palate, or velum, as it is often called, is attached anteriorly to the posterior free border of the palatine bones. Attachment is by means of a palatal aponeurosis, which is particularly well developed anteriorly and less so posteriorly. Laterally, muscle fibers of the soft palate are continuous with those of the superior pharyngeal constrictor muscle. The soft palate is directed posteriorly and when relaxed hangs curtain-like into the oropharynx.

The arrangement of muscle fibers in the soft palate is such that it may be elevated, lowered, or tensed. Five muscles are responsible for the mobility of the soft palate. Two are depressor relaxors (glossopalatine and pharyngopalatine), two are soft palate elevators (levator palatine or levator veli palatine and uvular), and one is an elevator tensor (tensor palatine or tensor veli palatine).

As the soft palate is raised or lowered, it modifies the general configuration and consequently the resonant characteristics of the vocal tract. In the production of various nasal sounds the palate is lowered, thus adding length and complexity to the vocal tract and, as we might expect, a concomitant modification of the quality of the emitted tone. Normally, the soft palate is elevated, as in Figure 5–57A, for the production of vowel sounds and is lowered for those sounds we identify as nasals. The palate is also lowered, as in Figure 5–57B, during normal breathing. A closer look at the anatomy of the soft palate ought to put us in a better position to appreciate its capabilities and contributions to the production of speech.

The Levator Palatine Muscle. The bulk of the soft palate is formed by the levator palatine muscle. It is a deceptively complex muscle, arising from the apex of the petrous portion of the temporal bone and from the medial plate of the cartilaginous framework of the Eustachian tube. It courses downward and medially to insert into the palatine aponeurosis, where it interdigitates with its fellow from the opposite side. It is shown schematically in Figure 5–58. Upon contraction, it lifts the soft palate upward and backward. In doing so, however, it also has a tendency to open the

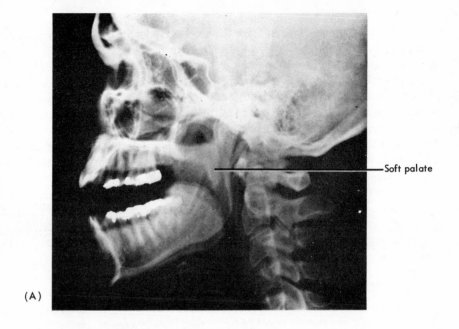

(A)

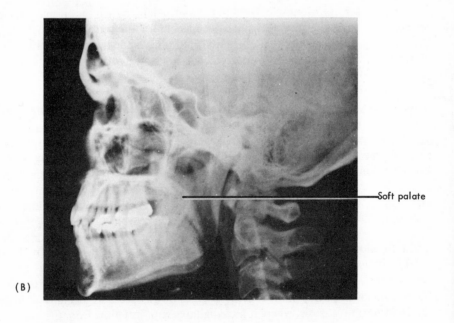

(B)

Fig. 5–57. *Lateral head X-rays showing the position of the palate during vowel production (A) and during breathing (B).*

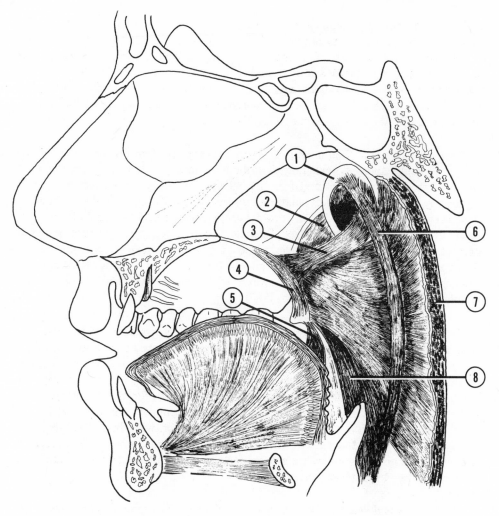

1. Orifice of Eustachian tube
2. Tensor palatine muscle
3. Levator palatine muscle
4. Uvular muscle
5. Glossopalatine muscle
6. Salpingopharyngeus muscle
7. Superior constrictor muscle
8. Palatoglossal muscle

Fig. 5–58. Schematic of the palatal musculature and adjacent structures.

Eustachian tube. This latter action and the structures associated with it will be considered in detail in the next chapter.

The Tensor Palatine Muscle.   The tensor palatine, shown schematically in Figure 5–58, is a ribbon-like muscle, located anterior and lateral to the levator palatine muscle. It arises from the base of the medial pterygoid plate, from the spina angularis of the sphenoid bone, and from the lateral wall of the Eustachian tube. The fibers course at first along the medial pterygoid plate, ending in a tendon which winds around the hamulus of the medial pterygoid plate. The tendon then passes medialward, and is inserted into the palatal aponeurosis and into the horizontal plate of the palatine bone. The significance of its complex action is easily overlooked, Upon contraction it exerts force in a lateral direction and flattens, tenses, and lowers (slightly) the soft palate. At the same time this muscle pulls the membranous lateral wall of the Eustachian tube away from the stationary cartilaginous medial wall, thereby opening the normally closed tube. The significance of this action, which may affect the hearing mechanism, will be discussed in the following chapter.

The Uvular Muscle. The uvular, or azygos muscle, is often regarded as a paired muscle, although anatomy texts may describe it as unpaired. It arises from the nasal spines of the palatine bones and from the adjacent palatine aponeurosis. It courses posteriorly the length of the soft palate and inserts into the uvula, a mid-line pendulous structure of the soft palate. Upon contraction this muscle shortens and lifts the soft palate. Its function is not entirely free of debate. For example, it may function as an important articulator in some languages, although it seems to play no particular role in the English language. The uvula, which may be seen in Figure 5–22, is often regarded as a degenerate or vestigial remnant; however, it is only present in the higher mammals (Kaplan, 1960; Palmer and LaRusso, 1965).

The Glossopalatine (Palatoglossus) Muscle. The glossopalatine, which was discussed with the extrinsic muscles of the tongue, arises from the anterior surface of the soft palate, where it is continuous with the muscle from the opposite side. The fibers pass down, forward, and laterally and insert into the sides of the tongue, where they blend with the longitudinal fibers in the dorsum. This muscle forms the glossopalatine arch, which, with its mucous membrane covering, comprises the anterior faucial pillar. Upon contraction it may depress the soft palate, or, with the soft palate fixed, it may raise the sides and back of the tongue. Because the course of this muscle is semicircular, it also acts somewhat as a sphincter and upon contraction decreases the distance between the anterior faucial pillars.

The Pharyngopalatine (Palatopharyngeus) Muscle. The pharyngopalatine is a complex muscle, difficult to visualize and also difficult to describe. It is a long fleshy bundle, which arises from the soft palate, where many of its fibers are continuous with those of the muscle from the opposite side. It courses, as shown in Figure 5–58, lateralward and downward, until it blends into the stylopharyngeus muscle, which terminates at the posterior border of the thyroid cartilage. Some fibers of the pharyngopalatine muscle blend into the sides of the pharynx. This muscle forms the pharyngopalatine arch, which with its mucous membrane comprises the posterior faucial pillars. Its principal action is in deglutition, where it acts to guide the bolus into the lower pharynx. Because of the semicircular course of the fibers, this muscle can also act as a sphincter to lower the palate and decrease the distance between the posterior faucial pillars, an action that is quite vigorous during swallowing and gagging, when the muscles nearly meet at the mid-line. This muscle may also be quite properly regarded as an extrinsic muscle of the larynx, since its contraction may raise the larynx or tilt the thyroid cartilage forward. Elevation of the larynx occurs during phonation at the extreme high end of the pitch range.

The tonsils

A small triangular space, wider below than above, exists between the anterior and posterior faucial pillars. This space, called the tonsillar fossa, is partially filled by masses of lymphoid tissue referred to as tonsils, or more properly, the palatine or faucial tonsils. They are part of a complete ring of lymphoid tissue surrounding the entrance to the oropharynx. This ring, known as Waldeyer's ring, consists of the palatine tonsils laterally, the pharyngeal tonsil or adenoids superiorly, and the lingual tonsil inferiorly. The lingual tonsil consists of a collection of lymph follicles that covers most of the root of the tongue.

The pharyngeal tonsil consists of an aggregate of lymphoid tissue located in the posterior wall of the nasopharynx. In childhood and even into the teens, the pharyngeal tonsil is usually greatly enlarged (hypertrophied). In a longitudinal study employing serial cephalometric laminagraphy, Subtelny and Koepp-Baker (1956) examined the growth of the adenoid tissue in fifteen subjects, some of whom were followed from shortly after birth to adolescence and/or adulthood. They found adenoid tissue to follow a rather predictable growth cycle. Shortly after birth the soft tissue which forms the roof of the nasopharynx slopes obliquely downward and backward to blend into the posterior pharyngeal wall. Adenoid tissue is not readily identifiable until at least six months of age, and by two years it is usually developed to the extent that it may occupy as much as one-half the nasopharyngeal cavity. Thereafter the adenoid tissue continues to grow, but at a slower pace, until the peak of growth, which may be reached by nine to ten years. After the peak of adenoid growth is reached, the growth pattern seems to reverse itself; that is, the tissue begins to atrophy, and its mass decreases substantially. By adulthood the adenoid tissue has usually completely atrophied. The growth pattern of adenoid tissue is shown schematically in Figure 5–59. Note the concave roof of the nasopharynx in the infant, which with the downward and forward growth of adenoid tissue becomes convex, as in the adolescent. In the adult, the nasopharynx once more resumes a concave appearance. The authors stress, however, that although the growth of adenoid tissue is in an anterior and downward direction, the growth of the facial skeleton is also in an anterior and downward direction. The result is that the dimensions of the nasopharynx are held in a fine state of balance. Facial growth will be discussed at greater length later in the chapter.

While the lingual and pharyngeal tonsils are not readily visible, the palatine tonsils are easily seen in an oral examination. They are relatively large in young children, sometimes to the extent that they almost obstruct the opening into the oropharynx. They shrink or atrophy, however, shortly after puberty. Although the medial or pharyngeal surface of the palatine tonsil is free and visible, the lateral surface is imbedded in the pharyngeal wall. It is retained in position by a fibrous capsule. The rough appearance of the visible portion of the tonsil is accounted for by the presence of from twelve to fifteen orifices which lead into crypts or recesses called tonsillar fossulae. The fossulae branch out and extend deeply into the tonsil structure. A small space superior to the tonsil is called the supratonsillar fossa, and, in cases of abscessed tonsil tissue, is frequently the site of pus collection. The tonsillar ring is probably a defense mechanism against bacterial invasion of the body, and for this reason it is often the locus of infection. Organisms fill the tonsillar crypts and appear

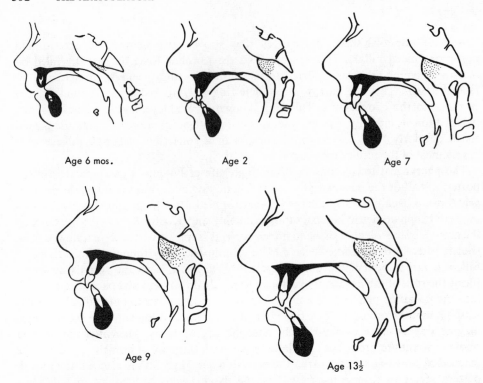

Age 6 mos. Age 2 Age 7

Age 9 Age 13½

Fig. 5–59. Tracings of lateral cephalometric X-rays of the same individual depicting the growth of adenoid tissue from infancy to the peak of adenoidal growth. (From Plastic and Reconstructive Surgery, *XVII, 3, 1956. Courtesy J. D. Subtelny and H. Koepp Baker.)*

as small whitish masses at the openings of the fossulae. In small children such whitish masses are almost continuously present, especially in the palatine tonsils. Chronic or repeated infections may result in a spread of the disease to the pharyngeal tonsil, the Eustachian tube, and the middle ear. Enlarged pharyngeal tonsils may affect the nasal emission of sounds and result in certain voice problems.

The pharyngeal tonsil may also contribute to establishing closure between the soft palate and pharyngeal walls (velopharyngeal closure). Sometimes the soft palate may be slightly short, or the pharynx particularly deep, as in the subject of Figure 5–60. This child has a normal palate, but the pharynx is too deep to allow velopharyngeal closure. The acoustic result, of course, is hypernasality. Occasionally a congenitally short soft palate may accomplish adequate pharyngeal closure because a normal pharynx is made shallow, due to an hypertrophied pharyngeal tonsil. Thus, a congenital velopharyngeal insufficiency is masked by the presence of adenoids. It may be unmasked, however, by surgical removal of the tonsil tissue; temporary (as is often the case) or permanent hypernasality may result. Brodnitz (1959) asserts that permanent hypernasality rarely results from adenoidectomy. However, the matter is not at all free of debate. On the basis of radiographic and longitudinal study of a large number of children and young adults, Subtelny and Koepp-Baker (1956) concluded that in some instances an irreversible nasal quality may appear in speech subsequent to adenoid removal.

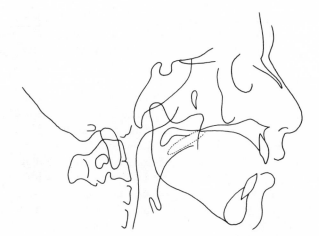

Fig. 5–60. Tracing of a lateral head X-ray of a child with a normal palate and deep phayynx. (X-ray from which tracing was made provided by Cleft Palate Center, University of Illinois. Courtesy Samuel Pruzansky.)

The Pharynx

From our description of the speech mechanism thus far, it is apparent that all of the various contributing structures have biological as well as nonbiological functions. The pharynx forms the upper portion of both the digestive and respiratory systems. As shown in Figure 5–61, the pharynx communicates with the nasal and oral cavities superiorly and with the laryngeal cavity and esophagus inferiorly. Thus it is a single tube that is common to both digestive and respiratory functions.

The contributions of the pharynx to speech production are not fully understood. It is known for certain that its function is one of resonance and that it probably is responsible for reinforcement of the lower-frequency partials in the complex laryngeal tone. The pharynx is not a particularly dynamic structure from a speech production standpoint. That is, variations in the size and configurations of the pharynx are mediated not so much by changes in the muscular walls, but rather by modifications resulting from movements of the base of the tongue and of the soft palate, with which

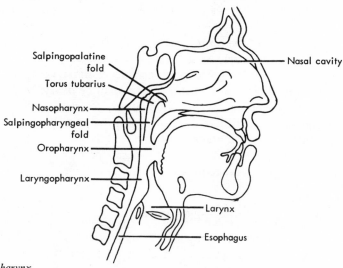

Salpingopalatine fold — Nasal cavity
Torus tubarius
Nasopharynx
Salpingopharyngeal fold
Oropharynx
Laryngopharynx
Larynx
Esophagus

Fig. 5–61. Schematic of pharynx and adjacent structures.

the pharynx is so closely associated. Recently, however, thanks to the contributions of cinefluorography, it has been shown that some not particularly well-understood changes in the configurations of the pharynx do take place during speech production. Movements of the soft palate are better understood, and more shall be said of these later.

The pharynx is a cone-shaped tube about 12 cm in length, and wider at the top than at the bottom. It is about 4 cm wide at its extreme width superiorly and about 2 cm from front to back. It narrows considerably until, at the level of the larynx in front and the sixth cervical vertebra behind, it is about 2.5 cm wide. At its lowest extreme the pharynx is continuous with the esophagus, and at this level the front and back pharyngeal walls are in direct contact with one another and separate only to permit the passage of food into the esophagus.

As stated earlier, the cavity of the pharynx may be divided into nasal, oral, and laryngeal portions.

The nasopharynx

The superior and posterior boundaries of the nasopharynx are formed by the rostrum of the sphenoid bone and by the pharyngeal protuberance of the occipital bone. The inferior boundary is set at the level of the soft palate. Anteriorly, the nasopharynx communicates with the posterior choanae of the nasal cavities; laterally it communicates with the pharyngeal orifice of the Eustachian tube. Thus, the nasopharynx has a posterior-superior wall and lateral walls. The anterior wall is deficient since the pharynx opens into the nasal cavities.

A prominent landmark of the lateral wall of the nasopharynx is the pharyngeal ostium of the Eustachian tube. This tube courses laterally, backward, and slightly upward to the middle-ear cavity. The pharyngeal end (medial end) of the cartilaginous skeleton of the Eustachian tube causes a distinct elevation of the mucous membrane. As a result, the posterior portion of the somewhat triangular-shaped ostium is characterized by a prominence called the torus tubarius (cushion of the tube). As shown in Figure 5–61, a fold of mucous membrane courses vertically downward from the posterior margin of the torus tubarius. This fold, called the salpingopharyngeal fold, contains the salpingopharyngeal muscle. A similar but smaller fold courses from the upper margin of the torus tubarius to the soft palate. It is called the salpingopalatine fold. The nasopharynx widens in a small area just posterior to the pharyngeal ostium and the torus tubarius. This prominent depression is called the pharyngeal recess or the fossa of Rosenmuller. It is at this point that the pharynx is at its widest.

The posterior wall of the nasopharynx, you will recall, is characterized by an aggregate of lymphatic tissue known as the pharyngeal tonsil. A second landmark in the nasopharynx is the pharyngeal bursa. It is a mid-line depression in the mucous membrane that extends from the superior part of the pharyngeal tonsil as far up as the pharyngeal protuberance of the occipital bone.

The oropharynx

The oropharynx extends from the soft palate, above, to the level of the hyoid bone, below. Anteriorly, it communicates by way of the fauces with the oral cavity. Structures in the oropharynx are located on the lateral walls. They are the palatine tonsils and the posterior faucial pillars.

Whereas the nasopharynx is relatively static in nature, and always patent, the oropharynx is comparatively dynamic. This is due to the mobile soft palate and base of the tongue which extend into its lumen.

The laryngopharynx

The laryngopharynx extends from the hyoid bone, above, to the level of the sixth cervical vertebra, below. It is funnel shaped, being much wider above than below, where it communicates with the entrance to the larynx (aditus laryngis).

The muscles of the pharynx

The pharyngeal tube is composed of three layers of tissue: a fibrous coat called the pharyngeal aponeurosis, a mucous membrane, and a strong muscular layer.

The pharyngeal aponeurosis is attached above to the pharyngeal tubercle of the occipital bone, the petrous portion of the temporal bone, the cartilage of the Eustachian tube, and the medial pterygoid plate. From the medial pterygoid plate it descends along the pterygomandibular ligament to the posterior end of the mylohyoid ridge of the mandible, from where it is continued to the lateral margins of the tongue, the stylohyoid ligament, the hyoid bone, and the thyroid cartilage. The aponeurosis is well-defined above, but below it loses its density and gradually disappears as a definite structure. The attachments of the pharyngeal aponeurosis to the base of the skull are schematized in Figure 5-62.

The mucous membrane of the pharynx is continuous with that of all the cavities with which it communicates.

The muscles of the pharynx consist of three pairs of constrictors: the inferior, middle, and superior. They are shown schematically in Figure 5-63.

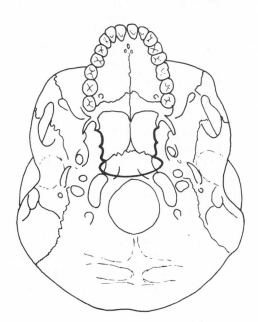

Fig. 5-62. Schematic illustrating attachments of pharyngeal aponeurosis to the base of the skull.

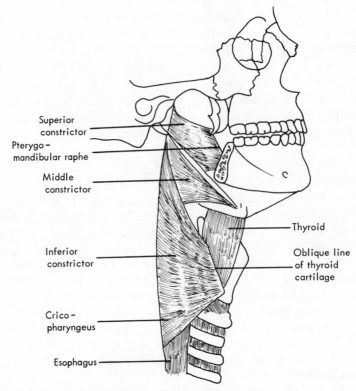

Superior
constrictor

Pterygo-
mandibular raphe

Middle
constrictor

Inferior
constrictor

Crico-
pharyngeus

Esophagus

Thyroid

Oblique line
of thyroid
cartilage

*Fig. 5–63. Schematic of the pharyngeal constrictor muscles
and adjacent structures.*

The Inferior Constrictor Muscle. The inferior constrictor is the thickest and the strongest of the pharyngeal muscles. It arises from the cricoid cartilage in the region of the articular facet of the cricothyroid joint and from the thyroid cartilage along the entire extent of the oblique line, back as far as its posterior limits. From their origins, the muscle fibers abruptly diverge fan-like as they course backward and medialward, where they interdigitate with their fellows from the opposite side, thus forming the mid-line pharyngeal raphe. The inferior-most fibers course in a horizontal direction to encircle and blend with muscle fibers of the esophagus. This band of muscle fibers is sometimes known as a separate muscle called the cricopharyngeus muscle, which probably contributes to the sphincter action of the esophagus. Its importance becomes more apparent in dealing with the esophageal speech of the laryngectomized, for it is the cricopharyngeus muscle that often functions as the pseudoglottis. The remainder of the fibers of the inferior constrictor course in an increasingly vertical direction, with the superior-most fibers coursing almost vertically. They overlap a good bit of the middle constrictor.

The Middle Constrictor Muscle. The middle constrictor is also fan shaped, but it is a somewhat smaller muscle than the inferior pharyngeal constrictor. It arises from the superior border of the greater cornu of the hyoid bone, from the lesser hyoid cornu, and from the stylohyoid ligament. The fibers radiate as they course backward and medialward to be inserted into the medial pharyngeal raphe. The inferior-most fibers course somewhat downward beneath the superior fibers of the inferior constrictor. The middle fibers course transversely, and the superior fibers course obliquely upward to overlap the inferior fibers of the superior constrictor.

The Superior Constrictor Muscle. The superior pharyngeal constrictor is the weakest of the pharyngeal muscles. It arises from the lower portion of the medial pterygoid plate and from its hamular process, from the pterygomandibular raphe, from the posterior part of the mylohyoid line of the mandible, and to a lesser degree from the sides of the tongue. The portion that arises from the pterygoid plate and from its hamular process is sometimes designated as a separate muscle called the pterygopharyngeus, and fibers from it have been consistently found to blend with those of the palatopharyngeus muscle. This finding has important implications with respect to the velopharyngeal mechanism to be discussed later in the chapter. The fibers course backward and medialward to be inserted into the mid-line raphe. Whereas the medial constrictor is overlapped by fibers of the inferior constrictor, the superior constrictor is overlapped by fibers of the medial constrictor muscle. The superior-most fibers fail to reach the base of the skull in an area lateral to the mid-line on either side. Consequently a nonmuscular space exists in a region between the levator palatine muscle and the base of the skull. This area, called the sinus of Morgagni, is filled in by the pharyngeal aponeurosis.

The Stylopharyngeal Muscle. A long slip of muscle, the stylopharyngeus, arises from the styloid process of the temporal bone. It courses downward along the side of the pharynx, with some fibers blending with those of the constrictor muscles, while others blend with the pharyngopalatine muscle, and are inserted into the posterior border of the superior horn of the thyroid cartilage. Contraction of the stylopharyngeal muscle dilates the pharynx laterally and contributes toward elevation of the pharynx and larynx. This muscle might be thought of as an extrinsic muscle of the larynx.

The Salpingopharyngeal Muscle. The salpingopharyngeal muscle is very closely associated with the stylopharyngeal and palatopharyngeal muscles. It is a long slip that originates from the inferior border of the medial cartilage at the orifice of the Eustachian tube. As shown in Figure 5–64, it courses vertically to blend with fibers of the palatopharyngeal muscle. Its principal action is in the initial stages of deglutition. Upon contraction the salpingopharyngeal muscles draw the lateral walls of the pharynx upward and medialward. This muscle and its action may be observed by eliciting a gag while the tongue is held immovable with a tongue depressor.

Passavant's pad and velopharyngeal closure

Until the middle of the nineteenth century, it was believed that palatal movement accounted for almost all velopharyngeal closure. In 1862, however, Gustave Passavant described anterior movement of the posterior pharyngeal wall during velopharyngeal closure. He noted that the pterygopharyngeal portion of the superior constrictor muscle contributes to a forward movement of the posterior wall at about the level of the arch or tubercle of the first cervical vertebra (Atlas). The result is a bulge of muscle

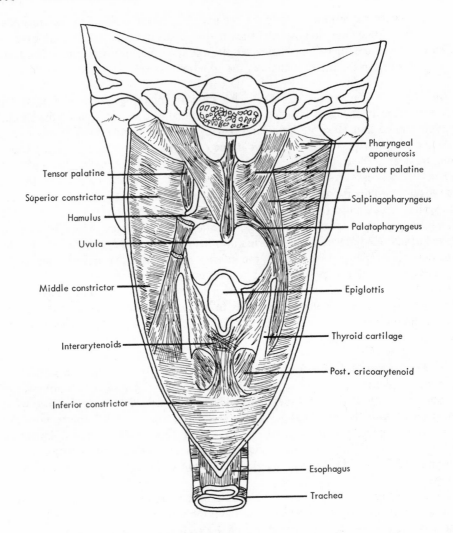

Fig. 5–64. The pharynx and palate as seen from behind.

tissue that is known as Passavant's bar, pad, or cushion. Although he observed this pad in a person with a cleft of the palate, he generalized its importance in speech production to the general population.

This cushion of muscle tissue called Passavant's pad has been found to be formed by a fusion of the fibers of the palatopharyngeal muscle with those of the pterygopharyngeal portion of the superior constrictor. The palatopharyngeal muscle, you will recall, originates from the soft palate and courses vertically downward to insert for the most part on the thyroid cartilage. Some fibers, however, do course posteriorly to fuse with the upper (pterygopharyngeal) portion of the superior pharyngeal constrictor. This anteriorly directed pad of tissue seems to be more prominent in some persons with a cleft of the palate than in those with normal palatal and pharyngeal structures. In these individuals, inadequate soft-palate tissue may be compensated for by active movement of the posterior and lateral pharyngeal walls. Under normal circumstances, however, active movement of the posterior pharygneal wall is not nearly so necessary to establish communication between the pharynx and soft palate. It seems that most persons do not possess a functional Passavant's pad, but such a pad may be acquired through use.

The contributions of Passavant's pad to the establishment of velopharyngeal closure has been both supported and contested, and even the existence of Passavant's pad has been questioned (Calnan, 1954). Hagerty, Hill, Pettit, and Kane (1958), in a laminagraphic study of posterior pharyngeal wall movement, analyzed films of eighty subjects producing the isolated sibilant [ʃ] and the vowel [a]. Their measurements indicated slight forward movement, except for nine subjects in which a Passavant's pad was evident. In six of the nine, however, actual velar contact with the posterior pharyngeal wall was made above the pad, and so strongly that it appeared the pad was not necessary for functional closure.

Currently, it is thought that in addition to upward and backward movement of the soft palate, there is also significant medial movement of the lateral walls of the nasopharynx. In other words, velopharyngeal closure is thought to be somewhat akin to a sphincter-like action.

In an exhaustive, and often quoted study of the velopharyngeal-closure mechanism, Harrington (1944) employed anatomical studies of the head and neck regions of ten specimens, a photographic study of three velopharyngeal mechanisms, and an X-ray study of velopharyngeal closure in three subjects, all of whom had cleft or repaired palates. As a result of these studies, Harrington was able to submit a more nearly complete account of the nature of velopharyngeal closure than had been feasible in the past. He concluded that the soft palate is elevated and drawn backward primarily by the action of the levator palatini muscles and that, at the same time, the posterior wall of the pharynx, mainly at the general level of the tubercle of the Atlas, is drawn forward due to contraction of palatal fibers of the superior constrictor muscles. Harrington noted that although velar activity varies considerably during the velopharyngeal closure, the extent of forward movement of the posterior pharyngeal wall, at least during speech seems to be relatively constant. He also found a considerable amount of medial movement of the lateral pharyngeal walls during velopharyngeal closure and attributed some of it to the hamular and palatal divisions of the pterygopharyngeus muscle. He noted, however, that because medial movement occurs over such a great vertical distance, the main contributor to this movement must be the salpingopharyngeus muscle, which, he stated, draws the lateral walls medially from as high as the orifice of the Eustachian tube to slightly below the level of Passavant's pad. He further noted that the extent of medial movement bears a direct relationship to the extent of velar elevation during velopharyngeal closure. Harrington found that the height of the velum increased progressively from [a] to [æ], to [i], to [u]. He suggested that the difference in velopharyngeal closure between the four vowels was related to the height of the tongue during vowel production.

Bloomer (1953), who investigated velopharyngeal movement by direct observation and photography of palatal and pharyngeal movements in patients who had undergone surgical removal of parts of their face, also found that complete velopharyngeal closure is not always found during vowel production. He noted that a greater degree of closure is obtained on the high than on the low vowels.

Hagerty and Hill (1960) also demonstrated incomplete closure during vowel production. In a previously mentioned study (Hagerty, *et al.*, 1958), he noted an incomplete closure for the [a] and a complete closure for the [s] sound.

In a cinefluorographic investigation of velopharyngeal closure, Moll (1962) concluded that the low vowels exhibit less velopharyngeal closure than the high vowels and that vowels adjacent to the nasal [n] exhibit incomplete closure, with the vowels preceding [n] having less closure than those that follow [n]. He also noted a tendency for less closure on isolated vowels than on those in nonnasal consonants contexts.

DEVELOPMENT AND GROWTH OF THE FACIAL REGION

Introduction and Early Embryonic Development

Because no living organism is immortal, the continuation of any species is dependent upon an unending succession of individuals, each of whom possesses the salient characteristics of its species. All animals reproduce, from the simplest protozoan to the most complex mammal. According to zoologists, the early forms of life probably duplicated themselves by a process not unlike fission, much like many bacteria and protozoa do today. The process is called mitosis, and is an example of asexual reproduction in which the parent simply divides into two parts, usually equal in size and rather exact duplicates. Since mitosis is a mechanism that maintains a constant chromosome number, all offspring have the same number of chromosomes as the parent cell.

A mature man is estimated to be composed of approximately 10^{14} cells. These cells not only must be formed and differentiated as the body grows, but also in many instances they must be replaced as they mature and die. Fortunately for biologists, in most organisms, the process of cell division is essentially the same. Thus, mitosis can be studied in an onion skin, in the root tips of growing plants, or in tissue culture, and the process is essentially the same as that in the living human or growing embryo.

The duplication of genes and chromosomes is the first step in the division of cells. It is immediately followed by a division of the cytoplasm, with the result that two cells, each identical in genetic characteristics, are formed. Biologists have divided mitotic cell division into five phases, shown schematically in Figure 5–65; in order of sequence they are interphase or resting phase, prophase, metaphase, anaphase, and telophase.

The term interphase or resting phase may imply that no activity is taking place in the nucleus of the cell, but this is hardly the case. It is during the interphase that nuclear growth is occurring at an accelerated rate. Toward the end of the interphase, however, the chromosomes, which are not normally visible, begin to take on a granulated appearance. The first sign that cell division is imminent is when the chromosomes become visible as long, thin threads, called chromatids. This stage of cell division is known as the prophase, throughout which the chromatids become increasingly visible, largely due to the fact that they become shorter and thicker. In addition, the nucleoli, which are formed by chromosomes, diminish in size and finally disappear. The metaphase begins with the disappearance of the nuclear membrane; at the same time a new structure appears in the cytoplasm. It is a long, thin chain of protein molecules, called the spindle, that is oriented between the two "poles" within

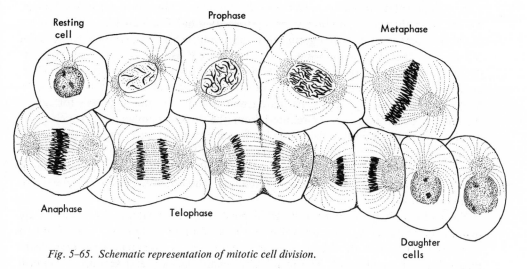

Fig. 5–65. Schematic representation of mitotic cell division.

the cell body. When the spindle is well-developed, the chromosomes move randomly through the cytoplasm at first and finally settle in a region midway between the poles of the spindle. The paired chromosomes are then seemingly pulled toward opposite poles (presumably by fine fibrils of the spindle). This migration toward the poles takes place in the anaphase of cell division. When the chromosomes form a densely packed group at the two poles, the telophase begins. Interestingly enough, the events that occur in prophase take place once more, but in reverse order. Thus, a nuclear membrane forms around the chromosomes, which uncoil to form slender threads again, and the nucleoli make their appearance. A cell wall forms in the region of the spindle, which slowly disintegrates leaving two cells, separated one from the other and ready to undergo a growth period before the next division is initiated.

Sexual reproduction, which is well-established in many simple forms of life, involves the union of two germ cells. Sometime during their life, complex organisms produce gametes, a general term denoting a sexual germ cell. Two gametes unite (one male and one female) to form a single new cell called a zygote, and it is this cell that gives rise to a new individual organism. In higher-order animals, including man, the female germ cell is called an ovum or egg. The human ovum has a diameter of about 200 microns (a micron is .001 millimeters). The male germ cell is called a spermatozoon or simply a sperm cell. It is about 50 microns in length, including the filament; the head alone is about 5 microns long.

It is important to recognize that when two sexual germ cells unite, their nucleic material and chromosomes are also combined. Every mature human cell contains 46 chromosomes. If mitosis were the only mechanism for the generation of new cells, each human germ cell would also contain 46 chromosomes, and the zygote, formed by the fertilization of an ovum by a sperm cell, would contain 92 chromosomes. Every cell in the mature individual that arose from this zygote would also contain 92 chromosomes, as would the germ cells of the new individual. Thus, the individual of the succeeding generation would possess 184 chromosomes, and, according to Swanson (1964), by the end of the tenth generation, each individual would have cells containing 23,332 chromosomes. This would be a disastrous state of affairs, for without some compensatory mechanism to reduce the number of chromosomes in the gamete, we simply would not remain human beings for very long! The reduction of the number of chromosomes in the sexual germ cell is accomplished by an extraordinary type of cell division called meiosis, which, very grossly, consists of two nuclear divisions during the maturation of the sex cell, with only one division of chromosomes. Thus, before any germ cell is capable of reproduction it must undergo meiosis. During the final phases of gametogenesis—spermatogenesis for sperms and oogenesis for eggs— the number of chromosomes is reduced from the diploid number (2N) which is the number found in all body cells, to the haploid number (N), just one-half the diploid number, which is the number found in the sex cells. Thus the mature sex cell contains one full set of chromosomes, not two as in the body cells. Gametogenesis is a fascinating process, but beyond the scope of the text. The interested reader is referred to Swanson (1964).

Normally, millions of sperm cells are deposited in the female, and when a mature ovum is present, they stream toward it at a rate of about 75 mm per hour. The first sperm cell that strikes the membrane surrounding the ovum enters, head first, dropping off its tail or filament. The membrane repairs quickly and sets up a chemical barrier which prevents additional sperm from entering. The fertilized cell is now known as a zygote (unpaired cell), and when the nuclei of the ovum and sperm unite, the first division of the cell follows shortly thereafter. With the union of the two sex cells the zygote is in possession of the full complement of 92 chromosomes. The cell division that follows is the mitotic division described earlier, and as a result each daughter cell possesses 92 chromosomes.

Early cell division of the fertilized human ovum has not been observed, and much of what is known has been learned from animal studies, in particular of the chicken and monkey. From what information there is, the process is probably as follows:

Initial cell division is probably accomplished within twenty-four hours after fertilization. Of the two cells, called blastomeres, one is larger than the other and this divides so that three cells are present after the second division. The other cell then divides, producing four cells, and so on, until a rounded mass containing from twelve to sixteen cells is formed. Such a round mass of cells, called a morula, has been recovered from the uterine cavity on or about the third day after fertilization. The morula remains in the uterine cavity, bathed in the fluid secreted by the uterine glands. This fluid passes between the cells of the morula, and as the morula grows it forms a fluid-filled sphere known as a blastocyst. The fluid-filled cavity is called a blastocoele. An early form of cell differentiation begins to take place during the blastocyst phase.

A mid-section of a blastocyst, shown schematically in Figure 5–66, reveals an outer layer of cuboidal cells called the trophoblast, which surrounds an inner cell mass. During this phase of development, the blastocyst becomes attached to the deciduous tissue of the uterine lining in such a way that the inner cell mass (known as the animal pole) is deepest. The trophoblast will not contribute toward the formation of any structure of the embryo, but rather, it forms only the fetal membranes such as the placenta. The inner cell mass, on the other hand, forms only embryonic tissue.

The first indication of cell differentiation in the inner cell mass is when certain cells proliferate to form the endoderm of the embryo. They proliferate at the periphery of the inner cell mass, between it and the trophoblast. Two distinct layers of endodermal

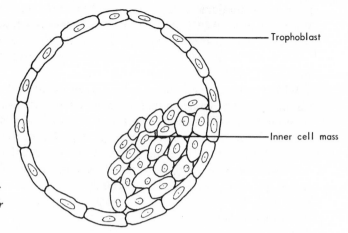

Fig. 5–66. Schematic section of a blastocyst revealing the inner cell mass.

cells become evident. One consists of cuboidal cells and lies against the inner cell mass. These endodermal cells proliferate at the periphery of the inner cell mass and ultimately completely line the inside of the trophoblast to form a sac called the primary yolk sac. These cells continue to proliferate until the yolk sac completely lines the blastocoele and finally folds or buckles. This folding causes the sac to be constricted so that it consists of two parts, a primary yolk sac that later atrophies and disappears and a secondary yolk sac that persists for some time. About the time the yolk sac is being formed, cells from the inner surface of the trophoblast proliferate to form a loose network of extraembryonic mesoderm (it does not contribute to formation of the embryo). This developing mesoderm, called magma reticulare, fills the blastocoele and it pushes the primary yolk sac away from the trophoblast whereupon it shrivels and atrophies. The remaining secondary yolk sac is confined to a small area in the vicinity of the inner cell mass.

During this same period, certain cells in the inner cell mass begin to secrete fluid, so that a layer of cells is separated from the inner cell mass. The result is a fluid-filled cavity, the amnionic cavity, which is covered by amnionic membrane, or simply the amnion. The early amnion and its relation to the inner cell mass is shown schematically in Figure 5–67. At the same time as the amnion is being formed, cells in the

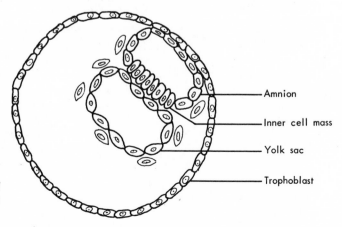

Fig. 5–67. The early amnion and its relation to the inner cell mass and yolk sac.

floor of the amnionic cavity become tall and columnar to form a layer of ectoderm. When this has taken place, the inner cell mass is known as the embryonic disc. It consists of columnar ectodermal cells in the floor of the amnionic cavity and a subadjacent layer of cuboidal endodermal cells which forms the roof of the yolk sac, as shown in Figure 5–68.

While these changes have been taking place, extraembryonic mesoderm has continued to proliferate so that it almost completely fills the blastocoele. This extraembryonic mesoderm forms two layers of tissue, one of which (called the somatopleuric extraembryonic mesoderm) lines the inside of the trophoblast. The inner cells of the trophoblast and its extraembryonic mesoderm lining together form an important fetal membrane called the chorion. The outer layer of extraembryonic mesoderm (called splanchnopleuric extraembryonic mesoderm) comes in contact with the outside of the yolk sac. The relationship of extraembryonic mesoderm to the embryonic disc is shown schematically in Figure 5–69.

While the blastocyst is implanting and the yolk sac and amnion are being formed, rapid and significant changes are taking place in the trophoblast which is rapidly proliferating. Enzymes, produced by the cells of the trophoblast, erode the deciduous

Fig. 5–68. Schematic of inner cell mass and adjacent structures.

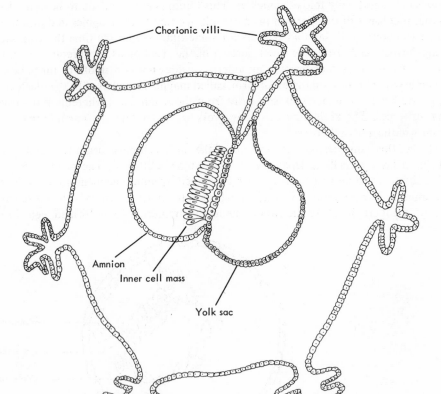

Chorionic villi

Amnion

Inner cell mass

Yolk sac

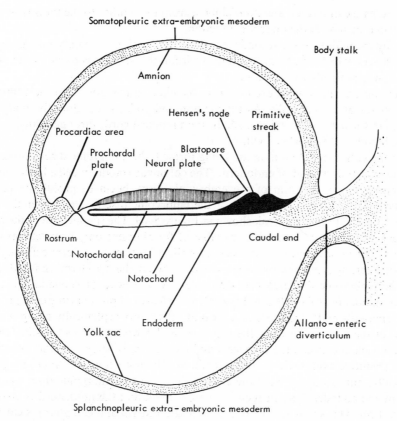

Fig. 5–69. Diagrammatic representation of a bilaminar embry-onic disc as seen in a longitudinal section. Extra-embryonic mesoderm is shown in stipple.

tissue of the uterine lining and facilitate interstitial implantation of the blastocyst. Proliferation of the trophoblast produces two types of cells, one of which (the syncitiotrophoblast) proliferates so rapidly that the individual cells do not produce cell boundaries. The other type (the cytotrophoblast) does produce cell boundaries. As proliferation of the trophoblast continues, finger-like processes (trophoblastic villi) begin to extend out in all directions from the blastocyst. At first the villi are composed only of syncitiotrophoblast and cytotrophoblast, but later somatopleuric extra-embryonic mesoderm invades them, and they are called chorionic villi (the chorion, you will recall, is formed by extraembryonic mesoderm cells from the trophoblast). As shown schematically in Figure 5–68, villi at first develop all over the surface of the blastocyst. Later, however, they degenerate, except at the region of the inner cell mass (embryonic pole), where they continue to invade the decidua of the uterus and become more complex. This restricted area, where villi continue to develop, is known as the chorion frondosum. It is the chorion frondosum that forms the fetal portion of the placenta, while the maternal portion is formed by the deciduous uterine tissue immediately surrounding the blastocyst. Eventually the chorionic villi invade the maternal blood supply, and when the fetal blood vessels grow into the chorionic villi, an exchange of oxygen and nourishment from the mother to the fetus is possible. Waste materials pass in the opposite direction.

Thus, by the middle of the second week after fertilization the embryo is surrounded by three layers, which are, from without to within, the deciduous tissue of the uterus, the chorion, and finally the amnion.

Extraembryonic mesoderm extends from the chorion frondosum to the embryonic disc by means of a body stalk. As the amnion and yolk sac develop, the body stalk elongates to form the connective tissue of the umbilical cord, through which courses the fetal blood to the chorionic villi.

While the yolk sac and amnion are being formed, the embryonic disc consists only of a layer of ectoderm and of endoderm. The columnar ectoderm cells, in the floor of the amnionic cavity (dorsum of the embryonic disc), begin to proliferate rapidly, particularly at the future caudal end of the embryonic disc (the end near the body stalk) to form the primitive streak shown in Figure 5–69. The significance of the primitive streak lies in the fact that it is capable of forming not only new ectoderm and endoderm, but *intraembryonic mesoderm* as well. A layer of mesoderm cells begins to grow out laterally from the primitive streak between the ectoderm and endoderm. Thus, the embryonic disc becomes trilaminar. At the head or cephalic end of the primitive streak (away from the body stalk), a small area of proliferating cells produces a node, Hensen's node, from which a strip of cells grows cephalically along the mid-line axis of the embryo between the ectoderm and endoderm. This mid-line strip of cells, sandwiched between the ectoderm and endoderm, is known as the notochord. It is the primitive axial skeleton of the embryo. The notochord continues its growth cephalically, but is stopped near the extreme limits of the embryonic disc, where the ectoderm and endoderm are in such intimate contact that the notochord is unable to separate them. This small area of tightly bound ectoderm and endoderm is called the prochordal plate. It forms the buccopharyngeal membrane, to be discussed later. Just ahead of the prochordal plate, an area of intraembryonic mesoderm, produced from the primitive streak, continues to proliferate, until finally it forms an intermediate layer between the ectoderm and endoderm everywhere in the embryonic disc except in the procardiac area, where it is found only in the mid-line. As the intraembryonic mesoderm continues to grow laterally, it finally meets and becomes continuous with the extraembryonic mesoderm that forms the chorion. During this stage of development a thickening of the ectoderm occurs in an area immediately overlying the notochord. This thickening is called the medullary, or neural, plate, the lateral margins of which grow upward to form the paraxial neural folds, between which lies the neural groove. Eventually the neural folds meet at the mid-line, fuse, and form the neural tube, from which all the future central nervous system is developed. The ectoderm once again becomes a continuous layer over the dorsum of the embryo. These developments, shown schematically in Figure 5–70, usually have occurred by the beginning of the third week.

A schematic representation of a longitudinal section through a three-week embryo was shown in Figure 5–69. Note the discontinuity between the caudal end of the neural plate and Hensen's node. This perforation is known as the blastopore, behind which is the primitive streak. Note further a small diverticulum at the caudal end of the yolk sac extending into the body stalk. It is called the alanto-enteric diverticulum, which ultimately extends into the body stalk.

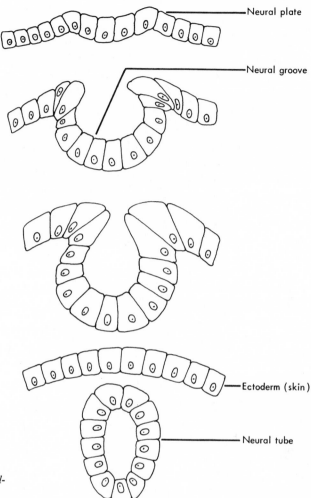

Neural plate

Neural groove

Ectoderm (skin)

Neural tube

Fig. 5–70. Schematic of the development of the neural tube.

About the beginning of the third week, mesoderm on either side of the neural tube and notocord (paraxial mesoderm) begins a progressive caudal transverse segmentation to form blocks or somites. They occupy the entire length of the trunk of the embryo on either side of the mid-line. The somites are subadjacent to the ectoderm, and are located lateral to the notocord and neural tube. A schematic transverse section through a somite is shown in Figure 5–71. There are three occipital, eight cervical, twelve thoracic, five lumbar, and from five to eight coccygeal somites. The occipital somites disappear early in the development of the embryo.

The tissue of the somites becomes differentiated into three parts, the medial-most of which is called the sclerotome. The cells of the sclerotome migrate to surround the notochord and the neural tube. This tissue differentiates into the vertebrae and the intervertebral discs. The migration dorsally around the neural tube forms the neural arch of the vertebra, and when the paired migrating sclerotomes meet, they join to form the neural spine. Cells immediately lateral to the sclerotome become elongated

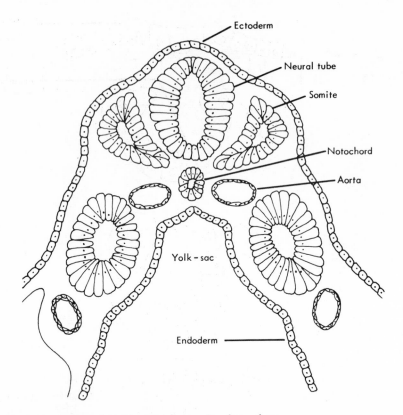

Ectoderm

Neural tube

Somite

Notochord

Aorta

Yolk-sac

Endoderm

Fig. 5–71. A schematic section through a somite of an embryo.

and spindle shaped. They are known collectively as a myotome or myomere. The myomeres differentiate into the muscles of the trunk of the body. The posterior portion of each myomere remains associated with the vertebral column and, by union with myomeres above and below, becomes the intrinsic musculature of the back. The anterior portion of each myomere divides into parts that give rise to the muscles just anterior to the vertebral column and parts that migrate around to the sides and front of the trunk to form abdominal muscles. The most lateral portion of the somite forms the dermatome which develops into the dermis or chorium of the skin. The overlying ectoderm forms the epidermis.

During the latter part of the third week, a very significant development occurs, the flexion of the embryo, in which a reversal of the head and tail ends occurs. Because of the extremely rapid growth of the intraembryonic structures, they cannot maintain themselves in a platelike position, and the entire embryo is thrown into a series of folds. Very rapid growth of the cephalic end of the embryo causes a cephalic fold in which the prochordal plate (now known as the buccopharyngeal membrane) is folded under the embryonic head. This flexion also carries the procardiac area under the developing head, so that both the buccopharyngeal membrane and the developing heart are ventral to the neural plate. Thus, the original rostral wall of the procardiac area now forms the caudal wall. Successive stages of flexion of the embryo are shown schematically in Figure 5–72.

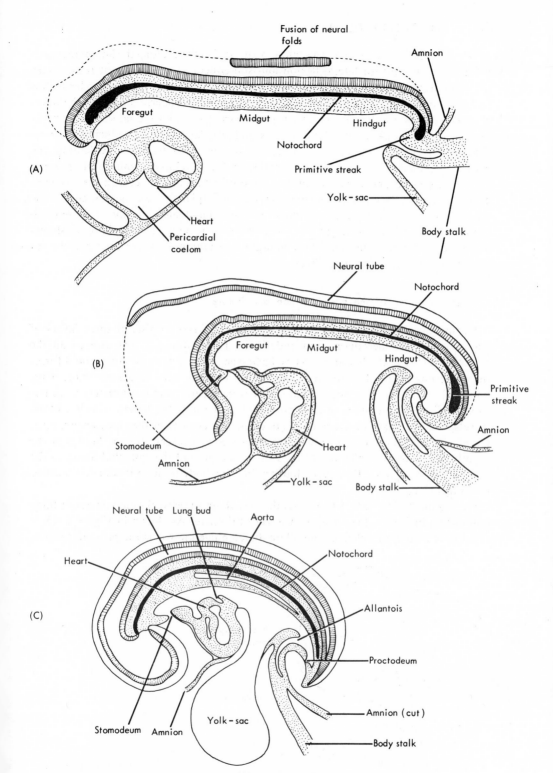

Fig. 5–72. Schematic sagittal sections of human embryos showing the longitudinal flexion and the establishment of the digestive tract.

While the embryo is flexing in a sagittal plane, it also flexes along the lateral margins. In order to account for lateral flexion and subsequent developments, it is necessary to elaborate on the developmental progress of the intraembryonic mesoderm thus far. It becomes divided into three parts: the paraxial mesoderm alongside the notochord (which is ectoderm), the intermediate mesoderm, and the lateral plate mesoderm. The lateral plate mesoderm divides into two layers, thus producing a cavity, the intraembryonic coelom, between them. It subsequently becomes divided into the pericardial, pleural, and peritoneal cavities in the developing embryo. The upper layer, called somatopleuric intraembryonic mesoderm, is in contact with the ectoderm of the dorsum of the embryo. The lower layer, called splanchnopleuric intraembryonic mesoderm, is in contact with the endoderm. Sagittal and lateral flexion of the embryo constricts the yolk sac, which in effect is taken into the body of the embryo, as shown in Figure 5–72, and forms part of the mid-gut. Formation of the remainder of the gut is also shown schematically in Figure 5–72.

Development of the Facial Region and Palate

During the flexion phase of development the embryo consists of three layers of tissue: ectoderm, mesoderm, and endoderm. They ultimately give rise to all the structures of the body. Ectoderm, as we have seen, is the outermost layer, and it forms the epidermis of the skin, much of the teeth, the entire nervous system, hair, nails, and epithelial tissue. The intermediate layer is mesoderm, and it ultimately gives rise to all the connective tissue in the body; that is, it forms the bones, muscles, blood vessels, and cartilages of the body. Endoderm, the deepest of the three layers, gives rise to the epithelial lining of the entire digestive tract (except for the linings of the mouth and pharynx, which are formed by ectoderm) and the epithelial lining of the entire respiratory tract. Because endoderm lines the body cavity it is sometimes called the "inner skin."

During the flexion state, when the embryo is about three weeks old and about three millimeters in length, the facial area is very primitive. As shown in Figure 5–73, it consists of a smooth, relatively undifferentiated bulge known as the prosencephalon,

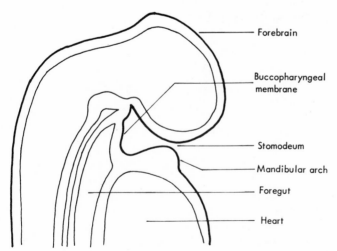

Forebrain

Buccopharyngeal membrane

Stomodeum

Mandibular arch

Foregut

Heart

Fig. 5–73. Schematic sagittal section through the head of a three-week embryo.

which is the forebrain or anterior brain vesicle of the embryo. It is covered by a thin layer of ectoderm and mesoderm. Immediately caudal (tail-ward) to the prosencephalon lies a transverse furrow known as the oral groove or stomodeum. The stomodeum is the primitive mouth, and it might be regarded as the topographical center of the developing facial structures (Patten, 1961). As the stomodeum deepens, its ectodermal floor comes into contact with the endodermal lining of the foregut. This two-cell-layered membrane, known as the oral plate or buccopharyngeal membrane, separates the oral groove and foregut. When, during the fourth week, this membrane ruptures and is absorbed by surrounding tissue, communication is for the first time established between the oral groove and the foregut.

The lateral walls of the anterior part of the foregut in the branchial region become differentiated into a series of transversely placed elevations with depressions between them. These depressions are known as branchial grooves or gill clefts. They are not true clefts, however, because the space is filled in with ectoderm and endoderm. The mesoderm has been pushed aside to that the ectoderm and endoderm are in direct contact. Later, the mesoderm again penetrates between the two layers. The branchial grooves are so closely homologous with similar true clefts of fishes and amphibians that the term gill cleft seems appropriate. As the paired (right and left) elevations between adjacent branchial grooves grow, they meet at the mid-line in such a manner that each pair forms a branchial arch. According to Gray (1966), six branchial arches make their appearance, but of these, only the first four are visible externally. The first of the branchial arches is known as the mandibular arch. It ultimately gives rise to the lower lip, the muscles of mastication, the mandible proper, the anterior portion of the tongue, and some of the structures of the middle ear. The second branchial arch, known as the hyoid arch, gives rise to such structures as the lesser cornua of the hyoid bone and the stapes, which is located in the middle-ear cavity.

The remaining branchial arches are designated only by number, and have no names assigned to them. The third arch gives rise to the body of the hyoid bone and to the posterior portion of the tongue. The fourth and fifth branchial arches give rise to the cricoid and arytenoid cartilages of the larynx and cartilages of the trachea. The first gill slit or branchial groove eventually develops into the concha of the pinna and into the external auditory meatus.

The ventral aspect of the forebrain, shown stippled in Figure 5–74, is crucial to the development of the face. Although it is relatively undifferentiated during the third week, it eventually develops into the frontonasal process. During this same period the first branchial, or mandibular, arch appears as a single transverse bar located immediately caudal to the oral groove. Some limited proliferation may have taken place, giving rise to as yet undifferentiated maxillary processes, one on either side.

Sometime during the latter part of the third or beginning of the fourth week, two areas, one on either side of the frontal process, begin to proliferate to form thickenings called nasal or olfactory placodes. Proliferation is of the ectoderm layer. During the fourth week rapid growth in the areas immediately surrounding the olfactory placodes results in the formation of two nasal pits. As shown in Figure 5–75, the nasal pits now divide the previously undifferentiated frontonasal process into a medial and two lateral nasal processes, one on either side. The olfactory placodes ultimately form the lining of the nasal pits and also the olfactory epithelium which contains the olfactory sensory cells. Although the maxillary processes continue to

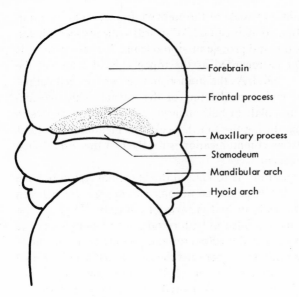

Forebrain

Frontal process

Maxillary process

Stomodeum

Mandibular arch

Hyoid arch

Fig. 5–74. Anterior view of an embryo during latter part of the third or beginning of the fourth week.

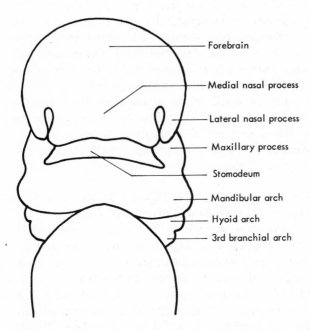

Forebrain

Medial nasal process

Lateral nasal process

Maxillary process

Stomodeum

Mandibular arch

Hyoid arch

3rd branchial arch

Fig. 5–75. Anterior view of a four-week embryo.

develop, they are still relatively undifferentiated from the mandibular arch. During the fourth week the hyoid arches appear as two sac-like pouches, located in the antero-lateral region of the neck. Their continuity is interrupted by the anterior growth of the pericardial swelling. The third branchial arch has grown considerably smaller by the end of the fourth week, when the embryo has attained a length of about 4.5 millimeters.

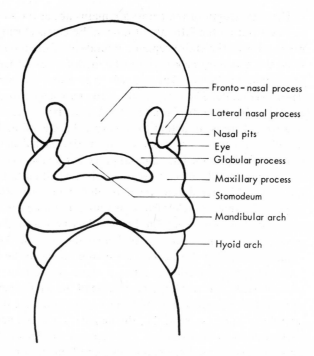

Fig. 5–76. Anterior view of a five-week embryo.

The fifth week finds the embryo about nine millimeters in length. During this period the branchial arches are at the height of their external development, and the face can now be divided into four primordial areas:

1. The frontonasal process. It is still relatively undifferentiated, with the exception of the lateral angles, which are rapidly growing in a caudal direction. During this stage of development the lateral nasal processes do not grow as rapidly as the medial nasal process. As proliferation of the medial nasal process continues, the two lateral angles become more and more prominent, and are known as the globular processes. They are shown in Figure 5–76.

2. The maxillary processes. Although they are becoming more and more prominent, the maxillary processes cannot as yet be easily differentiated from the mandibular arch from which they arose as cephalically directed swellings. The maxillary processes, as shown in Figure 5–76, are located between the lateral nasal processes and the mandibular arch. Sometime during the fifth week, a fusion of the frontonasal and the maxillary processes constricts the opening of the nasal pits.

3. The mandibular arch. Due to a pronounced constriction medially, as it crosses the mid-ventral line, the mandibular arch appears as two transverse bars, joined at their medial ends. The mandibular arch, however, is actually a single bar with a free cephalic border. It forms the entire caudal border of the oral pit. This free border is broken only where the mandibular arch is joined with the maxillary processes at the extreme lateral and rostral margins.

4. The hyoid arch. During the fifth week of development the hyoid arch is partially interrupted by the ventral bulge of the rapidly growing heart. The hyoid arch, therefore, appears as two sac-like processes, one on each antero-lateral portion of the neck region.

The total length of the embryo remains about the same throughout the sixth week as it was during the fifth, about nine millimeters. During this period the medial nasal process forms the entire cephalic boundary of the mouth opening. Also, by the sixth week the maxillary processes can be identified as wedge-shaped prominences located just caudal to the eye. The eye, which is shown in Figure 5–76, is just beginning to develop laterally. The medial tips of the maxillary processes are projected toward the caudal ends of the medial and lateral nasal processes. At this stage of development, however, there is no actual fusion with the medial and lateral nasal processes. The maxillary processes are separated from the medial nasal processes by the oronasal grooves and from the lateral nasal processes by the naso-optic grooves. These grooves are of considerable interest because failure of either to be normally obliterated during the course of later development results in malformations of the face. The oblique facial cleft, which is a cleft from the upper lip to the eye, has in the past been explained by a failure of fusion between the maxillary process and the nasal process. This fusion, however, normally occurs only below the nostril. An alternative explanation for oblique facial cleft is a general traumatic injury to the face of the embryo.

A fusion of the medial and lateral nasal processes results in a further constriction of the nostrils. The result is a narrowing of the medial nasal process and the beginnings of an anteriorly directed growth. The eyes, which are developing at the border of the lateral nasal process, rostral to the maxillary process, are drawn somewhat anteriorly. At this point in development, the superior border of the mandibular arch is a continuous ledge forming the caudal border of the mouth.

Except for its extreme lateral portion, the first branchial groove disappears during the later part of the sixth week. This groove, you will recall, develops into the concha of the pinna and the external auditory meatus. Several small buds begin to appear at the hyoid-mandibular arch area. These buds are the beginnings of the margins of the pinna. The third and fourth arches are no longer visible. They have been obliterated to form the cervical sinus, a temporary structure located between the hyoid arch in front and the thoracic wall behind. Due to the fusion of its walls, the sinus eventually disappears.

During the latter part of the sixth week fusion between the maxillary and medial nasal processes (globular processes) begins. When this fusion is completed, a shelf of tissue separates, for the first time, a portion of the oral and nasal cavities. This shelf is known as the primary palate. At the same time as the maxillary and medial nasal processes fuse, the tissue in the area of the globular processes is projected posteriorly into the nasal cavity to form two plates called the nasal laminae. During subsequent development, as the nasal pits come closer together, these nasal laminae ultimately fuse to form the nasal septum. The nasal septum divides the nasal cavity into two halves on the medial plane. A facial landmark known as the philtrum indicates the point of fusion between the maxillary and globular processes.

From what has been said thus far, it is apparent that the lateral nasal processes do not ultimately form any of the opening of the oral cavity. Rather they form the alae of the nose.

The seventh week sees a pronounced change in the face of the embryo. The nasal area is beginning to become prominent, with a corresponding reduction in width. The eyes have moved onto the anterior surface of the face. During this period the mandible has shown little change. The latter part of the sixth and the beginning of the seventh week are important in the development of the palate in the embryo. Because we are concerned primarily with the formation of the palate, a separate section dealing with the primary and secondary palates follows. Further development of the face of the embryo will be treated only incidentally.

Development of the Primary and Secondary Palates

The primary palate actually begins to develop during the fourth week when formation of the olfactory pits is taking place. Beginning at the inferior border of the olfactory pit, the medial nasal process fuses with the maxillary processes. During the sixth week fusion between the lateral nasal and medial nasal processes takes place. Because of the growth of the nasal processes, the olfactory pits are now actual choanae, each being closed off by a thin epithelial wall, the bucconasal membrane. During the latter part of the seventh or early part of the eighth week, this membrane ruptures and is absorbed by surrounding tissues. When this occurs the primary choana communicates directly with the oral cavity. A bar of tissue located between the nasal duct and the oral cavity at the edge between the facial and oral surfaces is the primary palate. This is the tissue that is formed when, during the sixth week, the maxillary and nasal processes fuse.

During the time of the formation of the upper facial regions, an interesting alteration occurs in the mandibular arch. Up until the sixth week it is an undifferentiated arch. Around the beginning of the fifth week, however, three constrictions appear on the exterior surface of the mandibular arch. A rather pronounced constriction known as the median sulcus divides the arch into halves. On either side, small furrows called lateral sulci develop. It is interesting to note that these sulci disappear at the same time the nasal and maxillary processes fuse in the upper facial region.

Differential facial growth accounts for much of the further development of the palate. An example is the rapid growth of the lateral nasal and the maxillary processes relative to the growth of the medial nasal process, which grows more slowly in a lateral direction. While this is taking place, the whole facial area grows in an anterior direction to form the prominence in the nasal region, at the same time causing a movement of the eyes from the antero-lateral to the anterior surface of the face. This differential growth is depicted schematically in Figures 5–77 and 5–78. The openings of the nares are closed during this stage of development by proliferating epithelium. The eyes, too, are covered by epithelium until after the development of the lids.

Until about the eighth week the mouth opening is very wide, becoming smaller with the fusion of the lateral areas of the mandibular arch and the maxillary processes to form the cheeks and at the same time narrowing the width of the mouth opening.

At the time of the development of the primary palate the nasal cavity is a short duct leading from the nostrils to the primitive oral cavity. The outer and inner openings of the nasal cavity are separated by the primary palate, which later will develop into the upper lip, the anterior portion of the alveolar process, and the premaxillary part of the palate.

During about the eighth week the growth of the head moves into a vertical plane. This change in direction of growth results in an increase in the height of the oral

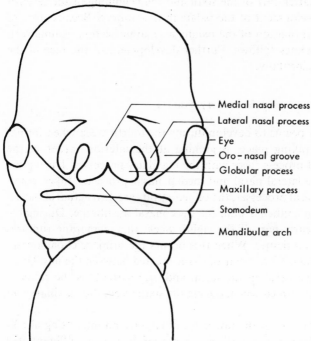

Fig. 5–77. Anterior view of a six-week embryo.

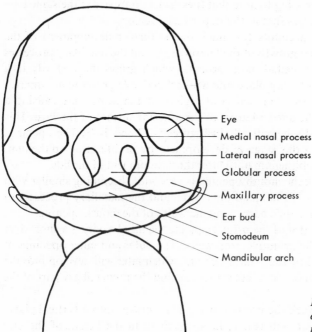

Fig. 5–78. Anterior view of an embryo during the latter part of the seventh or the beginning of the eighth week.

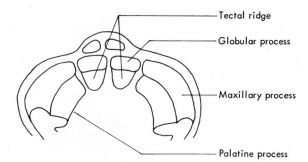

Fig. 5–79. Schematic of roof of the mouth of a nine-week embryo illustrating the processes which contribute to formation of the palate.

cavity. A direct result of this is that the tissue separating the primitive choana grows posteriorly and in a caudal direction to form part of the future nasal septum. The oral cavity communicates with the nasal cavities at this time, although an incomplete palate is formed by the primary palate anteriorly and medially directed swellings from the maxillary processes laterally. (We identify this medially directed portion later, in adult anatomy, as the palatine process of the maxillary bone.) Thus, medially, the oral cavity communicates with the nasal cavity on either side of the nasal septum. A schematic primary palate, as seen from beneath, is shown in Figure 5–79.

Before considering the development of the secondary palate, the embryological development of the tongue ought to be discussed very briefly.

The primordial areas which give rise to the mucous membrane of the tongue first appear during the seventh or eighth week. According to Patten (1961), they can best be seen in preparations made by cutting from either side through the visceral (branchial) arches to the lumen of the pharynx and then removing the brain and oropharyngeal roof so that the floor of the pharynx can be viewed from above, as in Figure 5–80.

Embryos in their fifth week often show evidence of paired lateral thickenings (lateral lingual swellings) on the internal surface of the mandibular arch. They consist of rapidly proliferating mesenchyme covered by epithelium. A small elevation located between the lateral lingual swellings is known as the tuberculum impar. Just behind it, as shown in Figure 5–80, is a second mid-line swelling known as the copula. It bridges the second and third branchial arches. Behind the copula are two swellings, placed on either side of the mid-line. They are the beginnings of the arytenoid cartilages, and between them may be seen a third mid-line swelling that will eventually become the epiglottis. These structures are shown schematically in Figure 5–81. Tissue on either side of the copula proliferates rapidly until, by the end of the seventh week, a distinct tongue-like structure is evident. A small pit, which we later identify as the foramen caecum in the adult, separates two pairs of bilaterally symmetrical tongue primordia. The cephalic pair, called the anterior lingual primordia, is located at the level of the first branchial arch, while the caudal pair, called the root primordia, is located at the level of the second branchial arch. At first the tongue is composed only of mucous membrane, but later, striated muscle fibers grow into it, causing a rapid expansion in its dimensions. The musculature does not come from the branchial arches but rather from the three occipital somites. When the tongue is well-developed, it is composed of two primary muscles, the genioglossus and the hyoglossus. The transverse and vertical muscles are derived from the hyoglossus.

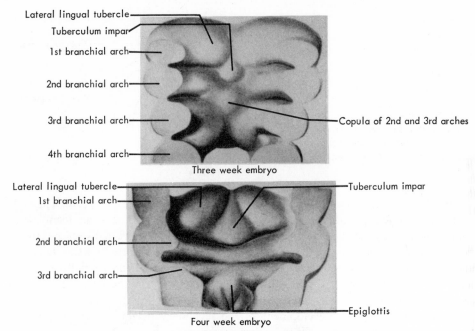

Lateral lingual tubercle

Tuberculum impar

1st branchial arch

2nd branchial arch

3rd branchial arch — Copula of 2nd and 3rd arches

4th branchial arch

Three week embryo

Lateral lingual tubercle — Tuberculum impar

1st branchial arch

2nd branchial arch

3rd branchial arch

Epiglottis

Four week embryo

Fig. 5–80. Anterior wall of pharynx and floor of the oral cavity, as seen from within, showing development of tongue and adjacent structures. (From H. Sicher and J. Tandler, Anatomie für Zahnärzte. *Julius Springer, Vienna and Berlin, 1928.)*

Fig. 5–81. Anterior wall of pharynx and floor of the oral cavity, as seen from within, showing the development of the tongue and adjacent structures. (From Sicher and Tandler, Anatomie für Zahnärzte.)

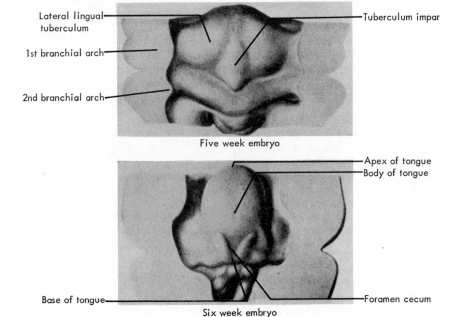

Lateral lingual tuberculum — Tuberculum impar

1st branchial arch

2nd branchial arch

Five week embryo

Apex of tongue

Body of tongue

Base of tongue — Foramen cecum

Six week embryo

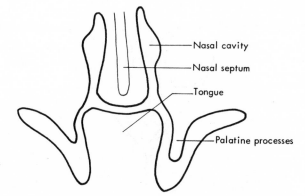

Fig. 5–82. Schematic section through the face of an embryo during the eighth week. The tongue extends into the nasal cavity thus separating the palatine processes.

In the earlier stages of the formation of the secondary palate, the tongue is extended in height so that it almost completely fills the oral cavity and, in fact, touches the tissue which will eventually develop into the nasal septum. This is illustrated in Figure 5–82. Folds of tissue, lateral on either side of the tongue, grow in a downward direction. These folds are the palatine processes of the maxillae. They extend posteriorly to the lateral walls of the pharynx.

The secondary palate is formed primarily by a fusion of the palatine processes of the maxillae. Fusion can occur, however, only when the tongue has moved down. This downward growth is made possible by a sudden spurt of growth in the mandibular arch. The tongue then drops, leaving a space between the palatine processes. When this occurs, as shown in Figures 5–83 and 5–84 schematically, mesoderm cells on the lateral (oral) surface of the palatine processes begin proliferating rapidly, causing a change in growth from the vertical to the horizontal plane. The palatine processes fuse with each other and with the nasal septum as well, as shown in Figures 5–84 and 5–85. This fusion takes place in an anterior to posterior direction. Thus, the palatine processes form only the soft palate and the medial portion of the hard palate. As was shown in

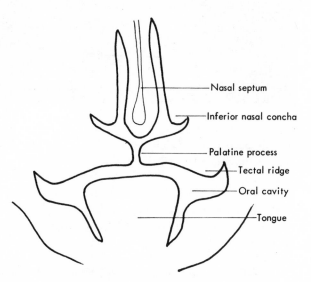

Fig. 5–83. Schematic section of a nine-week embryo. Tongue has evacuated the space between the palatine processes.

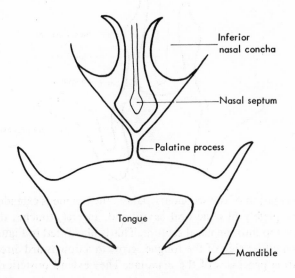

Fig. 5–84. Frontal section through face of an embryo slightly older than that in Fig. 5–83.

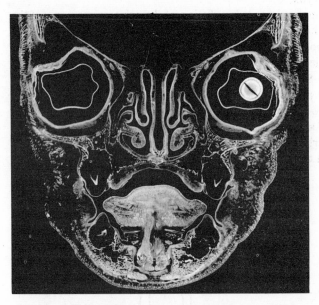

Fig. 5–85. A frontal section through the head of a five-month fetus.

Figure 5–79, the tegmen oris (roof of the mouth) is bounded laterally and anteriorly by the tectal ridge, which is a medial projection of the globular process. The tectal ridge is the equivalent of the premaxillary process.

Later in the developmental sequence the alveolar ridge will arise from a layer of mesoderm tissue that is located in a sulcus between the palate and lip. A swelling on the posterior alveolar ridge disappears as the ridge approaches maturity.

The following is a summary of the development sequence that leads to the formation of the palate:

2nd week: Appearance of stomodeum or primitive mouth

3rd week: Formation of the mandibular arch on either side; maxillary processes bud out from mandibular arch; nasal placodes appear

4th week: Rupture and disappearance of buccopharyngeal membrane

5th week: Appearance of frontonasal processes; olfactory pits widely separated; appearance of globular processes

6th week: Union of lateral nasal with maxillary processes; partial division of stomodeum into an upper and lower cavity

8th week: Union of the three portions of the palate commences anteriorly; completion of the upper lip by fusion of globular processes

10th week: Completion of union of palatine segments, the uvula being the last to be completed

The embryonic development as just described has been very schematic and highly idealized. Unfortunately, facial development is sometimes interrupted during the period when the fusion between the primitive palate and the palatine processes of the maxillae is normally taking place. As a result, facial deformities of various degrees of severity may occur, the most common of which is a cleft of the palate. A cleft may assume any one of a number of forms: complete, incomplete, unilateral, or bilateral. The cause or causes of cleft palate are not known with certainty. Such factors as intrauterine anoxia, toxic poisoning, high concentrations of cortisone, an inherent lack of mesoderm, and heredity seem to be related to cleft palate. After an exhaustive study of etiological factors, Fogh-Anderson (1942), in Denmark, concluded that heredity is in all likelihood the most essential etiological factor in cleft palate and cleft lip. Cleft palate occurs in one out of about a thousand births, and it seems that males are far more subject to the deformity than are females. The ratio is about 2 to 1. Interestingly enough, it seems that boys are less subject to the minor palatal defects than girls, but considerably more subject to the severe types of defects, such as complete lip and palatal clefts. Further discussion of cleft palate is beyond the scope of this text, and the interested reader is referred to Pruzansky (1961) and to *Proceedings of the Conference: Communicative Problems in Cleft Palate*, ASHA Publication (1964).

Postnatal Growth of the Head

By this time it ought to have been adequately demonstrated that the skull is not simply a static organic hitching post for the speech musculature but rather that it is a dynamic, living structure, capable of differential growth, capable of adjusting to environmental influences, and capable of disease. It might be of some value to consider some of the features of facial growth. This may facilitate a better understanding of some of the consequences of proper dental health and it might reinforce an awareness of the continuing nature of the development of the speech mechanism.

Aside from measurements of the various structures of the skull, two principal methods of study of skull growth have been employed. The first technique is known as vital staining. It involves injection of bone-penetrating dyes such as alizarin red into growing animals, usually monkeys. Preparations reveal layers of stained bone and provide, therefore, an index of growth. The second technique involves serial X-ray

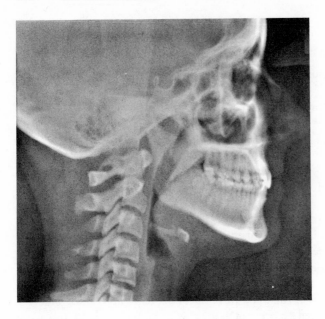

Fig. 5–86. A lateral head plate of a normal adolescent (female). (Courtesy Claft Palate Center.)

studies of animal and human skulls during the period of growth. X-ray studies have the distinct advantage of being applicable to living humans, and they also reveal the growth of soft tissue, such as the soft palate and pharynx. The value of any X-ray film is largely dependent upon the methods used to analyze it. Still cephalic radiograms have been used successfully in studies of the growth of the skull structures (Broadbent, 1930; 1937), (Brodie, 1940; 1941), and (Subtelny, 1957), as well as soft tissues (King, 1952), (Subtelny and Koepp-Baker, 1956), (Subtelny, 1957), and (Willis, 1952).

A major problem is in the selection of meaningful measures to be made. Because the skull is so complex, measurements must be made from certain recognizable reference points and planes. A lateral head X-ray is shown in Figure 5–86, and a partial tracing of the same X-ray, containing a number of abbreviated reference points used in cephalometric studies, is shown in Figure 5–87. A number of reference lines or planes is also shown. Below is a list of reference points, lines, and their definitions. A more complete list has been given by Lundstrom (1960).

Reference Points

1. ARTICULARE (ar)—Intersection between the contour of the external cranial base and the dorsal contour of the condylar head.

2. BASION (ba)—Normal projection of the anterior border of the occipital foramen on the occipital foramen line.

3. GNATHION (gn)—Lowest point of the mandibular symphysis.

4. GONION (go)—A point on the bony contour of the gonial angle determined by bisecting the tangent angle.

5. INFRADENTALE (id)—Highest and most prominent point on the lower alveolar arch.

6. NASION (n)—Most anterior point of the frontonasal suture.

7. ORBITALE (or)—The deepest point of the infraorbital margin.

8. Pogonion (pg)—The most prominent point of the chin.

9. Porion (po)—The point on the upper margin of the external auditory meatus.

10. Prosthion (pr)—Lowest and most prominent point on the upper alveolar arch.

11. Pterygomaxillare (pm)—Point representing the dorsal surface of the maxilla at the level of the nasal floor. The point is located on the pterygopalatine fossa, where this contour intersects that of the hard and soft palates.

12. Sella (s)—Center of the bony crypt known as the sella turcica.

13. Sphenoidale (sphen)—The most superior point of the tuberculum sellae.

14. Spinal point (sp)—Apex of the anterior nasal spine, also known as the anterior nasal spine (ans).

Reference Lines

1. Base Plane (BP)—Line joining nasion to basion.

2. Chin Line (CL)—Tangent to the chin through the infradentale.

3. Frankfort Horizontal Line (FM)—Line through porion and orbitale.

4. Mandibular Line (ML)—Tangent to the lower border of the mandible through the gnathion.

5. Nasal Line (NL)—Line through the spinal point (ans) and the pterygomaxillare.

6. Nasion-Sella Line (NSL)—Line joining the nasion to the sella.

Fig. 5–87. A partial tracing of the X-ray in Figure 5–86 showing some reference lines and planes that are used in cephalometry.

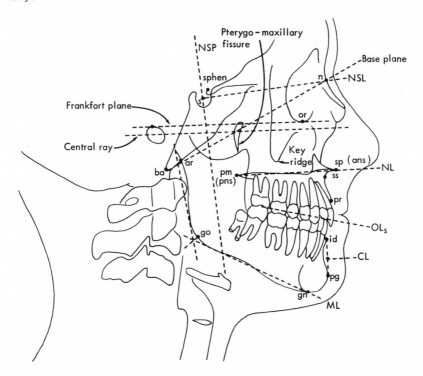

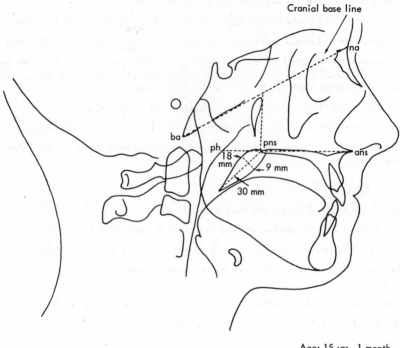

Age: 15 yrs, 1 month

Soft palate length mm. 30	Soft palate thickness mm. 9	Vertical ht. nasopharynx 29	Horizontal depth nasopharynx mm 18
(Norms) (32.9±1.397)	(8.9±.617)	(27.5±2.117)	(22.9±3.831)

$$\frac{\text{Pns} - \text{Ph}}{\text{S. Pal. leng.}} = 60\% \qquad \text{(Norms)} \quad (70.5 \pm 8.789)$$

Fig. 5–88. Tracings of lateral head X-ray showing measures to assess adequacy of velopharyngeal tissue. (Norms taken from "A cephalometric Study of the Growth of the Soft Palate," by J. Daniel Subtelny in Plastic and Reconstructive Surgery, xix, no. 1, 1957, pp. 49–62.)

7. NASION-SELLA PERPENDICULARE (NSP)—Line through the sella and perpendicular to the NSL.

8. OCCLUSAL LINE, SUPERIOR (OLS)—Line through the incision superior and the distobuccal cusp of the upper first molar. (If tooth is missing, use the mesiobuccal cusp of the upper second molar.)

Most of these references are in general use, and the reader is likely to encounter many of them in literature that deals with orthodontic and cleft-palate problems, as well as normal and abnormal speech functions. Although the references are often used to analyze still radiographs of the head, most of them are applicable to frame-by-frame analysis of cineradiographic films. Certain specific measurements are made in the study of velopharyngeal closure and in studies of the growth of the oropharyngeal and facial regions. A partial tracing of a lateral X-ray of an oropharyngeal region, including some soft tissues, is shown in Figure 5–88.

Measurements frequently made include the length and thickness of the soft palate and the vertical height and horizontal depth of the nasopharynx. These measures are frequently made from X-rays taken with the subject at rest and during sustained phonation of the vowel [ɑ]. In addition, the ratio between the length of velar tissue and horizontal pharyngeal depth is also evaluated (Subtelny, 1957). These measures may be defined as follows: The base of the skull is delineated from the face and pharynx by drawing a line from the nasion (junction of the frontal and nasal bones) to the basion (anterior-most point of the foramen magnum). According to Subtelny (1957), this line, called the cranial base line, effectively delineates the base of the skull from the face and pharynx. A second line, drawn through the reference points for the anterior and posterior nasal spines and extended to the soft tissue of the posterior pharyngeal wall, indicates the plane of the hard palate; by measuring the distance from the posterior nasal spine (pns) to the posterior pharyngeal wall (ph), an effective measure of the horizontal depth of the nasopharynx may be obtained. In order to study the vertical height of the nasopharynx, the linear distance from the posterior nasal spine to the cranial base line is measured. According to Subtelny (1957), this distance is measured along a line perpendicular to the cant of the hard palate and projected to intersect the cranial base line, as in Figure 5–88. The length of the soft palate at rest may be obtained by measuring the linear distance from the posterior nasal spine to the tip of the uvula; when the oral surface of the soft palate can be delineated from the dorsum of the tongue, the greatest thickness may also be measured.

An example of the uses to which such measures may be put is seen in a longitudinal cephalometric radiographic study by Subtelny (1957), who in an attempt to facilitate long-range rehabilitation planning for young children with a cleft of the palate, studied the progressive growth and development of the velum, nasopharynx, and associated structures. Serial cephalometric X-rays of thirty normal subjects, with X-ray records from infancy to early adulthood, were evaluated. The sample included an equal number of males and females. The X-rays were taken using a technique developed by

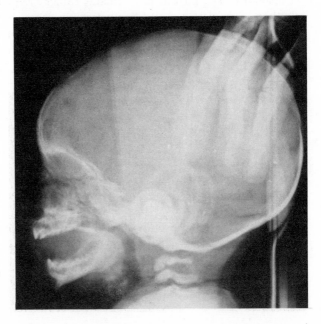

Fig. 5–89. Lateral head plate of normal infant. (Courtesy Cleft Palate Center.)

Broadbent (1930; 1931), in which the subjects' heads were stabilized by means of a specially constructed head holder. Thus, the subjects could be repositioned to obtain comparable successive X-rays over intervals of time. The X-ray films studied were taken every three months during the first year of life, every six months from one to three years, and at yearly intervals through the eighteenth year.

Some of Subtelny's findings are summarized as follows: Growth in length of the soft palate was most rapid during the early years of life, with a marked and consistent increase in length until about $1\frac{1}{2}$ to 2 years, at which time there was a leveling off of growth until approximately four to five years of age. Thereafter, the average growth was consistent but not as rapid as during the first years of life. Changes in thickness of the soft palate were the most rapid during the first year of life, and in succeeding years the average growth was slight until maximum thickness was reached at fourteen to sixteen years. Subtelny found that in the infant, the soft palate, as it rests against the dorsum of the tongue, gives the appearance of being almost in line with the hard palate as it slopes downward toward the oropharynx, as shown in Figure 5–89. With growth, however, the soft palate was found to approach more of a parallel relationship with the posterior pharyngeal wall, as in Figure 5–90. Subtelny noted that this change in angularity of the soft palate is closely correlated with the downward and forward growth of the facial skeleton described by Broadbent (1937) and Brodie (1941) and the increased vertical height of the pharynx found by King (1952). As shown in Figure 5–91, with growth of the facial skeleton, the hard palate moves in a parallel manner away from the base of the skull. Subtelny was interested in determining the concomitant changes of the vertical height of the nasopharynx. He found that the average vertical height doubled from early infancy to early adulthood, with the most profound changes occurring during the first year and a half of life. These findings support those of King (1952).

Along with the downward and foward growth of the facial skeleton and the increase in height of the nasopharynx, there is an increase in the horizontal depth of the nasopharynx. The growth rate remains rather gradual from infancy through early adulthood. The data revealed fluctuations in depth, however, which probably reflect the growth of adenoid tissue on the posterior pharyngeal wall. Subtelny also determined the proportional amount of velar tissue available for establishment of velo-

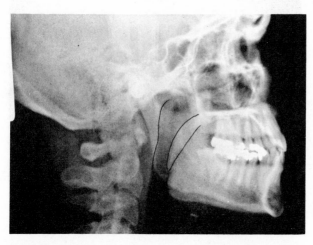

Fig. 5–90. Lateral head X-ray showing the slope of the soft palate and its relationship to the slope oJ the posterior pharyngeal wall.

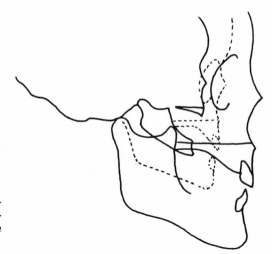

Fig. 5–91. Schematic of superimposed lateral head X-rays illustrating downward and forward growth of the facial bones.

Table 5-4

Means and Standard Deviations Based on Ratios Computed From Horizontal Measurements of the Nasopharynx Over the Length of the Soft Palate

Age in Years	Number of Ratios	Percentage Means $\dfrac{(Pns\text{-}Ph)}{Soft\ Palate\ Length} = \%$	Standard Deviations
$1/4$	10	73.8	12.7516
$1/2$	14	66.3	8.6944
$3/4$	14	65.2	8.9528
1	17	68.6	14.6142
$1^1/2$	16	62.5	11.5912
2	18	67.1	14.1381
$2^1/2$	19	60.0	8.6470
3	27	65.1	11.3986
4	27	65.1	14.1092
5	26	68.7	9.6563
6	23	66.3	15.0549
7	27	69.6	14.1922
8	23	68.7	13.6498
9	24	66.0	13.1667
10	26	68.3	9.8647
11	25	66.3	10.1304
12	23	68.3	9.5014
13	22	66.2	8.3813
14	17	70.0	9.1434
15	17	70.5	8.7881
16	17	71.4	6.9858
17	10	72.6	11.4739
18	6	70.2	6.9927

From J. D. Subtelny, "A Cephalometric Study of the Growth of the Soft Palate," *Plastic and Reconstructive Surgery*, XIX, 1957.

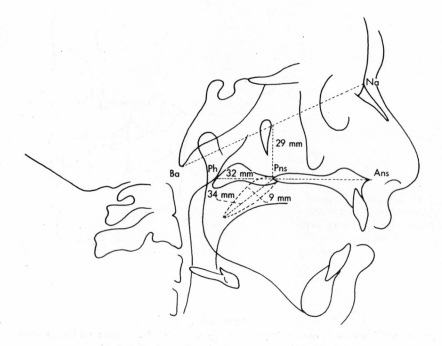

Age: 18 yrs, 4 months.

Soft palate length mm.	Soft palate thickness	Vertical ht. nasopharynx	Horizontal depth nasopharynx mm.
34	9	29	32
(Norms) 35.2=1.4142	none given	28.1 = 1.7029	24.2 = 1.8668
(ok)		(ok)	(deep)

$$\frac{Pns - Ph}{L.\ Pal.\ leng.} = 97\% \quad (Norms)\ 70.2 = 6.9927$$

Fig. 5–92. *Tracing of a lateral head X-ray of a subject with questionable velopharyngeal competence.*

pharyngeal closure. That is, the horizontal depth of the pharynx was stated in proportion to or as a percentage of the length of the soft palate. He found that the depth of the nasopharynx approximated a 2:3 ratio, relative to the length of the soft palate. Individual differences, which varied considerably, are reflected by the large standard deviations in Table 5–4. The results, however, suggest that a figure of 60 to 70 per cent would indicate adequate tissue for velopharyngeal closure. Higher percentages would suggest less likelihood of proper closure. The subject in Figure 5–92, for example, has a much higher percentage, in spite of considerable adenoid tissue. Such a value suggests that with atrophy or surgical removal of adenoid tissue, the result might well be an irreversible hypernasality.

Study of the growth of the skull is necessarily complicated by the fact that its two parts, the brain capsule and the masticatory facial skeleton, are integrated into one anatomic and biological unit. The complications arise because the growth of the brain capsule is entirely dependent upon the growth of the brain itself, whereas growth of the facial skeleton is dependent upon muscular influences and growth of the teeth and tongue. The two parts of the skull not only follow different paths of development, but their chronological sequence is different. For example, the brain has reached about 90 per cent of its physical development by the age of ten years, whereas the dentition and jaws are but beginning their final growth period, which goes on until about the twentieth year.

It is important in the study of the growth of the skull to appreciate the mechanisms of bone and cartilage growth. Because of the rigidity of the calcified bone, interstitial (expansive) growth is impossible. Bone tissue, therefore, can grow only by apposition or addition. Other connective tissue, such as muscle and cartilage, grows interstitially. In the case of cartilage, this entails mitotic cell division to produce fibroblasts (connective tissue cells) plus new collagenous (elastic fibers) and cementing substances. Hyaline cartilage is capable of both interstitial and appositional growth. Interstitial growth is initiated by mitotic division of the cartilage cells (chondrocites), which then grow to produce new hyalin substance. Appositional growth can take place only where the cartilage is covered by a layer of perichondrium. Cells in the perichondrium (which is connective tissue) differentiate into chondroblasts, which in turn produce the ground substance of hyaline cartilage. Hyaline cartilage is found at three primary locations at birth: parts of the nasal skeleton, the spheno-occipital synchondrosis (plus parts of the occipital bone which are joined by a synchondrosis), and the mandibular condyle. Growth at sutures is initiated by proliferation of connective tissue at the suture, and not by apposition of new bone.

At birth the skull, relative to the body, is quite large. During the first two years of life the brain capsule and brain just about triple in volume. The rate of growth then begins to slow down until about the seventh year, after which the annual growth is very slight. The brain capsule reaches about 90 per cent of growth and volume by the tenth year.

After the first year, the facial skeleton grows considerably faster than the cranium. During this growth period, in which the skull grows in all three dimensions—height, width, and depth—the original relationship between the facial skeleton and the neurocranium is maintained. That is, the plane of the palate, the occlusal plane, and the plane of the lower border of the mandible maintain a constant angular relation to the base of the skull. During periods of growth the parallel relationships of these three planes vary only slightly.

There are three primary sites of growth of the maxillary complex, which include the maxillae and the palatine bones. These three sites are the frontomaxillary, the zygomaticomaxillary, and the zygomaticotemporal sutures. As shown in Figure 5–93, they lie in planes in such a way that growth has the effect of shifting the entire maxillary complex downward and forward. During this growth period the antero-posterior depth of the bony palate almost doubles, whereas the transverse growth is much less. This is illustrated schematically in Figure 5–94. Growth of the palate is due to apposition. The increase in transverse diameter of the maxillae is brought about by appositional growth at the medial palatine suture and also by the influence, at the junction of the palatine processes and the maxillary complex, of the downward and lateral growth of the pterygoid plates of the sphenoid bone. By the end of the

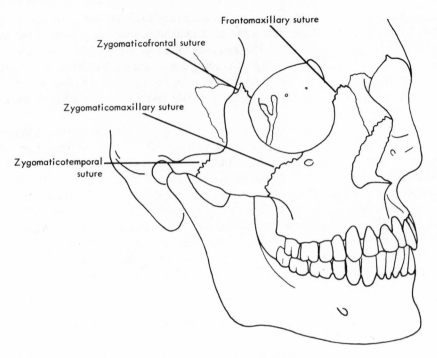

Fig. 5–93. Schematic of the primary sites of growth of the maxillary complex, which have the effect of shifting the face downward and forward.

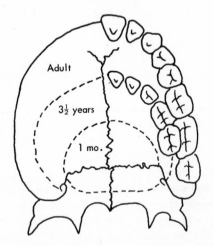

Fig. 5–94. Schematic of anterior and transverse growth of the palate and dental arch.

fifth year the palate has attained about five-sixths the width of a mature palate, and it has reached maximum transverse development by ten years.

Growth in facial height is most pronounced during the first six months of life, while the deciduous incisor teeth are developing, and between the ages of seven and eleven, when the permanent incisors and cuspid teeth are erupting. Studies of the antero-posterior growth of the maxillae show three periods of rapid growth: at ages

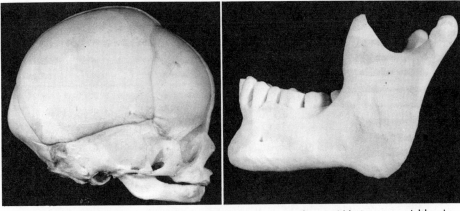

The mandible in an infant skull.   The mandible in young adulthood.

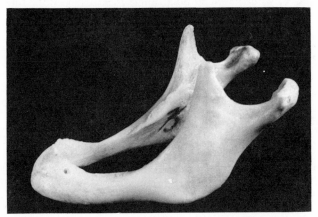

The mandible in old age, following the loss of the teeth.

Fig. 5–95. Changes in the mandible with age.

five to six, when the first molars are developing and erupting; at age eleven; and at age sixteen, when the second and third molars are descending and erupting.

The height of the body of the mandible is gained by apposition of bone on its external (labial) surfaces. Growth is much the same as that on the alveolar process of the maxilla. That is, growth in the lingual direction is accomplished by a heavy deposition of bone on the posterior edge of the ramus. Continual proliferation of hyaline cartilage below the articulating surface of the mandibular condyle and replacement of cartilage by deposition of bone account for the development that lowers the mandible and its occlusal plane. As evidence of the extent of the growth of the mandible, the height and length of the posterior border of the ramus, as measured from the angle to the temporomandibular joint, more than doubles during the period of development. Compared with the growth mechanism of the maxilla, the growth of the mandible is unique. Whereas maxillary growth is primarily sutural and appositional, growth of the mandible is due to interstitial growth in the hyaline cartilage of the condyle.

At birth, the body of the mandible is but a mere shell, containing the alveoli (tooth sockets) for the deciduous dentition. There are two incisors, one cuspid, and two molar teeth in each quadrant. As shown in Figure 5–95, the angle of the ramus with the mandibular plane is obtuse, about 170°. Shortly after birth the two halves of the mandible become joined at the symphysis, beginning from below, a process that is usually completed by the end of the first year. As stated previously, the body of the mandible elongates in an antero-posterior direction to provide room for the three additional permanent teeth which will be developing in the region behind the mental foramen. Because of the increasing dental development and consequent growth of the alveolar process, the depth of the body of the mandible increases. The mandibular angle becomes less and less obtuse, and at four years is about 140°. In the adult mandible the alveolar and subdental portions occupy about equal space. The ramus is almost vertical with the mandibular angle, being about 110° to 120°. In old age the body of the jaw becomes reduced in its vertical dimension. This is due to absorption of the alveolar process subsequent to the loss of teeth. The ramus again becomes increasingly oblique, with the mandibular angle measuring about 140°.

SELECTIVE READING LIST

Angle, E. H., "Classification of Malocclusion," *Dental Cosmos*, XLI, 1889, 248–64, 350–57.

Bloomer, H. H., "Observations of Palatopharyngeal Movements in Speech and Deglutition," *Journal of Speech and Hearing Disorders*, XVIII, 1953, 230–46.

———, "A Palatopograph for Contour Mapping of the Palate," *Journal of the American Dental Association*, XXX, 1943, 1053–57.

Broadbent, B. H., "The Face of the Normal Child," *Angle Orthodontist*, VII, 1937, 209.

———, "New X-ray Technique and Its Application to Orthodontia," Angle Orthodontist, I, 1931, 45.

———, "Roentgenographic Method of Measuring Biometric Relations of the Face and Cranium," White House Conference on Child Health and Protection, 1930, Report of Committee A, Growth and Development, Section 1, page 23.

Brodie, A. G., "On the Growth Pattern of the Human Head from the Third Month to the Eighth Year of Life," *American Journal of Anatomy*, LXXXIX, 1941, 209.

———, "Some Recent Observations on the Growth of the Face and Their Implications to the Orthodontist," *American Journal of Orthodontia and Oral Surgery*, XXVI, 1940, 741.

Brodnitz, F. S., *Vocal Rehabilitation*. Rochester, Minn: Whiting Press, Inc., 1959.

Calnan, J., "The Error of Gustav Passavant," *Plastic and Reconstructive Surgery*, XIII, 1954, 275–89.

Carrell, J. and W. Tiffany, *Phonetics: Theory and Application to Speech Improvement*. New York: McGraw-Hill Book Company, 1960.

Cates, H. and J. V. Basmajian, *Primary Anatomy*. Baltimore: The Williams & Wilkins Co., 1955.

Cooper, F. S., "Research Techniques and Instrumentation: EMG," *Proceedings of the Conference: Communicative Problems in Cleft Palate*, American Speech and Hearing Association Report No. 1, 1965, 153–68.

Crane, E. and G. Ramstrum, "A Classification of Palates," Unpublished Master's thesis, University of Michigan, 1943.

Denes, P. and E. Pinson, *The Speech Chain*. Baltimore: Waverly Press, Inc., 1963.

Fogh-Anderson, P., *Inheritance of Harelip and Cleft Palate*. Copenhagen: Nyt Norkisk Forlag, Arnold Busk, 1942.

Fujimura, O., "Bilabial Stop and Nasal Consonants: a Motion Picture Study and Its Acoustical Implications," *Journal of Speech and Hearing Research*, IV, 1961, 233–247.

Gray, H., *The Anatomy of the Human Body*, 28th ed., ed. C. M. Goss. Philadelphia: Lea & Febiger, 1966.

Hagerty, R. F. and M. J. Hill, "Pharyngeal Wall and Palatal Movement in Post-operative Cleft Palates and Normal Palates," *Journal of Speech and Hearing Research*, III, 1960, 59–66.

———, M. J. Hill, H. S. Pettit, and J. J. Kane, "Posterior Pharyngeal Wall Movement in Normals," *Journal of Speech and Hearing Research*, I, 1958, 203–10.

Hardy, J. C., "Air Flow and Air Pressure Studies," *Proceedings of the Conference: Communicative Problems in Cleft Palate*, American Speech and Hearing Association Report No. 1, 1965, 141–152.

Harrington, R., "A Study of the Mechanism of Velopharyngeal Closure," *Journal of Speech Disorders*, IX, 1944, 325–44.

Holbrook, R. T., and F. J. Carmody, "X-ray Studies of Speech Articulations," *University of California Publications in Modern Philology*, XX, 1937, 187–238.

Hudgins, C. V. and R. H. Stetson, "Relative Speed of Articulatory Movements," *Archives Neerl. Phon. Exper.*, XIII, 1937, 85–94.

Kaplan, H. M., *Anatomy and Physiology of Speech*. New York: McGraw-Hill Book Company, 1960.

Keaster, J., "Studies in the Anatomy and Physiology of the Tongue," *Laryngoscope*, 1940, 222–57.

Kelly, J. and L. B. Higley, "A Contribution to the X-ray Study of Tongue Position in Certain Vowels," *Archives of Speech*, I, 1934, 84–95.

King, E. W., "A Roentgenographic Study of Pharyngeal Growth," *Angle Orthodontist*, XXII, 1952, 23.

Lundstrom, A., *Introduction to Orthodontics*. New York: McGraw-Hill Book Company, 1960.

MacNeilage, P. F. and G. N. Sholes, "An Electromyographic Study of the Tongue During Vowel Production," *Journal of Speech and Hearing Research*, VII, 1964, 209–32.

Martone, A. L., "The Phenomenon of Function in Complete Denture Prosthodontics," a collection of reprints from *The Journal of Prosthetic Dentistry*. St Louis: The C. V. Mosby Company, 1963.

Massler, M. and E. Schour, *Atlas of the Mouth*. Chicago: American Dental Association, 1958.

Moll, K. L., "Photographic and Radiographic Procedures in Speech Research," *Proceedings of the Conference: Communicative Problems in Cleft Palate*, American Speech and Hearing Association Report No. 1, 1965, 129–39.

———, "Velopharyngeal Closure on Vowels," *Journal of Speech and Hearing Research*, V, 1962, 30–37.

Orban, B. J., *Oral Histology and Embryology*, 4th ed. St. Louis: The C. V. Mosby Company, 1957.

Palmer, J. M. and D. A. LaRusso, *Anatomy for Speech and Hearing*. New York: Harper and Row, Publishers, 1965.

Patten, B. M., "The Normal Development of the Facial Region," in *Congenital Anomalies of the Face and Associated Structures*, ed. S. Pruzansky. Springfield, Ill.: Charles C. Thomas, Publisher, 1961.

Pruzansky, S., ed., *Congenital Anomalies of the Face and Associated Structures*. Springfield, Ill.: Charles C. Thomas, Publisher, 1961.

Russell, G. O., *The Vowel*. Columbus: Ohio State University Press, 1928.

Sicher, J., "The Growth of the Mandible," *Journal of Periodontia*, XVI, 1945, 87–93.

———, *Oral Anatomy*. St. Louis: The C. V. Mosby Company, 1949.

Subtelny, J. D., "A Cephalometric Study of the Growth of the Soft Palate," *Plastic and Reconstructive Surgery*, XIX, 1957, 49–62.

——— and H. Koepp-Baker, "The Significance of Adenoid Tissue in Velopharyngeal Function," *Plastic and Reconstructive Surgery*, XII, 1956, 235–50.

Swanson, C. P., *The Cell*, 2nd ed. Englewood Cliffs, N. J.: Prentice-Hall, Inc., 1964.

Trevino, S. N. and C. E. Parmenter, "Vowel Positions as Shown by X-ray," *Quarterly Journal of Speech*, XVIII, 1932, 351–69.

Willis, R. H., *A Cephalometric Study of Size Relationships of the Normal Male Soft Palate*. Master's thesis in Dentistry, Department of Orthodontia, University of Washington, 1952.

Zemlin, W. R. and S. Stolpe, *The Structure of the Human Skull*. Champaign, Ill.: Stipes Publishing Co., 1967.

6

The Ear

INTRODUCTION

The Nature of Sound

Simple harmonic vibration
Wavelength, frequency, and velocity
Complex sounds
The decibel

ANATOMY OF THE EAR

Introduction
The External Ear

The auricle
The external auditory meatus

The Middle Ear

The tympanic membrane
The tympanic cavity
The Eustachian tube
The auditory ossicles

The Ligaments and Articulations of the Ossicles

The tympanic muscles

The Tensor Tympani Muscle
The Stapedius Muscle
The Action of the Tympanic Musculature

The transformer action of the middle ear

The Inner Ear

The bony labyrinth
The membranous labyrinth

346

INTRODUCTION

Sometime during the early 1700's a British philosopher, George Berkeley, asked if a falling tree makes noise when no one is nearby to hear the sound. Ever since that time writers have been introducing any discussion of sound and hearing by asking that same question. It is raised here only to point out the dual nature of sound. That is, a physicist might say that in falling the tree dissipated energy, setting up a propagating disturbance in the air . . . a wave of sound, while the psychologist might reply with the notion that such a propagating disturbance must first be perceived in order to be called sound. In the next few pages we shall concern ourselves with the mechanism that serves as the receptor of sounds and permits us to perceive propagating disturbances of air, such as those produced by falling trees or the rustling of leaves.

Before proceeding to the structure and workings of the hearing mechanism, it may prove beneficial to review briefly some of the basic properties of sound.

The Nature of Sound

Undisturbed air may be said to be in a state of equilibrium; that is, with the exception of random air-particle movement and atmospheric variations, the density of air particles remains relatively constant over time. When an external force impinges upon them, however, they may move closer together (compression) or farther apart (rarefaction) than when in a state of equilibrium. Because air is a fluid, it tends to flow from regions of higher pressure to regions of lower pressure. In addition, since air has mass, it exhibits inertial properties and, when once put into motion, tends to remain in motion until the energy imparted to it has been dissipated. Thus, once a disturbance of the air particles has been initiated, by a sharp clap of the hands, for example, a layer of compressed air will move outward in all directions, compressing the air ahead, with rarefied air trailing behind.

It is important to note that disturbed air particles exhibit a minute forward-and-backward motion, imparting their energy to the air particles ahead, while they return to a state of equilibrium behind. It is the disturbance, and not the air particles, which moves in a wave-like fashion through the air. For this reason, sound may be thought of as a flow of power or a transfer of energy from one place to another.

Although the sounds with which we are most familiar are almost invariably generated by a vibrating element, it is important to realize that vibratory motion and wave motion are not the same thing. A vibrating body produces waves when it is coupled

349

to some elastic medium, and the waves that are generated travel through the medium. Vibratory motion may be defined as motion back and forth along a path in such a manner that there is a restoring force, increasing with displacement, and always directed toward the position of rest. The motion is called periodic when it occurs in equal time intervals. There are five important measurable characteristics of vibratory motion: displacement, amplitude, frequency, period, and phase. Fortunately, these characteristics are also useful in describing wave motion.

1. Displacement of a vibrating body at any instant is the distance from equilibrium to the position of the body at that instant.

2. Amplitude of vibration is the maximum displacement of the body from its position of equilibrium and is usually equal to half the total extent of vibratory motion.

3. Frequency, f, is the number of complete vibrations or cycles per unit time, and is usually measured in vibrations or cycles per second.

4. The period, T, of a vibrating body is the time elapsed during a single complete vibration. Thus, frequency and period are inversely proportional. If a body makes 60 vibrations per second, each vibration or cycle occurs in 1/60 seconds. The relation between frequency and period is $T = 1/f$ and $f = 1/T$.

5. Phase is a term used in describing vibratory as well as wave motion and is useful in describing the relationship between two or more sound waves. Since in a complete vibratory cycle, the body swings through its position of equilibrium and back to it again, the process may be compared to circular motion. For this reason, phase may be defined as the portion of a cycle through which a vibrating body has passed up to a given instant; it is usually expressed in terms of degrees of a circle. The phase change in a complete vibratory cycle is 360°. The phase changes of a pendulum swinging through a small arc are shown schematically in Figure 6–1.

Simple harmonic vibration

The simplest form of vibratory motion, that executed by the tines of a tuning fork, by a pendulum swinging through a small arc, or by a weight bobbing up and down on

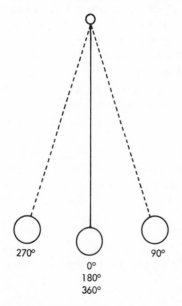

270°

0°
180°
360°

90°

Fig. 6–1. Illustration of phase changes in a complete cycle of a pendulum swinging through a small arc.

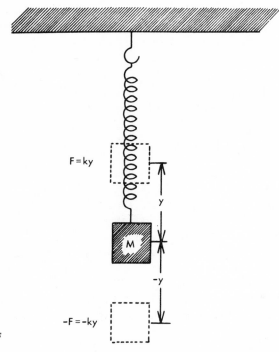

$$F = ky$$

$$-F = -ky$$

Fig. 6–2. Illustration of Hooke's law.

an ideal spring, is called simple harmonic motion, often abbreviated SHM. It is simple because of the simple relation between restoring force and displacement. In accordance with Hooke's law the restoring force is proportional to the displacement. In Figure 6–2, if k is the spring constant (force per unit stretch or compression), the restoring force, F, for a displacement, y, is ky, and k is proportional to F/y. Thus, no matter whether the mass, m, is displaced downward or upward, there will always be a restoring force proportional to the displacement; and in addition, since acceleration of a vibrating body is proportional to the force acting on it, acceleration is also directly proportional to the displacement from equilibrium, and is directed toward it. Simple harmonic motion can be produced only when the above conditions have been satisfied.

Simple harmonic motion, or sinusoidal motion, is sometimes defined as projected uniform circular motion. Thus, in Figure 6–3, if point P moves around the circle in

Fig. 6–3. Graphic projection of uniform circular motion.

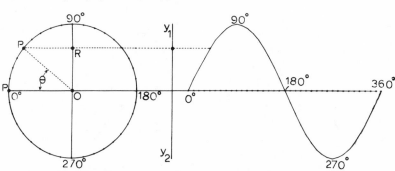

a clockwise direction, its projection on the vertical axis $y_1 y_2$ is represented by the point, R. As point P rotates at constant velocity, R moves along the vertical axis in simple harmonic motion. This motion may be represented graphically by plotting the distance, OR, against the angle swept by the line, OP. Thus, the displacement, y, at any point is proportional to the sine of the angle, θ, through which P has rotated on the circle, and the amplitude of the wave at any time can be obtained from the equation of simple harmonic motion:

$$y = A \sin \theta = A \sin \omega t$$

where A is the amplitude (equal to the radius of the generating circle or to the length of the line OP), ω is the angular velocity (measured in radians per second) of the point, P, on the generating circle. The number of times P goes around the circle in one second is the frequency, and since there are 2π radians in a complete circle, the relation between frequency, F, and angular velocity is $\omega = 2\pi F$.

If we assign a value of 1 to the line, OP, then the vertical distance, or the displacement plotted on the vertical scale ($y_1 y_2$), is the same as the sine, and the resultant graph is referred to as a sine curve. The graph in Figure 6–3 shows the extent of the vertical displacement plotted for each 10° of rotation of point P on the circle.

Sound waves generated by a simple harmonic vibration may also be graphed in the manner shown in Figure 6–3. The crests represent regions of compressed air and the troughs the regions of rarefied air. The number of waves generated in a second

Fig. 6–4. Illustration of the compression and rarefaction of air particles in a sine wave.

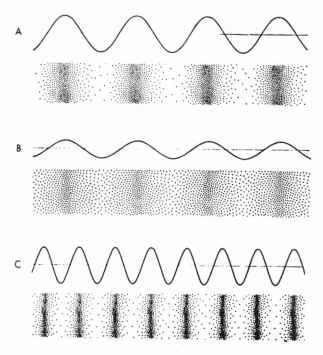

determines the frequency, *F*, while the time required for a complete cycle is the period, *T*, and it, of course, is the reciprocal of frequency *F*, or: $T = 1/F$.

It is possible to demonstrate visually what happens to air particles when a sound generated by simple harmonic motion passes through the air. The dots in Figure 6–4 represent air-particle movement. In a state of equilibrium air particles will be rather evenly distributed. In A, the particles are alternately compressed and rarefied. Graphic representation of the compressions and rarefactions may take the form of a sine curve, also shown in A. Note that the frequency in A and B is the same but that the extent of compression and rarefaction in wave A is approximately twice that of B. Since the air particles in A must move a greater distance, but at the same frequency as those in B, it should be apparent that they must move with greater velocity. Thus, a sine curve can represent the velocity of air-particle movement as well as the extent and frequency of movement. The sine curve in C has the same amplitude as that in A; however, the frequency of wave C is twice that of either wave A or B.

Thus, all sine waves are not the same. They may differ in amplitude, phase relationships, and/or frequency. Consider the two waves in Figure 6–5A, for example. Both are the same frequency and have the same amplitude, but whereas one begins at 0°, the other is at maximum displacement at 0°. These waves are 90° out of phase, or there is a phase lag of 90° between them. In Figure 6–5B, the two tones are 180° out of phase. Compression in one wave occurs when rarefaction is occurring in the other, and the result, in air-borne sound, is a cancellation of the energies in both waves. In general, such interference is only partially complete, but ideally, if interfering waves

Fig. 6–5. Oscillographic recordings of phase relationships between sound waves.

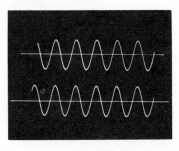

A. Waves 90° out
of phase

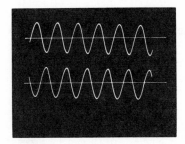

B. Waves 180° out
of phase

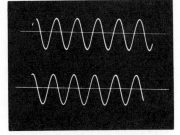

C. Waves in phase

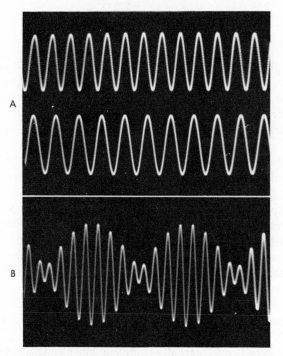

Fig. 6–6. (A) Beating effect produced by two sound waves of slightly different frequencies. (B) An oscillogram of the interference pattern.

have opposite phase and the same frequency and amplitude, they will exactly cancel. As we shall see, this fact may be a very useful laboratory technique in the study of hearing. In C, the two waves are in phase.

Interference may also result from tones that are of slightly different frequencies. When two tuning forks of slightly different frequencies are struck, the ear not only detects the two tones, but there is also a periodic swelling and decay of the tones. They are beating with one another. This beating effect may be explained by means of an illustration. In Figure 6–6, two wave trains of equal amplitude but slightly different frequencies are shown in superposition. Because one wave is vibrating at a rate greater than the other, the compression phase of one periodically overtakes, coincides, and moves ahead of the compression phase of the other, as in A. When the compression phases coincide, they reinforce, and when the compression phase of one coincides with the rarefaction of the other, they interfere or cancel, as shown in B. The result is a periodic waxing and waning of the amplitude of the sound. Since a beat or swelling of the tone occurs every time one wave is in phase with the other, the number of beats produced per second will be the difference in frequency between the two tones. When the frequency of beats (beat frequency is a better term) is high enough, a separate tone will be detected. It is called the beat note or difference tone. The use of beats is a simple way to tune musical instruments or electronic sound generators. In addition, when beats come too fast to be separately distinguished, they affect the tone, imparting a rough or dissonant quality to it.

Sound vibrators generally fall into one of three categories, those exhibiting free, forced, or maintained vibrations. Examples of free vibrators include tuning forks, pendulums, and vibrating strings. Once they have had energy imparted to them, they continue to vibrate periodically until the energy has been dissipated. It is characteristic of a free vibrator to vibrate at its natural frequency. We have seen how the natural frequency of a string is dependent upon its tension, mass, and length as expressed by the formula:

$$f = \frac{1}{2L} \sqrt{\frac{T}{M}}$$

Thus, no matter whether a string is plucked, struck, or bowed, its rate of vibration is the same. It is also characteristic of a free vibrator to absorb energy best when the energy source has a frequency rate exactly the same as the vibrator. This characteristic is known as resonance, which is easily demonstrated with the aid of three tuning forks, two of which have the same natural frequency. If one fork is struck and held in the vicinity of another fork matched in frequency, some of the energy radiated by the vibrating fork will be absorbed by the second fork, which will soon go into vibration on its own. There has been a transference of energy from one fork to the other. This transference of energy can be facilitated by touching the handles of the forks together. Whereas in the first instance the forks were loosely coupled, they are now closely coupled, and the transference of energy ought to be more efficient. If two forks with different natural or resonant frequencies are used in the same experiment, there will be little or no transference of energy, especially if they are loosely coupled. If, however, they are tightly coupled for a few seconds and then separated, the second fork may vibrate, not at the frequency of the first fork but rather at its own natural frequency.

Sometimes vibratory or sound energy is imparted to a structure at a frequency rate other than its own natural frequency. The structure is literally forced into vibration. If the base of a struck tuning fork is held firmly against a table top, for example, the whole table will be set into vibration at the same rate as the tuning fork. There is a transference of energy, but it is very inefficient. If the vibrating fork is removed from the table, the vibrations of the table cease almost instantly. In other words, the table offers a great deal of resistance to vibrations at the rate of the fork, and the vibrations are highly damped. Oscillograms of free and damped vibrations are shown in Figure 6–7. An extreme example of damping occurs when a displaced body returns to its position of equilibrium without passing through it. Such a condition is known as critical damping, and no free vibrations can occur. Critical or nearly critical damping can be demonstrated by releasing a displaced pendulum weight that is immersed in water. The human ear is highly, but not quite critically, damped. Imagine the state of confusion if the structures of the ear continued to vibrate for some time after a sound had ceased.

Maintained vibration is not very different from free vibration. A constant quantity of energy is applied to the vibrator at an integral multiple of the natural frequency of the vibrator, and any damping effects will be overcome, permitting the vibrator to maintain a constant amplitude vibration. Common examples of maintained vibration include a child "pumping" on a swing and the spring-driven pendulum of a clock.

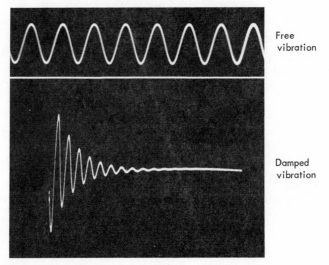

Fig. 6–7. *Oscillograms of free and damped vibrations.*

Wave length, frequency and velocity

In Figure 6–8, the distance between crests has been designated by the Greek letter λ (lambda). This is a commonly used symbol to represent wave length. As shown earlier, a complete cycle of simple harmonic motion represents a phase change of 360°; for this reason, wave length can be measured from any two points that represent a 360° phase change.

The velocity with which sound waves travel through air is about 1,130 feet per second (at room temperature). If the frequency of the sound wave is known, the wave length in feet can be determined by the following simple, but very basic formula: $λ = v/f$ where v is the velocity in feet per second and f is the frequency in cycles per second. On the other hand, if the wave length is known, the frequency is $f = v/λ = 1130/λ$. The frequency of a sound wave is, of course, determined by the frequency of vibration of the source of the sound. A particular tuning fork, when properly struck, may vibrate at 440 cycles per second, and the air particles surrounding the fork are set into vibration at the same rate. The result is a sinusoidal note (often called a pure tone) with a frequency of 440 cycles per second (cps), or A_4 on the musical scale.

One might at first expect the energy of a sound wave to be directly proportional to its amplitude; actually it is proportional to the square of the amplitude. In other words, a wave in which the amplitude of vibration is twice that of another actually represents four times as much energy. When an elastic medium such as air is deformed, the potential energy is given by the product of the average force and the distance through which it acts. We have seen that the value of the average force depends upon the distance through which the medium is displaced (Hooke's law). As a result, the work done, or energy of the wave, depends on the product of the two, or the square of the amplitude.

A tuning fork (and most other sound vibrators) generates a sound wave that is propagated out in all directions. In other words, it generates a spherical wave composed of layers of compressions and rarefactions, radiating in all directions from the sound source. Any specific direction in which this wave travels is often called a ray of sound, and the advancing disturbance is called a wave front. Since intensity is the rate of energy flow per unit of area of surface receiving the flow, it follows that, as the distance from the sound source increases, the distribution of energy flow must necessarily decrease. The wave front of a spherical sound wave, as it advances, is a sphere of increasing area $4\pi r^2$, where r is the radius (equal to the distance from the sound source). If the total quantity of energy at the sound source is P, the energy crossing a unit of area of surface would be $p/4\pi r^2$. From this it is apparent that the intensity of a sound wave varies inversely as the square of the distance from the source, or, $I = 1/d^2$. Thus, a sound with an intensity, I, at a certain distance from the source will have one-fourth the intensity at twice the distance and one-sixteenth the intensity at four times the distance. This relationship is known as the inverse square law, and is one of the fundamental laws of physics.

Complex sounds

Thus far we have been dealing with sine waves or pure tones. Pure tones, however, are relatively rare acoustic events in our day-to-day lives. The sounds to which we are most accustomed are usually quite complex; that is, they are composed of more than one frequency. The implication is, of course, that the vibrating structures which generate sound do not vibrate in a sinusoidal manner, but rather they vibrate in a complex manner. That is, a body may vibrate as a whole or it may vibrate in segments in various ways. Each mode of vibration contributes to the shape of the resultant wave as a whole, and each separate frequency that is generated contributes to the sound that is heard.

Early in the nineteenth century, a French physicist, Fourier, demonstrated that any wave form, as long as it is specifiable, can be broken down into a finite number of sinusoidal components of different amplitudes, frequencies, and phases. Furthermore, each of the components is an integral multiple of the fundamental (or lowest tone in the series), which has a period equal to that of a single cycle of the whole complex tone.

Any partial mode of vibration whose frequency is higher than the fundamental

Fig. 6–8. Illustration of wavelength.

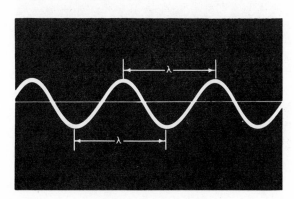

(any partial whose period is less than that of the whole wave of which it is a component) produces an overtone. When there are a number of partial modes of vibration there will be an equal number of overtones. The more complex wave forms are made of a larger number of overtones and it is these overtones which are largely responsible for a tone's characteristic quality. When the frequencies of the overtones are integral multiples of the lowest frequency, f, of the fundamental, they are called harmonics as well as overtones. In a harmonic series $1f$, $2f$, $3f$, $4f$ . . ., the lowest frequency or fundamental is also the first harmonic, while the first overtone, $2f$, is the second harmonic, and the second overtone is the third harmonic. The overtones of some vibrators are not quite harmonically related. Bells, for example, generate a series of overtones, some of which are not integral multiples of the lowest component in the tone. This accounts for a certain degree of dissonance characteristic of a bell tone.

Musical tones are, for the most part, complex tones composed of a fundamental frequency and a harmonically related series of overtones. The vowel sounds in speech are also composed of a fundamental frequency and harmonically related overtones. When the frequency composition, amplitude, and phase relationships of the components of a tone are constant over time, the sound is said to be a steady-state sound, an example of which is a sustained vowel sound. An important characteristic of speech, however, is that it is rarely in steady state; it is constantly changing. That is, speech is a series of transient sounds. Thus, a change in steady state is known as a transient. Transients are generated, for example, when a vowel is abruptly terminated by the articulators. The steady-state and transient features of a speech sample can be grossly examined by a display of its wave form, as in Figure 6–9. The wave form is of the word "Speech" as spoken by the author and displayed on an oscilloscope. Note the wave form of the [s] phoneme, which seems to be aperiodic when compared to the wave form of the [i] sound.

A sound that has little or no periodicity is usually called noise, and noises are characteristically nonspecifiable. Noises can be produced in a number of ways, by the turbulence of air as it passes through a constriction or by a body vibrating in an aperiodic manner. Noise is often defined as any undesired sound; and it is also defined as

Fig. 6–9. Oscillogram of the word "Speech," as spoken by the author.

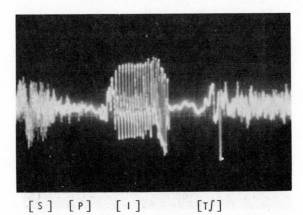

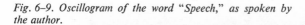

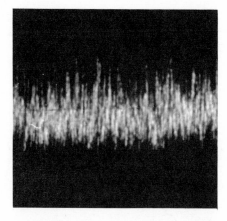

White noise

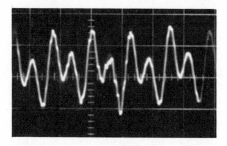

Complex tone

Fig. 6–10. Oscillograms of white noise and of a complex tone.

an erratic, intermittent, or statistically· random vibration. It is apparent that noise is not rigidly defined. A well-recognized and often used term is white noise. It may be produced by mixing all the pure tones in the audible spectrum without regard to phase, just as white light is produced by mixing all the colors in the visible spectrum. White noise sounds much like the hissing produced by steam escaping from a radiator. An oscillographic display of white noise, as compared to a complex tone, is shown in Figure 6–10. Because white noise contains so many components it has a tendency to interfere with almost any other sound. Such interference is called masking.

When sound, traveling through air, encounters a medium of a different density, it has a tendency to be reflected away. When sound strikes a wall, for instance, almost all of it is reflected away, and without a change in phase. Since the wall is relatively immovable, the total velocity of air particles (the sum of the velocity of the incident wave and of the reflected wave) must be zero, and if the velocities of the incident and reflected waves cancel, their combined pressures against the wall produce twice the pressure of that produced by the incident wave alone. If the direction of travel of an incident wave is to the right, as in Figure 6–11A, the amplitude of particle movement at the wall must be zero. Suppose for a moment that a sound wave were allowed to pass uninterrupted through the wall. The represented sound wave would then look as in B. Now earlier we stated that a sound is reflected away and without a change in phase. Imagine that the wave which has passed through the wall has been folded back on

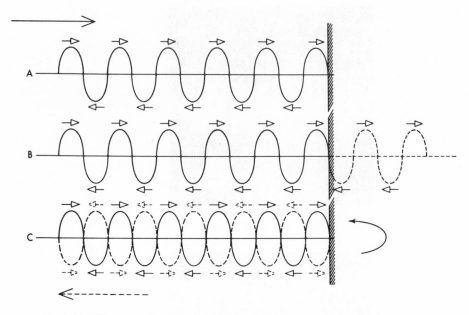

Fig. 6–11. Illustration of particle movement in a standing wave.

itself, thus representing a wave which has reflected without a change in phase, as in
C. The direction of travel of the incident wave is shown by the bold solid arrow,
while the direction of travel of the reflected wave is shown by the bold dotted arrow.
The direction of particle movement in the compression phase of the incident wave
is to the right, as indicated by the small solid arrows, while the direction of particle
movement in the rarefaction phase of the reflected wave is also to the right, as shown
by the small dotted arrows. The direction of particle movement in the rarefaction phase
of the incident wave is to the left while the direction of particle movement in the compression phase of the reflected wave is also to the left. For this reason, the forces acting
on the air particles are the sum of the forces in the compression phase of one wave
and the forces in the rarefaction phase in the other. When a wave is reflected back
without change in phase, a pattern of cancellations and reinforcements is quickly
set up. This phenomenon is known as a standing wave, which is an appropriate term,
since by moving the head slightly when a continuous tone is sounding in a room,
easily detected changes in loudness are experienced. In fact, with a little searching,
regions can be found where the sound is all but completely canceled, while others
can be found where the sound is very loud. The sound wave seems to be standing
still! Standing waves can be useful in the laboratory, but they are often a bothersome
nuisance in the concert hall.

The decibel

In everyday applications of acoustics, the ratios of intensity, pressure, and velocity
are often measured. We should come to grips with the way in which these comparisons are usually made. Most often a ratio scale is used, but since the intensity ratio of

the loudest tolerable sound to the just audible sound is in the order of 100,000,000,-000,000 to 1, the ratio scale is far too unwieldy. In order to avoid such cumbersome numbers, the ratio scale has been changed to an interval scale by means of logarithms.

Conventionally we count simply by adding a numerical unit to each successive number. For example, if the numerical unit is 1, we count by adding as follows: $1 + 1 = 2, 2 + 1 = 3, 3 + 1 = 4, 4 + 1 = 5$, and so on. Such a scale is called an interval scale, in which the intervals between successive values are equal or linear. We may also count by successive multiplication of a numerical unit. For example, if the numerical unit is 2, the scale would progress as follows: $2 \times 1 = 2, 2 \times 2 = 4$, $2 \times 4 = 8, 2 \times 8 = 16, 2 \times 16 = 32$, and so on. It is apparent that each successive product has twice the numerical value of its predecessor, or that the ratio between successive products is always 2:1. Such a scale is called a ratio scale. A ratio scale with a base of 2 may be expressed in other ways, as shown below:

$$
\begin{array}{lll}
2 \text{ (the base)} & = 2^1 = & 2 \\
2 \times 2 & = 2^2 = & 4 \\
2 \times 2 \times 2 & = 2^3 = & 8 \\
2 \times 2 \times 2 \times 2 & = 2^4 = & 16 \\
2 \times 2 \times 2 \times 2 \times 2 & = 2^5 = & 32 \\
2 \times 2 \times 2 \times 2 \times 2 \times 2 & = 2^6 = & 64 \\
2 \times 2 \times 2 \times 2 \times 2 \times 2 \times 2 & = 2^7 = & 128
\end{array}
$$

On the other hand, if the multiplying unit is 10, the scale would appear as:

$$
\begin{array}{lll}
10 \text{ (base)} & = 10^1 = & 10 \\
10 \times 10 & = 10^2 = & 100 \\
10 \times 10 \times 10 & = 10^3 = & 1,000 \\
10 \times 10 \times 10 \times 10 & = 10^4 = & 10,000 \\
10 \times 10 \times 10 \times 10 \times 10 & = 10^5 = & 100,000 \\
10 \times 10 \times 10 \times 10 \times 10 \times 10 & = 10^6 = & 1,000,000 \\
10 \times 10 \times 10 \times 10 \times 10 \times 10 \times 10 & = 10^7 = & 10,000,000
\end{array}
$$

In each scale the multiplying unit is called the base. It was 2 in the first scale and 10 in the second. Any scale whose successive units are multiplied by a specific base is called a logarithmic or exponential scale. Each time a unit is multiplied by the base, it has been raised by 1 power. Thus, 10^6 (read ten to the sixth power) means that ten has been multiplied by itself six times. It also means that 10^6 has a numerical value of 1,000,000. If we know the base of a logarithmic scale, 10, we need not write the number 10, because it does not tell us anything. All we need to write down is the value of the power to which 10 has been raised. Thus, we deal only with the exponent in our mathematical manipulations.

Logarithms are a valuable labor-saving device, especially when large numerical values must be dealt with. Since the exponents of a logarithmic scale in reality form an interval scale, such complex manipulations as multiplication and division are reduced to adding and subtracting exponents. Supposing we are faced with the problem of multiplying $1,000,000 \times 10,000$. We know that 1,000,000 is the same as 10^6 and that 10,000 is the same as 10^4. To solve the problem we need only add the exponents, to give 10^{10}, which may be expressed as 10,000,000,000. In order to divide 1,000,000 by 10,000 we need only express the numbers logarithmically and subtract

TABLE 6-1

Commonly Encountered Pressure and Intensity Ratios and Their Values
Expressed in Decibels

A Ratios	B Decibels (dB) for intensity	C Decibels (dB) for pressure
1	0	0
2	3.0	6.0
3	4.8	9.6
4	6.0	12.0
5	7.0	14.0
6	7.8	15.6
7	8.45	16.9
8	9.0	18.0
9	9.5	19.0
10	10.0	20.0
20	13.0	26.0
30	14.8	29.6
40	16.0	32.0
50	17.0	34.0
60	17.8	35.6
70	18.5	37.0
80	19.0	38.0
90	19.6	39.2
100	20.0	40.0

their exponents as follows: $10^6 - 10^4 (6 - 4) = 2 = 10^2 = 100$. The intensity ratio of the loudest to the faintest tone can therefore be represented logarithmically by determining the power to which 10 must be raised in order to equal 100,000,000,-000,000. It turns out to be 10^{14}. The 10 does not carry any information, so just the logarithm of the ratio is used, and it is expressed in units called bels. Thus a ratio of 10^{14}:1 may be expressed as 14 bels. The bel is not satisfactory, however, because the entire intensity range encompassed by human hearing amounts to only 14 bels. In order to specify smaller intensity ratios without using fractions, the term decibel has been introduced. It is one-tenth the power ratio in bels. The bel is rarely used today, being supplanted by the more convenient decibel. Therefore, any power ratio or intensity ratio may be expressed in decibels (dB) by the following formula: $dB = 10 \ Log_{10} I_2/I_1$.

Intensity is a measure of energy flow per unit of area per unit of time; cm^2/second. Energy per second is also power, measured in watts per square centimeter. Because a logarithmic scale has no true zero, it is a scale of ratios, always comparing two values. If we are interested in the relationship between two sound intensities or powers, one must become the reference for the other. Certain standard reference intensities have been adopted. The intensity level (*IL*) of any sound is the ratio of that intensity (expressed in dB) to the standard intensity of 10^{-16} watt/cm^2. (A negative exponent may be thought of as the reciprocal of the same number with a positive exponent. For example 10^{-2} is $1/10 \times 1/10$, or $1/10^2$, or $1/100$.)

Because the ear is a pressure-sensing device, comparisons between sound pressures are very often made, especially in reference to hearing. The power of a sound is proportional to pressure multiplied by itself or, in other words, to the square of the pressure. Thus, if pressure is doubled, the power becomes four times as great. To express pressure ratios in decibels, therefore, the formula may be written

$$dB = 10 \, Log_{10} \frac{(P_2)^2}{(P_1)^2},$$

or

$$dB = 10 \, Log \left(\frac{P_2}{P_1}\right)^2, \quad \text{or} \quad dB = 20 \, Log \frac{P_2}{P_1}$$

Pressure is a familiar term, but it is often used improperly, being equated with force. Force may be defined simply as a push or pull, whereas pressure is defined as force per unit area, when the force is at right angles to a surface: Pressure $(P) = $ Force/Area and $F = PA$. Sound pressure is often measured in dynes per square centimeter (dyne/cm^2), and the standard reference pressure which has been adopted is .0002 dynes/cm^2. Any pressure when compared to .0002 dyne/cm^2 is known as sound pressure level, abbreviated SPL. Thus SPL is the difference in dB between a particular pressure and the standard reference of .0002 dyne/cm^2. For reference purposes, commonly encountered intensity and pressure ratios, and their values expressed in dB, are given in Table 6–1.

ANATOMY OF THE EAR

Introduction

The ear is an extraordinary sound-detecting device, so sensitive it can almost hear the random Brownian movements of the air particles as they strike the eardrum. Yet, such a sensitive instrument is able to tolerate the sound waves generated by an entire symphony orchestra! The ear can also respond to a wide frequency range. It just misses detecting the low-frequency rumblings caused by muscle contractions and by blood rushing through the veins and arteries in the vicinity of the ear mechanism. The ear can also detect such things as shrill whistles that have extremely high frequencies. The range of audibility is often stated to be from 15 or 16 cycles per second (cps) to about 20,000 cps. In most adults, however, the upper limit of the frequency range is in the vicinity of 14,000 or 15,000 cps, while in some young children the upper limit of hearing is somewhere in the neighborhood of 30,000 cps.

The ear's power of discrimination is very impressive. Suppose a single pure tone is sounded at a moderate intensity level (comfortable to the listener) to a person with normal hearing. Then suppose we should change, very slightly, the frequency of that tone, sound it again, and ask our listener to tell us when he is just able to detect a change in frequency. He could detect, even without special training, at least 1,000 different pitches of sound, and at frequencies below 1,000 cps he could detect a change of only 3 cycles per second. In addition to having fine powers of pitch discrimination, the ear can also do quite well in detecting different levels of sound intensity. Within the total intensity range to which the ear can safely respond, a listener can detect over 250 different intensity levels, which, of course, are perceived as changes in loudness.

Thus the number of just noticeable differences within the dynamic range of hearing amounts to about a quarter of a million!

We are privileged to listen to simple or "pure" tones on very few occasions in our everyday lives. The discrimination powers of the hearing mechanism are not, however, confined to just pure tones. Consider the fact that we can usually keep our wits about us and carry on a relatively normal conversation in a room crowded with people all talking at the same time, or almost. In fact, we are quite able to suppress all sorts of sounds about us in such an environment and "tune in" on a conversation on the other side of a room. It helps, of course, if we can see the person who is talking.

Our task in the remainder of the chapter will be to examine the anatomical structure of the ear mechanism. We should also spend some time trying to figure out how some of the structures we examine might work. If we are successful in our undertaking, we ought to emerge from this chapter more impressed than ever with the remarkable structure we call simply, "the ear."

The hearing mechanism may be thought of as consisting of three divisions, the external, middle, and inner ears. This division is based largely on the anatomical relationships between the various structures of the auditory system. On a functional basis, however, it may be divided into an outer and an inner ear. The outer ear is the part of the system that has to do with absorption and transformation of acoustic energy into mechanical energy. The inner ear, on the other hand, is the part of the system that has to do with transduction of the mechanical energy; that is, the inner ear must absorb and transform mechanical energy into a series of neural impulses, the characteristics of which are somehow analogous to the original acoustic energy. For the sake of convention we will adhere to the anatomical divisions and begin with the external ear, which is composed of the auricle, or pinna, and the ear canal, or external auditory meatus.

The External Ear

The auricle

The auricle or pinna is the visible, flap-like part of the hearing mechanism that is fastened to the side of the head at an angle of about 30 degrees. It is funnel-like and functions, even though very poorly, to direct sound waves through the external auditory meatus to the tympanic membrane or eardrum. In animals like the horse and rabbit, the auricle can be moved in several directions, which is very important in localizing the source of sound, and the particularly large ears in some animals double as temperature-regulating mechanisms, since their size and elaborate vascular systems serve as excellent radiators of heat. In man, however, the function of the auricle is open to some question. The sensitivity of hearing (auditory acuity) seems to be about the same in those of us endowed with generous ears as it is in those who have small or, indeed, no ears.

According to Békésy and Rosenblith (1958), a number of experiments were conducted during the second half of the nineteenth century to determine the contributions of the external ear. The experimenters introduced hollow glass tubes into the ear canal and filled the irregularities with wax or dough. The results were consistent; although the sensitivity for sounds in the middle range was not substantially affected, the ability to localize the source of sounds suffered, especially if the source was directly in front or in back of the head.

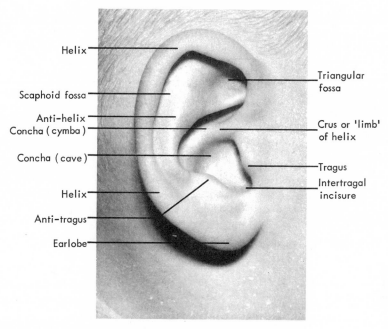

Helix

Scaphoid fossa

Anti-helix
Concha (cymba)

Concha (cave)

Helix

Anti-tragus

Earlobe

Triangular fossa

Crus or 'limb' of helix

Tragus

Intertragal incisure

Fig. 6–12. The auricle or pinna.

It becomes quite obvious, even from casual observation, that the surface of the auricle is very uneven and filled with pits, grooves, and depressions. The deepest of these depressions is called the concha, while the rimlike periphery of the auricle is known as the helix, which, as shown in Figure 6–12, descends into the concha anteriorly. This part of the helix is called the arm or crus, and it divides the concha into the skiff or cymba superiorly and the cave inferiorly. A frequently found variation of the helix, near the tip posteriorly, is a thickened portion called Darwin's tubercle. We ought not generalize about phylogenetic regression in persons with Darwin's tubercle, even though such an ear resembles that found on the Macaque Rhesus monkey. A second semicircular ridge, just anterior to the helix, is called the antihelix. A depression between the helix and antihelix is called the scaphoid fossa, or "boat-shaped ditch." At the level of the external auditory meatus anteriorly is a cartilaginous flap, which partially occludes the opening into the meatus. This flap is called the tragus, while just opposite it, forming the inferior boundary of the concha, is a smaller ridge, the antitragus. The tragus and antitragus are separated by a notch called the intertragal incisure. In some lower animals, particularly the aquatic animals, the tragus is modified so as to form a valve that closes to protect the ear from water pressure. The inferior extremity of the ear is called the earlap or ear lobe. This structure, which contains no cartilaginous framework, varies greatly in shape from person to person. The ear lobe seems to have no definite biological function.

The core of the auricle consists of a fibrous cartilage, which has a shape roughly similar to that of the ear. Medially the auricular cartilage, as it is called, is continuous with the cartilaginous skeleton of the external auditory meatus. It fastens anteriorly to the zygomatic arch by a cartilaginous spine and posteriorly to the mastoid process of the temporal bone by a cartilaginous tail. Although three auricular muscles attach to the auricle they are, for all practical purposes, vestigial and serve very little function in man. The auricularis anterior, when functional, draws the auricle upward and forward, the auricularis raises the auricle, and the auricularis posterior pulls it backward. Some very small intrinsic muscles extend from one part of the auricle to the other. In man they have no known function. Muscles of the auricle are very highly developed in some lower animals, however, even to the extent that the ears may exhibit independent movement like the eyes of the chameleon.

The external auditory meatus

Communication between the actual ear mechanism and the external environment is provided by the external auditory meatus, or, simply, the ear canal. It has one primary function, and that is to conduct sound to the eardrum.

The external auditory meatus is a curved and irregularly shaped tube that may vary from about 25 mm to 35 mm in length and from 6 mm to 8 mm in diameter. The diameter is largest at the auricular (external) orifice, becoming gradually smaller toward the isthmus, which is the junction of the cartilaginous framework with the bony framework. The diameter expands again, only to decrease in size just before the meatus terminates medially at the tympanic membrane. The external auditory meatus is also somewhat oval shaped, having its greatest diameter vertically.

Fig. 6–13. Coronal section of the human ear. (From Max Brodel, Three Unpublished Drawings of the Anatomy of the Human Ear. W. B. Saunders Company, Philadelphia, 1946.)

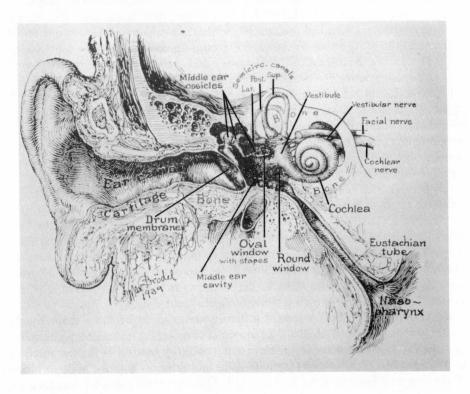

The drawing shown in Figure 6–13 was made by the late Max Brodel, a renowned medical illustrator. It is probably the most accurate and lucid drawing of the human ear ever made. As the drawing reveals, the supporting skeleton of the lateral one-third to one-half of the meatus is cartilaginous, while the skeleton for the medial portion is osseous. Whereas the bony portion of the canal is fixed in diameter, the cartilaginous portion is variable, and its diameter is dependent upon such things as movements of the mandible. At birth there is no osseous canal, and it does not become fully developed until about the end of the third year. The bony canal develops from an incomplete cartilaginous ring known as the tympanic annulus.

As shown in Figure 6–13, the axis of the external auditory meatus is such that it is slightly lower at the orifice than it is medially. The significance of this lies in the fact that water and other foreign materials are not liable to collect or remain in the ear canal as they might were the axis of the canal directed the other way. The course of the meatus is such that it forms an S-shaped curve. The most external part (pars externa) of the meatus is directed inward, slightly forward, and upward. The course then changes so that the middle portion (pars media) is directed inward and backward. The most medial portion (pars interna) is directed inward, forward, and slightly downward. The curvature, which is slightly variable from person to person, may be straightened out somewhat by gently pulling the auricle upward and back. With adequate illumination this will afford a view of the tympanic membrane. The course of the ear canal in infants and small children is much more horizontal than it is in the adult, and for this reason there is a tendency for foreign materials to accumulate in it.

The skin lining the external auditory meatus is closely adherent to the periostium and perichondrium of the supportive skeleton. The lateral one-third of the canal presents numerous hairs and modified sebaceous glands which produce, in conjunction with the ceruminous glands, the wax-like cerumen or "earwax." Cerumen protects the ear canal from drying out and, since it is bitter, noxious, and sticky, prevents the intrusion of insects and other foreign bodies.

The meatus has certain acoustic properties that are of vital importance both to physiologists and to engineers interested in hearing. According to Wever and Lawrence (1954), the estimated speed of sound in the meatus is 350 meters per second. If we can assume the meatus resonates best when its length is one-fourth the wave length of the applied sound, it ought to resonate at a frequency very near 4,000 cps. Wiener and Ross (1946) found the average length of the meatus in their subjects to be 2.3 cm, which means that the meatus should resonate to a sound whose wave length is 2.3 × 4 cm or 9.2 cm. Thus, the meatus ought to resonate at a frequency very near 3,800 cps, which is close to the resonant frequency observed. These results are in close agreement with earlier results obtained by Fleming (1939).

The Middle Ear

The medial limit of the external auditory meatus is formed by the eardrum or tympanic membrane, which also serves as the boundary for much of the lateral wall of the tympanic or middle-ear cavity. The middle ear was described in some detail by Fallopius, in 1561, who saw in it some resemblance to an Army drum or "tympanum," whence the cavity gets its name. The middle ear is composed of the tympanic membrane, the air-filled middle-ear cavity proper, and the structures contained within it, such as the auditory ossicles (the malleus, incus, and stapes), middle-ear muscles, and the mucous membrane which lines the structures in the middle-ear cavity.

The tympanic membrane

The tympanic membrane is placed obliquely in the external auditory meatus in such a manner as to form an obtuse angle (140°) with its upper wall and an acute angle with its lower wall. The periphery of the membrane, except for a small section superiorly, is thickened to form a fibrocartilaginous ring (annulus), which is accommodated by a groove in the bony wall of the meatus called the tympanic sulcus. It is by means of this attachment that the tympanic membrane is fixed into position. The tympanic sulcus is deficient superiorly at the notch of Rivinus, and while it is not easily seen in the adult temporal bone, it is readily visible in the temporal bones of lower primates and very young children. The sulcus shown in Figure 6–14 is in the temporal bone of a young adult ape.

Structurally the eardrum consists of three layers of tissue: a thin outer cutaneous layer, which is continuous with the lining of the external auditory meatus; a fibrous middle layer, which is responsible for the resilience of the eardrum, and an internal layer of mucous membrane, which is continuous with the lining of the tympanic

Fig. 6–14. Two views of the middle ear cavity of a young ape.

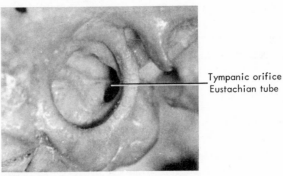

—Tympanic sulcus

—Oval window

Niche of round window

A. Lateral view showing oval and round windows, and the tympanic sulcus.

Tympanic orifice
Eustachian tube

B. Postero-lateral view showing tympanic orifice of Eustachian tube

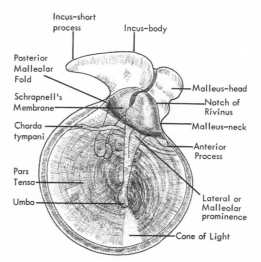

Fig. 6–15. Schematic of tympanic membrane and some associated structures.

cavity. The fibrous layer actually contains two layers closely connected one with the other. The more superficial of the two consists of fibers that radiate from the center toward the periphery. These fibers are rather evenly distributed throughout most of the tympanic membrane, giving the fibrous layer a fancied resemblance to spokes in a wheel. The deeper layer is composed of concentric rings of fibrous tissue which have an uneven distribution. Their density is greatest toward the periphery, becoming sparse in the center. A small triangular area, bounded by the notch of Rivinus, contains very few fibers, accounting for the flaccid nature of that portion of the eardrum, which is known as the pars flaccida, or Schrapnell's membrane. It is said to function in a very limited manner in maintaining equalization of the air pressure between the external and middle ears. The remainder of the eardrum is held rather tense, and is known as the pars tensa.

The eardrum may be examined by means of an otoscope, and normally appears as a concave, smooth, translucent, pearl-gray membrane. The fact that it is concave may easily be derived from a wedge-shaped reflected spot of light, usually seen radiating from the center toward the periphery, as in Figure 6–15. It is called the cone of light, and its presence is regarded as the hallmark of a healthy eardrum. In fact, many otologists regard the cone of light as the highlight of an otological examination. Upon close examination several important landmarks may be seen on the eardrum.

Extending from the center to the periphery of the membrane, at about 1 o'clock in the right ear and about 11 o'clock in the left, is an opaque, whitish streak, the malleolar stria, which is formed by the handle or manubrium of the malleus. The manubrium is firmly attached to the medial surface of the drum membrane, as far as its center, which is drawn inward toward the tympanic cavity to form the "navel," or more properly, the umbo. This is the spot from which the cone of light radiates. Another highlight may be seen at the upper end of the malleolar stria. It is due to light reflecting from the malleolar prominence, which is formed by the attachment of the lateral process of the malleus to the eardrum. Two ligamentous bands, the anterior and posterior malleolar folds, progress from the notch of Rivinus to the lateral process of the malleus. The triangular area above these folds is the pars flaccida, or Schrapnell's membrane.

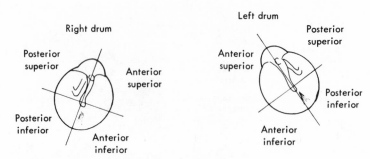

Fig. 6–16. Schematic of the division of the tympanic membrane into quadrants.

For descriptive purposes the tympanic membrane is often divided into four areas or quadrants. This division is illustrated schematically in Figure 6–16.

The tympanic cavity

The tympanic cavity, shown in Figures 6–17 and 6–18, is an irregular space within the petrous portion of the temporal bone. It is narrow, varying in width from 2 to 4 mm, while its vertical dimension is about 15 mm. Usually the tympanic cavity is considered in two parts, the attic or epitympanic recess, which is the portion extending upward beyond the superior border of the tympanic membrane, and the tympanic cavity proper, which is the portion of the cavity lying medially to the tympanic membrane. The epitympanic recess is largely occupied by the head of the malleus and the bulk of the incus. Its posterior wall is perforated by an orifice, the tympanic aditus, which forms the connecting link between the tympanic cavity and the tympanic antrum (sinus). Because the tympanic antrum communicates with the mastoid air cells, there is indirect communication between the middle-ear cavity and the mastoid air cells. In addition, the mucous membrane that lines the middle-ear cavity is continuous with that which lines the tympanic antrum and mastoid air cells. Thus, there is a relatively resistance-free path established for the spread of infection from the middle-ear cavity, or indeed from the nasal cavity, to the mastoid air cells. This is just one reason earaches and infections ought not to be taken lightly.

The tympanic cavity is bounded superiorly by a paper-thin plate of bone called the tegmental wall or tegmen tympani, which separates the tympanic cavity from the cranium and the meningeal coverings of the brain. The tegmen tympani is continued posteriorly so that it forms the roof of the tympanic antrum as well. The floor of the tympanic cavity, somewhat narrower than the roof, is formed by the tympanic plate. It separates the tympanic cavity from the jugular fossa, a groove that accommodates the jugular vein.

As implied earlier, most of the lateral wall of the tympanic cavity is formed by the tympanic membrane, and for this reason the terms lateral and membranous wall are often used synonymously. Above the tympanic membrane, however, in the epitympanic recess, the lateral wall is formed by part of the squamous portion of the temporal bone.

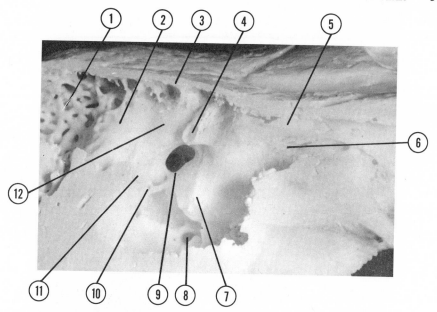

1. Tympanic antrum
2. Aditus to tympanic antrum
3. Tegmen tympani
4. Cochleariform process
5. Septum canalis musculotubarii
6. Bony part of auditory tube
7. Promontory
8. Niche of round window
9. Oval window
10. Pyrimidal eminence
11. Epitympanic recess
12. Prominence of lateral semicircular canal

Fig. 6–17. Photograph of the medial wall and part of the posterior and anterior walls of the right tympanic cavity, lateral view.

The labyrinthian or medial wall, shown in Figure 6–18, is vertically directed, and has as its landmarks the fenestra vestibuli, the fenestra rotunda, the promontory, and the prominence of the facial nerve canal. The fenestra vestibuli, popularly known as the oval window, is a somewhat kidney-shaped opening into the vestibule of the inner ear. During life the oval window is occupied by the footplate of the stapes, the periphery of which is fixed into place by an annular ligament. The fenestra rotunda, commonly referred to as the round window, is a circular opening into the basal turn of the scala tympani of the cochlea (to be discussed later). It is located beneath the oval window in a cone-shaped depression partially hidden from view by the promontory. The round window is closed by a thin membrane, the secondary tympanic membrane. The round window of a cat, as seen during life, is shown in Figure 6–19. The promontory is a rounded prominence projecting into the middle-ear cavity. It is formed by the lateral projection of the basal turn of the cochlea. Just superior to the oval window is a small prominence, formed by the lateral projection of the canal (aqueduct of Fallopius), through which courses the facial nerve.

The posterior or mastoid wall has as its landmarks the previously described tympanic aditus, which is the entrance to the tympanic antrum, the pyramidal eminence, and the fossa incudis. The pyramidal eminence is located just behind the oval window

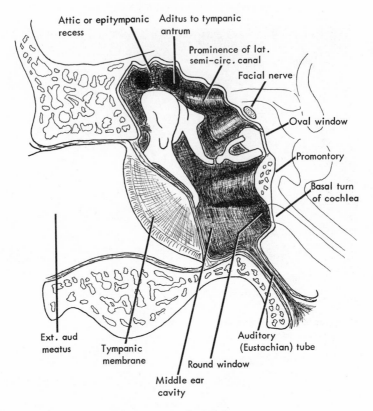

Fig. 6–18. Schematic of middle ear cavity, frontal view.

near the prominence of the facial canal. It is hollow and contains the stapedius muscle, one of the middle-ear muscles to be described later. The apex of the eminence is
pierced by a small aperture through which courses the tendon of the stapedius. The
fossa incudis is a small evacuation in the lower and back part of the epitympanic
recess which accommodates the short process of the incus. At the angle of the junction of the mastoid and membranous walls of the tympanic cavity, behind the tympanic
membrane and on a level with the lateral process of the malleus, is a small aperture
through which courses the chorda tympani nerve, a small branch of the facial nerve.
It enters the tympanic cavity, courses just medially to the neck of the malleus, and
leaves the cavity by way of the canal of Huguier (iter chordae anterius), which opens
just above and in front of the tympanic sulcus. The chorda tympani was shown schematically in Figure 6–15.

The anterior or carotid wall is somewhat wider at the top than at the bottom. It
is separated from the carotid canal (formed by the carotid artery) by a very thin plate
of bone. The upper part of the anterior wall is perforated by the tendon for the tensor
tympani muscle and by the orifice of the Eustachian tube. The canals for the Eustachian tube and for the tensor tympani are roughly parallel, and are separated by a
very thin plate of bone called the septum canalis musculotubarii, which is shown in
Figure 6–17.

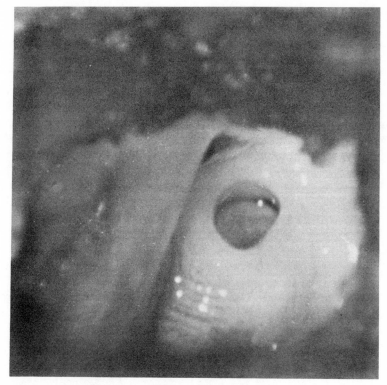

Fig. 6–19. Round window and promontory of a cat, as seen during life. (Modified Weber technique.)

The Eustachian tube

The Eustachian or auditory tube was described in detail by the sixteenth-century anatomist Eustachius, and has since borne his name. It is the canal which establishes communication between the middle-ear cavity and the nasopharynx. It is about 35–38 mm in length, and in the adult is directed downward, forward, and medialward, to the extent that it forms an angle of about 45 degrees with the sagittal plane and an angle of about 35 degrees with the horizontal plane. It may be divided into four sections, the osseous, cartilaginous, and membranous portions and the isthmus. The osseous portion, about 12–14 mm in length, begins in the carotid wall of the tympanic cavity just beneath the septum canalis musculotubarii. Thus, as seen in Figure 6–17, the tympanic opening of the Eustachian tube is about 3 mm above the floor of the tympanic cavity. This is a rather important point because in cases of infection of the middle ear or as a result of allergies, the middle-ear cavity may partially fill with exudate. Under normal conditions, and with an intact eardrum, this fluid may collect until it reaches the level of the tympanic opening of the tube before it can drain into the nasopharynx. The lumen through the osseous portion is normally open and varies from about 3 to 6 mm in diameter. It is narrowest at its medial limit where it ends at the junction of the squamous and petrous portions of the temporal bone as a ragged margin, which serves as the attachment for the cartilaginous portion. The junction

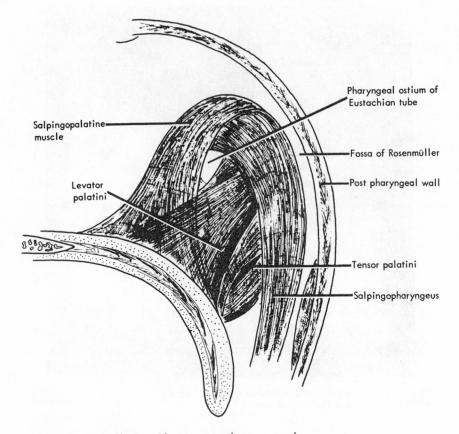

Fig. 6–20. Torus tubarius with mucous membrane removed.

of the osseous and cartilaginous portions is known as the isthmus. The cartilaginous portion varies in length from about 18 mm to 24 mm. It begins as a rounded shelf located above the lumen of the tube and gradually widens to form an incomplete ring whose upper edge is curled upon itself laterally so as to present the appearance of a hook when seen in transverse section. The tube is completed by soft connective tissue.

At the pharyngeal ostium the cartilage and its coverings form a prominent elevation, the torus tubarius. As shown schematically in Figure 6–20, the anterior fold of the torus is made by a small muscle called the salpingopalatine, which arises from the superior lateral border of the cartilage and courses downward and forward to blend with the muscle tissue of the soft palate. The posterior fold of the torus is made by the salpingopharyngeus, which arises from the medial superior border of the cartilage and arches downward and lateralward to blend into the lateral wall of the pharynx and with the palatopharyngeal muscle. Two other muscles, the levator palatini and the tensor palatini muscles, also arise from the cartilage. The levator palatini originates from the medial surface of the petrous portion of the temporal bone below the junction of the osseous and cartilaginous portions of the tube. A few fibers arise from the medial fold of the cartilage. The course of the muscle is roughly parallel to the cartilage until the fibers radiate and blend into the soft palate. Some fibers of the tensor palatini arise from the lateral side of the cartilage, but for the most part the muscle arises from adjacent bone. This muscle, you will recall, converges on the hamulus where the tendon courses at right angles to blend with the palatal aponeurosis.

The torus tubarius is liberally covered with ciliated mucous membrane that is continuous with that of the nasopharynx. The mucous membrane lining the lumen is a modified nasal type, which is continuous with that of the tympanic cavity. Near the pharyngeal orifice may be found a mass of pharyngeal tonsil tissue, which in many instances may actually penetrate into the lumen of the tube. This partially accounts for the rapid spread of upper respiratory infections through the Eustachian tube and into the middle ear.

Due to its elastic properties, the cartilaginous portion of the tube is normally collapsed, its walls folded parallel with its long axis. Simpkins (1943) has noted, however, that the passive elasticity of the cartilage is supplemented by active contraction of the salpingopalatine and salpingopharyngeus muscles.

The primary biological functions of the Eustachian tube are (1) to permit middle-ear pressure to equalize with external air pressure and (2) to permit drainage of normal and diseased middle-ear secretions from the middle-ear cavity into the nasopharynx. Almost all of us have experienced the uncomfortable sensation in our ears just after a rapid descent in an elevator. We may have also experienced an uncomfortable feeling in our stomachs, but this is another matter, not completely removed from the hearing mechanism, however. The uncomfortable sensation in our ears is the result of a sudden increase in air pressure outside with respect to the pressure in the middle ear. This discomfort may also be accompanied by strange, low rumblings in the ear. Such conditions, which may cause temporary partial deafness, can be alleviated simply by yawning, swallowing, or shouting loudly (depending upon your immediate circumstances, of course), all of which will open the normally closed pharyngeal orifice of the Eustachian tube, allowing air pressures to be equalized. Swelling (edema) in the lining at the tympanic or pharyngeal orifice may cause the tube to become closed. In chronic cases, air is absorbed by the mucous-membranous lining of the middle-ear cavity, and a negative pressure results. As a consequence, the eardrum is forced inward, and fluid exudes from the mucous membrane. Such conditions may increase both the stiffness and damping of the middle-ear structures and result in temporary hearing impairment, with losses confined especially to the lower frequencies (Wever and Lawrence, 1954).

Fortunately, the Eustachian tube may be temporarily dilated to permit pressure equalization and middle-ear drainage. It is opened by contraction of the levator and tensor palatini, mainly the latter (Lederer and Hollender, 1942), which pull the membranous lateral wall away from the relatively stationary medial wall, uncurling the cartilage in the process. The mechanism responsible for dilating the Eustachian tube is shown schematically in Figure 6–21. Wever and Lawrence (1954) point out that in instances where significant negative pressure has developed in the middle-ear cavity, the Eustachian tube may collapse and resist dilation. In these cases prompt medical attention is strongly advised.

The Eustachian tube is about half as long in children as it is in adults, and no bony canal exists at birth. In children the tube lies in a plane almost parallel to the pharyn-

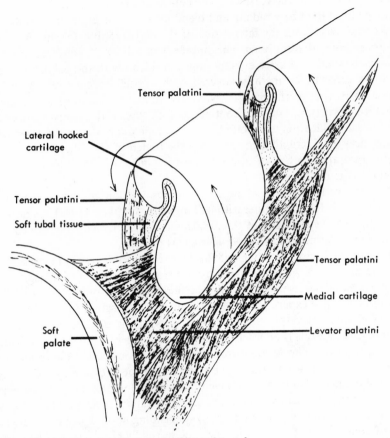

Fig. 6–21. Mechanism of dilation of the Eustachian tube.

geal lumen. In addition, it is more horizontal and wider, and for this reason the middle ear is particularly susceptible to the spread of infection from the pharyngeal regions.

The auditory ossicles

As stated earlier, much of the space within the middle-ear cavity is occupied by the ossicular chain, which consists of the malleus, incus, and the stapes. These three bones, the smallest in the human body, are shown greatly enlarged in Figures 6–22 and 6–23. Although all of the middle-ear structures ought to be regarded as a single functional unit, the ossicles themselves seem to have two main purposes: (1) to deliver in an efficient manner sound vibrations to the inner-ear fluids and (2) to serve as a protective device and help prevent the inner ear from being overdriven by excessively strong vibrations. The action of the middle ear will be discussed in greater detail after a brief description of the ossicular chain and some associated structures.

The largest and most lateral of the ossicles is the malleus, which is attached to the middle, connective tissue fibers of the tympanic membrane. The attachment is most intimate at the middle of the membrane, becoming less so toward the superior border.

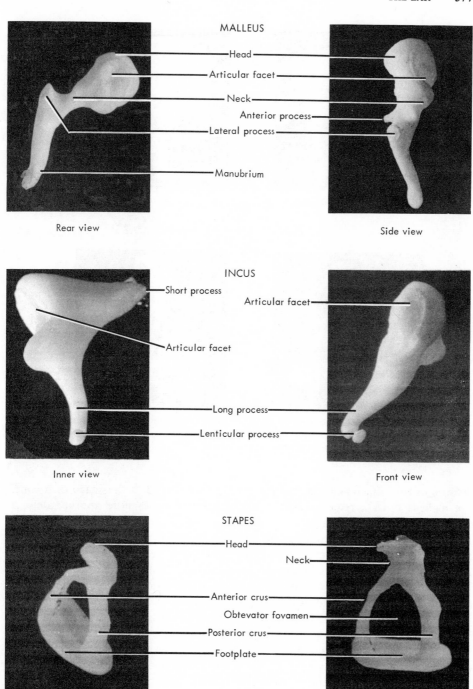

MALLEUS

Head
Articular facet
Neck
Anterior process
Lateral process

Manubrium

Rear view

Side view

INCUS

Short process

Articular facet

Articular facet

Long process
Lenticular process

Inner view

Front view

STAPES

Head
Neck

Anterior crus
Obtevator fovamen
Posterior crus
Footplate

Perspective view

Top view

Fig. 6–22. Various views of disarticulated human ossicles.

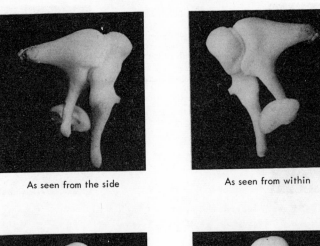

As seen from the side   As seen from within

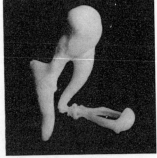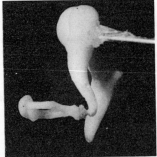

As seen from the front   As seen from behind

Fig. 6–23. Various views of an articulated ossicular chain.

Because of this attachment the membrane is pulled inward in the shape of a cone. The malleus bears a remote resemblance to a hammer or, more appropriately, a club, whence it gets its name. It consists of a head, neck, and three processes (the handle or manubrium, an anterior process, and a lateral process). The head is the bulbous portion that projects up into the epitympanic recess, as shown in Figure 6–18. Its posterior surface contains an articular facet that provides an attachment for the incus, the second ossicle in the chain. A constriction in the center divides the articular facet into upper and lower portions, placed nearly at right angles to one another. The neck of the malleus is simply a constriction between the manubrium and the head. In an earlier discussion of the tympanic membrane, the shadow of the manubrium was seen as a long, narrow process directed downward, somewhat backward, and medially. At the point where the manubrium joins the neck, a small projection forms the point of attachment for the tensor tympani, one of the middle-ear muscles. The anterior process is a spine-like structure at the junction of the manubrium and the neck, while the lateral process is directed laterally from about the same level and is attached to the upper part of the tympanic membrane. In otoscopic views of the tympanic membrane, the lateral process may be seen as a highlight near Schrapnell's membrane.

The second of the ossicles, the incus, derives its name from a resemblance to an anvil. Actually it does not look like an anvil at all, but it does look something like a premolar tooth with two diverging roots. It consists of a body and two arms (crura) or processes. As shown in Figure 6–22, the anterior surface of the body presents an articular facet. It joins with the articular facet of the malleus. The processes of the incus arise from the body at nearly right angles to each other. The short process is directed almost horizontally backward, as shown in Figure 6–18, and occupies the space of the fossa incudis in the epitympanic recess. The other, long process courses vertically, almost parallel to the manubrium of the malleus. Inferiorly, the end of the long process bends sharply medialward and terminates as a rounded projection called the lenticular process, which is tipped with cartilage, and articulates with the head of the stapes, the innermost of the ossicles.

The stapes, so named because of its resemblance to a stirrup, consists of a head, neck, two crura, and a footplate. In life, the footplate, which is partly osseous and partly cartilaginous, occupies the fenestra vestibuli, or oval window, as shown in Figure 6–18. The footplate is connected to the neck by the anterior and posterior crura, which almost invariably originate from points nearer the inferior than the superior margin of the footplate. The anterior crus is somewhat slenderer, shorter, and less curved than the posterior crus. Each is markedly channeled on the inner surface, which significantly reduces the mass of the stapes. The crura and footplate enclose a triangular-shaped space, named the obturator foramen. The neck, which is usually well defined, is simply a constriction between the junction of the crura and the expanded head of the stapes. The head, which is highly variable among specimens, presents a concave articular facet for reception of the lenticular process of the incus. Not infrequently the head or the neck presents a small spine, indicating the attachment of the tendon of the stapedius muscle. A photograph of the tympanic membrane and ossicular chain, as seen from within the tympanic cavity, is shown in Figure 6–24.

Fig. 6–24. Photograph of middle ear structures, as seen from within the tympanic cavity.

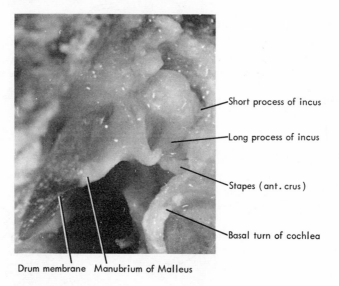

Short process of incus

Long process of incus

Stapes (ant. crus)

Basal turn of cochlea

Drum membrane   Manubrium of Malleus

The Ligaments and Articulations of the Ossicles.   The principal ligaments responsible for the suspension of the ossicular chain within the tympanic cavity are shown in Figure 6–25. A small, superior malleolar ligament extends from the head of the malleus to the tegmen tympani. It is highly variable and sometimes consists only of a thin fold of mucous membrane. Its action is complemented by the lateral malleolar ligament, which extends from the neck of the malleus to the bony wall near the notch of Rivinus. Another ligament, the anterior malleolar ligament, extends from the anterior process to the anterior or carotid wall of the middle-ear cavity. A single ligament lends support to the incus. It courses from the tip of the short process to the fossa incudis in the epitympanic recess. Both the vestibular surface and periphery of the oval-shaped footplate of the stapes are covered with a thin layer of hyaline cartilage fastened to the bony walls of the fenestra vestibuli by means of an elastic annular ligament, which is usually more pronounced anteriorly than it is posteriorly. A section through the stapes showing the annular ligament may be seen in Figure 6–26. Although this section was made through the temporal bone of a young dog, the structures closely resemble those of the human. When the stapes is acted upon by the lenticular process of the incus, it executes a motion that is largely dictated by the characteristics of the attachments of the footplate to the vestibular opening. This does not complete the picture, however, and the relationship between the ligamentary system and ossicular movement will be discussed in somewhat greater detail later in the chapter.

The malleus and incus are articulated by a diarthrodial joint, sometimes described

Fig. 6–25. Schematic illustration of middle ear ligaments and stapedius muscle.

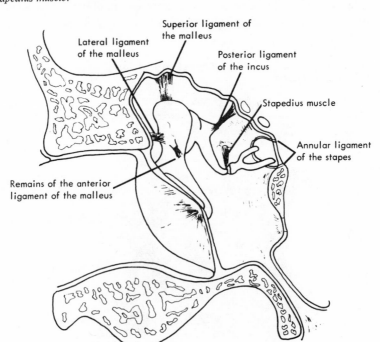

Superior ligament of
the malleus

Lateral ligament
of the malleus

Posterior ligament
of the incus

Stapedius muscle

Annular ligament
of the stapes

Remains of the anterior
ligament of the malleus

(perhaps more accurately) as a double saddle joint. The malleolar articulatory facet has a depression, as shown in Figure 6–22, into which the malleus fits. The joint is effected by a typical articular capsule, and the joint cavity is partially divided in two by a wedge-shaped articular disc or meniscus. Helmholtz (1868), an early investigator of the hearing mechanism, described the malleoincudal joint as a form of cog mechanism which locks, causing the incus to move with the malleus during rotation in one direction but leaving the malleus and incus free during rotation in the other direction. According to Helmholtz, the cog is engaged during inward movement of the manubrium and disengaged during outward movement; while the joint is disengaged, articulation is maintained by the articular capsule. Such a cog mechanism would have

Fig. 6–26. Serial section through dog cochlea showing stapes and some associated structures.

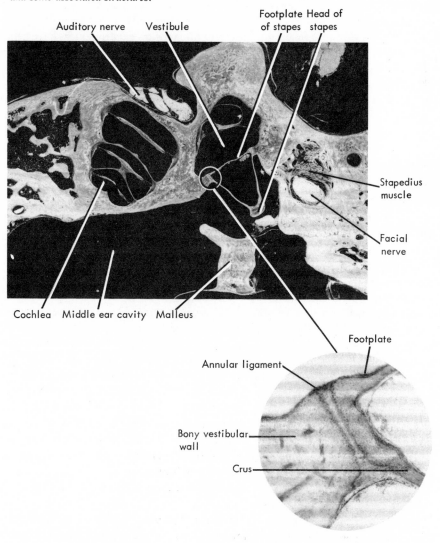

serious theoretical implications, and although Dahmann (1929) also noted some of the relative motion between the ossicles reported by Helmholtz, subsequent experiments by Fry and Fumagalli, as reported by Wever and Lawrence (1954), have supported the notion that the two ossicles move as a single mass, except perhaps when driven by extremely powerful stimuli. Fry reported that in most mammals the articular cartilages become ossified with the result that the joint becomes a synarthrosis. In addition, experiments carried out by Wever and Lawrence (1954) quite clearly demonstrate that the malleus and incus move as a single mass, even when driven by excessively powerful stimuli.

While some anatomists consider the incudostapedial joint to be of the syndesmosis type (immovable or just slightly movable), it is usually regarded as a true enarthrodial (ball and socket) joint. Helmholtz (1868) correctly described the joint as an enarthrodial type. He further stated, however, that the incus can be drawn away from the stapes without causing the stapes to follow. He supposed that the nature of the joint prevented the stapes from being torn from its attachments due to excessive movements of the incus. Subsequent findings by contemporary experimenters have generally failed to corroborate these findings by Helmholtz. A generally accepted description of the incudostapedial joint is that it is an enarthrodial type with an articular disc surrounded by an articular capsule.

Because of the way in which the ossicular chain is suspended by the ligamentous system, its inertia is very small, and its rotational axis is very near the center of gravity (they are balanced). As a result, once a sound has ceased, the vibrations of the ossicles also terminate abruptly. This is an important feature, minimizing distortion in the middle ear.

The entire ossicular chain is covered with a mucous membrane that is continuous with the lining of the middle-ear cavity.

The tympanic muscles

As mentioned briefly earlier, the middle-ear structures include two muscles, the tensor tympani and the stapedius, which are the smallest striated muscles in the body. They are pennate muscles, consisting of many short fibers directed obliquely to impinge on a tendon at the mid-line. Such an arrangement gives a muscle great capacity for exerting tension with very little linear displacement. That is, the tension exerted by a pennate muscle is the sum of the combined forces from contraction of all the muscle fibers, taking into account the angle at which they exert their force, whereas the total displacement is just the amount permitted by contraction of the shortest fibers. The tendons of the tympanic muscles differ from usual tendons due to an abundant amount of elastic tissue. According to Jepsen (1963), the elastic properties of the tendons may serve a dual purpose: (1) to damp the vibrations of the ossicles and (2) to render muscular traction slower and less sudden in onset. A second unique feature of the tympanic muscles is that they are completely encased in bony canals, and only their tendons (in man) enter into the tympanic cavity. According to Békésy (1936), this arrangement reduces muscular vibrations which might interfere with sound transmission. It also reduces the effective mass of the ossicular chain.

The Tensor Tympani Muscle. The tensor tympani, described by Eustachius in 1564, is the larger of the tympanic muscles. It is about 25 mm in length, has a cross-sectional area of about 5.85 sq mm, and is contained within a bony semicanal that runs nearly parallel with and superior to the osseous framework of the Eustachian tube. The muscle fibers originate from the cartilaginous portion of the framework of the Eustachian tube and from the walls of the canal in which the muscle is contained. A thin partition of bone, the septum canalis musculotubarii, separates the canal of the tensor tympani from the canal of the Eustachian tube. The curved lateral terminal of the muscle canal is called the cochleariform process. It forms a sort of pulley over which the tendon of the muscle plays. As the tendon emerges from the orifice of the canal it makes a rather sharp bend, conforming to the curvature of the cochleariform process, and is then directed to its point of insertion on the upper part of the manubrium of the malleus, as illustrated in Figure 6–27.

Contraction of the tensor tympani draws the malleus medially and anteriorly. The force is almost at right angles to the direction of rotation of the ossicular chain, and, when acting by itself, the muscle increases the tension of the tympanic membrane, as the name of the muscle suggests.

The Stapedius Muscle. The stapedius, considerably smaller than the tensor tympani, is about 6 mm in total length, with a cross-sectional area of about 5 sq mm. It originates within a bony canal running almost parallel to the facial nerve canal on the posterior wall of the tympanic cavity. Its direction is almost vertical, but the direction of its tendon is nearly horizontal. The muscle fibers originate from the walls of the canal and converge upon a tendon, which emerges from an aperture at the apex of the pyramidal eminence. The tendon and its attachment to the stapes are shown

Fig. 6–27. Schematic illustration of the tensor tympani muscle.

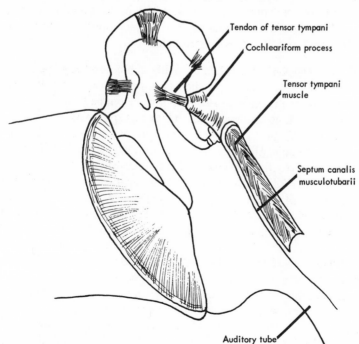

Tendon of tensor tympani

Cochleariform process

Tensor tympani muscle

Septum canalis musculotubarii

Auditory tube

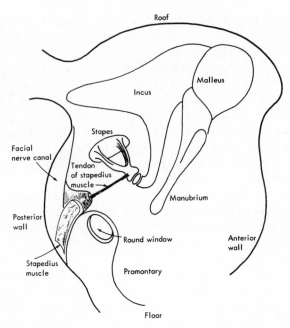

Fig. 6–28. Schematic of the stapedius muscle and the attachment of its tendon to the neck of the stapes.

schematically in Figure 6–28, and a microscopic view of a stapedius muscle and its attachment to a stapes is shown in Figure 6–29. Contraction of the stapedius exerts a force on the head of the stapes, drawing it posteriorly, at right angles to the direction of the movement of the ossicular chain. Thus, it may be seen that the stapedius and tensor tympani exert force in directions opposite to each other and perpendicular to the primary rotational axis of the ossicular chain.

The Action of the Tympanic Musculature. Although a number of persons seem to have some limited voluntary control of their tympanic musculature, its contraction is usually mediated by sound energy. The action of the tympanic muscles is generally thought of as an important acoustic reflex. Until rather recently most information regarding the behavior of the tympanic musculature has come from animal experiments. In 1878, for example, Hensen inserted a thin metal sliver into the tensor tympani of dogs and observed the movement of the sliver when the ear was stimulated with sound. Pollak, in 1886, conducted similar experiments in which he demonstrated that the acoustic reflex of the tensor tympani is dependent upon the adequacy of the stimulus. He further demonstrated that unilateral stimulation resulted in bilateral contraction of the tensor tympani, a finding subsequently used in clinical applications of the acoustic reflex (Jepsen, 1963). Kato, in 1913, was able to elicit acoustic reflexes of the tensor tympani and the stapedius. He noted a direct relationship between the duration of the stimulus and the duration of muscle contraction.

Although the acoustic reflex has been studied less extensively in man, Lüscher in 1929 was able to observe stapedial reflex movements in a person with a perforated eardrum. He found that a response could be elicited by either ipsilateral or contralateral stimulation and also that contraction could be elicited simply by expectation

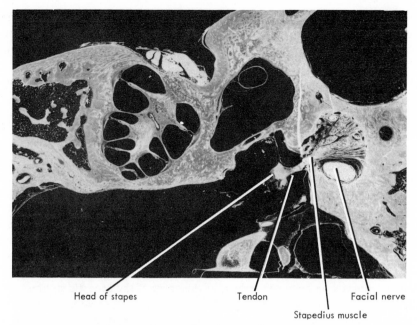

Head of stapes   Tendon   Facial nerve

Stapedius muscle

*Fig. 6–29. Photograph of stapedius muscle and its attachment
to the head of the stapes.*

of a loud sound. The acoustic reflex has also been observed during surgical exposure
of the middle ear.

In recent years electromyography has become an important laboratory technique
for investigation of the acoustic reflex. Perlman and Case, in 1939, recorded muscle
action potentials from the stapedius muscle in humans. This technique is especially
valuable for studying the latency of the acoustic reflex.

Because the acoustic reflex changes the mechanical properties of the transmission
system of the middle ear, the mechanical resistance (acoustic impedance) may be
measured by indirect means (Metz, 1946; Jepsen, 1963). This has become a valuable
research and clinical tool for studying hearing in humans.

Several functions have been attributed to the tympanic musculature. Wever and
Lawrence (1954) and Jepsen (1963) have listed four theories which have been proposed: (1) the intensity-control or protective theory, (2) the frequency-selection or
accommodation theory, (3) the fixation theory, and (4) the labyrinthine-pressure
theory. Jepsen (1963) also lists a fifth theory of the activity of the tympanic muscles
in the formation of overtones. This theory has not been put to test to the extent that
a discussion is warranted. In all of these theories the stapedius and tensor tympani
are regarded as forming a functional unit; that is, although morphologically they are
antagonists, physiologically they are synergists.

The intensity-control theory supposes that the muscles contract in response to certain critical levels of sound intensity. The function of such contraction is to prevent
the inner ear from being overdriven by excessive stapedial vibrations. Since both
muscles exert a force at right angles to the direction of ossicular movement, they
act as a damping mechanism that tends to suppress the degree of ossicular movement.

The frequency-selection or accommodation theory attributes a quite different function to the tympanic musculature. It supposes that the muscle contraction acts as a damping mechanism, which selectively absorbs sound energy at certain frequencies, thereby selectively increasing the sensitivity of hearing.

The fixation theory describes the function of the tympanic musculature as supplementing the suspensory ligaments in maintaining the appropriate position of the ossicles. Also, as the ossicular chain rocks back and forth during the transmission of sound, contraction of the tympanic musculature simply prevents the excursions from surpassing certain critical limits.

The labyrinthine-pressure theory asserts that the tympanic musculature can, by assuming various degrees of contraction, produce a change in pressure of the inner ear or labyrinthine fluids. Such a pressure change is brought about by inward or outward movements of the stapes footplate mediated by the tympanic musculature via the ossicular chain. An increase in inner-ear pressure will, according to the proponents of the labyrinthine-pressure theory, produce an increase in the mechanical impedance of the inner ear and a corresponding loss of low-frequency transmission.

The acoustic reflex is elicited at sound intensities well above the threshold of hearing. Muscle contraction begins shortly after the onset of the acoustic stimulation and continues until the sound is terminated. Both muscles seem to contract at the same time, and although the tensor tympani seems to exert more force, the stapedius seems to be the more effective muscle. In man the acoustic reflex is elicited at intensities in the vicinity of 80–90 dB above the threshold for hearing, with the lowest threshold for the reflex in the frequency range for which the threshold for hearing is lowest (Jepsen, 1963). These characteristics of the acoustic reflex place some serious limitations on the accommodation theory. For example, if the reflex serves to enhance the transmission of certain tones, the quality of a rapid succession of complex tones (music, for example) should change with changes in intensity. The threshold for the elicitation of the acoustic reflex is dangerously close to intensity levels that can be damaging to the hearing mechanism. It is doubtful if the reflex would facilitate transmission of sounds that are already threatening to the hearing mechanism.

The tympanic muscles have been shown to contribute to the strength of the ossicular chain. This can be demonstrated quite easily by severing the tendons of the tensor tympani and stapedius. Whereas the ossicular chain is normally quite resistant to mechanical manipulation, it is now loose and flaccid, and inner-ear damage can easily result. Thus there is a certain amount of support for a fixation theory, which also may be interpreted as evidence in support of an intensity-control or protection theory.

There has been little supportive evidence for a labyrinthine-pressure theory. Békésy (1936) and Lempert, Wever, Lawrence, and Meltzer (1949), in separate experiments, found that middle-ear muscle contraction does indeed cause increases in labyrinthine pressures, but not to the extent that sound transmission is significantly affected.

Increased tension due to muscle contraction ought to raise the acoustical impedance of the ossicular chain, thus resulting in a damping of low-frequency sounds. On the other hand, a reduction of muscle tension ought to lower the acoustic impedance, thus favoring the transmission of low-frequency sounds. Low-frequency components are almost always the strongest in complex tones, and if the acoustic reflex results in a damping of low-frequency sounds, it will act, in a limited way, as a protective mechanism.

A number of animal experiments have strongly supported the intensity-control theory. Almost without exception, these experiments showed a definite reduction in sound transmission due to the acoustic reflex, with a diminution greatest for the low-frequency tones (Jepsen, 1963; Wever and Lawrence, 1954). It should be pointed out, however, that some investigators (Wever and Bray, 1942; Wever and Vernon, 1956) have shown that the acoustic reflex (in animals) can slightly enhance some high-frequency tones. The loss in transmission of a 100-cps tone may be as much as 40 db. At about 1,000 cps the transmission is not reduced by much, and at frequencies of about 1,500 cps there is a slight increase in the sensitivity of the hearing mechanism. Above 2,000 cps little change can be detected.

There can be little doubt that these results support an intensity-control or protective theory. In addition, there is little question that the tympanic muscles also contribute to the action of the suspensory ligaments in maintaining the position of the ossicles. Thus it is not unreasonable, in light of the accumulated data, to accept the intensity-control theory, as well as the fixation theory, in accounting for the function of the tympanic muscles.

A rather important limitation to the protection that the tympanic muscles can supply is due to the latency of the muscle contraction. That is, there is a certain interval between the time that the sound impinges upon the drum membrane and the onset of contraction of the muscles. Some early experiments by Hensen in 1863, Kato in 1913, and Kobrak in 1930 produced latencies ranging from .01 to .13 seconds for the stapedius muscle and from .01 to .29 seconds for the tensor tympani. Wever and Lawrence (1954), in summarizing the results of both early and later experimentation, cite mean values of .06 seconds for the stapedius and .15 seconds for the tensor tympani.

Intense sounds, carrying steep wave fronts (transients), such as those resulting from explosions and industrial noise, may impinge upon the ear mechanism and cause damage before the musculature can contract. Too, prolonged exposure to unduly intense sounds (usually man-made) may result in a decrease in protection due to fatigue. By observing the stapedial reflex in humans with perforated eardrums, Lüscher (1929), Kobrak (1930), and others, by direct observation of the stapedial tendon, noted that upon sustained sound stimulation, a continued contraction was first observed, followed by a gradual decrease until the resting state was reached. A new contraction could only be elicited by changing substantially the frequency of the stimulating tone. In similar experiments with animals, Kato (1913) and Wersäll (1958) found the tensor tympani to be the more easily fatigable of the tympanic muscles.

In addition to the protection offered by the tympanic muscles, another mechanism seems to protect the inner ear to a certain extent. In 1936 Békésy noted that at very low frequencies an increase in sound pressure produced an increase in loudness . . . up to a certain point, beyond which further increases in sound pressure seemed to produce a sudden decrease in loudness. He found, as shown in Figure 6–30A, that when the ossicles were stimulated by a moderate sound pressure, the rotation of the stapes was about an axis indicated by the dotted line. Because the footplate is more rigidly fixed posteriorly than it is anteriorly, the stapes rocks about an axis near the posterior edge. As sound pressure is increased beyond a certain critical limit, however, the stapes

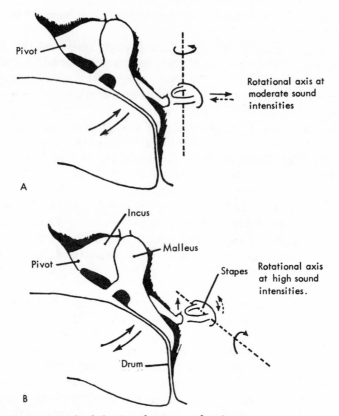

Fig. 6–30. Changes in mode of vibration of stapes as a function of sound intensities. (Courtesy Georg von Békésy.)

begins to turn about an axis that runs horizontally through the footplate, as in Figure 6–30B. As a result, the cochlear fluids flow only from one edge of the footplate to the other, with much less fluid displacement than when the mode of vibration is through a vertical axis and the footplate is acting like a piston. This shift of rotational axes, which seems to be due to a certain amount of freedom in the anchorage of the ossicular chain, is an effective protective mechanism occurring primarily with intense sounds at low frequencies.

The transformer action of the middle ear

A well-known principle in acoustics states that sound waves traveling in a medium of some given elasticity and density will not pass readily into a medium with a different elasticity and density but, rather, that most of the sound will be reflected away. The amount of sound reflected is a positive function of the differences between the media. Acoustic resistances, which are used to calculate sound transmission from one medium to another, can be determined if the density and the bulk modulus of elasticity of each medium are known. Acoustic resistance, R, is the square root of the product of density, ρ, and bulk modulus of elasticity, S, or $R = \sqrt{\rho S}$. Wever and Lawrence

(1954) have computed the amount of sound energy that passes from air to a body of water. For air at 20°C, the density, ρ_1, = 0.0012 grams per cu cm, and the bulk modulus of elasticity, S_1, = 1.42×10^6 dynes per sq cm. For sea water at 37°C (near body temperature), the density, ρ_2, = 1.024 grams per cu cm, and the bulk modulus of elasticity, S_2, = 2.53×10^{10} dynes per sq cm. For air, the acoustic resistance, R, = $\rho_1 S_1$ = 41.5 mechanical ohms per sq cm. For sea water, $R = \rho_2 S_2$ = 161,000 mechanical ohms per sq cm. The ratio of these resistances, $r = R_2/R_1$ = 3,880. Energy transmission can be computed by the formula, $T = 4r/(r + 1)^2$ = 0.001. Thus, one-tenth of 1 per cent of the sound in air will pass into the water, while the remaining 99.9 per cent is reflected back. Expressed in decibels, the transmission loss is 30 dB. Wever and Lawrence also point out that if sound waves acted directly upon the cochlear fluids, we might expect a transmission loss of about 30 dB.

In any system where there is to be efficient transmission of energy, the resistance (or impedance) of the source ought to match that of the load. Frequently encountered impedance-matching devices include the gear train of a bicycle, levers of various types, and the transmission of an automobile. In each of these, high-impedance energy sources, arms, legs, and high-speed engines, are matched to low-impedance loads. Or, to put it another way, the source moves through a great distance with comparatively little force, while the load moves through correspondingly little distance with a great deal of force. Energy, which is force times the distance moved, is the same at the source and at the load, neglecting friction, of course, but the force is much greater at the load than at the source.

This brings us to the problem with which the middle ear is faced. If somehow the acoustic resistance (impedance) of the ear could be made to approach that of air, efficient transmission would result. In order to match the acoustic resistance of air to that of the inner-ear fluids, which for the moment we will assume are the same as sea water, we need to find the required transformation ratio, which is the square root of the ratio of the two acoustic resistances. Earlier we found the ratio to be 3,880. Thus, in order to have maximum transmission of sound energy, we must have a mechanism that increases the pressure at the oval window, over what it is in the air, by a factor of about 63.

Evidence that the middle-ear mechanism facilitates hearing sensitivity may be gained from clinical cases where a disruption of the ossicular chain results in a hearing loss of 30 dB or greater. Figure 6–31 shows an audiogram of a person with a disruption of the ossicular chain and presumably no other ear pathology. Experimental removal of the middle-ear mechanism in animals permits a more exact determination of the contributions of the middle ear. In a series of experiments, Wever, Lawrence, and Smith (1948) removed the drum membrane, malleus, and incus from animals, after determining their hearing sensitivity with the structures intact. The resultant hearing loss was greatest for tones in the 500 to 2,000 cps range and in the 5,000 to 7,000 cps range. The average loss was about 28 dB. These losses are probably representative of the transformer action of the middle ear.

In 1863, Helmholtz first formulated the transformer action of the middle ear, and his description of middle-ear action may be found in the fourth edition of his outstanding classic, *On The Sensations of Tone*, published in 1877. Although his description of middle-ear function has enjoyed general acceptance for the most part, it is only

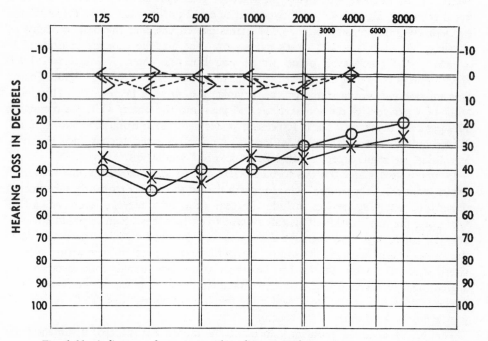

FREQUENCIES IN CYCLES PER SECOND

Fig. 6–31. Audiogram of a person with a disruption of the ossicular chain.

rather recently that the contributions of the middle ear have been quantified. Helmholtz supposed that the transformer action of the middle ear was due to the combined effects of (1) the lever action of the drum membrane itself, (2) the lever action of the ossicular chain, and (3) the mechanical advantage due to the ratio of effective drum-membrane area to stapedial-footplate area. Helmholtz assigned a dominant role to the lever action produced by the drum membrane.

Helmholtz stated that pressure exerted by sound waves on the cone-shaped drum membrane are transformed into a much greater pressure at the apex of the cone. This viewpoint necessitates (1) that the tympanic membrane be cone-shaped, (2) that the drum be slightly curved as shown in Figure 6–32A, and (3) that the shape of the membrane is not changed appreciably by the forces exerted by the sound waves. The principle by which this lever action was said to occur is illustrated in Figure 6–32B. It is known as the catenary principle. Note that as force, F, impinges upon the curved portion of the membrane, it is transformed into a much larger shearing force at points v. Since points v are fixed in position, the point at v_1 is caused to move in the direction of the arrow at H with a force much greater than that impinging upon the tympanic membrane.

A lever effect as described by Helmholtz requires that the drum membrane execute a rather piston-like in-and-out movement. Although the very gross movements of the drum membrane may be observed directly with a speculum, quantitative measurements of the magnitude of movement are very difficult to obtain. Békésy, in 1941,

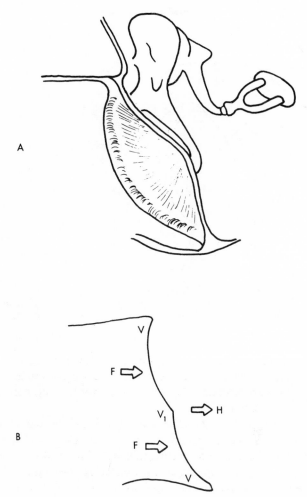

Fig. 6–32. (A.) Illustration of curved drum membrane as required for a catenary principle. (B.) Schematic of catenary principle. Helmholtz supposed this principle was responsible for an increase in force F at H.

was successful in plotting the mode of drum vibration by using the membrane itself as one plate of a condenser microphone and a fine wire inserted into the ear canal to a distance of about .5 mm from the membrane as the other plate. Vibration of the drum membrane modulated a high-frequency current passing through the condenser, and the modulation frequency corresponded to the extent of the vibration.

The mode of vibration of the drum membrane, as determined by Békésy, is shown in Figure 6–33. The closed curves represent equal amplitude contours while the numbers represent the relative magnitude of drum-membrane excursion. These results indicate that for a frequency of 2,000 cps the drum membrane vibrates not in a piston-like fashion but, rather, like a solid disc pivoted on an axis (shown as a dotted line). Note that the greatest amplitude of vibration occurs near the lower edge of the membrane. Such a mode of vibration may be accounted for by a critical inspection of the anatomy of the drum membrane. As shown in Figure 6–34, a fold on the lower edge of the membrane permits greatest mobility with a rotational axis through the neck of

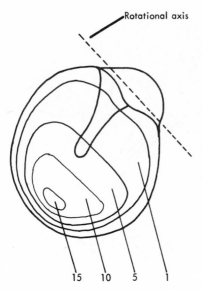

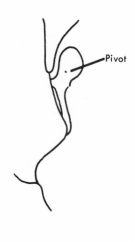

Fig. 6–33. Mode of vibration of the drum membrane for a 2,000 cycle tone. (Courtesy von Békésy.)

Fig. 6–34. Sectional view of the drum membrane illustrating round-ed fold on lower edge.

the malleus. The pattern of vibration shown in Figure 6–33 holds for frequencies up to about 2,500 cps. At higher frequencies the pattern begins to break up, and the drum vibrates segmentally. These results do not lend support to a catenary principle in the drum membrane.

The hypothesis of Helmholtz might also be put to test by direct measurement. That is, a known amount of pressure on the drum membrane ought to produce an increased pressure on the manubrium of the malleus. He reversed the procedure and carried out an experiment by measuring the degree of drum-membrane movement caused by a known amount of displacement of the manubrium. His results supported a lever principle in the drum membrane; however, replication of the experiment by Wever and Lawrence (1954), using refined techniques, has shown that as the manubrium is moved from its equilibrium position, the displacement of the drum membrane rises at first linearly followed by a decreasing rate. Further contradictory evidence can be seen in the effects of positive and negative pressures within the middle-ear cavity. According to Helmholtz, negative pressure in the middle ear should reduce the curvature of the membrane, thereby facilitating hearing, while positive pressure ought to raise the threshold of hearing. Clinical evidence, however, consistently demonstrates that any pressure differences between the middle and external ears, whether they be positive or negative, will decrease the sensitivity of hearing, with hearing impairment more severe for the low-frequency tones.

Examination of the experimental evidence that has been published to date fails to yield much in the way of support for lever action in the drum membrane. For an explanation of the transformer action of the middle ear, we shall have to turn either to the ossicular chain or to the ratio of effective drum-membrane area to stapedial-footplate area.

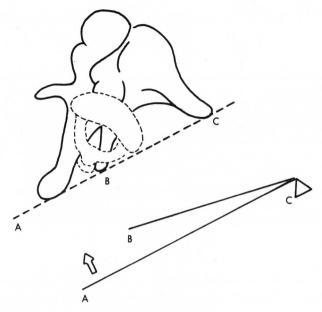

Fig. 6–35. Schematic of ossicular chain as described by Helmholtz.

In his attempt to account for a lever action by the ossicular chain, Helmholtz proposed that the lateral and anterior malleolar ligaments formed the principal rotational axis for the malleus. According to Helmholtz, sound waves impinging upon the drum membrane cause the end of the manubrium to swing the malleus about the rotational axis. However, the unique and complicated articulations of the ossicles cause the initially simple rotary movement to be modified so that a complex twisting action results. Helmholtz envisioned the ossicular chain as constituting a lever system. As shown in Figure 6–35, the fulcrum is at point, *c*, with the lever arms being the distances, *ca* and *cb*. Measurements of these lever arms yielded values of 9.5 mm and 6.3 mm respectively, for a lever ratio of 1.5 to 1, values that are in close agreement with subsequent findings. Thus, the amplitude of movement by the lenticular process, compared with that of the manubrium of the malleus, would be reduced by a ratio of 1.5 to 1, with a comparable increase in pressure. Note, however, that the lever system just described denies a rotational axis about the axial ligament which Helmholtz initially proposed.

The nature of an ossicular lever system was also investigated by Dahmann (1930), who, by placing tiny mirrors on the ossicles and observing the deflections of a light, was able to describe the movements of the ossicular chain. As shown in Figure 6–36A, the rotational axis of Dahmann runs from the anterior process of the malleus through the point of attachment of the short process of the incus to its ligament. The lever arms run perpendicular to the axis of rotation. As shown in Figure 6–36B, the line, *ab*, is the malleolar lever arm and the line, *cd*, is the incudal arm. Measurements of the lever arms yield a lever ratio of 1.31 to 1, which means that the pressure at the lenticular process would exceed the pressure applied to the manubrium by a comparable

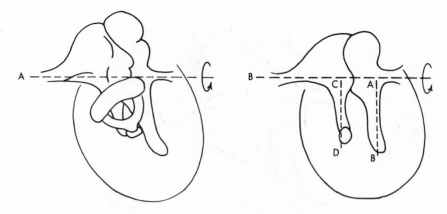

Fig. 6–36. The ossicular lever system as described by Dahmann.

ratio. Wever and Lawrence (1954) investigated the action of the ossicular chain by measuring the electrical output of the inner ear when the ossicular chain was stimulated at audio frequencies by a mechanical vibrator. They noted that vibrations had maximum effects when they were applied to the manubrium of the malleus and to the long process of the incus and that the vibrations had minimum effects when applied at points that agree very closely with the rotational axis described by Dahmann. Using laboratory animals, Wever and Lawrence obtained a lever ratio in the order of 2.5 to 1. If either value is accepted as representative of the mechanical advantage provided by the ossicular chain, it does not adequately account for the degree of hearing loss that results from destruction of the middle ear. Evidently, additional transformer action is provided by the differences in effective areas of drum membrane and stapes footplate.

Once again Helmholtz was an early contributor, estimating an areal ratio of from 15 to 20 to 1. Other researchers have obtained values that range from 14–40 to 1. These values, however, were obtained from different species of animals and from very small samples. Earlier in the chapter (page 368) the tympanic membrane was described as rigidly fastened to the tympanic ring. Therefore the periphery of the eardrum is rendered rather immovable, and something less than the total area can be regarded as effective in transmitting vibrations. Békésy (1941), observing drum-membrane movements in fresh cadaver ears, obtained an effective area of about two-thirds that of the total area.

Wever and Lawrence (1954) found an areal ratio between drum membrane and stapes footplate for humans to be in the order of 21 to 1. Using the Békésy data on effective area, they obtained an effective areal ratio of about 14 to 1. That is to say, the force exerted by the stapes footplate is applied over an area that is about 14 times smaller than the area of the eardrum. Pressure at the stapes, therefore, is multiplied by the ratio of the two effective areas.

In everyday language force and pressure are often used as synonyms, but in scientific language they mean entirely different things. Pressure is defined as force per unit area, when the force acts at right angles to a surface. It may be expressed by the following formula:

$$\text{Pressure} = \frac{\text{Force}}{\text{Area over which force acts}} \quad \text{or} \quad P = \frac{F}{A}.$$

From the above formula we see that pressure involves force as well as the area against which force is directed. Force, on the other hand, is given by the product of pressure and area, or: $F = PA$. The following example may illustrate the difference between force and pressure. In Figure 6–37A, the weight (force) is distributed over the entire base, and the pressure is not very great. In B, however, the pressure is much greater because the area of contact is much less. The downward force, however, is the same in each instance.

As shown in Figure 6–38, the total force acting upon the drum membrane is equal to the pressure multiplied by the area, or $F = PA$. The force is conducted by the ossicular chain to the stapes footplate, where the pressure is given by the force divided by the area, A_2, or, $P_2 = F/A_2 = P_1A_1/A_2$. Thus, pressure is simply the product of the ratio of the two areas. Using an ossicular lever ratio of 1.31 to 1, as obtained by Dahmann, the combined ratio provided by the transformer action of the middle ear is the product of the ossicular lever ratio and effective areal ratio, or $14.0 \times 1.31 =$ 18.3 to 1. Assuming these values to be representative, the total mechanical advantage afforded by the middle ear is 18.3, which when expressed in decibels amounts to 25.25 dB. For the present this mechanical advantage will have to suffice, although new data are constantly being provided, and the values may have to be re-evaluated.

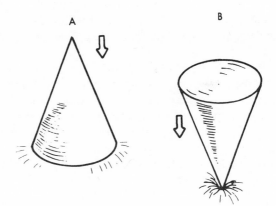

A   B

Fig. 6–37. Illustration of force and pressure.

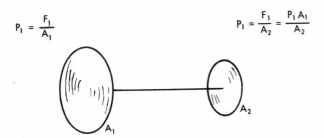

$P_1 = \dfrac{F_1}{A_1}$

$P_1 = \dfrac{F_1}{A_2} = \dfrac{P_1 A_1}{A_2}$

A_1

A_2

Fig. 6–38. Pressure increase due to differences in area.

Having got sound vibrations safely delivered to the stapes footplate, our next immediate task ought to be to examine the structure of the inner ear, after which we will be faced with two remaining problems. One of these deals with the manner in which sound vibrations are transmitted within the inner ear and converted to neural impulses, and the other has to do with the manner in which these neural impulses are conducted to the auditory area of the brain.

The Inner Ear

The inner ear may be divided into two cavity systems; one houses the organs of equilibrium and the other houses the essential organ of hearing. Although such a division may be justified on a functional basis, the two systems enjoy an intrinsic anatomical relationship. Actually the inner ear contains two labyrinths. One, called the osseous labyrinth, is a complex series of cavities; the second, contained within the first, is a series of communicating membranous sacs and ducts collectively known as the membranous labyrinth. The location of the inner ear within the temporal bone is shown schematically in Figure 6–39.

The bony labyrinth

The bony labyrinth consists of a system of canals and cavities within the dense petrous portion of the temporal bone. In the fetus and newborn, a capsule immediately surrounding the bony labyrinth is distinguishable from the adjacent spongy bone. Removal of the spongy bone reveals the periotic capsule, an illustration of which is shown in Figure 6–40. The capsule consists of three parts: the vestibule, semicircular canals, and the cochlea. Their spatial relationships may be seen in Figure 6–40.

The vestibule, which forms the central portion of the bony labyrinth, is continuous with the semicircular canals and the cochlea. It is ovoid in shape, measuring about 5 mm in its anteroposterior and vertical dimensions and about 3 mm across. Its lateral or tympanic wall (which forms part of the vestibular wall of the middle-ear cavity) is perforated by the fenestra vestibuli. Its medial wall presents a number of small perforations in addition to the orifice of the vestibular aqueduct, which extends to the posterior surface of the petrous portion of the temporal bone. This small but important canal transmits an extension of the membranous labyrinth, the ductus endolymphaticus, which terminates as a cul-de-sac within the layers of the dura mater (a strong protective covering of the brain) in the cranial cavity.

The three semicircular canals, superior, posterior, and lateral, open into the vestibule by way of five orifices. As shown in Figure 6–40, each canal presents a dilation, called an ampulla, at the point where the canal joins the vestibule. The superior and posterior canals join to form a common canal, which opens into the vestibule on the upper and medial wall. The semicircular canals lie in three planes, perpendicular to one another, to the extent that any two form nearly a right angle.

The medial-most portion of the osseous labyrinth is called the cochlea (snail). It is a bony canal, about 35 mm in length, which is coiled in upon itself around a central core or pillar of bone called the modiolus. The base of the modiolus is broad, and is located at the bottom of the internal auditory meatus, which is shown in Figure 6–41. It is perforated by numerous small orifices, which transmit fibers of the

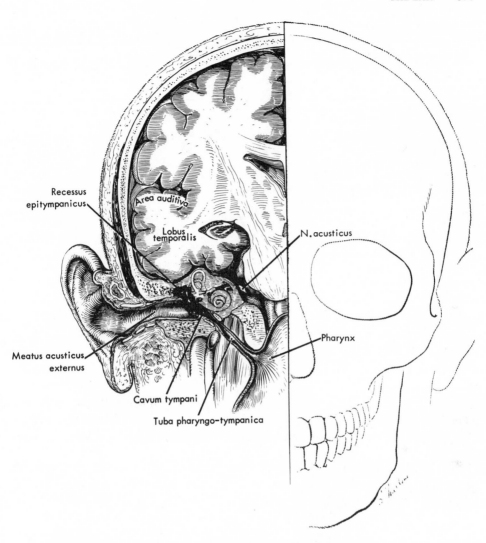

Fig. 6–39. *Schematic of the location of the inner ear within the temporal bone.* (From An Atlas of Some Pathological Conditions of the Eye, Ear, and Throat. *Courtesy of Abbott Laboratories, Chicago.*)

auditory branch of the eighth cranial (auditory) nerve. The distribution of these nerve fibers will be considered in greater detail a little later. The cochlea, which is actually a continuation of the vestibule, consists of a base followed by two and three-quarters turns which terminate at the apex or cupola. The spiral-shaped canal is partially divided into an upper duct, the scala vestibuli, and a lower duct, the scala tympani, by a thin bony shelf called the osseous spiral lamina. It projects from the modiolar wall as shown in Figure 6–42. This division is further completed by the interposition of the membranous cochlear duct, which will be discussed in some detail later. The spiral lamina actually consists of two layers of bone, each of which is continuous

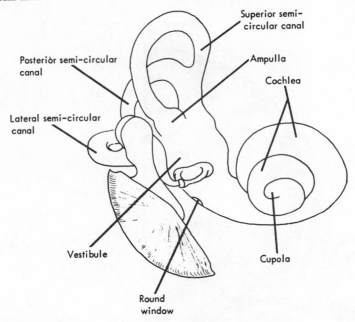

Fig. 6–40. The bony labyrinth and its parts in relation to the ossicular chain and drum membrane.

with structures that form the cochlear duct of the membranous labyrinth. Near the apex of the cochlea, the spiral lamina terminates as a hooklike process called the hamulus, which assists in forming the boundary of a small opening, the helicotrema. The helicotrema establishes communication between the scala vestibuli and scala tympani.

The cochlear canal has three openings, one of which is the round window or fenestra rotunda (or cochlear fenestra), located at the basal extreme of the scala tympani. The round window opens into the tympanic cavity; in life, however, it is closed off by the

Fig. 6–41. Section through a cochlea showing auditory nerve and base of the modiolus at the bottom of the internal auditory meatus.

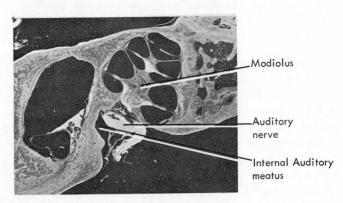

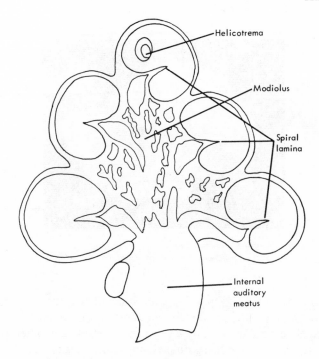

Helicotrema

Modiolus

Spiral
lamina

Internal
auditory
meatus

Fig. 6–42. Schematic section through the bony cochlea.

secondary tympanic membrane. The round window may be seen as a small opening in the medial wall of the tympanic cavity, tucked in a niche formed by the promontory. The function of the round window seems to be to permit pressure to equalize between the scala vestibuli and the scala tympani. Near the round window, in the scala tympani, is a very small aperture, the cochlear aqueduct, which is continued to the inferior surface of the temporal bone. The cochlear aqueduct establishes communication between the scala tympani and cerebrospinal fluid of the subarachnoid spaces, a point that will be returned to later. The third opening is elliptical in shape and joins the cavity of the vestibule with the scala vestibuli.

The bony labyrinth is lined with a thin, fibroserous membrane that is closely adherent to the bone. Its free surface is covered ·with epithelium that secretes an ultrafiltrate of blood serum called perilymph. Perilymph is a clear, thin, watery fluid, almost identical in nature to the cerebrospinal fluid that bathes the brain. It fills the scala vestibuli, the scala tympani, and the large perilymphatic spaces around the vestibule and semicircular canals. You will recall that communication between the perilymphatic and subarachnoid spaces is established by means of the cochlear aqueduct, shown in Figure 6–43. Whereas cerebrospinal fluid bathes the brain, perilymph bathes the membranous labyrinth.

The membranous labyrinth

The membranous labyrinth is shown in Figure 6–44. It is important to keep in mind that this labyrinth is contained within the bony labyrinth. The membranous labyrinth is filled with a fluid called endolymph, which is similar to perilymph but is very viscous

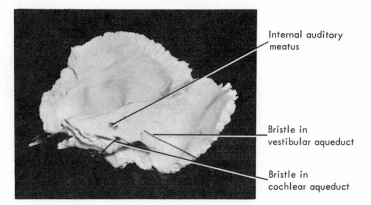

Internal auditory
meatus

Bristle in
vestibular aqueduct

Bristle in
cochlear aqueduct

Fig. 6–43. Right temporal bone, inner surface, showing internal auditory meatus, vestibular aqueduct, and cochlear aqueduct.

and differs somewhat in its chemical composition. Thus, there is an endolymph-filled membranous labyrinth, completely contained within a bony labyrinth, which in turn is filled with perilymph. To put it another way, the outer surface of the membranous labyrinth is in contact with perilymph, and the inner surface is in contact with endolymph. In certain places, however, the membranous labyrinth is adherent to the walls of the bony labyrinth. The membranous labyrinth has three divisions, the semicircular canals, the utricle and saccule, and the cochlear duct. Functionally the cochlear duct comprises the system for hearing, and the utricle, saccule, and semicircular canals comprise the system for equilibrium. The latter can be further divided into a static system, which functions in the perception of position in space in the vertical plane, and a kinetic system, which functions in the perception of rotation and acceleration of the head.

As may be seen in Figure 6–44, the membranous semicircular canals are similar in shape to the osseous semicircular canals in which they are housed; except, of course, they are smaller in diameter. The membranous canal system has five openings, all entering the sac-like utricle located in the vestibule. The membranous ampullae correspond in their location to the osseous ampullae, and are characterized by marked dilations. The membranous canals are lined with a layer of epithelium which is closely adherent to a thin layer of connective tissue. The membranous canals do not fully occupy the space in the bony labyrinth; however, they are fixed into position by small bundles of connective tissue that course to the bony canal wall. The ampullae contain small aggregations of connective tissue, upon which are situated highly developed ciliated sensory cells, the crista ampularis. The cilia of these cells are imbedded in a gelatinous mass, which contains minute crystalline grains of carbonate of lime. This gelatinous mass, termed the cupola, together with the ciliated or hair cells, forms the sense organ that is found in each ampulla. Very slight movements of the head or the body to which it is attached produce disturbances of the endolymph, which in turn affects the hair cells. The hair cells are supplied by the vestibular branch of the acoustic nerve. Sensory organs are also found in the utricle and saccule. They are similar to

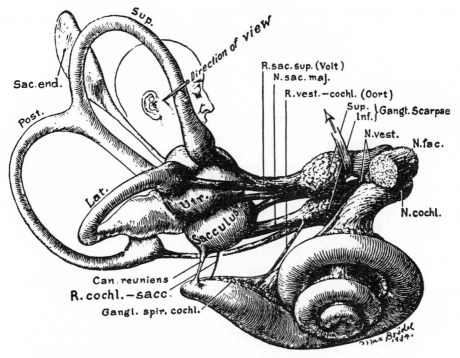

*Fig. 6–44. The membranous labyrinth. (From E. G. Wever,
Theory of Hearing. John Wiley & Sons, Inc., New York, 1949.)*

those in the ampullae, consisting of a mound of connective tissue, one on the anterior wall of the utricle and another on the medial wall of the saccule. These mounds of tissue, their epithelial cells, hair cells, and gelatinous cupola constitute the maculae. They contain the terminal fibers of the saccular and utricular branches of the vestibular part of the acoustic nerve. The maculae respond to linear forward and sideway movements of the head. According to Lederer and Hollender (1942), the labyrinth is fundamentally an organ of reflex action for the maintenance of equilibrium and the preservation of a constant field of vision. Under ordinary conditions this function is accomplished in an automatic manner, without preliminary or accompanying sensation, as is the case with vision and audition.

As shown in Figure 6–45, the utricle and saccule communicate indirectly by way of the utricular and saccular ducts, which join to form a common endolymphatic duct. It, you will recall, courses through the vestibular aqueduct to end in a blind pouch located between the layers of the dura mater. The saccule and cochlear duct communicate directly by means of the canal reuniens, which some authorities believe to be obliterated in the adult human. Others believe that it is always open and permits passage of endolymph from the cochlea to the saccule and indirectly to the utricle. Because of its small size, however, high-frequency disturbances of endolymph are prevented from being transmitted from the cochlea to the structures in the vestibule (Vinnikov and Titova, 1964).

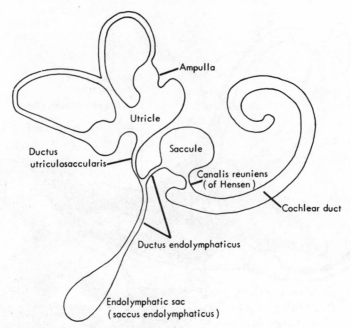

Fig. 6–45. Schematic of the membranous labyrinth.

The cochlear duct

As described earlier, the cochlea is a bony, spiral-shaped cavity about 35 mm in length incompletely divided into the scala vestibuli and scala tympani by the osseous spiral lamina, a narrow shelf of bone arising from the inner or modiolar wall of the cochlea. This division is completed by the membranous cochlear duct or scala media. It is a spirally arranged tube, about 31 mm in length, that complies with the general shape of the osseous cochlea and lies along its outer wall. Its floor is formed by the basilar membrane, which extends from the spiral lamina to the outer wall of the cochlea. Thus, the basilar membrane completes the roof of the scala tympani and also forms the membranous portion of the floor of the cochlear duct. The roof of the cochlear duct is formed by an extremely fragile membrane, the vestibular membrane of Reissner, which extends obliquely from thickened periosteum covering the spiral lamina to the outer wall of the cochlea. It is attached to a thickened spiral ligament which, as shown in Figure 6–46, lies along the outer wall of the cochlea.

It is crucial for an appreciation of the hearing mechanism to have a clear understanding of the relationship between the vestibule, the scala vestibuli, scala tympani, and the cochlear duct. This relationship is shown schematically in Figure 6–47. Note that the bony spiral lamina and basilar membrane (heavy line), which divide the cochlea into an upper and lower duct, are joined with the vestibule at the basal end in such a manner that the only direct communication is between the scala vestibuli and the vestibule. The scala tympani (lower duct), on the other hand, is also terminated basally at the bony wall of the vestibule, but does not communicate with the vestibule proper, except very indirectly through the helicotrema at the apex. Reissner's membrane, which forms the roof of the cochlear duct, terminates blindly at the

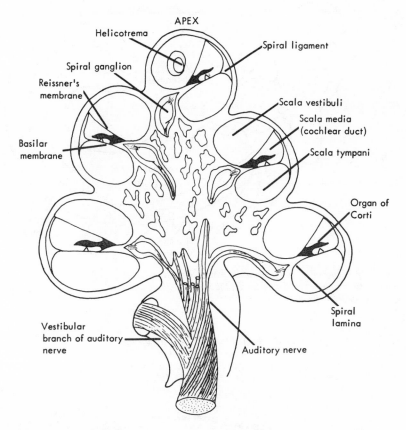

APEX

Helicotrema

Spiral ligament

Spiral ganglion

Reissner's
membrane

Scala vestibuli

Scala media
(cochlear duct)

Basilar
membrane

Scala tympani

Organ of
Corti

Vestibular
branch of auditory
nerve

Spiral
lamina

Auditory nerve

*Fig. 6–46. Schematic section of cochlea, illustrating modiolus
in relation to adjacent structures, including the cochlear duct.*

vestibular wall and also at the apex. As a result, the cochlear duct is essentially a closed
tube, its only outlet being the ductus reuniens.

Some of the structures forming the boundaries of the cochlear duct ought to be
described in greater detail. The spiral lamina is a very narrow shelf of bone at the
apical end, becoming gradually wider toward the basal end. Upon close examination
the spiral lamina is seen to consist of two thin plates of bone, between which are canals
for the transmission of fibers of the acoustic nerve. The upper layer is continuous with
a thickening of periosteum known as the spiral limbus. It is shown in Figure 6–48.
The spiral limbus is markedly concave at its outer edge, forming the internal spiral
sulcus and at the same time giving rise to an upper extremity, the vestibular lip, and
a lower extremity, the tympanic lip, which is continuous with the lower plate of bone,
often called the perforate habenula, and with the basilar membrane.

As shown in Figure 6–48, the outer wall of the cochlea is characterized by a marked
thickening of the periosteum known as the spiral ligament (of Kölliker). It projects
inward to form a shelf-like prominence, the basilar crest. The basilar membrane
extends from the tympanic lip to the basilar crest of the spiral ligament. The portion
of the membrane nearest the spiral lamina is thin and fragile, and is known as the

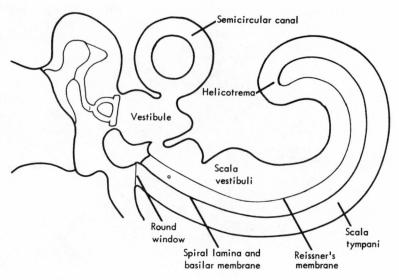

Fig. 6–47. Schematic of the hearing mechanism, illustrating the relationship between the vestibule, the scala vestibuli, scala tympani, and the cochlear duct.

Fig. 6–48. Illustration of the division of the cochlea into the scala vestibuli, scala media (cochlear duct), and the scala tympani. (From S. S. Stevens, ed., Handbook of Experimental Psychology. *John Wiley & Sons, Inc., New York, 1951.)*

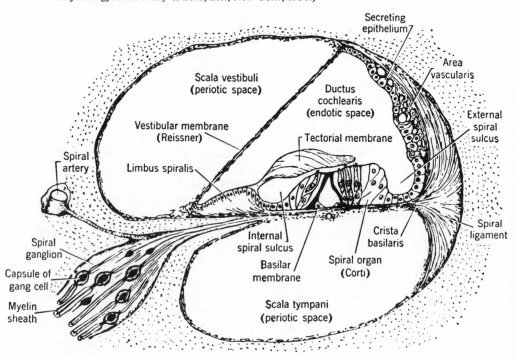

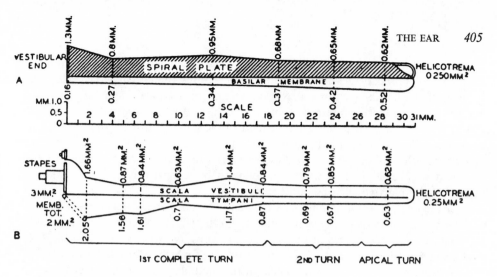

Fig. 6–49. *Schematic representation of the dimensions of the basilar membrane and of the scalae of the human cochlea.* (*From Fletcher's* Speech *and* Hearing in Communication, *Copyright 1953, D. Van Nostrand Company, Inc., Princeton, N.J.*)

zona arcuata. The outer portion is thick and relatively rigid, and is known as the zona pectinata.

The basilar membrane seems to be composed of a series of transverse fibers that course perpendicular to the axis of the cochlear duct. These fibers are imbedded in a rather homogenous interstitial substance. According to Retzius (1905) there are about 24,000 fibers in the basilar membrane. When viewed from above, without its superstructure, the basilar membrane might be said to bear a fancied resemblance to a corrugated or "washboard" road. The tympanic surface of the membrane is covered by a layer of epithelium containing vascular tissue. One of the vessels, larger than the rest, is called the vas spirale. The width of the basilar membrane is variable, a fact that has had a tremendous impact on the history of theories of hearing. Results obtained by numerous investigators vary considerably, so that absolute values cannot be given with certainty. In 1863, Hensen reported that the width of the basilar membrane varies from 0.041 mm at the basal end to 0.495 mm at the apex, and in 1918 Wrightson and Keith, in an extensive study, reported values that varied from 0.16 mm at the basal end to 0.52 mm at the apex. Guild, in 1927, reported values obtained on the ears of guinea pigs; they varied from 0.062 mm at the base to 0.209 mm at the apex. In 1938 Wever reported his results, obtained from a study of twenty-five human ears; the values ranged from 0.08 mm at the basal end to 0.498 mm at the apex. Wever also found that the basilar membrane is not uniformly tapered. The width increases from the basal end, at first slowly, and reaches maximum width at the end of the second turn, after which the width decreases sharply. The dimensions of structures of the inner ear, shown to scale, may be seen in Figure 6–49. This illustration by Fletcher (1952) is based on the data of Wrightson and Keith. It shows the dimensions and shape of the human basilar membrane and osseous spiral lamina and the sectional areas of the scala tympani and scala vestibuli.

The upper or vestibular surface of the basilar membrane bears an important organ, which contains the sensory cells essential to hearing. It was described in detail by

Corti, in 1836, and has borne his name since. The organ of Corti is extraordinarily complex, composed of a series of epithelial structures that occupy the length and breadth of the basilar membrane. A cross section of a typical mammalian cochlea and the organ of Corti contained within the cochlear duct is shown schematically in Figure 6–48, and a greatly enlarged schematic of the organ of Corti is shown in Figure 6–50. The cells that comprise the organ of Corti may be classified as either receptor or supporting cells. In an attempt to preserve a sense of continuity, the organ of Corti will be described, at first very grossly, followed by a more detailed description of some of the supportive cells and of the receptor cells.

Near the osseous spiral lamina may be seen two conspicuous structures, the inner and outer rods of Corti. They are supportive cells which, when seen in transverse section, are widely separated at their bases, and converge to meet at the top. They enclose a triangular inner tunnel of Corti, the floor of which is formed by the bases of the rods and by the basilar membrane. On the modiolar side of the inner rods is a single row of ciliated or hair cells, which are flanked on the inner side by numerous supportive cells. On the outer side of the outer rods are three (sometimes four) rows of outer hair cells, held in position at their bases and tops by a complex network of supportive cells, particularly the cells of Deiters and Hensen. The ciliated ends of the hair cells perforate a delicate reticular membrane and extend toward a rather structureless fibrogelatinous mass called the tectorial membrane.

The Supporting Cells.   The very complex supporting cells of the organ of Corti are shown schematically in Figure 6–51. The surface of the vestibular lip of the spiral

Fig. 6–50. Illustration of the organ of Corti. (*From Stevens, Handbook of Experimental Psychology.*)

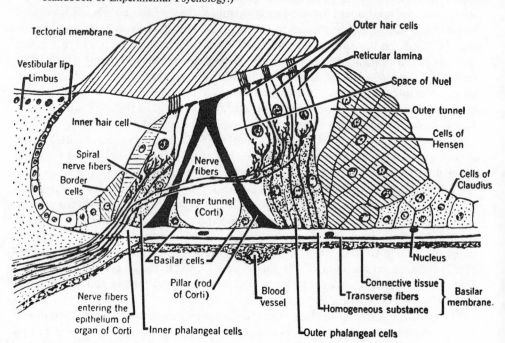

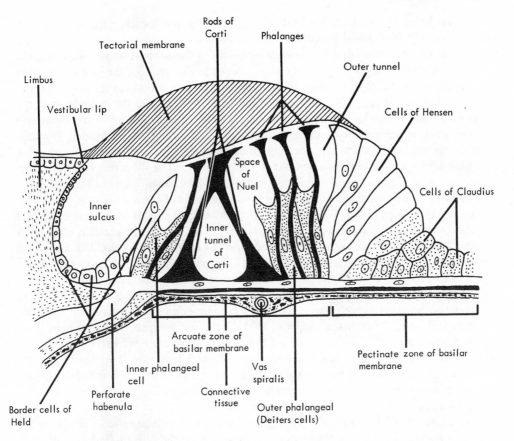

Fig. 6–51. Schematic representation of the supportive structures of the organ of Corti.

lamina is covered with a very distinctive layer of epithelium. Its cells are arranged in parallel rows, and, when viewed from the vestibular side, the vestibular lip has a serrated appearance. Early anatomists referred to the cells as "auditory teeth." Recently, Vinnikov and Titova (1964) have shown these cells to exhibit a secretory activity. The cells on the vestibular lip are continuous with the epithelial lining of the internal spiral sulcus. They are large, flat, polygonal cells directly continuous with the supporting cells for the inner hair cells. One or two rows of cells bordering the inner hair cells on the modiolar side are known as the border cells of Held. They are distinguished by a flattened head closely connected with similar flattened heads of adjacent cells.

The supporting cells most closely associated with the inner row of hair cells are remarkable structures. They are called phalangeal cells, and consist of two parts. The main body of the cell, with its small basal end, rests directly on the spiral lamina in the region of the habenula perforata. The cell body extends to the lower limit of the inner hair cell, where, at about that level, a rather rigid process is given off that extends almost to the level of the apex of the hair cell. At its upper limit this phalangeal process expands to form a flattened lamella. The inner hair cells are strongly supported at their bases by the bodies of the phalangeal cells and loosely supported at their apexes by the phalangeal processes.

At first glance, probably the most conspicuous of the supporting structures are the inner and outer rods or pillars of Corti. As shown in Figure 6–51, the base of the inner rod rests at the point of junction of the tympanic lip of the osseous spiral lamina and the basilar membrane, while the base of the outer rod rests on the outer limit of the arcuate zone of the basilar membrane. The widely expanded bases of the outer and inner rods, which actually come into direct contact, contain the cell nuclei. The rods converge and meet at the top, forming an acute angle with each other. The angle of inclination of the outer rods is somewhat greater than that of the inner. In a transverse section, as in Figure 6–51, the rods enclose a triangular-shaped "inner tunnel of Corti." The floor of the tunnel is formed by the expanded bases of the rods and by the subadjacent basilar membrane. When viewed from the side, the walls of the tunnel are not solid. The pillars, which are epithelial cells stacked alongside one another, have small slit-like spaces between them. These spaces permit endolymph to circulate and nerve fibers to pass through as they course toward the modiolus and the nerve-cell bodies contained therein. At their heads and bases, however, the pillars are continuous.

The headplates of the rods of Corti are complex. The outer surface of the head of the inner rod presents a deep concavity which accommodates a convexity on the head of the outer rod. In addition, the head of the inner rod presents a laminar headplate, which overlaps a similar headplate on the outer rod. These headplates bridge a gap between the inner hair cells and the first row of outer hair cells. The thin headplates of the outer rods are known as phalangeal processes, and they unite with the phalangeal processes of other supporting cells to form the reticular membrane, a delicate net-like structure which lies over the organ of Corti.

In contact with the bases of the outer rods is a row of phalangeal cells similar to the inner phalangeal cells described earlier. They are called the cells of Deiters. Although the bases of the first row of the cells of Deiters are in direct contact with the bases of the outer rods, their main bodies become rather widely separated above to enclose an inverted, triangular-shaped endolymphatic space, the space of Nuel. The Deiters cells are arranged, usually in rows of three, although occasionally four.[1] The bases of the Deiters cells rest on the pectinate zone of the basilar membrane. The main body of a Deiters cell is cylindrical; however, it becomes quite complex where it comes into contact with the base of the hair cell it supports. As shown schematically in Figure 6–52, its shape is modified to form a cup which snugly accommodates the basal end of an outer hair cell. At about the level of the cup, or lower head as it is sometimes called, the cell also gives off an ascending phalanx, which reaches the upper level of the organ of Corti between adjacent hair cells. There it quickly expands to form a thin lamella which contributes to the reticular membrane and also separates the apexes of neighboring hair cells. Thus, the reticular membrane, or lamina, is not an independent structure, but, rather, is composed of the inner phalanges, the headplates of the inner rods, the phalangeal processes of the outer rods, and the upper heads of the Deiters cells. The reticular membrane lends support to the apexes of the outer hair cells, whose

---

[1] Although there are but three rows of outer hair cells, four, five, and even more have been reported. The number of cells observed on serial sections of the cochlea is dependent upon the angle at which the section has been made. Increasingly tangential cuts result in an increasingly larger number of cells observed.

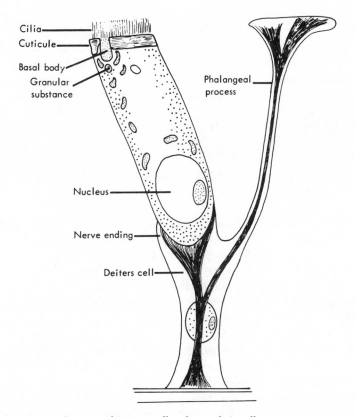

Cilia

Cuticule

Basal body

Granular
substance

Phalangeal
process

Nucleus

Nerve ending

Deiters cell

Fig. 6–52. Schematic of Deiters cell and outer hair cell.

tufts of cilia occupy the spaces in the net-like matrix. The apexes of the inner hair cells, however, rise above the reticular membrane, and their cilia form a continuous row.

Immediately adjacent to the outer row of Deiters cells are five or six rows of tall columnar cells, the supporting cells of Hensen. The narrow bases of the innermost row rest on the basilar membrane in direct contact with the bases of the outer row of Deiters cells. Toward their apexes, however, they are separated slightly from the outer row of hair cells, thus giving rise to a narrow, outer tunnel, shown in Figure 6–51. Additional rows of columnar cells, in decreasing height, lie outside Hensen's cells. They are the cells of Claudius and are continuous with a highly vascular layer of epithelium lining the spiral ligament. These latter cells, which are secretory, together with the vascular tissue, form the important stria vascularis. There is little question that the stria vascularis secretes endolymph, and since the organ of Corti does not enjoy a blood supply per se, the nutritive function of endolymph is vital to hearing.

An extraordinarily delicate membrane, the tectorial membrane, is connected to the epithelial covering of the vestibular lip of the spiral lamina, extends over the internal sulcus and the hair cells, and in life is evidently continuous with the cells of Hensen. It is often described as a semitransparent, gelatinous membrane, with a density scarcely exceeding that of endolymph. Others see it as a fluid-filled tube; however, it does contain numerous interwoven fibrils, which apparently contribute to its physical properties. The tectorial membrane is narrow at the basal end of the cochlea, becoming gradually wider toward the apex. In spite of the recent advances in electron microscopy and in histological techniques, the function and contributions of the tectorial membrane are not known for certain. There is no positive evidence that the cilia of the hair cells are imbedded in it during life (as is frequently claimed). On the basis of their electron microscopy, Engstrom, Ades, and Hawkins (1962) were unable to find supportive evidence that the hairs of the outer cells are either directly continuous with the tectorial membrane or that the hairs are imbedded in it. They suggest that only the tips of the hairs are in contact with the tectorial membrane and in some way adherent to it. They also point out the uncertainty as to whether the hairs are even in contact with the membrane during a state of rest.

The Receptor Cells.   The inner hair cells are droplet shaped, wide at their nucleated bases. They are arranged in a single row between the inner phalangeal cells and the inner rods of Corti, and have the same angle of inclination as the inner rods. According to Vinnikov and Titova (1964), the inner hair cells are arranged between supportive structures, but they have no special supportive apparatus; that is, well-defined intercellular spaces are present between the hair cells and adjacent supporting cells. The apex of an inner hair cell is slightly convex and bears two rows of cilia aligned parallel to the axis of the basilar membrane. The number of cilia varies from about 40 per cell in the basal end to more than 60 per cell in the apical turn. Each hair-cell body (inner and outer) is capped by a delicate cuticular plate into which the rootlets of the cilia (stereocilia) are anchored, and the entire cell, including the cilia, is surrounded by a plasma membrane. Just beneath the cuticular head, near the modiolar side of the cell, is a cylindrical structure known as the basal body. It is surrounded by granular materials. Basal bodies, from which a single, coarse cilium (kinocilium) arises, are found in the vestibular sensory cells, and although the basal bodies of cochlear hair cells strongly resemble those in the vestibular epithelium, the presence of a cilium protruding from the basal body is open to some question. The stereocilia, however, are easily identified in both cochlear and vestibular hair cells. They appear to be stiff and resistant to bending and in fact actually break off if excessive force is used (Engstrom, *et al.*, 1962). Some implications of the physical properties of the cochlear hair cells will be discussed in a separate section later in this chapter.

The outer hair cells are cylindrical in shape, with a rounded, nucleated base (like a miniature test tube) that nestles snugly into the cup-shaped head of the Deiters cells. The outer cells are also capped with a cuticular membrane from which numerous cilia protrude, rising above the recticular membrane. Their length, even in the same hair cell, varies considerably, as does the number per cell, which increases from about 40 in the basal turn to about 120 in the apical turn. As shown schematically in Figure 6–53, the cilia are characteristically arranged in the form of the letter W. This arrangement suggests the hair cells respond to shearing movements in the radial direction, a point to be considered in greater detail later. The outer hair cells also contain a basal body, which seems to lack the coarse kinocilium characteristic of the vestibular sensory cells. Endolymph circulates to the cells by means of intercellular spaces which are ultimately continuous with the tunnel of Corti and space of Nuel. The outer hair cells are covered with a well-defined plasma membrane, and membranous layers may be

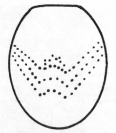

Fig. 6–53. Arrangement of the cilia on the surface of an outer hair cell.

distinguished within the lightly granulated cytoplasm of the cell. The cells are characteristically arranged in three parallel rows in the basal turn of the guinea pig cochlea, four rows in the middle turn, and sometimes five rows in the apical turn. According to Retzius (1905), the total number of inner hair cells is about 3,500, and the total number of outer hair cells from 12,000–20,000.

The cytoarchitecture of the cochlear hair cells has important implications regarding their highly specialized functions. The interested reader is urged to turn to the works of Wersäll (1956), Smith (1957), Flock, Kimura, Lundquist and Wersäll (1962), Engstrom, *et al.* (1962), Davis (1962), and Vinnikov and Titova (1964).

The nerve supply to the organ of Corti

Communication between the peripheral receptor organ of the ear, the membranous labyrinth, and the central organ, the brain, is established by means of the acoustic, or eighth (VIII) cranial nerve. Although the acoustic nerve is relatively thick, it contains a surprisingly small number of nerve fibers, about 50,000, according to Rasmussen (1940). Upon entering the internal auditory meatus, the acoustic nerve abruptly divides into a vestibular branch containing about 18,500 nerve fibers and a cochlear branch containing about 31,500 fibers. The cell bodies of the neurons which innervate the hair cells of the cochlea are located within the canal of Rosenthal in the modiolus, and form a long ganglion called the spiral ganglion of Corti. When the cochlea is seen in a plane parallel to the axis of the modiolus, the spiral ganglion is easily identified by an aggregate of nerve-cell bodies located very near the osseous spiral limbus (as in Figure 6–54). The ganglion cells are not evenly distributed in Rosenthal's canal. When counted, by means of serial sections, their density varies from 983 cells per millimeter of cochlear length in the lower basal turn to 1,215 cells per millimeter in the upper basal turn, 1,144 cells per millimeter in the lower middle turn, and 608 per millimeter in the upper middle and apical turns (Guild, Crowe, Burch, and Polvogt, 1931).

Each nerve-cell body gives rise to two nerve processes, a central one and a peripheral one. The peripheral courses from the cell body to its terminal ending at the hair cells, while the central courses from the cell body to the brain stem. Let us trace the path of the fibers of the acoustic nerve by first following the course of the peripheral fibers to their terminal endings at the hair cells and then tracing the course of the fibers from the cell bodies through the various levels of the brain stem and brain to their terminal endings at the cerebral cortex.

The peripheral processes of the nerve cells of the spiral ganglion possess a myelin

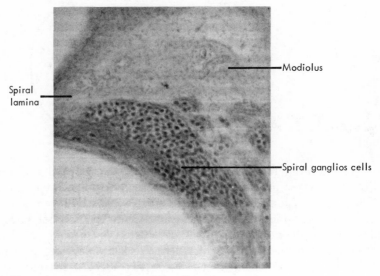

Fig. 6–54. Photomicrograph of spiral ganglion cells.

sheath encased by the sheath of Schwann, or neurilemmal sheath. For the most part the fibers pass in small bundles in a direction radial to the axis of the modiolus through numerous channels between the plates of the osseous spiral lamina and enter the cochlear duct through the small perforations on the vestibular surface of the tympanic lip of the spiral lamina, where they abruptly shed their myelin sheaths and neurilemma. Having entered the cochlear duct, the fibers can be divided, largely by virtue of their distribution to the hair cells, into two or quite possibly three groups. Many of the fibers (5 and 6 in Figure 6–55) course from their point of emergence in small radial bundles, and without much deviation are directed to the inner hair cells where they give off a few collateral branches, which come into close approximation with their basal surfaces.

Some fibers, which form the intraganglionic spiral bundle (1 and 2 in Figure 6–55), take a course that departs radically from the orderly course just described. These fibers, while still in the ganglionic spaces of the modiolus, cross over the main radial bundles and run for at least a quarter of a cochlear turn toward the apex. Each fiber gives off several collaterals, which turn outward and follow the course of the radial bundles in that part of the cochlea. Other fibers in the radial bundles form an internal spiral bundle (2a and 3a in Figure 6–55), which, when they approach the inner hair cells, turn abruptly and take an apical course, also giving off collaterals to supply the inner hair cells and an occasional outer hair cell. According to Lorente de Nó (1937), the fibers that form the internal spiral bundle are the collaterals given off by the intraganglionic spiral bundle mentioned above. Thus, most inner hair cells are innervated by more than one neuron, and each nerve fiber, in turn, innervates more than one hair cell.

Another group of nerve fibers, called the external spiral fibers (4 in Figure 6–55), are directed in a rather straight (radial) course from the spiral ganglion to the outer

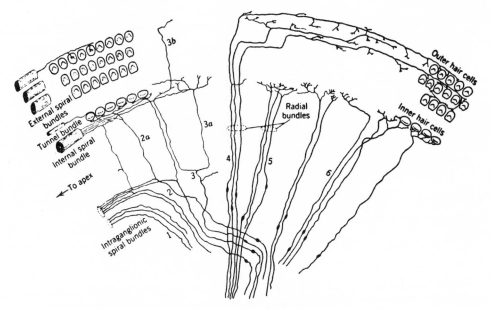

Fig. 6–55. The innervation of the cochlea. (From Wever, Theory of Hearing.)

hair cells, at which point they abruptly turn and course in a longitudinal direction toward the basal end of the cochlea, giving off secondary and tertiary collaterals which terminate as minute swellings on the sides and bases of the outer hair cells. These processes may also serve a very limited number of inner hair cells in addition to groups of three or four or more rows of outer hair cells. There is also a limited number of "diffuse" fibers in the cochlea. They are extremely thin and, due to a wandering, almost random course, give off collaterals that serve a wide segment of the inner hair cells.

The neurons comprising the auditory tract do not course uninterruptedly through the brain stem to the auditory area of the cerebral cortex. Rather, there is a succession of at least four neurons between the cochlea and cerebral cortex. Those at the level of the spiral ganglion are called first-order neurons, while those at the level of the cerebral cortex are called fourth or fifth-order neurons, depending upon the total number of successive neurons in the pathway.

The nerve pathway of hearing is shown schematically in Figure 6–56. The central processes of the spiral ganglion cells pass to the core of the modiolus where they form the cochlear nerve. The most apical fibers follow a straight course and form the core of the nerve, while the basal fibers are added in a twisted fashion to form the periphery of the nerve. The reason for the twisted feature seems to be due to the way in which the ear develops embryologically. The acoustic nerve evidently appears rather well developed before the cochlea has begun to form. The cochlea begins to develop at the basal end and grows in a spiral fashion toward the apex. As growth progresses, the nerve elements are "dragged" along, so that when the structure is completed, the basal fibers have been twisted around the apical fibers, and the nerve takes on a gross

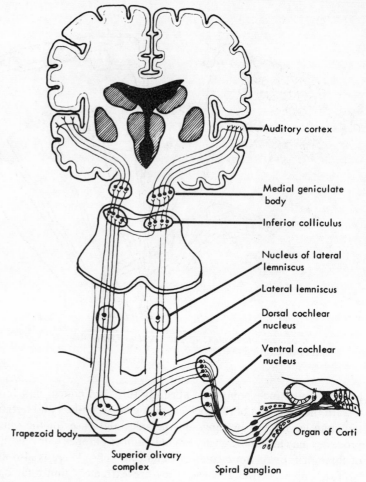

Auditory cortex

Medial geniculate body

Inferior colliculus

Nucleus of lateral lemniscus

Lateral lemniscus

Dorsal cochlear nucleus

Ventral cochlear nucleus

Organ of Corti

Trapezoid body

Superior olivary complex

Spiral ganglion

Fig. 6–56. A schematic nerve pathway for hearing.

appearance not unlike that of a manila rope. As we shall see in some detail later, the fibers serving the apical region of the cochlea are associated with low-frequency sounds, while the fibers of the basal region are associated with the high-frequency sounds. Because of the anatomical architecture of the cochlear nerve, the high-frequency fibers are the most exposed and subject to trauma, while the more essential (for speech reception) lower-frequency fibers are somewhat protected.

As the cochlear nerve enters the internal auditory meatus, it is joined by the two divisions of the vestibular nerve to complete the auditory nerve, which lies in close proximity to the facial nerve. The auditory nerve is quite short, only about five millimeters in length. It enters the medulla oblongata laterally at the level of the lower pons, where the cochlear bundle courses directly to the cochlear nucleus, and there it divides into two branches. One branch decends to the dorsal cochlear nucleus, often referred to as the tuberculum acusticum (acoustic tubercle), while the other ascends to the ventral cochlear nucleus. The fibers of both branches terminate in synaptic connections with second-order neurons of the cochlear nuclei. About half the cell bodies of the second-order neurons send axon fibers across the median plane through the trapezoid body, where some terminate by means of synapses with cells in other bulbar nuclei, mainly the superior olivary complex, which is located at the same level as, but somewhat lateral to, the trapezoid body. Decussation of the nerve fibers at the level of the cochlear nuclei has important implications. Since about half the fibers from one ear course directly upward from a cochlear nucleus, while the remainder cross over the mid-line to the cochlear nucleus on the opposite side, nerve impulses from each ear reach both the left and right temporal lobes of the brain. For this reason, destruction of the nerve pathway on one side does not result in complete deafness for the corresponding ear. The mechanism is reciprocal.

The superior olivary complex gives rise to third-order neurons, which course upward, forming a tract known as the lateral lemniscus. The third-order neurons are accompanied by second-order neurons, which pass uninterruptedly through the superior olivary complex. The lateral lemniscus contains a nucleus, which forms the point of synapse for some second- and third-order neurons, while other neurons pass uninterrupted from the lenticular nucleus on to the inferior colliculus of the midbrain, where synapses may once again occur. Also, at the level of the inferior colliculus, fibers decussate from one side of the brain to the other. The inferior colliculus, also known as the inferior quadrigeminal body, apparently contains centers for reflex responses to sound. A few fibers continue through the inferior colliculus to the medial geniculate body of the thalamus. Most of the fibers of the lateral lemniscus, however, terminate at the medial geniculate body, where they synapse with third- and fourth-order neurons whose axons course through the sublenticular portion of the internal capsule and end in the anterior transverse temporal (Heschel's) gyrus. There is good evidence for an orderly correspondence between the cochlea and the acoustic projection on the cerebral cortex. The arrangement of the cells within the medial geniculate body and of the fibers that radiate to the cortex also seems to be rather orderly and predictable.

Efferent nerve fibers have long been recognized in the cochlea. We have thus far been directing our attention only to the afferent nerve pathway. That is, it has been well established that the cochlea has a two-way nerve supply, one which goes from the hair cells to the auditory cortex, and another which courses from the central auditory pathway of one ear to the auditory organ of the opposite side. The efferent pathway was described in some detail by Rasmussen in 1946, and has since been called the tract of Rasmussen, although the descriptive term olivo-cochlear bundle is more informative. The efferent tract, shown very schematically in Figure 6–57, has a nuclear origin in the region of the olivary complex. The nerve fibers (about 400) form a bundle which runs toward the fourth ventricle and around the nucleus of the abducens nerve (a motor nerve that supplies the muscles of the eye) and follows a course parallel to the vestibular nerve through the internal auditory meatus where the fibers are distributed throughout the cochlea (of the opposite side) and probably terminate as the intraganglionic spiral bundle described earlier. It, you will recall, innervates mainly the inner hair cells. The large bulbous nerve endings of the efferent fibers seem to differ from the nerve endings of the afferent fibers. This feature not only makes identification of the efferent fibers possible but also suggests that they make contact with and are able to influence adjacent neural structures. A full discussion of the olivo-cochlear tract and its possible contribution to hearing is far beyond the scope of this text. The interested reader is referred to Davis (1962), Galambos (1958;

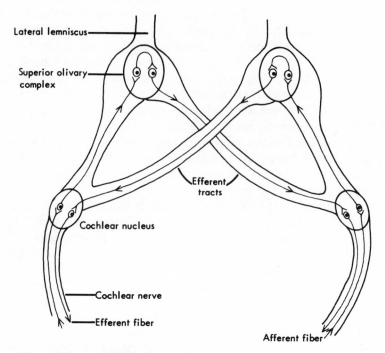

Lateral lemniscus

Superior olivary complex

Efferent tracts

Cochlear nucleus

Cochlear nerve

Efferent fiber

Afferent fiber

Fig. 6–57. Highly schematized olivo-cochlear tract.

1956a; 1956b; 1954), Galambos and Davis, 1948; 1943), Rasmussen and Windle (1960), and Vosteen (1963).

Two questions, however, can be posed regarding the function of the efferent or olivo-cochlear tract. Does the efferent system affect the sound-transformation functions of the cochlea, and is there a reciprocal effect of the two cochleae upon each other? Galambos and Davis (1948) convincingly demonstrated that stimulation of one ear inhibits the nerve impulses generated by the opposite ear, when the latter is stimulated simultaneously or with a short delay. In addition, electrical stimulation of the efferent pathway inhibits the electrical activity of the cochlear nerve. The findings of Galambos and Davis also suggest that the efferent tract is connected with the afferent tract, not only at the level of the olivary nucleus but also at higher levels, possibly even at the cortex. In general, the research findings suggest that the only physiological effect produced by the efferent tract is inhibitory.

The Function of the Inner Ear

Introduction

We are now faced with the problem of propagation of sound within the cochlea and the way in which vibratory energy is transformed into a train of neural impulses. From our previous description of the inner ear, it is evident that the entire membranous labyrinth forms a closed system. That is, since the walls of the bony labyrinth cannot yield to pressures and the labyrinthine fluids are practically incompressible,

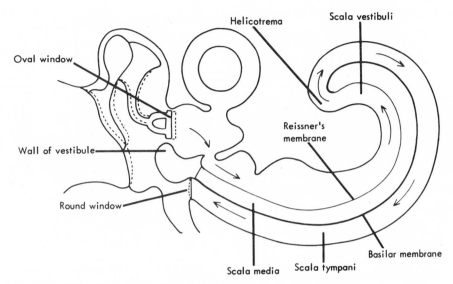

Fig. 6–58. Schematic of mass-action fluid flow through the cochlea.

vibrations of the stapes footplate must cause the cochlear fluids somehow to be displaced. The exact mechanism of fluid movements within the cochlea has important theoretical implications and has a direct bearing on the form many of the theories of hearing have taken.

One point of view is that the movements of the stapes are transmitted directly to the fluid column in the cochlea which responds as a whole—a mass-action mechanism. As illustrated in Figure 6–58, inward movement of the stapes footplate causes the perilymph to flow up the scala vestibuli, through the helicotrema, and then down the scala tympani, where the round window is distended by an amount directly proportional to the inward movement of the stapes. During outward movement, the direction of flow of the fluid column is reversed. Thus, the movements of the stapes and round window may have a proportional relationship, but with a reversal of phase. Sound energy, transmitted by the vibrating fluid column, is selectively absorbed by the structures on the basilar membrane.

An alternate viewpoint is that the pressure generated in the scala vestibuli is transmitted across the scala media to the scala tympani. As shown in Figure 6–59, such a transmission of pressure results in a distortion of Reissner's membrane and, in turn, the basilar membrane. As before, however, there will be displacements of the round window that are out of phase with the direction of movement of the stapes. The fluid movements may be distinctive for a particular frequency and thus produce distortion of the basilar membrane at a specific frequency-related locus. In either of these mechanisms disturbances of the hair cells located on the basilar membrane transform the mechanical energy into electrical disturbances that stimulate the fibers of the cochlear nerve.

The exact nature of the movements of the cochlear fluids and of the mechanism by which the hair cells are stimulated has been the subject of speculation and intensive

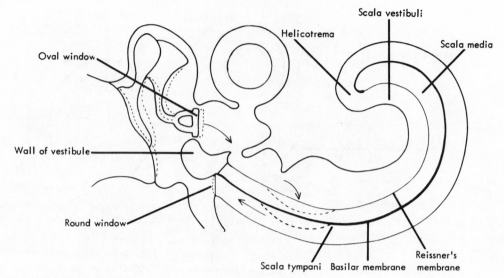

Fig. 6–59. Schematic of the path of vibrations through the cochlea.

research for many years. More than one researcher has devoted an entire lifetime to an attempt to explain the physiology of hearing. To date, the problem has not been completely resolved. The research has given rise to a number of theories of hearing, which may be broadly divided into two classes, each of which has two subclasses. They are, first, the place theories, which have as subclasses the resonance and non-resonance or travelling-wave theories and, secondly, the frequency theories, which have the telephone or nonanalytic and the frequency analytic theories as subclasses. In most of these theories the primary emphasis has been on the passage of sounds through the cochlea and the characteristics of the disturbances produced in the basilar membrane. The neurophysiology of the cochlea and the contributions of the central pathway have received less emphasis and in some instances have all but been excluded in the scheme of the hearing theory.

Our first objective will be to review briefly some of the theories of hearing, after which some features of the neurophysiology of the cochlea will be considered.

A word about theories

Any theory that attempts to explain a particular phenomenon, such as hearing, is bound to encounter complex problems like pitch analysis, discrimination, masking effects, and so forth. A theory, in order to be adequate, must withstand the rigors of a vast number of tests, and if it fails, the theory must be revised, not the test. It is curious, when one surveys the long evolution of theories of hearing, that they have become increasingly complex probably in order to account for such complex aspects of hearing as tonal interaction and loudness. As new auditory phenomena are encountered or discovered, the theory must be able to withstand new tests or undergo revisions. These revisions, if they occur, do not reflect a weakness in the theory nearly so much as they reflect a virtue in the scientific attitude of the theorist. In this spirit then, any theory, regardless of its degree of complexity or of its ability to meet the tests to which it is subjected, can at the very least advance knowledge. What more fruitful goal can science have?

Place theories

Resonance Theory.   One of the earliest, well-formulated theories of hearing was advanced by Helmholtz in 1857. His resonance theory was well received, and probably no theory of hearing has enjoyed such long-lived popularity. It closely followed on the heels of three important developments of the same period. They were Ohm's law of auditory analysis, Johannes Müller's doctrine of specific energy of nerves, and the then recent anatomical findings of Corti. Ohm's law stems from a fundamental mathematical theorum developed earlier by Fourier. Very briefly, Ohm's law states that any sound wave, so long as it is specifiable (periodic), consists of the sum of a series of sine (or cosine) waves, whose frequencies are integral multiples of the fundamental frequency. Also, a series of sine waves may be added to form a complex wave, the form of which is specific for any given series when the amplitudes and phase relationships are given. According to Ohm's law, the ear performs a type of Fourier analysis when it is stimulated by a complex wave and breaks the wave down into its sine-wave components. This law formed the very basis for Helmholtz's theory of hearing. He was also influenced by Müller's doctrine of specific nerve energy, which stated that the effects produced by stimulation of a nerve are specific to the particular sense with which the nerve is associated. For example, although the eye is normally responsive to light energy, electric, chemical, or physical stimulation of the optic nerve will produce sensations of light, and not shock or pressure. Although Müller applied his doctrine just to the "five senses," his contemporaries extended it to include the various attributes of the senses. This liberalization of Müller's doctrine enabled Helmholtz to state that every fiber in the auditory nerve is associated with a specific pitch.

Helmholtz also found support for his theory in the discovery of the rods of Corti. He theorized the outer rods made up a series of individually tuned resonators, with high-frequency resonators located at the basal end of the cochlea and low-frequency resonators in the apical region. He used as his analogy piano or harp strings, which, as everyone knows, may be set into vibration by singing or playing a loud musical tone into them. According to Helmholtz, a note of a given pitch causes a specific resonator to be set into vibration, and because each resonator is supplied with a separate nerve fiber, pitch analysis is accomplished within the cochlea. In a later presentation of his theory Helmholtz apparently yielded to some of the criticism leveled at him by his adversaries, for he no longer considered the rods of Corti to be the resonators, but, rather, the transverse fibers of the basilar membrane were thought to be the crucial resonating elements. The analogy of piano or harp strings is still applicable in this, the revised and final form of the Helmholtz resonance theory of hearing. Unfortunately, this analogy, which appears to be erroneous, is still being alluded to in some "authoritative" publications intended for public consumption. As a result, parents and teachers alike go through life supposing they have tiny pianos, harps, or marimbas inside their heads.

Helmholtz's theory was developed at a time when knowledge of the microscopic anatomy and the physical properties of the cochlea were not nearly so advanced as they are today. Yet, except for Helmholtz's specification of resonating elements, his theory bears a remarkable resemblance to the current place theories. The results of intensive research on the physical properties of the basilar membrane make it seem unlikely that actual resonators do exist. In order for the transverse fibers of the basilar membrane to be capable of resonating at specific frequencies, they must exhibit some peculiar acoustical and mechanical properties. For example, since Helmholtz located high frequencies at the basal end and low frequencies at the apical end of the cochlear duct, we would expect the transverse fibers to be longer in the apical region than at the basal end. As support for his hypothesis Helmholtz cited anatomical observations of Hensen, who found that the length of the transverse fibers of the basilar membrane increases from 0.04 mm at the basal end to .495 mm at the apical end. Thus, the length of the resonators was found to vary about twelvefold from base to apex. Subsequent experiments by Keith (1918) and Guild (1927) produced results that indicated a difference in length does indeed exist, but in the order of three- or fourfold. More recent experiments by Wever (1938) on large samples (25 ears) indicate a mean width of 0.1 mm at the basal end and 0.5 at the apex, for a variation of about sixfold. By applying principles derived from the basic laws of physics, it can be readily shown that a sixfold variation in length of the transverse fibers will account for only about 20 per cent of the frequency range in normal ears.

A second condition necessary to support the theory of Helmholtz is that the resonators exhibit a certain degree of independence one from the other; that is, the transverse tension ought to be very great with respect to the longitudinal tension. Helmholtz, in examining a basilar membrane from a cadaver, failed to find anatomical support for differential tension in the basilar membrane, and he assumed that the transverse tension present in life was lost in death. Recently Békésy (1941) examined a basilar membrane from a fresh cadaver to determine the ratio between longitudinal and transverse tension. He exposed the apex of the scala tympani by drilling away the bony wall of the otic capsule, and in this manner the tympanic surface of the basilar membrane was revealed. He then very carefully touched the basilar membrane with a thin glass thread. The deformed area was slightly elliptical in form, with the long axis running longitudinally. With absolutely equal tension transversely and longitudinally, the deformed area would be perfectly circular. Békésy found the ratio of longitudinal to transverse axes was very small and never exceeded 1:2. On the basis of the experimental evidence gathered in this manner he concluded that the basilar membrane did not demonstrate the physical properties one would expect from a membrane under differential tension. A schematic of the impressions produced by exerting pressure on a membrane under equal tension and of the basilar membrane in the region of the apex is shown in Figure 6–60.

Early opposition to the Helmholtz resonance theory was strengthened by Wien in 1905, who pointed out that a highly selective (undamped) resonator will be slow to respond to a driving force and equally slow to decay once the force has ceased to act.

Traveling-wave Theories.   In order to distinguish the rapid changes of frequency and intensity that occur in music and speech, resonators would of necessity have to be highly damped. This dilemma places serious limitations on a resonance theory; as a result, other principles of cochlear action were proposed as a basis for a theory of hearing. A number of nonresonance place theories followed which applied hydro-

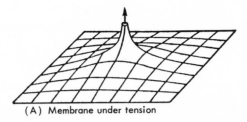

(A) Membrane under tension

Fig. 6–60. Schematic of impressions produced by placing tension on the basilar membrane and on a membrane under even tension. (Courtesy von Békésy.)

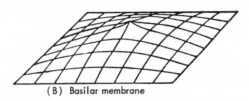

(B) Basilar membrane

dynamic principles to the cochlea. These theories recognized a spatial distribution of basilar-membrane displacement, which is a function of frequency, but they are not dependent upon the existence of resonating elements in the cochlea. That is, the distance the traveling wave progresses along the cochlear partition is a function of the frequency or rate of vibration and not of the resonance characteristics of the basilar membrane. In the nonresonance theories, as in the resonance theory, however, frequency analysis takes place within the cochlea.

One of the first of the nonresonance place theories was a traveling-wave theory advanced in 1895 by Hurst. Basically the theory proposes that stapes vibration sets up waves within the cochlear fluids and that these waves move up and down the cochlea. Stated very simply, the mechanism is as follows: As shown in Figure 6–61, inward movement of the stapes footplate causes the basilar membrane to be displaced. This displacement, which begins as a bulge at the basal end of the cochlea, moves toward the apex. When the wave reaches the apex, it is reflected, and begins a downward journey. If, however, the stapes begins to move inward before the "round trip" has been completed, two waves moving in opposite directions appear on the basilar membrane. The second wave meets the first wave somewhere along the cochlear partition. Thus, stimulation of the hair cells takes place at the point where the incident (upward-moving) wave meets the reflected (downward-traveling) wave. In the case of low frequencies the initial wave has time to travel up the cochlea, reflect, and travel down toward the basal end before the next wave is initiated. The theory of Hurst, therefore, ascribes low-frequency hearing to the basal end and high-frequency hearing to the apical region. This basic assumption regarding the locus of hearing for various frequencies contradicts recent experimental results, for it has been shown repeatedly that the location for high tones is at the basal end and the location for low tones is at the apical end of the cochlea.

About 1900, Emile ter Kuile advanced a variation of the Hurst theory in which the traveling wave was said to progress toward the apex during inward movement of the stapes and back toward the basal end during outward movement of the stapes. The result, of course, is that just one wave appears on the basilar membrane, with the

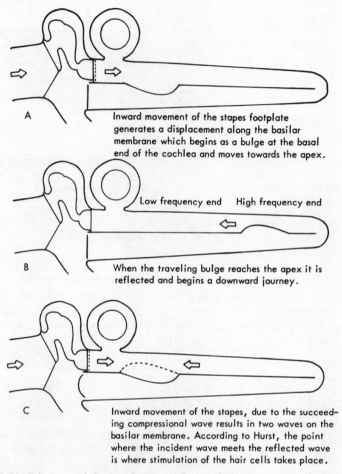

A   Inward movement of the stapes footplate
generates a displacement along the basilar
membrane which begins as a bulge at the basal
end of the cochlea and moves towards the apex.

Low frequency end   High frequency end

B   When the traveling bulge reaches the apex it is
reflected and begins a downward journey.

C   Inward movement of the stapes, due to the succeeding compressional wave results in two waves on the
basilar membrane. According to Hurst, the point
where the incident wave meets the reflected wave
is where stimulation of the hair cells takes place.

Fig. 6–61. Schematic of the traveling wave theory of Hurst.

position of the wave a function of the period of stapes vibration. As shown in Figure 6–62, inward movement of the stapes generates a bulge on the basilar membrane that immediately begins to travel toward the apex. When inward movement of the stapes has been completed, the propagating disturbance will have traveled one-half wave length along the basilar membrane. As the stapes begins outward movement, the cochlear fluid is sucked back, and erasure of the bulge begins. Erasure is initiated basally, and continues all during outward movement of the stapes. All this while, however, the original bulge had continued on its journey toward the apex. At the instant when outward stapes movement has been completed, one entire cycle of vibration will have occurred. The original bulge will have progressed one full wave length along the basilar membrane, and the erasing action of the second bulge will have just caught up with it. Pitch sensation is determined by the length of the disturbed portion of the basilar membrane, measured from the basal end to the farthest point reached by the original bulge before it was erased. At high rates of vibration the disturbances of the basilar membrane do not have time to get very far along before

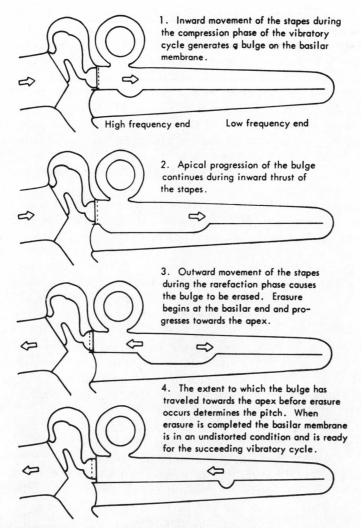

1. Inward movement of the stapes during the compression phase of the vibratory cycle generates a bulge on the basilar membrane.

High frequency end   Low frequency end

2. Apical progression of the bulge continues during inward thrust of the stapes.

3. Outward movement of the stapes during the rarefaction phase causes the bulge to be erased. Erasure begins at the basilar end and progresses towards the apex.

4. The extent to which the bulge has traveled towards the apex before erasure occurs determines the pitch. When erasure is completed the basilar membrane is in an undistorted condition and is ready for the succeeding vibratory cycle.

Fig. 6–62. Schematic of the traveling wave theory of ter Kuile.

outward movement of the stapes begins. At low frequencies, however, the disturbances have more time to progress toward the apex before erasure occurs. The result is that hearing for high frequencies takes place at the basal end and hearing for low frequencies occurs at the apical end. Some basic assumptions regarding fluid movement have not been supported experimentally, and the theory, therefore, has some serious limitations. For example, the erasing bulge generated by outward movement of the stapes has a half period in which to travel the exact same distance that the original disturbance traveled in a full period. Therefore, the speed of the second bulge must somehow be twice that of the original bulge. There is no accounting for this difference.

A number of traveling-wave theories made their appearance toward the end of the nineteenth and beginning of the twentieth centuries. A complete review of them is beyond the scope of this text, and the interested student is urged to refer to Wever

(1949) and Wever and Lawrence (1954). It ought to be pointed out, however, that many of the early traveling-wave theories suffered from a lack of empirical data regarding the physical properties of the cochlea. In 1928, Georg von Békésy embarked on a long series of brilliant experiments, attempting to describe the physical properties of the cochlear partition. He worked at first with ingenious models of the cochlea and later with fresh and preserved human and animal cochleas. In 1961 he was awarded the Nobel prize in medicine in recognition of his important contributions toward furthering an understanding of the physical mechanism of excitation in the cochlea. From his early experiments emerged a theory of hearing that has since gained an important place in the field of physiological acoustics. It is usually classified as a traveling-wave theory, but as we shall see, the term "traveling wave" must be used with some reservation.

In his initial experiments Békésy observed the movements of the "basilar" membrane in an enlarged mechanical model of the cochlea. He discovered that when a rubber membrane was suitably constructed, with appropriate thickness, stiffness, and tension, the model would show a very definite pattern of response, with a locus of maximum disturbance that was dependent upon the frequency of stimulation. In particular he noted that an undulating wave generated at the basal end of the membrane traveled along the membrane, constantly varying in amplitude at any point from moment to moment. The amplitude reached a maximum somewhere along the course of the membrane and then fell sharply to zero, as illustrated in Figure 6–63. Békésy also observed that the locus of maximum disturbance of the membrane systematically varied with the frequency of the driving force, as illustrated schematically in Figure 6–64. High-frequency stimulation resulted in maximum displacement at the narrow or basal end, while low-frequency stimulation produced maximum displacement at the wide or apical end of the membrane.

Békésy also suspended very fine silver particles in the fluid of his cochlear model and by means of microscopic observation under stroboscopic light observed a well-defined eddy current at the locus of maximum membrane response. The eddy also moved toward the basal end for high frequencies and toward the apex for low frequencies, along with the response pattern of the membrane. Békésy believed that these eddies generate a steady pressure on the cochlear partition at the locus of maximum membrane response and that this pressure was the actual stimulation agent for the hair cells. Thus, although large portions of the membrane may be displaced, the actual location of hair-cell stimulation is restricted to the narrow region where the eddy is generated. Békésy proposed that further frequency analysis takes place in the central pathway.

One additional, very important observation ought to be made. Békésy found that rather drastic modifications in the resistance of the cochlear fluids, changes in the dimensions of the fluid columns, or changes in the location of the driving force failed to change the vibratory pattern of the membrane and the location of the eddy current. The crucial factor seems to be the physical properties of the cochlear partition. Thus, it seems that Békésy does not describe a traveling-wave theory. At least the term ought not to be thought of in quite the same context as previous traveling-wave theories. Békésy has noted that in man there is no mechanical frequency discrimination for tones below 24 cps and that the discrimination reaches a peak in the frequency range of from about 300 to 1,000 cps. Complete data are not yet available at frequencies

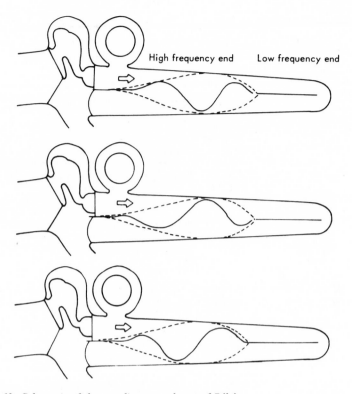

High frequency end   Low frequency end

Fig. 6–63. Schematic of the traveling wave theory of Békésy.

above 1,000 cps, but it seems that with an increase in frequency the region of membrane disturbance moves just so far toward the basal end and then remains there as frequency is increased further.

Several traveling-wave or place theories have been developed subsequent to Békésy's theory. For the most part they are quite compatible with his theory and differ only in certain details. That is, the mass and stiffness of the basilar membrane (or cochlear partition), plus the friction of the fluid columns, determine the speed of propagation of sound through the cochlea and the pattern of basilar-membrane displacement. Among the most recent traveling-wave theories are those of Zwislocki (1946), DeRosa (1947), Peterson and Bogert (1950), Huggins (1950), and Fletcher (1951). The interested reader is referred to the original presentations of these theories and also to Wever and Lawrence (1954) for a brief review and an evaluation of these and other traveling-wave theories.

Frequency theories

Nonanalytic Theory.   The frequency theories do not endow the cochlea with any sort of analytic function as do the place theories. Rather, they suppose the ear mechanism to be a transducer, which transforms the mechanical or vibratory energy into coded patterns of neural impulses, which are then conveyed by the acoustic nerve to the brain where discrimination and analysis occur. The pattern of impulses,

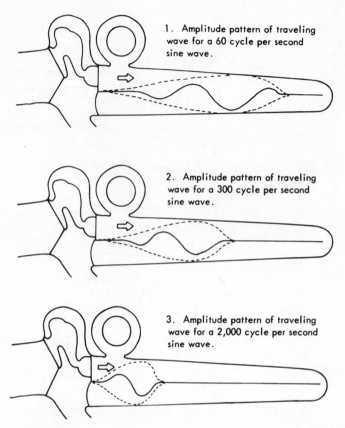

1. Amplitude pattern of traveling wave for a 60 cycle per second sine wave.

2. Amplitude pattern of traveling wave for a 300 cycle per second sine wave.

3. Amplitude pattern of traveling wave for a 2,000 cycle per second sine wave.

Fig. 6–64. Schematic of amplitude patterns of traveling waves for various frequencies of sine waves.

of course, corresponds to the pattern of the original sound. Such a system so closely resembles the theoretical basis for the telephone that the frequency theories are sometimes called the telephone theories. Although the first frequency or telephone theory was outlined in 1865 by Rinne, the telephone theory of Rutherford, advanced in 1886, has received the most publicity. This theory, as do some earlier frequency theories, supposes that any hair cell may be stimulated anywhere along the basilar membrane by sound of any frequency or complexity. The stimulated hair cells initiate a series of nerve impulses with parameters somehow analogous to those of the sound energy. Although Rutherford realized his theory was very demanding of the auditory-nerve fibers, he did not regard a firing rate of up to 15,000 impulses per second beyond the limits of any single nerve fiber or hair cell. Rutherford did not attribute pitch and quality analysis to the ear but rather to the brain. This capacity to discriminate, he said, is something that must be acquired through training. Interestingly enough, Rutherford admitted that a very gross place mechanism may also take place and, in fact, suggested that his theory and the place theories may be compatible. Numerous theories have followed Rutherford's, all of which are characterized by the telephone principle. They are all limited by the severe demands they place upon the individual fibers in the nervous system.

Extensive research on the frequency of discharge of single nerve fibers has revealed maximum firing rates that range from 24 to 1,000 impulses per second. In 1926 Adrian and Zotterman, among the first to conduct and report such experiments, obtained maximum discharge rates of 190 impulses per second on a frog muscle. Since that time many similar experiments have been conducted on animal tissues of various types, and the maximum rate has been, with few exceptions, something below 300 impulses per second, when stimulation was continuous. For brief intervals, the maximum discharge rate may exceed 1,000 impulses per second. The evidence, however, fails to support a strict single-fiber theory such as Rutherford's and necessitates a modification of the telephone theory.

Analytic Theory.   In an early study of auditory-nerve responses, Wever and Bray (1930) observed auditory-nerve discharges that were synchronous with auditory stimulation to a frequency as high as 4,000–5,000 per second. In subsequent studies, Davis, Derbyshire, and Lurie (1934) and Derbyshire and Davis (1935) noted synchronization up to 4,000 per second. The results also indicated that the synchronization does not abruptly cease at a specific frequency but, rather, gradually gives way to asynchronous nerve discharges to as high as 15,000 per second. The fact that synchronous nerve discharges failed to reach the upper limits of hearing led Wever and Bray to reject the simple telephone theory. They felt that the frequency of nerve discharges could not represent pitch throughout the entire hearing range from 20 to 20,000 cps. As a result, the telephone theory was modified to include certain features of both the telephone and place theories. One development was the volley principle, which states that when frequency limits are reached for any single nerve fiber, an additional nerve cell and its fibers may come into play. These two nerve cells, discharging alternately, double the response rate of the auditory system. If the frequency increases beyond the limits of the two fibers, three, four, or more nerve cells begin firing, thus raising the frequency limit three- or fourfold. This alternate firing of individual nerves has come to be known as the volley principle, and a full account of it may be found in Wever (1949). The volley principle is illustrated schematically in Figure 6–65.

Wever notes that when first developed, the place and frequency theories were exclusive and vigorously opposed conceptions of the action of the inner ear. In the volley theory the two traditional conceptions are combined and compromised so that the contributing virtues of each are retained and fused into a single harmonious theory of hearing. Pitch analysis, for example, is dependent upon the place of disturbance on the basilar membrane and on the composite nerve-impulse frequencies. The place and frequency theories are assigned various roles according to tonal region. Frequency serves for the low tones, place for the high ones, and both perform in the transition region between them. This assignment is based on the experimental evidence that sound-nerve discharge rate is synchronous for the low and intermediate frequencies but fails at the high-frequency rates. On the other hand, place representation seems to hold for high frequencies but because of spread of response fails for the lows. Wever notes that the boundaries of the place and frequency regions gradually blend into one another. He suggests that the frequency principle holds for a tonal range of from 15 to 400 cps, both frequency and place operate in the middle range of from 400 to 5,000 cps, and place alone functions in the high-tone range.

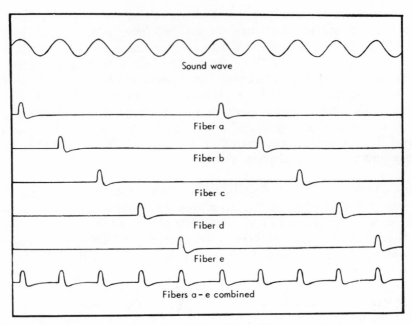

Fig. 6–65. Illustration of the volley principle. (From Wever, Theory of Hearing.)

Loudness, according to this theory, is dependent upon two factors: the spatial extent of basilar-membrane displacement and the number of active fibers. Intensity representation in the volley principle is illustrated schematically in Figure 6–66. Wever suggests that at low-intensity stimulation, only in a central region of the displaced basilar membrane is sensory action strong enough to excite nerve fibers, but as intensity is raised, adjacent nerve fibers previously inactive are brought into play. Stimulus intensity is represented by the number of active nerve fibers and by the rates at which they act. Thus, the message that is sent off to the brain consists of a sequence of electrical impulses, which together form some kind of representation of the vibrating motions of the basilar membrane. According to the volley theory, the representation is best for the low-frequency sounds where a number of neurons convey pitch information and is comparatively poor for the high frequencies where the neurons can supply only a "sketch" of the pitch information. This is probably not a particularly serious shortcoming, however, for as mentioned earlier, neurons leading from the basilar membrane retain their frequency identity in the auditory nerve, the cochlear nuclei, and, in fact, to the level of the cerebral cortex. The volley or place-frequency theory has been well received, and in recent years has gained a prominent position in physiological acoustics.

A form of frequency theory, called the frequency analytic or hydraulic theory, was advanced by Meyer in 1899. This theory, although it rejects the resonance principle essential to Helmholtz's theory, does assign frequency analysis to the cochlea. Meyer supposed that the displaced basilar membrane functioned to equalize pressures in the scala tympani and scala vestibuli. Certain unique characteristics of the basilar membrane cause the locus of the displacement to be a function of the frequency of stapes

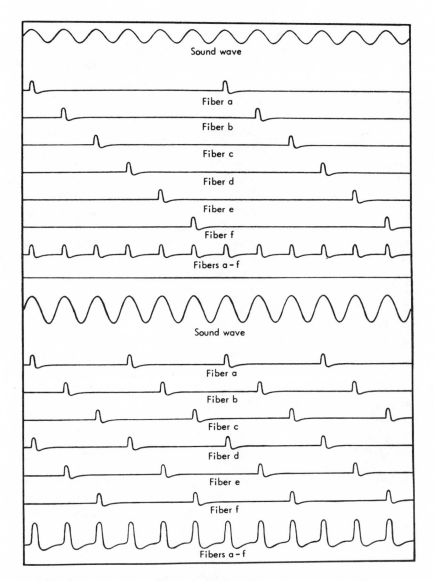

Fig. 6–66. *Schematic of intensity representation in the volley principle.* (*From Wever,* Theory of Hearing.)

vibration. This theory, which might be thought of as a hybrid traveling-wave theory, described the basilar membrane as completely damped and responsive only to positive pressures. It possesses no elasticity.

Very simply, the hydraulic theory states that inward movement of the stapes generates a positive pressure in the cochlea, which produces a bulge on the basilar membrane. Bulging continues until the limits of response of the basilar membrane at the basal end are reached. The bulge then continues to spread toward the apex until enough room has been created to accommodate the amount of cochlear fluid displaced by the stapes. Outward movement of the stapes generates a second displacement in the negative direction, and the basilar membrane is drawn upward. The second displacement begins at the basilar end of the membrane and spreads toward the apex. In the case of a sine wave, the amplitude of inward and outward movement is exactly the same, and the first bulge is "erased." Pitch sensation is dependent upon the extent of the spread of the bulge. It is important to note that the spread of the bulge on the membrane is brought about by the forces produced by cochlear fluids and not by a wave motion of the membrane. This theory is a good deal more complex than most, and the reader is referred to Wever (1949). The theory is presented in its entirety by Meyer (1950).

The development of improved research techniques and instrumentation during the past decade has resulted in a great deal of light being shed upon the physiology of the inner ear. Electron microscopy, for example, has proved to be a very rewarding avenue for research on the cytoarchitecture of the organ of Corti (Engstrom, *et al.*, 1962; Smith and Sjöstrand, 1961). New methods of specimen preparation have also facilitated research on the inner ear. In addition, the development of electronic instrumentation and data-treatment devices such as digital counters and computers has provided new approaches to the study of neurophysiology. On the basis of the accumulated research to date, it seems reasonable to assume that the pressure patterns of air-borne sound are transmitted rather faithfully by the middle-ear mechanism to the cochlea. Although no single theory of hearing seems to quite fill the bill, a place theory like Békésy's, together with a volley principle like Wever's, provides a satisfactory hypothetical construct upon which to base a concept of the way in which the peripheral hearing mechanism functions. Also, it seems quite probable that cochlear analysis, provided by a place-volley theory, combined with cortical analysis is an important factor in the hearing mechanism. The exact way in which vertical displacement of the basilar membrane produces stimulation of the hair cells has been a subject of research for quite some time. What seems to be a very adequate explanation has been given by Békésy (1960).

The pivot points for the tectorial and basilar membranes are shown in Figure 6–67. Because the membranes are hinged at different points, equal vertical displacement of the tectorial and basilar membranes results in a shearing force, the magnitude of which is considerably greater than the vertical force that produces the vertical displacement. In this way, minute pressure on the basilar membrane is transformed into a shearing force many times greater. As shown in Figure 6–68, the shearing force causes lateral distortion of the hair cells that initiate the nerve impulses. Thus, the inner ear provides a certain amount of mechanical gain, which increases the sensitivity of the hearing mechanism.

Neurophysiology of the cochlea

Up to this point we have been regarding the ear as a mechanical system. We turn now to a brief consideration of its behavior as a transducer, capable of converting acoustic or mechanical energy into nerve impulses. The discussion here will be rather limited in scope, and the interested reader is referred to Davis (1960; 1962) for a more comprehensive discussion of the excitatory process in the cochlea.

It has long been recognized that all living cells exhibit certain measurable electrical

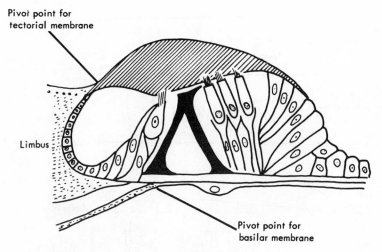

Fig. 6–67. Schematic of organ of Corti showing pivot points for the tectorial and basilar membranes.

properties. Biochemists have repeatedly demonstrated that cells and intercellular fluids contain electrolytes capable of conducting electricity. In order to account for the electrophysiological properties of cells a membrane theory is commonly used. It states that a cell is surrounded by a semipermeable membrane separating a double layer of ions, the positive ions outside and the negative ions inside. In a condition of rest the positive and negative charges are stable, and as a result a small electrical potential difference exists between the inside of a cell and its surrounding fluids. This potential usually amounts to about 70 millivolts. When a cell is disturbed or injured (by insertion of an electrode, for example), the membrane breaks down, a rapid exchange of ions takes place, and the surface of the cell becomes depolarized; that is, its electrical charge changes. Presumably, this rapid flow of minute quantities of electrical energy serves as the initiator of the nerve impulse. Immediately after depolarization the ionic cell membrane begins to restore itself to normal and in just a few milliseconds is capable of another depolarization or firing. In the cochlea, a shearing force, acting on the cilia of the hair cells, is thought to be the agent responsible for an initial disturbance of the cell membrane and the resultant depolarization.

With the development of suitable electrodes, surgical techniques, and electronic instrumentation, many of the electrical or bioelectrical properties of the inner ear can be measured. In 1930, Wever and Bray placed an electrode in the auditory nerve of an experimental animal and detected an electrical potential that accurately reproduced the frequency and wave form of the sound stimulus. When the electrical energy was amplified and channeled into a telephone receiver, Wever and Bray found that speech was reproduced with remarkable fidelity. Initially they suspected that the electrical activity represented the nerve impulses in the auditory nerve, but subsequent experiments by Wever and Bray, Adrian (1931), and others soon demonstrated that the same electrical activity could be detected by placing an electrode in the vicinity of the cochlea and that a lead from the auditory nerve was unnecessary. Adrian (1931)

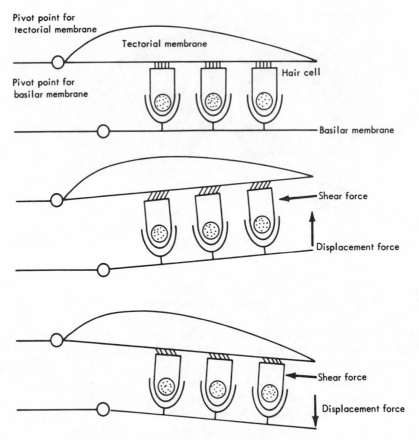

Fig. 6–68. Schematic illustration of how vertical displacement of the basilar and tectorial membranes produces a shearing force on the cilia of the hair cells.

suggested that the cochlea was acting like a biological microphone, and the electric energy produced was not to be confused with the nerve action potentials of the auditory nerve.

The microphonics of the cochlea seem to be generated by the hair cells or at least seem to be dependent upon the presence of healthy hair cells. Several reasons have been offered in support of this viewpoint. For example, microphonics continue to be produced after the acoustic nerve has been severed, and may persist even though the spiral ganglion cells degenerate. They disappear, however, when the outer hair cells are destroyed by toxic agents such as streptomycin (Davis, Deatherage, Rosenblüt, Fernandez, Kimura, and Smith 1958). Also, certain species of animals with a congenital absence of hair cells lack the microphonics present in animals with apparently healthy inner ears. Talley (1965) found that a particular breed of Dalmatian which appeared to be behaviorally deaf consistently lacked the characteristic cochlear microphonics present in his control animals. Microscopic examination of serial cochlear sections revealed a complete absence of the normal structures in the organ

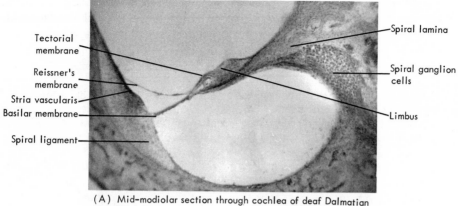

Tectorial membrane

Reissner's membrane

Stria vascularis

Basilar membrane

Spiral ligament

Spiral lamina

Spiral ganglion cells

Limbus

(A) Mid-modiolar section through cochlea of deaf Dalmatian

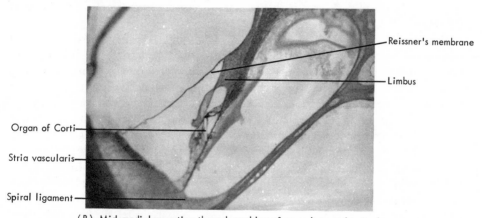

Reissner's membrane

Limbus

Organ of Corti

Stria vascularis

Spiral ligament

(B) Mid-modiolar section through cochlea of normal control animal

Fig. 6–69. *Photomicrographs of normal and abnormal dog cochleas.*

of Corti and, in particular, the hair cells and supportive structures. A mid-modiolar section through a Dalmatian cochlea is shown in Figure 6–69A, and a comparable section through the cochlea of a control animal is shown in B.

The amplitude of the cochlear microphonics is proportional to that of the stimulating signal up to the limit where further intensity might prove damaging. In addition, there is no real threshold, its determination being limited by the measuring instrumentation. Also, the microphonics demonstrate no adaptation to the stimulating signal, no fatigue, and seemingly no frequency limits, within reasonable limits. Cochlear microphonics, however, are highly dependent upon blood supply to the inner ear. When blood flow is interrupted, they decline rapidly in amplitude to a value approximately 10 per cent that of the original amplitude, where they remain for several hours after blood deprivation or death. The high-amplitude (oxygen-dependent) microphonics are designated CM-1, and the "oxygen-independent" microphonics are called CM-2.

The role of microphonics in hearing has been a subject of speculation and research ever since their discovery. At one time it was thought that they served to stimulate the terminal endings of the auditory nerve, but because the microphonics have no latency as opposed to a latency of about 0.5 milliseconds for nerve impulses, this interpretation seems highly unlikely. Stevens and Davis (1938) point out that it is not essential to assume that microphonics have any real functional significance:

> They are possibly an incidental by-product of the auditory process, an epiphenomenon, like the noise of an automobile—but, just as the noise may help us in determining whether or not an engine is running properly, so may the cochlear microphonics serve us in analyzing normal and abnormal functions in the inner ear.

Indeed microphonics are useful in determining the functional integrity of the inner ear. The literature on the properties and implications of these potential has grown to awesome proportions. There can be little doubt that the microphonics reflect very closely the mechanical events taking place on the basilar membrane. For this reason they have been used to determine the localization of frequency reception on the basilar membrane.

The experiments generally have taken one of two forms. In one, the ear is stimulated by tones of extreme intensity until the potentials are impaired. Presumably the ear has suffered hair-cell damage at a frequency-related area on the basilar membrane. It is important to note that the impairment in microphonics is not confined to the stimulating frequency but rather is reflected in a general depression of amplitude throughout the frequency range of the ear. Histological examination of the ears, however, reveals some striking findings. The area of cochlear damage has a direct relationship to the stimulating frequency. Ears exposed to low-frequency sounds suffer extensive damage in the apical region, while ears exposed to high-frequency sounds suffer restricted damage in the basal region (Smith and Wever, 1949). These results offer strong support for a place theory, especially for the high-frequency tones, and, since damage from low tones is so diffuse, they also offer strong support for a volley principle.

A second form of experiment involves mapping the cochlea with an electrode, searching for a maximum microphonic response to a tone with a particular frequency. Topographical mapping has been done over the frequency range of from 60 to 7,500 cps. These experiments have led to the formulation of cochlear maps, an example of which is shown in Figure 6–70. Note that high-frequency tones are spread out over the basal region, while the lower frequencies are all crowded into the apical region. Results such as these also seem to be consistent with a place-volley theory of hearing.

Electrical activity, which takes a form quite different from cochlear microphonics, may be recorded from the inner ear and from the nerve pathway. Action potentials from the acoustic nerve may be detected by placing an electrode into individual nerve fibers or on the trunk of the auditory nerve. These potentials have the same properties as action potentials of any other peripheral nerve. For example, they obey the all-or-none principle, described in the following chapter. Experiments have shown repeatedly that the integrated responses of the acoustic nerve demonstrate synchrony with a stimulating frequency as high as 2,000 cps, and quite possibly higher.

Other electrical activity, not fully understood, can also be detected from the inner ear. In 1952, Békésy reported that a direct current potential of about 80 millivolts exists between the scala media and the scala vestibuli or scala tympani. This voltage,

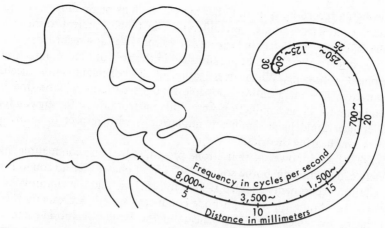

Fig. 6–70. Frequency location along the basilar membrane.

which seems to come from the stria vascularis, is confined to the endolymphatic space of the cochlea, and is absent in the utricle, saccule, and semicircular canals. Both Békésy (1952) and Davis (1957) have suggested that this DC resting potential serves to sensitize the hair cells of the cochlea. This potential, like the action potential and CM-1, is dependent upon oxygen supply and, when the blood supply to the cochlea is cut off, drops rapidly to zero, or may actually become negative for a while before returning to zero. When the ear is stimulated with sound, the DC resting potential seems to change in a manner proportional to the intensity of the stimulus. The source of this changing potential, which is known as the summating potential, is not known, but it may arise from the same mechanism that gives rise to cochlear microphonics. It does not seem to be a change in the status of the endolymphatic potential, however, but rather is apparently a separate electrical phenomenon that can be detected within the endolymphatic space.

Bone conduction

So far we have been discussing what is referred to as hearing by air conduction. Another avenue by which we hear sounds is bone conduction. Whenever there is direct physical contact between the skull and a vibrating body or when air-borne sounds are intense enough, the vibratory energy produces compressions in the skull bones and, as a consequence, disturbances in the ossicular chain and the inner ear. The importance of hearing by bone conduction is often overlooked. Bone-conducted sound, for example, provides us with an important feedback channel by which we are able to monitor our own voices. We are provided with at least two feedback channels, the system already described (air conduction) and bone conduction. Both the air- and bone-conducted feedback stimulates our own ears when we speak, but only the air-borne sound stimulates the ears of our auditors. This fact partially explains why a person is often so shocked when he hears a recording of his own voice for the first time. The recording apparatus or other auditor hears only the air-borne sounds, and since some low-frequency components produced by the larynx do not become air-borne, we hear our own voices as much more powerful and "full" sounding than appears through a recording system. Other factors, such as phase differences between air- and bone-conducted sounds, and differences in time of arrival to the ear, help augment the differences we detect in hearing our voices "live" and recorded.

Probably as much research has been published in the area of bone conduction as in any other phase of hearing. When investigation of the bone-conduction mechanism was first initiated, it seemed entirely possible that the patterns of vibration on the basilar membrane for bone conduction were different from those for air conduction. Such a difference would have significant implications with respect to resolving the controversies over hearing theories.

Békésy (1932) found, however, that a tone presented by bone conduction could be so completely canceled by air-borne sound, 180° out of phase, that no sound is heard. Such cancellation experiments enabled Békésy to conclude that the vibratory patterns on the basilar membrane for air- and bone-conducted sounds are exactly the same. The mechanisms by which the disturbances on the basilar membrane are caused are quite different, however. The results of extensive research in bone conduction suggest at least three avenues by which bone-conducted sounds result in basilar-membrance displacement. The first of these avenues is called labyrinthine bone conduction.

If a vibrating body is brought into contact with the skull, the bones undergo various types of vibration patterns, depending upon the frequency of the vibration. As shown in Figure 6-71, for low frequencies the skull vibrates as a rigid body; that is, the entire skull moves back and forth as a single unit. At about 800 cps, however, the mode of vibration undergoes a pronounced change. The forehead moves anteriorly, and the back of the head moves posteriorly, with a node occurring at the mid-point. The skull is said to be resonating at this frequency. At about 1,500 cps, the skull executes an entirely different form of vibration. It vibrates segmentally, a pattern not unlike the vibratory pattern of a bell. These displacements of the skull cause compressions of the fluid within the membranous labyrinth.

Rejto (1914) and Herzog (1930), in independent works, pointed out that if the elastic characteristics were equal above and below the basilar membrane, the pressures in

Fig. 6-71. *Illustration of the modes of vibration of the skull bones at various frequencies. (Courtesy von Békésy.)*

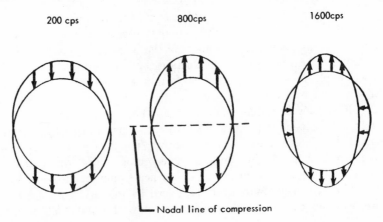

200 cps   800cps   1600cps

Nodal line of compression

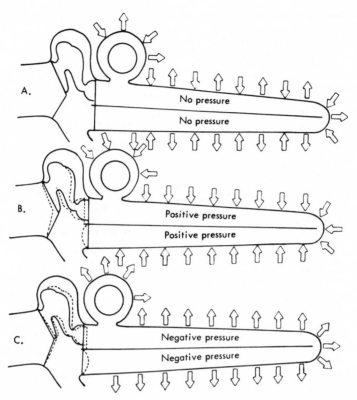

Fig. 6–72. Schematic of cochlea illustrating absence of basilar membrane displacement when the elastic characteristics of the cochlear scalae are equal.

the scala vestibuli and scala tympani would be exactly the same. As a consequence, the oval and round windows would be distended by equal amounts, and the basilar membrane would not be deformed. This is illustrated in Figure 6–72. In A the cochlear fluids are in equilibrium, the positive and negative pressures are the same, and no force is brought to bear upon the cochlear partition. In B positive pressure causes pressure within the cochlear scalae, but because the elasticity of the oval and round windows is the same, the basilar membrane is not subjected to differential pressures. In C, negative pressure decreases the pressure in the cochlear scalae, but because of equal elasticity of the oval and round windows, the basilar membrane is not deformed. If the conditions in Figure 6–72 should actually exist we would hear no sound at all. Occasionally such a condition arises. Abnormal bone growths that occlude both the oval and round windows (advanced otosclerosis) or exudate with or without accompanying pressure changes may hinder movement of both the round-window membrane and the stapes footplate, and although the clinical picture may suggest a sensorineural loss, the problem actually lies in the conduction pathway.

Actually the elasticity in the scala tympani is greater than it is in the scala vestibuli, and compression of the cochlear fluids results in a differential pressure between them. Consequently, the basilar membrane is displaced into the scala tympani when positive

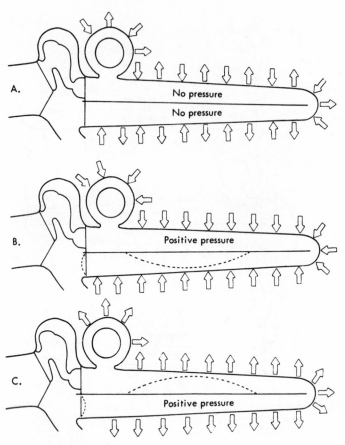

Fig. 6–73. Schematic of cochlea illustrating displacement of the basilar membrane under conditions of greater elastic characteristics in the scala tympani.

pressure is being generated, and it is displaced into the scala vestibuli when negative pressure is being generated. This is illustrated in Figure 6–73. Since the cochlear ducts are continuous with those of the labyrinth, displacement of the skull bones produces compression of the labyrinthine canals as well as the cochlear ducts. This results in additional fluid being forced into the scala vestibuli, with a corresponding increase in basilar-membrane displacement. The additional fluid resulting from labyrinthine compression augments the compression of the cochlear fluids, and the result is heightened activity on the basilar membrane.

You will recall the manner in which the ossicular chain is suspended within the middle-ear cavity. When the temporal bone is set into vibration, the walls of the middle-ear cavity undergo vibratory movement. The inertia of the ossicles prevents them from following the skull vibration; as a consequence, while the middle-ear cavity is moving outward, along with the inner ear, the ossicles remain relatively motionless. Mechanically, of course, the effect is exactly the same as when the temporal bone remains at rest while the ossicular chain moves in. Conversely, when the temporal bone

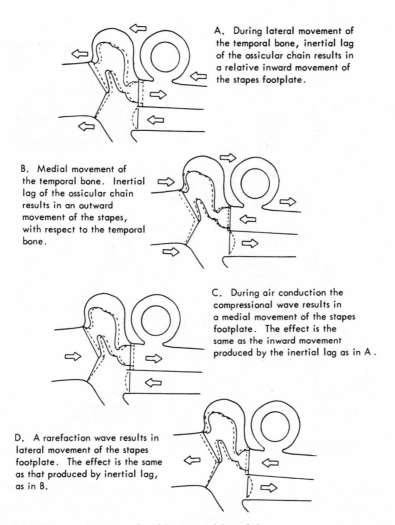

A. During lateral movement of the temporal bone, inertial lag of the ossicular chain results in a relative inward movement of the stapes footplate.

B. Medial movement of the temporal bone. Inertial lag of the ossicular chain results in an outward movement of the stapes, with respect to the temporal bone.

C. During air conduction the compressional wave results in a medial movement of the stapes footplate. The effect is the same as the inward movement produced by the inertial lag as in A.

D. A rarefaction wave results in lateral movement of the stapes footplate. The effect is the same as that produced by inertial lag, as in B.

Fig. 6–74. Bone conduction produced by intertial lag of the ossicular chain.

is moving medially, the ossicles, by remaining still, exert a force in the opposite direction or outward. This inertial effect augments the compression that takes place within the cochlear scale. Bone conduction due to inertial lag of the ossicular chain is illustrated in Figure 6–74.

A third route by which bone-conducted sounds may be heard results from the nature of the temporomandibular joint, shown schematically in Figure 6–75. If a finger is inserted into the auditory meatus while the mandible is being moved, slight displacements in the ear canal may be felt. When the bones of the skull are driven by a vibrator, the lower jaw does not follow exactly, but lags behind. It may be said that the mandibular condyle is vibrating at the same frequency as, but out of phase with, the remainder of the skull bones. This results in displacements, at the vibratory rate, of the cartilaginous skeleton of the auditory meatus. Such displacements cause air-

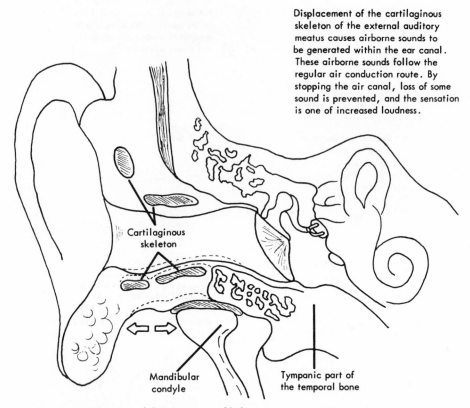

Displacement of the cartilaginous skeleton of the external auditory meatus causes airborne sounds to be generated within the ear canal. These airborne sounds follow the regular air conduction route. By stopping the air canal, loss of some sound is prevented, and the sensation is one of increased loudness.

Cartilaginous skeleton

Mandibular condyle

Tympanic part of the temporal bone

Fig. 6–75. Schematic of the temporomandibular joint.

borne sounds to be generated within the ear canal. These sounds follow the conventional air-conduction route. By stopping the ear canal, there arise variations in air pressure that act upon the drum membrane, and the sensation is one of increased loudness. This is easily demonstrated. Simply hum a tone while alternately opening and closing off the external meatus. Note the increase and decrease in the loudness sensation. This is known as the occlusion effect, first described by Wheatstone in 1827; it forms part of the basis for the Weber test in clinical audiometry. It is important to note, however, that the occlusion effect is confined to frequencies below about 2,000 cps.

This introduction to hearing by no means completes the picture. Hopefully, it has provided the student with sufficient background information to permit him to pursue some of the important behavioral aspects of hearing that belong to the domain of psychoacoustics. They include threshold detection, pitch, loudness, and speech discrimination, masking and distortion effects, and spatial localization. Hopefully too, the contents of this chapter will have served to sharpen the reader's appetite and to send him in full pursuit of some of his own prodding questions about the amazing mechanism we call simply, the ear.

SELECTIVE READING LIST

Adrian, E. D., "The Microphonic Action of the Cochlea: An Interpretation of Wever and Bray's Experiments," *Journal of Physiology*, LXXI, 1931, 28–30.

—— and Y. Zotterman, "The Impulses Produced by Sensory Nerve Endings; Part 2, The Response of a Single End-organ," *Journal of Physiology*, LXI, 1926, 151–71.

——, "The Impulses Produced by Sensory Nerve Endings; Part 3, Impulses Set up by Touch and Pressure," *Journal of Physiology*, LXI, 1926, 465–83.

Békésy, G. von, "Zur Theorie des Hörens. Die Schwingungsform der Basilarmembran," *Physik. Zeitschrift*, XXIX, 1928, 793–810.

——, "Zur Theorie des Hörens. Über die eben merkbare Amplituden-und-Frequenzänderung eines Tones. Die Theorie der Schwebungen," *Physik. Zeitschrift*, XXX, 1929, 721–45.

——, "Zur Theorie des Hörens bei der Schallaufnahme durch Knochenleitung," *Annalen Physik*, XIII, 1932, 111–36.

——, "Physikalische Probleme der Hörphysiologie," *Elektr. Nachr. Techn.*, XII, 1935, 71–83.

——, "Zur Physik des Mittelohres und über das Hören bei fehlerhaftem Trommelfell," *Akustik. Zeitschrift*, I, 1936, 13–23.

——, "Über die Messung der Schwingungsamplitude der Gehörknöchelchen mittels einer kapizitiven Sonde," *Akustik. Zeitschrift*, VI, 1941, 1–16.

——, "Über die Elastizität der Schneckentrennwand des Ohres," *Akustik. Zeitschrift*, 6, 1941, 265–78. Also, "On the Elasticity of the Cochlear Partition," *Journal of the Acoustical Society of America*, XX, 1948, 227–41.

——, "Über die Frequenzauflösung in der Menschlichen Schnecke," *Acta Otolaryngologica*, XXXII, 1944, 60–84.

——, "Vibration of the Head in a Sound Field, and its Role in Hearing by Bone Conduction," *Journal of the Acoustical Society of America*, XX, 1948, 749–60.

——, "The Vibration of the Cochlear Partition in Anatomical Preparations and in Models of the Inner Ear," *Journal of the Acoustical Society of America*, XXI, 1949, 233–45.

——, "Microphonics Produced by Touching the Cochlear Partition with a Vibrating Electrode," *Journal of the Acoustical Society of America*, XXIII, 1951, 29–35. (a)

——, "DC Potentials and Energy Balance of the Cochlear Partition," *Journal of the Acoustical Society of America*, XXIII, 1951, 578–82. (b)

——, "Cross Localization of the Place of Origin of the Cochlear Microphonics," *Journal of the Acoustical Society of America*, XXIV, 1952, 399–409.

——, *Experiments in Hearing*. New York: McGraw-Hill Book Company, 1960.

—— and W. A. Rosenblith, "The Mechanical Properties of the Ear," in *Handbook of Experimental Psychology*, ed. S. S. Stevens. New York: John Wiley & Sons, Inc., 1958.

Dahmann, H., "Zur Physiologie des Hörens: experimentelle Untersuchungen über die Mechanik der Gehörknochelchenkette, sowie über deren Verhalten auf Ton und Luftdruck," *Zeitschrift für Hals-Nasen-Ohrenheilkunde*, XXIV, 1929, 462–97; and XXVII, 1930, 329–68.

Davis, H., "The Electrical Phenomena of the Cochlea and the Auditory Nerve," *Journal of the Acoustical Society of America*, VI, 1935, 205–15.

——, "Biophysics and Physiology of the Inner Ear," *Physiology Review*, XXXVII, 1957, 1–49.

——, "Mechanism of Excitation of Auditory Nerve Impulses," in *Neural Mechanisms of the Auditory and Vestibular Systems*, ed. G. L. Rasmussen and W. Windle. Springfield, Illinois, Charles C. Thomas, 1960.

——, "Advances in the Neurophysiology and Neuroanatomy of the Cochlea," *Journal of the Acoustical Society of America*, XXXIV, 1962, 1377–85.

————, B. H. Deatherage, B. Rosenblut, C. Fernandez, R. Kimura, and C. A. Smith, "Modification of Cochlear Potentials Produced by Streptomycine Poisoning and by Extensive Venous Obstruction," *Laryngoscope*, LXVIII, 1958, 596–627.

————, A. J. Derbyshire, E. H. Kemp, M. H. Lurie, and M. Upton, "Functional and Histological Changes in the Cochlea of the Guinea Pig Resulting from Prolonged Stimulation," *Journal of General Psychology*, XII, 1935, 251–78.

———— and M. H. Lurie, "A Modification of Auditory Theory," *Archives of Otolaryngology*, XX, 1934, 390–95.

———— and L. J. Saul, "The Electric Response of the Cochlea," *American Journal of Physiology*, CVII, 1934, 311–32.

Derbyshire, A. J. and H. Davis, "The Probable Mechanism for Stimulation of the Auditory Nerve by the Organ of Corti," *American Journal of Physiology*, CXIII, 1935, 35.

————, "The Action Potentials of the Auditory Nerve," *American Journal of Physiology*, CXIII, 1935, 476–504.

DeRossa, L. A., "A Theory as to Function of the Scala Tympani in Hearing," *Journal of the Acoustical Society of America*, XIX, 1947, 623–28.

Engstrom, H., H. Ades, and J. Hawkins, "Structure and Functions of the Sensory Hairs of the Inner Ear," *Journal of the Acoustical Society of America*, XXXIV, 1962, 1356–63.

Fleming, N., "Resonance in the External Auditory Meatus," *Nature*, CXLIII, 1939, 642–43.

Fletcher, H., "A Space-time Pattern Theory of Hearing," *Journal of the Acoustical Society of America*, I, 1930, 311–43.

————, "On the Dynamics of the Cochlea," *Journal of the Acoustical Society of America*, XXIII, 1951, 637–45.

————, "The Dynamics of the Middle Ear and its Relation to the Acuity of Hearing," *Journal of the Acoustical Society of America*, XXIV, 1952, 129–31.

————, *Speech and Hearing in Communication*. New York: D. Van Nostrand Co., Inc., 1953.

Flock, A., R. Kimura, P. G. Lundquist, and J. Wersäll, "Morphological Basis of Directional Sensitivity of the Outer Hair Cells in the Organ of Corti," *Journal of the Acoustical Society of America*, Supplement XXXIV, 1962, 1351.

Galambos, R., "Neural Mechanisms of Audition," *Physiological Review*, XXXIV, 1954, 497–528.

————, "Some Recent Experiments on the Neurophysiology of Hearing," *Annals of Otology, Rhinology, and Laryngology*, LXV, 1956, 1053–59.

————, "Suppression of Auditory Nerve Activity by Stimulation of Fibers to the Cochlea," *Journal of Neurophysiology*, XIX, 1956, 424–37.

————, "Neural Mechanisms in Audition," *Laryngoscope*, LXVIII, 1958, 388–401.

———— and H. Davis, "The Response of Single Auditory-nerve Fibers to Acoustic Stimulation," *Journal of Neurophysiology*, VI, 1943, 39–57.

————, "Action Potentials from Single Auditory-nerve Fibers?" *Science*, CVIII, 1948, 513.

Guild, S. R., "The Width of the Basilar Membrane," *Science*, LXV, 1927, 67–69.

————, S. J. Crowe, C. C. Bunch, and L. M. Polvogt, "Correlations of Differences in the Density of Innervation of the Organ of Corti with Differences in the Acuity of Hearing," *Acta Oto-laryngologica*, XV, 1931, 269–308.

Helmholtz, H. von, "Die Mechanik der Gehörknöchelchen und des Trommelfells," *Pflügers Archiv für die geschichte Physiologie*, I, 1868, 1–60.

————, *Die Lehre von den Tonempfindungen als physiologische Grundlage für die Theorie der Musik* 4th ed. 1877, trans., *On the Sensations of Tone*, 2nd English ed. A. J. Ellis. New York: David McKay Co., Inc., 1912.

Hensen, V., "Zur Morphologie der Schnecke des Menchen und der Saugetheire," *Zeitschrift für wissenschaftliche Zoologie*, XIII, 1863, 481–512.

————, "Beobachtungen über die Thätigkeit des Trommellspanners bei Hund und Katze," *Archiv. fur Physiologie*, II, 1878, 312–19.

Herzog, H., "Die Mechanik der Knochenleitung im Modellversuch," *Zeitschrift für Hals-Nasen-und-Ohrenheilkunde*, XXVII, 1930, 402–8.

Huggins, W. H., "Theory of Cochlear Frequency Discrimination," *Quarterly Progress Report. Research Laboratory of Electronics, Massachusetts Institute of Technology*, Oct. 1950, 54–59.

—— and J. C. R. Licklider, "Place Mechanisms of Auditory Frequency Analysis," *Journal of the Acoustical Society of America*, XXIII, 1951, 290–99.

Hurst, C. H., "A New Theory of Hearing," *Transactions of the Liverpool Biological Society*, IX, 1895, 321–53.

Jepsen, O., "Middle-ear Muscle Reflexes in Man," in *Modern Developments in Audiology*, ed. J. Jerger. New York: Academic Press, 1963.

Kato, T., "Zur Physiologie der Binnenmuskeln des Ohres," *Pflügers Archiv für die geschichte Physiologie*, CL, 1913, 569–625.

Keith, A., "An Appendix on the Structures Concerned in the Mechanism of Hearing, in Wrightson, Sir T. and A. Keith," *An Enquiry Into the Analytical Mechanism of the Internal Ear*. London: MacMillan & Co., 1918.

Kobrak, H. B., "Zur Physiologie der Binnenmuskeln des Ohres I. (Untersuchungen zur Mechanik der Schalleitungskette) *Beitr. Anat., etc., Ohr.*, XXIX, 1932, 383–416.

——, "Zur Physiologie der Binnenmuskeln des Ohres II," *Beitr. Anat., etc., Ohr.*, XXIX, 1932, 383–416.

Kuile, E. ter, "Die Ubertragung der Energie von der Grundmembran auf die Horzellen," *Archiv für Physiologie*, LXXIX, 1900, 146–57.

——, "Die richtige Bewegungsform der membrana basilaris," *Archiv für Physiologie*, LXXIX, 1900, 484–509.

Lederer, F. L. and A. R. Hollender, *Textbook of Ear, Nose, and Throat*. Philadelphia: F. A. Davis Company, 1942.

Lempert, J., E. G. Wever, M. Lawrence, and P. E. Meltzer, "Perilymph: Its Relation to the Improvement of Hearing Which Follows Fenestration of the Vestibular Labyrinth in Clinical Otosclerosis," *Archives of Otolaryngology*, L, 1949, 377–87.

Lorente de Nó, R., "The Sensory Endings in the Cochlea," *Laryngoscope*, XLVII, 1937, 373–77.

Luscher, E., "Die Funktion des Musculus stapedius beim Menschen," *Zeitschrift für Hals-Nasen-und-Ohrenheilkunde*, XXIII, 1929, 105–32.

Metz, O., "The Acoustic Impedance Measured on Normal and Pathological Ears," *Acta Otolaryngologica, Supplement* LXIII, 1946.

Meyer, M., "Zur Theorie des Hörens," *Pflügers Archiv für die geschichte Physiologie*, LXXVIII, 1899, 346–62.

——, "The Hydraulic Principles Governing the Function of the Cochlea," *Journal of General Psychology*, I, 1928, 239–65.

Ohm, G. S., "Über die Definition des Tones, nebst daran geknupfter Theorie der Sirene und ahnlicker tonbildener Vorrichtungen," *Annalen der Physik*, LIX, 1843, 497–565.

Perlman, H. B. and T. J. Case, "Latent Period of the Crossed Stapedius Reflex in Man," *Annals of Otology, Rhinology, and Laryngology*, XLVIII, 1939, 663–75.

Peterson, L. C. and B. P. Bogert, "A Dynamical Theory of the Cochlea," *Journal of the Acoustical Society of America*, XXII, 1950, 369–81.

Pollak, J., "Über die Function des Musculus tensor tympani," *Medizinisch Jahrbuch*, LXXXII, 1886, 555–82.

Rasmussen, A. T., "Studies on the VIIIth Cranial Nerve of Man. *Laryngoscope*, L, 1940, 67–83.

Rasmussen, G. L., "The Olivary Peduncle and Other Fiber Projections of the Superior Olivary Complex," *Journal of Comparative Neurology*, LXXXIV, 1946, 141–219.

—— and W. F. Windle, *Neural Mechanisms of the Auditory and Vestibular Systems*. Springfield, Ill.: Charles C. Thomas, Publisher, 1960.

Rejto, A., "Beitrage zur physiologie der Knochenleitung," *Verhandlungen der Deutschen Otologische Gesellschaft*, XXIII, 1914, 268–85.

Retzius, G., "Die Endigungsweise des Gehörnerven," *Biol. Untersuchung*, V, 1893, 35–38.

———, "Weiteres über die Endigungsweise des Gehörnerven," *Biol. Untersuchung*, V, 1893, 35–38.

———, *Das Gehörorgan der Wirbeltheire, eine Morphologisch-histologische Studien*. Stockholm: Samson & Wallin, 1905.

Rutherford, Wm., "A New Theory of Hearing," *Journal of Anatomy and Physiology*, XXI, 1886, 166–68.

Simpkins, C. S., "Functional Anatomy of the Eustachian Tube," *Archives of Otolaryngology*, XXXVIII, 1943, 478–84.

Smith, C. A., "Electron Microscopic Studies of Cochlear and Vestibular Receptors," *Anatomical Record*, CXXVII, 1957, 483.

——— and F. S. Sjöstrand, "Structure of the Nerve Endings on the External Hair Cells of the Guinea Pig Cochlea as Studied by Serial Sections," *Journal of Ultrastructure Research*, V, 1961, 523–56.

Smith, K. R. and E. G. Wever, "The Problem of Stimulation Deafness; the Functional and Histological Effects of a High-frequency Stimulus," *Journal of Experimental Psychology*, XLIX, 1949, 238–41.

Stevens, S. S. and H. Davis, *Hearing, Its Psychology and Physiology*. New York: John Wiley & Sons, Inc., 1938.

Talley, J., "Hearing Mechanisms in the Behaviorally Deaf Dalmation Dog." Unpublished Master's thesis, University of Illinois, 1965.

Vinnikov, Ya. A., and A. K. Titova, *Kortiev organ-gistofiziologia i gistokhimia*. Moscow: Academy of Sciences, 1961. English ed. New York: Consultants Bureau, 1964.

Vosteen, K. H., "New Aspects in the Biology and Pathology of the Inner Ear," *Translations of the Beltone Institute for Hearing Research*. XVI, 1963.

Wërsall, J., "Studies on the Structure and Innervation of the Sensory Epithelium of the Cristae Ampulares in the Guinea Pig," *Acta Oto-laryngologica. Supplement* CXXXIX, 1958.

———, "The Tympanic Muscles and Their Reflexes," *Acta Oto-laryngologica*, CXXXIX, 1958.

Wever, E. G., *Theory of Hearing*. New York: John Wiley & Sons, Inc., 1949.

———, "The Width of the Basilar Membrane in Man," *Annals of Otology, Rhinology, and Laryngology*, XLVII, 1938, 37–47.

——— and C. W. Bray, "Action Currents in the Auditory Nerve in Response to Acoustical Stimulation," *Proceedings of the National Academy of Science*, XVI, 1930, 344–50.

———, "The Stapedius Muscle in Relation to Sound Conduction," *Journal of Experimental Psychology*, XXXI, 1942, 35–43.

——— and M. Lawrence, *Physiological Acoustics*. Princeton: Princeton University Press, 1954.

———, M. Lawrence, and K. R. Smith, "The Middle Ear in Sound Conduction," *Archives of Otolaryngology*, LXVIII, 1948, 19–35.

——— and J. A. Vernon, "The Control of Sound Transmission by the Middle Ear Muscles," *Annals of Otology, Rhinology and Laryngology*, LXV, 1956, 5–10.

Wien, M., "Ein Bedenken gegen die Helmholtzsche Resonanztheorie des Hörens," *Feschrift Adolph Wullner*, Leipzig, 1905, 28–35. (Not seen; reported by Wever and Lawrence, 1954.)

Wiener, F. M. and D. A. Ross, "Pressure Distribution in the Auditory Canal in a Progressive Sound Field," *Journal of the Acoustical Society of America*, XVIII, 1946, 401–8.

Wrightson, T. and A. Keith, *An Enquiry into the Analytical Mechanism of the Internal Ear*. London: MacMillan & Co., 1918.

Zwislocki, Jósef, "Über die mechanische Klanganalyze des Ohres," *Experientia*, II, 1946, 415–17.

———, "Theorie der Schneckenmechanik," *Acta Oto-laryngologica*, Supplement CXXII, 1948.

———, "Theory of the Acoustical Action of the Cochlea," *Journal of the Acoustical Society of America*, XXII, 1950, 778–84.

7

The Nervous System

INTRODUCTION

EMBRYONIC DEVELOPMENT OF THE NERVOUS SYSTEM

GROSS ANATOMY

The Central Nervous System

The meninges
The brain

The Telencephalon (Endbrain)
The Ventricular System
The Cerebral Cortex
The Basal Ganglia
The Diencephalon
The Mesencephalon
The Rhombencephalon

The spinal cord

The Peripheral Nervous System

The cranial nerves

Cranial Nerve I (Olfactory)
Cranial Nerve II (Optic)
Cranial Nerve III (Oculomotor)
Cranial Nerve IV (Trochlear)
Cranial Nerve V (Trigeminal)
Cranial Nerve VI (Abducent)
Cranial Nerve VII (Facial)
Cranial Nerve VIII (Acoustic)
Cranial Nerve IX (Glossopharyngeal)
Cranial Nerve X (Vagus)
Cranial Nerve XI (Accessory)

The spinal nerves

INTRODUCTION

Almost all of our behavior, the observable as well as the unobservable, is, in the final analysis, mediated by the nervous system. The nervous system is extraordinarily complex, being composed of millions of highly specialized cells called neurons. A neuron is a unique type of cell in that its response to an adequate stimulus results in a short-duration change of state, or response, which in turn can act as an adequate stimulus for adjacent nerve cells. Some of our behavior, however, is not so directly under the control of the nervous system; changes in body and blood chemistry may also result in modifications of our behavior. These changes often are the result of the sections of the glandular system, in particular the endocrine system.

In systemic anatomy the nervous and endocrine systems are regarded as two separate mechanisms. Functionally, however, they are very closely related. Certain endocrine glands, for example, stem from the same embryonic tissue that gives rise to the nervous system. The endocrine and nervous systems constitute a highly integrated behavior-controlling mechanism that is responsible for almost all of what we do. Very grossly, the internal activities, such as the life processes, are mediated to a large degree by the endocrine system, while the observable behavior is mediated by the nervous system. We may also say that the nervous system is responsible for quick actions while the endocrine system functions in producing much slower reactions which may extend over some period of time.

The nervous system can be described in a number of ways. We can be concerned with the spatial distribution of nerve tissue within the brain and within muscle tissues or with the manner in which these effectors, as they are more properly called, are provided with nerve impulses. Thus, the nervous system can be considered at the anatomical or at the physiological level. It is crucial for even a remote understanding of the nervous system to be acquainted with the basic structure and properties of nerve cells, as well as the gross anatomical relationships of the structures that comprise the nervous system. We are interested in the means by which the musculature of the speech mechanism is controlled. Thus we shall have to consider the structure and essential properties of the neuron, the essential characteristics of the nerve impulse, the gross anatomical relationships of the structures within the nervous system, and the distribution of nerve tissue within the various structures that comprise the speech mechanism.

Simple animals living in their uncomplicated environments do not require a complex nervous system, as is evident from the simple nerve net of the hydra. Larger animals, composed of a larger number of cells, make more frequent and complex adaptations to their environment and thus require increasingly complex nervous systems. Even in the lowly planaria, for example, there is a well-defined anterior brain, with large lateral nerves coursing posteriorly. Among some of the higher invertebrates and all the vertebrates, the network of nerve fibers, in spite of its complexity, has apparently proved inadequate in some respects, and a supplementary, endocrine system has evolved. In this system, specific chemical agents, released either directly or indirectly into the blood, circulate to various parts of the body, where they produce a specific effect. Because the endocrine system is such an important part of our adaptive mechanism, and is so closely linked with the nervous system, the chapter will conclude with a brief description of the endocrine glands and some of their effects.

Embryologists and zoologists have demonstrated quite conclusively that phylogeny is reflected remarkably well (in spite of some important omissions) in ontogeny. This holds true for the nervous system as well as the rest of the individual animal. Each organ and system in complex, high-order animals is laid down in a very primitive stage, and with growth of the embryo continues to develop until it reaches a stage that is representative for that particular species. Our appreciation and understanding of the nervous system may be facilitated by following its embryonic development from the simple neural tube to the complex, high-order development characteristic of man.

EMBRYONIC DEVELOPMENT OF THE NERVOUS SYSTEM

As mentioned briefly in Chapter 5, the entire nervous system is of ectodermal origin, and it first makes its appearance in the form of the neural folds, which lie alongside the dorsal mid-line of the embryonic disc. The neural folds begin just behind the anterior end of the embryonic disc, where they are continuous one with the other, and from there extend back, one on either side of the primitive streak (which, you will recall, is a temporary structure that gives rise to mesoderm). Between the neural folds is a shallow neural groove, which gradually deepens as the folds become elevated. Ultimately the folds meet and fuse in the mid-line to form the neural tube, as shown in Figure 7-1. Fusion begins anteriorly in the region of the hind brain and from there extends both forward and backward. Prior to the fusion of the neural, or medullary folds, a ridge of ectodermal cells appears just lateral to each fold. It is called the neural crest or ganglion ridge and gives rise to spinal and cranial nerve ganglia and the ganglia of the sympathetic nervous system (to be discussed later). Also on either side of the neural groove there is an upward growth of mesoderm, which soon invades the space between the neural tube and the overlying ectoderm which forms the dorsum of the embryo. In effect, the ectoderm, which gives rise to the nervous system, has migrated toward the interior of the embryo. Upon completion of the fusion of the neural folds, ectoderm once again forms a continuous layer over the dorsum of the embryo, as shown in Figure 7-1, and it is separated from the neural tube by the interposition of mesoderm.

The anterior part of the neural tube is somewhat broad and flat and ultimately forms the brain, while the narrow posterior part forms the spinal cord. The lumen of the tube forms the ventricles of the brain and the central canal of the spinal cord. At first the wall of the neural tube is composed of but a single layer of columnar

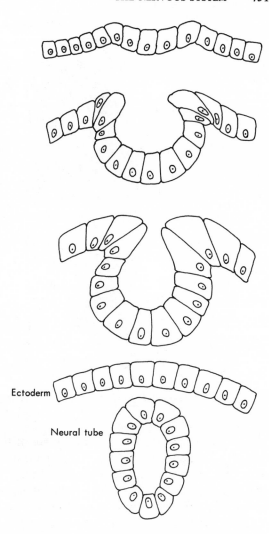

Fig. 7–1. Formation of the neural tube.

ectodermal cells whose nuclei are located toward the lumen side of the cell. They are known as the primitive, medullary, epithelial cells, from which almost all the cells in the future nervous system are developed. The fate of the primitive medullary epithelium and the forms its cells may take provide an important avenue for an understanding of the nervous system.

One form of cell differentiation that may occur is when the nucleus migrates toward the middle of the cell, whose body then takes on a spindle shape. Such a cell is called a spongioblast, and it gives rise to an astrocyte, which is a particular type of supportive or neuroglial cell. These cells send out processes which join with those of other neuroglial cells to form a network of supportive fibers or neuroglial tissue. Because neuroglial tissue stems from primitive medullary epithelium, it should come as no surprise that it is found only in the spinal cord and brain. Another form of cell modification occurs when the cytoplasm of the cell shrinks away from the outside of the

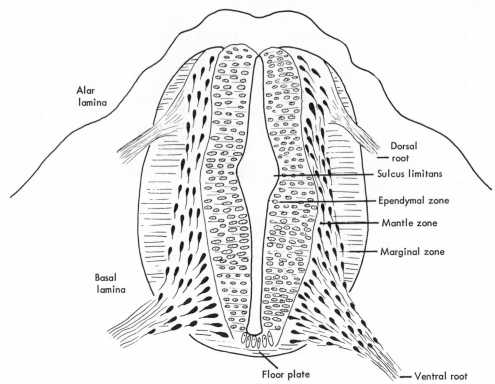

Alar
lamina

Dorsal
— root

Sulcus limitans

Ependymal zone

Mantle zone

Marginal zone

Basal
lamina

Floor plate

Ventral root

Fig. 7–2. Section of spinal cord of a four-week embryo.

neural tube and moves toward the nucleus at the lumen side of the tube. Such a cell seems to have one of two fates. It may remain unchanged and form an epithelial cell, lining the cavity of the neural tube, or it may form a germinal cell which undergoes rapid mitotic cell division. The resultant daughter cells may form medulloblasts, which can differentiate into astrocytes or oligodendrocytes, or they may form medulloblasts, which may ultimately differentiate into neuroglial cells or into neuroblasts, which are primitive nerve cells. Neuroblasts form mainly in the ventral region of the neural tube. Oligodendrocytes are unique cells responsible for forming myelin around the nerve fibers of cells in the brain and spinal cord. Myelin is a white, fatty substance which surrounds nerve fibers. It does not make its appearance until the nerve processes are well developed, and has been supposed to act as a sort of electrical insulator which insures isolated conduction within any given nerve fiber.

Because of the rapid growth of the cells, the central canal takes on a lozenge shape, the widest portion or lateral sulcus being called the sulcus limitans. As shown in Figure 7-2, it divides the lateral wall into a dorsal zone, called the alar lamina, and a ventral zone, called the basal lamina. Neuroblasts, which form mainly in the basal lamina, become motor in function while cells in the alar lamina become sensory. The lateral walls of the central canal are connected dorsally and ventrally by the thin dorsal roofplate and the ventral floorplate, whose cells retain their epithelial characteristics. Neuroblasts in the basal lamina begin to send out processes which course toward the periphery as motor nerve fibers, and they eventually form the ventral (motor) roots of the spinal nerves.

Earlier it was pointed out that ectoderm on either side of the neural tube known as the neural crest, gives rise to nerve tissue and in particular forms the posterior root ganglia and posterior (sensory) roots of the spinal nerves. The primitive nerve cells in the neural crest develop processes, one of which grows out to the periphery and forms the peripheral (afferent) process of the cell, while the other invades the neural tube and forms the central (efferent) process of the cell. Thus, the posterior root ganglion cells and their processes are formed outside the embryonic central nervous system. It may be worth noting that while these peripheral fibers may be myelinated, the myelin cannot stem from oligodendrocytes (which are confined to the neural tube). Presumably the myelin sheath on fibers peripheral to the neural tube arise from supportive cells in the neural crest. These cells give rise to an additional neurilemmal sheath which encases peripheral nerves, and since it arises from the neural crest, there are no neurilemmal cells inside the central nervous system. In addition to posterior (sensory) root ganglion cells, the neural crest also gives rise to the sympathetic nervous system and the medulla of the adrenal gland.

As a result of proliferation and differentiation of the cells in the neural tube, three layers or zones may be defined—an internal or ependymal, an intermediate or mantle, and an external or marginal zone. The ependymal layer ultimately forms the ependyma or epithelial lining of the central canal. The neuroglia and neuroblasts or young nerve cells together form the mantle layer, which eventually comprises the gray matter of the spinal cord, or medulla spinalis, as it is more properly called. Outside the mantle layer is the marginal layer, which is relatively free of nerve cells. It is this layer into which processes from the mantle layer extend and which will eventually form the white matter of the medulla spinalis. Continued proliferation of the neuroblasts in the mantle zone of the basal lamina results in obliteration of the ventral part of the central canal, and since growth is also in a ventral direction, swelling occurs on either side of the mid-line. As a result, a longitudinal anteromedian sulcus is produced.

At the same time, proliferation of neuroglia and neuroblasts in the alar lamina compresses and obliterates the dorsal part of the central canal, thus producing a postero-median septum. With continued cell proliferation the central canal is markedly reduced in size, until it occupies only the center of the neural tube. Local proliferation of the neuroblasts in the mantle zone results in aggregates of cell bodies, which form four columns, two in the alar lamina and two in the basal lamina. As shown in Figure 7–3, one group is located in the dorsal portion of the lateral wall of the alar lamina. It forms the somatic afferent column, which is recognized as the dorsal column or horn in the mature spinal cord. Similarly, a collection of neuroblasts in the basal lamina forms the somatic efferent column, which is recognized as the ventral column or horn. Visceral afferent and efferent columns also form in a region lateral to the sulcus limitans. As we shall see later in the chapter, they are associated with the autonomic nervous system.

Processes of the afferent columns traverse the marginal zone of the alar lamina and emerge from the spinal cord as the dorsal (afferent) roots of the spinal nerves, while processes of the efferent columns traverse the marginal zone of the basal lamina

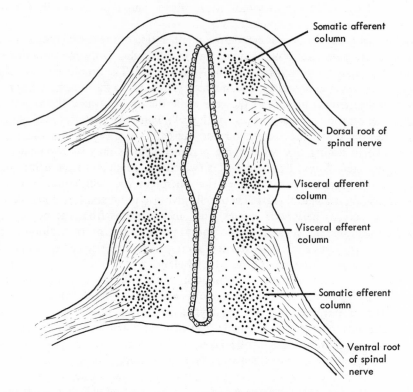

Fig. 7–3. Formation of columns in the embryonic spinal cord.

and leave the spinal cord as the ventral (efferent) roots of the spinal nerves. This differential arrangement of neuroblasts partially accounts for the rule of thumb that the dorsal half of the spinal cord is sensory in function and the ventral half is motor, sometimes known as Bell's law. This basic division, however, is restricted to the spinal cord and brain stem, and does not apply to the cephalic portion of the neural tube which develops into the brain.

A longitudinal section of the embryonic spinal cord would reveal periodic regions of intensified proliferation which correspond to segments of the spinal cord and their sensory and motor roots. Each segment is known as a neuromere. Each neuromere supplies an area of the body that roughly corresponds to a transversely oriented segment of the embryo, and although a nerve fiber may become "lost" in plexuses that develop later, its ultimate termination in a segment of the body is retained. The muscles which the ventral root supplies initially develop from the myomeres that lie in close proximity to the neural tube. The first axons that emerge from the neural tube grow into the muscles and thus establish a path which subsequent fibers seem to follow. The growing tip of the nerve fiber bears an ameboid swelling, which projects small searching fingers into the muscle and connective tissues through which the fiber is growing. Although the general path a nerve fiber follows seems to be determined by hereditary factors, the specific course of individual nerve fibers is influenced by certain barriers which may lie in its prospective path. Generally, the tip of the growing nerve fiber follows the course of previously laid down blood vessels, muscles, and connective tissue. Thus, the growing nerve fiber exhibits stereotropism. Once a pathway is established by the initial nerve fibers, others may follow to form a nerve bundle, and their path will be less haphazard than that of their predecessors.

As implied earlier, the cephalic portion of the neural tube undergoes a differentiation different from that of the spinal cord. Initially three dilations or primary brain vesicles appear. As shown in Figure 7-4, they are known as the prosencephalon, mesencephalon, and rhombencephalon. Shortly after the appearance of the three primary brain vesicles, the prosencephalon develops diverticula on either side at its cephalic extreme to form the telencephalon. The remainder of the prosencephalon is now known as the diencephalon. As the neural tube continues to grow in a cephalic direction, it is thrown into a fold which divides the rhombencephalon into a cephalic part called the metencephalon and a caudal part known as the myelencephalon. The three primary brain vesicles and their subsequent subdivisions are shown in Figure 7-4, and the early brain and its adult derivatives are shown in Table 7-1.

Due to the rapid growth and flexion of the cephalic end of the neural tube, its lateral walls thicken and become widely separated. The roofplate is stretched and very much

Fig. 7–4. Differentiation of the neural tube to form the brain vesicles.

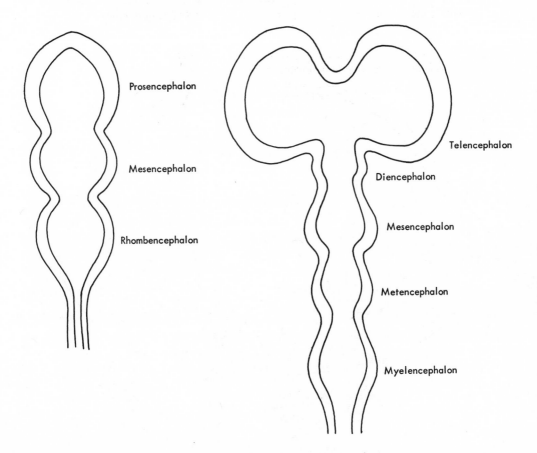

Table 7-1.
Adult Derivatives of the Primary Brain Vesicles

Primary Vesicle	Subdivision	Derivatives	Cavity
Prosencephalon	Telencephalon	Cerebral cortex, striate bodies, and rhinencephalon	Lateral ventricle and part of third ventricle
	Diencephalon	Thalamus and hypothalamus	Third ventricle
Mesencephalon	Mesencephalon	Collicular structures and cerebral peduncles	Cerebral aqueduct
Rhombencephalon	Metencephalon	Pons and cerebellum	Fourth ventricle
	Myelencephalon	Medulla oblongata	Fourth ventricle and part of central canal
Medulla spinalis		Spinal cord	Central canal

thinned. In spite of the rapid changes that occur, the sulcus limitans and consequently a division of the lateral walls into the alar and basal laminae are somewhat retained. As illustrated in Figure 7-5, the lateral portion of the rhombencephalon (hind brain) contains cells that are sensory in function, while the medial portion is motor. These groups of cell bodies form the ganglia of many of the cranial nerves.

Fig. 7–5. Schematic transverse section through embryonic hind-brain showing columns of neuroblasts.

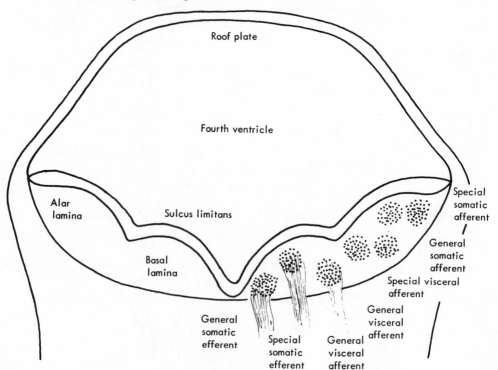

Roof plate

Fourth ventricle

Alar lamina

Sulcus limitans

Special somatic afferent

General somatic afferent

Basal lamina

Special visceral afferent

General somatic efferent

General visceral afferent

Special somatic efferent

General visceral afferent

The myelencephalon forms the medulla oblongata, and with proliferation of cells in the lateral walls, the lumen of the tube is partially obliterated to form the fourth ventricle and part of the central canal. The dorsal edges of the alar plate in the metencephalon become greatly thickened and fuse on the roofplate to form a thickened transverse band in the anterior part of the roof of the fourth ventricle. This structure is the anlage of the cerebellum. It continues to grow, especially laterally, to form the cerebellar hemispheres. Their point of fusion forms the vermis.

The most lateral aspect of the alar lamina in the metencephalon contains a highly specialized region called the rhombic lip. It undergoes rapid mitotic division to provide neuroblasts which migrate cephalically and caudally to form the pontine and olivary nuclei. During this stage of development the pharyngeal-arch region lies directly ventral to the rhombencephalon. The hypoglossal nerve (cranial nerve XII) supplies the occipital somites, the myotomes of which later migrate forward to form the extrinsic and intrinsic musculature of the tongue; in doing so, they drag their nerve supply along with them.

Flexion of the neural tube does not result in any great change in the gross structure of the mesencephalon, and so initially it retains the characteristics of the spinal cord. The dorsal aspect of the mesencephalon is known as the tectum or roof, while the ventral aspect (the basal lamina) is known as the tegmentum. The lumen of the mesencephalon forms the cerebral aqueduct. Thickening of the roof, on either side of the mid-line, produces two longitudinal elevations which undergo a transverse constriction to form the paired superior and inferior colliculi (the corpora quadrigemina); at the same time aggregates of neuroblasts in the basal lamina form two prominent nuclei, the red nucleus and the substantia nigra. As differentiation of the brain occurs, nerve tracts develop and pass either up or down through the mesencephalon to link the hindbrain with the cerebral cortex. Rather late in the initial development of the brain, large nerve tracts from the telencephalon pass down the ventral part of the mesencephalon, and they, along with the tegmentum, form the cerebral peduncles. They establish functional continuity between the cerebral hemispheres and the remainder of the nervous system.

Progressing in a cephalic direction, the next division of the brain encountered is the diencephalon. It, you will vividly recall, is that part of the forebrain which remains after the development of the telencephalic vesicles. As shown in Figure 7-6, they grow in a caudal direction, overlap the diencephalon, and compress it toward the mid-line. The lumen of the diencephalon becomes the third ventricle, and on either side of it proliferating neuroblasts collect into large nuclei constituting the hypothalamus, thalamus, and epithalamus. The floor of the diencephalon develops a diverticulum which becomes the neural portion of the pituitary gland. (Here we see evidence of the relationship between the nervous and endocrine systems.)

The cerebral hemispheres develop from the telencephalon. One of the first signs of differentiation is a thickening of the walls of the inferior aspect of the telencephalon to form structures called the corpus striatum. At this stage of development the remainder of the telencephalon is known as the pallium. The cephalic end of the diencephalon begins to proliferate and invaginates into the cavity of the cerebral vesicle, thus forming the choroid plexus. The pallium, in the mid-line region, begins to thicken and forms the hippocampus, while additional thickening in a region just lateral to the

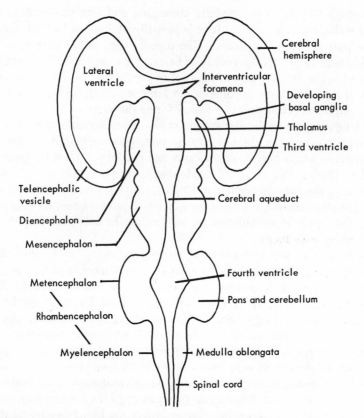

Fig. 7–6. Schematic of differential growth of the telencephalic vesicles and their relationship to the diencephalon.

corpus striatum forms the pyriform cortex. It, along with the hippocampus, is associated with the olfactory sense. The remainder of the pallium is now known as the neopallium, and it undergoes considerable growth and increase in thickness. Neuroblasts which differentiate within it pass nerve fibers down to the diencephalon as the corticopontine and corticospinal tracts. They grow through the corpus striatum and divide it into a lateral lentiform nucleus and a medial caudate nucleus. The tract that divides the corpus striatum forms a rather prominent band of white matter known as the internal capsule.

A small region in the middle of the pallium fails to grow rapidly and becomes overlapped by the remainder of the cerebral hemispheres. Thus, a portion of the cerebral cortex called the insula (island) lies below the surface of the brain; the folds of cerebral cortex that overlap it are called the opercula.

The pallium, like the remainder of the neural tube, at first contains ependymal, mantle, and marginal layers. Later in development, however, the neuroblasts migrate from the mantle to the marginal layer. The gray matter thus comes to occupy the marginal zone, and the nerve processes pass, for the most part, toward the depth of the brain to form the white (medullary) matter. Similar cell migration occurs in the cerebellum. Although the cerebral cortex grows rapidly, cell proliferation is uneven or differential, and as a result ridges or gyri, separated by fissures or sulci, are formed. Initially the surface of the cerebral hemispheres is relatively smooth, but with continued growth, more and more gyri are formed.

GROSS ANATOMY

The fibers and cells that make up the nervous system are distributed unevenly through the body. We know, for example, that the brain contains literally billions of neurons and nerve fibers, while the ear lobe has very few sensory nerve fibers. It is extremely difficult to discuss the nervous system as it really is, a single, highly integrated behavior-regulating system. With the realization that no single element of the nervous system can be justifiably treated in isolation from the remainder of the nervous system, we can divide it into individual subsystems, at least for descriptive purposes. Here again, however, we may encounter difficulties. Some of our divisions may be made on an anatomical basis, while others may be made on a functional basis. With these potential hazards in mind, let us proceed.

On a functional basis, almost all the fibers in the nervous system can be categorized as either somatic or autonomic. Somatic fibers are those involved either with the production of observable events or with the reception of environmental changes. Autonomic fibers, on the other hand, are involved chiefly with life processes, such as those that occur in the viscera, blood vessels, and glands; they are often referred to as the unconscious activities of the body. In addition, we might also broadly state that somatic fibers are involved in voluntary activities, while autonomic fibers are involved with involuntary activities—within limits of course.

On an anatomical basis we can divide the entire nervous system into the central and peripheral nervous systems. As most of us well know, the central nervous system is surrounded and protected by the cranial bones and vertebral column, and consists of the brain and spinal cord. The peripheral nervous system can be divided into the cranial and spinal nerves, plus their peripheral combinations, and the autonomic nervous system. The autonomic system, in turn, can be subdivided, but largely on a functional basis, into an afferent[1] and an efferent system, and finally, the autonomic efferent system can be divided both functionally and anatomically into the sympathetic and parasympathetic systems. These subsystems of the nervous system will be discussed in greater detail later in the chapter.

The Central Nervous System

The meninges

In addition to the protection provided the central nervous system by the skull and vertebral column, the brain and spinal cord are completely surrounded by three layers of nonnervous tissue collectively known as the meninges. The outermost layer is the dura mater. It is a very tough fibrous membrane that acts as a lining for the

---

[1] The afferent portion of the autonomic nervous system is often regarded as part of the peripheral nervous system, and the autonomic nervous system, in that event, is exclusively an efferent system.

cranium and also serves as the periosteum for the cranial bones. Its outer layer is closely adherent to the inner surface of the cranium, the adhesions being most pronounced in the regions of the sutures and around the margin of the foramen magnum. Its inner surface is lined by a smooth layer of mesothelium. The inner and outer layers, known as the endoseal and meningeal layers, respectively, are separated in places to form venous channels or sinuses which carry blood from the brain to the veins in the neck region

The middle meningeal layer is called the arachnoid, a delicate membrane of reticular fibers, the outer and inner aspects of which are lined by cuboidal or pavement mesothelium. The arachnoid loosely invests the brain and spinal cord, but does not follow the convolutions except at the longitudinal fissure, where the arachnoid and dura form a longitudinal septum called the falx cerebri. A potential subdural space exists between the dura and arachnoid mater.

The deepest layer of meninges, called the pia mater, is an extremely vascular membrane, held together by a loose network of areolar tissue. The pia mater closely follows the convolutions and irregularities of the surface of the brain and spinal cord. A space between the arachnoid and pia mater is known as the subarachnoid space. It contains cerebrospinal fluid, which is discussed on page 464.

The brain

The brain is characteristically described as being composed of three major derivatives of the embryonic neural tube from which subdivisions are formed. They are the forebrain, midbrain, and hindbrain. The forebrain, or prosencephalon, forms the endbrain or telencephalon and the interbrain or diencephalon. As we have seen, during embryological development, the telencephalon gives rise to the paired cerebral hemispheres, which form the most conspicuous part of the brain. The midbrain, or mesencephalon, is formed by two large nerve tracts, the cerebral peduncles, which connect the cerebral hemispheres with the hindbrain or rhombencephalon. The hindbrain includes such structures as the pons, medulla oblongata, and cerebellum. The three major divisions of the brain and their subdivisions were shown schematically in Figure 7-6.

The Telencephalon (*Endbrain*).   The cerebral hemispheres, which are very nearly mirrored images of one another, are partially separated by a deeply penetrating longitudinal fissure. The hemispheres are joined at the bottom of the longitudinal fissure by an elaborate system of interconnecting nerve fibers, the most conspicuous of which is known as the corpus callosum. It is shown in Figure 7-7. Each hemisphere has three surfaces, lateral, medial, and inferior, all of which are characterized by a maze of folds and depressions, or convolutions. Each fold is known as a gyrus, while a depression is called a sulcus or fissure, depending upon its depth of penetration. Although the deepest depressions are properly referred to as fissures, the terms sulcus and fissure are sometimes used interchangeably. For example, the central sulcus is sometimes referred to as the fissure of Rolando, and the lateral sulcus is referred to as the fissure of Sylvius. Once popular eponyms have largely fallen into disuse in recent years, and the student may avoid embarrassment by adhering to contemporary nomenclature. As shown in Figure 7-8, the central sulcus begins about midway

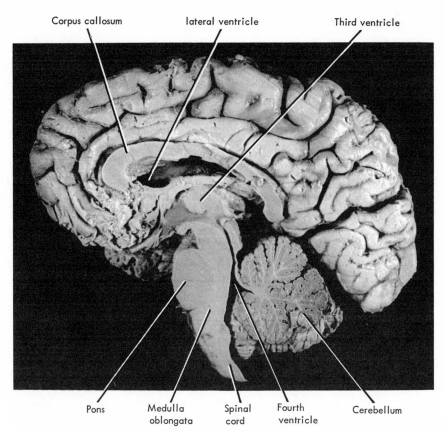

Corpus callosum   lateral ventricle   Third ventricle

Pons   Medulla oblongata   Spinal cord   Fourth ventricle   Cerebellum

Fig. 7–7. Photograph of a brain sectioned through the median plane showing the lateral ventricle and some associated structures.

Fig. 7–8. Schematic lateral surface of cerebral hemispheres, cerebellum, pons, medulla oblongata, and spinal cord.

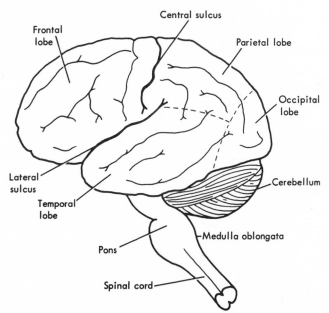

Frontal lobe   Central sulcus   Parietal lobe

Occipital lobe

Lateral sulcus

Temporal lobe

Cerebellum

Pons

Medulla oblongata

Spinal cord

between the inferior and superior borders. It courses obliquely upward and backward to terminate near the mid-point of the superior border. The lateral sulcus begins at the inferior border and courses back and somewhat upward to terminate on the lateral surface, slightly more than halfway back. These sulci roughly divide the hemispheres into four lobes: frontal, temporal, parietal, and occipital, as shown in Figure 7-8. The frontal lobe is that portion anterior to the central and lateral sulci, while the temporal lobe is located in the area below the lateral sulcus. The parietal lobe is bounded in front by the central sulcus and below by the lateral sulcus. The occipital lobe is not clearly defined, and its approximate boundaries are outlined in Figure 7-8.

Gyri and sulci may vary considerably among individuals, but the location of the more significant ones is rather predictable. Some of them are shown in Figure 7-9.

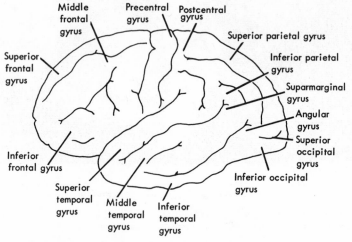

Fig. 7-9. Schematic lateral surface of cerebral hemisphere showing some gyri.

The frontal lobe is divided into four distinct gyri: the superior frontal, middle frontal, inferior frontal, and precentral. The precentral gyrus is particularly noteworthy because it is the area associated with the common motor pathway to the skeletal muscles. The parietal lobe contains the very important postcentral gyrus in addition to the superior parietal and inferior parietal gyri or lobules, as they are often called. The inferior parietal lobule is divided into the angular and supramarginal gyri, also shown in Figure 7-9. The occipital lobe, which is relatively small and pyramidal in shape, bears a superior and inferior gyrus, both of which are continuous in front with the parietal and temporal lobes. The temporal lobe is divided into superior, middle, and inferior temporal gyri by two sulci which course roughly parallel with the lateral sulcus.

The medial surface of a cerebral hemisphere also bears some noteworthy landmarks, some of which are shown in Figure 7-10. The parieto-occipital fissure, not clearly defined on the lateral surface, is easily seen on the medial surface. It courses down and forward as a rather deep cleft and joins the calcarine fissure just below and behind the corpus callosum. The cingulate fissure, which begins near the anterior limits of the corpus callosum, runs nearly parallel with its upper surface and terminates on the superomedial border of the hemisphere, just behind the upper limit of the central

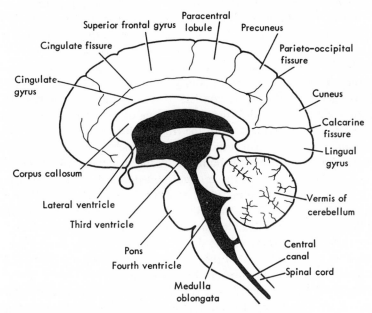

*Fig. 7–10. Schematic medial section of brain showing gyri,
fissures, and some significant structures.*

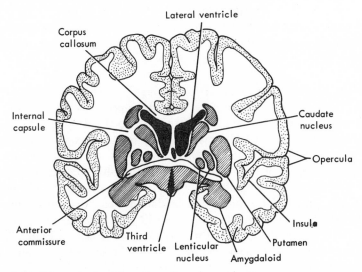

*Fig. 7–11. Schematic frontal section of cerebrum showing
ventricles, the insula and some associated structures.*

sulcus. The calcarine fissure extends from the occipital pole to the region of the
temporal lobe. Its course is roughly parallel with the inferior border of the hemisphere.

An additional lobe, called the insula, lies deeply in the lateral fissure, and can be
seen only when the lips of the fissure are separated. The insula is easily identified in
a frontal section through the brain, as in Figure 7-11.

The Ventricular System.   A frontal section of the cerebral hemispheres reveals the cerebral ventricles. They are part of the adult derivatives of the cavity in the embryonic neural tube. As shown in Figure 7-11, each hemisphere contains a lateral cerebral ventricle. They communicate with a smaller mid-line cavity known as the third ventricle. The lateral ventricle is bounded above by the corpus callosum, laterally by the caudate nucleus, and inferiorly by the thalamus (structures to be considered later). Each lateral ventricle consists of a body and three horns or cornua. These structures are shown by drawings of a casting of the ventricles in Figure 7-12. The lateral ventricles communicate with the front of the third ventricle by means of an interventricular foramen. The third ventricle, which is a rather narrow space between the cerebral hemispheres, is bounded by the structures comprising the diencephalon, and is continuous with the cerebral aqueduct (of Sylvius). It is a narrow canal, which courses through the midbrain and in turn is continuous with the fourth ventricle. As shown in Figure 7-10, the fourth ventricle is bounded by the cerebellum behind and the pons and medulla oblongata in front. These structures, which form the hindbrain or rhombencephalon, will be discussed later. The fourth ventricle is continued below into the central canal of the spinal cord. A schematic of the relationship of the ventricles to the brain is shown in Figure 7-13.

A collection of specialized epithelial cells in the ventricles manufactures lymph-like cerebrospinal fluid. These cells constitute the choroid plexus. Cerebrospinal fluid begins its circulation in the lateral ventricles, passes into the third and from there to the fourth, where it diffuses, by means of small apertures, into the subarachnoid spaces. It continues to circulate around the brain, and is finally absorbed by an elaborate venous system that drains blood from the brain. Thus, the brain and spinal cord are surrounded by cerebrospinal fluid which functions as a very efficient shock absorber and offers protection to the nervous system.

The Cerebral Cortex.   A frontal section through a cerebral hemisphere will reveal certain structural features. The surface or cortex appears somewhat gray in fresh specimens, and is termed gray matter, in contrast to the depths of the hemisphere which contain large tracts of white matter. Gray matter is composed largely of the bodies of nerve cells, while white matter is formed by the myelinated processes of nerve cells. The interior of the cerebral hemispheres also contains well-demarcated regions of gray matter known collectively as the basal nuclei or basal ganglia. They include a medial group, consisting of the caudate nucleus, thalamus, hypothalamus, and the subthalamus, and a lateral group formed by the putamen and globus pallidus which together constitute the lentiform nucleus. As shown in Figure 7-14, these lateral and medial groups are separated by a V-shaped tract of white matter called the internal capsule. The thalamus, hypothalamus, and subthalamus are components of the diencephalon, and are often not included with the basal ganglia.

The cerebral cortex forms a sort of closely fitting cap for the cerebral hemispheres. It varies somewhat in thickness, from about 1.25 mm in the occipital region to about 4 mm in the region of the anterior central (precentral) gyrus. Only about half of the actual surface of the cortex is visible in an intact brain, the walls of the sulci forming the unexposed area. Macroscopic views of the cortex reveal alternating light and dark bands formed by layers of nerve-cell bodies and myelinated nerve fibers. Microscopic views of the cerebral cortex reveal rather definite and consistent structural

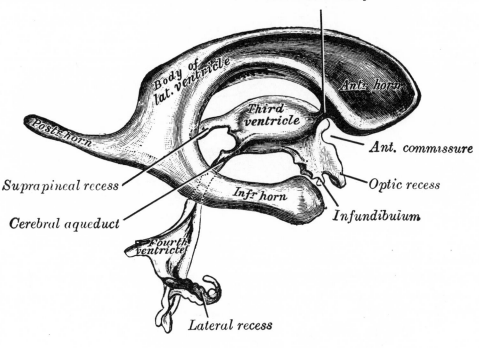

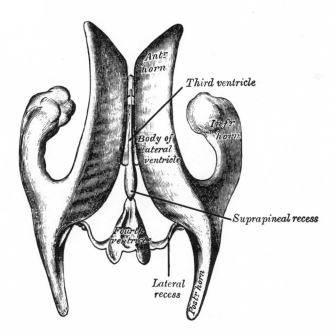

Fig. 7–12. Drawings of a casting of the ventricles as seen from
the side (top figure) and from above (bottom figure). (From
Gray's Anatomy, 28th edition, 1966. Courtesy Lea & Febiger,
Publishers, Philadelphia.)

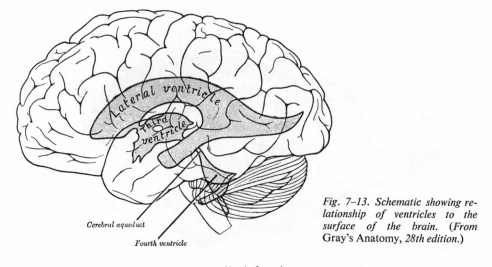

Fig. 7–13. Schematic showing relationship of ventricles to the surface of the brain. (From Gray's Anatomy, *28th edition.)*

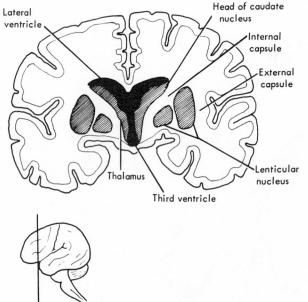

Fig. 7–14. Schematic of internal capsule and adjacent structures.

features. For example, there seem to be five types of cells organized in a stratified fashion throughout most of the cortex. Probably the most numerous, and certainly the most conspicuous cells are known as pyramidal cells. They can be classified as small, medium, large, and giant pyramidal cells. When seen microscopically, as in Figure 7-15, the cell body appears pyramidal in shape. Their axons extend into subadjacent white matter, while the dendrites are directed toward the surface where they give off branch-like collaterals. Small granule or stellate cells can be found throughout the cortex, although they are located in rather definite layers. They are characterized by short branching axons, which terminate in the vicinity of the cell body. The cells of Martinotti bear long axons, which are directed toward the surface of the

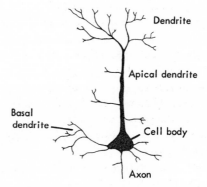

Dendrite

Apical dendrite

Basal
dendrite

Cell body

Axon

Fig. 7–15. Drawing of a pyramidal cell.

cortex where they give off numerous collaterals. The deepest cells in the cerebral cortex are fusiform or polymorphous, and their axons are directed toward the subadjacent white matter. While the superficial layer of cerebral cortex also contains fusiform cells, their dendrites are long and horizontally directed, and their penetrating axons reach into the deeper cortical substance.

Cell distribution varies among the regions of the cerebral cortex but is sufficiently consistent to permit a general description in terms of layers. Campbell (1905), Cajal (1906), and Brodmann (1909) have listed six layers of nerve cells and nerve fibers within the cortex. They are, beginning from without:

1. The molecular layer, containing the horizontal cells of Cajal, neuroglial cells, and stellate or granular cells. In addition, the apical dendrites of the pyramidal cells terminate in the molecular layer.

2. The external granular layer, containing small pyramidal plus some granular cells.

3. The pyramidal cell layer, sometimes divided into a superficial layer composed of medium-sized pyramidal cells and a deeper layer composed of large pyramidal cells. This layer also contains stellate cells plus cells of Martinotti, the axons of which are directed toward the surface of the cortex.

4. The internal granular layer, which is composed largely of stellate or granular cells plus a small number of small pyramidal cells.

5. The ganglionic layer, composed of large pyramidal cells. In the motor cortex they are particularly large, and are usually referred to as the giant pyramidal cells of Betz. These giant pyramidal cells give rise to the fibers of the corticospinal tract. The apical dendrites of these cells course to the molecular layer where they ramify. According to Ranson and Clark (1959), the axons of some of the giant pyramidal cells appear to run through the corpus callosum to the opposite cortex.

6. The fusiform layer, composed of irregular or polymorphous cells, the axons of which penetrate into the immediately subadjacent white matter.

Just as the thickness of the cerebral cortex varies from region to region, so do the arrangement and distribution of the layers of the various types of cells. In the past the areas of the cortex manifesting a certain histological homogeneity have been described as having individual and, in some instances, functional characteristics. Cortical areas differ, for example, in the relative thicknesses of the various layers, in the number of afferent and efferent fibers, and so forth. The locations and boundaries of some of these regions have been rather well-established. Numerous maps of the cortex, based on arrangements of cells, have been made, and many of them bear certain similarities. Ranson and Clark (1959) state that while over a hundred structurally different cortical areas have been distinguished, all can be classified in one or another of five fundamental types. In addition, there does in fact seem to be a certain relationship between cytoarchitecture and function.

Cortex Type 1 lacks the external and internal granular layers characteristic of much of the cortex. It is found in the motor and premotor areas of the frontal lobe. Cortex of Types 2 and 3 has well-developed granular layers and rather extensive distribution over much of the cortex, the occipital pole being a notable exception. Cortex of Type 4 is relatively thin but nevertheless has well-developed granular layers and numerous medium-sized pyramidal cells. It is found chiefly in the frontal and occipital poles and is sometimes referred to as polar cortex. Cortex of Type 5 contains mostly small granular or stellate cells and a few scattered, small pyramidal cells. It is found in those areas which receive the sensory projection fibers.

As mentioned earlier, Cortex of Type 1 is found in the superior frontal gyrus and also in the motor cortex of the anterior central gyrus. Although the cell structure in these two regions is very similar, the motor cortex is distinctive because of the presence of giant pyramidal cells (of Betz) within the fifth layer. A popular cortical map or architectonic chart is Brodmann's (1909). He assigned numbers to the various areas of the cortex on the basis of cell distribution, and today reference is often made to an area of the brain by means of a number. The motor cortex, for example, is known as area 4, while the somatosensory area is known as area 7 (see Figure 7-48).

The Basal Ganglia.   As stated earlier, the basal ganglia of the cerebral hemispheres include the caudate nucleus, the lenticular nucleus, and the internal capsule, which together form the corpus striatum or striate bodies. Basal ganglia also include the amygdaloid nucleus and the claustrum. The striate bodies are so named because of a striped appearance due to layers of white matter separating the basal ganglia, thus leaving stratified layers of white and gray matter. The caudate nucleus, shown schematically in Figure 7-16, is an elongated mass of gray matter, which is bent over on itself and conforms throughout its course to the wall of the lateral ventricle. In fact, its swollen rostral extremity or head bulges into the anterior horn of the lateral ventricle, where it is continuous with the lenticular nucleus. The remainder of the caudate nucleus is drawn out into a highly arched tail which turns sharply in a caudal direction and, conforming to the shape of the lateral horn of the third ventricle, bends sharply again in a rostral direction where it is continuous with the amygdaloid

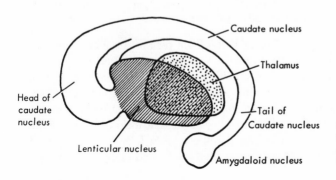

Fig. 7–16. *Schematic showing interrelationship of caudate nucleus, thalamus, lenticular nucleus, and amygdaloid nucleus.*

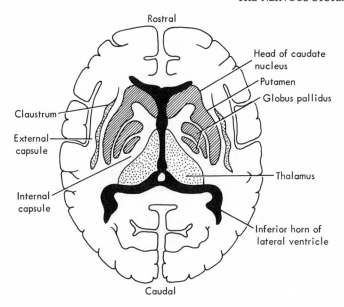

Fig. 7–17. Schematic of horizontal section through cerebrum showing interrelationships of the ventricles, thalamus, caudate nucleus, lenticular nucleus (putamen and globus pallidus), claustrum, and the internal and external capsules.

nucleus. Because of its curved course the caudate nucleus is cut through twice in any frontal section of the hemisphere, if the cut is behind the amygdaloid nucleus with which the tail is continuous. Throughout much of its extent the caudate nucleus is separated from the lenticular nucleus by a layer of white matter called the internal capsule, except anteriorly where the two portions unite to form the head.

The lenticular nucleus, shown in Figure 7-17, is located in the midst of the cerebral white matter. Its shape is somewhat similar to that of a biconvex lens, thus the name lenticular or lentiform. The structure is composed of two separate nuclei, the putamen and the globus pallidus. As shown in Figure 7-17, the putamen is a rather thick, convex mass, located just lateral to the globus pallidus and internal capsule. It is the larger portion of the lenticular nucleus. Its lateral surface is separated from the cortex of the insula by the interposed claustrum and external capsule, also shown in Figure 7-17. The cortical projection of the fibers from the putamen is not well defined. The globus pallidus is located medially to the putamen and is separated from it by the internal capsule. In addition, the globus pallidus is subdivided into external and internal parts by the internal medullary lamina. On cross section the globus pallidus appears roughly triangular, as may be seen in Figure 7-17. Because of its many myelinated fibers, it has a lighter color than the putamen, and so the name globus pallidus seems quite appropriate. Due to the presence of the medullary laminae and fine myelinated fiber bundles, the globus pallidus and putamen take on a somewhat striated appearance, hence the term corpus striatum.

The claustrum, shown in Figure 7-17, is a thin lamella of gray matter located between the lateral margin of the putamen and the cortex of the insula. The claustrum is bounded laterally and medially by a tract of white matter known as the external capsule and is sometimes regarded as a detached portion of the gray matter of the insula. Its cellular structure strongly resembles that of the deepest layer of the cerebral cortex.

The amygdaloid body is located in the roof of the anterior (rostral) limits of the inferior ventricular horn, where it is continuous with the anteriorly directed tail of the caudate nucleus. The amygdaloid bodies of the two sides are connected by commissural fibers through the anterior commissure.

The internal capsule, shown in Figure 7-17, is a rather broad band of white matter that separates the lenticular nucleus from the caudate nucleus and thalamus. It is somewhat V shaped, with the apex of the V directed medially. From the apex or genu, the anterior limb extends in a lateral and rostral direction, while the posterior limb is directed in a lateral and caudal direction. The anterior limb contains thalamo-cortical fibers (from the lateral nucleus of the thalamus to frontal lobe), corti-cothalamic fibers (from the frontal lobe to the thalamus), frontopontine fibers (from frontal lobe to nuclei of pons), as well as collaterals from the above tracts to the basal ganglia. The genu also contains corticothalamic and thalamocortical fibers, plus corticobulbar fibers (from the motor cortex to the motor nuclei of the cranial nerves).

The Diencephalon. The diencephalon, which stems embryologically from the prosencephalon, is so completely surrounded by the cerebral hemispheres as to appear to be a part of them, and only its ventral surface can be observed in the intact brain. The diencephalon consists of the thalamus, metathalamus, hypothalamus, epithalamus, and the subthalamus or ventral thalamus. When observed from above, following the removal of the cerebral hemispheres and corpus callosum, the thalami are seen to consist of oval-shaped masses, on either side of the third ventricle. Each thalamus is greatly expanded caudally, and the expansion is termed the pulvinar. It is continued laterally into an oval swelling known as the lateral geniculate body which, together with the medial geniculate body, forms the metathalamus. The medial geniculate body, which receives auditory fibers from the lateral lemniscus and inferior colliculus, is located beneath the pulvinar. The paired medial geniculate bodies are connected, one with the other, by a commissure which passes through the posterior part of the optic chiasma. The lateral geniculate body receives fibers of the optic tract.

The dorsal and lateral surfaces of the thalamus are covered by thin layers of white matter. The dorsal covering is termed the stratum zonale, while the lateral covering is called the external medullary lamina. These coverings are continuous with a Y-shaped reflection, the internal medullary lamina, which extends into the thalamus and divides it into medial, lateral, and anterior parts. The substance of the thalamus is largely gray matter, which is composed of a number of thalamic nuclei. One of these , the mid-line nucleus, often bridges the third ventricle and connects the thalami of the two sides. It contains mostly glial tissue and few, if any, nerve fibers or cells.

The epithalamus consists of the trigonum habenulae, the pineal body, and the posterior commissure. These structures are located at the posterior limits of the third ventricle, and the pineal body and posterior commissure can be seen in a sagittal section of the brain, as in Figure 7-18. The trigonum habenulae receive olfactory fibers. The pineal body is a small, cone-shaped structure located in a depression between the superior colliculi (structures of the mesencephalon). The posterior com-

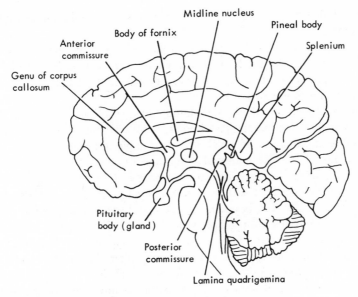

Fig. 7–18. Schematic sagittal section of brain showing some structures which join the cerebral hemispheres.

Fig. 7–19. Schematic of base of the brain.

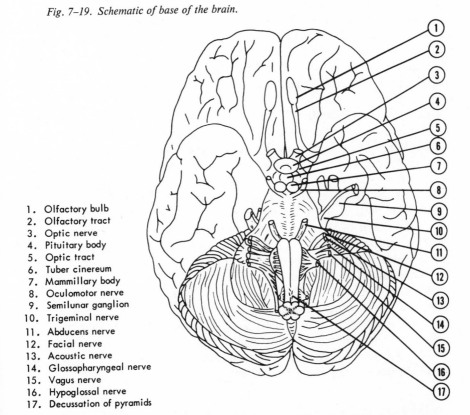

1. Olfactory bulb
2. Olfactory tract
3. Optic nerve
4. Pituitary body
5. Optic tract
6. Tuber cinereum
7. Mammillary body
8. Oculomotor nerve
9. Semilunar ganglion
10. Trigeminal nerve
11. Abducens nerve
12. Facial nerve
13. Acoustic nerve
14. Glossopharyngeal nerve
15. Vagus nerve
16. Hypoglossal nerve
17. Decussation of pyramids

missure is a rounded band of white fibers which crosses the mid-line just above the cerebral aqueduct.

Although the structure of the subthalamus has been well outlined, its function is not particularly well understood. It is located on the ventrolateral aspect of the thalamus, and separates it from the internal capsule. It is partially responsible for regulation of certain motor activities.

The structures constituting the hypothalamus form much of the floor of the third ventricle. They include the mammillary bodies, tuber cinereum, infundibulum, hypophysis, and optic chiasma, all of which are identifiable in a view of the base of the brain, as in Figure 7-19. The mammillary bodies are two rounded masses, placed on either side of the mid-line, just beneath the floor of the third ventricle. The tuber cinereum, located immediately rostral to the mammillary bodies, is a hollow eminence of gray matter. Laterally it is bounded by the optic tracts and cerebral peduncles. Anteriorly it is continuous with a hollow stalk, the infundivulum, which projects down and forward to join the neural portion of the hypophysis. The optic chiasma is an X-shaped structure located just rostral to the tuber cinereum. It receives fibers from the optic nerve. Many of the fibers decussate at the chiasma and continue to the lateral geniculate body where they continue to the occipital lobe of the cerebrum.

The Mesencephalon. The mesencephalon is a short, constricted segment connecting the pons and cerebellum (structures of the hindbrain) with the diencephalon and telencephalon. It consists of two lateroventral cerebral peduncles and a dorsal portion, the corpora quadrigemina or tectum. As was shown in Figure 7-10, the midbrain is pierced by the cerebral aqueduct, which connects the third with the fourth ventricle. The cerebral peduncles, which lie ventrally to the cerebral aqueduct, emerge from the lower surface of the cerebral hemispheres, converge toward the mid-line, and enter the upper surface of the pons. They are flanked on either side by the optic tracts. Each peduncle consists of a dorsal part named the tegmentum and a ventral part called the base. These parts are separated by a layer of dark gray matter called the substantia nigra.

The base contains large bundles of efferent (motor) fibers, which, for the most part, arise from the cerebral cortex and continue to the nuclei of the cranial nerves and to the spinal cord. The fibers are divided into tracts, the names of which suggest their connections or course. The cerebrospinal fibers, which occupy the middle portion of the base, arise from cells in the motor area (precentral gyrus) of the cerebral cortex and continue to the pyramids of the medulla oblongata. The frontopontine fibers occupy the middle portion of the base. They arise from cells in the frontal lobe and terminate in the nuclei of the pons. Temporopontine fibers are located in a tract lateral to the cerebrospinal tract. As the name implies, the fibers arise from cells in the temporal lobe and terminate in nuclei of the pons. This tract, however, also contains fibers originating from cells in the parietal and occipital lobes. The midbrain also contains the lemniscus, which is divided into a lateral and medial lemniscus. Other important tracts course through the midbrain. They include the ventral and lateral spinothalamic tracts, the spinotectal tracts, and others. In addition, the gray matter of the tegmentum contains nuclei for some cranial nerves. As shown in Figure 7-20, a layer of gray matter surrounds the cerebral aqueduct. It contains the nuclei of the oculomotor and trochlear nerves.

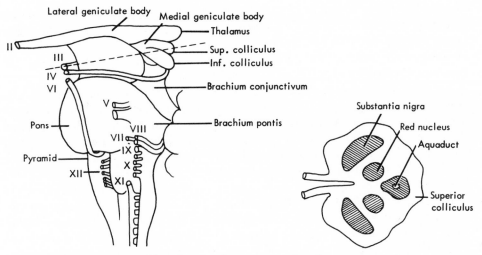

Fig. 7–20. Schematic of lateral view and transverse section of brain stem.

The dorsal part of the midbrain presents the corpora quadrigemina, which consists of the inferior and superior colliculi. They are paired structures, placed one above the other, on either side of the mid-line. Normally they are not visible in the intact brain because they are tucked in between the occipital lobe of the cerebrum and the upper surface of the cerebellum. The superior colliculi contain nuclear masses that roughly describe a ring aound the cerebral aqueduct, plus masses ventral to the aqueduct, very near the cerebral peduncles. In fresh specimens these masses are slightly red in color, and are known appropriately as the red nuclei of the tegmentum. The interior colliculi are composed of compact masses of nuclei. From cells in their gray matter, fibers pass to the medial geniculate bodies. This, you will recall, is part of the auditory pathway.

The Rhombencephalon.   The rhombencephalon or hindbrain is usually subdivided into the myelencephalon or medulla oblongata and the metencephalon, which consists of the pons and cerebellum. The medulla oblongata is continuous with the spinal cord, and is rather arbitrarily limited caudally at the level of the upper surface of the first cervical vertebra. This is a rather convenient boundary, however, for it also designates the level of the emergence of the first pair of cranial nerves. Above, the medulla oblongata is continuous with the pons, but the boundary between these two structures is defined by the foramen cecum, a small triangular expansion of the anterior median fissure. The lower part of the anterior median fissure is interrupted for a considerable distance by bundles of efferent nerve fibers, which cross over the mid-line and continue downward on the opposite side. This region constitutes the pyramidal decussation. The posterior median fissure is rather ill-defined throughout most of the medulla oblongata; however, the anterior (ventral) and posterior (dorsal) median fissures divide the structure into symmetrical halves, between which lie the central canal and fourth ventricle. The external surface of the medulla oblonata is further divided into anterior, middle, and posterior areas by the longitudinally directed antero-lateral sulcus (from which fibers of the hypoglossal nerve emerge) and the postero-lateral sulcus (from which the accessory, vagus, and glossopharyngeal nerves emerge).

The anterior portion of the medulla oblongata is commonly referred to as the pyramid. Situated between the anterior median fissure and the antero-lateral sulcus at a level just beneath the pons, it appears as paired, pyramidal-shaped eminences. The pyramids contain large bundles of motor fibers, about 60 per cent of which cross over the mid-line at the pyramidal decussation described earlier. The fibers that decussate continue downward as the lateral cerebrospinal fasciculus (an important voluntary motor tract which is part of the pyramidal motor system to be described later). The fibers that descend uncrossed (direct fibers) form the anterior cerebrospinal fasciculus.

The lateral portion of the medulla oblongata is bounded in front by the antero-lateral sulcus and behind by the posterolateral sulcus. It contains a prominent, oval-shaped mass called the olive. It also contains ascending nerve tracts, some of which will be described later in the chapter. The posterior portion, located behind the postero-lateral sulcus, contains a number of ascending nerve tracts including the fasciculus gracilis and the fasciculus cuneatus. They are located laterally to the posterior median fissure, and are continuous with ascending tracts of the spinal cord. The upper limit of the posterior portion is continued to the cerebellum by means of the paired, inferior cerebellar peduncles (often referred to as the restiform bodies). They carry fibers from the spinal cord and medulla oblongata to the cerebellum. Besides the important motor (descending) and sensory (ascending) nerve tracts, the medulla

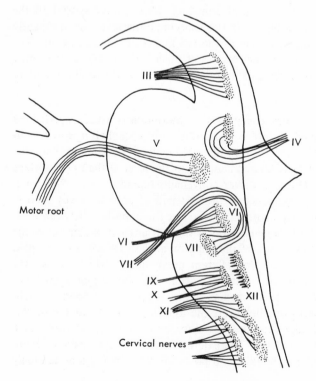

Fig. 7–21. Schematic of the location of motor nuclei and points of energence of the motor roots of the cranial nerves.

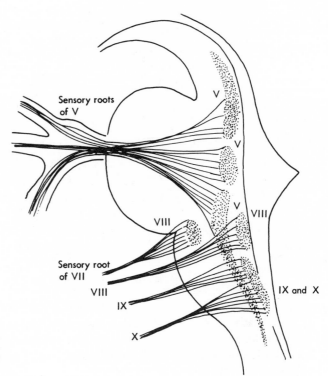

Fig. 7–22. Schematic of the location of the terminal nuclei of some of the afferent (sensory) cranial nerves.

oblongata also contains nuclei of some cranial nerves. The location of these nuclei will be deferred until a description of the pons has been completed.

When viewed from the side, as in Figure 7-18, the hindbrain presents a rounded, anteriorly directed eminence known as the pons. Below, the pons is continuous with medulla oblongata, above, with the cerebral peduncles. It consists largely of transverse fibers which bridge the mid-line and collect on either side to form the middle cerebellar peduncles. The dorsal portion of the pons is continuous with the tegmentum of the cerebral peduncles. The ventral portion contains bundles of longitudinal fibers, which enter through the cerebral peduncles. They include the corticospinal tract which gives off collaterals as it continues to the pyramids of the medulla oblongata, corticobulbar fibers, and corticopontine fibers. The pons also contains a number of cranial-nerve nuclei. The location of motor nuclei and points of emergence of the motor roots of the cranial nerves are shown schematically in Figure 7-21. The sensory nuclei and points of emergence of the sensory roots of the cranial nerves are shown schematically in Figure 7-22.

The cerebellum, shown in Figure 7-7, makes up the greater part of the hindbrain. It is somewhat oval in shape, with a pronounced constriction at the mid-line. It is also somewhat flattened, and its surface is marked by numerous transversely directed sulci, which give the cerebellum a laminated or foliated appearance. It consists of two lateral hemispheres and a vermis between and partially covered by them. Deep fissures divide the cerebellum into several lobes which are shown schematically in Figure 7-23. The flocculonodular lobe consists of the nodulus of the vermis and the

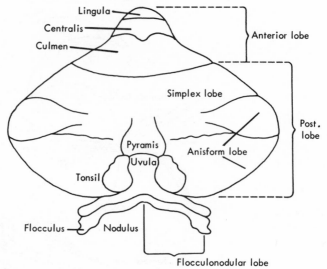

Fig. 7–23. Schematic of the divisions of the cerebellum

flocculi attached to it. The corpus of the cerebellum is divided into an anterior and posterior lobe by deeply penetrating fissures. As shown in Figure 7-23, the anterior lobe consists of the lingula, the central lobule, and the culmen monticuli. The larger posterior lobe consists of the simplex lobe, the medial lobule (tuber and folium of the vermis), the ansiform lobules, and the postero-median lobule. The latter consists of the pyramis and uvula of the vermis.

The cerebellum may also be considered in terms of a cortex and white matter, plus nuclei. The white matter includes three bundles of projection fibers connecting the cerebellum to other parts of the brain. It is connected to the midbrain by the paired superior peduncles, to the pons by the paired middle peduncles, and to the medulla (and spinal cord) by the paired inferior peduncles. In all then, six peduncles connect the cerebellum to other parts of the brain. They have been given special names. Each superior peduncle is known as a brachium conjunctivum. Fibers emerge from the white matter of cerebellar hemispheres and enter the midbrain where they decussate completely, turn upward, and continue to the diencephalon. The middle peduncles (sometimes called the lateral peduncles) are called the brachia pontis. As the name implies, the fibers arise from the pontine nuclei, decussate, and course to the cerebellum. Many of the fibers from the frontal and temporal lobes end in the pontine nuclei. Thus, a crossed corticopontocerebellar pathway is established. The inferior peduncles are known as the restiform bodies, and they contain afferent fibers from the proprioceptors and from the vestibular system. Other white matter in the cerebellum forms the cerebellar commissures, which connect the cerebellar hemispheres and the association fibers (arcuate fibers), which connect various parts of the cerebellar cortex with one another.

Gray matter is found in the cerebellar cortex and in deep masses (nuclei) located within the white matter. The cerebellar cortex has an inner granular layer composed of numerous small neuroglial and nerve cells, a middle layer composed of large

Purkinje cells, and an outer molecular layer formed mainly by nerve-cell processes. Purkinje cells are characterized by a single axon and elaborate bush-like dendritic processes which are somewhat flattened. The axons of Purkinje cells synapse with cells in the cerebellar nuclei. There are four nuclei on either side of the mid-line, the dentate, emboliform, globose, and fastigial. The cells of the dentate nucleus give rise to fibers that form much of the brachium conjunctivum, while those of the emboliform nucleus receive fibers from the vermis and send fibers into the brachium conjunctivum. The globose nucleus also receives fibers from the vermis but gives off efferent fibers to the red nucleus. The fastigial nucleus receives fibers from the vestibular branch of the auditory nerve and sends efferent fibers into the brain stem.

The spinal cord

The lower end of the medulla oblongata is prolonged into, and is continuous with, the spinal cord. It extends from the level of the upper border of the first cervical vertebra to about the lower border of the first lumbar vertebra. The remainder of the vertebral canal is occupied by lumbar and sacral nerves. During the early stages of embryological development the spinal cord occupies the full extent of the vertebral canal, and the spinal nerves leave and pass through their respective intervertebral foramina almost at right angles to the cord. The spinal column, however, grows faster than the spinal cord; as a result, the cord becomes shorter than the column. Consequently, the nerve roots become more and more oblique in the direction they take when leaving the cord. The lumbar and sacral nerves, for example, descend almost vertically to reach their points of exit from the spinal column. The location of the lower limit of the spinal cord is somewhat variable among specimens, and it also varies with movements of the vertebral column. For example, it is drawn slightly upward when the spinal column is flexed. The spinal cord does not end abruptly, but rather it gradually tapers to a point, the tip of which is prolonged into a fine filament of fibrous tissue known as the filum terminale. The full extent of the spinal cord is pierced by a central canal, which is a remnant of the lumen of the embryonic neural tube. In the adult, however, the central canal is frequently obliterated.

Thirty-one or thirty-two pairs of spinal nerves emerge from the spinal cord, eight in the cervical region, twelve thoracic, five lumbar, and five sacral. One and sometimes two coccygeal nerves also emerge from the lower extremity of the spinal cord. Although no segmentation of the cord is visible, it is often regarded as being built up of a series of spinal segments, each of which occupies a length equivalent to the extent of the attachment of a pair of spinal nerves. The spinal cord is often described as being roughly cylindrical in shape; however, its transverse diameter is slightly greater than the antero-posterior diameter. It is about 13 mm across, except at the level from the third cervical to the second thoracic and from the ninth through the twelfth thoracic vertebrae, where increased nerve tissue associated with innervation of the extremities results in enlargements of the cord. The cervical enlargement is the more pronounced.

Like the medulla oblongata, the spinal cord is incompletely divided into right and left halves by an anterior and posterior median sulcus. The anterior median sulcus or fissure is the deeper of the two, and its floor is formed by a transverse band of white matter, the anterior white commissure. Although the posterior median sulcus is rather shallow, a septum of neuroglial tissue extends from it more than halfway into the spinal cord. An additional longitudinal sulcus, the posterior lateral sulcus, further divides the spinal cord, and, as shown in Figure 7-24, the portion of spinal cord that lies between it and the posterior median sulcus is termed the posterior funiculus. In the upper two-thirds of the cord, a shallow furrow, the posterior-intermediate sulcus, divides the posterior funiculus into a medial fasciculus gracilis and a lateral fasciculus cuneatus. The portion of the cord anterior to the posterolateral sulcus is termed the antero-lateral region and is further divided by the region of emergence of the anterior roots of the spinal nerves into a lateral fasciculus and an anterior fasciculus. The major divisions and tracts of the spinal cord are shown in Figure 7-24 and 7-25.

A transverse section of the spinal cord reveals a central core of gray matter surrounded by white matter. The gray matter consists of two crescent-shaped bodies joined across the mid-line by a transverse commissure of gray matter, thus giving the gray matter the appearance of the letter H, or the shape of a butterfly. An imaginary frontal plane through the transverse commissure divides each crescent into an anterior or ventral and a posterior or dorsal horn. Since they extend the full length of the spinal cord, they are also called the ventral and dorsal columns. The same frontal plane also divides the transverse commissure into an anterior and posterior gray commissure. The anterior column consists largely of motor-nerve cells, the fibers of which leave the spinal cord as motor roots of the spinal nerves. In the upper cervical, thoracic, and mid-sacral regions, the gray matter in the region of the transverse commissure is extended laterally as the lateral horn or column. It contains cells of the autonomic nervous system. The posterior column contains large numbers of sensory cells, the fibers of which enter the spinal cord as sensory roots of the spinal nerves. As stated earlier, the spinal cord has rather pronounced enlargements in the cervical and lower thoracic regions. The gray matter is also enlarged at these levels.

In a region between the anterior and posterior columns, about opposite the trans-

Fig. 7–24. *Some major divisions of the spinal cord.*

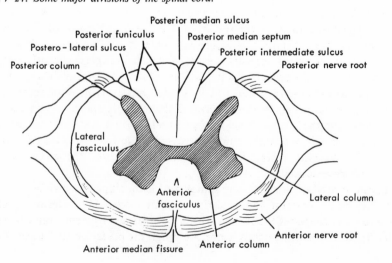

Posterior median sulcus

Posterior funiculus

Posterior median septum

Postero – lateral sulcus

Posterior intermediate sulcus

Posterior column

Posterior nerve root

Lateral fasciculus

Anterior fasciculus

Lateral column

Anterior nerve root

Anterior median fissure

Anterior column

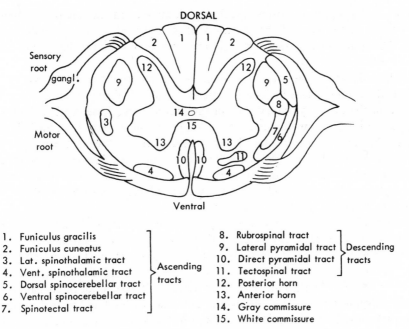

1. Funiculus gracilis
2. Funiculus cuneatus
3. Lat. spinothalamic tract
4. Vent. spinothalamic tract   } Ascending tracts
5. Dorsal spinocerebellar tract
6. Ventral spinocerebellar tract
7. Spinotectal tract

8. Rubrospinal tract
9. Lateral pyramidal tract   } Descending tracts
10. Direct pyramidal tract
11. Tectospinal tract
12. Posterior horn
13. Anterior horn
14. Gray commissure
15. White commissure

Fig. 7–25. Schematic transverse section through the spinal cord.

verse commissure, the gray matter extends into the white matter as a net-like series of processes which forms the spinal reticular formation.

Generally speaking, the cells in the anterior and lateral columns are associated with motor functions, while those in the posterior columns are associated with receptor and coordinating functions. The white matter in the spinal cord may be divided into (1) fibers that either connect the spinal cord with the brain or convey impulses from the brain to the spinal cord, or (2) fibers that are confined to the spinal cord and interconnect various areas and levels of the cord with one another. That is, they are association fibers. The white matter is divided by the posterior roots and the lateralmost of the anterior nerve roots into the anterior, lateral, and posterior white columns, each of which contains both ascending and descending tracts, some of which are shown in Figure 7-25.

The anterior white column is bounded by the antero-median fissure and the antero-lateral sulcus. Its descending tracts include the ventral corticospinal (direct pyramidal) tract close to the anterior median fissure. This is a motor tract which originates in the precentral motor gyrus and is distributed to the mid-thoracic region. The vestibulospinal tract extends from the vestibular nerve nuclei to the sacral region and constitutes part of the balance-reflex mechanism. The tectospinal tract arises from the contralateral superior colliculus of the midbrain, decussates, and descends to supply the effectors of audiovisual reflexes. The reticulospinal tract arises from the reticular substance of the medulla oblongata and midbrain and has a widespread distribution to the skeletal muscles.

The ascending tracts include the ventral spinothalamic tract, which originates from the cells in the opposite posterior column, decussates in the anterior commissure, and ascends to the level of the thalamus. It is supposed to carry impulses of light touch. The spino-olivary tract carries proprioceptive impulses to the olivary complex of the medulla oblongata.

The lateral white column is bounded by the antero-lateral and postero-lateral sulci. Its descending tracts include the lateral corticospinal or pyramidal tract, which arises from the giant pyramidal cells in the motor area of the cerebral cortex. The fibers decussate at the pyramids of the medulla oblongata and descend. It is a most important voluntary motor tract. The rubrospinal tract arises in the red nucleus of the superior colliculi. The descending fibers carry impulses associated with cerebellar functions, and are involved in the coordination of motor acts. The olivospinal tract arises in the region of the inferior olivary nucleus and carries motor fibers, which apparently function in reflex activities.

The ascending tracts of the lateral white column include the dorsal spinocerebellar tract, which is uncrossed and which carries sensory impulses from the leg and trunk regions to the cerebellum. It functions in reflex proprioception. The ventral spinocerebellar tract carries impulses to the cerebellum via the medulla, pons, and anterior medullary velum and enters the cerebellum by way of the superior cerebellar peduncle. The lateral spinothalamic tract decussates at the spinal level and ascends to the level of the thalamus. Its fibers arise from cells in the opposite posterior column and cross via the anterior white commissure. They carry impulses for sensations of pain and temperature. The spinotectal tract, which arises from the contralateral posterior gray column, terminates in the corpora quadrigemina.

The posterior white column is located between the postero-lateral and postero-median sulci. It contains a single, small, descending, comma-shaped tract of fibers located between the larger fasciculus gracilis and fasciculus cuneatus, both of which are ascending tracts. The fasciculus gracilis, located next to the postero-median septum, receives fibers from the posterior roots and terminates in the medulla. It carries sensations of muscle and joint movement, vibration, and passive movement. The fasciculus cuneatus is located between the fasciculus gracilis and posterior gray column, and receives fibers from the posterior nerve roots, primarily from the thoraco-cervical regions. They terminate in the medulla. They carry proprioceptive sensations.

Thus far in the discussion of the nervous system we have confined our attention to the central nervous system. Having arrived at the level of the spinal nerves, we ought to examine some of the more important aspects of the peripheral nervous system. By definition the peripheral nervous system is that portion lying outside the bony confines of the central nervous system. It includes the spinal and cranial nerves and their somatic sensory and motor fibers as well as autonomic fibers.

The Peripheral Nervous System

The peripheral nervous system includes the cranial nerves, and the spinal nerves with their ventral and dorsal roots and peripheral branches, plus portions of the autonomic nervous system. It might also be defined as that portion of the nervous system which conducts impulses either toward or away from the central nervous system. A nerve may be defined simply as a collection of nerve fibers. A single nerve fiber is so small it cannot be seen without the aid of a microscope, while nerves may reach diameters in excess of a lead pencil. Earlier, we learned that a nerve fiber is a process or extension of a nerve cell and that a nerve cell with all its processes is known as a neuron. We also learned that neurons which carry impulses toward the central nervous system are called afferent or sensory neurons, while those that carry impulses away from the central nervous system are called efferent or motor neurons. Almost all nerves are mixed, that is, they contain both efferent and afferent fibers. Some cranial nerves, however, are exclusively sensory or motor in function. Also, certain cranial nerves contain fibers which are part of the autonomic nervous system.

On a *functional* basis, the peripheral nervous system is composed of seven types of nerve fibers; that is, on the basis of the tissues supplied, seven types of nerve fibers are identified. They are:

1. General somatic afferent fibers, present in all spinal and some cranial nerves. They conduct impulses to the central nervous system from receptors in the integument, muscles, and connective tissues.

2. Special somatic afferent fibers, found only in the optic and auditory nerves.

3. General visceral afferent fibers, present in both cranial and spinal nerves and distributed to the viscera of the neck, thorax, abdomen, and pelvis and to blood vessels and glands throughout the body.

4. Special visceral afferent fibers, restricted to the special senses of smell and taste and carried, therefore, only by the olfactory, glossopharyngeal, and vagus nerves.

5. Somatic efferent fibers, distributed to the striated muscles in the body and found in some cranial and all spinal nerves.

6. General visceral efferent fibers, found in both cranial and spinal nerves and distributed to the peripheral ganglia of the autonomic nervous system (to be discussed later in the chapter). In general, these fibers supply the smooth muscles and glands throughout the body.

7. Special visceral efferent fibers are also recognized. Unfortunately, the name is misleading, because they supply the striated muscles of the larynx, pharynx, and soft palate, and those involved in mastication and facial expression. The fibers are found only in the cranial nerves.

The cranial nerves

Twelve pairs of cranial nerves are usually recognized and are referred to by Roman numerals and by names. They are numbered according to their superficial points of emergence from the brain stem. Accordingly, the rostral-most nerve is designated as cranial nerve I (olfactory), and the caudal-most nerve is designated as cranial nerve XII (hypoglossal). The names of the cranial nerves reflect either function (e.g., optic and olfactory), structure (e.g., trigeminal), or distribution (e.g., vagus). Because they are referred to by number in some instances and by name in others, the student ought to become familiar with both the names and associated numbers of the cranial nerves. The mnemonic device on page 482 may be helpful.

The area of the brain where a cranial nerve appears or attaches is known as its superficial origin, and the origin of all twelve cranial nerves, as seen in a view of the base of the brain, is shown schematically in Figure 7-26. Cranial nerves or branches

THE CRANIAL NERVES

I.	on — Olfactory	Sensory (smell)
II.	old — Optic	Sensory (vision)
III.	Olympus — Oculomotor	Motor (visual convergence and accommodation)
IV.	towering — Trochlear	Motor (rotates eye down and outwards)
V.	tops — Trigeminal	Sensory and Motor (sensations to eye, nose, and face: meninges) (muscles of mastication and tongue)
VI.	A — Abducent	Motor (supplies lateral eye muscles)
VII.	Finn — Facial	Sensory and Motor (sensations to tongue and soft palate) (muscles of the face and the stapedius)
VIII.	and — Acoustic	Sensory (hearing and balance)
IX.	German — Glossopharyngeal	Sensory and Motor (sensation to tonsils, pharynx, and soft palate) (muscles of pharynx and stylopharyngeus)
X.	vended — Vagus	Sensory and Motor (sensations to ear, pharynx, larynx, viscera) (muscles of pharynx, larynx, tongue, and smooth muscles of the viscera)
XI.	at — Accessory (spinal)	Motor (muscles of pharynx, larynx, soft palate, and neck)
XII.	hopps — Hypoglossal	Motor (strap muscles of neck, extrinsic and intrinsic muscles of the tongue)

Fig. 7–26. Illustration of the emergence of the cranial nerves from the base of the brain.

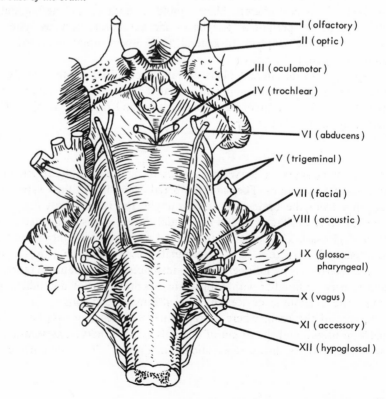

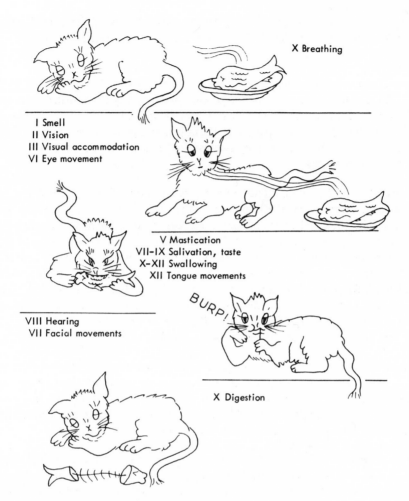

X Breathing

I Smell
II Vision
III Visual accommodation
VI Eye movement

V Mastication
VII-IX Salivation, taste
X-XII Swallowing
XII Tongue movements

VIII Hearing
VII Facial movements

BURP!

X Digestion

Fig. 7–27. Illustration of cranial nerve functions.

of cranial nerves, which have a motor function, arise from motor nuclei deep within the brain stem. These nuclei develop from the embryonic basal plate. Thus, the motor-nerve nuclei are closely analogous to ventral horn cells of the spinal cord. The sensory cranial nerves (or sensory branches) arise from ganglia located outside the brain stem. These ganglia, according to Chusid and McDonald (1960), may be considered analogous to the dorsal-root ganglia of the spinal nerves. Upon entering the brain stem the sensory nerves course to sensory-nerve nuclei, which develop from the alar plate of the neural tube. A schematic of the locations of the cranial nerve nuclei was shown in Figures 7-21 and 7-22.

Not all the cranial nerves are directly associated with speech production or speech reception. The olfactory (cranial nerve I) nerve, for example, is associated with smell. It may facilitate communication but not speech production or reception per se. Since we are primarily concerned with the nerves that supply the speech and hearing mechanisms, we need do no more than recognize some of them, while others may deserve a rather detailed description. The gross functions of the cranial nerves are shown schematically in Figure 7-27, and the brief description that follows may enhance an understanding of their functions.

Cranial Nerve I (Olfactory).   The olfactory nerve is actually not a nerve at all but, rather, an elongated extension of the brain. Olfactory fibers are distributed over the mucous membrane of the superior nasal concha and adjacent nasal septum. About twenty branches of the nerve penetrate the cribriform plate of the ethmoid bone and enter the olfactory bulb. There they synapse with neurons that course to the pyriform area and hippocampus.

Cranial Nerve II (Optic).   The optic nerve, or nerve of sight, is also regarded as an elongated extension of the brain rather than a cranial nerve in the true sense of the word. The rods and cones of the retina form first order neurons which synapse with second-order neurons also located in the retina. These neurons course to ganglion cells, the axons of which form the optic-nerve fibers. Third-order fibers course to the optic chiasma, where the fibers from the medial half of each retina decussate. The lateral fibers from each retina are uncrossed or direct. The fibers continue to central connections, and fourth-order neurons terminate in the occipital cortex, as well as in other cortical and subcortical areas. Because of these "secondary associations," reflex reactions to optic stimuli are made possible.

Cranial Nerve III (Oculomotor).   The oculomotor nerve, which supplies motor-nerve fibers to the eyelid (levator palpebrae) and ocular muscles, also carries parasympathetic fibers which supply the sphincter muscles of the iris and the ciliary muscles of the lens. The fibers arise from a nucleus near the floor of the cerebral aqueduct, pass forward, and emerge from the medial side of the cerebral peduncle.

Cranial Nerve IV (Trochlear).   From its origin at the trochlear nucleus, the fibers of the trochlear nerve, which are motor, course posteriorly, decussate in the anterior medullary velum (a thin layer of medullary fibers which forms the roof of the anterior portion of the fourth ventricle of the brain), and from there wind around the cerebral peduncles where they enter the superior orbital fissure, The fibers terminate in the superior oblique muscle of the eye, which moves the axis of vision downward and outward.

Cranial Nerve V (Trigeminal).   The trigeminal is the largest of the cranial nerves and is important in speech production. It emerges from the side of the pons by a large sensory and a smaller motor root. Grossly, the sensory portion serves the superficial and deep structures in the face, mouth, and lower jaw, while the motor portion serves the muscles of mastication, the soft palate, and the mylohyoid and anterior belly of the digastric muscles. The motor root follows a rather independent course from the sensory root. It arises from a motor nucleus in the mid-level of the pons, passes beneath the semilunar ganglion (to be described later), and leaves the cranium by way of the foramen ovale. Immediately below the foramen it joins with the mandibular branch of the sensory portion of the trigeminal. Thus, the mandibular branch contains both sensory and motor fibers. The motor fibers (motor root of the trigeminal) divide into two branches, one of which supplies the internal pterygoid muscle. The other branch supplies the masseter, external pterygoid, and buccinator muscles. The motor root also sends small filaments to the otic ganglion (largely sensory) and thus supplies the tensor tympani and tensor veli palatini muscles with motor fibers. The inferior alveolar nerve, which is primarily sensory, does contain a few motor fibers. They supply the mylohyoid and anterior belly of the digastric muscle.

The distribution of the fibers of the sensory root is extremely complex, and only a partial description will be permitted. The fibers of the sensory root arise from the semilunar ganglion located near the apex of the petrous portion of the temporal

Fig. 7–28. Schematic of distribution of trigeminal nerve.

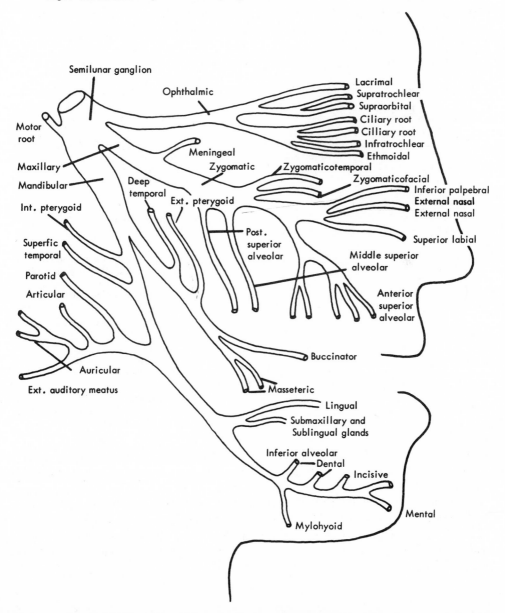

bone. From there they pass into the pons and terminate in the sensory nucleus of the trigeminal nerve (Figure 7-22). As shown schematically in Figure 7-28, the semilunar ganglion gives rise to three large branch nerves called the ophthalmic, maxillary, and mandibular nerves.

The ophthalmic nerve is sensory. It leaves the cranium by way of the superior orbital fissure, and its branches supply the lacrimal gland, eyelid, cornea, and iris of the eye, as well as the mucous membrane of the nasal cavity, paranasal sinuses, and the integument in the upper facial region and anterior scalp.

The maxillary nerve (also sensory) is larger than the ophthalmic. It leaves the cranium by way of the foramen rotundum and enters the pterygopalatine fossa, where it gives off branches. It then enters the infraorbital canal, branches again, and continues along the floor of the orbit to emerge finally through the infraorbital foramen of the maxilla. The inordinately complex distribution of the maxillary nerve and the structures served by its many branches are shown in outline form below.

DISTRIBUTION OF THE MAXILLARY BRANCH OF THE TRIGEMINAL NERVE

Primary Branches	*Secondary Branches*	*Structure Served*
Middle meningeal		Dura mater.
Zygomatic	Zygomaticotemporal	Integument at side of forehead.
	Zygomaticofacial	Integument of cheek.
Posterior-superior alveolar branches		Maxillary sinus, upper molar teeth.
Middle-superior alveolar		Bicuspid teeth.
Anterior-superior alveolar	Nasal	Mucous membrane of inferior part of auditory meatus and floor of nasal cavity. Incisor and canine teeth.
Inferior palpebral branches		Integument and conjunctiva of lower eyelid.
External nasal branches		Integument of nose and cartilaginous septum.
Superior labial branches		Integument of upper lip, mucous membrane of mouth, and labial glands.

The sphenopalatine ganglion, located in the pterygopalatine fossa, receives many fibers from the nearby maxillary nerve. It receives both sensory and motor fibers, and the ganglion in turn gives off a number of branches, the orbital, palatine, posterior-superior nasal, and pharyngeal. The orbital branches supply the mucous membrane of the ethmoidal and sphenoidal sinuses, while the palatine branches supply the gums, mucous membrane of the hard and soft palates, and mucous membrane of the nasal cavity. The posterior-superior nasal branches supply the mucous membrane of the lateral wall of the nasal cavity, while the pharyngeal branch supplies the mucous membrane of the nasopharynx.

The mandibular nerve, the largest branch of the trigeminal, contains both sensory and motor fibers. Grossly, it supplies the lower teeth and gums, the muscles of mastication, the integument of the ear and adjacent temporal regions, the lower facial region, and the mucous membrane of the anterior two-thirds of the tongue. Just after leaving the semilunar ganglion, it divides into two large branches and a single small branch, the nervous spinosus. It supplies the dura mater and mastoid air cells. The large branches of the mandibular nerve are known as the anterior and posterior divisions. The anterior division is primarily motor, and, as mentioned briefly earlier, it supplies the muscles of mastication. The anterior portion does carry sensory fibers, however, and they supply the integument and mucous membrane of the cheek. The anterior portion is usually considered in four parts, the masseteric, deep temporal, buccinator, and external pterygoid.

The masseteric nerve supplies the masseter muscle and also sends fibers to the temporomandibular joint. The deep temporal nerve supplies the temporalis muscle. The buccinator nerve supplies the external pterygoid muscle as well as the buccinator muscle and, in addition supplies sensory fibers to the integument and mucous membrane in the region of the buccinator. The external pterygoid nerve supplies the external pterygoid muscle.

The posterior division of the mandibular nerve is primarily sensory but does carry a few motor fibers. It gives rise to the auriculotemporal, lingual, and inferior alveolar nerves.

The auriculotemporal branch supplies the integument of the ear and the lining of the external auditory meatus; a filament also supplies the tympanic membrane. The nerve also supplies the temporomandibular joint, the parotid gland, and the integument over the temporal region.

The lingual nerve, which supplies the sublingual gland, mucous membrane of the anterior two-thirds of the tongue, and the mucous membrane of the mouth and gums, communicates with the facial nerve by way of the chorda tympani. It, you will recall, passes through the tympanic cavity.

The inferior alveolar nerve is the largest branch of the mandibular nerve. It branches are the mylohyoid, dental, incisive, and mental nerves. The mylohyoid nerve supplies the mylohyoid muscle and the anterior belly of the digastric. The dental nerves supply the lower molars and bicuspids, while the incisive nerve supplies the lower cuspid and incisor teeth. The mental nerve emerges via the mental foramen and supplies the integument of the chin and mucous membrane and integument of the lower lip.

Cranial Nerve VI (Abducent).   The abducent nerve is motor. Its fibers arise from the adbucent nucleus, enter the orbit through the superior orbital fissure, and terminate in the lateral rectus muscles of the eye.

Cranial Nerve VII (Facial).   The facial nerve is large, complex, and important in speech production. It consists of motor and sensory roots and also carries fibers of the autonomic nervous system. A striking characteristic of the facial nerve is that it communicates with many other cranial nerves. The functional significance of the branches of communication is not well-understood, but it is interesting to note that the facial nerve communicates with the acoustic, trigeminal, vagus, glossopharyngeal, and even with cervical nerves. The motor root, which forms the main part of the nerve, arises from the motor nucleus located deep in the substance of the pons. Initially the motor root courses backward and medialward; it then makes a complete bend and emerges at the lower border of the pons, between the olive and inferior cerebellar peduncle, in the immediate vicinity of the acoustic nerve. The sensory root arises from the genicular ganglion. The central processes of the ganglion cells leave the trunk of the facial nerve in the internal auditory meatus as the sensory root. It enters the pons near the motor root and terminates in a nucleus called the tractus solitarius. From their superficial points of origin the two roots course (in the company of the acoustic nerve) to the internal auditory meatus and enter the facial nerve canal located at the bottom of the meatus. The facial nerve canal takes a rather complex course through the petrous portion of the temporal bone, at first coursing lateralward; then bending abruptly it courses backward and downward where it terminates at the stylomastoid foramen. The point where the facial nerve canal changes course is known as the geniculum, and it contains the genicular ganglion or nucleus of the sensory root. Several nerves emerge from the genicular ganglion, one of them being the greater superficial petrosal nerve. It is mainly sensory and supplies the mucous membrane of the soft palate. While still in the canal the facial nerve sends off motor-nerve fibers to the stapedius muscle and also gives off the chorda tympani, the fibers of which join the mandibular branch of the trigeminal nerve and ultimately terminate in the mucous membrane of the anterior two-thirds of the tongue, where they constitute the nerve of taste for that part of the tongue. Upon emerging from the stylomastoid foramen, the facial nerve gives off branches which supply the auricular muscles, the posterior belly of the digastric muscle, and the stylohyoid muscle. The main trunk of the nerve courses forward through the substance of the parotid gland and continues behind the ramus of the mandible. During its course it gives off numerous small branches which have an extensive distribution over the side of the head, face, and upper-neck region.

The temporal branch supplies the anterior and superior auricular muscles, the frontalis, orbicularis oculi, and the corrugator muscles. The posterior auricular nerve supplies the posterior auricular muscle. Zygomatic branches supply the orbicularis oculi, while the buccal branches supply the superficial muscles of the face and the small muscles of the nose. Other fibers of the buccal branch supply the buccinator muscle and the orbicularis oris. The mandibular branch supplies the muscles of the lower lip, while the cervical branch supplies the platysma muscle.

Cranial Nerve VIII (Acoustic). The acoustic nerve is a composite sensory nerve, consisting of two separate parts known as the cochlear and vestibular nerves. These nerves differ in their peripheral endings, functions, and central connections. They form a common trunk only when entering the internal auditory meatus. The cochlear nerve was considered in some detail in the previous chapter. A brief review will suffice. It arises from the cells in the spiral ganglion of the cochlea. The peripheral fibers pass to the cochlea, while the central fibers course through the canal of the modiolus and continue into the internal auditory meatus. Its fibers end in the ventral and dorsal cochlear nuclei. The vestibular nerve arises from cells in the vestibular ganglion (of Scarpa). Three peripheral branches supply the utricle, ampullae, and the saccule.

The central fibers follow the course of the cochlear nerve and terminate in the vestibular nucleus, which is located on the lateral floor and wall of the fourth ventricle in the pons and medulla oblongata.

Cranial Nerve IX (Glossopharyngeal).   The glossopharyngeal nerve contains both motor and sensory fibers, which, as the name implies, supply the tongue and pharynx, It also carries fibers of the autonomic nervous system. From its superficial origin in a groove between the olive and inferior cerebellar peduncles, the nerve courses lateralward and emerges from the cranium by way of the jugular foramen. In the foramen the nerve presents two enlargements, the superior and inferior ganglia. For our purposes the superior ganglion may be disregarded. The inferior ganglion contains cell bodies for the sensory fibers of the glossopharyngeal nerve, although motor fibers course through it. The glossopharyngeal nerve gives off several branches, some of which are directly associated with the speech mechanism. The tympanic branch, for example, supplies parasympathetic fibers to the parotid gland and also supplies the mucous membrane of the middle-ear cavity and the Eustachian tube. The carotid sinus nerve supplies the internal carotid artery with sensory fibers for the blood-pressure receptors. The pharyngeal branches supply the mucous membrane of the pharynx, while a single motor branch supplies the stylopharyngeal muscle. A complex system of tonsillar and lingual branches supplies the mucous membrane of the palatine tonsils, the fauces, soft palate, and posterior portion of the tongue. In addition, special visceral sensory fibers innervate the taste buds on the posterior portion of the tongue and constitute the nerve of taste for that part of the tongue.

Cranial Nerve X (Vagus)   The vagus nerve, so named because of its wandering course, has an extensive distribution through the neck and thorax and extends into the abdomen. The superficial origin of the vagus nerve consists of a number of small rootlets, which emerge between the olive and inferior peduncle just beneath the roots of the glossopharyngeal nerve. The nerve leaves the cranium by way of the jugular foramen, at which point it presents two enlargements, the jugular and nodose ganglia. They contain cells for the sensory portion of the nerve. Branches from the ganglia join several of the other cranial nerves, and others supply sensory fibers to the dura mater and the integument of the posterior portion of the external ear and external auditory meatus. In the neck the vagus gives off several branches, some of which directly serve the speech mechanism. In addition, the vagus receives fibers from other cranial nerves. Motor fibers from the accessory nerve, for example, enter the vagus and emerge as the recurrent nerve. Thus, although many of the nerve fibers which supply the larynx emerge from the vagus nerve, they actually arise from the accessory nerve.

The pharyngeal branch of the vagus contains both sensory and motor fibers, which supply the muscles and mucous membrane of the pharynx and soft palate (except the tensor veli palatini). The superior laryngeal branch divides into external and internal branches. The external branch is motor and supplies the cricothyroid muscle and part of the inferior pharyngeal constrictor. The internal branch is sensory. It supplies the mucous membrane of the base of the tongue and also pierces the thyrohyoid membrane to supply the mucous membrane of the supraglottal portion of the larynx.

The recurrent nerve is so named because it arises from the vagus at a point on the

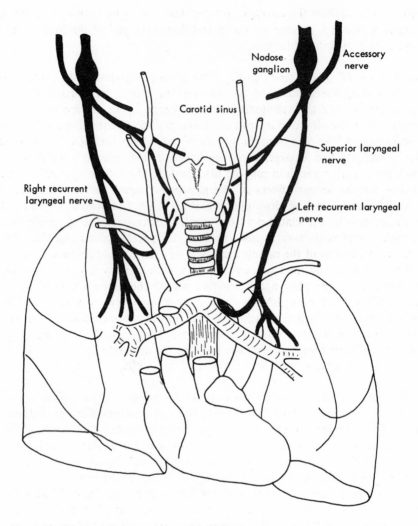

Fig. 7–29. Course of the laryngeal branches of the vagus nerve.

nerve considerably below the larynx. It ascends to terminate at the larynx, where it supplies the subglottal laryngeal mucosa and all of the intrinsic muscles of the larynx except the cricothyroid. The right recurrent nerve loops behind the right common carotid and subclavian arteries at their junction and courses vertically to the larynx. The left recurrent laryngeal nerve leaves the vagus at a lower level than does the right. It loops under and behind the aortic arch and ascends in a groove located between the trachea and esophagus to enter the larynx through the cricothyroid membrane. It is also distributed to the subglottal laryngeal mucosa and all the intrinsic laryngeal muscles, excepting, as noted before, the cricothyroid. The course of the recurrent nerve is shown in Figure 7–29. Small branches leave the recurrent nerve and supply the mucous membrane and muscles of the esophagus and trachea. As the vagus continues in its downward course, it gives off branches that supply such structures as the pericardium, stomach, pancreas, spleen, kidneys, intestines, and liver.

Cranial Nerve XI (Accessory).   The accessory is a motor nerve and consists of a cranial and a spinal portion. The fibers of the cranial part arise from the nucleus ambiguous and emerge from the side of the medulla oblongata by means of four or five small rootlets. It then courses laterally and passes through the jugular foramen. Branches from the accessory connect with the jugular ganglion of the vagus. The remainder of the fibers are distributed to the pharyngeal and superior branches of the vagus nerve. The cranial portion of the accessory nerve thus supplies the uvula and levator veli palatini. Other fibers of the cranial portion continue into the trunk of the vagus, and are distributed with the recurrent nerve. The fibers of the spinal portion arise from the motor cells in the anterior horn of the spinal cord and emerge as motor roots from the cervical nerves one through four or five. The fibers unite to form a single nerve trunk, which ascends alongside the spinal cord and enters the cranium through the foramen magnum. It then follows the course of the cranial portion, emerging through the jugular foramen, at which point it receives fibers from the cranial portion. The spinal portion supplies motor fibers to the sternocleido-mastoid and trapezius muscles.

Cranial Nerve XII (Hypoglossal).   The hypoglossal is primarily a motor nerve and, as the name implies, supplies the tongue. The fibers arise from the hypoglossal nucleus and emerge from the brain between the pyramid and olive. The nerve leaves the skull by way of the hypoglossal canal, located just lateral to the foramen magnum. The nerve then descends, coursing between the internal carotid artery and jugular vein and at the same time giving off communicating branches to other cranial nerves and to the first cervical nerve. Its motor fibers are distributed to extrinsic muscles of the tongue. They include the sternohyoid, sternothyroid, thyrohyoid, styloglossus, hyoglossus, genioglossus, geniohyoid, mylohyoid, and the anterior belly of the omohyoid muscle. In addition, the nerve supplies all the intrinsic muscles of the tongue, and may supply the tongue with some sensory nerve fibers.

The spinal nerves

Ordinarily thirty-one pairs of nerves arise from the spinal cord. They leave the vertebral canal by way of intervertebral foramina. The spinal nerves emerge in the form of dorsal (afferent) and ventral (efferent) roots. For the most part, the ventral root arises from the ventral and lateral regions of spinal gray matter, while the dorsal root arises from the dorsal and medial gray matter. Near or in each intervertebral foramen is an oval-shaped swelling of the dorsal root, the spinal ganglion. It contains the cell bodies of the somatic and visceral afferent neurons in the nerve root. As shown in Figure 7–30, the dorsal and ventral roots join just beyond the spinal ganglion to form a completed spinal nerve, which then makes its exit through the intervertebral foramen. The spinal nerves are divided, on a topographical basis, into eight cervical pairs, twelve thoracic, five lumbar, five sacral, and one coccygeal. Conventionally they are referred to in an abbreviated form. Thus, the third cervical nerve appears as C–3, while the first lumbar is L–1.

The first pair of cervical nerves leaves between the first cervical vertebra and the occipital bone, and the remaining cervical nerves leave above their corresponding vertebrae, with the exception of the eighth cervical nerve, which leaves above the first thoracic vertebra. The remainder of the spinal nerves leave below their numerically corresponding vertebrae. Because of the relationship of the spinal nerves with

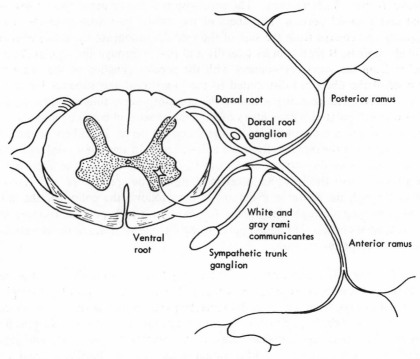

Dorsal root

Posterior ramus

Dorsal root ganglion

Ventral root

White and gray rami communicantes

Sympathetic trunk ganglion

Anterior ramus

Fig. 7–30. Schematic of the arrangement of a typical spinal nerve.

the segmented vertebral column, the spinal cord is often divided into segments, one for each pair of nerves. Although there is no visual evidence of actual segmentation of the cord, a certain segmental characteristic is retained in the ultimate distribution of the spinal nerves. Due to the comparatively slow growth rate of the spinal cord in relation to the spinal column, the mature spinal cord extends only to about the lower border of the first lumbar vertebra. Consequently, successive roots take an increasingly vertical course toward their respective foramina. The roots of the cervical nerves run horizontally, those of the thoracic nerves course obliquely downward, and those of the lumbar and sacral nerves course vertically, as shown schematically in Figure 7–31. The collection of vertically directed lumbar and sacral nerve roots is known as the cauda equina.

Immediately after leaving the intervertebral foramen, each spinal nerve divides into a posterior or dorsal and an anterior or ventral ramus, shown in Figure 7–30. Each ramus carries fibers from both the ventral and dorsal roots; that is, each ramus carries both sensory and motor fibers.

The posterior rami are distributed to the deep and superficial muscles of the back and to the integument of the back. The muscles supplied by the posterior rami are, for the most part, postural.

The anterior rami of the spinal nerves have a rather extensive distribution, which will be discussed very grossly. Later in the chapter the specific muscles of the speech mechanism supplied by the anterior rami will be discussed. The anterior rami of the first four cervical nerves join by communicating branches to form the cervical plexus, and

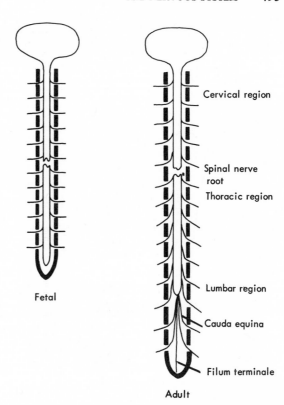

Fetal

Cervical region

Spinal nerve root

Thoracic region

Lumbar region

Cauda equina

Filum terminale

Adult

Fig. 7–31. The course of the spinal nerves in the spinal columns of a fetal and an adult nervous system.

bundles of fibers from the cervical plexus, in turn, communicate with some of the cranial nerves, especially those that supply the facial and anterior neck regions. An important branch of the cervical plexus is the phrenic nerve. It contains both sensory and motor fibers, and is distributed to the diaphragm.

The anterior rami of the lower four cervical nerves, plus the first thoracic, unite to form the brachial plexus. It supplies muscles and integument of the chest and upper limb.

The anterior rami of the upper eleven thoracic nerves course between the ribs, and are known appropriately as intercostal nerves. Unlike the cervical nerves they follow independent courses. As might be expected these nerves supply the sacrospinalis and intercostal muscles and the integument of the thorax. Sensory branches also supply the parietal pleura. The lower six thoracic nerves also supply the muscles of the abdominal wall.

The anterior rami of the lumbar, sacral, and coccygeal nerves join to form the lumbosacral plexus. It is a very elaborate network, and for descriptive purposes is usually divided into the lumbar, sacral, and pudendal plexuses, which together supply the trunk and lower limbs.

The Autonomic Nervous System

Although the autonomic system is very complex and difficult to describe, it can be defined simply as a division of the peripheral nervous system which supplies the

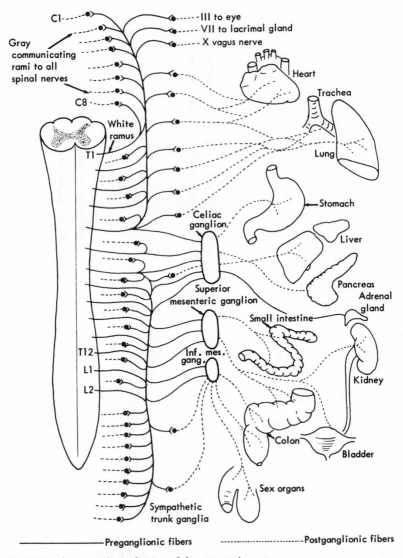

Fig. 7–32. The sympathetic division of the autonomic system.

smooth muscles and glands throughout the body. Because of the nature and functions of the structures supplied by it, the autonomic nervous system is also known variously as the visceral efferent system, involuntary, or vegetative nervous system. Although there is not a great deal of difference between the somatic efferent and visceral efferent systems, there is an interesting morphological difference between them. Two neurons are required to carry an impulse from the central nervous system to an effector in the viscera, while only a single neuron is required to carry an impulse from the central nervous system to a skeletal effector.

By definition the autonomic system is a motor (efferent) system. Autonomic nerves, however, do carry visceral afferent fibers, and so in the past the autonomic system has been described as being composed of an afferent and efferent division. Strictly

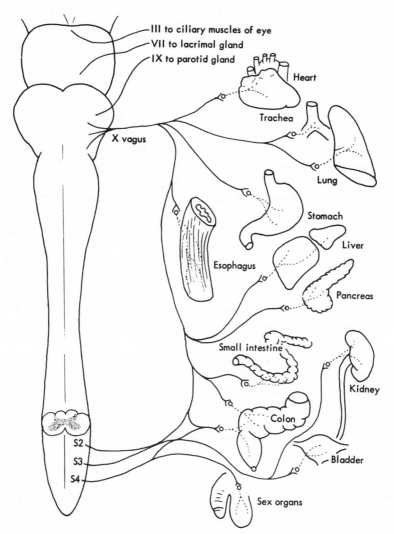

Fig. 7–33. Parasympathetic division of the autonomic system.

speaking the visceral afferent fibers are part of the peripheral, and not the autonomic nervous system. The autonomic nervous system can be divided, however, on both a morphological and a physiological basis, into the sympathetic or thoracolumbar and the parasympathetic or craniosacral systems. The sympathetic system receives outflow from the thoracic and lumbar segments of the spinal cord, and its ganglia are located near the spinal column. The parasympathetic system receives outflow from the cranial and sacral portions of the central nervous system, and its ganglia tend to be located peripherally, near the structures that are supplied.

Together, the sympathetic and parasympathetic systems constitute a highly integrated mechanism that helps maintain a constant internal body environment. As may be seen in Figures 7–32 and 7–33, many visceral structures are supplied by both systems. In certain situations the sympathetic system may dominate the function of these structures and prepare the body to cope with emergencies or periods of excitement. In other situations the parasympathetic system may dominate the functions of the same structures and act in antagonism to the effects of the sympathetic system. Generally speaking the sympathetic system mobilizes the body for emergency or threatening situations, while the parasymphathetic system acts to conserve body resources.

The Sympathetic or Thoracolumbar System.   In addition to the anterior and posterior rami, some spinal nerves, especially in the thorax and lumbar regions, give rise to additional branches known as the white rami communicantes. These branches contain myelinated fibers whose cell bodies are in the lateral column of spinal gray matter. The axons of these cells constitute the preganglionic fibers of the sympathetic nervous system. As illustrated in Figure 7–30, they leave the spinal cord as part of the ventral root and continue to the trunk ganglia of the sympathetic chain. They are two nerve cords, extending from the base of the skull to the coccyx, one on either side of the vertebral column. Each cord consists of a series of swellings or ganglia, placed one above the other and interconnected by short nerve bundles. There are 21 or 22 ganglia in each chain, 3 or 4 associated with cervical nerves, 10 or 11 with thoracic, 4 with lumbar, and 4 with sacral nerves.

Upon entering the trunk (or chain) ganglia, the preganglionic fibers may synapse with a number of ganglion cells, course up or down in the sympathetic trunk, and synapse with ganglion cells at higher or lower levels, or they may continue through the trunk ganglia and course to collateral ganglia located deep in the body. These preganglionic fibers may give off collaterals during their course through the sympathetic trunk, so that a single preganglionic fiber may communicate with a dozen or more postganglionic neurons. Postganglionic fibers have their cell bodies located in the trunk ganglia. Their axons, which are largely unmyelinated, course back to the spinal nerves by means of delicate nerve bundles called the gray rami. While each spinal nerve receives a gray ramus, the distribution of white rami is more limited and is confined to the thoracic and first four lumbar nerves. Thus, the white rami carry preganglionic fibers from the central nervous system to the sympathetic trunk,[2] and the gray rami carry postganglionic fibers from the sympathetic trunk to the spinal nerves. After joining the spinal nerves, the postganglionic (visceral efferent) fibers are distributed along with somatic fibers, and ultimately supply the smooth muscle and glandular tissue throughout the body.

The Parasympathetic (Craniosacral) Division.   The preganglionic fibers of the parasympathetic division arise from cell bodies in the gray matter of the brain stem and from the middle three segments of the sacral portion of the spinal cord. In general, they course uninterruptedly from their origin to the structures they supply, where they synapse with ganglion cells that give rise to postganglionic fibers. Thus, preganglionic parasympathetic fibers are very long when compared with preganglionic sympathetic fibers.

---

[2] The white rami also carry visceral afferent fibers. They traverse the autonomic ganglia and continue on to supply the viscera. The course of the visceral afferent fibers follows a pattern very similar to the course of somatic afferent fibers.

Parasympathetic fibers are carried by the occulomotor, facial, glossopharyngeal, and vagus nerves, and they supply the muscles of the eye, the salivary glands, and the glands in the mucous membrane of the nose, soft palate, tonsils, lips, and gums. They also supply muscles of the heart, and may supply the mucous membrane of the larynx to some extent. Parasympathetic fibers arising in the sacral region supply the pelvic viscera.

The Structure of Neurons

Imagine two persons, each faced with the task of describing a city. One sees it at night from the window of a plane, and he describes a wide, multicolored expanse, characterized by orderly rows of tiny lights, elaborate systems of freeways, and almost never-ending streams of traffic that suggest pleasant suburban living, away from the city. The other person sees the city in early morning from the window of a train, and he describes junkyards, sagging back porches, dust and rubbish blowing about tall, gray buildings, and almost never-ending streams of people, facing a biting wind and always in a hurry to get somewhere without ever quite knowing why. Both persons may produce accurate, vivid descriptions that are representative of the city in terms of the way in which they viewed it, yet both are aware that neither description is truly characteristic of the city when seen in all its aspects.

A person bent on describing the nervous system or, indeed, a single nerve cell is faced with problems that are not unlike those encountered by our two sightseers. Structures revealed in the study of a neuron are largely dependent upon the techniques used to view it and equally dependent upon the method of preparation of the specimen. A microscopic view of a freshly killed neuron is completely different from a view of a fixed and stained specimen, mounted on a glass slide. In addition, ordinary tissue-staining techniques reveal little of a neuron, except its nucleus and cell body, while special (silver) stains reveal many of the intricate details of nerve fibers and the shapes of the cell bodies. Other stains may produce certain artifacts, structures that do not even exist in the living neuron.

A neuron, which is commonly regarded as the functional unit of the central nervous system, consists of a nucleated cell body and cytoplasmic extensions or processes, which may be classfied as axons or dendrites (sometimes called dendrons). Often, a functional distinction is made between axons and dendrites; that is, it is often stated that axons conduct impulses away from the cell body and dendrites conduct impulses toward it. While this is often true, such a generalization may be hazardous and in fact may contradict the histological distinctions that can be made between axons and dendrites.

The primary process of a neuron is the axon, or axis cylinder. Axons are characterized by a rather uniform thickness, a lack of side branches, and often their length. As shown in Figure 7–34, an axon's point of attachment to a cell body is characterized by a cone-shaped expansion called the axon hillock. Axons vary considerably in length, from less than a millimeter to a meter. Although a neuron usually has but a single axon, it may give off side branches, or collaterals, usually near the cell body. The terminal endings of axons usually consist of a multitude of fine filaments called telodendria, and they, collectively, are known as the end brush. The very tips of the telodendria often appear as minute loops or swellings called the terminal buttons (*boutons terminaux*). They occur most frequently in the central nervous system.

Neurons are often classified on the basis of the length of their axons. Those with long axons are known as Golgi's type I, while those with short axons that branch repeatedly in the vicinity of the cell body are Golgi's type II cells.

Most neurons possess several dendrites, and their cytoplasm retains most of the characteristics of the cell body from which they arise. Their origin is by means of a wide, ill-defined base, but they taper rapidly and terminate very near the cell body. It seems that dendrites effectively increase the surface area of a neuron, thus facilitating association with other neurons.

Like other cells, a nerve-cell body (which may also be called perikaryon or cyton) consists of a nucleus surrounded by cytoplasm. The nucleus is comparatively large, generally spherical, and contains a rather large nucleolus. The cytoplasm is enclosed by a cell membrane that seems to consist of alternating layers of proteins and lipids (fat-like substance). According to Gardner (1964) the cell membranes are less than 200 Å in thickness. Lipids have the property of insolubility in water and probably provide an effective barrier to diffusion of water through the membrane. Small pores in the membrane (3 Å) are large enough to permit diffusion of certain ions, a point to be considered in some detail later.

When properly fixed and stained, the cytoplasm reveals mitochondria (cytoplasmic filaments) and Golgi apparatus, plus Nissl granules and neurofibrils, which are especially characteristic of nerve cells. The Nissl granules, or bodies, appear to be a granular-like substance, which differs among the various types of nerve cells. For example, primary somatic motor neurons are characterized by large flakes of Nissl substance, while visceral motor neurons contain slightly smaller flakes. Sensory neurons, on the other hand, usually contain fine granules of Nissl substance. In addition, Nissl substance is present in the dendrites of cells, while the axons and their hillocks are usually free of it. It seems that Nissl substance is in a state of solution or suspension in living neurons. It is not visible in living cells and seems to be precipitated in the form of granules either by death or by the fixing process. Ranson and Clark (1959) state that although Nissl substance, as it appears in fixed preparations, represents a fixation artifact, similar cells always present similar Nissl Patterns after fixation. A peculiar "behavioral" characteristic of Nissl substance has proved valuable in the study of neurons and the nervous system. When the primary process of a neuron is severed or injured, the cell body usually demonstrates a phenomenon called chromatolysis (a disintegration of Nissl substance), and the cytoplasm appears lightly stained and without granules after preparation. Thus, the status of Nissl substance (in fixed and stained specimens) seems to be fairly valid index of the functional integrity of a neuron. The results of research within recent years strongly suggests that Nissl substance has a metabolic function. It has been found to consist chiefly of a nucleoprotein, ribose nucleic acid (RNA), which seems to be depleted during intense nerve activity and must constantly be replaced.

Depending on the staining techniques used, neurofibrillae may appear to be fine, filament-like fibers which are unevenly distributed throughout the neuron, or they may appear (probably correctly) as fibers which anastomose with each other to form a true network. Neurofibrillae extend into the nerve processes, and can be traced to the terminal endings of both axons and dendrites. Neurofibrillae may have a function

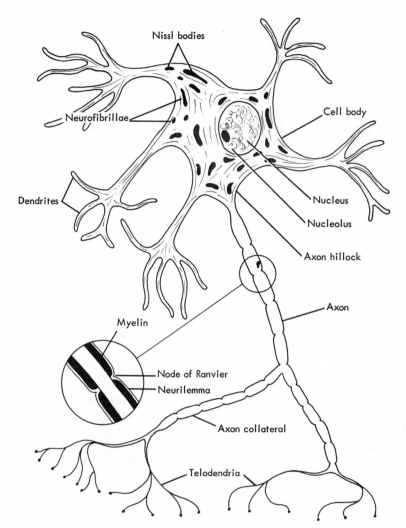

Fig. 7–34. Illustration of a neuron showing cell body and processes.

related to the metabolism of the neuron, but exactly how is not known. An alternate theory is that they contribute to the transmission of nerve impulses. The fact that they can be traced through the full extent of the neuron may provide supportive evidence for this latter line of thought. Neurofibrillae are helpful in histological studies of nerve tissue. They stain differentially and help distinguish nerve tissue from surrounding supportive tissue.

Pigment granules are also found in the cytoplasm of nerve-cell bodies. In certain areas of the brain, for example, the substantia nigra, the cells contain large amounts of melanin (a black pigment). This accounts for the dark appearance of the nucleus. In addition, yellow granules appear and accumulate with advancing age. No significance has been assigned to this pigmentation.

Neurons vary widely in the complexity of their forms depending on the shape of the perikaryon and on the number and shapes of their processes. Although the diversity is almost without limit, neurons are all too often categorically typed as unipolar, bipolar, or multipolar. These terms have persisted for years, but do not clarify much of anything; in fact at times they contribute to confusion. It may be of value to give a few examples of the forms of neurons and, at the same time, assign the commonly used descriptive terms employed to type them.

Early in the development of the embryo, many neuroblasts in the neural crest develop two processes which extend in opposite directions from the cell body. These cells are termed, quite appropriately, bipolar. Later, however, rapid growth of the cell body causes the poles of the cell to move together, until the nerve processes fuse at their point of emergence from the cell body. The resultant cell is now called unipolar, and its single short process is abruptly divided into a central and a peripheral branch. The peripheral process normally conducts an impulse toward the cell body and serves the office of a dendrite, while the central process conducts the impulse away from the cell body (toward the central nervous system) and functions as an axon. The peripheral process may be referred to as a dendrite or as an afferent axon. On a histological basis, however, it ought to be called an afferent axon, and not a dendrite.

In a few selected regions, particularly the spiral and vestibular ganglion, the bipolar cells retain their embryonic structure, and their peripheral processes are properly referred to as afferent axons, while the central processes are efferent axons. You may recall that in the previous chapter the peripheral processes of the spiral ganglion cells were referred to as dendrites. This terminology was used solely as a matter of expediency (at the expense of accuracy). Thus, the author has been guilty (knowingly) of perpetuating the confusion between function and structure. Perhaps it would clarify matters to state that the duties of a dendrite are always to conduct impulses toward the cell body, while the duties of axons are to conduct impulses either toward or away from the cell body; that is, an axon may be afferent or efferent. Thus, the "axiom" that a neuron has but a single axon also turns out to be rather tenuous. The pyramidal cells of the motor cortex and the primary motor neurons provide adequate examples of the multipolar neurons. They are characterized by numerous dendrites and a single, rather long axon.

Inasmuch as axons constitute the major communicating pathways from central nervous system to effectors, from receptors to the central nervous system, and from one part of the central nervous system to another, it ought to come as no surprise to learn that a great deal of the bulk of the nervous system is axionic. The transmission paths are composed of axionic nerve fibers.

Nerve-cell bodies are somewhat brown or gray in color, and when they appear in vast numbers, the tissue takes on a gray color. Nerve fibers, on the other hand, may appear either gray or white when they appear in the aggregate. Many nerve fibers (axons) are ensheathed either by a lipoid tissue called myelin, by a tubular covering called neurilemma, or by both myelin and neurilemma. Other fibers are devoid of a covering, and are referred to as naked fibers. Depending on their coverings, four possible types of nerve fibers can be identified.

1. Naked fibers (without myelin or neurilemma)
2. Unmyelinated fibers with a neurilemma
3. Myelinated fibers without a neurilemma.
4. Myelinated fibers with a neurilemma.

Naked fibers are particularly common in the gray matter and in some paths in the brain and spinal cord. Unmyelinated fibers with a thin neurilemma were first described by Remak in 1838, and so are most often referred to as Remak fibers. They are particularly abundant in the autonomic nervous system. Many afferent fibers of the cerebrospinal nerves are also unmyelinated, but possess a neurilemma. Such fibers tend to occur in groups with a single, common neurilemmal sheath. Myelinated (medullated, white) fibers without a neurilemma are found in the brain and spinal cord. These fibers are invested by the fibers and nuclei of neuroglial cells. In all probability the myelin sheaths of the fibers in the central nervous system are formed by oligodendrocytes. Myelin does not form simultaneously with the nerve fibers, but rather makes its appearance after the nerve process has reached a rather advanced stage of development. In fact, myelinization of some nerve fibers is not completed until late childhood. Myelin forms a segmented covering around the nerve fiber, but it does not continue to the final termination of the fiber, and it usually does not continue past the axon hillock. The cell bodies of the spiral and vestibular ganglia, however, are exceptional in that they are covered by myelin.

The bulk of the peripheral nervous system contains fibers surrounded by a relatively thick myelin sheath, over which is a covering of a nucleated neurilemma. Neurilemma is a very thin membranous sheath consisting of cylindrical cells placed end to end along the nerve fiber. As shown in Figure 7–34, a rather pronounced constriction appears at fairly regular intervals, marking the limits of an individual cell. As a result, a nerve fiber ensheathed with neurilemma is characterized by rather equally spaced constrictions, called the nodes of Ranvier. At each constriction, the underlying myelin is completely interrupted. The gross appearance of such a nerve fiber is sometimes likened to a string of long sausages. Neurilemma apparently has an ectodermal origin from cells in the neural crest that are similar to oligodendria in the neural tube. Myelin also seems to be produced by the same cells that give rise to neurilemma. Or, to put it another way, the neurilemma is responsible for the formation of the myelin sheath. All axons in the peripheral nervous system, myelinated or not, possess a neurilemma. In addition to forming myelin, neurilemma also plays an important role in the regeneration of damaged nerve fibers. It might be worth deviating from our relatively strict anatomical description of the nervous system just long enough to examine briefly the way an injured nerve fiber may regenerate.

Degeneration and regeneration of peripheral nerve fibers

When a peripheral nerve fiber is cut or severely injured, it cannot be replaced by mitotic cell division. Permanent loss of the nerve fiber, however, is not inevitable, for under favorable conditions it may regenerate. At first the distal portion of the severed axon begins to degenerate slowly (Wallerian degeneration), a process that may require several days. The axis cylinder and myelin sheath disintegrate, forming small, fat droplets along the course of the nerve fiber. The degeneration begins distally and progresses proximally toward the cell body, but usually does not involve the next neuron. The neurilemmal sheath, however, does not degenerate, but rather its cells near the site of injury proliferate to form a scar tissue. At this stage, the situation may become rather static. The remaining distal portion of the neurilemmal tube may persist for months, but if development of a new axon fails to occur, the tube may slowly shrink.

Changes also occur in the proximal portion of the neuron. It may undergo a limited "retrograde" degeneration, usually to the first node of Ranvier, or the entire proximal portion of the process may completely degenerate, in that event the entire cell soon dies. If, however, the cell should survive the trauma, the stump of its axis cylinder will begin to grow distally. Fine filaments find their way through the scar tissue. Usually their path is tortuous, and may be misdirected, until eventually a few fibers find their way into the distal part of the neurilemmal tube. Some fibers may never cross the scar tissue, and in fact they may even turn back and course for a short distance toward the cell body. When the fibers finally reach the distal segment of the neurilemma, their rate of growth is substantially accelerated. Once the new axis cylinder has reached the site of its predecessor, terminal endings develop, and the nerve fiber is once again functional.

A rather important point to note is that the nerve fibers of the central nervous system, which do not possess a neurilemma, are not able to regenerate, at least to any significant extent. Although it is probably a gross oversimplification, the neurilemma seems to provide the path for growth of new axis cylinders, and in addition, may provide the necessary nutrition to the developing axon. Also, new axons tend to become myelinated shortly after their development, a condition which may be produced by the neurilemma or by the axis cylinder itself. Ranson and Clark (1959) credit the axon for the production of new myelin.

Neuroglia

Aside from nerve tissue and blood vessels, another type of tissue is found in the central nervous system. It is called neuroglia, and forms the primary supportive tissue of the brain and spinal cord. Neuroglia has acquired a sort of generic connotation, for it includes neuroglia proper, astrocytes, oligodendroglia, microglia, and ependyma. Neuroglial cells are also known as protoplasmic astrocytes. The cells, which stem from ectoderm, are characterized by an elaborate system of freely branching protoplasmic processes. Because of their appearance they are often called mossy cells. Fibrous astrocytes are confined primarily to the white matter of the central nervous system and are characterized by long, unbranching fibers, which project from the cell body in all directions. Because of their appearance they are often called spider cells. Oligodendroglial cells, smaller than the astrocytes, closely resemble embryonic neurons (bipolar cells); that is, they bear relatively few branches. Oligodendroglia are frequently credited with assisting in the formation of myelin in the central nervous system. It has also been suggested that they have a metabolic function and facilitate the exchange of metabolic products between nerve cells and the brain fluids. Microglial cells have a mesodermal origin. They are found in both white and gray matter and are distinctive because of their small cell bodies and relatively few (two or three) frequently branching processes. They resemble very small protoplasmic astrocytes.

Numerous functions, in addition to a supportive one, have been assigned to neuroglial tissue. Microglial cells, for example, assume the role of scavenger cells in damaged nerve tissue, and oligodendrocytes seem to form much of the "scar tissue" in regions of destruction. The ependyma, which forms a single layer of columnar epithelial cells, seems to have a secretory function. Ependymal cells are particularly abundant in the covering of the choroid plexuses, and seem to function in the manufacture of cerebrospinal fluid.

Neuron excitation and conduction

It has long been recognized that all living tissue, plant and animal, is capable of developing electrical potentials. These potentials, which rarely exceed 100 mV (0.1 Volts), are of special interest to the physiologist, and have been the subject of much attention and speculation for many years. Although these bioelectrical potentials are of a rather small magnitude, with appropriate techniques and instrumentation they can easily be measured and recorded. This is fortunate, for it is widely believed that the measurable bioelectric phenomena are a direct reflection of the excitation states responsible for such vital functions as muscle contraction, impulse transmission in a nerve, and secretion of glandular tissue. In a state of quiet, any two points on the surface of a cell membrane exhibit the same electrical potential. If, however, a suitable electrode is placed on the surface of a cell, without damaging it, and a specially constructed electrode, usually a saline-filled microscopic glass pipette (microelectrode) is thrust into the cytoplasm of the cell, an electrical potential amounting to -50-90 mV will be detected.

Such potential differences have been found to be due to an unequal ion distribution and concentration on either side of the plasma membrane of the cell. An ion is an atom that has either gained or lost an orbital electron and as a consequence has acquired an electrical charge. An atom is normally in a state of balance or electrical equilibrium. This is because the negatively charged electrons just balance the postively charged protons in the nucleus. A chlorine atom, for example, normally contains seven electrons in its outer orbital ring; if it accepts a free electron to make up a full complement of eight in the outer ring, it assumes a negative charge, and is no longer known as an atom but, rather, a negatively charged ion, or anion. Potassium and sodium atoms contain a single electron in their outer ring, and the next outermost ring contains eight electrons. If these atoms lose an electron, they assume a positive charge, and are known as positive ions or cations. As everyone who has taken high school chemistry knows, an exchange of ions across a membrane constitutes a flow of electrical current and, by the same token, current flow causes ions to move.

Chemical analysis of the cytoplasm of nerve cells reveals a concentration of potassium ions (K^+), which may be 20 to 50 times higher than that in extracellular materials. The cytoplasm also contains a high concentration of negative organic ions. On the other hand, the extracellular fluids contain a much higher concentration of positive sodium ions (Na^+), as well as chlorine ions (Cl^-). Thus, although both the intracellular cytoplasm and extracellular tissue contain positive ions, the concentration outside the cell is so much higher than inside that the cell cytoplasm is negative relative to the outside of the membrane. This bioelectrical potential is often spoken of as a membrane potential, and is due to polarization of the cell membrane. If electrodes are carefully placed, one on either side of the cell membrane, a continuous steady or resting potential amounting to as much as 100 mV is recorded. Even if the recording apparatus draws current, the resting potential remains the same. Thus, the charge on the cell membrane must somehow be maintained, and this seems to be due to a selective permeability of the cell membrane.

Potassium (K^+) and chlorine (Cl^-) ions are small and can pass through the membrane, but sodium ions (Na^+) are hydrated (contain water), and are too large to diffuse through the membrane without difficulty. In a resting state the potassium ions (K^+) diffuse through the cell membrane, being attracted by the organic negative ions in the cell. At the same time potassium ions inside the cell diffuse through the cell membrane, being attracted by a lower external concentration. This twoway diffusion is nearly a balancing process, but there is also a steady but slight diffusion of sodium ions (Na^+) from a region of high concentration (inside the cell membrane). If it were not for an additional mechanism, positive sodium ions would ultimately equalize inside and outside the cell membrane, and the resting potential would diminish. It turns out, however, that there is an active process which extrudes sodium ions as fast as they enter the cell, so that the sodium-ion concentration is always kept to about one-tenth of that outside the cell. This active mechanism, which seems to be due to the expenditure of energy by the cell, acts on both potassium and sodium ions, and has been called the sodium-potassium pump, or simply the sodium pump. It operates continuously and maintains the resting potential as long as the cell is intact and alive.

If a neuron retained its resting potential indefinitely, it would be of little use to the nervous system. Many forms of stimuli, heat, mechanical, electrical, or chemical, may produce a sudden change in the resting potential of a neuron. Once stimulated, the only function a neuron has to perform is to conduct impulses, either afferent from peripheral sense organs to the central nervous system or efferent from the central nervous system to the muscles or other effectors. Electricity is most often used as a source of artificial stimulation for neurons. It can easily be controlled and measured and can be applied to either muscle or nerve tissue without causing damage. With suitable electrodes and instrumentation, a number of the electrical changes that follow nerve stimulation can be detected and measured.

Briefly, when a neuron or a nerve fiber is stimulated adequately, a transistory reversal of the resting potential occurs at the excited point. This electrical change travels along the fibers, away from the point of excitation, at a definite velocity, and is quickly followed by a recovery period during which the resting potential is restored. It must be emphasized that to say an electrical disturbance travels up or down a nerve fiber, is not the same as saying that electricity travels along the neuron. An electrical current can be conducted through a killed nerve specimen, but a propagated disturbance (nerve impulse) cannot. A nerve impulse may be described as a short-duration local electrical disturbance which causes a similar disturbance to the adjacent portions of the nerve fiber consecutively along the extent of the fiber. Sometimes a nerve impulse is likened to a train of gunpowder which has been ignited at one end (or in the middle). As the powder burns, it ignites the power ahead of it, and so the combustion moves along the train. This analogy is quite incorrect and is often misleading, because, for one thing, once the combustion has occurred, only the residue of the gunpowder remains.

Rather than resort to analogy, it might be better to demonstrate the wave-like

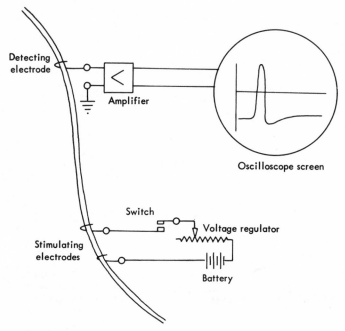

*Fig. 7–35. Method of stimulating a nerve fiber and of detecting
the nerve impulse.*

progression of the electrical changes that occur along the excited nerve fiber by portraying them on an oscilloscope. In Figure 7-35, a small electrode is hooked around a nerve fiber or inserted into it, and a ground electrode is inserted into some adjacent nonnervous tissue fluid. These electrodes are connected to an amplifier and from there to an oscilloscope. Stimulating electrodes are located farther down the nerve fiber.

Suppose that the stimulating current is direct or constant, and can be delivered to the electrodes in varying strengths. In addition, a switch is provided so that the current can be turned on when the switch is made and turned off when the switch contacts break. In order to avoid damaging the neuron, a minimal current strength is used in an initial attempt to excite the neuron, but it turns out that no matter how long the switch is made, the nerve fiber does not demonstrate any electrical changes. As current strength is slowly increased, however, a certain minimal value is finally reached that excites the nerve if the current is left on long enough. This minimal strength of current, which, when left on for an indefinite period of time, produces a nerve stimulation, has been termed the rheobase.

Further experimentation reveals that if the current strength is increased, a shorter current duration time is required for stimulation. In addition, a certain current strength may be reached which does not shorten the required current duration that produces nerve excitation. Also, a certain minimal current duration time is found to exist, and if shorter duration times are used, no amount of current strength excites a nerve fiber or nerve. High-frequency, pulsating currents, for example, may not stimulate

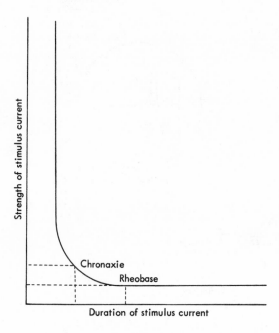

Fig. 7–36. Illustration of the relationship between current strength and duration.

a nerve, regardless of the current strength. The relationship of current strength and duration may be seen when these two parameters are plotted, as in Figure 7–36. It has become common practice to select a current strength that is twice that of rheobase and to determine the current duration required for exicitation at that strength. This time is known as chronaxie or excitation time. Although chronaxie is an arbitrary measure, it has rather predictable values for various types of tissues and for that reason has a very real use in the clinical and laboratory setting.

Having determined values of current strength and duration that constitute an adequate stimulus, we must still determine our criteria measures for what constitutes a response to the stimulus. Some information can be obtained by a close examination of a tracing on the face of the oscilloscope, as in Figure 7–37. At the left of the tracing is a short-duration vertical deflection. It represents the shock or stimulus artifact. The large vertical variation to the right of the stimulus artifact is called the spike potential. Notice that its value changes from that of the resting potential (−50 mV) to almost plus 40 mV, a total of 90 mV. Earlier it was shown that a typical resting potential was about −60 mV. If nerve excitation resulted in complete cell depolarization, the maximum change in amplitude would not reach the value shown in Figure 7–37.

This puzzling state of affairs can be accounted for by the status of ion concentrations during excitation. The application of an adequate stimulus results in a sudden current flow through the cell membrane, and it causes rapid ion flow, which seems to increase the cell-membrane permeability. Quite suddenly, an electrical disturbance caused by ion movement begins to move away from the region of local disturbance. Sodium ions pass readily into the nerve fiber and decrease its negative resting potential. At the same time, of course, the fluid outside the cell membrane has become somewhat devoid of the positive soduim ions. As a result, the potential difference across the membrane is greatly reduced. About the time the concentration of sodium ions reaches maximum inside the cell membrane, the permeability to potassium ions is increased, as rapid outward flow reduces the positive value inside the cell and simultaneously increases the positive value outside it. Concurrent with outward potassium-ion movement, the sodium-ion movement is held back. All of these events, which change the resting potential from a -50 mV value to $+40$ mV take place in about .0005 seconds (.5 mSec).

Later, and much more slowly, the sodium pump begins to transport sodium ions out through the cell membrane, and with the decrease in positive potential due to the loss of sodium ions, the potassium ions begin slowly to permeate through to the inside of the cell membrane, and a gradual repolarization is once again established. The electrical changes which accompany repolarization can also be displayed on an oscilloscope. They are called the after-potentials.

The sharp reversal of potential due to cell depolarization is called the spike potential, or simply the spike, and it, together with the after-potentials, represents the nerve-action potential or nerve impulse. Or, perhaps more accurately, the spike and after-potentials represent the electrical disturbance which occurs at a point on a cell membrane as the disturbance passes that point. The ion movement just described, which consitutes a current flow, sets current flowing through the immediately adjacent and, for the moment, normal membrane. That is, sodium and potassium ions are caused to flow, sodium inward, potassium outward, through the membrane, followed by a restoration process. Meanwhile, however, the normal portion of membrane immediately adjacent to the newly disturbed region, in turn, reacts to the current flow, and the process of cell-membrane disturbance and current flow spreads rapidly over the cell membrane.

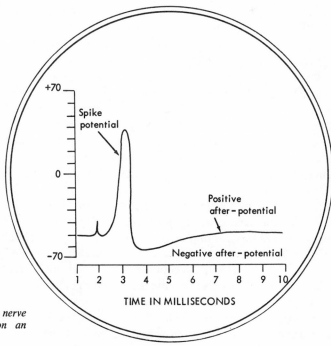

Fig. 7–37. Illustration of a nerve impulse when displayed on an oscilloscope.

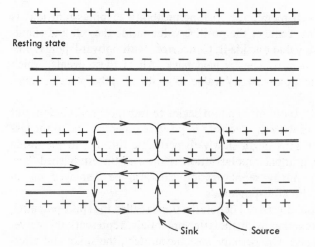

Resting state

Fig. 7–38. Illusiration of the direction of current flow in a nerve fiber during the passage of an impulse.

In Figure 7–38, arrows represent ion flow inward through the depolarized membrane; they also indicate that current (ions) flows longitudinally inside the fiber. It reaches polarized membrane ahead of the depolarized region and also behind it. Current flow in the polarized region is outward. The point where inward current flow occurs is often referred to as the sink, and the point where outward flow occurs is called the source. We see, then, that the source acts as a stimulus to propagate the breakdown of cell membrane. Thus, once a stimulus (electric shock, for example) initiates an impulse, it is self-propagating and is no longer dependent upon the presence of a stimulus. The stimulus simply instigates the process.

When adequate constant current is used, excitation occurs when the circuit is closed and again when it is opened. In the interval between the make and break of the circuit, current flows between the electrodes but does not excite the neuron, provided the current magnitude remains unchanged. The closing, or make, current causes excitation at the cathode (where the current leaves the tissue), while the break current causes excitation at the anode (where current is entering the tissue). The make current is usually the stronger of the two, so that near rheobase, for example, a response may occur with only the make current, the break current being inadequate. During the interval between the make and break of a constant current, the excitability and conductivity of nerve fibers is changed, an effect called electrotonus. Both excitability and conductivity are increased in the region of the cathode (where outward current or ion flow occurs) when current is made, and both these properties are depressed in the region of the anode (inward current or ion flow) during the make. These effects are reversed when the current is broken; that is, there is a momentary increase in excitability and conductivity at the anode and depression of these properties at the cathode. Electrotonus may influence the results obtained in experiments.

An isolated nerve-muscle preparation is shown in Figure 7–39A. Note that the electrodes are located with the cathode nearer the muscle and that during current make the direction of the nerve impulse is descending. During break, however, the depressed excitability and conductivity at the cathode provides an effective block, and so excitation occurs only on the make. With the electrodes reversed, as in Figure 7–39B, excitation does not occur on the make because the depression at the region of the

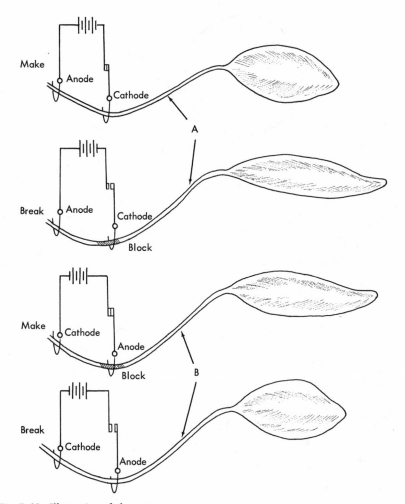

Fig. 7–39. Illustration of electrotonus.

anode provides an effective block. When the current is broken, however, there is an increase of excitability at the anode and a depression at the cathode, so that there is no block between the anode and muscle preparation. Thus excitation can occur only on the current break.

We have seen that if a pair of recording electrodes are spaced along a resting nerve fiber, there is no electrical difference between them. We have also seen that the active or excited part of a nerve fiber is electrically negative with respect to an inactive part. In Figure 7–40, a pair of recording electrodes, connected to a sensitive oscilloscope, is spaced along a nerve fiber. The small arrows indicate the direction of current flow. When a nerve fiber is excited, the impulse travels from the excited portion to the unexcited portion (from − to +). The current flow in the electrodes and apparatus, however, is just the opposite, from the unexcited (+) to the excited (−) portion. Thus, as the arrows indicate, the circuit is a complete one. Earlier we saw that the electrical disturbance detected in such an experiment is called the action potential.

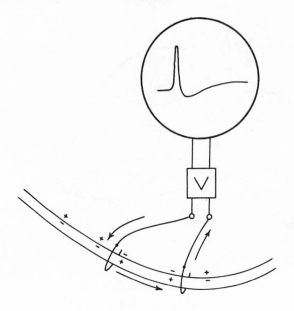

Fig. 7-40. Illustration of direction of current flow in recording
apparatus and in nerve fiber during
passage of a nerve impulse.

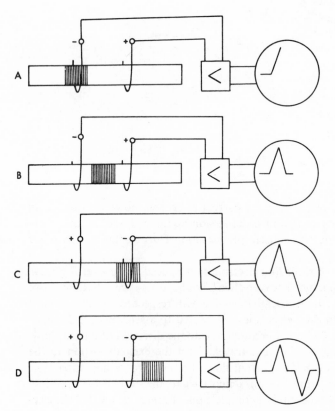

Fig. 7-41. Method of recording
a nerve impulse.

Injured nerve tissue is also somewhat negative with respect to healthy tissue, and when electrodes are placed, one on an injured portion and the other on a healthy portion, current flows through the recording apparatus. It is called the current of injury, or demarcation current.

Depending on the experimental procedure, different types of electrical disturbances may be seen on the oscilloscope. For example, if electrodes are placed on healthy nerve tissue, as in Figure 7–41, it is possible to detect the passage of impulses, whether they are initiated naturally or artificially. When one end of the nerve fiber is stimulated, the impulse arrives at the first electrode (A) and causes it to become negative relative to the second electrode. This is shown on the oscilloscope as a rapid vertical deflection. When the impulse is between the first and second electrodes (B), the difference in potential between them is zero, and so the deflection on the oscilloscope returns to the base line. When the impulse reaches the second electrode (C), it becomes electrically negative with respect to the first, but current through the instrument flows in the opposite direction, and the deflection is downward. And finally, as the impulse passes the second electrode, the potential difference between the first and second electrodes suddenly becomes zero again, and the oscilloscope deflection returns to the base line, as in Figure 7–41D. The tracing observed on the oscilloscope represents the potential changes at each electrode, and a *diphasic* curve is produced.

If, in a slightly different experiment, one electrode is placed on healthy nerve tissue and the other on a portion of nerve fiber that has been crushed or otherwise injured (by insertion of an electrode), the electrical potential resulting from the difference in potential between the injured and uninjured portions will be sharply reduced when the impulse reaches the first electrode; that is, the action potential will be canceled by the current of injury. As a result, the deflection on the oscilloscope will only record the negative variation of the injury current, and since the impulse cannot reach the electrode located on the crushed part of the nerve fiber, a second deflection, in the opposite direction, cannot occur. The electrical disturbance, shown in Figure 7–42, is called a monophasic curve.

Probably the most conspicuous electrical change that is evident in a recording of a nerve impulse is the spike potential. Because the cell membrane is completely depolarized during the presence of a spike potential, it is rendered physiologically incapable of further depolarization or of being receptive to another stimulus. This period corresponds to the absolute refractory period and in motor nerves lasts for about .5 msec. The absolute refractory period is continued into the relative refractory period, during which the threshold of excitability is less than that in the resting state and during which time the impulses, if they occur, are of smaller magnitude. The duration of the relative refractory period is about 3 or 4 msec in motor fibers. Because repolarization of cell membrane is not complete during the relative refractory period, a stronger than usual stimulus is required to initiate an impulse, and for the same reason the magnitude of response is reduced. This period of diminished excitability is continuous with one during which the nerve fiber is more excitable than in the resting state. It is called the supernormal phase, which may last 10 msec or longer, and it corresponds in time to the duration of the negative after-potential. Finally the nerve fiber enters a subnormal phase during which time excitability is less than normal. It lasts up to 70 msec and corresponds in time to the positive after-potential. When

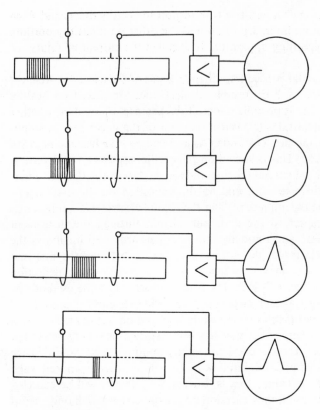

Fig. 7–42. Method of recording a nerve impulse.

a nerve fiber has been subjected to several rapid and successive stimuli, the duration of the supernormal phase and negative after-potential may become sharply reduced, with a proportionate increase in the duration of the subnormal phase and positive after-potential.

Because a nerve fiber is refractory to stimuli during the passage of a spike potential, the number of impulses per unit time is limited. For example, if the total refractory period amounts to 1 msec, the maximum frequency of impulses could not exceed 1,000 per second, and this frequency rate is only an ideal one. The refractory period has been shown to lengthen during continuous transmission at high frequencies.

It has been shown that, within limits, the individual nerve impulse cannot be varied in magnitude or duration by increasing the strength of the stimulus. In other words, a single spike potential carries no information other than that the stimulus was adequate. Yet, in terms of common everyday experience, a stronger stimulus produces an increase in sensation or in response. The increase turns out to be a result of an increase in frequency of nerve impulses, and not due to a change in the characteristics of the individual impulses. When a strong stimulus is applied to a whole motor nerve (as is usually the case in the laboratory) rather than a single fiber, it excites a greater number of nerve fibers than a weak stimulus. Earlier in the text we saw how a single electric shock applied to a muscle produces a single, short-duration contraction. If a motor nerve is stimulated by a succession of stimuli, the resulting contractions tend to become fused into a single sustained contraction, or tetanus. An increase in the magnitude of stimuli causes more nerve fibers to become active and thus facilitate tetanus.

The velocity of nerve impulses was first measured by Helmholtz in 1852. He used a muscle-nerve preparation from a frog leg and measured the difference in time between the application of a stimulus and muscle contraction, when the stimulus was delivered at the extreme upper end of the nerve. He then moved the stimulus electrodes a known distance toward the muscle and repeated the experiment. The difference in latencies obtained in the two experiments was taken as the velocity of nerve impulse, and it amounted to about 30 meters per second. In man, the velocity may be as high as 120 meters per second. With the development of the oscilloscope and other sensitive apparatus, nerve velocity can be determined by recording the times at which a monophasic potential passes two points at a known distance along a nerve fiber.

On the basis of velocity of conduction, mammalian nerve fibers have been divided into three groups. Group A consists of the somatic, medullated fibers, both sensory and motor. They are large fibers, have the shortest chronaxie, and have a conduction velocity of up to 120 meters per second. Collaterals of type A fibers conduct at lower velocities. For this reason, the different fiber components of a single neuron may have quite different conduction rates. Group B consists of the medullated fibers, such as those of the autonomic nervous system. They are smaller in diameter than type A and have longer chronaxies. Their conduction velocities range from 3 to 14 meters per second. Group C consists of fine, nonmedullated fibers, such as those found in the dorsal roots. They have velocites in the vicinity of 0.5 to 1.5 meters per second. Thus, there seems to be a very definite relation between nerve-fiber diameter and conduction velocity. This relationship is such that the product of nerve-fiber diameter in microns and a constant factor of 6 gives the approximate conduction velocity in meters per second. For example, an axon with a diameter of 15 microns has a conduction velocity of about 90 meters per second. The velocity conduction seems to be due, in part, to the presence of myelin. It acts as an electrical insulator and prevents the outward flow of ions, except at the nodes of Ranvier. Consequently, conduction is characterized by outward current flow only at the nodes, and takes place from node to node rather than continuously, as in unmyelinated fibers. In effect, the conduction jumps from node to node in what has been termed saltatory conduction.[3]

Inasmuch as current flows not only inside the cell membrane but outside as well, the question may well be asked whether resting fibers in a nerve might not be affected when adjacent fibers are conducting impulses. It turns out that there is indeed an effect which modifies the excitability of a resting fiber. As the nerve impulse passes a given point of a resting fiber, it becomes at first less excitable, then more excitable, and finally less excitable. Another example of the effect of extracellular current flow is seen when conduction in a portion of a nerve fiber is blocked by cold or pressure (or other effective agents). A nerve impulse may reach the block and suddenly cease, or it may jump the blocked area and continue. That is, the nerve impulse may stop at the block, but the current flow may, under favorable conditions, initiate a new impulse on the other side of it. In effect, the first nerve impulse acts as an artificial stimulus

---

[3] The mechanism of saltatory conduction may be open to some question, and certain research has failed to offer support this type of conduction.

to initiate an impulse on the far side of the block. In the event an actual stimulation fails to occur, the nerve fiber beyond the block may become more susceptible to stimulation.

Once a nerve fiber is stimulated to the extent that cell depolarization is initiated, the process is complete. That is, if a single weak, but nevertheless adequate stimulus initiates a nerve impulse, its characteristics (magnitude of spike potential and duration of after-potential) will be very much the same as an impulse initiated from a much stronger stimulus. This "behavioral characteristic" is often referred to as the all-or-none character of a nerve impulse, or the all-or-none principle. This is not to imply, however, that a "subliminal" stimulus will result in no changes in a nerve fiber. On the contrary, an inadequate stimulus may increase the excitability of a neuron without actually resulting in a nerve impulse.

Very often a nerve impulse is likened to the flow of electric current, but there is a very real and fundamental difference between current flow and a nerve impulse that ought to be pointed out. Electric current is transmitted passively along the conducting medium, and gets progressively weaker as it travels along. A nerve fiber, however, contributes energy that maintains the nerve impulse and transmits it without a decrement. In this sense, a nerve impulse *is* somewhat analogous to combustion along a train of gunpowder. An interesting testimony to the active characteristic of a nerve impulse is seen in an experiment where a nerve impulse, diminished in magnitude due to a local narcosis, suddenly recovers after passing the partial drug block. In other words, if a small portion of a nerve fiber is drugged, the action potentials are reduced in magnitude in the narcotized part of the fiber, and if they are not completely blocked, quickly become normal again when they have passed it.

Synapses

Up until now we have been talking about excitation and conduction in individual nerve cells and nerve fibers. In order that the nervous system may function as the highly integrated, behavior-controlling mechanism it is, excited neurons must somehow initiate impulses in adjacent neurons. Dorsal-root fibers, for example, enter the spinal cord and branch repeatedly. Some branches ascend in the dorsal columns of the spinal cord and terminate at the level of the medulla oblongata, while others terminate in the gray matter of the spinal cord, either at or below the level of entrance. As these fibers terminate they form functional connections with other nerve cells, and their axons, in turn, travel to other nerve cells (or effectors) and establish additional functional connections. In this manner, long and intricate pathways are established in the nervous system. The functional connections between neurons are known as neuronal junctions or synapses. The term functional connection is a good one. It implies, quite accurately, that there is no cytoplasmic continuity of neurons at the synapse.

Although it has long been suspected that individual neurons in a pathway retain their anatomic identity, only in recent years has the electron microscope revealed the structural details of the synapse. A schematic of a pre- and postsynaptic neuron is shown in Figure 7–43, and a schematic electron micrograph of a synapse in shown in Figure 7–44. As an axon approaches another nerve cell, its telodendria terminate by making contact with the surface of a dendrite or with the surface of the body

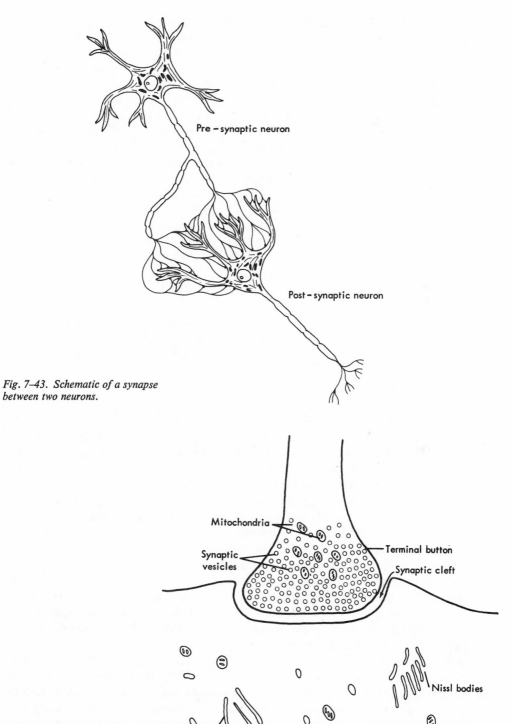

Fig. 7–43. Schematic of a synapse between two neurons.

Pre – synaptic neuron

Post – synaptic neuron

Mitochondria

Synaptic vesicles

Terminal button

Synaptic cleft

Fig. 7–44. Schematic of an electron micrograph of a synapse.

Nissl bodies

Nissl bodies

of the postsynaptic cell. As mentioned earlier in the chapter, each telodendron terminates as a small swelling or loop where it makes synaptic contact with the succeeding cell. These endings, you will recall, are called terminal buttons (*boutons terminaux*). Or, a telodendron may make a synaptic junction by means of a *bouton de passage* and then continue on to synapse with a number of additional nerve cells. A single axon, then, may synapse with a large number of cells, and by the same token any single cell may form synaptic junctions with a number of axons.

The synaptic arrangement by which functional communication may be established between contiguous neurons varies considerably in size, complexity, and arrangement. In spite of the diversity, most synapses have certain characteristics in common. As shown in Figure 7–44, a slight indentation occurs at the point where the dendrite or the cell body is in contact with the terminal button. The two cell membranes have been shown to be distinctively separated but by a "synaptic cleft" of only about .01 microns, a distance beyond the limits of resolution of the light microscope. Mitochondria are especially numerous in the terminal button, and they are thought to supply the cell with energy required for synaptic transmission. In addition, a high concentration of synaptic vesicles is found in the terminal button. These vesicles are thought to contain a vital chemical transmitter which depolarizes the cell membrane below the synaptic cleft.

Although the anatomical arrangements between the axon and the postsynaptic neuron may vary considerably in different regions throughout the body, there is no reason to suppose that the function of different types of synapses is different. It has been repeatedly demonstrated, especially in the laboratory, that a single nerve fiber is able to conduct impulses in both directions. Normally, however, an impulse is conducted in just one direction. Usually the afferent fibers are stimulated at their peripheral endings, while the efferent fibers are activated at their origins within the central nervous system. Functional distinctions are based, not on morphology, but on the connections of nerve fibers. An additional mechanism that dictates the direction of conduction of nerve impulses lies in the properties of the synapse. That is, it is possible to account for unidirectional propagation of nerve impulses on the basis of the properties of the synapse and on the receptiveness of contiguous neurons.

The literature on the subject of synapses has reached inordinately awesome proportions, and a comprehensive discussion of the subject is simply beyond the scope of the text. A very schematic account of synaptic transmission will have to suffice. When action potentials arrive at the terminal button of a presynaptic neuron, the ion flow apparently causes the synaptic vesicles to release or ejaculate a transmitter substance through the cell membrane into the synaptic cleft. This transmitter substance, which has been identified as acetylcholine in the mammalian central nervous system, presumably produces a small, localized ion flow through the post- or subsynaptic cell membrane. Acetylcholine seems to be released at the terminal buttons of the axon, and nowhere else along the course of the neuron. Axionic nerve endings elsewhere in the nervous system seem to release substances similar to acetylcholine. It has been further demonstrated that acetylcholine has a stimulating effect upon the postsynaptic cell. Its presence, however, does not seem to effect the irritability or excitability of the presynaptic axon but only increases the excitability of the postsynaptic neuron at the dendrite or cell body. Picture an impulse traveling in both directions over a neuron, with release of acetylcholine only at the axionic ending (where the synaptic vesicles are concentrated). If such an active neuron is located within a chain of neurons, acetylcholine will be released at the axionic end, thus activating (or tending to activate) the next adjacent (postsynaptic) neuron. No acetylcholine will be released at the dendritic end of the presynaptic neuron, however, and the impulse will not be reinitiated in the adjacent neuron. Thus, it is possible to account for unidirectional propagation of nerve impulses on the basis of the nerve impulse and the receptiveness of adjacent neurons.

With the release of acetylcholine, current flows in the postsynaptic cell membrane, but only for about a millisecond, and the transmitter substance soon becomes ineffective, either through diffusion or by the effect of localized enzymes. It has been demonstrated with reasonable certainty that acetylcholine is destroyed by an enzyme called acetylcholinesterase. Nevertheless, during the short duration acetylcholine is effective, it produces a small depolarization known as the excitatory postsynaptic potential, often abbreviated EPSP. This local effect may not be adequate and may fail to reach threshold; in that event, the nerve impulse simply terminates. The total time required for the generation of an EPSP, even though it may be inadequate, is only a few microseconds. The effect of subsequent (by a very short time interval) or simultaneous impulses from other terminal buttons may significantly alter the magnitude of the EPSP, however, and ultimately prove adequate, in which case the postsynaptic spike potential appears. The cell is said to have fired, and a message is on its way.

At times there is a certain advantage to thinking of a synaptic event in a spatial as well as in a temporal sense. We have seen that the arrival of a nerve impulse at a synaptic region may fail to arouse the succeeding neuron. But if two or more closely successive impulses should arrive, synaptic transmission is more likely to occur. That is, nerve impulses may summate, in a temporal sense, until they are adequate stimuli for the postsynaptic neuron. This summation of impulses is often referred to as temporal summation, and it is shown schematically in Figure 7–45. On the other hand, terminal buttons from one or more axons may impinge upon a single dendritic ending or cell body (as is usually the case), in the event a single impulse from one axon should fail to accomplish the synaptic event, the simultaneous or near simultaneous arrival of impulses from a number of axons may result in synaptic transmission. This type of summation of impulses is called spatial summation, and it is illustrated in Figure 7–46.

It seems that without exception, stimulation of peripheral motor neurons leads to muscle contraction. Most normal motor functions involve two muscles, one acting

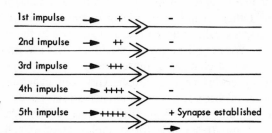

Fig. 7–45. Schematic of temporal summation.

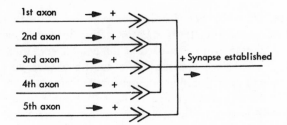

Fig. 7–46. Schematic of spatial summation.

as a flexor and another acting as an extensor. In order that even the simplest reflex response may occur, relaxation of an antagonistic muscle usually takes place. This relaxation seems to be due to an important regulatory activity called nervous inhibition. According to Wilson (1966), inhibition affecting voluntary muscles must reside in the central nervous system, and it can take one of two possible forms. Inhibition of a response may be the result of a reduction of the excitability of a motor neuron or a reduction of the excitatory input reaching it. Most of the research to date has been centered around the mechanism in which the receptiveness of the postsynaptic neuron is reduced, in other words, postsynaptic inhibition.

Much of the pioneer work in inhibitory synapses has been by Sir John Eccles (1965) and his colleagues. They propose a synapse that can inhibit the firing of a neuron in spite of a volley of excitatory impulses, and they further suggest that the inhibitory synapse causes the postsynaptic cell to become more negative than it is during the resting state and thus less likely to be stimulated by excitatory stimuli. One explanation of the inhibitory mechanism is that the transmitter substance released at the inhibitory synapse causes a very selective ion permeability that permits outward flow of potassium ions but not inward flow of sodium ions. The result, of course, would be an increase in extracellular positive-ion concentration and a corresponding decrease in intracellular positive-ion concentration . . . in a word, an increase in negativity and, therefore, a decrease in excitability. Researchers also suggest that a given nerve cell cannot have both excitatory and inhibitory synapses. Rather, two different kinds of nerve cells are required, one for inhibitory and another for excitatory transmission.

Receptors

We have yet to consider how nerve impulses may be initiated in order to effect a response to environmental change. An organism must be able to detect environmental changes and carry out an appropriate response if it is to survive. Environmental changes are detected by highly specialized receptors called exteroceptors. They include receptors which give rise to such sensations as touch, pain, and temperature. Other receptors are sensitive stimuli which usually originate some distance away. They are called teloceptors, and give rise to the special senses of sight, audition, and smell. We are all aware of sensations that are generated within the body. They are the result of changes in muscle or tendon or in position of the body, which are detected by proprioceptors. Other sensations generated within the body are due to stimulation of visceral receptors in such structures as mucous membrane in the nose and throat, bladder, and so forth. Other highly specialized receptors respond to chemical stimuli (taste buds, for example). They are called chemoreceptors. In regions of the skin, where hair is sparsely distributed, tactile nerve endings form a complex network around the root of the hair, and when it is bent or deformed, stimulation occurs. Pain receptors in the skin consist of free nerve endings, which can be stimulated directly. In deep tissues, free nerve endings are often encapsulated by layers of connective tissue. These structures, called Pacinian corpuscles, are receptive to pressure and deformation, rather than pain. The sensation initiated by Pacinian corpuscles is often known as deep touch.

Several types of proprioceptors are located in muscles, tendons, and around joints. The most common seem to be neuromuscular spindles, which are usually located near the junction of muscle and tendon. Each spindle consists of small motor fibers (collaterals) and a limited number of sensory fibers (afferent may be more appropriate), which form either annular spiral endings, or are splayed out on the muscle fibers. These endings are receptive to changes in muscle length caused by tension; that is, they are responsive to being stretched and are often called stretch receptors. On the other hand, contraction of muscle fibers also stimulates the nerve endings. According to Gardner (1964), neuromuscular spindles are concerned chiefly with reflex rather than sensory mechanisms. A schematic of a neuromuscular spindle is shown in Figure 7–47. Although Pacinian corpuscles are present in joints, the most

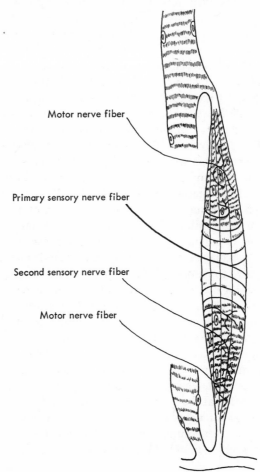

Motor nerve fiber

Primary sensory nerve fiber

Second sensory nerve fiber

Motor nerve fiber

Fig. 7–47. Schematic of a neuro-muscular spindle.

common ending is a modified free nerve ending called the Ruffini-type ending. It is sensitive to position and movement at the joints.

The local electrical changes that occur when a receptor is subjected to stimulation are known as receptor potentials. If a subthreshold stimulus (one that fails to excite the neuron) is applied, a small receptor potentials results, and as the magnitude of the subthreshold stimulus is increased, it is reflected by an increase in the receptor potential. As stimulus values are increased, the receptor potential finally reaches threshold value, and the neuron fires. Receptors also exhibit summating properties.

In accordance with the all-or-none principle, individual nerve impulses, once they are initiated at a receptor, are always the same, regardless of the magnitude of the stimulus. The frequency of impulses, however, will increase with an increase in the value of the adequate stimulus. If a strong stimulus is applied at a receptor, the initial train of nerve impulses will persist for a short duration and then gradually diminish in frequency, until there is only an occasional nerve impulse. This decrement of nerve-impulse frequency is known as adaptation. There is a cessation or decrement of nerve-impulse frequency in spite of continuous stimulation. Adaptation is a characteristic of the nervous system that probably relieves us of many of the conscious consequences of body position that would otherwise be purely redundant. In other words, once a limb has been moved to a certain resting position, there is no need for the receptors to continuously "remind" us where it is. We only need new information when the limb is moved to a new resting position or when continuous movements are involved.

In spite of their specialization, receptors are not exclusively responsive to a specific type of stimulus. Chemical, thermal, and electrical stimuli, when intense enough, can arouse most receptors. Receptors do exhibit a relatively selective sensitivity to certain stimuli, however. Some respond primarily to mechanical stimuli, while others respond to chemical stimuli, and still others respond to light or thermal stimuli. Along with specialization of function, receptors also exhibit specialization in their form. Some receptors seem to be highly differentiated neurons, while others are composed of neurons and specialized epithelial cells, which together make up receptors, especially for the special senses of sight, smell, and audition.

Although you cannot always tell the function of a receptor by its structure, there is a certain relationship between form and function. The sensation of light touch, for example, is initiated by receptors that are responsive to deformation. The nerve endings, which may take the form of small expanded lamellas (tactile discs), are primarily responsive to deformation and not to other stimuli, such as heat.

Having got a nerve impulse generated in an afferent nerve fiber in response to an environmental change, it might be worthwhile to examine briefly the mechanism whereby an efferent nerve impulse is transmitted to the muscles that may effect a response. Whereas nerve impulses are transmitted from one neuron to another at synapses or neural junctions, they are transmitted from neuron to effector at neuroeffector or myoneural junctions. The mechanism of transmission of an excitatory state from neuron to neuron has so many features in common with the transmission from neuron to muscle fiber that the myoneural junction is also known as the myoneural synapse.

As a motor axon approaches skeletal muscle, it first loses its myelin sheath and then usually divides into a number of secondary branches, each of which terminates on the surface of a single muscle fiber on an end plate. Each skeletal muscle fiber has at

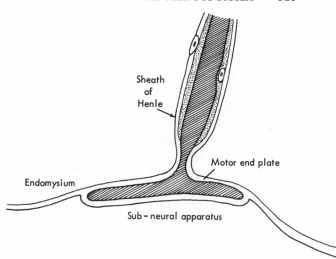

Fig. 7–48. Schematic cross section
of a motor end plate.

least one motor ending, while many have more than one, often derived from different neurons. By the same token, each axon may, and often does, supply a number of skeletal muscle fibers. A nerve cell, its axon, and the muscle fibers supplied by it are known as a motor unit.

As the secondary branch approaches a muscle fiber it divides repeatedly to form fine filaments that arborize in an end plate. These fine filaments are sometimes known as alpha fibers to distinguish them from the main root of the nerve fiber or axis cylinder. They lie flat upon the surface of the sarcoplasm of the muscle fiber, separated from it by a thin membrane called the endoneurium or sheath of Henle. It is a delicate membrane, apparently continuous with the endomysium that binds muscle fibers together. A diagram of a section across a motor end plate is shown in Figure 7–48.

The sarcolemma beneath each end plate is specialized to form what might be called simply the subneural apparatus. It possesses properties similar to the synaptic junction in the central nervous system. For example, it is rich in mitochondria. Sarcolemma, like nerve-cell membrane, is characterized by differences in ion concentrations between its inner and outer surfaces. The interior of a resting muscle fiber is about 50 to 100 mv negative, relative to its surroundings. When an impulse arrives at the motor end plate, acetylcholine is released. It traverses the myoneural gap or synapse and, upon combining with a receptor chemical, forms a complex compound that increases the permeability of the sarcolemma to ion flow. The result is a local depolarization. When it is sufficient, a propagated depolarization results, and the muscle contracts. The effect of acetylcholine is quickly negated by acetylcholinesterase, just as in the neuron synapse. A muscle fiber responds once each time a nerve action potential is transmitted across the myoneural junction. Muscle-fiber depolarization produces an action potential very similar to that resulting from neuron depolarization. Muscle-action potentials, you may recall, form the basis for electromyography. If a number of whole motor units are active at a single time, the individual muscle twitches are combined into a single whole muscle contraction which may produce a tetonic or tetanous contraction, and if motor impulses arrive slightly out of phase, the combined contraction of groups of muscle fibers results in a sustained muscle contraction.

The events that occur at a myoneural junction occupy a small amount of time, usually less than a millisecond. Thus, when the latencies of receptor cells, synaptic transmission, and myoneural transmission are combined, even the simplest motor acts are certain to form a time interval sometimes called the reaction time.

Skeletal muscle is dependent upon a nerve supply if it is to function normally. Smooth muscle and glands are somewhat independent of a nerve supply Their activity may be initiated by chemical stimulation.

If electrodes are placed over a normal muscle and electric shock applied, the resultant contractions are due to stimulation of the motor-nerve supply to the muscle, and the motor impulses in turn initiate the muscular contraction. Strength-duration curves may be obtained for muscle-nerve preparations, and the curves are very similar to those obtained from nerve fibers. If a muscle is denervated, the electric stimulation, when intense enough, may cause the muscle tissue to contract. The chronaxie, however, will be many times longer than in a healthy specimen. Normal muscles are usually in a state of slight, constant contraction, or tone. If the peripheral nerve supply for a muscle is destroyed, the muscle simply becomes limp, and the usual tone is lost. If the tendon of a denervated muscle is pulled, it offers only passive resistance, and is easily stretched. If the nerve destruction is such that the organism is decerebrate, at least for a particular muscle, and the peripheral nerve supply left intact, the stretched muscle offers more than passive resistance. It returns, pull for pull, and actively contracts in opposition to stretching forces. The response is called a stretch reflex. If the afferent fibers from the muscle are carefully sectioned (by cutting the dorsal nerve root, for example), the stretch reflex disappears completely.

The implication of such an experiment is that the stretch receptors initiate a train of impulses when the muscle is stretched. The impulses reach the spinal cord by way of afferent fibers, which synapse with the large multipolar ventral horn cells, or lower motor neurons, as they are often called. The transmitted impulses then travel out of the spinal cord in the ventral roots of the spinal nerve to the muscle originally

Fig. 7–49. Schematic of a two neuron reflex arc.

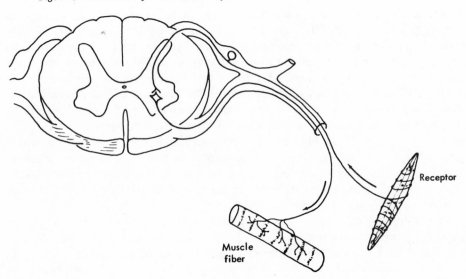

Receptor

Muscle
fiber

stretched, which then contracts. As stretching is increased, impulses follow each other more frequently and along an increasing number of fibers. As a result, the muscle contracts more and more forcefully. The paths taken by the afferent and efferent nerve impulses constitute what is often called the reflex arc. The particular example just cited is known as the two-neuron arc, and it is illustrated in Figure 7–49. The reflex arc, sometimes called the functional unit of behavior, is probably an oversimplification, but it does illustrate a very basic form of behavior, seen in the familiar knee jerk, for example.

Another basic form of behavior is seen in the withdrawal of the hand from a painful stimulus. The afferent nerve fibers enter the dorsal horn of the spinal gray matter, and may synapse with a number of internuncial neurons, which in turn can activate a large number of motor neurons. For this reason, painful stimuli delivered to the tip of a finger be followed by withdrawal of the entire hand or arm. In addition, impulses may reach the cerebral hemisphere by way of an ascending tract. The reflex activity, however, may have occurred before the individual is aware of the painful consequences of the stimulus.

SOME ASPECTS OF FUNCTIONAL NEUROANATOMY

The Cerebral Cortex

In our brief introduction to the cerebrum, four lobes were identified, the frontal, parietal, temporal, and occipital. In addition, there is an area located deep to the lateral fissure at the level of the lower end of the postcentral gyrus. In a normal, whole brain this area, which is known as the insula, is not visible.

The cerebral cortex is characterized by a high density of neurons, which are laid down in six identifiable layers. The most superficial layers of cells are afferent as well as efferent in nature. They are the association neurons, which course to other parts of the cortex. The fourth layer of cells contains nerve endings from radiations of the thalamus, while the fifth layer contains motor cells or the giant pyramidal cells of Betz. They are responsible for the initiation of motor-nerve impulses.

It must be stressed that interconnections between the various regions in the brain have not been completely documented. It is known, however, that certain regions

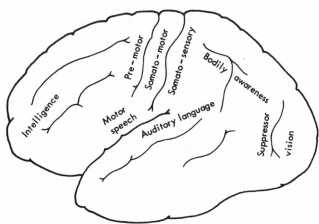

Fig. 7–50. Schematic localization of cerebral functions.

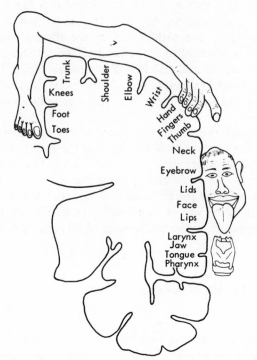

Fig. 7–51. Body representation in the motor cortex.

of the cortex are related to rather specific functions. By various experimental techniques, including electrical stimulation of various areas of the surgically exposed brain, researchers have succeeded, at least in part, in mapping some of the functionally homogenous regions of the cerebral cortex. The cerebral cortex and some areas which have had functions assigned to them are shown in Figure 7–50. One of the most thoroughly mapped regions of the brain is the motor cortex, which is located in the precentral gyrus.

A semigraphic technique often used to schematize body representation in the motor cortex is called a homunculus. An example is shown in Figure 7–51. As seen from the homunculus, there is almost an inverse relationship between the volume or area of the body and its degree of cortical representation. The area of the cortex that supplies the legs, for example, is not significantly larger than the area that supplies the tongue. The implication is that there is a direct relationship between cortical representation of a structure and the amount of nerve supply.

If a surgically exposed motor cortex is stimulated in the region near the longitudinal fissure, movements occur in the hip and trunk. If an area midway between the longitudinal fissure and the lateral fissure is stimulated, movements are produced in the wrist and fingers, and if an area near the lateral fissure is stimulated, movements are produced in the facial region. Because of the decussation of the motor fibers at the level of the medulla, stimulation of the left motor cortex produces movements on the right side of the body. You will recall, however, that the motor fibers for the cranial nerves leave the brain stem above the level of decussation at the pyramids. For this reason stimulation of the cortical area representing the facial regions usually produces unilateral movement on the ipsilateral side.

The topographic arrangement of the sensory area is approximately the same as the arrangement of the motor area. Some specific regions that are of particular interest to us include a small triangular area, anterior to the central sulcus, known as the inferior frontal gyrus. Commonly, however, it is called Broca's center, and lesions in this area often result in the inability to produce coordinated movements of the speech musculature. By the same token, lesions in the region immediately surrounding the superior terminal of the lateral sulcus may result in language disabilities.

The Proprioceptive and Exteroceptive Pathways

Sensory impulses have either proprioceptive or exteroceptive origins. Proprioceptors are located in muscles, tendons, and the joints of the body, while exteroceptors are located in the surface of the skin. Once initiated, the afferent impulses travel over the sensory fibers in the spinal or cranial nerves to terminate, for the most part, in the postcentral gyrus of the parietal lobe. Afferent fibers at the spinal level enter the spinal cord to synapse with ganglion cells of the posterior or dorsal root. Impulses are then relayed to the posterior funiculus, or funiculus cuneatus. At this level some nerve fibers carry relayed messages to the anterior horn. These impulses leave the spinal cord by way of efferent fibers and course to the effectors. This, of course, is the familiar reflex arc. The sensory impulses are carried through the funiculus cuneatus to the nucleus cuneatus in the lower region of the medulla oblongata. Other messages from the lower extremities are carried by the funiculus gracilis. At the level of the medulla these fibers decussate to ascend in the contralateral medial lemniscus.

A few fibers, those carrying pain and temperature, cross over at the level at which they enter the spinal cord and ascend as part of the spinothalamic tract. These tracts merge with the medial lemniscus at the level of the medulla, where they ascend as a common tract to the ventrolateral nucleus in the thalamus. From the thalamus the impulses are relayed through the internal capsule to terminate finally at the posterior gyrus of the parietal lobe. At the level of the cranial nerves, the afferent fibers enter the medulla as sensory branches of their respective nerves. Sensory impulses are carried primarily by three of the cranial nerves. They are the trigeminal, facial, and vagus nerves. They relay impulses from their nuclei to the trigeminal lemniscus on the contralateral side of the midbrain. The fibers then ascend to terminate in the arcuate nucleus of the thalamus, where they may be once again relayed through the internal capsule to the postcentral gyrus of the parietal lobe.

The Pyramidal Pathway

All the motor impulses that originate at the cortical level travel through an important motor tract that is commonly referred to as the pyramidal tract. We have already traced part of this tract but have referred to it as the corticospinal tract. The motor impulses originate from the giant pyramidal cells of Betz. These cells, you will recall, are located in the deeper layers of cortical substance. The impulses are carried by upper motor fibers through the internal capsule to the roots of the cerebral peduncles.

At this level, fibers are diverted from their path to form the motor nuclei of the oculo-motor and trochlear nerves. The remaining fibers continue in their descending course to the level of the pons where more collaterals are given off. They course to the motor nuclei of the trigeminal, facial, and abducens nerves. The pyramidal tract continues its descent to the level of the pyramids, where more fibers are given off to the motor nuclei of the glossopharyngeal, vagus, accessory, and hypoglossal nerves. The olfactory, optic, and acoustic nerves, being sensory in function, have no motor nuclei. At the pyramids, from 70 to 90 per cent of the fibers decussate to descend as the lateral cerebrospinal or lateral pyramidal tract. The remaining fibers do not cross over but rather descend as the ventral cerebrospinal or direct pyramidal tract.

The Extrapyramidal Tract.   Whereas description of the pyramidal tract, at the schematic level, appears to be a relatively straightforward task, the extrapyramidal tract is not quite so amenable to description. Motor cells in the prefrontal gyrus (premotor area) transmit impulses by way of extrapyramidal fibers through the internal capsule to the cerebral peduncles, where they are continued to the level of the pons. As they course through the internal capsule, however, they give off collaterals that course to the lenticular nucleus. In addition, efferent fibers originate at the lenticular nucleus to merge with the descending extrapyramidal tract. The extrapyramidal fibers terminate at the pontine level in pontine nuclei. Impulses are then relayed to the cortex of the contralateral cerebellar hemispheres via the middle cerebellar peduncle or brachium pontis.

The cerebellar cortex contains a layer of specialized cells called the Purkinje cells, which send axons to the dendate nucleus of the ipsilateral hemisphere, where they are relayed via the brachium conjunctivum to the red nucleus. At this level the fibers decussate and descend as the rubrospinal tract. Apparently the various nuclei along the extrapyramidal tract, the Purkinje cells, are capable of initiating efferent impulses that travel directly to the rubrospinal tract. In addition, the impulses may take an ascending course back to the striate bodies.

The extrapyramidal tract is indirectly associated with voluntary movements. It forms along with the pyramidal tract, an inordinately complex but nevertheless beautiful integrating network that makes possible the fine, smooth, voluntary motor activities in which most of us effortlessly engage. Certain areas in the premotor part of the frontal lobe, called the suppressor areas, give rise to many of the extrapyramidal fibers.

The extrapyramidal system is sometimes described as an alternate pathway for motor impulses. Certainly it functions as a coordinated pathway. Inasmuch as the pyramidal and extrapyramidal tracts are combined functionally into a complex servo-mechanism, we ought not to attempt to dichotomize them into strictly separate systems.

The nervous control of breathing

Breathing is controlled at the voluntary level and at the involuntary or vegetative level. Depending upon the circumstances, one or the other may be dominant. We shall be primarily concerned with breathing at the voluntary level, which, as we all know, consists of an inhalation phase and an exhalation phase.

At the involuntary level of breathing, the stimulus for inhalation apparently is the accumulation of carbon dioxide at the level of the lung, as well as the chemical status of the blood in the arteries. Afferent impulses are conducted via the afferent fibers of the vagus nerve to nuclei in the medulla and cerebellum. The exact nature of the inhalation control mechanism is open to some question, but it appears to be part of a vast integrating network, called the reticular formation, in the brain stem. Impulses are relayed from the nuclei in the inhalation control center to motor fibers of the phrenic nerve, which is a spinal nerve that arises at the cervical level (C–3, C–4, and C–5) and innervates the diaphragm. In addition, motor impulses are relayed to supplementary muscles of inhalation, such as the intercostals. When the lung is inflated, specialized stretch receptors initiate inhibitory afferent impulses which travel over the vagus nerve back to the inspiratory nuclei, and contraction of the inhalation muscles is terminated. When active inhalation is terminated the passive forces of exhalation, such as tissue elasticity, are released, and the lung deflates.

Inhalation for speech purposes is controlled not only by the same mechanism responsible for involuntary inhalation but by proprioceptive impulses from the muscles of exhalation and from the lungs. The amount of air we inhale and the rate of inhalation are also dependent upon the particular speech task in which the individual is engaged. The muscles required when breathing for speech purposes include those involved in involuntary breathing and, in addition, supplementary muscles of inhalation and the muscles of active exhalation.

We have seen that as the spinal nerves emerge from the spinal cord, certain of them combine to form large bundles of nerves called plexuses. They include the cervical plexus, which is formed by the cervical nerves C–1, C–2, C–3, and C–4. The phrenic

Table 7-2

Motor Nerve Supply for the Muscles of Breathing*

Muscles of Inhalation	*Innervation Plexus and Nerves*
Diaphragm	Phrenic nerve (C–3, C–4, and C–5)
Pectoralis Major	Medial and lateral anterior thoracic (C–5, C–6, C–7, C–8, and T–1)
Pectoralis Minor	Brachial (C–5, C–6)
Subclavius	Brachial (C–5, C–6)
Serratus Anterior	Long thoracic (C–5, C–6, C–7)
External Intercostals	Intercostal nerves (Anterior rami of T–2 through T–12)
Costal Elevators	Intercostal nerves (Anterior rami of T–2 through T–12)
Serratus Posterior Superior	T–1 through T–4
Sternomastoid	Accessory (XI)
Scalenes	C–2, C–3 (Anterior rami)
Latissimus Dorsi	Thoracodorsal (C–6, C–7, C–8)
Sacrospinalis	Thoracic Nerves (Posterior rami)
Muscles of Exhalation	
Triangularis Sterni	T–6 through T–12 (Anterior ramus)
Internal Intercostals	T–2 through T–12 (Anterior ramus)
External Oblique	T–6 through T–12 (Anterior ramus)
Internal Oblique	T–6 through T–12 (Anterior ramus)
Transversus Abdominis	T–7 through T–12 (Anterior ramus)
Rectus Abdominis	T–6 through T–12 (Anterior ramus)

*As noted in Chapter 2, the contributions of some of the above muscles are open to question. They are included here because they may in fact contribute to respiration in a compensatory role.

plexus is formed by cervical nerves C–3, C–4, and C–5, and the anterior thoracic plexus is formed by cervical nerves C–5, C–6, and C–7, plus some fibers from T–1. The long thoracic plexus is formed by cervical nerves C–5, C–6, and C–7, and the thoracodorsal plexus is formed by cervical nerves C–6, C–7, and C–8. These plexuses are largely responsible for innervation of the muscles of respiration. The sequence of muscle action for speech purposes was discussed to a limited extent in the chapter on breathing, so we need not attempt to do more than summarize the innervation of the various muscles that may be involved in breathing.

Table 7–2 lists muscles to which a breathing function has often been assigned, with their nerve supply. You may recall that the contributions of some of those muscles, under normal circumstances, are open to some question. However, they may contribute to breathing under abnormal circumstances, and are therefore included in the table.

The nervous control of the tongue

The muscles of the tongue are innervated by the trigeminal, facial, glossopharyngeal, and hypoglossal nerves. These nerves supply both intrinsic and extrinsic tongue muscles with sensory as well as motor fibers. The hypoglossal nerve supplies the intrinsic muscles of the tongue. As the hypoglossal descends from its origin, it gives off a descending branch, or ramus, which follows the course taken by the vagus nerve. This branch unites with branches of the cervical nerves C–2 and C–3 and then begins a sharp ascent. An abrupt change in the course of a nerve is called an ansa. Thus, the ascending nerve, which contains fibers of the hypoglossal and cervical nerves C–2 and C–3, is known as the ansa hypoglossi. It supplies the omohyoid, sternohyoid, and sternothyroid muscles. Table 7–3 lists the muscles of the tongue and their nerve supply.

Table 7-3
Nerve Supply for Muscles of the Tongue

Intrinsic Muscles	*Innervation Nerves*
Superior longitudinal	Hypoglossal (XII)
Inferior longitudinal	Hypoglossal
Transversus	Hypoglossal
Verticalis	Hypoglossal

Extrinsic Muscles	
Styloglossus	Hypoglossal (XII)
Palatoglossus	Accessory (XI)
Hyoglossus	Hypoglossal
Genioglossus	Hypoglossal

The nervous control of the muscles of mastication

The muscles of mastication, which include the jaw depressors as well as the elevators, are supplied by the cranial nerves. The jaw depressors are supplied by the trigeminal and hypoglossal nerves. The elevators are supplied by the anterior trunk of the mandibular branch of the trigeminal nerve. Sensory fibers to the lower teeth and adjacent structures are supplied by the posterior trunk of the mandibular branch of the trigeminal nerve. Table 7-4 lists the muscles of mastication and their innervation.

Table 7-4
Nerve Supply for the Muscles of Mastication

Muscle	Innervation Nerve
Masseter	Trigeminal, anterior trunk of mandibular branch
Temporalis	Trigeminal, anterior trunk of mandibular branch
Internal pterygoid	Trigeminal, anterior trunk of mandibular branch
External pterygoid	Trigeminal, mandibular branch
Depressors of mandible	See extrinsic laryngeal muscles (Table 7–5)

The nervous control of the pharynx

As it courses inferiorly, the vagus sends off two rami. They originate from the nodose ganglion and form the motor branch of the pharyngeal plexus. These fibers supply the pharyngeal constrictor muscles. Sensory fibers from the glossopharyngeal nerve are also contained in the pharyngeal plexus. They supply the mucous membrane of the pharynx, the faucial pillars, the pharyngeal orifice of the Eustachian tube, and the soft palate.

The nervous control of the soft palate

The motor fibers for the muscles of the soft palate are derived from the mandibular branch of the trigeminal nerve and from the accessory nerve. The latter supplies motor fibers to the uvula. The nerves that supply the palate with both sensory and motor fibers are contained in the pharyngeal plexus, and arise from the sphenopalatine ganglion located in the pterygopalatine fossa. The sphenopalatine ganglion receives sensory fibers from the facial nerve and from the maxillary branch of the trigeminal nerve. It sends off numerous branches, some of which descend to enter the hard palate through the incisive foramina. They are called the nasopalatine nerves. Others course forward to innervate the mucosa of the nasal cavities, while some enter the posterior portion of the hard palate by way of the greater and lesser palatine foramina, located just medial to the third molar teeth. The mucosa of the hard palate and of the entire soft palate is supplied by these latter palatine nerves.

The nervous control of the larynx

We have seen how the intrinsic muscles of the larynx are supplied by the vagus nerve. Other muscles associated with phonation include the laryngeal elevators and depressors. These muscles are supplied by the cranial nerves and by the nerves contained in the cervical plexus. A sensory branch of the superior laryngeal nerve, called the internal branch, supplies fibers to the laryngeal mucosa, the base of the tongue, and the epiglottis. Cortical representation of the larynx was shown in Figure 7–51, and Table 7–5 lists the muscles of phonation, extrinsic muscles of the larynx, and their nerve supply.

Table 7-5
Nerve Supply for the Muscles of Phonation

Extrinsic Muscles	*Innervation*
Digastricus, anterior belly	Trigeminal, mylohyoid branch
Digastricus, posterior belly	Facial, digastric branch
Stylohyoid	Facial, stylohyoid branch
Mylohyoid	Trigeminal, mylohyoid branch
Geniohyoid	Hypoglossal, geniohyoid branch
Sternohyoid	Hypoglossal, C–1, C–2, and C–3
Omohyoid	Hypoglossal, C–1, C–2, and C–3
Thyrohyoid	Hypoglossal, C–1 and C–2
Sternohyoid	Hypoglossal, C–1, C–2, and C–3

Intrinsic Muscles	
Thyroarytenoid	Vagus, inferior recurrent branch
Lateral cricoarytenoid	Vagus, inferior recurrent branch
Posterior cricoarytenoid	Vagus, inferior recurrent branch
Arytenoid muscles	Vagus, inferior recurrent branch
Cricothyroid	Vagus, superior recurrent branch

This account of the nervous system by no means completes the picture. It has been but a thumbnail sketch, which hopefully has pointed the way for further study. The content of the chapter has been restricted to some specific topics, and was but an introduction to the nervous system. Although we have examined the nervous system in a piecemeal fashion, in retrospect a very valuable concept seems to emerge: the function of the nervous system is far more than the combined separate functions of all its components. What seems to be a fitting and appropriate close to this part of the chapter has been given to us by Sir John Eccles, ". . . the task of understanding in a comprehensive way how the human brain operates staggers its own imagination."

AN INTRODUCTION TO THE ENDOCRINE SYSTEM

The endocrine system is largely glandular, but the endocrine glands ought to be distinguished from other glands in the body, such as the lacrimal, mammary, and sweat glands, which discharge to the surface of the body, or other glands, such as those in the mouth (salivary glands), stomach, and intestines, which discharge their secretions into the alimentary tract. Contents of the endocrine glands are delivered directly into the blood stream and are then carried to the various tissues of the body. The secretions of the endocrine glands are called hormones, and their effect is one of stimulation of other tissues in the body. As mentioned earlier, the endocrines evolved after the nervous system, and are found in the more highly specialized animals, where the nervous system alone has apparently proved inadequate in certain respects.

Three experimental approaches have shed a good deal of light on the functions of the endocrine glands. One approach, for example, is to prepare an extract of the glandular tissue and, following injection into an animal, to study its effects. A second technique is to remove the gland or glands under study and to observe carefully the subsequent life history of the animal. A third technique is to observe carefully the behavior of human subjects in whom glandular disorders have been diagnosed.

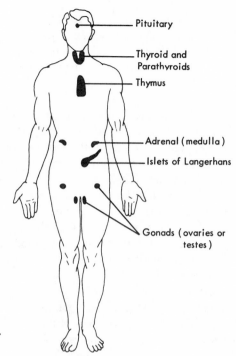

Pituitary

Thyroid and
Parathyroids

Thymus

Adrenal (medulla)

Islets of Langerhans

Gonads (ovaries or
testes)

Fig. 7–52. Illustration of the location of the endocrine glands.

The vertebrates have seven clearly recognized endocrine glands, the thyroid, parathyroids, adrenals, pituitary, gonads, pancreas, and the thymus. An eighth structure, the pineal body, is sometime recognized as an endocrine gland, but there is little evidence that such is the case. The location of the endocrine glands is shown in Figure 7–52.

The thyroid gland. The thyroid gland consists of two lobes, placed one on either side of the larynx and connected by a strip of thyroid tissue called the isthmus. When seen under the microscope, the glandular tissue appears to be composed of a mass of alveoli or follicles, each of which is lined by a single layer of cuboidal epithelial cells. The follicles contain a viscous material called colloid. This substance, which contains the thyroid hormone, is secreted by the epithelial cells. If an animal is deprived of a thyroid gland, stark metabolic changes occur, which if prolonged may result in death. If the thyroid hormone, thyroxin, is administered, however, the animal will remain perfectly healthy and normal in every respect. Deficiencies in thyroxin may produce cretinism in children and myxedema in adults. A child remains small and becomes badly formed, with puffy skin and a tongue that seems much too large for the mouth. Mental development is at a rather complete standstill, and deafness is frequent. A thyroxin deficiency in adults results in a familiar disease known as myxedema. Usual symptoms include a general lethargy, both mental and physical, an increase in weight, and thickening of the skin. It seems that the entire mechanism of the body is slowed down. The administration of proper amounts of thyroxin (or thyroid extracts) restores metabolism to its normal level, and subsequently all symptoms disapper. If given thyroxin at a very early age, a child usually responds well and can grow into a normal adult.

In the early part of the century an enlarged thyroid gland was quite commonplace in certain parts of the world. These areas were quite well-defined and all were characterized by a marked deficiency of iodine in the water and soil. With the addition of supplementary iodine to the diets of persons, an enlarged thyroid gland, or goiter, can be prevented. As might be expected, iodine is an important constituent of the thyroid hormone.

Occasionally the thyroid gland begins to produce more thyroxin than the body needs, and this condition (hyperthyroidism) may also be accompanied by a slight enlargement of the gland. Excessive thyroxin increases metabolism and speeds up the entire mechanism of the body. Along with nervousness and tremor and rapid action of the heart, the eyeballs may also become protruded, a condition called exophthalmos. Control of thyroxin secretion is mediated through the hypothalamus and the anterior lobe of the pituitary glands. The controlling mechanism is very complicated due to the reciprocal effects of a thyroid-stimulating hormone secreted by the pituitary and the level of thyroxin in the blood stream. A decrease in thyroxin stimulates the pituitary mechanism, and more thyroid-stimulating hormone is released. Exophthalmos is believed due not to an excess of thyroxin itself, but to the thyroid-stimulating (thyrotrophic) hormone of the anterior lobe of the pituitary gland.

The parathyroid glands. The parathyroid glands are two pairs of pea-sized structures. One pair is located behind the upper poles of the thyroid gland, and the other pair is just behind the lower poles. In animals, removal of the parathyroids results in increased excitability of the neuromuscular tissues, which eventually culminates in a severe and usually fatal convulsive disorder called tetany. Death is due either to exhaustion or asphyxia resulting from a spasm of the larynx. The parathyroids seem to function in maintaining proper levels of phosphorus and calcium in the blood. When the glands are removed, blood-calcium level falls off rapidly, which correlates with the symptoms of the disease. In the event the parathyroids become overactive, the calcium level in the blood rises too high. If prolonged, the calcium of the bones is sacrificed, resulting in a weak and twisted skeleton. In addition, the excessive blood calcium is brought to the kidneys for excretion, which may result in deposition of calcium, or kidney stones.

The adrenal glands. As the name implies, the adrenal glands are located on the upper surface of the kidneys. Each gland is composed of two parts, a central, dark-colored mass called the medulla and an outer covering called the cortex. The medulla and cortex have quite different embryonic origins, and there is little evidence that their functions are very closely related. The cortex is derived from the tissue that gives rise to the sex glands, whereas the medulla is a derivative of the neural crest. The medulla produces a hormone called adrenalin, sometimes called adrenin or epinephrine. Surgical removal of the medullary portion of the adrenal glands does not result in very great changes in an animal's behavior. If, however, adrenalin is administered to an animal, heart action becomes stronger, the spleen contracts, forcing its reserve into the blood stream, the skin blanches, the pupils dilate, and the hair "stands on end." The entire picture is very similar to that due to excitation of the sympathetic nervous system.

The cortex of the adrenal gland is essential for life. Animals die in about two weeks following complete removal of both adrenal glands. Numerous compounds have been isolated from the cortex, and it seems that their functions are complicated. If the cortex should fail, carbohydrate metabolism is affected, and the blood-sugar level drops drastically. Sodium chloride is lost from the blood and other tissues, and blood pressure falls. Overactivity of the cortex produces some changes of a different kind. In children, precocious development of the sexual organs and of the secondary sex characteristics is seen. In female children, a tendency toward virilism also occurs. In adult males, overactivity of the adrenal cortex may produce excessive hair growth, and a generalized increase in "maleness." Adult females fare even worse. The changes are toward maleness; facial hair may begin to appear, the body becomes muscular, and often the voice deepens. Even the sex organs may show signs of atrophy and become nonfunctional.

The pituitary gland. The pituitary or hypophysis is a very complex and important gland. It lies tucked in the sella turcica of the sphenoid bone and is continuous with the base of the brain by means of the infundibulum. It is a double gland, composed of an anterior lobe which develops from the roof of the embryonic pharynx and a posterior lobe which is a direct outgrowth of the floor of the brain. Because of its location in man, research has been difficult. The gland is easily removed in some lower vertebrates, however, and the effects of removal, especially in the young animal, are profound. Growth is immediately inhibited, and sexual maturity never occurs. In addition, atrophy of the entire adrenal gland also takes place. Clearly the pituitary is an important gland that regulates the functions of other endocrine glands and the growth and development of the entire mechanism of the body.

The effect of overactivity of the pituitary has given us some clues as to its function. The somatic effects of overactivity usually includes abnormal growth of the entire body which, in spite of awesome dimensions, remains rather well proportioned. On the other hand, gland failure may result in dwarfism. These effects only occur when the gland malfunctions in the young child. If the pituitary should become overactive after maturity is reached, a person may develop a syndrome known as acromegaly. It includes enlarged hands, a protruding lower jaw, and massive brows.

The effects of the pituitary on the thyroid gland have already been mentioned. A hormone from the pituitary probably initiates or stimulates the thyroid to produce thyroxin. The pituitary also regulates the adrenal cortex and its production of a hormone called cortisone. It seems to facilitate the body's potential for regenerating new tissue and also prevents shock and other symptoms associated with severe trauma. We have briefly encountered the effects of the pituitary on sexual development. It produces at least two gonad-stimulating hormones, one which affects the Graafian follicles in the ovaries and another which causes the follicles to release their egg cells or in the male to produce testosterone, a hormone which controls the physiological status of the secondary sex characteristics. The pituitary also produces a hormone called lactogen which controls lactation (secretion of milk by the mammary glands).

The posterior lobe of the pituitary seems to function in maintaining the proper water balance in the body.

The gonads. The testes and ovaries are also compound glands whose primary function is the production of sperm cells and eggs. They also have very important endocrine functions. The interstitial tissue of the testes produces testosterone, which stimulates the development of the secondary sex characteristics in males. The fact that the testes are associated with these characteristics can be demonstrated by removal of these glands or castration, which, when performed in young humans, results in a high-pitched voice, a lack of beard, a tendency toward obesity, and few of the usual sexual and emotional characteristics associated with the adult male. Castration after maturity, however, results in few of these changes.

The onset of interstitial tissue activity and the production of testosterone are associated with puberty, when pubic hair appears and when growth of the larynx, change of voice, and increased development of the genitalia occur. Occasionally the testes fail to descend into the scrotal sac during the latter part of gestation. This condition, known as cryptorchidism, results in impairment in the production of live sperm cells but does not affect the secretion of testosterone. As a result, these males are perfectly virile in all respects except fertility.

The ovary produces a complex battery of hormones, many of which are associated with care of the embryo, both before and after birth. As eggs mature in the ovary, a fluid-filled space develops around it. The egg and the space together form a Graafian follicle, which produces estrogen. It is the counterpart of testosterone in the male. Estrogen stimulates the onset of puberty and the development of the female secondary sex characteristics. Another hormone, progesterone is produced by a specialized part of the ovary called the corpus luteum. Subsequent to the release of a mature egg from the Graafian follicle, progesterone initiates the menstrual cycle in humans and the estrus cycle in other mammals.

The pancreas. The most obvious function of the pancreas is to produce enzymes that aid digestion. An additional function of a small group of cells, called the Islets of Langerhans, is to produce a homone called insulin, which is responsible for the retention and storage of sugar in the body. If these islets are destroyed, or become nonfunctional, as in the case of human diabetes, sugar is no longer stored in the liver and other tissues but is carried to the kidney and is excreted along with urine.

The thymus. The thymus lies behind the upper part of the sternum and extends upward into the root of the neck. It is relatively large in infants and at the time of puberty begins to shrink until at adulthood it is reduced to little more than a vestigial structure. Although the thymus has been the subject of considerable research, its specific function is not known with certainty. The structure of the tissue suggests that it is involved in the production of lymphocytes, but proof is lacking.

With this, the completion of the text material, the student ought to have become acutely aware that a complete and comprehensive understanding of the speech and hearing mechanisms is no simple task. It demands, first of all, a rather thorough knowledge of the basic structures involved, the way they function, and the manner in which they are interrelated. Secondly, it demands a continuous pursuit of new ideas, concepts, and research findings, as they appear in the professional literature. Old, well-established, and firmly implanted ideas may have to be cast aside in order to make way for the new. If this textbook has been successful at all, the student will have been motivated to ask pertinent questions, to seek out new ideas and research findings, and to add them judiciously to his rapidly expanding repertory of knowledge. In that event the student will be meeting his obligations, not only to himself, but to his profession.

SELECTIVE READING LIST

Brodal, Alf, *The Cranial Nerves*. Oxford: Blackwell Scientific Publications, 1959.

Brodmann, K., *Vergleichende Lokalization der Grosshirnrinde*. Leipzig: Barth, 1909.

Cajal, Ramón y Santiago, *Studien uber die Hirnrinde des Menschen*. Aus dem spanischen ubersetzt von Johannes Bresler, Leipzig, 1906.

Cajal, Ramón y Santiago, *Studies on the Diencephalon*. Compiled and translated by Enrique Ramon Moliner. Springfield, Ill., Charles C. Thomas publisher, 1966.

Campbell, A. W., *Histological Studies on the Localization of Cerebral Function*. Published by aid of a subsidy from the Royal Society of London. Cambridge: University Press, 1905.

Chusid, J. G. and J. J. McDonald, *Correlative Neuroanatomy and Functional Neurology*, 10th ed. Los Altos, Calif.: Lange Medical Publications, 1960.

Eccles, Sir John C., "The Synapse," *Scientific American*, CCXII, January, 1965, 56–69.

Gardner, E., *Fundamentals of Neurology*. Philadelphia: W. B. Saunders Co., 1964.

Hathaway, S. R., *Physiological Psychology*. New York: Appleton-Century-Crofts, 1952.

Hodgkin, A. L., *The Conduction of the Nervous Impulse*. Liverpool: University Press, 1964.

Netter, F. H., *Nervous System*. Summit, N. J., Ciba Pharmaceutical Products, Inc., 1953.

Penfield W. and L. Roberts, *Speech and Brain Mechanisms*. Princeton, N. J.: Princeton University Press, 1959.

Ranson, S. W. and S. L. Clark, *The Anatomy of the Nervous System*. 10th ed., Philadelphia: W. B. Saunders Co., 1959.

Wilson, Victor J., "Inhibition in the Central Nervous System," *Scientific American*, CCXIV May, 1966, 102–11.

Zentnay, P. J., "Motor Disorders of the CNS and their Significance for Speech," *Journal of Speech Disorders*, II, 1937, 131–38.

Glossary

Å: Symbol for angstrom, a unit of length equal to 10^{-8} cm.

AB-: Prefix meaning from, off, or away from the mid-line.

ABSCESS: A localized area of pus contained within a cavity.

ABDOMEN: That portion of the body lying between the thorax and pelvis.

ABDUCT: To draw away from the mid-line.

ABSCISSA: The horizontal line in a graph showing the relationship of two values, such as time and temperature.

ACETYLCHOLINE: A chemical substance, released in synaptic regions, which increases the irritability of neurons.

ACQUIRED: Obtained after birth. Not congenital.

ACROMEGALY: A chronic enlargement of the bones and soft tissues of the hands, feet, and face, due to excessive secretion by the pituitary gland.

ACROMION: A summit, as on the scapula.

ACTION POTENTIAL: Changes in electrical potential, occurring at the surface of nerve or muscle tissue at the moment of excitation. It consists of a short-duration period of negativity called the spike potential and secondary changes in potential called after-potentials.

ACUTE: With sudden onset and of short duration.

AD-: Prefix meaning to or toward.

ADAM'S APPLE: An anterior projection, especially of the male thyroid cartilage.

ADDUCT: Movement toward the mid-line.

ADENOIDS: The enlarged or hypertrophied pharyngeal tonsil.

ADIOPOSE: Fatty, fat.

ADITUS: An entrance.

ADRENALIN: A hormone secreted by the medulla of the adrenal gland.

AFFERENT: Carrying toward, as toward the central nervous system.

AFTER-POTENTIAL: *See* action potential.

ALA: A wing, or wing-like.

ALVEOLUS: A small hollow or pit.

AMEBOID: Resembling an ameba in form or in movement.

AMNION: A membrane surrounding the embryo.

AMPHIARTHRODIAL: A yielding joint.

AMPULLA: A flask-like structure or dilation of a tube.

AMYGDALOID: Almond-shaped.

ANASTOMOSE: To open, one into another.

ANATOMICAL POSITION: The body standing erect, facing the observer, with arms at the side and palms forward.

ANDROGEN: Male sex hormone.

ANEROID: *See* barometer.

ANGULAR VELOCITY: A term usually applied to rotational motion, it is the vector whose magnitude is the time rate of change of the angle θ rotated through. $\omega = d\theta/dt$

ANLAGE: A German word meaning predisposition. In embryology, the first structure or cell group indicating development of a structure.

ANNULAR: Ring-shaped.

ANOMALY: A deviation from the normal.

ANOXIA: Oxygen deprivation.

ANSA: A loop

ANSIFORM: Shaped like a loop.

ANTAGONIST: A muscle which acts in opposition to another.

ANTERIOR: Toward the front, away from the back.

ANTHROPOID: Resembling man.

ANTRUM: A cavity or hollow space. Usually pertaining to the bones.

APERIODIC: Not periodic.

APEX: The summit or top.

APHASIA: A collective term meaning the inability to express, recognize, or comprehend language or symbols.

APHONIA: Loss or absence of voice due to failure of vibration of the vocal folds.

APONEUROSIS: A broad sheet of connective tissue that forms the attachment of muscle to bone.

APPENDICULAR SKELETON: The skeleton of the extremities and of the pectoral and pelvic girdles.

APPOSITION: The fitting together.

AQ.: Abbreviation for water.

ARCOLA: A minute space in tissue.

ARCUATE: Arched, or bow-shaped.

AREOLAR TISSUE: A mesh-like form of connective tissue.

ARTHRO-: Pertaining to a joint.

ARTHRODIA: A joint permitting only gliding movements.

ARTICULATE: A joint or juncture of bones. Movement and placement of the articulators during speech production.

ARTICULATORS: Those structures responsible for modification of the acoustic properties of the vocal tract; i.e., tongue, lips, soft and hard palates, and teeth.

ARTIFACT: A structure or tissue which has been changed from its natural state by mechanical, electrical, chemical, or other artificial means.

ARYTENOID: Resembling the mouth of a pitcher.

ASTHENIA: Muscle weakness. Implying loss of strength.

ASTRO-: A combining form which signifies pertaining to the stars. Example, an astrocyte, which is a many-processed, star-shaped cell of neuroglial tissue.

ATAVISM: Reversion or the occurrence of a characteristic not usually found in more immediate progenitors.

ATAXIA: Lack of muscle control, due to incoordination.

ATMOSPHERIC PRESSURE: Pressure of the atmosphere, which amounts to about fifteen pounds to the square inch at sea level.

ATTENUATE: To decrease the amplitude or energy of a signal. To decrease.

ATTRITION: A wearing down or away, by friction.

AXIAL SKELETON: The skeleton of the head and trunk.

AXILLA: The arm pit.

AXILLARY: Pertaining to the arm pit.

AXIS: An imaginary line passing through the center of a body. The line about which a rotating body turns.

AXIS CYLINDER: The conducting core of a dendrite or axon.

AXON: The efferent (usually) process of a neuron.

BALLISTICS: The study of the motion of projectiles. Movements which result from sudden muscle contractions and which are continued by the forces of inertia.

BAROMETER: An instrument that measures atmospheric pressure. A mercury barometer consists of a glass tube filled with mercury and inverted into a reservoir. An aneroid barometer consists of a metal chamber from which the air has been evacuated. Pressure is indicated by the collapsing or bulging of a thin metal wall of the chamber, which in turn moves an indicating pointer.

BASAL GANGLIA: The striate bodies and the thalamus.

BASILAR MEMBRANE: The membrane in the cochlear duct which supports the organ of Corti.

BELLY: The fleshy portion of a muscle.

BERNOULLI'S PRINCIPLE: In the case of an ideal fluid, as velocity of fluid flow increases, pressure must decrease, so long as total energy remains at a constant. Pressure is perpendicular to the direction of fluid flow. Thus, if volume fluid flow is constant, velocity will increase at an area of constriction with a corresponding decrease in pressure at the constriction.

BIFID: Divided into two parts.

BIFURCATE: To divide into two branches.

BILATERAL: Pertaining to both sides.

BINAURAL: Pertaining to both ears.

BLADE: A wide, flat structure, such as the tongue or scapula.

BLASTO-, BLAST-: A combining form, often used in embryology, meaning germ.

BLASTOCOELE: The cavity of a blastula.

BLASTOCYST: A hollow cell mass. The intitial embryonic cell bud.

BLASTOMERE: One of the cells formed during the primary cell division of an egg.

BLASTULA: A hollow ball of cells, one cell layer thick.

BOLUS: A rounded mass, usually of food.

BONE: The dense, hard, supportive tissue of which most of the skeletal framework is comprised.

BOYLE'S LAW: At any given temperature the volume of a gas varies in inverse proportion to the pressure exerted upon it.

BRANCHIAL: Pertaining to the embryonic gill arches.

BREATHING: the process of inflating and deflating the lungs.

BREVIS: Brief, short.

BROCA'S AREA: An area in the inferior convolution of the frontal lobe of the brain that seems to be related to language or expression of language.

BRONCHIOLE: The smallest divisions of the bronchial tree.

BRONCHUS: The primary division of the trachea.

BROWNIAN MOVEMENT: A rapid, oscillatory movement often observed in fluid particles or fine particles suspended in liquids.

BUCCA: Pertaining to the cheek.

BULK MODULUS OF ELASTICITY: Also called the volume modulus of elasticity. When compressional forces act inward over the surface area of a body, the volume is compressed. The coefficient of compression is known as the bulk modulus of elasticity. It is determined by the restoring force of the compressed substance.

BURSA: A sac or sac-like cavity.

BUTTOCK: Either of the two protuberances that form the rump.

CANAL: A passageway or duct.

CANALICULI: A number of small canals.

CANINE: Pertaining to dog. The tooth next to the incisors.

CAPITULUM: A protrusion on the head of a bone.

CARDIAC: Near or supplying the heart. The anterior part of the stomach.

CARIES: Molecular destruction of bone or teeth. Decay.

CARNIVOROUS: Flesh eating.

CARTILAGE: A nonvascular connective tissue, softer and more flexible than bone.

CATHETER: A tube that is passed into body passages, often for drawing off fluid, such as urine.

CAUDA EQUINA: Shaped like the tail of a horse.

CAUDAL: Toward the tail, away from the head.

CAUDATE: Having a tail.

CAVITY: A hollow or space within or between structures.

CECUM: A blind pouch.

CELL: The smallest unit of life. Contains a nucleus, protoplasm, and a cell wall.

CEMENTUM: A very dense tissue which forms the outer surfaces of the root of a tooth.

CEPHALIC: Pertaining to the head.

CERUMEN: A Latin word meaning wax.

CERVICAL: Pertaining to the neck.

CERVIX: The neck of a structure.

CESIUM: Cs. An alkali similar to potassium and sodium.

CHIASMA: A decussation of fibers, as in the optic chiasma.

CHOANA: A funnel-like opening. *Pl.* choanae.

CHONDRAL: Cartilaginous, relating to cartilage.

CHORION: An embryonic membrane external to and enclosing the amnion. The hard shell of an egg.

CHOROID: A delicate and highly vascular membrane.

CHRONAXIE: Current duration required to excite a neuron or muscle tissue at a current strength twice that of rheobase.

CHRONIC: Of long duration.

CILIA: The thread-like cytoplasmic processes of cells which beat rhythmically.

CINEFLUOROGRAPHY: X-ray radiography combined with motion-picture photography.

CINEMATOGRAPHY: Motion-picture photography.

CINEREA: The gray matter of the nervous system.

CIRCUMDUCTION: When the end of a limb describes a circle, and the shaft describes a cone.

CLAUSTRUM: A bar-shaped structure. A thin layer of gray matter, lateral to the external capsule.

CLINKER: A mass of uncombustible material, fused together, usually formed during the burning of coal, which has the property of jamming up the works, especially in coal stokers.

COCCYX: The vestigial, inferior-most portion of the vertebral column.

COCHLEAR MICROPHONICS: Minute quantities of electrical energy generated within the cochlea. The electrical energy has properties analogous to those of the acoustic stimulus.

COELOM: Body cavity.

COLLICULI: The superior and inferior colliculi of the midbrain which compose the corpus quadrigemina.

COLLICULUS: A small eminence.

COMMISSURE: A joining together. A nerve tract connecting right and left halves of the nervous system.

COMPARATIVE ANATOMY: The comparison of the anatomy of different orders of animals or of plants, one with another.

COMPLEMENTAL AIR: Air which supplies a deficiency. Air which can be inhaled beyond that inhaled during quiet breathing.

CONCHA: A shell-like organ or structure. *Pl.* conchae.

CONDENSER LENS: A lens that concentrates light energy. Often called a positive lens.

CONDYLE: A rounded process.

CONDYLOID: Shaped like a knuckle.

CONGENITAL: Existing at birth. May or may not be hereditary.

CONTINUANT: A speech sound that remains relatively steady-state over a period of time, such as [s] or [m].

CONTRALATERAL: Associated with a part on the other side.

COPULA: A bridging or connecting structure.

CORACOID: Having the shape of a crow's beak.

CORNICULATE: Horn, or furnished with horns.

CORNU: A horn. *Pl.* Cornua.

CORONAL: A vertical plane or cut, from side to side, dividing the structure into front and back halves.

CORPUS: The body of a structure. A body.

CORPUS CALLOSUM: A prominent band of white fibers connecting the right and left cerebral hemispheres.

CORTEX: The outer layer of an organ.

COSTAL: *Adj.*, pertaining to the ribs.

COSTO: Pertaining to the ribs.

COXAL: *Adj.*, pertaining to the coxa, or hip bone.

CRANIAL: Pertaining to the head.

CRESCENDO: A gradual increase in intensity or loudness.

CREST: A ridge, as on the upper border of the ilium.

CRETIN: A person with a congenital lack of thyroid secretion. Characterized by hyponormal physical development and mental retardation.

CRIBRIFORM: Perforated, as the cribriform plate of the ethmoid bone.

CRICOID: Ring-shaped.

CRUCIFORM: Cross-shaped.

CRURA: *See* crus.

CRUS: A pillar or shank that is leg-like in function or appearance. *Pl.* crura.

CULMEN: A summit.

CULMEN MONTICULI: The highest lobule of the cerebellum.

CUNEIFORM: Wedge-shaped.

CUPOLA: A vault or dome, located on a roof, as on a caboose.

CUSP: A pointed eminence.

CUTANEOUS: Pertaining to the skin.

CUTICLE: The epidermis. A superficial membrane. The outermost layer of the skin.

CYMBA: The upper part of the concha of the ear.

CYTON: The cell body of a neuron.

CYTOPLASM: Protoplasm. The protoplasm of a cell other than the nucleus.

DAMPING: To cause a decrease in amplitude of successive oscillations or waves.

DEAD AIR: Air in the respiratory tract which does not enter into gas exchange, i.e., air in the mouth, nasal cavities, pharynx, larynx, and trachea.

DECIBEL: db. A quantitative unit of relative sound intensity or sound pressure, based on the logarithmic relationship of amplitudes or pressures of two sounds, one of which serves as the reference.

DECIDUOUS: Temporary. Falling off and shedding at maturity.

DECUSSATE: To cross over, as nerves or muscle fibers.

DEEP: Away from the surface. Toward the center of a structure or body.

DEFECATE: Evacuation of the bowel.

DEGLUTITION: Swallowing.

DEMI-: Prefix meaning half.

DEMULSCENT: An agent that protects a surface from the irritating effects of friction.

DENDRITE: The afferent process of a neuron.

DENTIN: The major substance of a tooth, enveloped by enamel on the crown and by cementum on the root. Often written dentine.

DERMATOME: Skin areas supplied by individual spinal nerves.

DERMIS: Pertaining to the skin.

DEXTRAL: Pertaining to the right side.

DI-: A prefix meaning two or twice.

DIAPHYSIS: Shaft of a long bone.

DIARTHRODIAL: A movable articulation between two bones.

DIASTEMA: A toothless space between two teeth.

DICHOTOMIZE: To divide into two.

DIGASTRIC: Having two bellies.

DIGITATE: Having finger-like branches that may intertwine.

DILATION: The process of expanding or enlarging.

DISTAL: Away from the body or from the medial axis.

DISTEND: To stretch apart, or to stretch out.

DIVERTICULUM: A blind tube, sac, or process.

DORSAL: toward the backbone.

DYS-: Prefix meaning abnormal or deficient.

DYSPHONIA: An impairment of the larynx which affects voice production.

ECTO-: Prefix meaning outside or external.

ECTODERM: The outermost of the three primary layers in the embryo.

EDDY: Current flow that diverges from the main stream of current flow, in a fluid.

EDEMA: Abnormal collection of tissue fluids, causing swelling.

EDENTULOUS: Toothless.

EDGE TONE: A method of setting air in a column into vibration by blowing a stream of air over a sharp edge.

EFFERENT: Conduction from a central region to the periphery.

ELASTIC TISSUE: Connective tissue consisting of yellow elastic fibers.

ELASTICITY: The property of returning to an original form subsequent to removal of a deforming force.

ELECTRODES: The surface of contact between a metallic and a nonmetallic conductor. A terminal or metal plate through which electrical energy is applied to or taken from the body.

ELECTROMYOGRAPHY: Recording the electrical energy generated by active muscles.

ELEIDIN: A semifluid granular substance found in the stratum lucidum (translucent layer of the skin).

EMG: Abbreviation for electromyography.

EMBOLIFORM: Wedge-shaped.

EMESIS: Vomit.

ENARTHRODIAL: A joint in which a rounded head fits into a socket of another, permitting motion in almost any direction. Ball and socket.

END ORGAN: Any terminal structure of a nerve or neuron.

ENDO-: A prefix meaning within.

ENDOTHELIUM: A form of epithelial tissue that lines the walls of the blood vessels.

ENSIFORM: Sword-shaped.

ENZYME: A catalytic substance, usually produced by glands, which has a specific effect in promoting a chemical change.

EPENDYMA: A layer of cells lining the cavities of the brain and spinal cord.

EPIDERMIS: The outer nonvascular, nonsensitive layer of the skin.

EPIGLOTTIS: A Greek word meaning upon the tongue. A thin lamella of elastic cartilage between the root of the tongue and entrance to the larynx.

EPITHELIUM: Tissue which forms the protecting and/or secreting surfaces of the body.

EPONYM: A person from whom a place or structure takes its name.

ESTROGENS: Female sex hormones.

ETHMOID: Sieve-shaped.

EVAGINATE: To grow outward.

EVERSION: A turning outward.

EXCISE: To remove a part, foreign body, or organ, by cutting.

EXHALATION: That phase of a breathing cycle during which air is expelled from the lungs.

EXPIRATION: That phase of a breathing cycle during which air is expelled from the lungs.

EXPIRATORY RESERVE VOLUME: The quantity of air which can be exhaled, beyond that which is exhaled during quiet breathing.

EXTENSION: An increase in the angle between two bones.

EXTENSORS: Muscles responsible for producing extension.

EXTERNAL: Toward the outside or farther from the mid-line.

EXTEROCEPTOR: Specialized sense organs that respond to pressure, temperature changes, and pain. The nerve endings are on the surface of the body.

EXTRAPOLATE: To estimate a quantity by extending data beyond its established and known range.

EXTREMITY: A limb of the body. The distal part.

EXTRINSIC: Originating outside the part.

EXTRUDE: To push. To extend outward.

EXUDATE: A discharge of fluid tissue.

FACET: A small plane area on a structure, usually bone.

FALX: Sickle-shaped, such as the falx inguinalis.

FASCIA: A sheet of fibrous connective tissue that encases the body beneath the skin and separates muscle bundles from one another.

FASCICULAR: Clustered together.

FASCICULUS: A bundle of nerve or muscle fibers. In the nervous system, nerves which presumably have common connections or functions.

FASTIGIAL: Pyramidal or conical in form.

FAUCES: Pertaining to the upper part of the throat. That space surrounded by the soft palate, palatine arches, and the base of the tongue.

FENESTRA: A window or opening.

FIBER: A thin strand of nerve or muscle tissue.

FIBRIL: A thread-like component of a fiber.

FIBROCARTILAGE: An elastic cartilage consisting of a predominance of white fibrous tissue.

FIRST-SURFACED: A mirror with the reflective coating on the side of the glass nearer the light source. Light does not have to pass through the glass, be reflected, and pass out of the glass again.

FISSION: Cleaving or splitting into parts.

FISSURE: A cleft or slit.

FISTULA: An opening formed by incomplete closure of a wound.

FLACCID: A condition of hypotonus of muscle fibers.

FLEXION: A decrease in the angle between two bones.

FLEXORS: Muscles responsible for producing flexion.

FLOCCULENT: Flaky, or downy.

FLOCCULUS: A prominent lobe of the cerebellum.

FLUX: A flowing or flow.

FOCAL LENGTH: The distance from a lens to the point where an infinitely distant source of light will converge to form a common point or focus.

FOLIUM: A lamina or leaflet of gray matter which forms part of the tree-like structure of the cerebellum.

FOLLICLE: A small, secretory cavity or sac.

FORAMEN: An opening or perforation in a bone or connective tissue.

FORCE: An influence which produces or tends to produce a change in motion.

FORMANT BANDS: Regions of prominent energy distribution in a speech sound. Broad-band resonant frequencies.

FOSSA: A pit or hollow.

FOSSULA: A small fossa.

FOVEA: A cup-shaped depression or pit.

FRENULUM: A small frenum.

FRENUM: A fold of skin or mucous membrane that limits the range of movement of a structure. A frenulum.

FRICATIVE: A speech sound generated by friction of air through a restricted opening.

FRONTAL: The anterior part of a structure or organ.

FUNCTIONAL RESERVE VOLUME: The functional air in the lungs which can be expelled.

FUNICULUS: A column of white matter in the nervous system, named with reference to the gray matter of the spinal cord. There are dorsal, ventral, and lateral funiculi.

FUSIFORM: Spindle-shaped.

GAMETE: A sexual germ cell; the female ovum or male sperm cell.

GAMETOGENESIS: The formation of gametes (sex germ cells).

GANGLION: A mass of nerve cells located outside the central nervous system.

GASTRO-: Pertaining to the stomach.

GENIAL-: Pertaining to the chin.

GENICULATE: Abruptly bent, like the knee.

GENU: A structure shaped like a knee, as the genu of the internal capsule or corpus callosum.

GERM: A small particle of protoplasm capable of developing into a complete individual.

GINGIVA: The gum. *Pl.* Gingivae

GINGLYMUS: A hinged joint.

GIRDLE: An encircling or confining structure.

GLAND: A cell, tissue, or organ which produces and discharges a substance used elsewhere in the body.

GLENOID: Like a socket.

GLIAL: From the Greek word *glia*, meaning glue. A binding or supporting tissue found in the nervous system—neuroglial.

GLOBOSE: Spherical or globe-shaped.

GLOSSO-: Pertaining to the tongue.

GLOTTAL TONE: The tone generated by the vibrating vocal folds, to be distinguished from the tone produced by the oscillation or ringing of the vocal tract.

GLOTTIS: The space between the vocal folds.

GLOW-LAMP: A light which incorporates the use of inert gases to produce a bright glow. Neon and Xenon are examples of glowlamps.

GOMPHOSIS: An articulation of a cone-shaped process with an accommodating socket. For example, the articulation of the teeth with the alveoli.

GRACILIS: Slender.

GROOVE: A furrow in a bone, or other structure.

GUTTURAL: Pertaining to the throat.

GYRUS: A fold in the cerebral cortex; a convolution.

HABENULA: Any frenum, or ribbon-like structure.

HALITUS: The expired breath.

HAMULUS: Hook-shaped.

HARMONIC: The partials of a complex sound which are integral multiples of the fundamental frequency.

HEAD: In bone, an enlargement at one end, beyond its neck.

HELIX: A spiral object or part.

HEMI-: Prefix meaning half.

HERBIVOROUS: Plant eating.

HG.: Abbreviation for mercury.

HIATUS: A perforation in fleshy tissue. Any large opening.

HILUM: The region where vessels, nerves, etc. enter or leave a part.

HISTOLOGY: A science of the study of tissues.

HOMO-: Prefix meaning similar.

HORMONE: A chemical secretion, usually of an endocrine gland, which is carried by body fluids, and specifically regulates a function of another organ.

HYDRA: A fresh-water polyp of the genus Hydra.

HYDRATED: Containing water.

HYOID: Shaped like the Greek letter v.

HYPER-: Prefix meaning excess.

HYPERKINESIA: Excessive movement.

HYPERTROPHY: The overgrowth or enlargement of an organ or tissue.

HYPO-: Prefix meaning deficiency, or under.

HYPODERMIC: Under the skin.

HYPOPHYSIS: Any outgrowth or process, especially of the nervous system. For example, the hypophysis cerebri or pituitary gland.

ILIUM: The superior broad portion of the hipbone.

IMPEDANCE: The apparent resistance of a mechanical or electrical system to the absorption of energy.

IMPRESSION: An indentation or dent.

IMPULSE: A stimulus carried by the nervous system.

INCIDENT: Falling upon. With light or sound, directly from the source; not reflected.

INCIDENT WAVE: A sound wave which falls onto a reflecting or refracting surface.

INCISIVE: Cutting. Pertaining to the teeth.

INCUS: The middle of the bones in the ossicular chain of the middle ear.

INERTIA: The tendency of a body to remain in a state of rest or of uniform motion in a straight line, unless acted upon by an external force.

INFERIOR: The lower of two parts. Situated below or underneath.

INFRA-: Prefix meaning below or underneath.

INFUNDIBULUM: A funnel-shaped structure or organ.

INGUINAL: Pertaining to the groin.

INHALATION: The phase of a breathing cycle during which air is drawn into the lungs.

INNERVATION: The supplying of any organ with nerve fibers.

INSCRIPTIONS: Transverse fibrous bands between segments of the rectus abdominis muscle.

INSERTION: The area of attachment of muscle to the bone it moves.

INSPIRATION: The phase of a breathing cycle during which air is drawn into the lungs.

INSPIRATORY RESERVE VOLUME: The quantity of air which can be inhaled beyond that inhaled during quiet breathing.

INSULA: Island.

INTEGUMENT: The skin.

INTERDIGITATE: The interlocking of similar parts, as the fingers of one hand with the fingers of the other.

INTERNAL: Away from the outside, toward the inside.

INTERNUNCIAL: Cells that serve as a connecting medium between two others.

INTERSTITIAL: Situated between. Occupying interspaces of tissue.

INTERVERTEBRAL: The space between the vertebrae.

INTRAPULMONIC: Within the lungs.

INTRATHORACIC SPACE: The space between the inner thoracic wall and the lung surfaces. The nonexistent intrapleural space.

INTRINSIC: Located within any given part.

INVERSION: The act of turning in.

INVERTEBRATE: Without a spinal column.

INVESTED: Usually meaning that a structure is covered by an outer sheath of connective tissue.

ION: An atom or group of atoms which, due to outside force, has lost or gained one or more orbital electrons and has thus become capable of conducting electricity.

IPSILATERAL: Conduction of impulses on the same side. Same side.

JUGULAR: Pertaining to the neck region.

KINESTHESIA: The sense of movement of muscles, and the perception of weight, resistance, and position.

KINETIC: Pertaining to motion.

KYMOGRAPH: An instrument, consisting of a motor-driven cylinder, which is used to record physiological and mechanical events. The rotating cylinder is covered with paper upon which the recording is made.

LABIAL: Pertaining to the lips.

LABIODENTAL: Pertaining to the lips and teeth.

LABYRINTH: A maze. A system of interconnecting pathways, as in the inner ear.

LACUNA: A small depression or space. The space in the matrix of dense connective tissue occupied by a cartilage cell or by a bone cell.

LAMELLA: A thin plate or scale.

LAMINA: A plate, or sheet. *Pl.* laminae

LAMINOGRAPHY: Sectional radiography. Radiographs of plane sections of a body.

LARYNGOSCOPE: A device for examination of the internal larynx.

LARYNGOSCOPY: Examination of the larynx.

LATERAL: Toward the side.

LEMNISCUS: A fiber tract within the central nervous system, such as the lateral lemniscus, which carries auditory impulses.

LENTICULAR: Pertaining to or shaped like a lens.

LEVATOR: That which raises or elevates.

LIGAMENT: A band of flexible, elastic, dense, fibrous connective tissue connecting the articular ends of bones. Sometimes found in a capsule, completely enveloping the joint.

LIMBUS: The border or edge of any flat organ or part, such as the limbus of the spiral lamina of the inner ear.

LINEA: A line, such as the linea alba.

LINEA ALBA: A white line.

LINGUA: The tongue.

LINGULA: A tongue-like structure. A small lobule of the cerebellum.

LIP: One of the fleshy folds surrounding the orifice of the mouth. A projecting margin or rim.

LIPID: A fat or fat-like substance that is insoluble in water.

LOBE: A rounded part or projection of an organ, separated from neighboring parts by fissures or constrictions.

LONGITUDINAL: Lengthwise, or in the direction of the long axis of a structure or the body.

LONGUS: Long.

LOUDNESS: The perceptual impression of the intensity of a sound. Loudness is also dependent upon the frequency of a sound.

LOW-PASS FILTER: A device, mechanical or electrical, which attenuates high-frequency energy and passes the low-frequency energy.

LUMBAR: Pertaining to the loin.

LUMEN: A cavity or space.

LUNG: The organ of respiration.

LYMPH: A colorless fluid derived from blood which carries with it waste from the blood.

MACRO-: A combining form meaning an enlargement or large.

MACULA: A spot or patch of color, or a small tubercle.

MAJOR: Primary or larger.

MAL-: Prefix meaning improper, bad, or wrong.

MALAR: Pertaining to the cheek. On the zygomatic bone, the malar surface or facial surface, as opposed to the temporal surface.

MALOCCLUSION: Any deviation from normal occlusion of the teeth.

MAMMAE: The breasts; the milk-secreting glands.

MAMMARY: Pertaining to the mammae.

MANDIBLE: The lower jaw.

MANOMETER: An instrument for measuring the pressure of liquids and gases.

MANUBRIUM: A handle. The upper portion of the sternum.

MASS: The quantity of matter in a body to which its inertial properties may be ascribed.

MASTICATION: Chewing.

MATRIX: A mold or the cavity in which anything is formed. The ground substance of connective tissue.

MAXILLA: The right or left upper jaw. *Pl.* maxillae

MAXIMUM MINUTE VENTILATION: *See* maximum minute volume.

MAXIMUM MINUTE VOLUME: The quantity of air that can be exchanged under conditions of forced breathing. Also known as maximum minute ventilation.

MEATUS: A tube or passage.

MEDIAL: Toward the axis or near the mid-line.

MEDIASTINUM: The space between the pleural investments of the lungs. It contains the heart.

MEDULLA: Anything resembling marrow in its structure, or in its relation to other structures. For example, a fatty sub-stance occupying cavities, as distinguished from the cortex. *Adj.* medullary.

MEIOSIS: The process of reduction division of germ-cell chromosomes from diploid to haploid number when completed.

MEMBRANE: A thin layer of tissue that binds structures, separates, or lines cavities.

MENINX: A membrane, especially one of the brain. *Pl.* meninges

MENISCUS: A crescent-shaped structure.

MENTAL: Pertaining to the mind. Also from the Latin mentum, pertaining to the chin.

MESENCHYME: The connective tissue of the embryo. Part of the mesoderm, it forms the connective tissues and the blood vessels.

MESOTHELIUM: A form of epithelial tissue which lines the primary body cavities.

METOPIC: Pertaining to the forehead.

MICRO-: A combining form meaning small.

MICRON: One-thousandth of a millimeter, or one-millionth of a meter (10^{-6} meters).

MICROSCOPE: An optical device that permits examination of minute objects.

MICTURITION: Urination.

MINOR: Lesser, smaller

MINUTE VOLUME: The quantity of air that is exchanged in a minute, usually expressed in cm^2.

MITOSIS: Asexual cell division.

MODALITY: A special sense, such as hearing.

MODIOLUS: The central core of bone, or columella within the cochlea.

MODULATE: To modify the intensity, frequency, or quality of the voice, as in vibrato, or inflection.

MOLECULE: The smallest unit into which a substance can be divided and still retain its characteristics.

MONAURAL: A single ear.

MORPHOLOGY: The study of form and structure of plants and animals.

MORULA: A solid cellular globular mass.

MOTOR UNIT: The muscle fibers supplied by a single axon. The supplying neuron is often included as part of the motor unit.

MUCOPERIOSTEUM: Periosteum with a mucous-membrane surface.

MUCUS: The viscous secretion of the mucous glands.

MYELIN: The fatty sheath on the axon of a neuron. Medullary sheath.

MYO-: A combining form meaning muscle.

NARIS: A nostril. *Pl.* nares.

NASAL: Pertaining to the nose.

NECK: The constricted portion of the body which connects the head with the trunk. A narrow portion of any structure serving to join its parts.

NECROPSY: The examination of a dead body.

NEO-: A combining form meaning new.

NEPHRO-: A combining form meaning kidney.

NERVOUS SYSTEM: The entire nervous apparatus of the body.

NEURAL: Pertaining to nerves or nervous tissue.

NEURILEMMA: The sheath encasing a nerve fiber.

NODE: A knob or protuberance, a point of constriction, or a small, rounded organ.

NODOSE: Characterized by nodes.

NODULE: A small node or an aggregate of cells.

NODULUS: A small node. One of the subdivisions of the vermis of the cerebellum.

NOISE: Any unwanted sound. A highly complex sound produced by erratic, intermittent, or statistically random oscillation.

NOMENCLATURE: A system of naming parts, structures, organs, etc.

NOTCH: A deep indentation.

NUCHAL: Nape of the neck.

NUCLEUS: An aggregate of cell bodies. The specialized protoplasm of a cell. *Pl.* nuclei.

OCCIPITAL: Pertaining to, or in relation to the back of the head. The occiput.

OCCIPUT: The back of the head.

OCCLUSION: The full meeting of the masticating surfaces of the upper and lower teeth.

OCTAVE: A 2:1 ratio in frequency comprises an octave.

OCULAR: Pertaining to the eyes or eyesight.

OHM: Originally, the unit of resistance of a conductor in which one volt produces a current flow of one ampere (named after George Ohm 1787–1854). Also used to denote resistance to the transference of other forms of energy, such as mechanical. For example, an acoustical resistance has a magnitude of one acoustical ohm when a sound pressure of 1 microbar produces a volume velocity of 1 cubic centimeter per second.

OLFACTION: Smell.

OLIGO-: Prefix meaning little, or deficiency.

ONTOGENETIC: Embryological.

OPERCULUM: A lid or flap.

OPHTHALMOSCOPE: An instrument for examination of the eye, consisting essentially of a concave mirror with a hole in it, through which the observer looks.

ORBICULAR: Circular, pertaining to circular muscles.

ORBIT: The bony cavity containing the eye.

ORGAN: An aggregate of tissues that exhibits functional unity in which one tissue predominates.

ORGANIC: A structural characteristic affecting the function of organs.

ORIFICE: An opening or entrance to a cavity or tube.

ORIGIN: The place of attachment of a muscle which remains relatively fixed during contraction.

ORTHO-: Prefix meaning straight.

OS-: Pertaining to bone, or to the mouth.

OSSEOUS: Bony, composed of bone.

OSSICLE: A small bone, especially of the middle ear.

OSSIFY: To convert or harden into bone.

OSTIUM: A mouth or aperture.

OTITIS: An inflammation.

OTO-: A combining form meaning ear.

OTOSCOPE: A speculum-like device for examination of the middle ear.

OVERTONE: Complex tones, produced by such generators as vibrating strings, contain component frequencies that are integral multiples of the lowest frequency. The first component is the fundamental frequency, or first harmonic, and the others are overtones.

OVUM: An egg.

OXIDIZE: To combine chemically with oxygen.

PALATE: The roof of the mouth.

PALLIUM: A mantle or a portion of the cerebral wall.

PALM: The inner or flexor surface of the hand.

PALPABLE: Perceptive by palpation.

PALPATE: To examine by the sense of touch.

PAPILLA: A small, nipple-like eminence. *Pl.* papillae.

PARENCHYMA: The essential part of an organ.

PARIETAL: Forming, or situated on a wall.

PARS: A part.

PARTIAL: In acoustics, a component of a complex tone.

PARTURITION: Giving birth to young.

PASSAGE: A channel or lumen.

PATENT: Open.

PATHOLOGY: A biological science dealing with the nature of disease, its courses and its effects.

PECTINATE: Comb-like.

PECTORAL: Pertaining to the chest.

PEDICLE: A process or projection that resembles a foot.

PEDUNCLE: A small foot or stalk.

PELVIC: Pertaining to the pelvis.

PELVIS: A basin, or basin-shaped cavity.

PENNIFORM: Feather-like in structure.

PERICARDIUM: The membranous sac that envelops the heart.

PERICHONDRIUM: A fibrous membrane investing the surface of cartilage.

PERIKARYON: The cell body of a neuron.

PERIOD: The time required for an oscillating body to make one complete oscillating or vibratory cycle.

PERIODONTAL: Surrounding a tooth, especially its root. Also written peridental.

PERIOSTEUM: A fibrous membrane investing the surfaces of bone.

PERIPHERAL: Away from the axis or midline.

PERITONEUM: The serous membranous lining of the abdominal cavity.

PETROUS: From the Greek "stone"; a very hard, dense bone, as the petrous portion of the temporal bone.

PHALANGES: The bones of the fingers and toes.

PHALANX: Pertaining to fingers or toes.

PHARYNX: Gullet.

PHASE: A particular point of advancement of a cycle, usually expressed in degrees of a circle. One complete cycle = 360°

PHILTRUM: The midline vertical depression of the upper lip, extending from the vermilion border to the nose.

PHONATION: The production of sounds by the vibration of the vocal folds.

PHONE: An individual speech sound.

PHONEME: The smallest distinctive group or class of phones in a language.

PHONEMIC: Concerning the discrimination of distincitve speech sounds in a language.

PHOTOCELL: An electronic device that is sensitive to light.

PHOTOMICROGRAPH: A photograph of a minute or microscopic object, usually made with the aid of a microscope.

PHRENIC: Pertaining to the diaphragm.

PHYLUM: One of the main divisions of the animal or plant kingdom.

PHYSIOLOGY: The science of the function of living organisms, or their parts.

PISIFORM: Pea-shaped.

PIT: A depression, as the pit of the stomach.

PITCH: That attribute of auditory sensation in terms of which sounds may be placed on a scale extending from low to high.

PLACENTA: A vascular, spongy tissue formed by the interlocking of fetal and maternal tissue in the uterus, which allows exchange of nutritive and respiratory products.

PLACODE: A local thicking of ectoderm. A plate-like structure.

PLANARIA: A small, free-living flatworm, of the phylum Platyhelminthes.

Plane: A flat, smooth surface either tangent to the body, or dividing it.

PLANTAR: Pertaining to the sole of the foot.

PLATE: A flattened part, especially a flattened part of a bone.

PLATY-: A combining form meaning flat or broad.

PLETHYSMOGRAPH: A device used for measuring changes in volume of an organ or structure. The structure to be examined is usually placed within an airtight container, and changes in volume produce a displacement of air or water, which is measured and taken as an index of volume change.

PLEURAE: The serous membranes that line the thoracic cavity and invest the surfaces of the lungs.

PLEURISY: An inflammation of the pleurae.

PLEXUS: A network of anastomosing vessels or nerves.

PLICA: A fold.

PLOSIVE: A complete stop that consists of a closure, stop, and release of air by the articulators or glottis.

PNEUMO-: A combining form meaning air or lung.

PNEUMOGRAPH: An instrument for recording the movements of the thorax during respiration.

PNEUMOTHORAX: The presence of gas or air in the pleural cavity.

POCKET: A blind sac or cavity.

POLY-: Prefix denoting many.

POLYGONAL: An adjective pertaining to a figure having many angles and sides.

POLYP: A sedentary type of animal form, usually with a fixed base, columnar body, and a free end with a mouth. Also, a projecting growth.

PONS: A process or bridge of tissue connecting two parts of an organ.

PORE: A minute opening on the surface.

POST-: Prefix meaning after, or behind.

POSTERIOR: Toward the back, or away from the front.

PRE-: Prefix meaning before.

PRESSURE: The force per unit area exerted at a given point.

PRIMORDIA: First-formed.

PROCERUS: From the Greek *pro*, and *keras*, horn. A pyramidalshaped muscle of the nose.

PROCESS: A prominence of bone, cartilage, or of the nervous system.

PROGENITOR: An ancestor in the direct line; a forefather.

PROGESTERONE: A female sex hormone.

PROLIFERATE: To grow by multiplication, as in cell division.

PRONE: Lying face down. Opposite of supine.

PROPRIOCEPTION: Awareness of one's own position, balance, and equilibrium, especially during locomotion.

PROTUBERANCE: A knob-like projection.

PROXIMAL: Nearest the body or medial axis.

PSEUDO-: Prefix meaning false.

PSYCHOGENIC: Originating in the mind.

PTERO-: A combining form meaning feather or wing.

PUBERTY: The beginning of sexual maturity.

PUDENDUM: Vulva, or external female genitalia.

PULVINAR: An angular (cushion-like) prominence on the thalamus.

PUNCTIFORM: Pointed in form.

PUTAMEN: The outer portion of the lenticular nucleus.

PYRIFORM: Pear-shaped.

QUADRILATERAL: A plane figure having four sides and four angles.

RADIAN: An angle at the center of a circle subtending its arc, and equal in length to the radius of the circle. Equal to 57.2958°.

RADIOGRAPHY: A photograph made by projecting roentgen (X) rays through a part of the body onto a sensitive film.

RAMUS: A branch of a vein or nerve, or a process of bone projecting from a main branch.

RAPHE: A seam or ridge indicating the line of junction of two symmetrical halves. Usually applies to muscles.

RECESS: A fossa, ventricle, or ampulla.

RECTUS: Pertaining to anything having a straight course.

REFLECTED WAVE: A sound wave that has been cast or thrown back.

REFLEX: An involuntary, relatively invariable adaptive response to a stimulus.

REFRACTORY PERIOD: The period of time during which a neuron or muscle fiber exhibits decreased sensitivity to a stimulus.

REGISTER: A range of pitch in voice for which the mode of vibration of the vocal folds is relatively the same, except for frequency of vibration.

RELAXATION PRESSURE: Intrapulmonic pressure due to tissue elasticity, torque, and gravity, which tends to expel air from the lungs.

RENAL: Pertaining to the kidney.

RENIFORM: Kidney shaped.

RESIDUAL: A remainder. That which cannot be evacuated or discharged, such as residual air in the lungs.

RESIDUAL VOLUME: The quantity of residual air, usually expressed in cm^2.

RESONANCE: The absorption by a structure of energy at a specific frequency band, and the emission of energy by the same structure at the same frequency band.

RESPIRATION: The interchange of gases of the living and gases in which they live.

RESPIRATORY PASSAGE: The nares, nasal cavities, pharynx, oral cavity, larynx, trachea, and bronchial tubes.

RESTIFORM: Cord-like.

RETICULAR: A network of connective tissue. A net-like structure.

RETRACT: Draw back, shorten.

RETRO-: A combining form meaning back, or behind.

RHEOBASE: A minimal strength of electrical current, which, when left on for an indefinite period of time, produces a nerve stimulation.

RHINO-: A combining form meaning nose.

RHOMBOID: Shaped like a rhombus.

RHOMBUS: An oblique-angled parallelogram.

RIDGE: An elevation or crest.

RIMA: A chink or cleft.

RISORIUS: A Latin word, meaning laughter. A cheek muscle extending from the masseter to the corner of the mouth.

ROENTGENOGRAPHY: A photograph made by projecting roentgen (X) rays through a part of the body onto a sensitive film.

ROSTRAL: Toward the head.

ROSTRUM: A beak, projection, or ridge.

RUDIMENTARY: In an imperfect or early stage of development.

RUGA: A wrinkle or fold. *Pl.* rugae.

SACCULE: A small sac.

SACRAL: Pertaining to the sacrum.

SACRO-: A combining form meaning pertaining to the sacrum.

SACRUM: The fused vertebrae, which, with the coccyx, form the inferior portion of the vertebral column.

SAGITTAL: Pertaining to the antero-posterior median plane of the body. Arrow-like, as the sagittal suture of the skull.

SALINE: A salt, or a solution containing sodium chloride.

SALPINGIAN: Trumpet-like, as the shape of the Eustachian tube.

SARCO-: A combining form meaning flesh.

SARCOLEMMA: The sheath of a muscle fiber.

SARCOPLASM: The longitudinal substance between muscle fibrils.

SCALA: A subdivision of the cavity of the cochlea, especially of the perilymphatic spaces.

SCAPHA: Boat shaped.

SCAPULA: The shoulder blade.

SCHINDYLESIS: An articulation where a plate of bone fits into a groove in another bone.

SCHISTO-: A combining form meaning split or cleavage.

SEBACEOUS: From the Latin word *sebum*, which means tallow. Thus, containing or secreting fatty matter.

SEBACEOUS GLANDS: Glands that secrete an oily substance called sebum.

SELECTIVE PERMEABILITY: A membrane that permits only certain substances to pass in or out.

SELLA: A saddle.

SEMILUNARIS: Half-moon in shape.

SENSATION: A change in the state of awareness due to stimulation of an afferent nerve.

SENSE ORGAN: A specialized sensory nerve terminal activated by a specific stimulus.

SEPTUM: A partition separating two cavities.

SEROUS: Characterized by serum.

SERRATED: Notched on the edge, like a saw.

SERUM: Any watery animal fluid.

SHAFT: The trunk of any columnar structure, especially the diaphysis of a long bone.

SHEATH: The connective tissue covering vessels, muscles, nerves, etc.

SIBILANT: Characterized by a hissing sound.

SIGMOID: Shaped like the letter S.

SINE: A trigonometric function equal to the ratio of the ordinate of the end point of the arc to the radius vector of this end point, the origin located at the center of the circle on which the arc lies, and the critical point of the arc located on the x-axis.

SINK: The point where inward current flow occurs during propagation of a nerve impulse.

SINUS: A cavity or depression within a structure, or existing between two adjacent structures.

Situ, in: In position.

SOFT PALATE: The mobile, muscular, posterior portion of the palate that separates the nasal from subadjacent cavities.

SOMA: Body.

SOMATIC: Pertaining to the body and especially the voluntary muscles and skeletal framework.

SPECIFIC GRAVITY: The ratio of the mass of a given volume of any substance to that of the same volume of some other substance. Water is usually the standard for liquids and solids, while air or hydrogen is the standard for gases.

SPECTRUM: The band of colors formed when visible light is passed through a prism or other light-dispersing device. In sound, a representation of the amplitude (sometimes also phase) of the components arranged as a function of their frequencies.

SPECULUM: An instrument for dilating the orifice of a cavity or tube in order that the interior may be observed.

SPHENOID: Wedge shaped. A basal compound skull bone.

SPHINCTER: A muscle that contracts to close an orifice or opening.

SPINE: A sharp projection. Sometimes taken to mean the vertebral column.

SPIROMETER: An instrument for measuring vital capacity, or volumes of inhaled and exhaled air.

SPLANCHNIC: Pertaining to the viscera.

SPONGIO-: Prefix meaning sponge-like.

SQUAMOUS: A flat plate or scale.

STAPES: The innermost of the ossicles of the middle ear.

STENOSIS: Narrowing of a duct or canal, especially of the blood vessels.

STEREOTROPISM: Growth or movement toward a solid body.

STIMULUS: Anything that acts as an excitant or irritant for the nervous system.

STOMODEUM: The embryonic mouth.

STRAIN: Deformation produced by stress.

STRATIFIED: Arranged in layers.

STRESS: The action of forces whereby deformation or strain results.

STRIATED: Characterized by parallel-placed transverse fibers.

STROBOLARYNGOSCOPY: Examination of the larynx utilizing a stroboscope for illumination. When the rate of the flashing light is equal to that of the vibrating vocal folds, they seemingly stand motionless, thus affording a critical inspection.

STROBOSCOPE: A device that utilizes a short-duration flashing light apparently to stop moving objects.

STYLO-: A combining form meaning pillar.

SUB-: Prefix meaning under, beneath, or deficient.

SULCUS: A furrow or groove, especially in the brain.

SUPER-: Prefix meaning above or excessive.

SUPERFICIAL: Toward the surface.

SUPERIOR: Upper, the upper of two parts.

SUPINE: Lying on the back, face upward. The hand, with palm upward.

SUPPLEMENTAL AIR: The air that can be exhaled, beyond that which is exhaled during quiet breathing.

SUPPURATIVE: Pus producing.

SUPRA-: Prefix meaning upon or above.

SURFACE TENSION: A supportive property on the surface of a liquid. An apparent tension in an actually nonexistent surface film due to attractive properties of the liquid molecules.

SUTURE: The point or line of junction of two structures, or parts of a structure. An immovable articulation.

SYMPHYSIS: The point of union between two structures.

SYN-: Prefix meaning with or together.

SYNAPSE: The region of communication between neurons.

SYNARTHROSIS: An articulation in which the bones are immovably bound.

SYNCHONDROSIS: An articulation between two bones that is characterized by an intervening cartilage.

SYNDESMOSIS: A joint fixed by means of fibrous tissue.

SYNERGY: The cooperative action of two or more muscle groups, or of two or more organs.

SYNOVIA: The fluid normally present in joint cavities.

SYNOVIAL: Pertaining to the secretion of synovia by the membranes in an articular capsule.

SYSTEM: A combination of parts into functional unity.

TAG: A flap-like appendage.

TEGMEN: A cover or roof.

TELA: A web of tissue.

TELENCEPHALON: The anterior part of the forebrain.

TELERECEPTORS: Receptors that are sensitive to stimuli from a distant source, such as light, sound, and smell.

TEMPLE: That portion of the head posterior to the eye and superior to the zygomatic arch.

TEMPORAL: Pertaining to the temple.

TENDON: A nonelastic band of connective tissue that forms the attachment of muscle to bone.

TENSOR: The part of a muscle that serves to make a structure tense.

TENUOUS: Minute, not dense.

TERTIARY: Third in order.

TETANY: The blending of discrete muscular contractions to form a sustained contraction.

TETRA-: A combining form meaning four.

TETRAHEDRAL: Having the form of a tetrahedron, which is a solid contained by four plane faces; a triangular pyramid.

THORACIC: Pertaining to the thorax.

THORAX: The portion of the torso bounded below by the diaphragm and above by the root of the neck.

THYROID: Shield shaped.

TIDAL AIR: The air exchanged during a cycle of quiet breathing.

TIDAL VOLUME: The quantity of air exchanged during a cycle of quiet, normal breathing, usually measured in cm^2.

TISSUE: An aggregate of cells similar in function.

TONSIL: An aggregate of lymph nodes and vessels, contained in the mucosa of the pharynx.

TOPICAL: Pertaining to a localized region.

TOPOGRAPH: A graphic description of the surface features of an area or figure.

TORQUE: A force that produces or tends to produce torsion (twisting) or rotation.

TORSO: The body, minus the head and extremities.

TORTUOUS: Twisted, turned.

TORUS: An elevation or prominence.

TRACHEOSTOMY: The making of an opening into the trachea.

TRACHEOTOMY: Cutting into the trachea.

TRACT: A pathway or course, especially of nerves. A group of structures with a specific purpose.

TRACTION: Drawing or pulling.

TRAGUS: A small pointed eminence in front of the concha of the ear. The hair in front of the concha is also called the tragus.

TRANSDUCER: A device that absorbs energy and emits energy either in the same form or in another form.

TRANSILLUMINATION: To illuminate the interior or lumen of a structure by passing light through the tissue.

TRANSVERSE: Crosswise, at right angles to the longitudinal plane.

TRAPEZOID: A four-sided figure with two parallel and two diverging sides.

TRIFOLIATE: Having three leaves or leaf-like parts.

TRIGONUM: A small, triangular-shaped cavity or structure.

TRITICEOUS: Shaped like a grain of wheat.

TRITURATION: Grinding. To reduce to a powder by grinding.

TROCHANTER: A very large, bony process.

TROCHLEAR: A structure shaped like a pulley. The fourth cranial nerve.

TROCHOID: A pivot joint, capable of rotating motion.

TROPHOBLAST: The outer layer of cells of a blastocyst.

TUBER: A rounded protuberance.

TUBERCLE: A small, round, bony projection on a structure.

TUBEROSITY: A large rounded projection on a bone.

TURBINATED: Scroll shaped.

TYMPANIC: Pertaining to the middle ear.

TYMPANUM: The middle ear.

UMBILICUS: The navel or central abdominal depression at the region of attachment of the umbilical cord.

UTERO: Pertaining to the uterus. The womb.

UTRICLE: In hearing, a membranous sac.

UVULA: Cone shaped. Hanging free, as a bunch of grapes.

VALLECULA: A shallow groove or depression. *Pl.* valleculae.

VELUM: A thin, veil-like structure. The muscular portion of the soft palate.

VENTRAL: Situated on the lower or abdominal surface.

VENTRICLE: A small cavity or pouch.

VERMIAN: Worm-like.

VERMILION: Brilliant red.

VERMIS: The annulated median portion of the cerebellum, so named because of its resemblance to a worm.

VERSION: A turning

VERTEBRA: One of the bones forming the vertebral column.

VERTEBRAL: Pertaining to the vertebrae.

VESICLE: A small sac containing fluid.

VESTIBULE: An approach or an antechamber.

VESTIGIAL: A degenerate remnant of a functional structure.

VILLI: Fine processes of the chorion which extend into the deciduous tissue of the uterus.

VIRILISM: Masculinity.

VISCERAE: The soft internal organs of the body.

VISCERAL: Pertaining to the viscerae.

VISCOSITY: The property of a fluid which resists change in the shape or arrangement of its elements during flow.

VITAL CAPACITY: The maximum amount of air that can be exhaled after maximum inhalation.

VOMER: Shaped like a plowshare. The inferior-most portion of the bony nasal septum.

WHEATSTONE BRIDGE: A sensitive instrument designed to measure the electrical resistance of a component in an electrical circuit.

XIPHOID: Sword shaped.

ZYGOMATIC: An adjective pertaining to the arch formed by the union of the zygomatic process of the temporal bone with the malar (zygomatic) bone.

ZYGOTE: The cell produced by the union of two sex cells.

Appendix

SUMMARY OF THE MUSCLES OF THE SPEECH MECHANISM

SUMMARY OF THE MUSCLES OF BREATHING

MUSCLES OF INHALATION

Thoracic muscles

Diaphragm
>Origin:
>>Sternal —Two fleshy slips from the posterior surface of the xiphoid.
>>Costal —From the inner surfaces of the cartilages and adjacent portions of the lower six ribs on either side.
>>Lumbar—From aponeurotic arches, lumbocostal, and from the lumbar vertebrae by two pillars or crura.
>Course:
>>Muscle fibers from periphery converge and meet at the central tendon.
>Insertion:
>>The fibers insert into the central tendon.
>Innervation:
>>Phrenic nerve.
>Function:
>>Acts as primary muscle of inhalation.

Pectoralis major
>Origin:
>>The clavicle and sternum and first six ribs. Also the aponeurosis of external oblique muscle of the abdomen.
>Course:
>>Muscle fibers course upward and lateralward.
>Insertion:
>>Inserts in the intertubercular sulcus of the humerus bone.
>Innervation:
>>Medial and lateral anterior thoracic.
>Function:
>>Adducts and medially rotates humerus, flexes shoulder joint, depresses shoulder. With shoulder fixed, it might raise the sternum and upper six ribs.

Pectoralis minor
>Origin:
>>Ribs three through five, near their cartilages.

552

Course:
Upward and lateralward, converging to form a tendon.
Insertion:
Coracoid process of scapula.
Innervation:
Medial and lateral anterior thoracic.
Function:
Draws shoulder forward, and with shoulder fixed might raise ribs three through five.

Subclavius
Origin:
First costal cartilage and first rib.
Course:
Fibers course obliquely upward and lateralward.
Insertion:
Into the groove on the under surface of the clavicle between the costoclavicular and conoid ligament.
Function:
Depresses lateral end of clavicle, and with shoulder fixed might help raise the upper rib.

Serratus anterior
Origin:
Upper eight or nine ribs, near their cartilages.
Course:
Fibers course backward, close to the chest wall.
Insertion:
Vertebral border of scapula.
Innervation:
Long thoracic.
Function:
Draws scapula forward and inferior angle laterally. With shoulder fixed, might raise the upper eight or nine ribs.

External intercostals
Origin:
Lower border of the rib above.
Course:
Down and out anteriorly, down and medially posteriorly.
Insertion:
Into the upper edge of the rib below.
Innervation:
Intercostal nerves.
Function:
Draws adjacent ribs together. With the first ribs fixed, lift the rib beneath.

Levator costalis
Origin:
Transverse processes of seventh cervical and upper eleven thoracic vertebrae.
Course:
The fibers course obliquely down and laterally.
Insertion:
Into the outer surface of the rib immediately below the vertebra from which it takes its origin. Some fibers cross over a rib and insert into the next rib below.
Innervation:
Anterior rami of thoracic.
Function:
Aids in raising the ribs in inhalation, presumably.

Serratus posterior superior
  Origin:
    Spines of seventh cervical and upper thoracic vertebrae.
  Course:
    Down and laterally.
  Insertion:
    Second through fifth ribs near their angles.
  Innervation:
    Second and third thoracic.
  Function:
    Accessory muscle of respiration, elevates the ribs, presumably.

Neck Muscles

Sternocleidomastoid
  Origin:
    From the anterior surface of manubrium and the upper surface of the medial end
    of the clavicle.
  Course:
    Almost directly upward, the fibers converging as they course.
  Insertion:
    Lateral portion of mastoid process and the base of the occipital bone.
  Innervation:
    Spinal portion of accessory nerve and branches from the anterior rami of second
    and third cranial nerves.
  Function:
    If the head is fixed, raises the sternum and, indirectly, the ribs. Rotates the head.

Scalenus anterior
  Origin:
    Transverse processes of third to sixth cervical vertebrae.
  Course:
    Descends almost vertically and inserts as a flat tendon.
  Insertion:
    Tubercle of first rib.
  Innervation:
    Anterior rami of third and fourth cervical.
  Function:
    Flexes vertebral column laterally, accessory muscle of inhalation.

Scalenus medius
  Origin:
    Transverse processes of second to sixth cervical vertebrae.
  Course:
    Descends alongside the vertebral column and inserts as a broad tendon.
  Insertion:
    First rib.
  Innervation:
    Anterior rami of third and fourth cervical.
  Function:
    Flexes vertebral column laterally and acts as an accessory muscle of respiration.

Scalenus posterior
  Origin:
    Tubercles of fourth through sixth cervical vertebrae.
  Course:
    Descends along side the vertebral column and sometimes blends with the scalenus
    medius.

Insertion:
Second rib.
Innervation:
Anterior rami of third and fourth cervical.
Function:
Flexes vertebral column laterally and acts as an accessory muscle of respiration.

Scalenus minimus
(Highly variable)

Back muscles

Latissimus dorsi
Origin:
Iliac crest, sacroiliac ligament, spines of the lumbar, sacral, and lower five thoracic vertebrae.
Course:
The muscle curves around the lower border of the teres major muscle, and is twisted upon itself so that the superior fibers become at first posterior and then inferior.
Insertion:
It inserts on the humerus, near the insertion of the pectoralis major.
Innervation:
Thoracodorsal nerve.
Function:
Rotates the arm medially, adducts the arm, and with the arm fixed might raise the lower ribs.

Sacrospinalis (Iliocostalis cervicis)
Origin:
Heads of ribs one through six.
Course:
Vertically upward.
Insertion:
Posterior tubercles of transverse processes of fourth, fifth, and sixth cervical vertebrae.
Innervation:
Posterior rami of cervical nerves.
Function:
Extends vertebral column, and might raise ribs one through six.

MUSCLES OF EXHALATION

Thoracic muscles

Triangularis sterni (transversus thoracis)
Origin:
Posterior surface of corpus of sternum and ensiform process and from the posterior surfaces of the costal cartilages of ribs five through seven.
Course:
Upward and outward.
Insertion:
Lower borders and inner surfaces of ribs two through six.
Innervation:
Branches of intercostal nerves.
Function:
Pulls ribs downward, decreasing thoracic cavity.

Subcostals
   Origin:
      The inner surface of the ribs, near their angle.
   Course:
      Down and medially near the vertebral column and down and laterally anteriorly.
   Insertion:
      Inner surface of the second or third rib below the origin.
   Innervation:
      Intercostal nerves.
   Function:
      Lowers the ribs, presumably.

Internal intercostals
   Origin:
      Lower border of the upper eleven ribs, and their costal cartilages in an area extending laterally to the angle.
   Course:
      Down and laterally anteriorly.
   Insertion:
      Upper surface of the rib immediately below.
   Innervation:
      Intercostal nerves.
   Function:
      May lower the ribs, decreasing the thoracic cavity.

Serratus posterior inferior
   Origin:
      From the spinous processes of thoracic vertebrae eleven and twelve and the lumbar vertebrae one through three.
   Course:
      Upward and laterally.
   Insertion:
      Inferior borders of lower four ribs, near their angles.
   Innervation:
      Anterior rami of thoracic nerves nine through twelve.
   Function:
      Pulls the lower ribs downward, presumably.

Back muscles

Illiocostalis dorsi
   Origin:
      Angles of ribs six through twelve.
   Course:
      Vertical and slightly medialward.
   Insertion:
      Angles of ribs one through six or seven and transverse process of the seventh cervical vertebra.
   Innervation:
      Posterior rami of thoracic nerves.
   Function:
      Pulls the ribs downward, presumably.

Iliocostalis lumborum
   Origin:
      Posterior iliac crest and sacrum.
   Course:
      Vertically upward.

Insertion:
Ribs three through twelve, at their angles.
Innervation:
Posterior rami of lumbar nerves.
Function:
Depresses the ribs, presumably.

Quadratus lumborum
Origin:
Iliac crest and iliolumborum ligament.
Course:
Vertically upwards, converging as they course.
Insertion:
Transverse processes of the lumbar vertebrae one through four and medial half of last rib.
Innervation:
The lower thoracic and the lumbar nerves.
Function:
Flexes the vertebral column and lowers the last rib.

Abdominal muscles

External oblique
Origin:
Exterior surfaces and lower borders of ribs four through twelve.
Course:
Down and medially
Insertion:
Anterior half of iliac crest and abdominal aponeurosis.
Innervation:
Intercostal nerves eight through twelve, iliohypogastric and ilioinguinal nerves.
Function:
Compresses abdominal contents.

Internal oblique
Origin:
Lateral half of inguinal ligament and anterior half of the iliac crest.
Course:
Up and medially.
Insertion:
Abdominal aponeurosis and inferior borders of the costal cartilages of ribs eight through twelve.
Innervation:
Same as external oblique.
Function:
Compresses abdominal contents.

Transversus abdominis
Origin:
Inner surfaces of ribs six through twelve, from lumbar fascia, from inner edge of anterior half of iliac crest, and lateral half of inguinal ligament.
Course:
Horizontally.
Insertion:
Abdominal aponeurosis.
Innervation:
Same as external oblique.
Function:
Compresses abdominal contents.

SUMMARY OF THE MUSCLES OF THE LARYNX

EXTRINSIC MUSCLES OF THE LARYNX

Suprahyoid muscles

Digastricus (anterior belly)
Origin:
Inner surface of mandible near symphysis.
Course:
Down and posteriorly.
Insertion:
Intermediate tendon at hyoid bone.
Innervation:
Mylohyoid nerve.
Function:
Depresses the jaw or raises the hyoid bone.

Digastricus (posterior belly)
Origin:
Mastoid process of temporal bone.
Course:
Down and anteriorly.
Insertion:
Hyoid bone and intermediate tendon.
Innervation:
Facial nerve.
Function:
Elevates and retracts hyoid bone.

Stylohyoid
Origin:
Styloid process of temporal bone.
Course:
Down and anteriorly.
Insertion:
Body of hyoid bone.
Function:
Elevates hyoid bone.

Mylohyoid
Origin:
Mylohyoid line.
Course:
Oblique, medially and posteriorly.
Insertion:
Median raphe and body of hyoid bone.
Innervation:
Mylohyoid nerve.
Function:
Elevates the hyoid bone and tongue. May assist in depressing the jaw.

Geniohyoid
Origin:
Mental spine of mandible.
Course:
Back and downward.
Insertion:
Body of hyoid bone.

Innervation:
　First and second cervical.
Function:
　Elevates and draws hyoid bone forward. Depress the jaw.

Supplementary laryngeal elevators

Hyoglossus
　Origin:
　　Body and greater cornu of hyoid.
　Course:
　　Vertically, radiating as it courses.
　Insertion:
　　Into the tongue at the sides.
　Innervation:
　　Hypoglossal.
　Function:
　　Depresses the tongue, raises the hyoid bone if the tongue is fixed or elevated.

Genioglossus
　Origin:
　　Mental spine of the mandible.
　Course:
　　Posteriorly, radiating as it courses.
　Insertion:
　　Superior fibers insert into the tongue from the root to the tip. Middle fibers, into the sides of pharynx, and inferior fibers into the body of hyoid bone.
　Innervation:
　　Hypoglossal.
　Function:
　　Protrudes the tongue, depresses the tongue, or elevates the hyoid bone.

Infrahyoid muscles

Sternohyoid
　Origin:
　　Manubrium sterni and clavicle.
　Course:
　　Vertically up.
　Insertion:
　　Lower border of body of hyoid bone.
　Innervation:
　　Descends cervicis and hypoglossi.
　Function:
　　Depresses the hyoid.

Omohyoid
　Origin:
　　Upper border of scapula.
　Course:
　　Forward, upward behind sternocleidomastoid where it changes direction at a central tendon, to course vertically upward.
　Insertion:
　　The lower border of the hyoid bone.
　Innervation:
　　Same as sternohyoid.
　Function:
　　Depresses the hyoid.

Thyrohyoid
  Origin:
    Oblique line of thyroid cartilage.
  Course:
    Vertically upwards.
  Insertion:
    Lower border of greater cornu of hyoid bone.
  Innervation:
    Descends hypoglossi.
  Function:
    Decreases distance between thyroid cartilage and hyoid bone. With hyoid fixed, raises the larynx. With larynx fixed, depresses the hyoid bone.

Sternothyroid
  Origin:
    Manubrium of sternum.
  Course:
    Vertically upward.
  Insertion:
    Oblique line of thyroid cartilage.
  Innervation:
    Descends cervicis and hypoglossi.
  Function:
    Depresses the thyroid.

Intrinsic muscles of the larynx

Thyroarytenoid

Thyromuscularis
  Origin:
    Posterior surface of the thyroid near the angle.
  Course:
    Posteriorly and laterally.
  Insertion:
    Muscular process and base of arytenoid cartilage.
  Innervation:
    Recurrent laryngeal.
  Function:
    Relaxes the vocal folds.

Thyrovocalis
  Origin:
    Posterior surface of the thyroid near the angle.
  Course:
    Posteriorly.
  Insertion:
    Vocal process and lateral surface of the arytenoid process.
  Innervation:
    Recurrent laryngeal.
  Function:
    Vocal fold tensor.

Abductor muscle

Posterior cricoarytenoid
  Origin:
    Posterior surface of cricoid lamina.

Course:
    Up and laterally.
Insertion:
    Muscular process of the arytenoid cartilage.
Innervation:
    Recurrent laryngeal.
Function:
    Dilates the glottis.

Adductor muscles

Lateral cricoarytenoid
    Origin:
        Lateral surface of cricoid arch.
    Course:
        Up and posteriorly.
    Insertion:
        Muscular process of arytenoid cartilage.
    Innervation:
        Recurrent laryngeal.
    Function:
        Approximates the vocal folds.

Glottal tensor muscle

Cricothyroid
    Origin:
        Arch of cricoid cartilage.
    Course:
        Vertical and slightly posteriorly.
    Insertion:
        Lower border of thyroid cartilage.
    Innervation:
        External branch of superior laryngeal.
    Function:
        Elongates, tenses the vocal folds.

SUMMARY OF THE MUSCLES OF THE TONGUE

Intrinsic muscles of the tongue

Superior longitudinal
    Origin:
        Base of tongue.
    Course:
        Horizontally anteriorly.
    Insertion:
        Tip of tongue.
    Innervation:
        Hypoglossal.
    Function:
        Shortens the tongue or turn up the tip.

Inferior longitudinal
    Origin:
        Base of tongue, laterally on either side.

Course:
   Horizontally anteriorward.
Insertion:
   Tip of tongue.
Innervation:
   Hypoglossal.
Function:
   Shortens the tongue or turns the tip down.

Transverse:
   Origin:
      Median raphe of tongue.
   Course:
      Laterally.
   Insertion:
      Submucous tissue at the lateral margin.
   Innervation:
      Hypoglossal.
   Function:
      Narrows the tongue.

Vertical
   Origin:
      Dorsum of tongue.
   Course:
      Vertically downward.
   Insertion:
      Sides and base of tongue.
   Innervation:
      Hypoglossal.
   Function:
      Flattens the tongue.

Extrinsic muscles of the tongue

   Genioglossus (see supplementary laryngeal elevators)

   Styloglossus
      Origin:
         Styloid process of temporal bone.
      Course:
         Down and anteriorly.
      Insertion:
         Sides of the tongue.
      Innervation:
         Hypoglossal.
      Function:
         Elevates and retracts the tongue.

   Palatoglossus:
      Origin:
         Inferior surface of the soft palate, anteriorly.
      Course:
         Down and laterally.
      Insertion:
         Sides of the tongue.
      Function:
         Raises the back of the tongue or lowers the soft palate.

   Hyoglossus (see supplementary laryngeal elevators)

SUMMARY OF THE MUSCLES OF THE PHARYNX

Inferior constrictor
Origin:
Oblique line of thyroid cartilage and cricoid cartilage at the side.
Course:
Radiates from its origin, especially upwards as it courses posteriorly.
Insertion:
Midline raphe.
Innervation:
Accessory and laryngeal branches of vagus.
Function:
Constricts the pharynx.

Middle constrictor
Origin:
Stylohyoid ligament and major cornu of hyoid bone.
Course:
Radiates from its origin, as it courses posteriorly.
Insertion:
Mid-line raphe.
Innervation:
Accessory.
Function:
Constricts the pharynx.

Superior constrictor
Origin:
Medial pterygoid plate and pterygomandibular raphe.
Course:
Posteriorly, radiating somewhat.
Insertion:
Mid-line raphe.
Innervation:
Accessory.
Function:
Constricts the pharynx.

Stylopharyngeus
Origin:
Styloid process of temporal bone.
Course:
Vertically downward and somewhat medially.
Insertion:
Lateral wall of pharynx and posterior border of the superior cornu of the thyroid cartilage.
Innervation:
Glossopharyngeal.
Function:
Elevates the pharynx.

Salpingopharyngeus
Origin:
Auditory tube.
Course:
Vertically downward.
Insertion:
Blends with fibers of palatopharyngeus.

Innervation:
Accessory.
Function:
Draws lateral walls of pharynx up and lateralwards.

Pharyngopalatinus (see muscles of the soft palate)

SUMMARY OF THE MUSCLES OF THE SOFT PALATE

Levator palatini
Origin:
Petrous portion of temporal bone and cartilage of auditory tube.
Course:
Down and medially.
Insertion:
Mid-line and aponeurosis of soft palate.
Innervation:
Accessory.
Function:
Elevates soft palate.

Tensor palatini
Origin:
Medial pterygoid plate, auditory tube.
Course:
Vertically downward to hamulus.
Insertion:
Mid-line and aponeurosis of soft palate.
Innervation:
Trigeminal (mandibular branch).
Function:
Tenses soft palate, dilates orifice of auditory tube.

Musculus uvulae
Origin:
Spine of palatine bone and palatine aponeurosis.
Course:
Posteriorly.
Insertion:
Aponeurosis of soft palate.
Innervation:
Accessory.
Function:
Shortens soft palate.

Palatoglossus (glossopalatinus) (see extrinsic tongue muscles)

Palatopharyngeus (pharyngopalatinus)
Origin:
Soft palate, some fibers from auditory tube.
Course:
Laterally and downward.
Insertion:
Blends with fibers from the stylopharyngeus and inserts into the lateral wall of the pharynx and posterior border of the thyroid cartilage.
Innervation:
Accessory.

Function:
   Depresses soft palate and constricts pharynx.

SUMMARY OF THE MUSCLES OF THE FACE AND LIPS

Buccinator
   Origin:
      Pterygomandibular raphe, alveolar process of mandible and maxilla.
   Course:
      Horizontally forward and medialwards with central fibers decussating at corner of the mouth.
   Insertion:
      Blend with fibers of orbicularis oris.
   Innervation:
      Facial:
   Function:
      Compresses lips and retracts corner of mouth.

Risorius
   Origin:
      Fascia of masseter muscle.
   Course:
      Horizontally forward.
   Insertion:
      Integument at corner of mouth.
   Innervation:
      Facial.
   Function:
      Retracts corner of mouth.

Quadratus labii superior
   Origin:
      By three heads in infraorbital region of maxilla.
   Course:
      Obliquely down and laterally.
   Insertion:
      Corner of mouth.
   Innervation:
      Facial.
   Function:
      Elevates corner of mouth.

Quadratus labii inferior
   Origin:
      Mandible, near mental foramen.
   Course:
      Obliquely upward and medially.
   Insertion:
      Corner of mouth.
   Innervation:
      Facial.
   Function:
      Depresses and retracts lower lip.

Zygomaticus
   Origin:
      Malar surface of zygomatic bone.

Course:
Down and medialward.
Insertion:
Blends with orbicularis oris at corner of mouth.
Innervation:
Facial.
Function:
Elevates angle of mouth.

Mentalis
Origin:
Mandible, at mental tuberosity.
Course:
Vertically upward.
Insertion:
Integument of chin and orbicular oris.
Innervation:
Facial.
Function:
Wrinkles the chin and everts lower lip.

Triangularis
Origin:
Oblique line of mandible.
Course:
Vertically upward.
Insertion:
Angle of mouth, fibers blending with orbicularis oris.
Innervation:
Facial.
Function:
Depresses angle of mouth, compresses the lips.

Caninus
Origin:
Canine fossa of maxilla.
Course:
Vertically.
Insertion:
Angle of mouth, fibers blending with orbicularis oris.
Innervation:
Facial.
Function:
Elevates angle of mouth, compresses the lips.

Incisivis labii superior
Origin:
Maxilla, near canine teeth.
Course:
Parallel with long axis of mouth.
Insertion:
Angle of mouth.
Innervation:
Facial.
Function:
Draws corner of mouth radially in.

Incisivis labii inferior
  Origin:
    Mandible, near lateral incisors.
  Course:
    Parallel with long axis of mouth.
  Insertion:
    Corner of mouth.
  Innervation:
    Facial.
  Function:
    Draws corner of mouth radially in and depresses angle of mouth.

Platysma
  Origin:
    Fascia of pectoral and shoulder region.
  Course:
    Upward, converging.
  Insertion:
    Lower portion of mandible body, integument of upper, anterior neck, and corner
    of mouth.
  Innervation:
    Facial.
  Function:
    Draws angle of mouth down and out.

SUMMARY OF THE MUSCLES OF MASTICATION

Digastricus (see suprahyoid muscles of the larynx)

Mylohyoid (see suprahyoid muscles of the larynx)

Geniohyoid (see suprahyoid muscles of the larynx)

External pterygoid
  Origin:
    Greater wing of sphenoid, lateral surface of lateral pterygoid plate.
  Course:
    Horizontally back, converging.
  Insertion:
    Condyle of mandible.
  Innervation:
    Trigeminal, mandibular branch.
  Function:
    Protracts mandible.

Masseter
  Origin:
    Zygomatic arch.
  Course:
    Down and somewhat posteriorly.
  Insertion:
    Ramus of mandible.
  Innervation:
    Trigeminal, mandibular branch.

Function:
Closes jaws.

Temporalis
Origin:
Temporal fossa.
Course:
Down, converging rapidly.
Insertion:
Anterior border of coronoid process, anterior border of ramus.
Innervation:
Trigeminal, mandibular branch.
Function:
Closes jaws, retracts lower jaw.

Internal Pterygoid
Origin:
Lateral pterygoid plate, perpendicular plate of palatine bone.
Course:
Down, lateral, and back.
Insertion:
Medial surface of ramus and angle.
Function:
Closes the jaws.

Index

Material in the Appendix and the Glossary has not been included in the index. Italicized page numbers indicate illustrations.

569

I

History

For many years I have been researching the history of dogs. It has become increasingly clear that most of the claims made as to the antiquity of the breeds are utterly unfounded. This is not true of the Irish Wolfhound. However, while he is of an ancient breed, many of the stories currently told about him are not factual. On the other hand, there are numerous tales of actual occurrences which are not generally known. I am constrained in my desire to summarize, in this book, the history of the Irish Wolfhound. I will not make statements without proof of their validity and, for two reasons, I cannot present in this book the evidence I already have in my possession:

1. My research, analysis, and synthesis have not been completed.

2. This chapter would exceed in length the balance of the book.

Revelation of the facts, therefore, will be made by me in a number of volumes to be published over the next few years.

What I shall do here is summarize the findings at which I arrived in one book already published[1] and make general statements as to the balance of the history. As my historical books are published, this chapter in *The Irish Wolfhound Guide* will be revised to include additional authenticated information. Meanwhile, the reader can obtain Father Edmund Hogan's *The Irish Wolfdog* (1897) and Captain George Augustus Graham's *The Irish Wolfhound* (1885) in a combined volume which, although dated 1972, was published in 1973 by the Irish Wolfhound Clubs of America and of Ireland.[2]

Fossilized remains of the Irish Wolfhound have been unearthed in Ireland. At a much later date, we find the Irish Wolfhound

---

[1] Alfred W. DeQuoy, *The Irish Wolfhound in Irish Literature and Law* (1971). Privately printed. Out of print.

[2] Orders from the Western Hemisphere should be sent to the Secretary, Irish Wolfhound Club of America, Inc., whose name and address may be obtained from the American Kennel Club, 51 Madison Avenue, New York, N.Y., 10010. Persons in other areas may place their orders with the Secretary, Irish Wolfhound Club of Ireland, whose name and address may be obtained from the Irish Kennel Club, 23 Earlsfort Terrace, Dublin 2, Ireland.

mentioned in Irish laws. The laws of Ireland predate Christianity and, to the best of my knowledge, these are the oldest laws in the world which make reference to a *breed* of dog.

The earliest Irish literature possibly dates from the fifth century and is centuries older than other European literature, with the exception of Greek and Latin. It is possible to assign approximate dates to its sagas and poems by considering the style of writing, and the description of swords, helmets, shields, gold dress ornaments, trumpets, method of fighting, use of horses. This analysis leads us to the conclusions that some of the stories are of the pre-Christian era and that they were transmitted orally from generation to generation by the *filid,* a professional class of poets who were ranked with the nobility in the courts of Irish Kings.

When Christianity came to Ireland in the fifth century, the clergy gave a written form to the Irish language. They wrote the ancient tales as well as religious subjects in Irish. After a while, Latin was used solely for liturgical purposes. The Vikings, in their ninth and tenth century raids, ravaged the monasteries and destroyed many of the precious manuscripts. Those that survived and those that have been produced since then, contain innumerable references to the Irish Wolfhound. Many of these stories are fanciful to the highest degree, but it is possible to prove that many are historically true. The stories give abundant evidence of the following:

1. In combat with their foes, the Irish used huge, swift, ferocious dogs called *cu.*

2. They also employed these dogs to hunt deer, boar and wolves by sight and to guard persons, cattle and other property.

3. These hounds were held in such high esteem that, when disputes arose over them, not only individual combats but also battles between large armed forces occurred.

4. Praise for the *cu* and the deep affection of their owners for them appear throughout Irish poems and prose.

5. Ownership was restricted to kings, nobles, and poets.

6. They constituted valuable gifts.

7. The chains and collars used on the *cu* often were of precious metal.

8. The word *cu* (genitive, *con*) appears in many Irish names, ancient as well as modern, to denote outstanding qualities.

9. Descriptions of the *cu* are included in Irish manuscripts from the earliest times to those of the nineteenth century and are identical to those of the present-day Irish Wolfhound.

10. All authorities agree that the *cu* was the Irish Wolfhound.

Evidence of the above has been presented in my previously-mentioned book which restricts itself to Irish literature and law. In the writings of other countries, in paintings and in sculpture, we have proof that the Irish Wolfhound has had a continuous history to this day, but details will be omitted until the entire case can be presented. Suffice to say that, throughout history, the Irish Wolfhound has been highly prized by the great of all nations and that, in the nineteenth century, when interest in *breeds* of dogs began to be aroused, Captain George Augustus Graham (1833-1909), a Scottish officer in the British Army, began a breeding program to prevent the extinction of Irish Wolfhounds. He had remarkable success and we are all deeply indebted to him.

II

Characteristics

Senator George Graham Vest, shortly after the Civil War, represented a client whose foxhound, Old Drum, had been killed by the defendant. The trial was held in Johnson County, Missouri. In his summation to the jury, Senator Vest said:

> Gentlemen of the Jury: The best friend a man has in this world may turn against him and become his enemy. His son or daughter whom he has reared with loving care may prove ungrateful. Those who are nearest and dearest to us, those whom we trust with our happiness and our good name, may become traitors to their faith. The money that a man has, he may lose. It flies away from him, perhaps when he needs it the most. A man's reputation may be sacrificed in a moment of ill-considered action. The people who are prone to fall on their knees to do us honor when success is with us may be the first to throw the stone of malice when failure settles its cloud upon our heads. The one absolutely unselfish friend that a man can have in this selfish world, the one that never deserts him and the one that never proves ungrateful or treacherous is his dog.
>
> Gentlemen of the Jury, a man's dog stands by him in prosperity and in poverty, in health and in sickness. He will sleep on the cold ground, where the wintry winds blow and the snow drives fiercely, if only he may be near his master's side. He will kiss the hand that has no food to offer, he will lick the wounds and sores that come in encounters with the roughness of the world. He guards the sleep of his pauper master as if he were a prince. When all other friends desert, he remains. When riches take wings and reputation falls to pieces, he is as constant in his love as the sun in its journey through the heavens. If fortune drives the master forth an outcast in the world, friendless and homeless, the faithful dog asks no higher privilege than that of accompanying him to guard against danger, to fight against his enemies, and when the last scene of all comes, and death takes the master in its embrace and his body is laid away in the cold ground, no matter if all other friends pursue their way, there by his graveside will the noble dog be found, his head between his paws, his eyes sad but open in alert watchfulness, faithful and true even to death.

4

It was Samuel Butler (1612-1680) who said: "The greatest pleasure of a dog is that you may make a fool of yourself with him and not only will he not scold you, but he will make a fool of himself, too."[1]

From these reviews of Dog's nature, let us turn to consideration of those attributes which specifically characterize the Irish Wolfhound. His motto is "Gentle when stroked, fierce when provoked". I do not know of a more gentle dog than the Irish Wolfhound. One of the locations where this quality is put to the test is a benched dog show, that is, a show where the dog must be chained to his bench during the day with the exception of brief periods when he is being shown or "exercised", the latter term being euphemistic for "allowed to relieve himself" (which some persons may consider euphemistic also). Thousands of persons pass by and many pause to pat the dogs despite the warning signs. Many dogs of other breeds, through boredom, irritation, or nervousness, growl, bark, and snap at the passersby. The Irish Wolfhounds are always calm and friendly. The quiet that prevails at the Irish Wolfhound bench is striking.

The question is frequently asked: "How are they with children and with animals?" I have never seen a child abuse a Wolfhound, but I know that should this occur, the hound would placidly leave; if he were unable to leave, he would bear the unjust punishment without retaliation. Of course, one could conjure up situations where this would not be likely.

An illustration of the manner in which Irish Wolfhounds become members of the family is provided by the following letter from Amy Glassner.[2]

> I can't begin to tell you what a pleasure our life has been since Conagh joined our family. She's a devoted companion to me and my husband as well as a gentle playmate to my three young children. She has infinite patience and a sense of responsibility that's truly amazing. About her responsibility—I have never seen anything like it in any of my previous dogs. Every night before we retire, Conagh makes a bed check of the children. First she sticks her wet nose into the face of our daughter (Robin) to make sure all's well, then she goes across the hall and repeats the same procedure with Adam. Finally she checks on the baby. Needless to say, Marty and I were flabbergasted when we first noticed this nocturnal ritual. After a while we took it for granted (although we told everyone about our dog's amazing "nanny" instincts).

---

[1] Samuel Butler, "The Note-Books," *Works of Samuel Butler* (20 vols.; 1926), XX, p. 217.
[2] Amy Glassner. *Letter to author* (25 February 1971).

One night not long ago, Marty and I went to our room while Conagh made her bed check. Suddenly I heard her running across the hall to Adam's room. Then I heard her race back to Robin's room. She did this several times when I realized something was amiss. I went to check, and noticed immediately that Robin's bed was empty. It seems she had a nightmare and went into Adam's room for company. When I checked his room I found her snuggled deep under the covers near the wall. The dog didn't notice her there and was obviously extremely distressed that she'd lost one of her children. I have never seen such relief when I showed her where Robin was. She jumped up on the bed, poked her nose into Robin's face, heaved a giant sigh, and settled down on Adam's bed for the night. That's where I left them—two kids and a giant Wolfhound, blissfully asleep in a twin bed.

So that's my dog. We are very proud of her and we all love her with all our hearts. I can guarantee you, we will never be without a Wolfhound again.

The Irish Wolfhound's gentleness is demonstrated when he is harassed by other breeds. I frequently take my hounds out for a walk, sometimes singly but most of the time as a pack, and always without a leash. It is surprising to observe the effrontery exhibited by dogs along our route. They bark ferociously. Ignored by the Wolfhounds, they advance menacingly—after we have gone by, of course—growling and barking. Should a hound go forth to meet them in his usual inquiring and friendly fashion, the dog will turn and run, yelping if small in size, silent if large. Occasionally, the owner of the strange dog will observe his animal, barking all the while, leave his property and follow us along the road. Some people laugh when they see the Wolfhound glance backward and trot away. I suppose they consider that the Wolfhound is cowardly. However, when one of my hounds decides to investigate the situation and the other dog runs, the owner is quick to shout: "Call off your dog!"

As we travel along the roads, the hounds will suddenly bound away, often toward some dog or cat. At my command, they immediately abandon the chase. Should I see the quarry before they do, all I have to do is caution "No!" and they will not leave me. This, of course, is due to their obedience training. One should not expect an untrained hound to react in the same way.

The great majority of Irish Wolfhound owners have only one of the breed. Their personal observations are that he is the soul of gentleness. I am in complete agreement with this judgment, but do not be deluded into believing that there is no danger of his getting into a fight with another dog.

Once, at a dog show, my first Irish Wolfhound, Champion Feasgar Bruadar of Ballylyke, U.D.[1] (nicknamed Gamine), whom I have called "the gentlest of animals", was attacked by an Airedale Terrier. She gave out a roar that reverberated all over the grounds and pinned her adversary down. Yet she did not bite him, merely emitting threatening growls. I could not pull her off by her chain collar. It was necessary for me to put an arm under her neck and, exerting full strength, lift her up and to the rear. This was a dangerous procedure as the other dog could have bitten me. However, he was glad to get away.

Such an incident is the rare exception. Much more typical is the very light knock on the door and then, when the door is opened, a little girl asking "Can Gamine come out to play?" My wife and I allow children to come onto our grounds to play with the dogs provided we are there to supervise. If the dogs start "roughhousing" or racing around, playtime is over because of the possibility that a dog could accidentally crash into one of the children.

If someone comes to your home with a dog—of any breed—have both dogs on leash until assured that no trouble will develop. Wherever there are two or more dogs, be on the alert for trouble. A growl, a stiffening of the body's muscles, a raised tail or hackles, a snarl, call for quick action. Remember that a dog, of any size, may feel overwhelmed by the size of the Wolfhound and may bite out of fear. The Wolfhound's reaction cannot be predicted. Each hound has his own personality and attitudes. If it is a small dog that bites him, he may ignore it. But one can never be certain. Dog fights involving Wolfhounds are fearsome.

In brief, while the Irish Wolfhound is extremely gentle, he can become aroused.

Mary Beynon wrote amusingly of her hound's role as peacemaker in dogfights.

> I have seen Grim often gallop in and with his nose toss first one of my fighting West Highland terriers to the right, and then one to the left, and so end the fight.[2]

We all like to think that if we were attacked by another person, our faithful dog would spring to our aid. I wonder how the dog would know whether or not his master was engaged in a little "horseplay". When, in order to test our dogs' reactions, my children would strike

---

[1]Utility Dog. See chapter on Obedience.

[2]Mary Beynon, "An Adventure in Africa," The Irish Wolfhound Association (Britain), *The Irish Wolfhound* (1925), p. 27.

me and I would cry for help, the dogs would bite me! Gently, of course. I know of only one instance where an Irish Wolfhound went to the aid of his master. There may be many such instances. This involved a man who owned an Irish Wolfhound and a Boxer. The latter constantly bullied the Irish Wolfhound without fear of reprisal. One day, the owner called his Boxer and, when he failed to come close to him, reached out and grabbed him by the collar. The Boxer bit the owner and the Irish Wolfhound promptly tore into the Boxer. In this case, I presume the Irish Wolfhound knew that the Boxer's action was antagonistic. I do not know whether he could properly evaluate human actions.

Mr. Ronald Monro, who used his Irish Wolfhound in hunting kangaroo and deer, has said of him:

> He will not let a stranger near me if I am in the bush, either sitting or lying down, but as soon as I get on my feet will then let them approach.[1]

Having inquired about their attitude towards children and other animals, people immediately ask, "Are they good watchdogs?" One can observe that the questioner wants a dog that can differentiate between the "good guys" and the "bad guys". He wants a dog that will affectionately welcome the rich uncle who has been away for twenty years, but will attack on sight the man who secretly intends to kidnap the child or to "case the joint" for a burglary. Men expect their dogs to have greater perception than they themselves possess. They may dislike salesmen and want their dogs to bark and snarl at them but they would be furious at the poor animal if the insurance adjuster was not allowed to enter with a large check for the beneficiary on a policy. The dog should bite the kidnapper but not the new pastor who takes the child in his arms. He should bark at a person with evil intent who is near the house at night, but he should not bark if the person is visiting the neighbors or is lost and is inquiring for directions. Poor dog!

One evening, prominent attorney Henry Weaver, who sold me my first Irish Wolfhound, was alone in his house. The servants, whose stone residence adjoined the garage, had been given the night off. Suddenly, his three hounds began growling and pleading to go out. They were turned loose. It soon became apparent that the dogs had some person or animal cornered near the garage and their growls and barks were not in the spirit of play. Mr. Weaver opened a

---

[1] Ronald K. Monro, "Irish Wolfhounds in Australia," The Irish Wolfhound Club (Britain), *Year Book* (1935-1937), p. 92.

window and cried out "Don't move!" He hurried out and found that the dogs had surrounded a man who stood in horror, frozen on the spot. Mr. Weaver called off the dogs, holding two of them by their collars, and inquired as to the reason for the intruder's presence. The explanation was that the man had had a flat tire and had come looking for a jack. In reply to Mr. Weaver's question as to why he had not gone to the main house where the lights were on, he said that he did not want to disturb anyone. Mr. Weaver warned him to get back to the road, three hundred yards away, as fast as he could because he did not know how long he could restrain the dogs. The man flew down the driveway.

Mrs. Winifred Heckmann, breeder, exhibitor and judge of Irish Wolfhounds, relates two incidents of the breed's protective characteristics.[1]

> Recently I gave Barn Hill Hopeful Sheila to some very personal friends of mine, Dr. and Mrs. Glenn Morrow of Johns Hopkins Hospital, who live in one of a new block of hospital-owned houses which, unfortunately, are located in a rather unsavory section of Baltimore.

> Only staff physicians of the hospital live in this block, and many of the doctors are home very little, spending most of their nights at the hospital. The natives seem to know this, and some very dreadful things have happened. Every night, it seems, some home is broken into.

> When Glenn and Phyllis and their eight-months-old daughter moved there, they wanted a big dog, so I offered them Sheila. They love her.

> Recently, they had a young student nurse in to baby-sit while they went out to dinner. It was raining, and Sheila had been outdoors and came in wet. So Phyllis closed the baby gate between kitchen and dining room to make Sheila stay off the rugs until she was dry. She forgot to tell the nurse to let her out later.

> Around 11:45 p.m., there was a gentle rapping at the front door. Assuming it was the Morrows returning and not ringing the doorbell in case the baby was asleep, the student nurse opened the door without question.

> There stood a big, burly hoodlum. He forced his way in. He struck the girl on the head with a milk bottle and started to choke her. The student nurse screamed and struggled. Likely she would

---

have been criminally assaulted, maybe murdered, had it not been for the Irish Wolfhound locked in the kitchen.

With a mighty roar, Sheila went into action. In one tremendous leap she cleared the baby gate and catapulted into the midst of the scene—eyes blazing and fangs bared.

Confronted by this apparition right out of the pages of the HOUND OF THE BASKERVILLES, the hood dropped his victim and bolted. Whether he got away with impunity is not known. He was the only witness; the girl had fainted.

The Wolfhound's sudden materialization had been as great a shock to her as the attacker. She had not known there was a dog in the house.

When the Morrows returned, they found the student nurse unconscious on the living room floor with Sheila beside her, licking her face. A peculiar thing about the incident is that Sheila did not know the girl, had never even seen her before all this happened.

The second incident involved Barn Hill Sheila, owned by Lt. Donald E. Rockwell, Jr. The lieutenant had often joked about Sheila being worthless as a guard dog. One evening, a gentleman who was being entertained by the Rockwells decided to pick up the baby. Sheila, friendly until then, jumped up and pinned him against the wall with her two front paws until the Rockwells called her off.

This canine approach is verified by the following accounts, the first being Mary Beynon's.

I have had personally several experiences of attacks on humans— and they have all been the same. A spring at the chest—human knocked on to his back, when they will usually stand with their forepaws on the man's chest and wait to hear what is wanted. This happened to me at Bournstream—where I lived in 1917, when old Biddy I. caught a man breaking in. I was also treated once in exactly this way by mistake in the dark. So I can speak with some inside knowledge. They can easily be taught to see anyone undesirable off by walking close behind them, and if they stop, the hound will growl and show his teeth. Grim always did this to any tramps if told so. They are not aggressive, but like to care for their masters' property. One of mine that I gave Colonel Durand (9th Lancers) during the war, and he took this hound to France, when they were very devoted to each other. One evening Colonel Durand went out from his billet to dine with some of his officers. While he was out the dog was let out into the garden, and while he was there, the Frenchman and his wife, owners of the house, wanted to return home—they also had gone out somewhere to dine. The dog, Tiger I., refused to allow them to return, and he refused to go into the house in spite of a fierce snowstorm coming on, till Colonel Durand returned. When he did, he found Monsieur and Madam very cold, but furiously angry. Likewise the maids indoors all shivering and crying and imploring Tiger I. to allow their master and mistress to come inside or to come inside himself! He was quite friendly with them, but till his master returned they remained with him outside. He sat on the steps of the chateau and was very polite but perfectly firm in his refusal to their entrance.[1]

Lieutenant-Colonel H. M. Durand relates a couple of other experiences.

I live close to a main road which is notorious for the number of tramps that stream along it, and the late occupant of this house told me that seldom did a summer's day pass without two or three of these gentlemen of the road calling in to ask for something— since the hounds have been here I have never had a single tramp through the gate, and yet there is not a tradesman or workman who has ever been molested or who has a bad word for the hounds. Once, during the War, a tramp did come to the house we then lived in in Gloucestershire. I suppose he knew full well that there were only three women in the house, so he quickly opened a conservatory door and walked in—the next second something big and heavy hit him on the chest and he went flat on his back on the floor. He there lay very still, for every time he moved an eyelash a most unpleasant rumble came from somewhere close to his chin. The lady of the house, hearing the crash, came to see what was happening and found our old Wolfhound bitch, Mistress Biddy, standing over a prostrate man. The lady stood about five feet high and the man was a burly great scamp with a very varied vocabulary, which he proved from the other side of the garden gate, but no churchwarden ever walked more soberly or quietly than he did when he got the order "Get up, don't talk, walk slowly down to the gate and shut it behind you."

I admit I nearly lost a friend through an Irish Wolfhound once. He is a dignified high official now who returns from dining out in a Rolls Royce with a wife and grown-up family, but this alas was years ago, before the Great War, and we were young officers at Aldershot—my friend and I and my Irish Wolfhound had two rooms at the top of a long flight of uncarpeted stone stairs. One night, and a very cold one at that, my friend who was dining in

---

[1]Mary Beynon, *op. cit.*, p. 26.

London unfortunately missed the last train back at night and had to come down by a milk train in the very early hours next morning. Arriving in barracks as the chill grey dawn was breaking he came to the flight of stone stairs, and, being a kindly fellow and not wishing to wake us all, he slipped off his shoes and crept noiselessly up the first flight—and there he stayed till my servant brought my early tea—my Wolfhound sat there steps above him, and was quite friendly but firm. No one walked about father's house in their socks, and if they tried to they sat quite still till father came to see about it.[1]

My son, who bears the same name as I, had an experience which left an indelible impression on his memory. One evening in 1966, when he was a lieutenant in the Army, he fell asleep while reading in a room located in the lower portion of our home. Awakening to find that darkness had fallen, he decided to go upstairs to his bedroom. He opened the door and walked into the adjoining room, the recreation room, where at that moment all the hounds happened to be asleep. Momentarily transfixed by the roars which greeted him and by the glowing eyes and bared teeth of the hounds, he reacted quickly and spoke to them. They advanced with wagging tails and lapping tongues. For some time, my son had been an infrequent guest at our home and both he and the hound pack had forgotten about the other's presence.

Please note that all of these stories illustrate the instinct of the Irish Wolfhound to guard his master's home. I am not being inconsistent when I say that, unlike some other breeds, the Irish Wolfhound is not inherently distrustful. If a stranger invites the dog into his car, he will probably go. He has a heart of gold and he thinks everybody else has. If you want a different temperament, buy a dog of another breed. Of course, the Irish Wolfhound could be trained to be unfriendly and even aggressive as is amply shown in Irish literature.[2] This might prove tragic. One snap of those powerful jaws will break a man's arm. A propelled weight of 120-170 pounds could kill or seriously injure a man. Moreover, it is possible that these newly-acquired characteristics would be transmitted by breeding[3] just as many German Shepherds are now either vicious or timid due to the breeding practices of some persons solely or mainly motivated by the prospects of financial gain.

---

[1]H. M. Durand, "A Short Chat on the Breed," The Irish Wolfhound Club (Britain), *Year Book* (1926), pp. 47, 48.

[2]Alfred W. DeQuoy, *op. cit.*, pp. 10, 18-24, 56, 84.

[3]See Index at Genetics, Characteristics, Inheritability of.

The Irish Wolfhound is a calm, dignified, majestic animal. He is not lethargic, but neither is he a "bundle of nerves" as some dogs are. He will run and play just as other dogs do, but only for brief periods. Usually, he will lie down and observe the passing scene, preferably at the feet of his master. Occasionally, to the surprise of the new owner, he will roll over on his back and rest with all feet in the air. He adapts himself to his owner's moods. He is alert, affectionate and responsive but not over-demonstrative. He craves human companionship. If you spend your time out-of-doors, so will he. If you prefer the indoors, he will remain at your side. On the question of differences of attitudes between the sexes, I refer you to the chapter on Sales.

There is a popular misconception that purebred dogs are more susceptible to disease than mongrels. And persons frequently inquire whether Irish Wolfhounds are hardy or are apt to be sickly. It will be seen in the chapter on Coursing and Tracking, the chapter on Hunting and in Appendix A that Irish Wolfhounds are subject to fewer problems than most breeds. In addition, these two chapters cover his speed and ability to hunt by scent as well as by sight. His scenting capabilities are also discussed under Obedience as is his aptitude for absorbing instruction.

One occasionally reads of how a dog pines for his master or canine playmate, fails to eat and dies of grief. I do not doubt that there is some element of truth in at least some of these stories, yet when my wife and I leave the house for a couple of months or when one of the hounds dies, the appetite and health of the dogs are not affected. This may be due to the fact that the hounds are not placed in a kennel during our absence—they remain at home under the care of persons known to the dogs. Also, the fact that there are several dogs must minimize loneliness over the absence of the masters or companions. Of course, the hounds are overjoyed when we return. My wife tells me that when I leave home for a few days, the dogs search the house in an attempt to find me and finally settle down at the foot of my bed awaiting my return.

When Henry Weaver had to part with his hounds because his new position required him to travel extensively and to reside most of the remaining time in Philadelphia and New York, rather than at his country estate in Virginia, he returned to my care Champion Keltic Ghost of Ballylyke whom he had purchased from me when she was three months old. She was then six years old. She adjusted very well to her new surroundings, ate well, romped with the other hounds, and lavished her affection on us. I trained her in obedience and she won her Companion Dog's degree. After a while, I took her and my other hounds out one evening for a run, without leashes. She stayed with the other dogs as they periodically ran out of sight and then checked back to make sure I was still with them. Then I noticed that on one occasion she had not returned with the others. I called her name, blew my silent dog whistle and ran towards the area where she had last disappeared into the darkness. I heard children laughing and headed towards them. They were looking at Ghost who had jumped onto the open tailgate of a station wagon and then lain down in the vehicle. Poor Ghost had figured that this was the way to get back to the Weavers! Some time later, after Ghost had died, Henry Weaver told me that he and his wife, Kitty, found it lonesome to return on a weekend to their Virginia estate and not to be greeted by Irish Wolfhounds. Could they borrow a hound for a few days? I loaned them Ch. Keltic Phantom II, CDX.[1]

In describing the accomplishments of their hounds, owners tend to exaggerate or color the specific activity reported. They will assert that the dog saw an automobile coming, ran across the street and either pushed the child out of the path of danger or pulled it away with its teeth. I tend to regard all stories of dog heroism with suspicion. I don't deny that the incidents actually occurred. I just wonder whether there wasn't something else involved. For example, did the dog bump the child in trying to escape from the automobile? Was he pulling the child's dress in play as he had been accustomed to doing? I have in mind the animals in motion pictures who are handicapped only in their inability to speak English. A horse sees his fallen and wounded master in danger from the rifle fire of Indians. In such a situation, one could expect the frightened horse to run back to the stable. But in the motion picture, he not only returns to the ranch, but also yanks at a cowboy's jacket with his teeth, and leads him and his posse back to the rescue!

This leads us to the question "Can dogs think?" Karl von Frisch, in discussing intelligence and insight, said:

> Perhaps one can really see in the conditioned reflex a bridge between innate reflexes and simple intelligent actions. When conditioned reflexes are produced very rapidly in a brain, and when not only simultaneous sensory impressions, but also recollections from the past, memorised visual images, are made use of, that easy play of thought is produced which makes use of every experience, seeks and finds connections and is considered as intelligent behaviour. In the highest vertebrates it has increased to a fantastic extent, but it not a privilege of man.

---

[1]Companion Dog Excellent. See chapter on Obedience.

He then relates experiments with chimpanzees and continues:

> Any dog lover will be able to relate similar intelligent exploits of his pet, different in degree but not in kind.[1]

Allow me to relate two incidents which appear to indicate canine intelligence.

On a cold wintry evening, my Sahib (Ch. Sulhamstead Samando Patrick, C.D.) began to bark outside the house. I opened the kitchen door to find the reason for this unusual action and Sahib came charging in. He dashed down to the recreation room and whined. When I followed him, he ran into the basement and over to the two-way swinging door that leads outside where he whined again. My perplexity was soon dispelled when I found that an old shoe which I had given to my two six-month-old puppies was firmly wedged so that the two-way door could not be opened in either direction. I then heard, for the first time, the puppies whining outside. I removed the shoe and the puppies came bounding in, joyful at being able to escape the wintry blasts.

Keltic Tara, one of the puppies, later decided to prowl around the neighborhood at night. This was easy to do as the grounds were enclosed only by a post and rails fence having three rails and standing three and a half feet high. At seven o'clock in the morning, I chanced to see her coming back into the yard. I scolded her and assumed she would not repeat her offense. At six o'clock the following morning, the other hounds gave forth low whines. Immediate investigation revealed Tara trotting down the road towards the house. Again, she was reprimanded. The next morning, I awoke at five o'clock and decided to check on the number of dogs present. Tara was missing. I started out to look for her and there she was, trotting home. It could have been mere coincidence that Tara decided to come home one hour earlier each morning after she had been caught, or it could have been native cunning. Wires were installed between the fence rails and a small electric charge run through them for one day. Tara's wanderlust seemingly vanished.

Despite numerous pleas made to Irish Wolfhound owners, I have been unable to accumulate sufficient data to arrive at a conclusion on the longevity of Irish Wolfhounds. Dr. Alex Comfort, University College, London, obtained from Miss Delphis Gardner (Coolafin Kennels), Ireland, her records on Irish Wolfhounds from 1927 to

---

[1] Karl von Frisch, *You and Life*. Trans. from the German by Dr. Ernst Fellner and Betty Inskip (1940), pp. 119, 120.

1945. I shall extract from the published results of his studies.[2] The article itself should be read by anyone interested in the parameters, assumptions, etc. Data pertain only to puppies whelped alive.

Of 189 hounds, exact dates of birth and death were known on 103; in 51 other cases, the exact date of death was not known, but the year was.

		Dates of Birth and Death Known Exactly		Birth Date Known Death Year Known	Date of Death Unknown
	Whelped Alive	Died Within 12 Months	Died After 12 Months	Died After 12 Months	
Dogs	94	36	17	26	15
Bitches	95	27	23	25	20
Total	189	63	40	51	35

Including accidental death, the probabilities at birth of reaching certain ages were:

Probability of Attaining

	1 Month	1 Year
Dogs	74%	61%
Bitches	88%	73%

Excluding accidental death, the life expectancy in years of hounds at various ages was computed as:

	Life Expectancy		Expected Age at Death	
Age	Dogs	Bitches	Dogs	Bitches
1	3.8	5.6	4.8	6.6
2	3.7	5.1	5.7	7.1
3	4.0	4.6	7.0	7.6
4	3.6	3.9	7.6	7.9
5	2.8	3.1	7.8	8.1
6	2.3	2.8	8.3	8.8
7	1.6	2.5	8.6	9.5
8	1.7	1.9	9.7	9.9
9	1.2	1.7	10.2	10.7
10	.5	2.5	10.5	12.5
11		2.2		13.2
12		1.2		13.2
13	.	0.2		13.2

[2]Alex Comfort, "Longevity and Mortality of Irish Wolfhounds," *Proceedings of the Zoological Society of London* (September, 1956) CXXVII, Part 1, pp. 27-34.

The mean ages at death of those Irish Wolfhounds who survived to one year were: dogs, 5.0 ± 1 years and bitches, 6.6 ± 1 years. Surprisingly, an article in the American Kennel Gazette[1] states that the average canine (all breeds) life expectancy is only six to seven years. The basis for this calculation is no longer known.

Stanley S. Flower wrote:

> Dogs get a reputation for longevity because they are so numerous. It comes as a surprise to most people to be told that the average age of a dog in England, without counting deaths among young puppies, is probably well under four years.
>
> The healthy mind dwells naturally on those dogs which have been long and faithful companions of oneself and of one's friends, and not on those which have been failures or have soon, by accidents, come to tragic ends.[2]

Pliny the Elder (A.D. c. 23-79) observed that male Laconian dogs live for 10 years and females 12, whereas other dogs live 15 and occasionally 20 years.[3]

Aelian (fl. second century A.D.) gave the maximum age of dogs as 14 years.[4]

The oldest dog in Miss Gardner's kennels was 10.5 years at the time of his death. The oldest bitch was 13.4 years.

Dr. Comfort concluded:

1. As expected, bitches live longer than dogs. However, the disproportion in Irish Wolfhounds is unusually large.

2. Adult Irish Wolfhound deaths occur at a steady rate, i.e. although older hounds are more likely to die than younger ones, the number of Irish Wolfhound deaths each year is about the same.

3. There was a high mortality of males in the second and third years of life.

In another article, Dr. Comfort concluded from a meager amount of data—all that was available—that large dogs have a smaller life span than small dogs. He noted:

---

[1] "AKC Tops a Registration Mark," The American Kennel Club, *Pure-Bred Dogs—American Kennel Gazette* (February, 1959), p. 10.

[2] Stanley S. Flower, "Contributions to Our Knowledge of the Duration of Life in Vertebrate Animals," *Proceedings of the Zoological Society of London* (1931), p. 171.

[3] Caius Plinius Secundus, "Naturalis Historiae," x. 83. 178, *Pliny*. Trans. by H. Rackham (10 vols.; 1940) III, pp. 404, 406.

[4] Claudius Aelianus, *On the Characteristics of Animals*, iv. 40. Trans. by A. F. Scholfield (3 vols.; 1958-1959) I, p. 259.

I can find no record of a wolfhound or mastiff older than 14 years, but ages of 16 and 17 are reported in spaniels and of nearly 19 in pekinese. Hubbard's records include fox terriers (age 20, 21, 21), Bedlington terrier (age 20), retriever (age 20), and Schipperke (age 24). He states that many toy breeds exceed the age of 12, some a few years longer, and a few exceed 20 years.[1]

The serious deficiency in our knowledge of longevity and mortality of the Irish Wolfhound could easily be remedied if *breeders* were to report to me, by sex, the number of puppies in each litter born alive, the number born dead, the date of whelp, and the dates at which live-born puppies later died. This would mean that they would have to get reports from purchasers as well as keep records of puppies retained. Specific data forwarded to me are revealed to no one, so that a breeder need not fear that he will be subject to unfavorable comment. The data are used to form an overall picture.

I am not optimistic about the cooperation which I may get. Here are a few of my experiences. Since 1956, I have been collecting registration data on Irish Wolfhounds. Breeders have been asked to supply me with this information for each puppy whelped: name of puppy, sex, date of whelp, year of registration, name of sire, name of dam, name and address of owner, name and address of breeder. The addresses were requested so that I could follow up on litters produced in later years by the puppies. By means of unremitting effort and letter writing, I was able to compile and edit *Irish Wolfhound Registrations in America—1956-1964*. This was published in 1969 by the Irish Wolfhound Club of America. I had hoped that those owners and breeders who were not sufficiently motivated to write to me out of interest in the breed would at least be anxious to see their names in print in future editions. This has not proven to be the case. Indifference prevails.

In pursuance of another project, I wrote this letter to the owners of sight hounds in the Washington, D.C., area.

For a number of years, I have been researching the history of the Irish Wolfhound. This study has now been expanded to include all dogs. In 1969, my wife and I toured some twenty-odd countries and measured many skulls of prehistoric dogs and wolves. I had hopes of being able to identify some of these dog skulls as belonging to a specific breed but, unfortunately, there are few measurements of the modern dog available for comparison. To

[1]Alex Comfort, "Longevity and Mortality in Dogs of Four Breeds," *Journal of Gerontology* (April, 1960) XV, No. 2, p. 128.

remedy this deficiency, I have enlisted the support of the Bird and Mammal Laboratories of the Fish and Wildlife Service, situated at the U.S. National Museum, more generally known as the Smithsonian. Heretofore, they have not been concerned with dogs but have confined their studies to wolves and coyotes. They have agreed to assist in my work.

I have written to the 95 veterinarians in the D.C. area asking them to donate to the Museum deceased purebred dogs which were mature and good specimens of the breed. I would appreciate your cooperation and that of your friends in this endeavor, especially in the greyhound-like breeds, i.e., Afghan, Borzoi, Greyhound, Irish Wolfhound, Saluki, Scottish Deerhound, and Whippet.

Upon the death of dogs belonging to you or your friends, would you be kind enough to call me. I will arrange to have the dogs picked up. Very few veterinarians have deep-freeze facilities. Therefore I should be called either before the animals are put down or soon thereafter and, if possible, the dogs should be put to sleep in time for me to get them to the Smithsonian before it closes for the weekend or a holiday. Your cooperation may enable me to substantiate claims of the early history of various breeds. It will certainly provide evidence of the differences between them.

The response from all sources has been very poor. The arrangement which I have with the Museum is that it will strip down the bodies and I will take measurements.

I then wrote to over 100 breed clubs in the United States and asked for the cooperation of their members:

I am asking that you request your veterinarian to sever the head of any of your dogs that may die, that you provide the veterinarian with a cardboard box, polyethylene bag and dry ice. he will place the head and the ice in the bag, and the bag into the box. You are then requested to seal the box and mail it air express collect to Bird and Mammal Laboratories, U.S. National Museum, Washington, D.C. Please enclose the name of the breed, sex and age, and notify me when the package is mailed so that I may assure its receipt. I realize that you are as deeply attached to your pets as I am, but I hope you can do what I ask so that valuable scientific studies can be made on your breed of dogs.

No skulls have ever been received. Only one club sent a reply. It said that its members would be reluctant to comply with my request. Dog magazines declined to publish my request. The net result will be that, in some future publication, I shall be able to authenticate osteologically the antiquity of the Irish Wolfhound but not that of other breeds. Owners of other breeds who claim that their dogs are prehistoric or early historic will have to rely on early representations such as statuettes, pottery, murals. This method is not always satisfactory.

With the passage of time, the Smithsonian may decide against receiving dog specimens. I suggest that I be contacted before any are sent. Residents of the Washington, D.C., area can notify me when their hounds have died or are to be put to sleep and I shall pick up the bodies for delivery to the Smithsonian.

I did have one other project in mind: a nationwide network of veterinary facilities to which Irish Wolfhounds would be delivered for autopsies with confidential reports then being forwarded to a central agency. Preliminary talks had been held with the Walter Reed Army Institute of Research with the view of having it act as the central repository and evaluator of data. But then I decided that I could not expect the complete cooperation from owners that would be needed to make such an organization worthwhile. Possibly this enterprise can be revived at a later date.

III

Standard of Excellence

Kennel clubs have been established in many countries of the world for the purposes of guiding and assisting breeders of purebred dogs. One of their functions is the supervision of dog shows where the quality of each breed is evaluated by comparison with a Standard of Excellence. Whereas all other countries describe their Kennel Clubs and Irish Wolfhound Clubs with a national title, e.g. the Irish Kennel Club and the Irish Wolfhound Club of Ireland, in Great Britain the organizations are simply called The Kennel Club and The Irish Wolfhound Club. To prevent confusion, I shall add to the names of these clubs the word "Britain" in parentheses. Dates of formation of Kennel Clubs in Britain, the United States and Canada are 1873, 1884 and 1888 respectively. Until 1922, when the Irish Free State was established, the Irish Kennel Club was only a show-promoting body under the jurisdiction of The Kennel Club (Britain). Now it serves the same functions as the others. The Fédération Cynologique Internationale (F.C.I.), located in Thuin, Belgium, comprises the Kennel Clubs of almost all continental European countries,[1] the six most populous South American countries,[2] Israel, Mexico, Morocco, Panama, and the Dominican Republic.

The first dog show was held in Newcastle, England, in 1859. Competition was limited to pointers and setters. In 1873, The Kennel Club (Britain) was formed for the sole purpose of promoting shows. It was not until January, 1880, that its charter was expanded. From that date on, a dog could not be entered in a show unless it had previously been registered. The first dog was registered in April, 1880.[3]

A class for Irish Wolfhounds was established by The Kennel Club in 1879[4] and Irish Wolfhounds appeared in the ring for the first time

---

[1] Except Albania, Bulgaria, Greece, Turkey, USSR, Liechtenstein, San Marino.
[2] Argentina, Brazil, Chile, Colombia, Peru, Venezuela.
[3] D. Chiverton, *Letter to author* (August 15, 1963).
[4] George A. Graham, "Irish Wolfhounds," *The Kennel Encyclopaedia*, edited by J. Sidney Turner (2 vols.; 1907-1908) II, p. 840. Irish Wolfhounds were classified in the Sporting Division as early as May 5, 1881, according to E. W. Jaquet, *History of the Kennel Club* (1905), p. 21.

at the Irish Kennel Club Show, in Dublin, in the same year. Judge Hugh Dalziel placed P. H. Cooper's Brian first, F. Adcock's hound—name unknown—second, and George Graham's Scot third. The next appearance of Irish Wolfhounds was at The Kennel Club (Britain) Show at Crystal Palace, London, in 1881. Judge Vero Shaw gave first to W. deB. Jessop's Hydra and second to Graham's Clutha. In 1882, Graham won a first and a second with Scot and Clutha, the only two Irish Wolfhounds entered. It is interesting to note that although Ireland was then a part of Great Britain, The Kennel Club's Calendar and Stud Books listed Irish Wolfhounds at the shows just mentioned under the caption "Foreign Dogs". In 1885, they were classified as Irish Wolfhounds. None was shown in 1883, 1884 and 1885.

The first Irish Wolfhound Club was formed in 1884[1] in Britain through the efforts of Captain George A. Graham. The Irish Wolfhound Club of Ireland dates from 1925. Other national breed clubs and the dates when they were organized are: Irish Wolfhound Club of America, Inc. (October, 1926), Nederlandse Verenigingvoor de Ierse Wolfshond en Deerhound (Netherlands, 15 April, 1934), Suomen Irlanninsusikoira r.y. (Finland, 27 April, 1969), Irish Wolfhound Club of Canada (1971), Rassemblement des Amateurs de Lévriers d'Irlande et d'Ecosse (France, April, 1974), Irländska Varghundsklubben (Sweden, 18 April, 1976) and Irish Wolfhound Club of New South Wales (Australia, 24 July, 1976). Names and addresses of the Secretaries may be obtained from the respective Kennel Clubs.[2]

---

[1]*Ibid.*, p. 857. On page 850, the date is erroneously given as 1886. The year 1886 is also reported in the Foreword to George A. Graham's *Irish Wolfhound Pedigrees — 1859-1906* (From his working Stud Book, edited for The Irish Wolfhound Club of Ireland by Delphis Gardner in 1959) and in Jaquet's *History of the Kennel Club*, p. 87. However, in the last paragraph of his 1885 monograph, Captain Graham said that a Club had been formed "quite lately." This prevails over J. H. Walsh's statement in *The Dog in Health and Disease* (1887) that the Club had been created in 1876. In the 1886 edition of J. H. Walsh's *The Dogs of the British Islands* it is stated at page 213 that the Irish Wolfhound Club had adopted a Standard in 1885. The *Kennel Chronicle* of 30 March, 1885, refers to the recent formation of the Irish Wolfhound Club.

[2]The Kennel Club (Britain), 1 Clarges St., Piccadilly, London W1Y 8AB, England.

The Irish Kennel Club, 23 Earlsfort Terrace, Dublin 2, Ireland.

The American Kennel Club, 51 Madison Avenue, New York, N.Y., 10010, USA.

Raad van Beheer op Kynologisch Gebied in Nederland, Emmalaan 16, NL Amsterdam Z, Netherlands.

Suomen Kennelliitto, Bulevardi 14a, Helsinki 12, Finland.

Canadian Kennel Club, 2150 Bloor St. West, Toronto, Ontario M6S 4V7, Canada.

Société Centrale Canine, 3, Rue de Choiseul, Paris (2e) France.

Svenska Kennelklubben, Box 1308, S-11183 Stockholm, Sweden.

R.A.S. Kennel Club, Endeavour House, 33 MacQuarie Place, Sydney, Australia.

While Captain Graham made some comments on the Irish Wolfhound Standard of Excellence in his 1885 monograph,[1] a full statement of the Standard developed in collaboration with others does not seem to have appeared in print until 1886.[2] Various organizations have made changes in it, most of them minor. Strangely enough we even find instances where the Standard of the breed club in Great Britain differs from that of the ruling body, the Kennel Club. The policy of the F.C.I. is that, for a particular breed, member clubs must follow the Standard of the country where the breed originated. It has designated the Irish Wolfhound as an "English Breed." A number of arguments could be advanced for calling it an "Irish Breed":

1. The Irish Wolfhound originated in Ireland.

2. Irishmen were members of the Irish Wolfhound Club (Britain) which approved the Standard in 1885, Ireland then being part of the British Empire. Captain Graham, the prime mover, was a Scotsman.

3. Irish Wolfhounds were first shown in breed competition at the Irish Kennel Club Show, in Dublin (1879).

4. Until 1885, Irish Wolfhounds were listed in the Calendar and Stud Books of Britain under the caption "Foreign Dogs".

5. The Irish Kennel Club was the first to adopt the Standard (1926). Britain did not do so until 1950.[3]

The Standard of Excellence given here is that followed by the kennel and breed clubs in the United States and Canada. There follows a comparison between the original text and that used by various kennel and breed clubs.

Standard of Excellence

1.   GENERAL APPEARANCE.—Of great size and commanding appearance, the Irish Wolfhound is remarkable in combining power and swiftness with keen sight.

---

[1] George A. Graham, *The Irish Wolfhound* (1885). Combined with Edmund Hogan's *The Irish Wolfdog* and published by The Irish Wolfhound Club of Ireland (1939), pp. 216-219. Republished by the Irish Wolfhound Clubs of America and Ireland (1972).

[2] John Henry Walsh ("Stonehenge"), *The Dogs of the British Islands* (1886), pp. 213, 214.

[3] The Kennel Club (Britain), *Letter to author* (June 10, 1971).

The largest and tallest of the galloping hounds, in general type he is a rough-coated, Greyhound-like breed; very muscular, strong though gracefully built; movements easy and active; head and neck carried high; the tail carried with an upward sweep with a slight curve towards the extremity.

The minimum height and weight of dogs should be 32 ins. and 120 lbs.; of bitches, 30 ins. and 105 lbs.; these to apply only to hounds over 18 months of age. Anything below this should be debarred from competition. Great size, including height at shoulder and proportionate length of body is the desideratum to be aimed at, and it is desired to firmly establish a race that shall average from 32 to 34 ins. in dogs, showing the requisite power, activity, courage and symmetry.

2. HEAD.—Long, the frontal bones on the forehead very slightly raised and very little indentation between the eyes. Skull, not too broad. Muzzle, long and moderately pointed. Ears, small and Greyhound-like in carriage.

3. NECK.—Rather long, very strong and muscular, well arched without dewlap or loose skin about the throat.

4. CHEST.—Very deep. Breast, wide.

5. BACK.—Rather long than short. Loins arched.

6. TAIL.—Long and slightly curved, of moderate thickness, and well covered with hair.

7. BELLY.—Well drawn up.

8. FORE-QUARTERS.—Shoulders, muscular, giving breadth of chest, set sloping. Elbows well under, neither turned inwards nor outwards. LEG.—Forearm muscular, and the whole leg strong and quite straight.

9. HIND-QUARTERS.—Muscular thighs and second thigh long and strong as in the Greyhound, and hocks well let down and turning neither in nor out.

10. FEET.—Moderately large and round neither turned inwards nor outwards. Toes, well arched and closed. Nails, very strong and curved.

11. HAIR.—Rough and hard on body, legs and head; especially wiry and long over eyes and under jaw.

12. COLOR AND MARKINGS.—The recognized colors are grey, brindle, red, black, pure white, fawn, or any color that appears in the Deerhound.

13. FAULTS.—Too light or heavy head, too highly arched frontal bone; large ears and hanging flat to the face; short neck; full dewlap; too narrow or too broad a chest; sunken or hollow or quite straight back; bent forelegs; overbent fetlocks; twisted feet; spreading toes; too curly a tail; weak hindquarters and a

general want of muscle; too short in body; lips or nose liver-
colored or lacking pigmentation.

Text Differences in Standard of Excellence[1]

The Irish Wolfhound should not be quite so heavy or massive as the Great Dane, but more so than the Deerhound, which in general type he should otherwise resemble.[2]	The Irish Wolfhound should be more massive than the Deerhound.
a, b, d, e	c
Of great size and commanding appearance.	The Irish Wolfhound is remarkable in combining power and swiftness with keen sight. The largest and tallest of the galloping hounds, in general type he is a rough-coated Greyhound-like breed.[3]
a, b, c, d, e	f
Strongly though gracefully built.	Strong though gracefully built.[3]
a, b, c, d, e	f

[1]a, Original text; b, The Kennel Club (Britain); c, The Irish Wolfhound Club (Britain); d, The Irish Kennel Club, The Irish Wolfhound Club of Ireland; e, F.C.I.; f, American Kennel Club, Canadian Kennel Club, Irish Wolfhound Club of America, Inc., Irish Wolfhound Club of Canada.

[2]Deleted in U.S. The Irish Wolfhound Club of America, *Harp and Hound* (1949) I, No. 1, p. 27; (1950) I, No. 4, p. 34.

[3]*Ibid.*

The minimum height and weight of dogs should be 31 in and 120 lb; of bitches, 28 in and 90 lb.[1]	The minimum height and weight of dogs should be 32 in and 120 lb; of bitches, 30 in and 105 lb; these to apply only to hounds over 18 months of age.[1,2]
a, b, c, d, e	f
Anything below this should be debarred from competition.	Anything below this should be heavily penalized.
a, c, d, f	b, e
It is desired to firmly establish a race that shall average from 32 to 34 in in dogs.	It is desired to firmly establish a breed that shall average 32 to 34 in in dogs.
a, c, d, f	b, e
Leg — Forearm muscular.	Leg and forearm muscular.
a, c, d, f	b, e
Hair — Rough and hard on body.	Coat — Rough and hardy on body.
a, c, d, f	b, e

Any colour that appears in the Deerhound.

a, b, c, d, e, f
(except that AKC says:
"any other color.")

---

[1]	In	Cm	Lb	Kg
	28	71.12	90	40.82
	30	76.20	105	47.63
	31	78.74	120	54.43
	32	81.28		
	34	86.36		

[2]The Irish Wolfhound Club of America, *Annual Reports* (1946-1947), p. 19.

No mention.	Eyes — Dark.
a, c, d, f	b, e
Faults — Large ears and hanging flat to the face.	Faults — Large ears; ears hanging flat to the face.
a, c, d, f	b,e
Faults — Sunken or hollow or quite straight back.	Faults — Sunken, hollow, or quite straight back.
a, c, d, f	b, e
Faults — Pink or liver-coloured eyelids.[1]	No mention.
b, c, d, e	a, f
Faults — Lips and nose any colour other than black.[1]	Faults — Lips or nose liver-colored or lacking pig-mentation.[2]
b, c, d, e	f
Faults — Very light eyes.[3]	No mention.
b, c, d, e	a, f
Note: Male animals should have two normal testicles fully descended into the scrotum.	The male with apparently two normal testicles descended into the scrotum.
b	c

Whenever it is suggested that the Standard be studied for possible revision, a hue and cry arise and a warning issued: "Don't trifle with the Standard." Yet, the Standard has been changed on several occasions: at times legally, at other times upon the whim of some individual. I do not see any need for a radical revision of the

[1]Appears for the first time in The Irish Wolfhound club (Britain), *Year Book* (1930-1932), p. 20.

[2]The Irish Wolfhound Club of America, *Annual Reports* (1939-1940), p. 21.

[3]The Irish Wolfhound Club (Britain), *Year Book* (1930-1932), p. 23.

Standard but its wording could be improved and any suggested significant modifications could be examined. Were representatives from the four countries with the largest Irish Wolfhound population (the United States, Ireland, Britain and Canada) to form a committee, the question could be studied and a report submitted to the breed clubs for their approval. It is possible that we might at least end up with a standard Standard of Excellence.

Every requirement stated in a Standard should have a sound reason for its existence. Preferably this reason should be that possession of the quality noted and absence of the faults enable the particular breed to perform its function better (or did so in the past) such as the pursuit and killing of wolves or that it adds to the beauty of the animal.

There are many misconceptions as to the reasons for certain physical requirements. I will point these out as they arise in this chapter. As an example from another breed, I quote from an article on Afghan Hounds where the author comments on the statement "High tail carriage is emphasized in Afghanistan, for the hounds hunt so much in thicket that it is only by watching the tails that the movement of the dogs can be detected":

> We understand that some, if not all, fanciers of various trailing and pointing breeds find high tail-carriage an asset in tracing their dogs. And we have seen it to be so when following these dogs on foot as they track, quarter, or freeze to a point, with head low and working in "dog high" grass or brush. But an Afghan?
>
> Here's a dog that pursues his game so fast his handlers properly must follow on horse back, seated high about the dog's level. The dog moves in great leaps, easily double his own height, and if cover is heavy, generally looking for his prey with head up at the top of the leaps. He closes in a great melee that would visibly shake all but the sturdiest thicket. If lost to sight, surely he's in a dense forest or over the horizon.
>
> But let's say our Afghan runs stealthily and closes quietly in an unshakable thicket. Even then would you seek him by his tail? It seems to us that would be slender evidence indeed and that no other part of an Afghan would blend so well with a thicket as that particular member. No, if this be the purpose of an Afghan's tail, a terrible error has been made over 4,000 years in not breeding a bushy appendage with a generous white flag.
>
> Finally—granting all else in the statement—in all that you know or have seen of Afghanistan's terrain have you noticed any great

prevalence of grass, brush, thicket—or anything¹ but rocks? The *National Geographic* may have misled us, but we have not.¹

It is sad to note that not only do some of the reasons advanced for the existence of requirements in the Standard have no basis in fact but that, in many cases, some of these requirements result in great suffering to the breeds. I shall cite only one example of the latter situation: the breeding of dogs with inordinately large skulls renders caesarean operation a necessity; ignorance of this fact results in the suffering, and frequently the death, of the dams. For a detailed listing of anatomical and physiological features of breeds which were considered detrimental by the Permanent Committee of the World Veterinary Association in 1967, and by the British Veterinary Association and The Kennel Club (Britain) in 1964, see Appendix A. The Irish Wolfhound is not one of the breeds listed.

Each item in the Irish Wolfhound Standard will now be reviewed. We shall examine the reasons ascribed for its existence and we shall discuss some points not in the Standard. Let us consider, in turn, type and size, then the parts of the body in the following order: head, ears, eyes, eyelids, lips, nose, teeth, neck, chest, back, shoulders, elbows, forelegs, feet, loins, hindquarters, and tail. Finally, let us comment on movement, coat, color, and temperament.

The illustrations of the skeletal and exterior anatomical parts of the dog will assist in the understanding.

TYPE

Captain Graham inserted in the Standard:

> The Irish Wolfhound should not be quite so heavy or massive as the Great Dane, but more so than the Deerhound, which in general type he should otherwise resemble . . . Of great size and commanding appearance.

In 1950, the Irish Wolfhound Club of America deleted the above. It felt that, while the particular wording had been needed in Graham's day because of the comparative rarity of the Irish Wolfhound and the more plentiful numbers of Great Danes and Deerhounds, it was no longer required since the Irish Wolfhound breed was, in 1950, well established and its desirable characteristics known. In the United States, the following was substituted:

---

¹Donald A. Smith, "Afghan Hounds," The American Kennel Club, *Pure-Bred Dogs—American Kennel Gazette* (November, 1957) LXXIV, pp. 47, 48.

Of great size and commanding appearance, the Irish Wolfhound is remarkable in combining power and swiftness with keen sight. The largest and tallest of the galloping hounds, in general type he is a rough-coated, Greyhound-like breed.

Mr. I. W. Everett, owner of the famous Felixstowe Kennels in England, related:

The late Captain Graham, in talking over Irish Wolfhounds one day with me, drifted on to type, and on my asking him his description of it, he described something of this sort:

An Irish Wolfhound should not be either like a Great Dane or a Deerhound, although he would lean more to the Deerhound than to the Dane. His head should show greater proportion of strength to the size of him than the Deerhound. His ears should be carried in repose tucked behind him, as a Greyhound's, and when looking at objects in the distance should be semi-erect. His eyes should at least harmonize with his general colour, a usual preference being given to dark rather than light eyes. His muzzle, distinctly not square; it should have the appearance of being undercut rather than square, until the teeth are inspected, when it is seen the teeth are level. The head should be of good length in proportion to the hound, with a very small drop before the eyes and frontal bones little raised. His throat should be clear of loose skin or dewlap. His skull, although not coarse, should give one the impression of strength. To finish up a nice typical head, a reasonable amount of eyebrow, muzzle hair, and beard, completed by the neck being set into the head nice and high up and showing a reasonable crest. The neck should be of fair length, but too long a neck gives an impression of weakness rather than strength. The body should give an impression of nice length rather than the idea of a short-coupled-up body; brisket down to elbows and nicely wide at the bottom; the ribs reasonably sprung, but not to the extent of a Great Dane, so as not to resemble a barrel-like appearance. The loin should be a little full, but not so exaggerated as to give the hound the appearance of being dipped behind the shoulder, but just sufficient to give a nice gradual sweep right down to the set-on of the tail, which should connect fairly low down. This all adds to the lines of a nice set of curves beginning with the crest of neck and finishing with the bend of the tail.

As to the legs, a fair amount of bone is needed to make a typical hound, and it is essential that the shoulders should be nicely laid back, not upright. The forelegs should be set in line with their shoulder points. The hindquarters are responsible for about two thirds of his movement, continued movement that is, given the hound is fit internally. He needs good strong hindquarters, well muscled up, as separated from a superabundance of fat; his heels nicely low to the ground, nicely bent stifles and second thighs, and in action his hind legs should come just past the forelegs, outside of course. Tail of good length, but certainly not thick and fleshy. His body just in front of hindlegs fairly drawn up, of course, for he is a galloping hound and does not need much encumbrance there when he is called upon for work. His coat should be dense next his skin, and longer and more wiry on the outside. It should be a double coat, and would more frequently be so if not so much over-groomed. Colours in various shades are recognized. Personally, I am very fond of orange-fawns and the various shades of brindle. I do not so much like the fainter shades unless accompanied by good black toenails and muzzles, and dark shadings round the eyes and under edges of tail.[1]

It can be seen that in discussing "type", Captain Graham covered all points in the Standard except height which, of course, he took for granted. In his monograph, Captain Graham said:

It will be well now to state the conclusions at which the writer has arrived as to the general appearance and character of the Irish Wolfhound, after a prolonged, searching, and careful study of the subject.

Form. That of a very tall, heavy, Scotch Deerhound, much more massive, and very majestic-looking; active and fast, perhaps somewhat less so than the present breed of Deerhound; neck thick in comparison to his form, and very muscular; body and frame lengthy.

Head. Long, but not narrow, coming to a comparative point towards the nose; nose rather large, and head gradually getting broader from the same, evenly up to the back of the skull—not sharp up to the eyes, and then suddenly broad and lumpy, as is often the case with dogs bred between Greyhound and Mastiff.

Coat. There can be little doubt that from the very nature of the work the dog was called upon to do this would be of a rough, and probably somewhat shaggy nature. . . .So it is with justice concluded that the coat was thoroughly rough; hard and long all over body, head, legs, and tail; hair on head, long, and rather softer than that on body, standing out boldly over eyes; beard under jaws being also very marked and wiry.

Colour. Black, grey, brindle, red, and fawn, though white dogs were esteemed in former times, as is several times shown us—

---

[1]George Augustus Graham. Quoted by I. W. Everett, "The Typical Irish Wolfhound," The Irish Wolfhound Club (Britain), *Year Book* (1933-1935), pp. 63, 64.

indeed they were often preferred—but for beauty the dark colours should be cultivated.

Ears. Small in proportion to size of head, and half erect as in the smooth Greyhound. If dark in colour it is to be preferred.

The tail should be carried with an upward curve only, and not be curled, as is the case with many Greyhounds.

Size . . . putting the matter on the grounds of simple necessity, we cannot but conclude that the dog should be not less than from 2 to 3 inches taller than the wolf. Now, the usual height of the wolf would range about 30 inches, therefore, we get the height of from 32 to 33 inches in the dog. Also arguing from the skulls, the dog would have stood 32 to 34 inches. We may, therefore, safely deduce that the height of these dogs varied from 32 to 34 inches, and even 35 inches in the dogs, probably from 29 to 31 inches in the bitches. The other dimensions would naturally be about as follows for well-shaped and true-formed dogs. Girth of chest— Dogs, 38 to 44 inches; bitches, 32 to 34 inches. Weight in lbs.— Dogs, 115 to 140; bitches 90 to 115. Girth of fore-arm—Dogs, 10 to 12 inches; bitches, 8-1/2 to 10 inches. Length of head—Dogs, 12-1/2 to 14 inches; bitches, 11 to 12 inches.[1]

The measurements just stated appeared in 1885. They may have been in Graham's original work in 1879. In 1909, Graham revised his estimates, increasing the height and weight measurements and decreasing those of girth and length—except for the body girth of bitches.

Capt. Graham's Desired Measurements[2]

Inches (Centimetres) and Pounds (Kilograms)

		Height	Weight	Body Girth	Forearm Girth	Head Length
Dogs						
	1885	32-33	115-140	38-44	10-12	12 1/2-14
		(81-84)	(52.2-63.5)	(97-112)	(25-30)	(32-36)
	1909	33-34	130-145	36-39	8-9 1/2	12-13 1/2
		(84-86)	(59.0-65.8)	(91-99)	(20-24)	(30-34)
Bitches						
	1885	29-31	90-115	32-34	8 1/2-10	11-12
		(74-79)	(40.8-52.2)	(81-86)	(22-25)	(28-30)
	1909	30-31	100-120	33-36	7 1/2-8 1/2	10 1/2-11 1/2
		(76-79)	(45.4-54.4)	(84-91)	(19-22)	(27-29)

[1]George A. Graham, *The Irish Wolfhound* (1939), pp. 216-219.

[2]*Id.* "Irish Wolfhounds," *The Kennel Encyclopaedia, op. cit.,* p. 851. Graham, in 1885, arguing from an assumed 30 inch height for a wolf, deduced that the male Irish Wolfhound should be 32-33 inches, but he also believed from the examination of skulls that the dog formerly was 32-34 inches and the bitch 29-31. His 1909 figures are also based on the assumed height of 30 inches for a wolf.

Irish Greyhound by P. Reinagle.

"Gentle when stroked."
Ard Ri of Ballylyke, C.D. (sitting) and Ch. Feasgar Bruadar of Ballylyke, U.D. (lying down)
(1959). First two Irish Wolfhounds owned by the author.

"Fierce when provoked."
Major Acres Tancred O'Magnus, C.D., chasing a ball (1977). Owned by Boardman Moore (Ballymor Kennel).

Ch. Keltic Tara, C.D.X., Ch. Keltic Banshee, U.D., Ch. Keltic Phantom II, C.D.X., Ch. Sulhamstead Samando Patrick, C.D. (1966). Owned by the author (Keltic Kennel).

In addition to "type", the words "soundness" and "quality" are often used by judges. Miss M.S. Kearns defined these terms very well:

> I always understood that type was that combination of points and qualities which distinguished a member of one breed from the members of all other breeds . . . Soundness is an essential attribute of all breeds of dogs . . . It is a formation of body and a state of health in that body which enables the animal to live a happy life and do the work for which it is intended. In my opinion, type and soundness are equally important in a show dog, and the combination of the two gives, what I like to call, Quality.[1]

SIZE

Graham wrote in the Standard:

> Of great size and commanding appearance, very muscular, strongly though gracefully built . . . The minimum height and weight of dogs should be 31 inches and 120 pounds,[2] of bitches, 28 inches and 90 pounds. Anything below this should be debarred from competition. Great size, including height at shoulder and proportionate length of body, is the desideratum to be aimed at, and it is desired to firmly establish a race that shall average from 32 to 34 inches in dogs, showing the requisite power, activity, courage and symmetry.

In 1950, the Irish Wolfhound Club of America substituted "strong" for "strongly". This change may have been the result of a typographical error. I prefer the latter wording. I also think that the words "to be aimed at" could well be eliminated as redundant since "desideratum" means "that which is desired". There are other improvements that could be made such as avoidance of split infinitives, e.g. "to firmly establish", but these are insignificant matters and, therefore, shall receive no further comment.

In 1947, a change in the American Standard was made by substituting 32 as the minimum height for dogs and 30 as that for bitches. The only minimum weight change was that for bitches. It

---

[1] M. S. Kearns, "Irish Wolfhound 'Quality,' " The Irish Wolfhound Club (Britain), *Year Book* (1928-1929), p. 60.

[2] The 1939 and 1972 editions of Hogan's *The Irish Wolfdog, op. cit.*, at page 87 have "128" instead of "120" for the minimum weight of dogs. The 1897 edition has the correct figure.

was increased from 90 to 105. A provision was added: "These to apply only to hounds over 18 months of age."

The tallest dog in a competition is not necessarily the best, but if two or more Irish Wolfhounds are equal in other respects, the tallest dog should be declared the winner. It is possible that even if the tallest dog is not quite so good as the others, his size might suffice to tip the scale in his favor.

In 1913, Judge F. H. Purchase said:

> When we come across a tremendously big hound, thoroughly good on the whole, but with a few comparatively minor faults, these faults should be regarded with a lenient eye, and he should be preferred to a smaller animal possessing fewer faults, perhaps, but fewer merits, also. It is so much more difficult to breed a good big one than a good little one.[1]

Judge J. F. Baily said in 1910:

> Remember that size, i.e., height at shoulder, is everything in this breed. It is a point hard to acquire, easy to lose, and almost impossible to regain.[2]

Captain Graham's view:

> An all-round sound dog of medium height, is far preferable to an overgrown, badly-shaped, crooked-legged giant, for size, though most important, cannot in any way make up for unsoundness.[3]

Mrs. Florence Nagle, prominent English breeder (Sulhamstead Kennels), wrote:

> Novice breeders are apt to think that size is the most important thing at which to aim. This is not so; type and conformation come first, all things being equal. Of course, a good big one will beat a good small one, but it is quite wrong to put a big hound of poor conformation or unsound over a really well-made smaller hound, provided that the latter is 32 inches tall (30 inches if a bitch). In my long experience of the breed since 1913, the few hounds of 37 inches or over have not been really good hounds, and would not have stood an earthly chance in a variety class.[4]

---

[1] F. H. Purchase, The Kennel Club (Britain), *The Kennel Gazette* (March, 1913) XXXIV, p. 112.

[2] John F. Baily, *ibid.* (January, 1910) XXXI, p. 6.

[3] George A. Graham, in *The Kennel Encyclopaedia, op. cit.,* p. 853.

[4] Florence Nagle, "Aids to Breeding Good Irish Wolfhounds," The Irish Wolfhound Club (Britain), *Year Book* (1955-1957), p. 38.

It should be remembered that dogs are puppies until a year old, that Irish Wolfhounds attain almost their full height at 1 year of age and that they are not fully developed until 3 or 4 years of age.

The Irish Wolfhound is the tallest of dogs. By this statement it is meant that the average Irish Wolfhound is taller than the average dog of any other breed. There are, of course, individual dogs of other breeds who are taller than certain individual Irish Wolfhounds.

The minimum and average height stipulations in Standards for some of the big breeds are:

	Height (in)			
	Dogs		Bitches	
Breed	Min.	Av.	Min.	Av.
Irish Wolfhound	32		30	
Great Dane	30		28	
Mastiff	30		27½	
St. Bernard	27½		25½	
Borzoi	28		26	
Scottish Deerhound		30-32		28 up
Great Pyrenees		27-32		25-29
Newfoundland		28		26
Afghan Hound		27±1		25±1
Bullmastiff		25-27		24-26

It will be observed that the minimum height for Irish Wolfhounds is greater than that of any other breed and is equal to or greater than the highest average for any other breed. The height of dogs is measured at the withers. Some Great Danes may give the impression of being taller than Irish Wolfhounds because they normally hold their heads more erect than do the Irish Wolfhounds. The latter often walk with the top of the neck level with the back. They will raise their heads above a 45° angle only when they have sighted or heard something of interest. Moreover, when a Great Dane's ears are cropped—as is the practice in the United States—and the dog is alerted by some sight or sound, his ears are held vertically, unlike those of the Wolfhound, whose ears are folded back. See illustrations.

When persons see me with one of my dogs, they often ask how tall he is. Although I know the heights of all my dogs, I usually do not provide the information. The reason for my evasiveness is that it would hardly be fair to have the accurate measurements of my dogs compared with measurements of other dogs which most likely were either taken inaccurately or estimated. Unfortunately, there are persons who will claim great heights for their dogs, for instance "37 inches", and disparage those of another owner as "only 34". Placed side by side, the difference may be revealed as only an inch or, as I have seen it happen, the allegedly smaller dog is taller.

Captain Graham kept a working stud book in which he listed 601 dogs.[1] He reported the heights of 242 of these, 138 being dogs and 104 bitches. Since it is desirable to consider the heights by periods and since the dates of measurements are not given, the time divisions in the accompanying table have been set by decades and the dogs have been assigned to these by whelping date. The dogs seem to have maintained a 2 to 3 inch advantage over the bitches. By the end of the period, the median for dogs was 32 inches and for bitches 30, that is there were as many hounds above this figure as below it. The arithmetic mean, that is the sum of the heights divided by the number of hounds, was approximately the same as the median. We do not know how old the dogs were at the time of measurement. This makes it a little difficult to compare the figures with those of modern dogs.

Mean Height Measurements Reported by Capt. Graham

| | **Dogs** | | | **Bitches** | | | **Total** | | |
Periods	No.	in	cm	No.	in	cm	No.	in	cm
1859-1868	5	30.5	77.5	4	27.9	70.9	9	29.3	74.4
1869-1878	9	30.8	78.2	4	27.8	70.6	13	29.9	75.9
1879-1888	40	30.4	77.2	30	28.4	72.1	70	29.6	75.2
1889-1898	74	31.5	80.0	59	28.8	73.2	133	30.3	77.0
1899-1902	10	32.0	81.3	7	29.8	75.7	17	31.1	79.0
Total	138			104			242		

From 1956 to date, my family and organizations in the United States and Canada to which I have provided guidelines have taken measurements of Irish Wolfhounds. All of this material will be referred to as North American measurements. They include, of course, many Irish and English imports. Although I encourage

---

[1]George Graham, *Irish Wolfhound Pedigrees, op. cit.*

individuals to measure the heights of their dogs, I do not include them in my calculations as they are most likely less reliable than those taken by organizations operating under a single supervisor. My guidelines are these:

> A uniform method of measurement can be had by the use of one type of device under the direction of one person. The hound should be set up so that his front legs are straight under him and so that he is not even slightly crouching. His head should be raised to a normal position and not so high that he is not firmly standing on his feet. The point of measurement is the most forward on the withers. Both the hound and the measuring stick should be on a level surface. If outdoors, use a platform and check it in length and width with a carpenter's level. If necessary, level the platform by inserting objects under it. The measuring stick should be perpendicular to the surface and a small level on the crosspiece resting on the withers should insure accuracy. In taking measurements, allowance should be made for the thickness of the crosspiece. Individual measurements should not be made known to any person other than the owner. To accomplish this, only the owner and his dog should be near the point where the measurements are taken. The purposes of this secrecy are twofold. First, so that the persons with smaller hounds will not be dissuaded from having their dogs measured. Second, to prevent disparagement by one person of the dogs of another. I hope that the measurements which have been and which will be taken will not lead to objectives of even taller dogs without regard to balance and proper conformation.

A device made of wood which can provide exact measurements is illustrated here. The base should have a spherical level or small levels in each direction. The vertical section which slides into the base has inscribed on it marks to an eighth of an inch up to 40 inches and to a half of a centimeter up to 102 centimeters. Allowance has been made for the fact that the vertical section does not rest on the ground. A horizontal crosspiece has a slit which enables it to be slid down the vertical piece. A small level taped onto the horizontal crosspiece tells us when to read the measurement. Readings are taken where the top of the horizontal crosspiece meets the vertical section since allowance for the thickness of the horizontal crosspiece has been made in the graduations of the scale.

Data on height and weight must be correlated with age to be meaningful. Moreover, the number of measurements at the various ages must be sufficiently large to be statistically valid as to the Irish Wolfhound breed. Ideally, one should have measurements of the same dogs at successive periods of their development. Otherwise,

Height 1956—1976

	Number of Measurements	Males						Number of Measurements	Females					
		Inches			Centimetres				Inches			Centimetres		
Age		Max.	Min.	Mean	Max.	Min.	Mean		Max.	Min.	Mean	Max.	Min.	Mean
Months														
3	10	22.5	21.5	22.0	57.2	54.6	55.9	11	21.5	21.0	21.2	54.6	53.3	53.8
4	10	25.5	24.0	24.6	64.8	61.0	62.5	9	24.5	23.8	24.1	62.2	60.5	61.2
5	10	28.5	25.5	27.4	72.4	64.8	69.6	4	27.0	25.0	26.2	68.6	63.5	66.5
6	10	31.5	27.8	29.6	80.0	70.6	75.2	4	28.0	28.0	28.0	71.1	71.1	71.1
7	15	32.5	29.8	31.0	82.6	75.7	78.7	4	30.0	27.3	29.3	76.2	69.3	74.4
8	13	33.8	30.3	32.0	85.9	77.0	81.3	5	31.0	28.3	30.2	78.7	71.9	76.7
9	13	34.0	31.5	33.0	86.4	80.0	83.8	12	32.8	29.5	31.1	83.3	74.9	79.0
10	18	34.5	32.8	33.7	87.6	83.3	85.6	10	32.5	30.0	31.5	82.6	76.2	80.0
11	26	34.5	32.0	33.8	87.6	81.3	85.9	28	35.0	30.0	31.9	88.9	76.2	81.0
Years														
1-2	130	36.3	31.3	33.9	92.2	79.5	86.1	71	34.5	29.0	31.9	87.6	73.7	81.0
2-3	40	36.8	30.5	34.0	93.5	77.5	86.4	46	34.5	29.8	31.9	87.6	75.7	81.0
3+	54	36.8	31.0	34.0	93.5	78.7	86.4	48	34.3	29.5	31.8	87.1	74.9	80.8

Weight 1956—1976

	Number of Measurements	Males						Number of Measurements	Females					
		Pounds			Kilograms				Pounds			Kilograms		
Age		Max.	Min.	Mean	Max.	Min.	Mean		Max.	Min.	Mean	Max.	Min.	Mean
Months														
Birth	35	1.8	0.6	1.2	.816	.272	.544	27	1.9	0.6	1.2	.862	.272	.544
1	20	14	8	10	6.4	3.6	4.5	27	13	6	9	5.9	2.7	4.1
2	22	37	23	30	16.8	10.4	13.6	28	37	19	25	16.8	8.6	11.3
3	18	56	41	45	25.4	18.6	20.4	29	51	32	41	23.1	14.5	18.6
4	13	82	45	71	34.9	20.4	30.4	12	69	52	64	31.3	23.1	27.7
5	10	97	67	83	44.0	30.4	37.6	13	89	62	80	40.4	28.1	36.3
6	16	110	80	96	49.9	36.3	43.5	16	107	79	92	48.5	35.8	41.7
7	8	117	95	106	53.1	43.1	48.1	5	112	89	101	50.8	40.4	45.8
8	5	126	100	114	57.2	45.1	51.7	7	125	92	109	56.7	41.7	49.4
9	11	135	106	120	61.2	48.1	54.4	10	145	108	114	65.8	49.0	51.7
10	9	143	105	126	64.9	47.6	57.2	3	143	100	119	64.9	45.4	54.0
11	9	138	113	130	62.6	51.3	59.0	5	138	100	120	62.6	45.4	54.4
Years														
1-2	70	185	91	134	83.9	41.3	60.8	52	151	79	121	68.5	35.8	54.9
2-3	32	170	102	139	77.1	46.3	63.0	30	144	97	122	65.3	47.6	55.3
3+	36	172	107	145	78.0	48.5	65.8	27	150	98	126	68.0	44.5	57.2

one's calculations might show, for example, that the mean height of males is 33 inches at 10 months of age and 32 inches at 11 months. We know that hounds do not decrease in height from the age of 10 to 11 months. The reason for any decrease is, obviously, that the dogs measured at 11 months were not the same as those measured at 10 months. For this reason, I request that dogs measured in prior years be remeasured each year.

The date being so meager, I found it advisable to group by year all those pertaining to hounds one year of age and over. When a dog is a

MEAN HEIGHT AND WEIGHT OF NORTH AMERICAN (1956 - 1976) IRISH WOLFHOUNDS

year old, he has come very close to his maximum height and, therefore, we can say that the figures fairly well represent the adult dog. We can conclude that the average male Irish Wolfhound in the United States is 34 inches high and the average female two inches less. This holds true regardless of the region where the hound lives. The tallest males measured were 36-3/4 inches tall, the tallest female was 35 inches. This should not be interpreted as meaning that there are no taller representatives of either sex. It merely means that these were the tallest of those whose owners presented them for measurement.

Graham said, and the Standard still reads: "It is desired to firmly establish a race that shall average 32 to 34 inches in dogs, showing the requisite power, activity, courage and symmetry." It may be possible to say that Captain Graham's objective, at least in heights, has been attained.

The breeder must beware of the temptation to breed for size alone. Such an objective will inevitably lead to malformed hounds to the detriment of the breed. It could also be a cause of physical pain to the dog.

The American Kennel Club evidently considers the Irish Wolfhound to be more agile for his size than some of the other large breeds since, in obedience trials, he must jump one and one-half times his height or three feet whichever is less, whereas the jump for the following large breeds is set at the height of the dog or three feet, whichever is less: Bloodhounds, Bullmastiffs, Great Danes, Great Pyrenees, Mastiffs, Newfoundlands, St. Bernards.

In addition to height, ranginess and weight are elements that constitute size. The Irish Wolfhound is the rangiest of dogs. The original Standard prescribed a minimum of 120 pounds for male Irish Wolfhounds and 90 for females. When, in the United States, the minimum height of dogs was raised from 31 to 32 and for bitches from 28 to 30, the minimum weight for bitches was raised to 105.

As for weight measurements, until a dog is over 100 pounds, I pick him up, weigh both of us on the bathscales, and then subtract my weight. Whenever a hound is over 100 pounds, he is taken to the junk yard and weighed. Apart from the fact that the scales are checked by the Weights and Measurements Office of the city, their accuracy can be assumed on the basis that no person would knowingly operate scales showing a greater weight than actuality if that person were buying by weight. Weekly measurements from birth are recorded in the chapter on *The Puppy* under "Feeding".

Graham does give us some weights. However, in only three cases are they tied in with age. One male weighed 120 pounds at 10 months, another 121 at 11 months and a third 104 at a year. The mean weight of the 16 males reported were 122 lb (55.3 cm), of the 13 females 100 lb (45.4 cm). So that the hounds measured by Graham were, on the average, just a little over the minimum weight prescribed in his Standard.

There are no significant differences in weight between Irish Wolfhounds of the same age and sex in the different sections of the United States. Dogs of one year and over average 138 pounds and bitches 123 pounds. The heaviest male weighed was 185 pounds and the heaviest female 151. There was one bitch present but not entered at the 1971 Irish Wolfhound Club of America Specialty that weighed 192 pounds and was 34-1/2 inches tall but she is not included in these calculations as she was exceedingly overweight. Occasionally some young dogs are underweight but as a rule Irish Wolfhound owners have their hounds either at the proper weight or somewhat over it.

From 1925 to 1947, Mr. and Mrs. L. O. Starbuck operated the Ambleside Kennels at Augusta, Michigan. After the death of Mr. Starbuck, Colonel William D. Dana became Mrs. Starbuck's kennel partner and gave an account of the sizes of Ambleside hounds from 1925 to 1947.[1] He points out that the averages for hounds six to eight months of age represent many more dogs than the averages of older hounds because at those ages many of the dogs were sold.

Measurements Reported by Ambleside Kennels
(1925-1947)

	Weight				Height			
	lb		kg		in		cm	
Age	Dogs	Bitches	Dogs	Bitches	Dogs	Bitches	Dogs	Bitches
(months)								
2	24.8	23.5	11.2	10.7				
3	44.7	41.7	20.3	18.9	21.2	20.8	53.8	52.8
4	64.9	58.2	29.4	26.4	25.1	24.2	63.8	61.5
6	98.3	87.2	44.6	39.6	30.1	28.6	76.5	72.6
8	117.1	102.8	53.1	46.6	32.9	31.1	83.6	79.0
10	129.7	114.8	58.8	52.1	34.2	32.3	86.9	82.0
12	136.1	116.7	61.7	52.9	34.9	32.5	88.6	82.6
18	144.7	120.1	65.6	54.5	35.5	32.9	90.2	83.6
24	149.8	129.0	67.9	58.5	35.9	33.6	91.2	85.3
36	161.8	132.0	73.4	59.9	36.0	33.7	91.4	85.6

---

[1] William D. Dana, "Mite to Mighty in 3 Years," The Irish Wolfhound Club of America, *Harp and Hound* (1951) II, No. 2, pp. 10, 11, 13.

Unfortunately, he does not tell us how many hounds form the basis for each of the averages. This information is not now available. Colonel Dana also says that the measurements given on hounds over a year old are probably greater than those of average Irish Wolfhounds since the Starbucks kept the best for breeding purposes and, because of their experience, gave them better care than the average dog owner.

In comparing the North American figures with the Ambleside figures, I took the mean of Ambleside measurements at 12, 18 and 24 months to arrive at the 1 to 2 years of age figure, and I took the mean of Ambleside measurements at 24 and 36 months to arrive at the 2 to 3 years of age figure. Thus:

Ambleside

Age (years)	Height (in)		Weight (lb)	
	Dogs	Bitches	Dogs	Bitches
1-2	35.4	33.0	144	122
2-3	36.0	33.7	159	131

I find it impossible to justify the height figures of the Ambleside hounds. It will be noted from the charts and graphs that after 10 months of age, the mean North American measurements increase by only 0.3″ for 196 males and by only 0.4″ for 145 females. The Ambleside males and females — number unknown — increased by 1.8″ and 1.4″ respectively. This is utterly inconsistent with the known fact that Irish Wolfhounds have attained almost their full height at one year of age. Since they do not decrease in height — at least until they are old — the maximum increase would be very little over the mean. One cannot use for comparison the North American maximum or minimum heights at different ages because, in almost all cases, these are not measurements of the same individuals, i.e. the hounds measured at 1 to 2 years of age were usually not measured again when they became older.

Beginning with the age of four months, Ambleside height measurements are greater than the North American. It may be that the measurement methods were equally accurate or it may be that they differed in accuracy. Regardless, all curves on the graph are fairly consistent until we reach the 1 to 2 year bracket at which point, the Ambleside curves rise sharply. This is an additional argument for stating that the Ambleside height figures for 1 year of age and over cannot be considered as accurate. One cannot argue that the

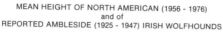

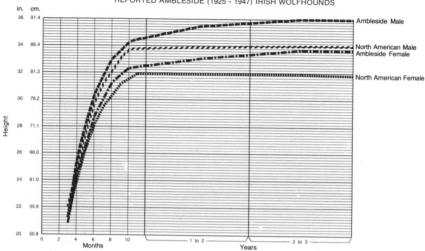

MEAN HEIGHT OF NORTH AMERICAN (1956 - 1976)
and of
REPORTED AMBLESIDE (1925 - 1947) IRISH WOLFHOUNDS

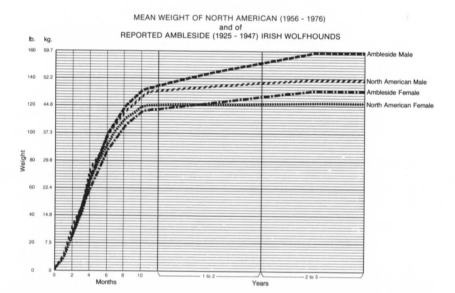

MEAN WEIGHT OF NORTH AMERICAN (1956 - 1976)
and of
REPORTED AMBLESIDE (1925 - 1947) IRISH WOLFHOUNDS

reason for the sharp rise beginning at 10 months is that the smaller hounds were then sold, since Col. Dana says that Ambleside retained most of its hounds until they were 6-8 months old and that those retained were probably greater than the average Irish Wolfhound. If this were so, then the differences between the North American and Ambleside curves should have increased between 8 to 10 months. Instead, they decreased!

Suppose we assume that Ambleside did not sell its hounds until they were 10 months old, then it could be expected that the curves would rise to the 1 to 2 year mark as the figures would represent the mean of the tallest Ambleside hounds, *but* they would then flatten out to the 2-3 year period. Instead, they continue to rise.

Additional support for my contention that the Ambleside height figures are erroneous can be obtained from analysis of the weight figures. Reported weight measurements can be relied upon more than height measurements because they are easier to take and also because people are less liable to exaggerate them. Until the hounds arrive at one year of age, the differences in weight between North American and Ambleside hounds are not over 4 pounds, with the Ambleside males being heavier than the North American and the Ambleside females not so heavy as the North American females. This difference in weight is insignificant. Moreover, the curves on the graph are about the same. But, when we get to the age of one year and over, the margin widens. Ambleside males and females increase by 29 and 16 pounds respectively, North American males and females by 13 and 3 respectively. Three possible reasons could be advanced in explanation:

1. The Ambleside hounds increased in height and correspondingly in weight. But it has been shown that Irish Wolfhounds increase very little in height after 1 year and certainly not as much as the Ambleside figures show.
2. The Ambleside hounds were allowed to get fatter than the average North American hound. This seems most unlikely.
3. The Ambleside hounds did increase in weight and someone at Ambleside estimated that a certain height increase had also taken place — without actually measuring the height.
4. The height figures from 1 year onward represent measurements reported by owners as well as Ambleside measurements and these were inaccurate.

It is my opinion that the Ambleside figures should be disregarded.

Compared to other breeds, the Irish Wolfhound is possibly the heaviest next to the St. Bernard. We have seen that the average grown Irish Wolfhound male weighs about 138 pounds and the female about 123. Some weight specifications in the Standards are:

	Dogs		Bitches	
	Min.	Av.	Min.	Av.
Irish Wolfhound	120		105	
Scottish Deerhound		85-110		75-95
Borzoi		75-105		60-85
Great Pyrenees		100-125		90-115
Newfoundland		150		120
Afghan Hound		60		50
Bullmastiff		110-130		100-120

Marlene Anderson, writing the St. Bernard column in *Popular Dogs*, says: "The largest Smooth I have ever seen is . . . 31-3/4 inches; weight, approximately 210".[1] This dog's height was measured with an American Kennel Club official standard measuring stand.

HEAD

The Standard of Excellence reads:

Head . . . carried high.
Head—Long, the frontal bones of the forehead very slightly raised and very little indentation between the eyes. Skull, not too broad. Muzzle, long and moderately pointed.
Faults—Too light or heavy a head, too highly arched frontal bone.

Graham expressed his belief:

His head should show greater proportion of strength to the size of him than the Deerhound . . . His muzzle, distinctly not square; it

---

[1]Marlene J. Anderson, "Saint Bernards," *Popular Dogs* (January, 1970), XLIII, p. 94.

should have the appearance of being undercut rather than square
. . . The head should be of good length in proportion to the
hound, with a very small drop before the eyes and frontal bones
little raised . . . His skull, although not coarse, should give one
the impression of strength. To finish up a nice typical head, a
reasonable amount of eyebrow, muzzle hair, and beard,
completed by the neck being set into the head nice and high up
and showing a reasonable crest.[1]

At another time, Graham said:

That the hair on the head should be long, and rather softer than
on the body, standing out boldly over the eyes and that the beard
should be very marked and wiry.[2]

A dog who carries his head low cannot lift his knees and feet as
well or advance them as well as one who holds his head at a normal
height.

The Irish Wolfhound in motion normally carries his head just
about level with his back unless he has sighted something which has
excited his interest, in which case he will raise it to a 45° angle. If
greatly excited, he will raise it even more.[3] Many handlers, anxious
to impress the judge that their Irish Wolfhounds hold their heads
high as prescribed in the Standard, pull up on the leads so that the
collars are tightened on the Irish Wolfhounds' necks and they are
forced to gait with their heads held abnormally high. It was because
of this that Mrs. Florence Nagle, after judging the IWCA Specialty
in 1959, stated with sardonic humor: "Your dogs have beautiful
long necks. It must be because of the way you drag them around the
ring!"

Actually, judges realize that this stranglehold on the dog
interferes with his natural movement and many therefore caution:
"On a loose lead, please!"

I will agree that the Irish Wolfhound looks more alert with his
head up. However, if it needs to be held up, it should be done only
when the gaiting is completed and the judge is examining the dogs
as they stand. The hound should be judged as he normally looks,
whether moving or standing, not in an artificial position.

---

[1]G. A. Graham. Quoted by I. W. Everett, "The Typical Irish Wolfhound," *op. cit.*, p. 63.

[2]*Id.*, "Irish Wolfhounds," *The Kennel Encyclopaedia, op. cit.*, p. 851.

[3]See *Index at Coursing, Head and neck carriage.*

EARS

On this point, the Standard reads:

Ears—Small and Greyhound-like in carriage.
Faults—Large ears and hanging flat to the face.

The Standard is clear enough. It means that the Irish Wolfhound should have a "rose ear", i.e., one which laps over to the rear revealing the inner ear. The Standard for Greyhounds reads: "Small and fine in texture, thrown back and folded, except when excited, when they are semipricked."
Graham said:

His ears should be carried in repose tucked behind him, as a Greyhound's, and when looking at objects in the distance should be semi-erect.[1]

I have read that a rose ear offers less wind resistance to a running dog. This does not appear to me to be a major factor for inclusion in the Standard. A better basis for the requirement might be that a rose ear is esthetically pleasing.

EYES

The American Standard does not specify the color of eyes. In 1931, the British, after much debate, added to the list of faults, "very light eyes". I have been unable to find the reason that The Kennel Club (Britain) changed the Standard to read "Eyes Dark." The Irish Wolfhound Club (Britain) does not appear to have proposed this change and it does not appear in its Standard.
I know of no reason that would make a dark eye preferable to a light one, other than appearance. Functionally, it would seem to make no difference. Lions and tigers have light eyes. So do wolves and bald eagles. I am told these animals are fairly good hunters. I am also informed that the color of the eye is not a factor in visual acuity.

I recently questioned Dr. Ralph Vierheller, the noted canine ophthalmologist, about eye color and its possible connection with eyesight. He said that there were no indications that dark brown or black eyes were healthier or functionally superior to yellow or light brown. However, he did say that blue eyes (or

---

[1]*Ibid.*

albinism in the iris, as he called it), frequently goes along with lack of pigment in the back of the eye—the tapetum or choroid membrane—which aids in seeing in dim light and also protects the eye from glare. Because of this he feels that blue or light grey eyes should be considered inferior and therefore undesirable.[1]

Reporting on "coursing meetings", Miss Marion Clark, who was associated with Mrs. Florence Nagle, wrote:

> We were interested in training the hounds to spot the hare in a field. The light-eyed dogs and bitches could spot quicker than the dark-eyed.[2]

In the chapter on Hunting contained in this book, Mrs. Mary Beynon expresses her conviction, based on experiences in Africa, that light-eyed dogs have more courage than dark-eyed ones. I cannot subscribe to this opinion.

Graham expressed the view:

> His eyes should at least harmonize with his general colour, a usual preference being given to dark rather than light eyes.[3]

Miss Kearns, a well-known English breeder and judge had strong feelings on this point:

> Many breeders say it is the colour and formation of the eyes that make or mar the expression. Light eyes are very objectionable in a dog of almost any breed, and no amount of nonsense talked about the colour of the eyes blending with the coat, put forward to excuse light eyes, can ever make me like them any better. The colour of the eyes, however, does not determine the expression. How often do we see two hounds with exactly the same coloured eyes, one hound having the correct expression, the other quite wrong? I have seen Irish Wolfhounds with beautiful dark eyes and quite the wrong expression in them. The expression has nothing to do with the colour, but is a reflex of the mind and character.[4]

I consider Mr. R. H. Smythe to be better qualified on the point of eye-color in association with coat-color:

---

[1]Patricia Ide, "Greyhounds", The American Kennel Club, *Pure-Bred Dogs — American Kennel Gazette* (August, 1976) XCIII, p. 92.

[2]Marion Clark, *Letter to author* (16 December 1969).

[3]G. A. Graham. Quoted by I.W. Everett, "The Typical Irish Wolfhound," *op. cit.*, p.63.

[4]M. S. Kearns, *op. cit.*, p. 61.

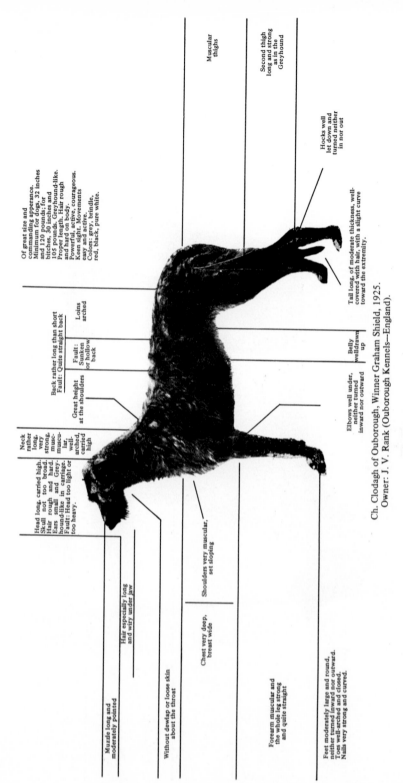

Muscular
thighs

Second thigh
long and strong
as in the
Greyhound

Hocks well
let down and
turned neither
in nor out

Of great size and
commanding apperance.
Minimum for dogs, 32 inches
and 120 pounds; for
bitches, 30 inches and
105 pounds. Greyhound-like.
Proper length. Hair rough
and hard on body.
Powerful, active, courageous.
Keen sight. Movements
easy and active.
Colors: grey, brindle,
red, black, pure white.

Tail long, of moderate thickness, well-
covered with hair, with a slight curve
toward the extremity.

Loins
arched

Back rather long than short
Fault: Quite straight back

Fault:
Sunken
or hollow
back

Belly
welldrawn
up

Great height
at the shoulders

Neck
rather
long,
very
strong,
and hard.
muscu-
lar,
well-
arched,
carried
high

Elbows well under,
neither turned
inward nor outward

Head long, carried high.
Skull not too broad.
Hair rough and hard.
Ears small and Grey-
hound-like in carriage.
Fault: Head too light or
too heavy.

Shoulders very muscular,
set sloping

Muzzle long and
moderately pointed

Hair especially long
and wiry under jaw

Without dewlap or loose skin
about the throat

Chest very deep,
breast wide

Forearm muscular and
the whole leg strong
and quite straight

Feet moderately large and round,
neither turned inward nor outward.
Toes well-arched and closed.
Nails very strong and curved.

Ch. Clodagh of Ouborough, Winner Graham Shield, 1925.
Owner: J. V. Rank (Ouborough Kennels—England).

Illustration of the Standard

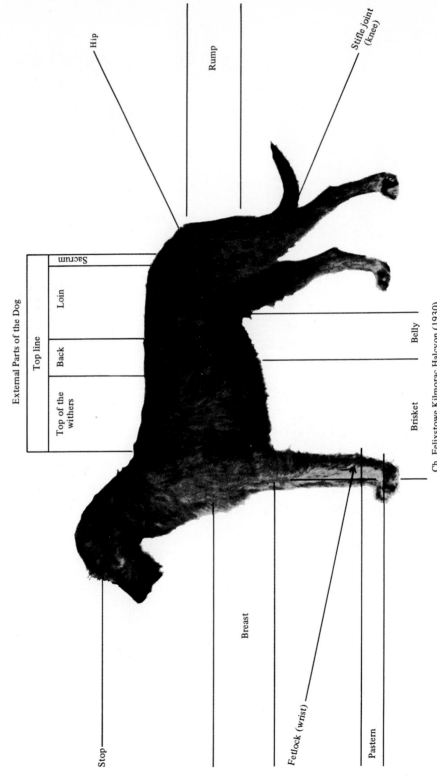

External Parts of the Dog

Ch. Felixstowe Kilmorac Halcyon (1930),
Owner: Mr. & Mrs. Edward Clark (Halcyon Kennels—USA).

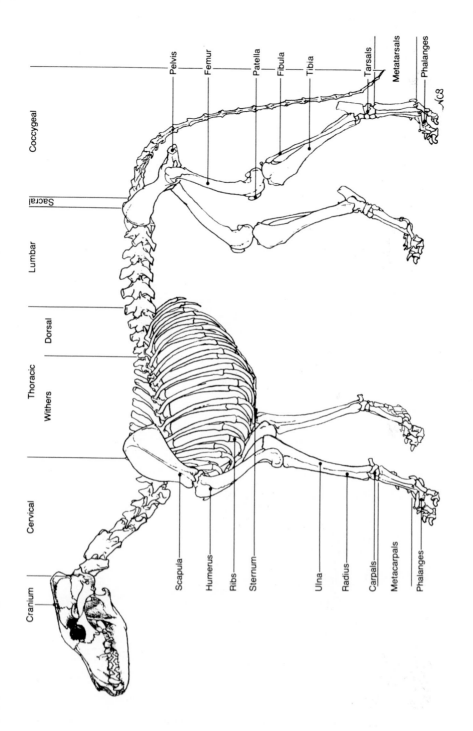

Coccygeal

Sacral

Lumbar

Dorsal

Thoracic

Withers

Cervical

Cranium

Pelvis

Femur

Patella

Fibula

Tibia

Tarsals

Metatarsals

Phalanges

Scapula

Humerus

Ribs

Sternum

Ulna

Radius

Carpals

Metacarpals

Phalanges

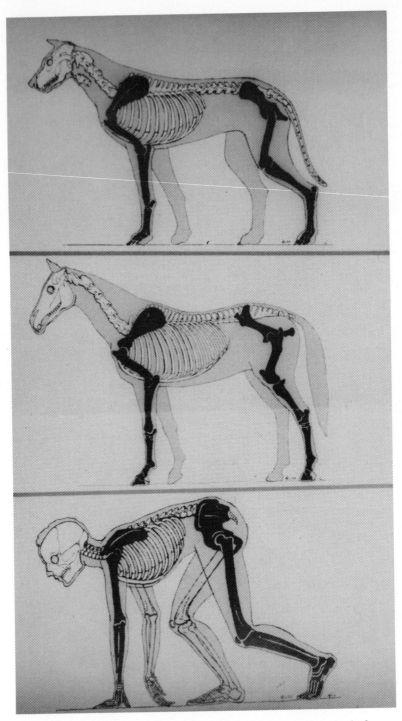

Skeletons of dog, horse and man with propulsion systems emphasized.

Scot owned by Capt. George A. Graham. Placed third in the first appearance of Irish Wolfhounds in the breed ring. Irish Kennel Club Show, Dublin (1879).

Ch. Sulhamstead Melba at the age of ten years (1963). Note the graying muzzle. Owned by Mrs. Florence Nagle and Miss Marion Clark (Sulhamstead Kennel — England).

An excellent male Irish Wolfhound type.

Ch. Wild Isle Warlock, winner of Irish Wolfhound Club of America Specialty in 1974, 1975 and 1976. Bred, owned and handled by Mrs. Louis (Jill) Bregy (Wild Isle Kennel).

An excellent female Irish Wolfhound type.
Ch. Kihone Mearose of Cu, winner of 1973 Irish Wolfhound Club of America Specialty.
Owned and handled by Miss F. Jeannette McGregor (Kihone Kennel). Bred by Mr. and Mrs.
Kelly (Rosalie) Fox (Cu Kennel).

Scottish Deerhound Ch. Lyonhils Highland Fortune. Owned by Mr. and Mrs. Fredrick Schlexer and handled by Mrs. (Nanse) Schlexer (Duncairn Kennel).

Greyhound Ch. Fawnglen's Fascination. Handled by Mrs. (Nanse) Schlexer.

Great Dane. Compare head and ear carriage with that of Irish Wolfhound below.

Chulainn Dauntless (1926) owned by Mrs. D. le B. Bennett and Captain R.C. Hartland-Rowe (Chulainn Kennel — England). "Muscular. Strongly though gracefully built. Head and neck carried high. Neck long, strong, muscular, well-arched. Rough hard coat. Back rather long, not straight. Arched loins. Belly well drawn up." Proper slope of croup. Tail long with upward sweep.

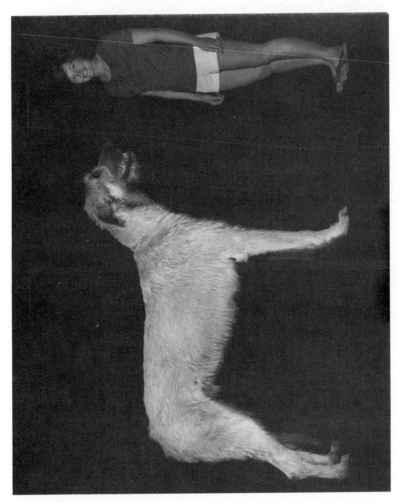

Picture of Irish Wolfhound enlarged to illustrate how one would appear if he were four feet tall and were standing near a five and half foot girl. Ballymor Ajax, owned by Boardman Moore, and Christine Moore.

Ambleside Finn of Erinn with breeder and owner Alma Starbuck (Ambleside Kennel).

Ch. Fuath of Ulaid (1960). Owned by Miss Celeste Hutton (Greysarge Kennel).

Ch. Ballykelly Dalkey (1971). Owned by Miss Elizabeth Murphy (Carrokeel Kennel — Ireland).

Well-proportioned head. Proper ear carriage. "Hair especially wiry and long over eyes and under jaw."

Short muzzle resulting in a "blocky" head.

"Fault: Large ears and hanging flat to the face."

Muzzle too broad.

Ch. Kihone Mearose of Cu

Soft expression. Dark eyes. "Head long, the frontal bones on the forehead very slightly raised and very little indentation between the eyes. Skull not too broad. Muzzle, long and moderately pointed. Ears, small and Greyhound-like in carriage."

Light eyes. Eyes are not mentioned in the U.S. Standard.

Blue eyes. Most likely a genetic defect.

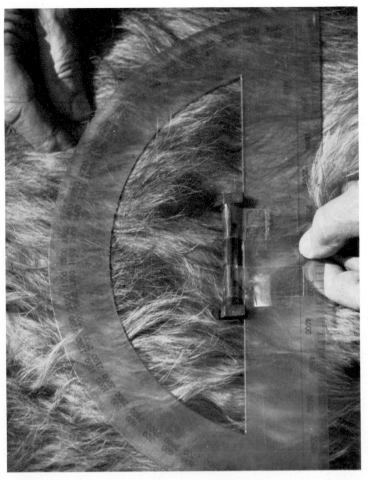

Measurement of scapular angle. Center of protractor's base at center of scapular spine near its base. Left hand adjusts protractor so that bubble is centered. Center of spine between fingers of the right hand is at 2130 mils from the horizontal or 530 from the vertical (2130 − 1600 = 530). This is equivalent to 29 degrees, 49 minutes.

Ch. Keltic Findabair, C.D., at 2 years being measured by the author's children, Glenna and Alfred (1971).

Correct. Level bite.

Correct. Scissors bite.

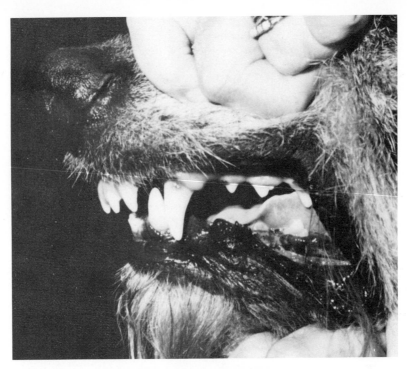

Overshot. Appearance of teeth.

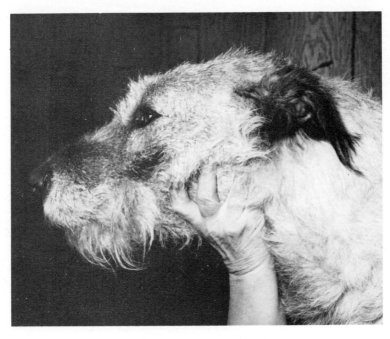

Overshot. Appearance of muzzle.

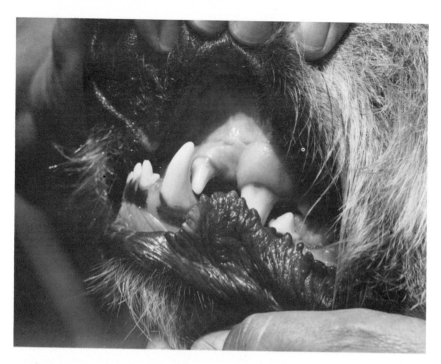

Undershot. Appearance of teeth.

Undershot. Appearance of muzzle.

"Breast wide. Elbows well under, neither turned inwards nor outwards. Forearm muscular, and the whole leg strong and quite straight. Toes, well-arched and closed. Nails very strong and curved."

Out at elbows.

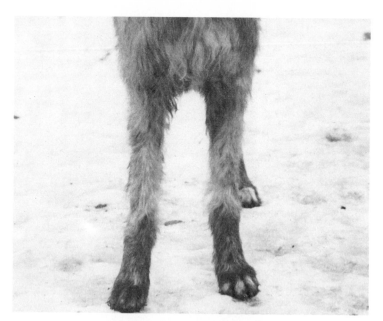

"Fault: Too narrow a chest." Feet turned out at carpal joint.

"Faults: Too broad a chest. Spreading toes." (Splayfeet).

Irish Wolfhound of Scottish Deerhound type. Too light a head. Neck short compared to length of head. Neck not muscular. Light bone. Weak pasterns. Shallow chest. Straight back. Too short in body ("close-coupled"). Weak thighs.

Feet flat and turned out.

"Neck rather long, very strong and muscular. Shoulders muscular, set sloping. Chest very deep. Feet moderately large and round neither turned inwards nor outwards."

Shallow chest. Light bone. Feet turned out at carpal joint.

Incorrect top line. Sloping.

"Fault: Sunken or hollow back."

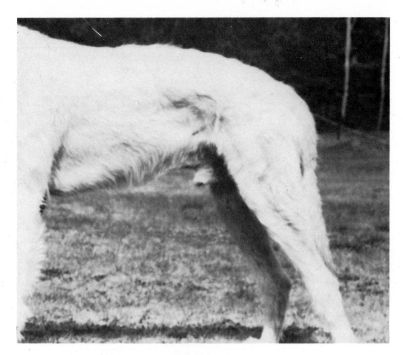

Roached back.

"Fault. Quite straight back." Back should be "rather long than short." Close-coupled.

Good rear angulation. "Muscular thighs and second thigh long and strong as in the Greyhound." Keltic Siobhan, C.D., also winner of Bred-by-Exhibitor, Bitches, Class. Shown with the author, breeder-owner-handler, and Mrs. Kelly (Rosalie) Fox.

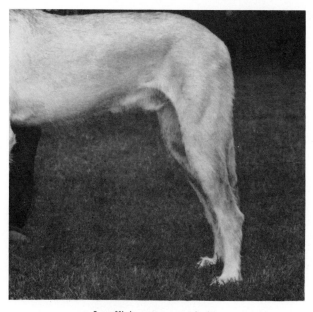

Insufficient rear angulation.

Rear over-angulated.

Thighs not "muscular." Second thigh (tibia) not "long and strong."

"Hocks well let down and turning neither in nor out." Broad rear. Keltic Siobhan, C.D.

Hocks turned in ("cowhocks").

Sacrum at too small an angle resulting in a high tail set.

Tail used for balance in turning.

Ch. Fleetwind Roise of Ronor, F. Ch., at 4 years, coursing (1977). Note head and tail carriage. Owned, trained, and handled by Royce M. and Eugene F. Northcott.

Ch. Sanctuary Fair Erin, F. Ch., coursing (1977). Note head and tail carriage. Owned, trained, and handled by Michael John Bowen (Dannybrook Kennel).

Long, heavy and silky coat.

Soft coat cut with clippers.

Crisp's Champion Sheelah (1890). Formerly owned by Captain George Graham. First Irish Wolfhound Champion. First winner of Graham Challenge Shield (1886).

Light eyes are the result of deficiency of sufficient quantity of pigment or of the presence of pigment possessing insufficient depth of colour. . . .Coat colour has a direct association with eye colour and dogs showing yellow or red in the coat are more likely to possess light eyes than are all-black dogs.[1]

Miss Phyllis Gardner, breeder and author, wrote:

Arrian did not like a light eye: and his preference for a "flame-coloured" eye was endorsed at a recent meeting of the Irish Wolfhound Club, when several breeders of great experience gave their opinion that a clear hazel eye is preferable to either a dark or a very light eye. In my mind, a "strong" or compelling eye, whose glance can be felt and has meaning, is a leading characteristic of the true breed.[2]

Dansey, in his translation of Arrian, calls the dogs in question "greyhounds", but the Greek words written in the Modern European alphabet would be *Keltikai onertragoi*,[3] i.e. Celtic vertragi. I have no wish to enter into a discussion on the nature of these dogs or the etymology of words since these matters will be covered in great detail in a planned work, *The Dog in Early History*. However, in amplification of Miss Gardner's remark, may I present a portion of Dansey's translation of Arrian (A.D. C. 96-C. 180):

But the swift-footed Celtic hounds are called in the Celtic tongue *onertragoi;*—not deriving their name from any particular nation, like the Cretan, Carian, or Spartan dogs: but, as some of the Cretans are named *diaponai* from working hard, *itamai* from their keenness, and mongrels from their being compounded from both; so these Celts are named for their swiftness. . . .

Their eyes should be large, up-raised, clear, strikingly bright. The best look fiery, and flash like lightning, resembling those of leopards, lions, or lynxes. Next to these are black eyes, provided they are wide-eyed and grim-looking; and last of all, grey: nor are these to be considered bad, nor indicative of bad dogs, provided they are clear, and have a savage look.[4]

---

[1]R. H. Smythe, *The Conformation of the Dog* (n.d. First published in 1957), pp. 32, 33.

[2]Phyllis Gardner, *The Irish Wolfhound* (1931), p. 167.

[3]Arrian , "De Venatione Libellus," iii. 6, *Arrianus*. In Greek and Latin. Ed. by Charles Muller (1846), p. 289.

[4]Arrian, *The Cynegeticus*, iv. 5. Trans. from the Greek by William Dansey (1831), pp. 74, 75, 77, 78.

Even though there is nothing in the American Standard on the subject of eyes, most American judges will only reluctantly place a dog with light eyes above another with dark ones. At three consecutive Irish Wolfhound Club of America Specialty dinners, the judges' principal and, in one case, only, critique was that there were too many dogs with light eyes! One judge placed one of my hounds fourth in the Hound Group two days after the Specialty and volunteered that she would have been second or third had she not light eyes!

Apparently, there are many who think of the Irish Wolfhound as "gentle when stroked" such as the English judge who said of one hound that he had a "lovely expression: Gentle, clever, faithful, benevolent, thoughtful". I too greatly admire such a dog but I also like the hound with what Miss Gardner called "a 'strong' or compelling eye". I have in mind that the Irish Wolfhound was a killer in combat against humans as well as wild animals: "Fierce when provoked." And I know that a light eye can be soft when the dog is in repose.

Blue eyes in an Irish Wolfhound over two months of age would appear to be a genetic defect. The Scottish Deerhound Standard of Excellence calls for disqualification of a hound with "blue or china-colored eyes." See Index at Eyes, Blue.

EYELIDS, LIPS, NOSE

Standard:

> *Faults*—In England: Pink or liver-coloured eyelids; lips and nose any colour other than black.
> In the U.S.: Lips or nose liver-colored or lacking pigmentation.

TEETH

While the Standard does not mention teeth, it is a factor in proper breeding. Most dental faults are hereditary.

Hold the dog's mouth closed and spread the lips apart. If the inside face of the upper incisors barely graze the outside face of the lower, the dog's bite is called "scissors". An "overshot" mouth means that the upper incisors advance farther than the lower and too much to be called "scissors", while "undershot" means that the lower incisors project beyond the upper. Puppies are often "overshot" a little. As they mature, the mandible increases in length and the lower teeth advance. With the exception of the lower canines, the teeth of the mandibles are all closely overlapped by the teeth of the upper jaws, thus allowing a firm clasp on any quarry. Overshot and undershot jaws disturb this relationship and change the appearance of the muzzle. The Standards for both English and French Bulldogs call for undershot jaws. There is some disagreement on the meaning of a "level bite". Some hold that this is the case when the incisors squarely meet. But Mrs. G. M. Angel is quoted as saying: "Level, in this case means even—i.e. not irregular or out of position—and it does not mean that the teeth should meet in a level line."[1]

Captain Graham has been quoted as saying of the Irish Wolfhound:

"The teeth are level."[2]

It is interesting to read the various Standards with regard to teeth.

Afghan Hound	Level. Scissors bite not to be penalized.
Basenji	Teeth must be level with scissors bite.
Basset Hound	Either a scissors or an even bite.
Beagle	Jaws level.
Black and Tan Coonhound	Teeth should fit evenly with slightly scissors bite.
Borzoi	Either an even or a scissors bite.
Dachshund	Scissors bite.
English Foxhound	Teeth must meet squarely.
Greyhound	Even in front.
Norwegian Elkhound	Scissors bite.
Rhodesian Ridgeback	Jaws level.
Saluki	Level.
Scottish Deerhound	Teeth and lips level.
Whippet	Teeth of upper jaw should fit closely over the lower.

---

[1]Mrs. G. M. Angel in *British Dog World*. Quoted in "Salukis," The American Kennel Club. *Pure-Bred Dogs—American Kennel Gazette* (May, 1971) LXXVIII, p. 54.

[2]G. A. Graham. Quoted by I. W. Everett, "The Typical Wolfhound," *op. cit.*, p. 63.

So-called "distemper teeth" are those which are pitted, and have erosions and permanent stains in the enamel. These changes occur during early puppyhood when the permanent teeth are being formed. They indicate that the puppy has had some ailment during this formative period. . .

The usual cause is a high fever during the time the permanent teeth are developing. Many illnesses produce high fevers but, inasmuch as canine distemper is probably the commonest fever-producing disease of puppies in most areas, such affected teeth have come to be called "distemper teeth". Keep in mind, however that just because a puppy has eroded teeth, he has not necessarily had distemper. Of course, the condition described is not to be confused with normal discoloration and tartar accumulation which can be removed by proper cleaning of the teeth.

There is no treatment, nor is one needed as "distemper teeth" serve the dog as well as normal ones. They are somewhat more susceptible to the collection of food and tartar, but not to any great extent. Of course, they may be unsightly if many teeth are involved, but otherwise innocuous.[1]

NECK

Standard

Neck—Rather long, very strong and muscular, well arched, without dewlap or loose skin about the throat.
Faults—Short neck; full dewlap.

Graham had the following comment:

Their necks should be thick in comparison to their form and very muscular.[2]

And on another occasion:

His throat should be clear of loose skin or dewlap. . . .The neck should be of fair length, but too long a neck gives an impression of weakness rather than strength.[3]

---

[1]"A Word from the Veterinarian," The American Kennel Club, *Pure-Bred Dogs—American Kennel Gazette* (October, 1960) LXXVII, p. 21.

[2]George A. Graham, "Irish Wolfhounds," *The Kennel Encyclopaedia, op. cit.*, p. 851.

[3]*Id.*, quoted by I. W. Everett, "The Typical Irish Wolfhound," *op. cit.*, pp. 63, 64.

A long neck puts more weight on the forehand. It creates instability to the front and results in greater speed as the dog strives to maintain his equilibrium. It is used by him in maintaining balance. It is helpful in the feinting, dodging and striking that occurs as the dog runs alongside the wolf and in the ensuing combat.

With regard to the neck being carried high, see comments on "Head".

A short neck usually means short backs and upright shoulders. This results in stilted action and in concussion when the dog is running.

CHEST, BACK

Standard:

> *Chest*—Very deep. Breast, wide.
> *Back*—Rather long than short.
> *Faults*—Too narrow or too broad a chest. Sunken or hollow or quite straight back. Too short in body.

Quoting Graham:

> Brisket down to elbows and nicely wide at the bottom. . . . The body should give an impression of nice length rather than the idea of a short-coupled-up body . . . the ribs reasonably sprung, but not to the extent of a Great Dane, so as not to resemble a barrel-like appearance. . . . This all adds to the lines of a nice set of curves beginning with the crest of neck and finishing with the bend of the tail. . . . His body just in front of hindlegs fairly drawn up, of course, for he is a galloping hound and does not need much encumbrance there when he is called upon for work.[1]

At the upper edges of the two scapulae, the cartilage projects about an inch and can be felt by the fingers. It is to this point (the withers) that a dog's height is measured. The space between these shoulder blades is greater when the dog's head is raised than when it is lowered.

Long dorsal bones mean a longer chest and therefore more lung room or breathing space. This makes it easier for the dog to gallop and endure.

---

[1]*Ibid.*, p. 64.

The ribs are curved outward from the center of the body and to the rear. When a dog inhales, the ribs rotate forward thus increasing the capacity of the thoracic cavity. The ribs return to their original position when the dog exhales. Spring of rib is what is desired to provide lung room. One should check the *midline* of the chest not the lower two inches or "deep chest" which is caused by the solid bone of the sternum. Actually one should be interested, not in the diameter of the chest at rest, but in the difference between the chest at inspiration and expiration.

When the Irish Wolfhound gallops, he flexes his spine. A long, well-muscled back will bend more easily, allowing the hind legs to go first under the body and then to the rear away from the body.

A dog with a short back has a gallop similar to a horse. The back is fairly rigid, the stride shorter than that of a dog with a long back. Most of the force then comes from the hips and stifles.

Note that a "quite straight back" is listed as a fault. Actually this refers not to the dorsal vertebrae but to the entire top line. In the Standard, the words "Loins arched" are included under the caption "Back."

SHOULDERS, ELBOWS

Standard:

> *Shoulders.*—Muscular, giving breadth of chest, set sloping.
> Elbows well under, neither turned inwards nor outwards.

"It is essential that the shoulders should be nicely laid back, not upright," said Graham.[1]

A sloping shoulder, say one at a 30° angle from the vertical, results in freer and faster action. It also results in less concussion than that which occurs when a dog has an upright shoulder. The latter is capable of only slight extension and therefore causes the dog to expend greater energy and become more quickly fatigued. In the center line of the scapula there is a ridge. The reach of a dog's foreleg can be judged by prolonging the center line to a point on the ground as the dog stands with his pads under the center of the blade. The upright shoulder may result in the over-development of muscles under the scapula, thereby pushing the blades out at the withers, a condition known as loaded shoulders. This, in turn, can force the

---

[1]*Ibid.*

elbows out. Among some of the causes of dogs being "out at the elbow" are insufficient exercise or improper feeding. These may result in soft chest muscles which, in turn, may cause the elbow condition.

Puppies who jump up against fences or gallop excessively may throw their shoulders out. The remedy is to curb this practice and *walk* them.

Oxen have blades that are more vertical. This is excellent for pulling. We find that the Alaskan Malamute Standard calls for "moderately sloping" shoulders.

> If the neck bones are long the dorsal bones will in all probability be long . . . this encourages the development of a well-laid-back shoulder. Conversely, if the neck bones are short, it is more than likely that the dorsal bones will also be short (and the lumbar bones long) and the result will be an upright shoulder. . . . The . . . upper end [of the scapula] will lie farther forward or farther backward in accordance with the placement of the dorsal vertebrae.[1]

It seems to have been unequivocally stated by all "authorities" that a sighthound's shoulder layback should be at a 45° angle from the vertical. My judging experience with Irish Wolfhounds and Scottish Deerhounds has been that the angle is much less. As a check, I measured 40 hounds at the 1977 Irish Wolfhound Club of America Specialty with a semicircular protractor on which a small level had been mounted. Its 6 inch radius allowed greater accuracy than a smaller one in measuring Irish Wolfhounds. As can be seen in the photograph, it is divided into mils, there being 6283 mils in a circle. Let us illustrate the procedure using the left side of the hound. First, move a finger repeatedly forward and rearward along the shoulder to find the scapular spine which is a prominent ridge. Then place an index and middle finger on each side of the spine and move them up and down along its full length so as to fix in your mind the general angle. Now set the center of the protractor's horizontal base at the base and center of the spine — not on the humerus. Level the bubble with the left hand and, keeping your eye on the level, place the thumb and index finger of the right hand on each side of the spine at the upper edge of the protractor. Quickly read the angle. Do not mistakenly measure to the posterior edge of the scapula. In the photograph, the angle from the horizontal to the center of the spine is 2130 mils; subtracting from this 1600, at which

---

[1]Smythe, *The Conformation of the Dog, op. cit.*, pp. 59, 60.

point a vertical line would interesect, one obtains the figure of 530 mils, or 29° 49′.

The question now arises: Does the spine run along the entire length of the scapula and in its exact center? From the Smithsonian Institution, I obtained all the scapulae of sighthounds in its possession. Five were of Irish Wolfhounds, two of Greyhounds, one of a Scottish Deerhound and one of a Borzoi. The anterior and posterior edges were marked with a pencil at the points of maximum scapular width. Using the protractor as previously described, it was found that the mean angles were 45° between the anterior and posterior edges, 25° 30′ from the spine to the posterior edge and 19° 30′ from the spine to the anterior edge (Figure 1). The center of the scapula at the line of maximum width would be at an angle of 22° 30′, half the full scapular measure of 45°, and 3° more than the angle from the anterior edge to the spine (Figure 2). Therefore, 3° should be added to any angular measurement from the vertical to the scapular spine and they have been added in the following report.

1977 IWCA Specialty Blue Ribbon Winners
(Includes Veterans and Best of Breed. Best of
Opposite Sex was Winner of Veterans Bitches Class)

Classes	No. of Hounds	Mean Age Yr Mo	Mean Shoulder Angle
Puppy, Novice	6	1 — 1	19°
Bred-by-Exhibitor and American-Bred	4	2 — 2	24°
Open, Veterans, Best of Breed	5	4 — 1	31°

The above figures would seem to indicate that the angle becomes greater as the hound grows older. However, the sampling is much too small to justify such a conclusion. Incidentally, there was no difference in angulation between sexes.

Summarizing all the results:

	No. of Hounds	Mean Shoulder Angle Minimum	Maximum	Mean
Blue Ribbon Winners	15	14°	37°	25°
Others	25	8°	31°	20°
	40	8°	37°	22°

This is quite a difference from the universally-stated 45°. It should be noted that precise measurement devices were not used by me. Angles were read directly from the protractor and, therefore, some variations from exact measurements should be expected.

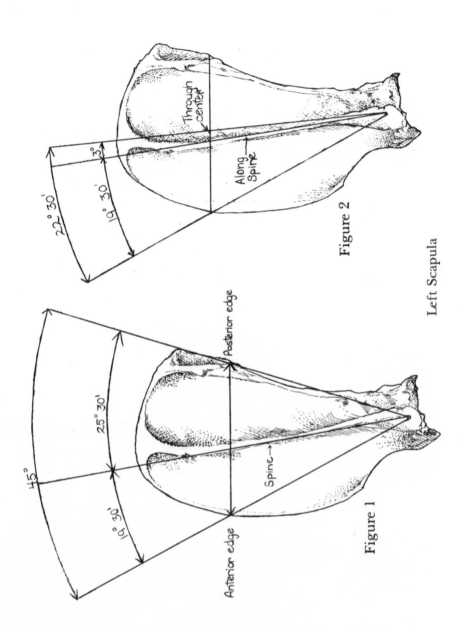

Figure 2

Figure 1

Left Scapula

Many "authorities" have dogmatically expounded the view that the ideal layback for sighthounds is 45°. They have advanced theories in support of their position. They have also been strongly critical of straight shoulders and given arguments in support of this view without, however, specifying how steep a shoulder must be to qualify as "straight." The same situation is true of rear angulation. Yet there are hounds without the so-called "desirable degree of angulation" who do well in coursing. It must be acknowledged that spirit, courage or, as it is commonly termed, "desire," will overcome many physical deficiencies.

I am unaware of any study that has scientifically proven what the optimum angles should be. Possibly such a study would require radiographic evidence of Irish Wolfhounds at a standstill and in motion at various gaits and then exhaustive tests of speed and endurance. While this would be a most interesting project — as well as time-consuming and expensive — the research on IWs which I am presently conducting will not allow me to undertake any new assignments. I hope some scientifically qualified individuals and organizations will delve deeper into form and function.

FORELEGS

Standard:

> Leg—Forearm muscular, and the whole leg strong and quite straight.
> Faults—Bent forelegs; overbent fetlocks.

Graham makes these points:

> As to the legs, a fair amount of bone is needed to make a typical hound. . . .The forelegs should be set in line with their shoulder points.[2]

The Standard calls for the leg to be "quite straight", but McDowell Lyon says:

> Sloping pasterns are not to be confused with broken-down pasterns. The slope should not start in the joint itself but either above it or below it, keeping this group of bones in compact harmony. . . .The bend does three things: (1) prevents knuckling over and undue tax on muscles involved in that; (2) absorbs the

---

[1]G.A. Graham. Quoted by I.W. Everett, "The Typical Irish Wolfhound," *op. cit.*, p. 64.

shock of concussion; (3) and provides greater lift to the center of gravity by letting the bones below the pastern enter into that action.[1]

FEET

Standard:

Feet—Moderately large and round, neither turned inwards nor outwards. Toes, well arched and closed. Nails, very strong and curved.
Faults—Twisted feet; spreading toes.

Graham adds:

His heels nicely low to the ground.[2]

The Standard requires a "cat foot" in the IW. This structure provides for greater endurance whereas the long "hare foot" provides early speed. A cat foot with the toes well set up,together and well padded is essential to absorb shock. Where, instead of being firmly together, the toes are widely separated, we have a condition known as "splay feet" which is due to slackness in muscles and tendons. Experiments by Ralston Purina showed that puppies of large breeds developed splay feet and straight toe joints when brought up on hard-surfaced runs. Increased exercise and a change of kennel run surface when puppies were six weeks of age stopped further deterioration but the condition remained permanent if the puppies' environment was unchanged until they were twenty-four weeks old.[3]

The Standard says that the feet should point straight ahead, but Lyon, generally considered to be an authority on movement in dogs, says that when the dog is standing the feet should be slightly turned out.[4] This position would seem to be advisable, just as in a human, in order that the body may be in better balance. Rachel Page Elliott agrees.[5] See Index at Standard of Excellence, Toes.

---

[1]McDowell Lyon. *The Dog in Action* (1963), pp. 154, 155.

[2]G. A. Graham. Quoted by I.W. Everett, "The Typical Irish Wolfhound," *op. cit.*, p. 64.

[3]Louis Pegram, "Flat Feet in Purebred Dogs," *Popular Dogs* (December, 1972).

[4]McDowell Lyon, "The Dog in Action, *Popular Dogs* (May, 1962), XXXV, p. 48.

[5]Rachel Page Elliott, *Dog Steps* (1973), p. 63.

LOINS

Standard:

Loins—Arched. *Belly*—Well drawn up.

Graham observed:

> The loin should be a little full, but not so exaggerated as to give
> the hound the appearance of being dipped behind the shoulder,
> but just sufficient to give a nice gradual sweep right down to the
> set-on of the tail, which should connect fairly low down.[1]

An arched loin functions like a spring. It enables the dog to draw
his hind legs well under him as a preliminary to a forceful drive with
his hind legs. It should be broad and strong to provide power.

While long dorsal bones are desirable, one should beware of
lumbar bones that are so long as to cause weakness.

Of interest is the fact that the Greyhound Standard in England
calls for "slightly arched" loins, whereas in the United States "well
arched" loins are desired.

HINDQUARTERS

Standard:

> *Hindquarters*—Muscular thighs and second thigh long and
> strong as in the Greyhound, and hocks well let down and turning
> neither in nor out.
> *Faults*—Weak hindquarters and a general want of muscle.

Graham:

> The hindquarters are responsible for about two-thirds of his
> movement, continued movement that is, given the hound is fit
> internally. He needs good strong hindquarters, well muscled up,
> as separated from a super abundance of fat . . . nicely bent stifles
> and second thighs.[2]

Breadth across the hips facilitates the passage of the hind legs on
the outside of the front legs in the gallop. The croup should be set at
about 30° from the horizontal to allow efficient propulsion.

---

[1]G. A. Graham. Quoted by I. W. Everett, "The Typical Irish Wolfhound," *op.
cit.*, p. 64.

[2]*Ibid.*

A steep croup, short upper thigh or cowhocks can cause stifles to turn outwards. However, a steep croup does enable a dog to get his feet under him and to turn more quickly.

The pelvis is attached to the sacrum by ligaments. Movement at this point is very limited. The propulsion provided by the hind legs acts against the spine through the pelvis. If the pelvis were vertical, the force from the hind legs would push the lower part of the pelvis upwards against the spine instead of forward. The more the pelvis is inclined and the more the hindquarters are angulated, the more do the bones come into line with the spine and thus exert a more direct influence. Well-bent stifles allow the dog to push forward rather than pound the ground. The German Shepherd has a more horizontal pelvis and a femur that is nearer the perpendicular. This means that the stifle is farther to the rear and results in greater angulation. If a dog is over-angulated, he has to restrict the movement of his hind legs to the speed of his front legs. While long thighs and marked angulation help endurance, it is generally the straight-stifled greyhound who is faster than one more angulated. The latter soon becomes worthless, however, because of the stress on his spine and feet.[1] Smythe relates that the Greyhound, Mick the Miller (c. 1930), was one of the fastest dogs ever and yet he had an extraordinarily long back and amazing angulations. The theory seems to be that the greater the angulation the more time it takes to extend the legs to the rear and then to recover. However, dogs with greater angulation may cover more ground with each bound![2] Galloping breeds have a greater degree of inclination of the pelvis than do some terriers.

The expression "hocks well let down" means that the hock joint is near the ground, i.e., that the metatarsal bones are relatively short. This condition sacrifices initial speed for endurance.

We read in Hutchinson's *Dog Encyclopaedia:*

> Dalziel gave the best description of the broad-hipped dog, perhaps, when he wrote: "With a very broad-hipped dog, the stifles are generally set outwards, thus throwing the hocks nearer together. This formation is greatly liked by some, as it enables the dog to bring its hindlegs well forward, clear of its sides, but some wiseacres confound this with cowhocks, which arise from the legs being bowed in at the hocks." It will be found that hounds so built gallop easily and powerfully and never tire, and can jump without effort.[3]

---

[1] Smythe, *The Conformation of the Dog, op. cit.,* p. 89.

[2] *Ibid.,* pp. 89, 90.

[3] Hutchinson, Walter Victor, *Hutchinson's Encyclopaedia* (3 vols.; 1939) II, pp. 996, 998.

TAIL

Standard:

> *Tail*—Long and slightly curved, of moderate thickness, and well covered with hair.
> *Fault*—Too curly a tail.

Graham said:

> The set-on of the tail, which should connect fairly low down.
> . . .Tail of good length, but certainly not thick and fleshy.[1]

> Slightly curved, of moderate thickness, and well covered with hair.[2]

The reasons given for certain physical features or characteristics of dogs often are pure guesswork. For instance, it has been said that dogs in the North carry their tails high because those dogs whose tails dragged in the snow were lost by reason of "natural selection", i.e., the principle of "survival of the fittest", since snow in their tails became frozen and they became prey to wild beasts. To this, one might ask "What about the wolf and his long tail?"

The usual view is that expressed by English breeders and judges, I.W. Everett and Miss Esther Croucher:

> A long tail is of considerable assistance to a dog travelling at speed, especially in turning when it is used as a rudder.[3]

> Tails in some cases only just reached the hocks and though I know they are a minor point they are essential to a coursing hound to give that extra weight and balance for a quick swing round if needed when hunting.[4]

Freeman Lloyd went so far as to say:

> A decent dog with a long tail can course and run down any game from a rabbit to a deer. Cut his tail off, and he's like a ship without a rudder.[5]

---

[1]G. A. Graham. Quoted by I. W. Everett,"The Irish Wolfhound," *op. cit.*, p. 64.

[2]*Id.*, "Irish Wolfhounds", *The Kennel Encyclopaedia, op. cit.*, p. 851.

[3]I. W. Everett, "Impressions at Bath Show," The Irish Wolfhound Club, *Year Book* (Britain) (1925), p. 26.

[4]Esther M. Croucher, "Irish Wolfhounds in America," The Irish Wolfhound Club (Britain), *Year Book* (1961-1963), p. 38.

[5]Freeman Lloyd, "Many Dogs in Many Lands," American Kennel Club, *Pure-Bred Dogs—American Kennel Club Gazette* (February, 1924) XXXVI, p. 149.

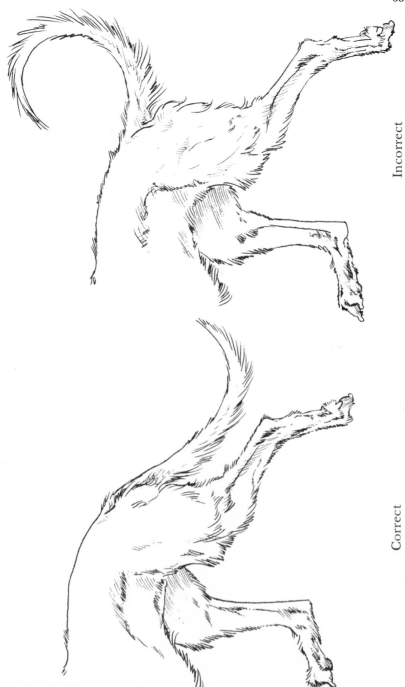

Tail Carriage

Incorrect

Correct

While it seems logical to say that the weight of the tail will help balance the dog, it seems to me Mr. Lloyd's statement might be an exaggeration. Are deer, who have short tails, and antelopes, who usually do, unable to change direction rapidly? Could they do so better if they had long tails? I have seen motion pictures of an impala making a right angle turn while at a full run.

In Irish Wolfhounds, it is considered desirable to have tails below the hocks, when extended by hand. I do not see that the curving upwards of the extremity, as indicated in the Standard, serves any purpose other than being more esthetic. A tail carried over the back would seem to indicate too high placement on the croup.

An interesting theory is that the dog's tail aids in blood circulation:

> The theory, according to W. R. McCuistion, D.V.M., in *Veterinary Medicine/Small Animal Clinician,* is that the long tail, with its elevated position and maneuverability, acts as a hydraulic ram, sending blood and lymph through the lymphatic system during moments of excitement (stress) when the heart is unusually taxed. . .

> When the tail is held erect, according to Dr. McCuistion, the descent of fluids within the lymph vessels and veins is facilitated. The side to side motion of the tail in this position evidently aids in maintaining body fluid equilibrium and in counteracting downward pressure from gravity. The piston-like motion propels the blood through a lacey network of capillaries and other small vessels to the principal circulatory vessels within the body. . . .

> The cat, skunk, horse, elephant, deer, dog, and others carry their tails high in moments of excitement. The possibility that these animals do this to facilitate the rapid flow through the lymph system is reasonable. However, it seems more likely among dogs than among elephants, whose tails are proportionately minute.[1]

MOVEMENT

Standard:

Power and swiftness . . .

Galloping hounds . . .

Movements easy and active.

---

[1]W. R. McCuistion. Article in *Veterinary Medicine/Small Animal Clinician.* Quoted in "Dog's Tail," *Gaines Dog Research Progress* (Summer, 1966).

In the field, an Irish Wolfhound will use a number of gaits.[1] In the ring, only two gaits are called for: the walk and the trot.

In the walk, the sequence of footfalls is left rear, left front, right rear, right front with support being alternately on three feet and two feet. In walking, the dog's hind foot just about covers the spot where the front foot was placed. The dog will have a short stride if he is long coupled, has short legs, does not stand up well on his hocks, has straight stifles, a flat croup, soft muscles or is in poor condition. If his hind foot steps beyond the place vacated by the front he may be short coupled or have straight shoulder blades and too much rear angulation.

At a trot, the sequence of footfalls varies but generally it can be said that the support alternates between the diagonals, i.e. the left rear and right front are followed by the right rear and left front. In between the support furnished by the diagonals, the Irish Wolfhound, at a fast trot, is suspended in air. At a normal trot, the hind feet of the dog strike the ground at about the same location as the front feet.

Lyon says: "The trot is admirably suited for rough, irregular ground and for traveling long distances at a fair rate of speed. It is the natural foraging gait of most wild animals. No one leg has more work to do than its opposite and the diagonal support makes it easier for the dog to maintain equilibrium."[2]

The canter may be either on the "left lead" or the "right lead" depending on which front foot is on the ground when the Irish Wolfhound propels himself in the air. When a hound is on the right lead, the sequence of footfalls is left rear, right rear and left front, right front. In effect, it is a three-beat gait followed by suspension. An animal uses the left lead when turning towards the left and the right lead when turning to the right. He is supported by one, two or three feet.

The transverse gallop is generally used by dogs other than the fast gazehounds. It is a four-beat gait resembling the canter: left rear, right rear, left front, right front, suspension. Support consists of one or two feet.

The rotatory gallop used by the Irish Wolfhound follows this pattern: left rear, right rear, suspension, right front, left front, suspension. Support is provided by one or two feet. The hind feet pass on the outside of the front feet and go beyond them.

---

[1]Descriptions of these may be found in: *Animals in Motion*—by Eadweard Muybridge (1957); *The Dog in Action*—by McDowell Lyon (1963); *The Conformation of the Dog*—by R. H. Smythe (n.d. First published in 1957).

[2]Lyon, *The Dog in Action* (1963), p. 48.

An impression often encountered in the working dog field, conveyed both by word and picture, is that, in motion as at a standstill, a dog's front legs are parallel and that this is equally true of the hind legs.[1] To a certain extent this is true in a slow walk but, as speed increases, the feet are gradually brought towards the center of the body. In the trot or the rotatory gallop, a dog never has more than two feet on the ground and at times only one foot. For efficient support these feet must be under the center of gravity of the body, converging on a center line under the body. This is called "single tracking". It does not necessarily mean that all four feet fall exactly on the same line.

The leg itself, when viewed from the front or the rear, must maintain a straight column of bones from the shoulder or hip joints to the pad. Neither pasterns nor hocks should deflect from this line. Any tendency toward "cowhocks" will interfere with this straight column and curtail efficient locomotion.

Here is McDowell Lyon's analysis:

> A good working dog will stand with his front feet slightly turned outward. The pastern is not bent outward as we see in a "French front", but the assembly from the pastern joint to the pad is rotated a few degrees. Slow motion pictures have definitely established that when this foot is brought in under the dog's center of gravity the feet face to the front and the action is over the two center toes. The same research shows that the foot, which faces straight forward when the dog is standing, is toed in slightly when it reaches this center line and the action is over one center toe and a smaller outside toe. If the dog is not moving fast, you can detect this by eye.[2]

The comments previously made about single tracking at a trot also apply to the canter and gallop. Judge John F. Baily is reported as saying, after praising the English Champion Cotswold, "He goes, perhaps, rather wide behind, but as I have seen many good horses do the same and still gallop fast, it may not be such a fault after all. He is unquestionably the most perfect specimen of the breed we have got, or that I have seen, and I think I have seen every good specimen that has come out since 1879."[3]

---

[1] To this effect, see Smythe, *The Conformation of the Dog, op. cit.*, pp. 103, 130. Also see The American Kennel Club's *The Complete Dog Book* (1975), p. 660, which shows in its anatomical drawings a Pointer coming and going at a trot. The widely separated feet are called "correct" and "good."

[2] Lyon, "The Dog in Action," *Popular Dogs* (May 1962) XXXV, p. 48.

[3] John F. Baily. The Kennel Club (Britain), *The Kennel Gazette* (July 1908) XXIX, p. 330.

"Paddling"   "Weaving"   Moving Wide   Correct
Convergence
("Single Tracking")

"Cow-hocked"   Moving Close   Moving Wide   Correct
Hound In Motion   Convergence
("Single Tracking")

Often, the movement of dogs of Greyhound-type is considered to be the same as horses. This is not true. The Greyhound, Irish Wolfhound, etc., bend their spines considerably in galloping. The horse's spine bends very little. In the horse, the femur and stifle are enclosed within skin and muscle and are close to the body and the hind legs swing more or less like a pendulum from the stifle, whereas the Irish Wolfhound's hind leg motion starts at the top of the pelvis. The horse uses the transverse gallop, the Irish Wolfhound the rotatory.[1] The horse gets most of his propelling power from his front legs, whereas in the dog it is the hind legs that provide the main power, assisted by the fore.[2]

Excellent conformation does not necessarily result in excellent gait. Lack of condition, overdevelopment of certain muscles, injuries and ailments such as arthritis will affect a dog's gait.

An Irish Wolfhound should have balance. A heavier front than rear results in insufficient propelling power. The reverse gives more power than is needed and puts the dog off balance.

The Irish Wolfhound should move energetically, flexing his feet so that, from the rear, one can see his pads. Observing the dog coming and going, one can see whether he is crabbing or paddling, whether he is out at the elbow, whether he is cow-hocked, or whether he is moving true. Excess rear stride occasioned by more rear than front angulation and legs insufficiently long or back too short will produce "crabbing", i.e. the dog moves forward but his body is at an angle to the forward movement.

Observing from the side one can evaluate the power with which the dog is driving, his reach, recovery, whether he is rolling, whether a stilted front is causing his withers to bounce up and down, whether his front and rear are in balance, whether he has a smooth, rhythmic gait. He should not shuffle along or otherwise present a sloppy appearance. Nor should he be a "dancer". He should cover ground smoothly, easily and efficiently at a good rate of speed.

COAT

Standard:

> *Hair*—Rough and hard on body, legs and head; especially wiry and long over eyes and under jaw.

In 1909, Graham wrote:

---

[1]Muybridge, *op. cit.*, pp. 49, 52.
[2]Smythe, *The Conformation of the Dog, op. cit.*, p. 100.

The coat should be thoroughly rough, hard and long all over the body, head, legs, and tail.[1]

I.W. Everett quotes Graham as saying:

His coat should be dense next his skin, and longer and more wiry on the outside. It should be a double coat, and would more frequently be so if not so much over-groomed.[2]

John F. Baily, who worked with Graham in the formulation of the Standard, said, speaking of the undercoat:

That it keeps its owner warm is very probable, that it keeps out the water is doubtful. It is generally woolly, absorbs damp like blotting paper and is kept from drying by the outer coat.[3]

Coats are inherited not acquired. However, I have seen a sparse coat on a puppy develop into a fairly dense one over a period of years. The same is true for hair on the head and muzzle.

COLOR

Standard:

Color and Markings—The recognized colors are gray, brindle, red, black, pure white, fawn, or any color that appears in the Deerhound.

Colors mentioned in the Deerhound Standard are: dark blue-gray, darker and lighter gray or brindle, yellow and sandy red and red fawn. In the American Kennel Club's *The Complete Dog Book,* the word "other" has been added to the Standard so that it now reads "or any other color that appears in the Deerhound."[4] This implies that colors previously named, including "pure white" are proper Deerhound colors, whereas the Deerhound Standard says: "White is condemned by all authorities" and "A white blaze on the head, or a white collar, should entirely disqualify." I believe that the introduction of the word "other" was inadvertent and that it should be deleted. No such change was ever recommended by the Irish

[1]George A. Graham, "Irish Wolfhounds," *The Kennel Encyclopaedia, op. cit.,* p. 851.
[2]*Id.* Quoted by I.W. Everett, "The Typical Irish Wolfhound," *op. cit.,* 64.
[3]John F. Baily, "My Interpretation of Irish Wolfhound Type," The Irish Wolfhound Club (Britain), *Year Book* (1927), p. 50.
[4]American Kennel Club, *The Complete Dog Book* (1975), p. 178.

Wolfhound Club of America and it does not appear in any of its publications. One color that is seen in Irish Wolfhounds is called "wheaten".

Over a period of years, a few blue-coated dogs have appeared. A concomitant characteristic has been blue eyes. Apart from the odd expression of a blue-eyed Irish Wolfhound, a more serious element is the susceptibility of such a hound and its progeny to becoming blind and deaf. See Index at Eyes, Blue. One American breeder, who had previously assured me that the colors of the kennel's blue-coated and blue-eyed hounds were not objectives, is now producing many of them and advertising blue as a rare color, thus implying its desirability.

Graham is quoted as saying about the Irish Wolfhound:

> Colours in various shades are recognized. Personally, I am very fond of orange-fawns and the various shades of brindle. I do not so much like the fainter shades unless accompanied by good black toenails and muzzles, and dark shadings round the eyes and under edges of tail. [1]

In his Working Stud Book, Graham assigned 26 variations of colors to 344 of the 601 hounds listed. I have reduced these to six more elementary groups: red, fawn, gray, wheaten, brindle, and black.

If we begin our study of colors with the whelping date of Graham's first Irish Wolfhound (1859) and end it with the lone entry for 1906, we can construct the table shown.

NUMBER OF HOUNDS BY COLOR

	1859 1868	1869 1878	1879 1888	1889 1898	1899 1906	Total
Red	5	3	14	32	3	57
Fawn	1	1	10	39	13	64
Gray		3	13	31	16	63
Wheaten				4	2	6
Brindle	1	7	39	76	27	150
Black		1			3	4
Total	7	15	76	182	64	344

---

[1] G. A. Graham. Quoted by I. W. Everett, "The Typical Irish Wolfhound," *op. cit.*, p. 64.

It can be seen that, initially (1859-1868), six out of the seven Irish Wolfhounds were red or fawn. In the next decade about half were brindle and the remainder were about equally divided between reddish (red and fawn) and gray hounds, with one being black.

From 1879-1888, again about half were brindle but, among the remainder, reddish hounds outnumbered grays by almost two to one. In the following ten years, there are almost as many reddish dogs as brindle; grays account for only 17% and wheatens make their first appearance. In the last years, 42% are brindle, 25% are reddish, 25% gray; black Irish Wolfhounds appear after a lapse of thirty years. Black dogs are comparatively rare today. Until recently, one very rarely saw a reddish hound.

In the U.S., the color of a dog must be declared when he is registered. In the case of Irish Wolfhounds, I consider this information practically worthless. A puppy can change color quite rapidly as he grows up, and occasionally more than once. The color may become darker, e.g. a red or wheaten yearling may become a gray brindle, or lighter, e.g. a red may become a fawn.

In 1904, English judge Edwin G. Salter had this to say:

> I have seen real good hounds relegated to inferior positions simply because of their wheaten or light colour, irrespective of their quality. Why should a good hound suffer because it happens to be born other than say a blue or a dark colour? The wheaten and light fawns were the original colours, and fashion or taste should not, as it unfortunately sometimes does, influence a judge's mind.[1]

TEMPERAMENT

It should be noted that the Standard calls for "activity" and "courage". A judge may obtain some indication of these qualities by observing the dog's bearing, his self-confidence, boldness in movement, and lack of shyness. An Irish Wolfhound who cringes at the approach of the judge and who moves sluggishly does not give evidence of "activity" and "courage". It is possible that this condition is not an inherent characteristic of the particular hound and that it is due to his youth, his state of health at the moment, the strange surroundings, the heat of the day, or the abrupt movements of the judge.

---

[1] Edwin G. Salter, The Kennel Club (Britain), *The Kennel Gazette* (Jan. 1904), XXV, p. 8.

POINTS

A Judging Committee, composed of Captain Graham, J. F. Baily and Hamilton-Adams, performed their duties at the 1903 Kennel Club Show in England using this point system for Irish Wolfhounds:

1. Head, 25; viz., length and shape, 12; ears, 7; beard and brows, 3; eyes, 3.

2. Body, 25; viz., height at shoulder, 12; substance and girth, 7; length and symmetry, 6.

3. Limbs, 25; viz., loins and hocks, 9; forelegs, 9; feet, 7.

4. Remainder, 25; viz., coat, 10; neck, 7; tail, 5; teeth, 2; nails, 1.[1]

In the above table, shoulder placement, bend of stifle, and movement were not given any values unless they were incorporated in "length and symmetry" and in "loins and hocks"? I do not see how it is possible to judge dogs by means of a Scale of Points without taking an extraordinarily long time to determine points to be awarded, and in recording and totaling them. A judge would then most likely end up with a selected dog that he would ordinarily not have placed above the others. Miss M. S. Kearns, referring to the 1904 show, said, "The hound awarded the most number of points was certainly not the most typical."[2]

The point system used had been approved by The Irish Wolfhound Club (Britain).[3] It varied slightly from one suggested by "Breeder" in *Our Dogs*[4] and appears to have been superseded at some unknown date by a "List of Points in Order of Merit". Neither of these systems is mentioned in books by Graham (1885) and Hogan (1897). We do find a "List of Points" in the 1925 Yearbook of the Irish Wolfhound Club (Britain) and in the Biennial Report of the Irish Wolfhound Club of America for 1928-1930,[5] both of these books being the first publications of the two clubs. At that time, the list read as follows:

---

[1]Percy Shewell. The Kennel Club (Britain), *The Kennel Gazette* (January, 1904), XXV, p. 9.

[2]M. S. Kearns, *op. cit.*, p. 60.

[3]Herbert Compton, *The Twentieth Century Dog* (2 vols., 1904) II, pp. 175, 176.

[4]W. D. Drury, *British Dogs* (2 vols., 1903) I, pp. 113, 114.

[5]The Irish Wolfhound Club of America, *Biennial Report* (March 1928-1930), p. 19.

LIST OF POINTS
In Order of Merit

1. The Irish Wolfhound should not be quite so heavy or massive as the Great Dane, but more so than the Deerhound, which in general type he should otherwise resemble.

1. Great size and commanding appearance.

3. Movements easy and active.

4. Head, long and level, carried high.

5. Forelegs, heavily boned, quite straight; elbows well set under.

6. Thighs long and muscular; second thighs, well muscled, stifles nicely bent.

7. Coat, rough and hard, specially wiry and long over eyes and under jaw.

8. Body, long, well-ribbed up, with ribs well sprung, and great breadth across hips.

9. Loins arched, belly well drawn up.

10. Ears, small, with Greyhound-like carriage.

11. Feet, moderately large and round; toes, close, well arched.

12. Neck, long, well arched and very strong.

13. Chest, very deep, moderately broad.

14. Shoulders, muscular, set sloping.

15. Tail, long and slightly curved.

16. Eyes, dark.

Note—The above in no way alters the "Standard of Excellence", which must in all cases be rigidly adhered to; they simply give the various points in order of merit. If in any case they appear at variance with Standard of Excellence, it is the latter which is correct.

Sometime between 1938 and 1954, the English Club changed point 6 from "stifles nicely bent" to "stifles slightly bent".[1] In 1950, the Irish Wolfhound Club of America changed the first paragraph to read:

> Typical—The Irish Wolfhound is a rough-coated Greyhound-like breed, the tallest of the coursing hounds and remarkable in combining power and swiftness.[2]

As for acceptance of the Standard of Points by the Kennel Clubs, that of Britain did not officially acknowledge its existence until January 1, 1950, when it did so for the Standards of all breeds which it recognized.[3] The first American Kennel Club record available of the Standard of Points is that in the 1929 edition of its book, *Pure-Bred Dogs.*[4] Possibly a Standard of Points accompanied the rules of the Irish Wolfhound Club of Ireland in 1926 when it was first affiliated to the Irish Kennel Club.[5]

It is my opinion that the List of Points serves no useful purpose. In the first place few judges, breeders, and owners would agree with the present ordering and they would undoubtedly present a wide variation if they individually prepared a ranking of their own. Even if they all agreed on a ranking, there would be disagreement on the importance of each feature. One might say that "Movements easy and active" is ten times as important as "Head, long and carried high". Another might say it is only twice as important. It also presents the danger that judges might fail to remember whether a fault was listed in the Standard or in the List of Points in Order of Merit. For example, in the United States, "Eyes" is covered by the List of Points but not in the Standard. It matters little that at the end of the former there is a note to the effect that in the event of contradiction between the terms of the Standard and those in the List of Points, the Standard shall be considered correct. Some American judges apparently believe that dark eyes are demanded by the Standard.

Now that we know a little of the history of the breed and what a good Irish Wolfhound should look and act like, let us see what a breeder must do to bring forth the puppy which you seek to purchase.

---

[1] The Irish Wolfhound Club (Britain), *Year Book* (1935-1937), p. 20; (1938-1954), p. 23.

[2] The Irish Wolfhound Club of America, *Harp and Hound* (1950), I, No. 4, p. 34.

[3] The Kennel Club (Britain) *Letter to the author* (June 10, 1971).

[4] The American Kennel Club, *Letter to the author* (May 20, 1971).

[5] The Irish Kennel Club, *Letter to the author* (May 24, 1971).

IV

The Breeder's Responsibilities

A. GENERAL

The Irish Wolfhound Club of America has adopted certain "Guidelines" proposed by me for owners and breeders. My recommendation that a bitch not be bred once she has reached the age of six years was changed to read seven years. Copies of the Guidelines are furnished by the Club to all persons inquiring about the breed. Regional clubs and breeders are encouraged to reproduce and distribute them.

IRISH WOLFHOUND CLUB OF AMERICA GUIDELINES

The purpose of this document is to provide guidance to owners and breeders of Irish Wolfhounds so that both the individual hound and the breed may benefit. It lists actions considered advisable as well as those that are generally deemed undesirable. These are not intended to be complete lists. Moreover, each of the actions listed as undesirable are not necessarily inherently bad. Reputable persons may well differ in their opinions and conditions may exist which would justify exceptions to the rules.

GUIDELINES FOR OWNERS

Humaneness is everyone's concern. For this reason and because the characteristics of the Irish Wolfhound could be seriously altered by improper care or conduct, the following guidelines are provided to owners and prospective owners:

1. The overwhelming concern of a person selling, giving away, or otherwise placing an Irish Wolfhound in another home is that this home be a good one. He carefully inquires into the reputation of the prospective owner and into the conditions of the home, e.g. knowledge, experience and judgment of the prospective owner with regard to other dogs, method of feeding, care, exercise.

75

2. Under no conditions will hounds be transferred to pet shops, commercial dog dealers, contest sponsors, or to persons whose intention to resell the dog is known. Persons desiring to purchase several hounds will be carefully interviewed to ascertain whether or not a "puppy mill" is being planned.

3. At the time of transfer, a dog should be in good health. The new owner should be advised to have him examined by a veterinarian within 48 hours of receipt.

4. If a dog has such faults, whether physical, mental, or temperamental, that it should not be bred, consideration should first be given to having him put to sleep. This is especially applicable if the dog is in pain or is likely to suffer. If a decision is made to transfer the ownership of the dog, provision should be made to prevent his being bred or shown. Preferably, neutering or spaying should be performed prior to transfer. If, because of the age of the hound or for some other valid reason, this is not done, then the two parties should enter into a written agreement that the new owner will have the operation performed by a certain date or the transfer will be void and the hound returned and that upon receipt of a veterinarian's statement that the operation has been done by the prescribed date, the registration certificate will be transferred.

5. Puppies under 12 weeks of age should neither be transferred nor imported.

6. The sales price of a dog should conform to accepted practice, i.e., it should be neither excessively high nor low.

7. If the transfer of a hound is made without restrictions, the new owner should be given its health, registration, and pedigree records.

8. An owner should take the following actions with regard to a new owner:

a. Inform him of available literature on the breed since the feeding, exercise and care of Irish Wolfhounds, especially puppies, differ in some respects from practices exercised with other breeds.

b. Provide him with a copy of these guidelines.

c. Provide him with the name and address of the Irish Wolfhound Club of America Secretary and urge him to apply for Associate Membership. Membership includes a subscription to the official publication *Harp and Hound.*

GUIDELINES FOR BREEDERS

The purpose of breeding Irish Wolfhounds is to bring their natural qualities to perfection. There exists a constant danger that disreputable or ignorant breeders may, by improper practices, produce physically, mentally, or temperamentally poor specimens to the detriment of the breed. For this reason, the following guidelines are provided.

1. Breeding should be done selectively and in accordance with genetic principles so as to reduce faults to a minimum and to improve the qualities of the breed.

2. Breeding should not be done solely to make money, to have a puppy, or to demonstrate to children the "miracle of life". It should not be done unless a good probability exists that the puppies can be sold at prices comparable to those charged by reputable breeders with stock of similar quality. It should not be done unless an absolute certainty exists that all puppies will have good homes.

3. Hounds in poor health or of unsound temperament should not be bred.

4. A bitch should be bred only between the ages of 2 to 7 years. She should not be bred if this might result in her having a litter more often than once every 12 months.

5. Where a bitch that has been bred fails to conceive, the owner of the stud will allow one repeat service on condition that the same stud is available and in good health and that the owners of both hounds can agree on time and place of breeding.

6. The owner of the stud is to some extent a sponsor of any resulting litter in that, prior to the breeding, he should have reason to believe that the breeder is following these guidelines.

7. Complete and accurate breeding and pedigree records should be maintained. These include:

a. For the mated pair: names of hounds and dates of whelp, names and addresses of owners, date bitch came in season, dates of attempted breedings, dates of ties, if any.

b. For the resulting litter: date of whelp, number and sex of puppies whelped alive, number and sex of puppies dead at birth.

c. For each live puppy: Name, sex, registration date, name and address of owner.

8. Since the above record is of great value in the study of Irish Wolfhounds, the breeder is urged to send the data to the Irish

Wolfhound Club of America Secretary. Information on any particular breeder or hound will not be revealed but merely incorporated into statistical records.

9. Each person inquiring about an Irish Wolfhound should be given a copy of these guidelines.

B.　BREEDING OBJECTIVES

Persons breed dogs for one or more of these reasons:

1. Ideally, to produce a dog that could be a model for the Standard of Excellence. More practically, to improve the breed by producing a dog that will be superior to his parents.

2. To have a puppy.

3. To make money.

Let us examine each of these motives.

1. *To improve the breed.*

This requires knowledge of the Standard of Excellence and of genetics, ability to evaluate the qualities and faults of Irish Wolfhounds, and practical experience in the exercise of such ability. The minimum age at which a bitch should be bred, as stated in the *Guidelines,* is to allow her to mature physically and psychologically; the minimum period between breedings that is mentioned is to allow her the opportunity of replacing calcium reserves and to allow the reproductive systems to come back to normal. Captain Graham was also of this opinion.[1]

> Are inherited defects of dogs really becoming more common? S. F. J. Hodgman and W. B. Singleton, prominent British veterinarians, think so and frankly spoke their thoughts at the recent congress of the British Veterinary Association . . . The list [of "hereditary abnormalities"] included extreme nervousness amounting to mental instability among Miniature and Toy Poodles and Labradors; patella luxation in Chihuahuas, King Charles Spaniels, and Pomeranians; hip dysplasia in German Shepherds, Boxers, Labradors, and Golden Retrievers; otitis due to hair in the outer ear canal; and intervertebral disc luxation in the long-backed, short-legged breeds; uterine inertia in Scotties; stomach distension and torsion in Bloodhounds and Irish Setters; lens luxation in Wirehaired Fox Terriers; cryptorchidism

---

[1]George A. Graham, in *The Kennel Encyclopaedia, op. cit.,* p. 853.

in Boxers, German Shepherds and Poodles. Given as among the causes for this deterioration in canine structure of performance are the high prices paid for pedigreed dogs, *the large number of "amateur" breeders and their reluctance to cull poor specimens, and a lack of understanding of the principles of breeding*.[1] The inventory of abnormalities is causing such concern among responsible breeders that the British Kennel Club has asked the British Small Animal Veterinary Associations to make a survey and report on the existing situation.[2]

2. *To have a puppy*

While this is a proper motive, it should be combined with reason 1: "To improve the breed".

A person who breeds solely to have a puppy may follow improper breeding practices and thereby adversely and seriously affect the breed. The damage which he will have done will remain with us for many years. At some time in the future, someone may innocently mate his good hound with a descendant of the poorly bred one which appears to be equally good, but which may have either a vicious or a shy temperament, or which may be carrying a defect as a recessive. It will be much more difficult than now to breed properly: all Irish Wolfhounds will be suspect. This has happened in other breeds. For example, when German Shepherds became popular, many persons bred without regard to breeding principles. As a result, one sees today Shepherds of poor temperament and hip dysplasia is prevalent among members of that breed.

Many persons who breed for the sole reason that they wish a puppy will often find that they are unable to sell the other puppies in the litter at the prices charged by regular breeders. They may lower the price or they may give the puppies away; many of the dogs go into homes where they are not properly taken care of; many are bred improperly. The stud owner should hold himself partially responsible for the proper disposition of a litter. Breeders should be prepared to keep the entire litter if necessary.

The individual who has a bitch and who desires a puppy should consider whether it might not be preferable to buy one. Puppies demand considerable time if they are to develop properly. There are also many expenses connected with the mating, the gestation period, the whelping and postnatal care of dam and puppies. Not

---

[1]Italics mine.

[2]Gaines Nutrition Center, "Inherited Defects Study," *Gaines Dog Research Progress* (Summer, 1963). The referenced survey will be found in Appendix A of this book.

all bitches are desirable as dams, not all males are desirable as studs. Breeding of inferior stock lowers the average quality of the breed. Contrary to the opinions of many, it is not essential to the welfare of the bitch that she have a litter.

3. *To make money*

Unless this objective is coupled to the first — "To improve the breed" — it is reprehensible. All the bad features involved in breeding only for a puppy (Objective 2) are present here, plus many others.

Usually, the derogatory term "puppy mill" is used to designate an enterprise involved in the production or sale of puppies where the primary, if not the sole, consideration is profits. It can be equally applied to individuals who disregard the *Guidelines for Owners and Breeders* reproduced in this chapter.

Puppy mills are numerous. No one should ever buy from one. The only persons who do so are either unaware that it is a malignancy or are unconcerned about humaneness towards animals. There can be considerable variance in the degree of reprehensibility of puppy mill management. For example, there is the honest citizen who owns an Irish Wolfhound bitch and who would like to be looked upon as active in the breed but who is unaware of the qualities and defects of hounds; he will request the services of a stud dog whom he has never seen and with whose lineage he is unacquainted. Puppies will be placed in good homes but if they are superior in quality to their parents it is mere chance. In my view, this is a puppy mill as the main objective has not been to improve the breed and measures to this end have not been taken. One should also approach with caution those *unqualified* breeders who breed "to have a puppy," or "to provide an experience for the children."

How does one recognize a puppy mill? I shall describe the worst kind imaginable, but please bear in mind that it is not necessary that all the following elements be present to justify the onerous title:

● Breeder is not thoroughly acquainted with the Standard of Excellence, or, if he is, is unable to apply the criteria to actual hounds. Therefore his breeding is unlikely to improve the breed.

● Breeder is unacquainted with the lineage of the stud and bitch. Even if he has this knowledge, his ignorance of genetic principles will most likely not result in improvement of the breed.

● The bitch has serious hereditary defects and is either extremely shy or vicious. The puppies will inherit these faults.

● The bitch is confined to a small cage in an unhealthful environment so that she suffers both physically and emotionally. She is allowed insufficient exercise. She is not fed an adequate and balanced diet. Results will be evident in the puppies.

● The bitch is physically abused by the breeder or others. Loud noises or high-pitched excitement are routine. She has neither other canines to play with or humans with whom she can reciprocate affection. The bitch and her puppies will be affected.

● Breeder's purpose in breeding is solely to make money. He is likely to breed a proven stud with the bitch who normally has the largest litters in order to increase his revenue. To obviate criticism of too frequent breeding or improper breeding, he will certify that the parents were other hounds of his. Under these circumstances, the owners of the puppies will be unsure of how to breed properly.

● The bitch may be left with several males so that the actual sire (or sires) is unknown.

● The stud dog selected is the nearest available; one whose stud fee is lowest; one who has serious hereditary physical and temperamental defects. He may have the same faults as the bitch thus reinforcing these in the progeny. Or he may be an outstanding dog, whose owner is more interested in a stud fee than in the welfare of the breed and therefore becomes, to a certain extent, a partner in the puppy mill operation. One, or even two, outstanding parents is not a guarantee of a quality litter. The pedigrees and the qualities and faults of the dogs themselves must be examined.

● The stud dog or bitch may be ill or diseased.

● The bitch may be in her first season or extremely old. The stud dog or the bitch, not having been examined by a veterinarian, may harbor the virus causing viremia resulting in either death of the puppies or kidney damage to them. The bitch may have been bred at every season. Her general condition may be thus weakened and her puppies may be similarly weak and susceptible to disease. Whelping may be extremely painful to her because of some obstruction.

● The actual mating is done haphazardly with the possibility of injuries to both animals, e.g. biting, pulling away prematurely after a tie.

● No written record is maintained of the mating so that, intentionally or not, the pedigrees may be erroneous.

● When the bitch is in whelp, she is not checked for parasites or wormed, or she is wormed late in her pregnancy so that the puppies are to some extent, poisoned. She is not fed an adequate balanced diet for a bitch in gestation for reasons of economy. She is not allowed to exercise in moderation.

● As the date for whelping approaches, the bitch is either left alone in her small cage or surrounded and harassed by other canines to her great distress. She may be cruelly treated by humans. Environmental influences will affect both the bitch and her puppies. See Index at Environmental influences.

● The whelping area may be unsanitary. The bitch, confined to her pen, may be unable to walk off her restlessness. She will be mentally distraught.

● The dam may give birth, without human supervision, in extreme heat or cold or exposure to rain, snow, or drafts. Environmental influences may affect her mentally and the puppies' temperament will also become poor. Complications may arise causing her death or that of the puppies or, at least, great pain. A veterinarian may not be summoned because of the cost. The breeder figures his losses in financial terms not in terms of canine suffering.

● The puppies' toe nails will not be cut, causing greater pain to the dam. Her breasts will not be properly massaged to alleviate pain. She will be kept confined with the puppies and be subjected to continuous harassment from them.

● The breeder will let the puppies suffer without calling a veterinarian (to save expenses) and hope that they live although, if they do, they will be deficient in health.

● At an early age, he may sell the puppies (possibly not weaned or barely so) without having them wormed, immunized, or checked by a veterinarian for any ailments. The reason for early sales is to avoid expenses of feeding and care and to reduce transportation costs since Irish Wolfhound puppies grow very rapidly.

● Since he wishes to sell puppies when very young, the breeder is not concerned with the effect on dam and puppies of early separation. Nor is he concerned with the qualifications of purchasers as providers of a good home. He may sell to pet shops, to wholesalers who resell to department stores and pet shops, to individuals for resale, or to individuals for personal ownership. If the puppy is particularly bad or if the breeder is unable to dispose of his "merchandise," he may sell the puppies for scientific research.

● Pet shops and persons who buy for resale want to buy young puppies so that, if there is some delay in reselling, the dogs won't have lost their puppy appeal. They import dogs as young as 5 weeks of age. Torn from their dam and littermates, they undergo a severe traumatic experience. Within the United States, puppies are shipped without provision of food, water or shelter in flimsy crates stacked in trucks that travel thousands of miles.

● Pet shops and other such dealers have no areas within which the dogs can run. They are kept cooped up with the result that, as shown by scientific studies, their intelligence, personality and stature are retarded. See Index at Confinement. This is cruelty. It also conveys to the owners the mistaken belief that Irish Wolfhounds are inordinately shy and stupid. The puppies are often kept in cages at a window where the sun's rays strike them directly. They are exposed to diseases of the other animals in the shop. All of this adds up to the fact that often the dogs sold are sick, infirm, diseased. Many soon die even after expensive veterinarian treatment undertaken by the new owner. The pet shop may have a "guarantee" in which case the buyer is entitled to another sick, infirm, and diseased dog or a cringing hound or a vicious one if the pet shop is still in business. Often, the new owner has become attached to the purchased puppy and will keep it out of pity and affection. Returned dogs are often shipped back to the breeder thereby increasing the suffering of the unfortunate puppy.

● Pet shops and other of similar ilk mark up the prices 100% so that buyers pay about the same price as they would for a sound, healthy, and typical Irish Wolfhound from a reputable breeder. The seller knows nothing about the Standard of Excellence, the lineage of the puppies, their qualities and faults, how they were initially cared for and what the care should now be. Therefore, the buyer can learn nothing from him. The reputable breeder, on the other hand, does not feel that his responsibilities cease with the sale. He informs the buyer of the breed's characteristics and of its proper care. He recommends books on the Irish Wolfhound. He is always available to answer questions long after the sale has been made.

● Pet shops are not interested in the conditions under which the puppy will be brought up. Pay the price and you own the dog.

● They may donate a puppy to the sponsor of a contest and the puppy becomes a chattel to be owned by someone who, by lack of knowledge or by bad character, is not a good master.

● Disreputable breeders make use of false or misleading advertisements. See Index at Advertisement.

Please do not labor under the misapprehension that a puppy mill must have *all* the above attributes. These represent the worst possible cases. A kind, loving person may operate a puppy mill merely by breeding without proper qualifications or by reason of an agreement whereby he must return one or more litters to the former owner of the dam. For details on puppy mill operations, the cruelties involved, and proposed legislation, write to The Humane Society of the United States, 1604 K St., N.W., Washington, D.C. 20006.

One interesting operation is that of a Japanese company which pays high prices abroad for Champion dogs of all breeds and above average prices for non-Champion bitches. The bitches are given to persons in Japan with the understanding that the company and the new owner will engage in a breeding program whereby the company selects the stud, determines the breeding schedule and is entitled to all puppies until the purchase price of $400 to $500 is paid at the rate of 5% of the purchase price per puppy, e.g. if the purchase price were $500, the company would allow $25 per puppy. In effect, the buyer must breed his bitch until he can give 20 of her puppies to the company before he owns her. The keeper of the bitch must buy all his dog food from the company. The female puppies that result from the breeding are placed in homes under similar agreements. Male puppies are sold for cash. Champion males purchased abroad are sold under a plan whereby the purchaser has three years to pay. During this period, the company furnishes free food and medical care for the dog but the company uses him as a stud whenever it wishes. It is obvious that this breeding program is not intended to improve the breed. The company, for financial reasons, must breed the nearest male to the nearest female regardless of genetic considerations; it must breed often without regard to the condition of the bitch; it cannot bother with the problems of selecting only the best homes for the puppies.

There are reputable persons who lease bitches to other persons either because they do not have the time to care properly for the dam and her puppies or because they consider it too great an inconvenience. In these cases, the lessees and not the owners of the dam are known as the breeders. When the bitch is due to whelp, she is sent to the kennel of the lessee. While this is perfectly legal, just as it is to sell a dog which a person has owned for many years, I, and I believe most dog owners, could not bring themselves to allow a dam to bring forth puppies in any environment other than the home to which she has become attached, because of the mental anguish involved. I would strongly condemn the leasing of a bitch if the purpose of the lessor is to make money.

Should a person purchase an Irish Wolfhound from a person or organization out of pity—to prevent further abuse of the animal? While it may seem heartless to say so, I would recommend that this not ordinarily be done. By buying the hound, you will be encouraging the owner to obtain more for resale and you will thus be compounding the problem and increasing the number of hounds who will suffer. An exception might be made if the cruel owner just happened to have one Irish Wolfhound and would not be likely to get more.

Some Irish Wolfhound Clubs have a Welfare Program manned by volunteers who agree to pick up Irish Wolfhounds who are strays, who are impounded by the Dog Warden, or who are no longer wanted by their owners. The Irish Wolfhound Association of the West Coast asks these questions of its members:

1. Can you pick up and deliver a hound?

2. Approximately how many miles can you reasonably travel to pick up a dog?

3. Can you take the dog to a Veterinarian if necessary (with Welfare Fund reimbursement)?

4. Can the dog be temporarily isolated from other pets or children?

5. How many days are you willing to care for a dog before it is placed in a permanent home?

6. Can you care for a convalescing dog (surgery, etc.)?

7. Are there any additional conditions you would like to have considered? Please explain.

How does one embark on a proper breeding program? The first requirement is to know the breed thoroughly. A beginner might start out by purchasing a good bitch, training her and showing her. By experience, by discussion with other breeders and by reading books and magazines on genetics and other matters briefly covered in this book such as the Standard of Excellence, he will be ready to begin. He will breed his bitch according to approved principles. The best one or two puppy bitches are retained. If only one, get a related bitch either by purchase or by another breeding to assure uniformity of stock and to guard against the possibility that disease or accident may end the strain begun with only one bitch. Males are appealing particularly because of their impressive size, but generally it is less expensive to operate a kennel by breeding to outside studs. However, if an outstanding male appears in a litter, it may be wise to keep him.

One breeder, with an outstanding record, has said on several occasions: "Breeding is an art, not a science. You cannot breed dogs by computers." It is true that breeding dogs is an art. The breeder and the show ring judge must both have an artistic objective in considering type, expression, etc. While it would be theoretically possible to make dog breeding a purely scientific endeavor and to have a computer make the calculations, it would be impossible as a practical matter. One must first remember that a computer is merely a very rapid calculating machine with the capability of storing data for future use. It cannot reason. If the product of its operations is "garbage", it is usually because a human being either has fed it erroneous data or has given it erroneous instructions. Let us consider all the difficulties that would exist were one to attempt to "breed dogs by computer" and thus make it purely a science. One would first have to place mathematical values on every portion of the dog's body. For example, one might say that the ideal relationship of head length to width would be 2 to 1 at the zygomatic arch, 3 to 1 at the carnassials, 5 to 1 at the canines. Then one would have to establish the proper proportion of the head with relation to the rest of the body. One would have to establish degrees of angulation, etc. Deductions would have to be made for variations from these standards. Then one would have to give relative weights to each item. What is the weight to be given to head as compared to forelegs, etc? A device would have to be created to judge whether the dog's movements were perfectly aligned or not, etc. Now it is obvious that the requirements are absolutely ridiculous. Even if they were not, one could never get a group of persons to agree on the proper proportions and the weights to be assigned.

I think we can therefore say with assurance that breeding dogs for the show ring is not an exact science, and that esthetics and judgment play important parts. I also think that we can say with equal assurance that breeding dogs for the show ring is not pure art and that one must also consider genetics. I do not think it is necessary for me to defend the well-known (and some less well-understood) principles of heredity. Cattle breeders follow genetic principles. So do the breeders of racing horses and many others. It is because of recent advances in the field of genetics that scientists are able to determine the presence of some defective genes and that attempts are now being made to eliminate or alleviate the effects. Genetics is the subject of the next chapter. At this point, all we shall do is look at dog breeding with a view of developing certain statistics. Statistics can be helpful. For example, they may show that fertility in one breed is not as great as in another, that one breed has greater puppy mortality than another, etc. These facts then become the subject of study to determine, first, the probable causes of the conditions and, then, the corrective action to be taken.

Unfortunately, there are very little data on Irish Wolfhound breeding programs. We are therefore forced to consider those of other breeds as well. Out interest lies in the probabilities in the following areas:

1. Fertility.
2. Litter size.
3. Live whelps.
4. Survival of live whelps.
5. Sex ratio.

The Ralston Purina Company has bred twelve to fifteen different breeds of dogs at its Research Farm near Gray Summit, Missouri, since 1925 resulting in almost 15,000 whelps. Dr. James Corbin, its director of research, has been most cooperative in providing me with much of the data which I shall now present.

1. *Fertility*

Infertility in dogs is influenced by many factors: genetics, age, physical condition, nutrition, time of mating, change of climate. Infertility is a problem with other animals as well. For example, only half of the breeding of horses is successful.[1] Dr. James Corbin wrote:

> The probability of barrenness in a bitch varies from kennel to kennel, with females from kennels where bitches are overfed with both total food intake and supplements having a poor conception rate. Well fed, exercised bitches will have a high conception rate. Less than 10% of bitches can be expected to be barren. We found this applicable to our females, those in kennels associated with us, and reports in the literature.[2] The major reason that bitches fail to conceive is a low grade infection. Other reasons are vaginal tumors, ovarian cysts and tumors, and pyometria.[3]

---

[1] *Morris Animal Foundation Newsletter* (May, 1968).

[2] James Corbin, Ralston Purina Company, *Letter to author* (November 5, 1965).

[3] *Id.* Quoted in "Collies," American Kennel Club, *Pure-Bred Dogs—American Kennel Gazette* (November, 1970), LXXXVII.

Studies conducted over a period of four years at the School of Veterinary Medicine, University of California, Davis, California, have provided very interesting data.[1] 234 litters consisting of 1,157 Beagle puppies were whelped. Dams and puppies received normal, not special, care. The ideal age for breeding was found to be 3 years. At that age, the estrous cycle was 6 months as compared to 8 or more months when the dam was over 4 years of age. The 3 year olds were more fecund, whereas those over 4 failed to conceive in one-third of the cases. Both these groups spent a minimum of time in "nesting". The 1 to 2 year olds delayed whelping by several hours while they prepared their whelping place. From the onset of labor to complete whelping the three year olds consumed less than 4 hours; those over 4 years required 8 to 12 hours. 3 year old dams whelped most easily.

When asked a number of questions, Dr. Corbin replied:

> We have no idea as to the percentage of males that are sterile but it will probably be less than 2 or 3% of the males. Male sterility depends on previous bouts with distemper, hepatitis, leptospirosis, brucellosis, and on how the stud is housed and used. We know that a male housed continuously in a hot apartment would more than likely become sterile, since he would not have a chance to keep cool as he would even in the summer when he could get down on the ground or concrete and have a high heat transfer to the ground. In olden days it was a custom with both man and animals to wrap the scrotum with some good insulating material to create sterility. In the summer our rabbits at our farm would frequently become sterile when they could not get down on the cool concrete; by placing them in a cool environment, their fertility could be improved or restored. The use of a male also influences his fertility level. The accumulation of semen in the Cowper's gland tends to deteriorate and unless the male ejaculates each week to ten days, it is entirely possible for him to remain "effectively" sterile. The most fertile males are those that are used several times a week.[2]

However, Dr. Corbin has also said that a stud dog may have "misses" if used too young, or too often, or if he has an infection.[3] Note also the following comment by Stephen J. Field:

> Young studs should not be overworked. It may not necessarily lower their sperm count to the danger point, but their ambi-

---

[1]A. C. Andersen, "Puppy Production to the Weaning Age," *Journal of the American Veterinary Medical Association* (February 15, 1957) CXXX, pp. 151-158.

[2]Corbin, *Letter to author* (November 25, 1966).

[3]Corbin. Quoted in "Collies," *op. cit.*

tion may sometimes be injurious to health, cause extreme lack of flesh and condition due to loss of appetite and fretting. I have frequently tested yearling males just shedding coat and recently off a show circuit and both by sperm count and proven results found many to be of low fertility—but not completely sterile—for a few months. Such males are usually restored to high fertility again by a good diet and rest—possibly vitamin supplements.

I have observed many cases of high sperm count in males under 10 months of age and also in males well over the usual life span. Likewise I have observed some low sperm counts in dogs in the prime of life and apparently in full bloom and vigor. Discovery of a few active sperm cells does not prove the stud to be fertile. Nor does failure to find any active sperm at one examination necessarily mean that the male may not at a later date become highly fertile and able to sire pups. This is especially so if steps are taken to improve his general physical condition.

This article should not result in shifting blame for all misses onto the stud. In reality, quite the contrary. If the dog sired litters the month before and the month after, the blame for a miss should lie with the bitch, or possibly breeding at the wrong time—usually too early.[1]

In a paper presented by A. E. Harrop of the Royal Veterinary College, University of London, at the 1968 British Small Animal Congress, it was reported that, of 200 infertile dogs examined, no reasons could be found for the infertility of 169.

Eleven had never been fertile, 158 were proven stud dogs which had become sterile. In some cases the onset of infertility had been gradual, but in the majority it had occurred suddenly. The history, in almost all cases, was similar. The dog, having been put to stud at about 10-12 months of age, served only a few bitches during the first year, in the meantime gained recognition in the show ring and as a result the frequency of use markedly increased.

The dogs had been fertile until reaching an average age of about 3½ years. Seventy-seven per cent of the bitches served by them conceived at their next heat when served by another sire, which demonstrated a satisfactory fertility rate in the bitches. It is interesting to note that all 158 dogs continued to serve willingly and without any inhibitions.[2]

---

[1] Stephen J. Field, "The Stud Dog, Too, Needs Management," *Gaines Dog Research Progress* (Fall, 1958).

[2] A. E. Harrop. *Journal of Small Animal Practice.* Quoted in "Infertility of the Male Dog," *Gaines Dog Research Progress* (Spring, 1967).

Fred J. Kingma relates another person's experience:

> An interesting, if difficult-to-explain cause of temporary sterility, is that reported by Huggins. It was noted that male dogs brought into his institution for research purposes invariably showed semen devoid of spermatozoa beginning within 8 to 60 days after confinement in cages. The return of spermatozoa in the semen occurred after the animals had been confined for a period of four months or longer. Treatment with male hormones did not prevent this condition. Increasing the amount of exercise, however, shortened the duration of the period of sterility.[1]

Purina reports:

> More than 90% of the matings made in the population of our kennel are successful, i.e. result in conception. These include:
>
> 1. New breeding stock raised from puppies on up.
>
> 2. Normal producers that have been having litters all along.
>
> 3. Old dogs that for one reason or another we want to continue to obtain litters from.[2]

Patricia Huntley (Balingary Kennel, Sepulveda, California) has obtained data from reputable Irish Wolfhound breeders who had two or more litters from August, 1965, to September, 1970. During this period, there were twenty-six successful breedings and seven unsuccessful, i.e., 79% of the attempted breedings were successful.

All of the hounds, both dogs and bitches, which were unsuccessfully mated had either already been proven or were proven later, except for one bitch who died at an early age. The following table indicates that a tie is not proof that a litter will be produced. It

UNSUCCESSFUL IRISH WOLFHOUND BREEDINGS

Proven		Tie	No Tie	Total
Dog	Bitch			
Yes	Yes	1	1	2
Yes	No	1	3	4
No	Yes	0	1	1
No	No	0	0	0
Total		2	5	7

---

[1] Fred J. Kingma, "Factors in Canine Sterility and Fertility," *Gaines Dog Research Progress* (Winter, 1952-1953).

[2] Corbin, *Letter to author* (November 25, 1966).

is equally true that a litter may be whelped even though a tie has not occurred. Data to show the probability of this outcome are not available to me at this time.

2. *Litter Size*

Field writes: "It has been well established that litter size is mostly determined by factors relating to the bitch. However, this phase of the topic is in need of additional research."[1]

According to Corbin:

> Litter size is dependent on:
> 1. The breed of the dog.
> 2. The size of the dog.
> 3. The strain of the dog.
> 4. The number of litters that a bitch has had.
> 5. Many other factors.
>
> Some of the top breeds tend to have 3, 4 and 5 puppies and this will also apply to some of the miniatures. Our larger breeds of dogs range from 6 to 12.[2]

The experiences of some breeders are set forth in the next table.

Breeder	Breed	Period	Number of Litters	Number of Puppies	Average Number of Puppies per Litter
Purina Dog Research Division[3]	12-15 different breeds	1956-1970	1,173	8,594	7.3
University of California[4]	Beagles	1951-1955	234	1,157	4.9
Mrs. Maurie G. Prager[5]	English Cocker Spaniels	1948-1964	56	331	5.9
Mrs. Leon C. Johnson[6]	Dachshunds	1937-1965	127	578	4.6
Evelyn Bryan[7]	Shetland Sheepdogs	1960-1965	20	83	4.2
Various[8] (Patricia Huntley, compiler)	Irish Wolfhounds	1965-1970	26	159	6.1
Various[9]	Irish Wolfhounds	1972-1975	1,220	5,318	4.4

[1]Field, *op. cit.*

[2]Corbin. *Letter to author* (November 25, 1966).

[3]*Ibid.*

[4]School of Veterinary Medicine, University of California, Davis, California, as reported by A.C. Andersen, *op. cit.*, pp. 151, 155. Number of puppies given as "whelped" were those whelped alive. Number of stillborn not given.

[5]Of "On Time Farm," Middle Valley, New Jersey. *Gaines Dog Research Progress* (Winter, 1963-1964).

[6]Leonca, Cygnet, Ohio. *Ibid.* (Spring, 1965). Standards had larger litters than miniatures.

[7]Meridel Kennels, Pearland, Texas. *Ibid.*

[8]Patricia Huntley. *Letter to author* (August 5, 1971).

[9]American Kennel Club records of litters and puppies *registered*. This is not a record of all the puppies in the litters.

The study on Miss Delphis Gardner's kennels reported one hundred and eighty-nine Irish Wolfhounds whelped alive from 1927 to 1945 (See Index at Gardner, Delphis). There were forty-nine litters, twenty-four consisting of one puppy and twenty-five being multiple births of from two to twelve puppies. The mean of multiple birth litters was 6.6 puppies. The mean of all litters was 3.9 puppies as shown here.[1]

	Number of Litters	Puppies			Average Number of Puppies per Litter
		Dogs	Bitches	Total	
Single births	24	8	16	24	1
Multiple births	25	86	79	165	6.6
Total	49	94	95	189	3.9

Unlike the data from Miss Gardner, Pat Huntley's figure of 159 puppies includes both those whelped alive and those who were born dead. All births were multiple. The respective numbers of dogs and bitches were: 75-84.

The largest litter of Irish Wolfhounds of which I am aware was one of nineteen in England.[2] There was one of seventeen in the United States.[3] As in all breeds, older dams produce fewer young per litter. R. Portman Graham believes that the progeny of old dams degenerate.[4]

Dr. Corbin comments: "Size of breed does not seem to be a factor in the mortality of the number born dead."[5] Pat Huntley informs me that, of the three Irish Wolfhounds listed as being born dead, two were large puppies and died in a forceps delivery. Seven puppies died later in the week: 3 of infection, 1 stepped on by dam, 2 culled as too small, 1 culled because of birth defect.

Pat Huntley comments that if one were to add the experiences of single litter breeders to the figures she provided, the Irish Wolfhound puppy mortality rate would undoubtedly be greater if for no other reason than the inexperience of the breeders.

---

[1] Comfort, "Longevity and Mortality of Irish Wolfhounds," *op. cit.*, p. 31.

[2] April 29, 1926. Sire: Chivalry Boy of Grevel. Dam: Thora of Ifold. Pat Huntley refers to *OUR DOGS*, December, 1926, as the source. She notes that the article erroneously calls the sire Chivalry of Grevel and she adds that only ten of the litter were registered.

[3] May 20, 1967. Sire: Ch. Balbrigan of Balingary. Dam: Finisk of Eagle. Breeder: Donna Turman. One puppy died on the third day when stepped upon by the dam. All others survived.

[4] R. Portman Graham, *The Mating and Welphing of Dogs* (1954), pp. 42, 44.

[5] Corbin, *Letter to author* (November 25, 1966).

3. *Live Whelps*

Breeder	Breed	Period	Number Puppies Born	Number of Puppies Born Alive	Percentage of Puppies Born Alive
Purina Dog Research Division[1]	12-15 different breeds	1956-1970	8,594	8,159	94.9
Mrs. Maurie G. Prager[2]	English Cocker Spaniels	1948-1964	331	320	96.7
Mrs. Leon C. Johnson[3]	Dachshunds	1937-1965	578	534	92.4
Evelyn Bryan[4]	Shetland Sheepdogs	1960-1965	83	71	85.5
Starberry Kennels[5]	Collies	1958-1964	251	241	96.0
Various[10] (Pat Huntley, compiler)	Irish Wolfhounds	1964-1970	159	156	98.1
In England[11]	Mixed	Five years	—	—	95.4

4. *Survival of Live Whelps*

Breeder	Breed	Period	Number of Puppies Born Alive	Number of Puppies Weaned	Percentage Weaned of those Born Alive
Purina Dog Research Division[1]	12-15 different breeds	1956-1970	8,159	7,444	91.2
Mrs. Maurie G. Prager[2]	English Cocker Spaniels	1948-1964	320	289	90.3
Mrs. Leon C. Johnson[6]	Dachshunds	1937-1965	534	484	90.6
Evelyn Bryan[7]	Shetland Sheepdogs	1960-1965	71	60	84.5
Starberry Kennels[5]	Collies	1958-1964	241	220	91.3
Mrs. Alice Reiss[8]	Chiefly Dachshunds	1958-1965	223	209	93.7
University of California[9]	Beagles	1951-1955	1,157	816	70.5
Various[6,10] (Pat Huntley, compiler)	Irish Wolfhounds	1965-1970	156	149	95.5
In England[7,11]	Mixed	Five years	—	—	67.0

---

[1]Corbin, *Letter to author* (November 25, 1966).

[2]*Gaines Dog Research Progress* (Winter, 1963-1964).

[3]*Ibid* (Spring, 1965). Standards had lower mortality rate than miniatures.

[4]*Ibid.*

[5]*Ibid.* In Southbury, Conn.

[6]*Ibid.* Deaths listed as occurring "within two weeks."

[7]*Ibid.* Deaths listed as occurring "later."

[8]*Ibid.* Kimball, Nebraska. Deaths listed as occurring "after birth."

[9]A.C. Andersen, *op. cit.*, pp. 151-158.

[10]Patricia Huntley, *Letter to author* (August 5, 1971).

[11]Cornell Research Laboratory for Diseases of Dogs, Cornell University, *Laboratory Report,* Series 2, No. 4 (May 1, 1974).

Based on a survey in various portions of the world, it has been estimated that about one-third of puppies born alive die by weaning age, i.e. by 6 weeks, and that most deaths occur within the first two weeks of life.[1] Naturally, the first week is the most critical.[2]

According to an advertisement of the Purina Dog Research Division, the average of puppies whelped alive throughout the United States who survive through weaning is between 50% and 70%, with 80% considered good. Referring to the activities of his organization, Dr. Corbin said:

> Approximately 4.5% to 5% of the puppies born in well-organized kennels are born dead or die within the first hour or so. This is generally caused by non-specific mortality, crushing by the bitch, suffocation because of the placental membrane, clearance failure, and from chilling. Our kennel normally is in operation from 8:00 in the morning until 5:00 at night. Since our fellows work during these hours, any puppies that are whelped during the night and die before the fellows see them at 8 o'clock are considered born dead . . . Loss of pups after weaning at 6 weeks is almost unknown.[3]

A Cornell Research Laboratory study concluded that the percentage of puppy losses gradually diminished as the bitch approached the age of three and gradually increased after she became 4 years old.[4] In the Davis California, study,[5] 70.5% of puppies whelped alive were weaned. The percentage in the case of puppies from three-year old dams was 80%. Dystocia, i.e. difficult birth, was also very rare in the case of the 3 year olds. 341 puppies, or 29.4%, died before they were 6 weeks of age. The causes of death and the number of puppies involved were:

Dams default (dystocia, carelessness, excessive licking, lactation failure, cannibalism)	105
Stillbirth	53
Exposure (heat and cold)	51
Malformation (fissue abdominal-thoracic, adactylia, facial cleft, rectal prolapse, mummified fetus)	30

---

[1] Dr. J. E. Mosier, "Puppy Diseases Involving Litter Problems," *Gaines Dog Research Progress* (Summer, 1970).

[2] Cornell, *op. cit.*

[3] Corbin, *Letter to author* (June 9, 1966).

[4] Cornell, *op. cit.*

[5] A.C. Andersen, *op. cit.*, pp. 151-158.

Disease	29
Undetermined	28
Accidents	20
Parasites	9

Percentages of losses of both sexes by periods were:

Birth to 24 hours	37.0%
1st week	28.1%
2nd week	10.0%
3rd week	6.1%
4th week	4.7%
5th week (weaned)	14.1%
	100%

Percentage of litters whelped, of puppies whelped, and of puppies weaned by season are shown in the next table, as well as the mortality by season.

Season	Litters	Puppies Whelped	Puppies Weaned	Mortality
Spring	33%	33%	34%	28%
Summer	26%	26%	26%	29%
Fall	19%	19%	17%	34%
Winter	22%	22%	23%	29%

The above table shows that, in this experiment, the average number of puppies in a litter was the same regardless of the season, i.e., five, and that mortality was highest in the fall.

5. Sex Ratio

A study of German Shepherds revealed that the percentage of male puppies was 53.2 in litters of one to eight puppies, and 52.2 in litters of nine or more. The number of males began to decrease when the dams became five years old[1]

According to the Handbook of Biological Data, males among German Shepherds number 55.0%, Terriers 56.0%, dogs of various breeds 51.0% to 54.0%[2] Whitney observed a 55.4 percentage among

---

[1]John L. Fuller, "Dog Genetics," *Gaines Dog Research Progress* (Summer, 1961).

[2]*Handbook of Biological Data.* Edited by W. S. Spector (1956), p. 519.

1,440 puppies of breeds not stated.[1] Pat Huntley's data show that 47.2% of the 156 Irish Wolfhounds whelped were males. Miss Gardner's data show 49.7% of the 189 live Irish Wolfhound whelps were male. Obviously, registration data are entirely different from whelping data but, as a matter of interest, 53% of the 3,080 Irish Wolfhounds registered in the United States through 1964 were males.

In the Davis, California, study 54% of the puppies who were dead at birth or within twenty-four hours were males.[2] Mortality of young males is usually greater than that of females.

I strongly urge that Appendix A be read. It includes reports by The World Small Animal Veterinary Association, The British Veterinary Association and The Kennel Club (Britain) on hereditary defects and on temperamental and physical requirements imposed by the Standards of Excellence which have deleterious effects on dogs. In view of the fact that these requirements, in effect, result in pain or susceptibility to injury, disease and physical discomfort, one would think that dog lovers would seek to change the Standards of Excellence. This is possibly too much to expect since, in many cases, the appearance of the breed would be entirely changed. The breeds listed below are those named in the critical reports:

Airedale Terrier
Alaskan Malamute
Australian Terrier
Basset Hound
Beagle
Bedlington Terrier
Bloodhound
Boston Terrier
Boxer
Bull Terrier
Bulldog
Bullmastiff
Cairn Terrier
Chihuahua
Chow Chow
Collie
Dachshund
Dalmatian
Dandie Dinmont Terrier

Doberman Pinscher
English Setter
English Toy Terrier
Finnish Spitz
Fox Terrier
French Bulldog
German Shepherd
Griffon (Brussels)
Irish Terrier
Japanese Spaniel
Karelian Bear Dog
Keeshond
Manchester Terrier
Mastiff
Newfoundland
Norwegian "Buhund"
Norwegian Elkhound
Pekingese
Pomeranian

---

[1]Hutt, *op. cit.*, p. 443.
[2]A. C. Andersen, *op. cit.*, pp. 151-158.

Poodle
Pug
Retriever (Golden)
Retriever (Labrador)
Rhodesian Ridgeback
Rottweiler
St. Bernard
Schipperke
Scottish Terrier
Shih Tzu
Spaniel (Cavalier King Charles)

Spaniel (Clumber)
Spaniel (Cocker)
Spaniel (English Springer)
Spaniel (Irish Water)
Spaniel (King Charles)
Swedish "Lapphund"
Tibetan Terrier
Weimaraner
Welsh Corgi
Welsh Terrier
Wirehaired Fox Terrier

C. GENETICS

Our knowledge of genetics dates back to the studies of an Austrian monk, Gregor Johann Mendel, who taught science in the high school at Brunn (now Brno, Czechoslovakia). They were published in 1865 but ignored by the world. Mendel was promoted to abbot of the monastery and was forced by his administrative duties to forgo further studies on inheritance. Thirty-four years later, after Mendel's death, his experiments and theories were again made known to the scientific community.

The subject of genetics is very complicated. There are very few people who are really experts in this field. Those who are thus qualified continually make discoveries which are featured in the daily press as well as in scientific journals. This section is merely an exposition, as simple, clear, and elementary as I can make it, of some of the principles and theories.

Genetics involves the inheritance of characteristics. A puppy derives all of his physical, mental and temperamental characteristics from his parents. This is done by the transmission of genes, half from the sire, half from the dam. They determine his sex, size, coat, color, the proportion of each part of the body to the rest, his intelligence and temperament.

Color, in an animal, is a qualitative character. Rather than begin with the acquisition of color in dogs—a more complex case—let us take as the *parental generation* a black and white Holstein-Friesian bull (whose characteristics are such that he cannot sire red calves) and a red cow (who is of Holstein-Friesian stock even though she can't be called Holstein-Friesian since these, by definition, must be black and white). Each animal has a pair of genes which determine color. We will use the second letter of the alphabet to show these. A capital letter (B) indicates that the gene is dominant, one in lower case (b) that the gene is recessive. When a dominant gene is allied with a recessive, the inheritor of these two displays only the dominant characteristic. It has been determined that black is dominant to red, so B will indicate black and b will indicate red. In our first matrix, the bull is *pure* for black, i.e. both of his genes are black (BB). The cow is *pure* for red, i.e. both of her genes are red (bb). It is apparent that, regardless of which gene of the bull is allied with those of the cow, all the calves (called F 1, i.e. the *first filial generation*) will possess both a dominant and a recessive gene (Bb) but will exhibit only the dominant characteristic (B). In other words, the calves will not be *pure* for color like their parents but will be hybrids. Their *genotype* will be Bb, but their *phenotype* (outward appearance) will be B, i.e. black.[1]

Bull

		B	B
	b	Bb	Bb
Cow			
	b	Bb	Bb

Now let us breed one of these progeny to another to get the *second filial generation* (F 2).

Bull

		B	b
	B	BB	Bb
Cow			
	b	Bb	bb

It can be seen that one calf is *pure* for black (BB), one is *pure* for red (bb) and two are hybrid (Bb). It can also be seen that three out of the four are black (BB, Bb, Bb) and the other is red (bb). Mendel's first law was that if the parents have contrasting characters, their offspring will show either one or the other, but not both. If the offspring are interbred, the characters will reappear in a 3 to 1 ratio with the dominant being the more numerous. This proportion, of course, is an average. That is, the probability of a calf being red is

---

[1] The forms of two genes possessed by an individual or the characters which they produce are called alleles. Germ cells that unite in fertilization are called gametes; their union results in a cell called zygote. If the genes are the same (e.g. BB or bb), then the animal is homozygous, otherwise heterozygous.

25%. It does not mean that if four calves are born, one will necessarily be red and that three will necessarily be black.

We know, by looking at the red calf, that his genotype is bb. But one cannot tell by looking at the F 2 calves which are BB and which are Bb. They all appear black, i.e. they all have the same phenotype although a different genotype. The only way we can determine whether there is a recessive is by breeding. The fastest way of doing this (at least for cattle which usually have only one calf per breeding) is to breed the black (that we want to check) with a red. If we bred black to black, we might have any of the following situations:

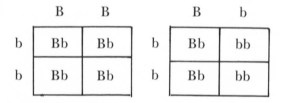

Probability of a red:

       0%   0%   25%

If we bred the black to a red, one of the two following situations would exist:

	B	B
b	Bb	Bb
b	Bb	Bb

	B	b
b	Bb	bb
b	Bb	bb

Probability of a red: 0%   50%

Let us consider probability for a moment, taking as our example the last matrix where it is shown that the probability of getting a red is 50%. This means that there is a 50% chance that any certain calf thrown will be red.

There is a 50% chance that the first calf dropped will be red. Regardless of the color of the first calf, the probability of the second calf being red is also 50%. The same hold true for every succeeding calf: the probability remains at 50%. It is the same situation that exists when a coin is tossed. Even though Heads may have shown up 6 times in a row, the probability of a Head on the next throw is still 50%.

We have a different situation when we seek to determine the probability of an event occurring several times in succession. The probability of having eight red calves and no black would be 50% to the eighth power: $.5^8$, or .004, or four-tenths of one per cent, or 1 out of 250. So that, in testing for a recessive, one can make a decision when one is satisfied with the odds. Obviously, it might take longer to test for a recessive in a cow than it would in a bitch, since a cow usually has only one calf per breeding whereas a bitch usually has several puppies. Checking for a recessive in a bull or a male dog is easier than checking for a recessive in a cow or bitch, since the male can be bred to several females pure for the recessive. This will result in more numerous progeny and, therefore, a larger sampling from which to check against the known probability.

We have determined that, where there is a 50% probability of getting a black or a red calf, the probability of getting eight consecutive blacks or eight consecutive reds is 0.4%. What is the probability of getting eight males in a litter of eight? While, in dogs of various breeds, the percentage of males at birth is over 50%,[1] we shall use the figure of 50%. A 50% probability carried to the eighth power gives us 0.4%. The probability of getting eight females in such a litter would be the same. The probability of getting *either* eight males *or* eight females in a litter of eight would be 0.4 plus 0.4, or 0.8. Remember that we have been talking of a "litter of eight". To determine the probability of a bitch having exactly eight males and no females in a litter, one would first have to compute the probability of having a litter of eight and then multiply that figure by the probability of having eight males. In arriving at these two probabilities, one must be consistent and either include or exclude in both the number of puppies whelped dead.

In the accompanying table, I have computed the probabilities of getting certain numbers of dominant and recessive characteristics in litters of up to eight puppies. To illustrate, where the probability of a recessive was 50% and where there was a litter of 8, we look under "Size of litter: 8" and under "Expected ratio 1:1." We see that the probability of getting 8 dominants and 0 recessives is 0.39 (I used 0.4 in the preceeding two paragraphs). The probability of getting 0 dominants and 8 recessives obviously is also 0.39.

Where *a* equals the probability of one event, *b* the probability of the other event and *n* equals the number of individuals to which either event might apply, the formula for the litter of eight and the

---

[1]Hutt, *op cit.*, pp. 442, 443.

actual calculation in the case of a 50% probability is

$$a^8 + 8a^7b^1 + 28a^6b^2 + 56b^5b^3 + 70a^4b^4 + 56a^3b^5 + 28a^2b^6 + 8a^1b^7 + b^8 = 100\%$$
$$0.39 + 3.13 + 10.94 + 21.87 + 27.34 + 21.87 + 10.94 + 3.13 + 0.39 = 100\%$$

For those persons who wish to compute for larger numbers, Pascal's triangle can be extended and the terms of the expanded binomial calculated.

PASCAL'S TRIANGLE

n	Coefficients								
1					1		1		
2				1		2		1	
3			1		3		3		1
4		1		4		6		4		1
5	1		5		10		10		5		1
6	1		6		15		20		15		6		1
7	1		7		21		35		35		21		7		1
8	1		8		28		56		70		56		28		8		1

Pct.

$a^8 + 8a^7b^1 + 28a^6b^2 + 56a^5b^3 + 70a^4b^4 + 56a^3b^5 + 28a^2b^6 + 8a^1b^7 + b^8$ = 100

$a^7 + 7a^6b^1 + 21a^5b^1 + 35a^4b^3 + 35a^3b^4 + 21a^2b^5 + 7a^1b^6 + b^7$ = 100

$a^6 + 6a^5b^1 + 15a^4b^2 + 20a^3b^3 + 15a^2b^4 + 6a^1b^5 + b^6$ = 100

$a^5 + 5a^4b^1 + 10a^3b^2 + 10a^2b^3 + 5a^1b^4 + b^5$ = 100

$a^4 + 4a^3b^1 + 6a^2b^2 + 4a^1b^3 + b^4$ = 100

$a^3 + 3a^2b^1 + 3a^1b^2 + b^3$ = 100

$a^2 + 2a^1b^1 + b^2$ = 100

$a + b$ = 100

Now let us turn to the subject of color in dogs.

It would be convenient if we could list a dozen genes which, in different combinations, might account for all the great range of colors and patterns to be seen in the various species of domestic animals. There are several good reasons why this writer will undertake no such venture.

One of these reasons is that, when authorities on the colors of dogs or horses cannot agree on the genes causing those colors, it is scarcely appropriate for a poultry expert to add fuel to the flames . . . From his investigations, Little was able to assign genotypes to many breeds, as for example:

Beagle (with no ticking): a^t B C D E g m P s^p t
Dalmatian (with black spots): A^S B C D E g m P s^w T
Weimaraner: A^S b C d E g m P S t

For simplicity in these examples, only single genes are shown. Pure breeds would be homozygous for each one.[1]

E is considered to be an extension of black pigment and is a complementary gene to B.[2] These genes provide the following characteristics:

Genotype	Phenotype
BB EE, Bb EE, BB Ee, Bb Ee	Black.
BB ee, Bb ee	Red with black eyes and nose.
bb ee	Yellow or pale red with brown nose.
bb Ee, bb EE	Brown, Chocolate, or Liver.

Limiting ourselves to these two types of genes, the possible combinations are shown on the next page in the form of a matrix. As an example, 75% of a litter of puppies whose black sire and black dam have genes BbEE should be black, 25% should be red. The appropriate square in the matrix shows this proportion.[3]

Now we shall consider the case of two hereditary factors (color and coat) located on two different chromosomes.[4] We mate a black (BB) shorthaired (hh) guinea pig with a white (bb) long-haired (HH) one. It can be seen from the matrix that all the progeny are black and long-haired. Therefore, black and long hair are the dominant characteristics.

	Bh	Bh
bH	BbHh	BbHh
bH	BbHh	BbHh

[1] *Ibid.*, pp. 483, 485.
[2] *Ibid.*, pp. 92, 94, 95.
[3] BbEe-BbEe also has a probability of 75% black and 25% yellow, or pale red.
[4] Frisch, *op. cit.*, pp. 221-224.

PROBABILITY OF COLORS IN DOGS

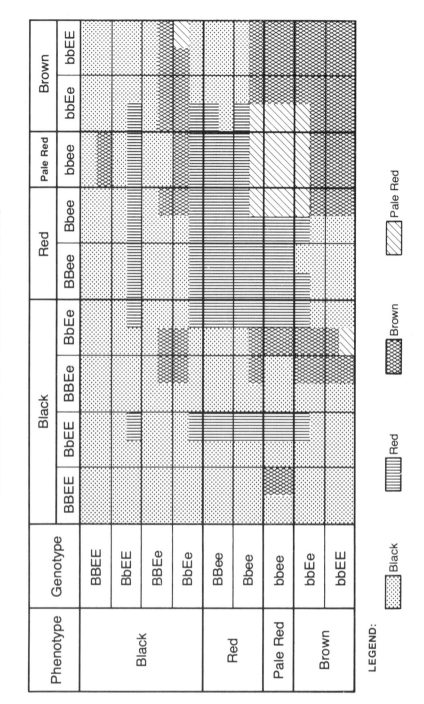

LEGEND: Black Red Brown Pale Red

If the hybrid progeny are crossed among themselves, we get the proper Mendelian ratio of 75% black to 25% white and 75% long-haired to 25% short-haired. But on the combination of color and coat, we get the following numbers and percentages of guinea pigs.

9 Black, long-haired (56.25%)   3 White, long-haired (18.75%)

3 Black, short-haired (18.75%)   1 White, short-haired (6.25%)

Color is a qualitative character. We now consider quantitative characters, i.e. those where very slight differences exist among individuals in a large group. Examples are height, weight, milk production, fat content of milk, strength, viability. Possibly Galton's Law[1] applies here: quantitative characters are inherited in the proportion 50% from both parents, 25% from both grandparents, etc. On the other hand, size is determined by the dam. A Shetland pony was artificially inseminated by a huge draft Shire. The foals were smaller than the normal Shetlands both at birth and at the age of three years.[2]

To ensure completeness of the record, here is what Captain Graham had to say:

> Breeders should remember that in breeding, the question of ancestors is a most important one, and that a small dog descended from large ancestors, is more likely to breed large dogs than is a large dog from small ancestors.

> A large dog from large ancestors is the dog, par excellence, to select. The writer believes, with Colonel Garnier, that the following rules are the correct ones to recognize, viz.:—(1) That quality (i.e., "blood", nervous development, vigour, energy and character) is very much more dependent on the dam than on the sire. (2) Bone or size, on the contrary, is far more dependent on the sire. (3) Colour is almost wholly dependent on the sire. (4) The coat is almost wholly dependent on the sire. (5) Muscular development and general form is chiefly dependent on the dam. (6) All these are modified by the fact that the purer bred parent will (other things being the same) influence the progeny more than any other.[3]

---

[1] Hutt, *op cit.*, pp. 267, 268. Onstott calls it "discredited". Kyle Onstott, *The New Art of Breeding Better Dogs.* Revised by Phillip Onstott (1967), p. 168. Francis Galton lived from 1822 to 1911.

[2] Hutt, *op cit.*, p. 313.

[3] George A. Graham, in *The Kennel Encyclopaedia, op. cit.*, pp. 853, 854.

The depth of pigmentation in a dog's eye probably depends upon a number of genes.[1] Blue eyes in Irish Wolfhounds over two months of age are portents of danger. Blue-eyed tigers have "white" coats and are wall-eyed.[2]

> The merle type of dilution . . . found in several breeds of dogs leaves heterozygotes with black (undiluted) blotches on a background that is either bluish-grey or dilute tan. Dogs homozygous for this gene are almost entirely white (except Foxhounds, which show some color) and their eyes are very pale blue, sometimes called "china" eyes. Such homozygotes are more or less sightless, and some lack an eye on one or both sides. They are also deaf. A similar association of eye defects with white spotting is known in the mouse, and most blue-eyed white cats are deaf.[3]

In 1906, Harding Cox mentioned that in the early 1870s, a number of outstanding fox terriers from one kennel were "mostly all white dogs (and by the same token some of them deaf or defective of hearing)."[4]

A trait which appears in an offspring but not in any known ancestor may be genetic, congenital, or a mutation. A genetic disease or condition is determined by factors present in the sperm cell of the sire or the ovum of the dam, or both. If not inherited but present at birth, it is called congenital. A congenital disease may be caused by injury during the development of the fetus. The puppy's ability to overcome the disease would be dependent upon the genes, however.

Hutt observed:

> Conditions passed in a germ cell from parent to offspring, but outside the nucleus and not through genes, are sometimes said to be transmitted by *cytoplasmic inheritance* to distinguish them from heredity through the genes.[5]

With regard to inheritable defects, dogs are normal (NN), carriers (Nn), or abnormal (nn). Normality is the dominant characteristic. There are six possible combinations if a simple recessive hereditary factor is involved.

---

[1]Onstott, *op. cit.*, p. 95.

[2]R. W. Guillery and J. H. Kaas, "Genetic Abnormality of the Visual Pathways in a 'White' Tiger." *Science* (22 June, 1973) CLXXX, pp. 1287-1289.

[3]Hutt, *op. cit.*, p. 485.

[4]Harding Cox, *Dogs* (1906) I, p. 19.

[5]*Ibid.*, p. 4.

One Parent	Other Parent	Notation	Probabilities (percentage)		
			Normality	Carrier	Abnormality
Normal	Normal	NN-NN	100		
Normal	Carrier	NN-Nn	50	50	
Normal	Abnormal	NN-nn		100	
Carrier	Carrier	Nn-Nn	25	50	25
Carrier	Abnormal	Nn-nn		50	50
Abnormal	Abnormal	nn-nn			100

Can acquired characteristics be inherited?

Certain character failings, such as viciousness, extreme nervousness, and hysterical or epileptic tendencies must be condemned.[1]

Two lines of Pointers, one bred for fearfulness and lack of friendliness toward man and the other for opposite traits, subjected to various behavioral tests, revealed surprising within-litter similarities and between-litter differences, particularly between the two most extreme lines of a bold and timid first generation. Investigators Drs. O. D. Murphee and R. A. Dykman of Little Rock, Ark., stated that since environmental factors were the same for all the dogs, there is little doubt but that the litter differences are of hereditary nature.[2]

He [Darwin] believed that the latter [environmental influences] could become heritable if the external influence lasted long enough.[3]

Dr. Fox wrote:

It can be stated that certain traits such as aggressiveness, fear-biting and timidity can be inherited. Actually, behavior is not inherited as such, but rather, genes modulate the capacity of an organism to react under different environmental circumstances. Behavior must therefore be considered as the outcome of a genotype (or innate capacities) and environment interaction.[4]

---

[1]"Scoring System Helps Reach Breeding Goals," *Gaines Dog Research Progress* (Summer, 1968).

[2]"Heredity Influences Behavior," *ibid.* (Spring, 1966).

[3]Frisch, *op. cit.*, p. 252.

[4]Michael W. Fox, "Guidelines to Behavior in Dogs," *Gaines Dog Research Progress* (Spring, 1968).

Hutt concluded:

> Sometimes the environmental influences far outweigh the genetic ones.[1]

Breeders have their own standards by which they determine the type of breeding entered into. The general belief, if I am not mistaken, is that inbreeding involves very closely related individuals and that linebreeding occurs when individuals not so closely related are mated. Here are definitions provided by the Society for the Advancement of Canine Genetics:

> Breeding methods are commonly subdivided into four general types. These are inbreeding, linebreeding, outbreeding, and crossbreeding. Each system has its place and its purpose and accomplishes certain results when properly used. It is senseless to argue the benefits of one system against another . . .
>
> *Inbreeding* is the mating of related individuals (usually not more than two generations removed from one another), where neither individual is an ancestor of the other. The most distantly related individuals included in this definition would be those having only one grandparent in common. It should be noted that this definition excludes such matings as mother to son, granddaughter to grandfather, etc. The reason for this will be explained in the discussion of linebreeding. The maximum inbreeding that can be achieved in a single mating is by breeding brother to sister . . .
>
> Inbreeding brings out recessive genes in the homozygous condition. Since these genes may be either desirable or undesirable, the effects of inbreeding vary considerably . . .
>
> Inbreeding in itself has no bad effects. This was proven most definitely by Dr. Helen Dean King at the Wister Institute in Philadelphia. She has bred rats brother to sister for over a hundred generations. Today the rats are larger, live longer, and produce larger litters than did the rats with which she began her experiment. The reason for these good results is that careful selection was practiced during the entire experiment. All undesirable animals were destroyed and only the best were kept for breeding.
>
> *Linebreeding* is the breeding of an individual to one of his (or her) ancestors. Linebreeding causes the progeny to resemble one particular individual in their ancestry more closely than the

---

[1]Hutt, *op. cit.*, p. 5.

others, and in this respect its effects are in direct opposition to those of general inbreeding . . .

The strongest possible linebreeding effect is obtained by breeding a stud to his own daughters for several generations . . .

Linebreeding also brings out recessive genes but in a more orderly manner than general inbreeding. Less variation will appear in linebred litters than in inbred litters . . .

Quite often linebred puppies are advertised as though there were some magic power about linebreeding that guaranteed good results. As with inbreeding, the results obtained depend entirely on the quality of the original stock, the skill with which the breeding program was planned and executed, and on the methods and amount of selection . . .

Outbreeding is a mating between individuals that are less closely related than average. A mating should probably be considered as outbreeding when the two individuals show no common ancestor in a four-generation pedigree.

Crossbreeding is a mating of one breed to another. This method has little to offer the commercial breeder but is useful to the research geneticist in learning more about the genetic composition of the different breeds.[1]

An example of proper inbreeding is that of cattle on the Channel Islands: Alderney, Jersey, and Guernsey. Inbred for hundreds of years, these strains are known throughout the world for their excellence. On the other hand Sewall Wright pointed out that twenty-five generations of guinea pig brother-sister mating resulted in some decline in weight, fertility, and vitality although it "may not cause any obvious degeneration".[2]

The degree of inbreeding may be determined by calculation.

Calculation of inbreeding coefficients is based on the assumption that each animal receives one-half of its inheritance (genotype) from each parent. While this assumption is not strictly accurate, it is a much better approximation than Galton's theory which asserted that each parent contributed one-quarter, each grandparent one-eighth and so on, or the Picardy system by

[1]Society for the Advancement of Canine Genetics, *Journal of Canine Genetics* (August, 1947). Quoted in "The 4 Systems of Breeding Defined," *Gaines Dog Research Progress* (Fall, 1947).

[2]Sewall Wright, "Mendelian Analysis of The Pure Breeds of Livestock," *Journal of Heredity* (November, 1923), p. 340.

which one-third of a dog's inheritance is assumed to be derived from its parents, grandparents, and great-grandparents respectively. Obviously, everything a dog gets from its grandparents it must get via its parents, so that at the time of fertilization the whole of its inheritance is derived from its parents, although not necessarily quite equally from each.[1]

Sewall Wright's formula for the calculation of degrees of inbreeding[2] is:

$$F_x = \Sigma \left[(.5)^{n+n'+1} (1 + F_A) \right]$$

x = coefficient of inbreeding of X.

n = number of generations from X's sire to an ancestor common to the paternal and maternal side. This is zero if the sire himself appears in the pedigree of the dam.

n^1 = number of generations from X's dam to the same common ancestor. This is zero if the dam herself appears in the pedigree of the sire.

Σ = summation (of separate contributions from each different common ancestor).

F_A = coefficient of inbreeding of the common ancestor, when that animal is itself inbred.

In the pedigree charts which will portray our examples, the usual procedure is followed. X is the Irish Wolfhound whose coefficient of inbreeding we seek. In the next column appear his sire, A (upper letter) and dam, B (lower letter). Similarly the parents of the sire, (C,D) and dam (C,E), are in the third column, etc.

$$\text{Example I:} \quad X \begin{cases} A \begin{cases} C \\ D \end{cases} \\ B \begin{cases} C \\ E \end{cases} \end{cases}$$

In the above example, X's paternal grandsire (C) is also his maternal grandsire. The number of generations from X's sire, A, to this common ancestor (C) is 1. The number of generations from X's dam, B, to this common ancestor is also 1.

$$.5^{1+1+1} = .5^3 = 0.125$$

---

[1]"Scoring System Helps Reach Breeding Goals," *Gaines Dog Research Progress* (Summer, 1968).

[2]Hutt, *op. cit.*, pp. 382-385.

The degree of relationship between A and B is thus 12.5% and, therefore, X is 12.5% inbred.

$$\text{Example 2:} \quad X \begin{cases} A & \begin{cases} C \\ D \end{cases} \\ B & \begin{cases} C \\ D \end{cases} \end{cases}$$

If X's paternal and maternal grandparents are the same, as in Example 2, then the contribution of granddam D, would be the same as grandsire C, i.e. 12.5% and the total of both contributions would be 25%.

Our third example involves the situation where a common ancestor is also inbred. The sire, A, is also the maternal grandsire. He is inbred since E appears as both his paternal and maternal grandsire.

$$\text{Example 3:} \quad X \begin{cases} A \begin{cases} C \begin{cases} E \\ F \end{cases} \\ D \begin{cases} E \\ G \end{cases} \end{cases} \\ B \begin{cases} A \begin{cases} C \begin{cases} E \\ F \end{cases} \\ D \begin{cases} E \\ G \end{cases} \end{cases} \\ H \begin{cases} M \\ G \end{cases} \end{cases} \end{cases}$$

To calculate E's contribution to A's inbreeding, we take the number of generations from A's sire and from A's dam to E and apply our formula:

$$F_A = .5^{1+1+1} = .5^3 = .125$$

Now we calculate A's contribution to X's inbreeding. A is a common ancestor appearing as he does on both the paternal and maternal side of X. The number of generations from X's sire (A) to the common ancestor (A) is zero. There is one generation between the dam and the common ancestor. A's contribution to the degree of inbreeding is:

$$(.5^{0+1+1}) (1 + F_A) = (.5^2) (1.125) = .28125 = 28.125\%$$

G is also a common ancestor. Her contribution is: $.5^{2+2+1} = .03125$ or 3.125%. X's inbreeding is the sum of A's and G's contributions: 28.125 + 3.125 = 31.25%.

D. PREMATING CONSIDERATIONS

Periods of ovulation are usually called "season" or "heat". The frequency of this occurrence in dogs varies. Usually, it is about six months. Basenjis ovulate once a year. Generally, Irish Wolfhound bitches ovulate for the first time at about fourteen to eighteen months of age, some at two years, and thereafter about every six to nine months. Some bitches come in season within an abnormally short period after a normal heat. Such a "false heat" will not result in a pregnancy should the animal be bred.[1] Some bitches do not come in season until they receive hormone shots. Some time before the bitch whom you are planning to breed is due to come in season, have her inoculated against distemper, hepatitis, and leptospirosis with modified live vaccine of chicken embryo or tissue culture origin.[2] Since a dam can pass worms on to her puppies, she should be examined for worms prior to mating, and wormed if necessary. She should not be overweight as such a condition reduces the conception rate and creates whelping problems. She should be in excellent physical condition and free of fleas, lice, and ticks.

The first phase of ovulation is called proestrus. Generally it lasts nine days, but this period could be anywhere from two to twenty-seven days in length.[3] The first indication may be the appearance of blood on the carpet (removed with cold water) and is referred to as "showing color". This is a discharge from the vulva which now becomes enlarged. The date when the bitch first showed color should be recorded as it is of importance in determining when to attempt breeding.

The standard way of determining when ovulation should occur is by daily microscopic examination of vaginal smears. If possible, one should select a veterinarian who has had considerable experience in this type of work. Another method is by establishing contact between a glucose strip, of the type used by diabetics to test the sugar level in the urine, and the cervical mucus.[4] A change in color of the strip indicates that ovulation has taken place. This method is not recommended.[5]

---

[1]Onstott, *op. cit.*, p. 35.
[2]See Index at Health Maintenance, Inoculation.
[3]Kingma, *op. cit.*
[4]Tes-Tape. Eli Lilly Co.
[5]See Index at Whelping, Milk.

Ordinarily, ovulation occurs thirty-six hours before the first appearance of leukocytes (observed by microscope), lasts one to four days and ends seventy-two hours before the bitch last accepts the male. These times may vary by twelve hours. During the period she is in season, the bitch dissipates an odor which attracts males. Until a day or two before the proestrus period ends, she will fiercely repel his advances. She may then allow him to mount but will not permit him to enter. After the first week, the vulva remains enlarged but becomes softer. The discharge gradually lightens and usually ends after two weeks.

> Only during estrus will the bitch accept the male . . . Although the average duration of estrus approximates 9 days, this figure is not always applicable. The possibility that estrus may last from 8-24 days is extremely important since conception is dependent upon the successful union of spermatozoon and ovum . . . Fertilization of the ovum is only possible following the first maturation division. In the bitch the first maturation division does not occur until 24 to 48 hours following ovulation.[1]

PHASES OF OVULATION

Proestrus 2-27 days. Usually 9		*Estrus* 8-24 days. Usually about 9	*Postestrus*
		Maturation Division 3 days	
	1-2 days		
Male not accepted	Male will mount. No entry	Male accepted	Male not accepted

We have learned that special nutrition and pampering the stud dog is of no value in improving his ability to produce sperm and in fact may reduce this capacity. He should, however, be firmly fleshed and vigorous. Animals not used frequently often produce inferior semen on their first service. A second sample 24 hours later will usually be much improved, arguing for more than a single breeding.

---

[1]Kingma, *op. cit.*

It has been found that males can be used regularly at 48 hour intervals or daily for three consecutive days without depletion of sperm reserves, or used at stud twice in the same day if rested for 48 hours before the next service.

Bitches to be bred should be thin but gaining.[1]

While the bitch is usually not responsive to males except during the middle portion of her season, it is advisable to keep her confined throughout. It she is kept in the house with a male, even though not together, the male will not eat, and will become quite nervous; his sexual desire may be decreased.[2] It is better, therefore, under those circumstances to keep the bitch away from the male. Make sure she cannot escape and that other dogs cannot enter. Should you wish to exercise her, take her in the car for some distance away from your home. There are preparations on sale which claim to mask the odor of the bitch. I am informed that they are ineffective.

Bitches should not be bred until their second season to allow them to mature. I recommend that, if they are to be bred, it be done between the ages of two to six years. A bitch who has not had a litter by four years of age is apt to have a difficult time whelping. In the Irish Wolfhound Club of America Specialty Shows, a bitch six years of age or over is called a "veteran". A dog may be used as a stud from the age of two to perhaps six years. He should never be allowed to be overweight. A "proven" stud or bitch is one which has been successfully mated. Naturally, matters are facilitated by having at least one proven participant.

The owner of the stud should assure himself, by examination of the registration certificate or otherwise, that the proffered bitch is registered.

Cryptorchidism is the condition which exists in male dogs when one or both of the testicles fail to descend through the inguinal canal into the scrotum. If only one testicle descends, the dog is called a unilateral cryptorchid. It is not correct to refer to him as a monorchid as this means "having only one testicle". Cryptorchids are barred from being shown in purebred competition in the United States. The complete cryptorchid is sterile; he may also be difficult to handle; a tumor may develop in the testicle; the dog may lose his masculinity. Unilateral cryptorchids may be fertile. Since the defect is hereditary, the British Veterinary Association recommends that

---

[1]Robert W. Kirk, "Kennel Management," *Gaines Dog Research Progress* (Summer, 1961).

[2]A. C. Andersen, *op. cit.*, p. 158.

one avoid breeding unilateral cryptorchids, any of their male progeny, as well as any littermates or parents of cryptorchids.[1] It is considered improper to operate on a unilateral monorchid to give him the appearance of being normal.[2]

Both the owner of the stud and of the bitch should know genetic principles, should study the pedigrees of the two animals, should observe their qualities and defects and should view the progeny which either may have had. If convinced that this would be a proper breeding, they may enter into a written agreement to breed, inserting whatever provisions they wish. One possibility is shown here.

BREEDING AGREEMENT

Agreement made this ＿＿＿＿ day of ＿＿＿＿＿ , 19 ＿ , in

＿＿＿＿＿ between ＿＿＿＿＿ owner of ＿＿＿＿ and ＿＿＿＿ ,
                                    (Dog)
owner of ＿＿＿＿＿ , whereby this dog will be bred to this bitch on
            (Bitch)
the following terms:

1. Payment will be due if a tie occurs or if a veterinarian certifies that a mating has taken place.

2. The fee for this mating will be: (Cross out inapplicable portion). ＿＿＿＿＿＿＿＿＿＿ dollars at time of mating.
   Choice made by owner of dog of any puppy in the litter. One puppy, dead or alive, constitutes a litter. Choice will be made at any time before puppies are ten weeks old. Payment will be considered to have been made if one or more puppies are whelped, dead or alive, but none survives to the age of ten weeks.

3. In the event that there is no pregnancy, the bitch will be entitled to a free return service at her next season to the same dog if he is available; otherwise, to any other dog owned and selected by the owner of the first dog used.

4. It is further agreed that the breeder will not transfer owner-ship of any puppy resulting from this breeding to any person or

---

[1] British Veterinary Association, "Cryptorchidism in the Dog," *Veterinary Records* (1955) LXVII, pp. 472-474.

[2] Frederick B. Hutt, *Animal Genetics.* Copyright © 1964, The Ronald Press Company, New York, p. 157.

organization whose intent is to resell, trade or give away the puppy, or to use it in laboratory experiments. This intent may be inferred from statements or from past conduct, e.g. operation of a pet shop. Should the buyer fail to comply with this provision, he shall pay to the seller $5000 in liquidated damages for the damage done to the reputation of the seller, his kennel operations, and to the Irish Wolfhound breed generally.

Witness our hands and seals this _____ day of _____ , 19 ___ .

The penalty clause may be difficult to enforce since intent is a factor, attorney's fees would be incurred, and the defendant may have his domicile or place of business quite some distance from the home of the plaintiff.

The amount of the stud fee is determined by the owner of the stud, of course, and is payable at the time of service. Views are widely divergent as to what is a proper charge. Some stud dog owners charge the price of a puppy, some vary the price depending on whether the stud is a champion and proven, some do not charge unless the dam whelps. One breeder charges the price of a puppy if the bitch has no championship points; if the bitch has points but is not a champion, the stud fee is cut in half; if the bitch is a champion, the charge is reduced by seventy-five per cent. In this manner, the breeder attempts to encourage the breeding of good show dogs and discourage the breeding of those who are not. I have heard the view expressed that a stud dog owner should not accept a puppy in payment unless he intends to keep it; otherwise, he may be encouraging breeding by persons who are not financially able to care properly for Irish Wolfhound puppies.

The bitch is usually brought to the stud for the "service" and not vice versa. Any charges for boarding, vaginal smears, veterinarian assistance are borne by the owner of the bitch. When she first shows color, notify the owner of the stud and make arrangements with him. It is a much better practice for the owner of the bitch to take her personally to be bred than it is to ship her. The bitch may be upset by her owner's absence in strange territory and, also, the owner may be able to assist in the mating. Moreover, shipping a large dog presents many problems. See chapter on Sales.

If records have been kept by you of the bitch's condition and behavior when she was in season on previous occasions, you will have a fairly good idea of when she should be mated. For instance, knowing the date she showed color, you will be able to predict with some accuracy when her vulva will become enlarged, what her reactions to males will be on various dates, etc.

The bitch will be ready approximately from the tenth day to the fourteenth, counting from the first day she showed color. This can vary considerably. Some bitches may accept the male only on one certain day, others will do so for two weeks. The period from the eleventh to the thirteenth day is usually considered the best. However, it could be the third or the twenty-first day. There are many popular beliefs: "The male will know when she is ready." But I have seen males who were willing from the onset of the bitch's season until it terminated three weeks later. The male indicates readiness by evidencing great excitement, head and ears erect, prancing, licking the bitch's vulva. "The bitch will welcome the male when she is ready." But I have known bitches who were "ready" physiologically and who gave the usual signs but who refused to be mated.

If the bitch is "ready", she may indicate this by being playful, by "flagging", i.e. raising her tale or turning it to one side, and/or by "standing" when approached by a male, i.e. inviting him to mount. Keep a record of her behavior. In some bitches, the vulvar discharge will change from red to pale yellow. The vulva, although still swollen, will become soft and pliable. Veterinarians, by means of vaginal smears, can inform you when to breed. Some persons rely on "Tes-Tape", made by Lilly. This is a test for glucose in urine. The paper is wrapped over the tip of the finger and introduced into the vagina. Dr. M. Josephine Deubler[1] does not look with favor upon its use because of the risk of infection and because she does not know of any scientific basis for the test. Since the tape can give false results because of its age or exposure to light, heat, or moisture, a piece should first be tested in a glucose solution, if it is to be used. I recommend reliance on a veterinarian. A blister with the appearance of a cold sore on the stud dog's prepuce or the bitch's vagina may harbor the virus causing viremia. An infected puppy will hemorrhage; if he does not die, he may, nevertheless, incur kidney damage.

E. MATING

There are advocates of the practice of turning the stud and bitch loose together and letting them mate when they are ready. I strongly

---

[1]Writer of column "Ask Your Doctor" in *Popular Dogs*.

recommend this not be done for reasons which shall presently appear.

Do not feed the stud for several hours prior to the mating. Both dog and bitch should be allowed to relieve themselves before being brought together. Wash their sexual organs with an antiseptic soap to reduce the possibility of infection. Make sure no residue of the soap is left on the bitch. Cut off the long hairs around the vulva. Some lubricant such as vaseline may be advisable if the vagina is unusually small. The hands should be washed or a sterilized rubber glove used.

Put chain collars on both hounds and attach strong leads. See Index at Obedience, Training, Collars, for the proper way to put on a collar and to control dogs. Take the hounds to an area where there will be no distractions and where the footing will be firm. Indoor-outdoor carpeting serves well indoors. Let them approach each other to become acquainted but be prepared to pull them apart should the bitch show resentment.

If the bitch is not ready or if the time has passed, she may attempt to escape from the dog, tuck her tail between her legs or sit down. Or, she may repel all advances, and violently. I have never seen such fury as that of an Irish Wolfhound bitch to whom unwelcome advances are being made and, under those circumstances, any intelligent male will keep his distance. Despite the strong male urge, he will henceforth approach hesitantly and a growl from the bitch will suffice to make him desist, especially if she has previously bitten him. There are Irish Wolfhound bitches that will growl at studs even when they are ready but will allow them to mount if someone is holding their own heads. In some cases, a muzzle may be necessary. Do not wait until the last day before purchasing a muzzle. Some difficulty may be encountered in locating one large enough. I suggest a wire muzzle since this does not interfere with breathing.

Another expedient is to place the center of a leash, or strip of cloth, etc., on the top of the bitch's muzzle with the ends downward. Cross the ends underneath the muzzle, over and under again. Tie under the muzzle, then around the neck. The bitch's mouth should not be clamped tight but merely enough to prevent her from biting. The excitement, the energy she will expend, and possibly the temperature will cause her to pant heavily. A leash should remain attached to her collar as fast action will be required if the muzzle should become loosened.

Some Irish Wolfhound bitches will never tolerate a male to mount. I have seen four men fail in an attempt to breed Irish Wolfhounds in such a circumstance. One recollects the saying

"Fierce when provoked". Although the bitches have never, to my knowledge, bitten the humans present at the mating, the latter have not been able to control them. It is quite possible that a bitch that will not allow herself to be bred should not in fact be bred. The hormone deficiencies which are evidently present may not augur well for the eventual birth and development of progeny. Some bitches will refuse one stud, yet will submit to another.

Should the bitch prove unwilling, a decision must be made whether to postpone the event on the theory that she is not ready (bearing in mind that she might always react this way) or to muzzle her and hold her head. Assuming the latter course, the male is allowed to mount. He may not know what is expected of him. In which case, raise him to the proper position. Some males may proceed at once to accomplish their task. Others, overanxious, may go through great exertions and accomplish nothing. Some males will allow humans to assist them in obtaining a penetration, others will promptly disembark if touched. Occasionally, a bitch will yelp at the moment of penetration and will then swerve to one side causing the male to withdraw; or she will crouch and prevent him from entering. In these cases, it may be necessary to place a knee under the bitch to prevent her from crouching. It may be necessary to have persons on each side of the bitch to prevent her from swerving, one also holding her head, while the other pulls the tail to one side, and holds his hand, palm upwards under the bitch's vulva as a guide. While supporting the bitch, try to keep away from the male as it may divert him from his work.

When the dog has penetrated the bitch, there may occur what is known as a "tie", i.e. the penis swells up especially at the rear, and the male is unable to withdraw for anywhere from a few minutes to an hour, usually about ten to twenty minutes. A tie is definite proof that the male has ejaculated seminal fluid into the female. It is not a guarantee of a litter, but it is that a service has been made.

A tie is not absolutely necessary for conception. It is recommended that if the male does effect a penetration, the handler push against his rump to prevent an exit for from five to ten minutes. Pregnancy should result as the sperm will have been ejected in the first two minutes and the alkalizing fluid will have been introduced in the next three to eight minutes.

It is possible for the puppies in a litter to have two sires but, of course, an individual puppy can have but one.

Once a penetration has been made, the handlers should take care that neither animal tears itself away. This could result in serious injury to either or both. When a tie has been effected, try to make both hounds maintain their positions. If either struggles to disengage, raise one of the stud's forelegs and front part of his body over the bitch's back and lower them to the other side. Hold them both in this position. Some persons go further. They take the hindleg that is on the same side as the foreleg that was raised and lift it over the bitch so that the two animals are standing rear to rear. Holding the tails of both will assist in keeping them together. Restrain both animals from moving until the tie is broken. Both Irish Wolfhounds should then be allowed to rest. Do not allow the bitch to urinate for one half an hour.

If the male has mounted and appears to be wasting his time, pull him off, let him rest a few minutes and try again. If it is observed that his penis is enlarged allow it to reduce in size before allowing him to try again.

A second service may be unnecessary if the first one resulted in a tie. If the stud has not been used for some time, wait a couple of days and try another mating.

For future reference, keep a detailed written record of the behavior of both stud and bitch when breedings are attempted. If there exists the possibility of having a litter, immediately start saving newspapers. They will be needed in large quantities.

If semen could be preserved, it could be of value in a number of situations, e.g. where an outstanding male has died or where he cannot be used because a long quarantine period has been established by some country. The problem has been that a dilutant was needed to allow semen to be frozen and to be thereafter effective. Dr. Stephen Seeger has discovered a method and, in its use, has produced five generations of dogs. At this time, it is envisioned that the procedure would be somewhat like this: Semen would be taken from a dog at a central location; it would be rigorously examined, frozen in ampules and stored. The owner of the stud would authorize delivery of the ampules to trained veterinarians in the area where the bitch to be mated is located.[1]

The American Kennel Club will register litters resulting from artificial insemination only if the dogs cannot be mated naturally. Both the sire and dam must be present at the time and extraction and insemination must be performed by the same recognized veterinarian. Check with the AKC for its requirements, preferably before the insemination but in any case not later than "immediately after the artificial mating".

---

[1]Haworth Hoch, The American Kennel Club, *Pure-Bred Dogs — American Kennel Gazette* (January, 1977), LXXXXIV, p. 168.

F. GESTATION PERIOD

The gestation period is always stated as being 63 days. Why people don't say "9 weeks", I don't know. It is possible for the date to be as early as the 58th day or as late as the 65th.[1]

> After mating, the bitch should be kept away from all other dogs and bitches, large and small, for at least a fortnight and should have her walking exercise entirely by herself. During this fortnight the exercise should consist of not less than 4 miles a day and not more than 6 or 7. During the last three weeks of "carrying" the exercise should be given in two or even three parts and even this must be adjusted according to the condition of the animal.[2]

Check the bitch for worms and worm her if necessary so that the puppies will not be infected either before they are born or while nursing. Do not worm her after 3 or 4 weeks from the time of mating.[3] Remove the tartar from her teeth or have a veterinarian do it to lessen the possibility of infection when she severs the umbilical cords. Clean her ears.[4] Make sure she has no fleas, ticks, or lice. It is the position of Gaines Dog Research Center that:

> Commercial dog foods are adequate for the bitch in gestation, the lactating dam, and the growing puppy alike. Experience shows that the caloric requirements of these animals are much greater than those of normal adult dogs that need satisfy only maintenance requirements. Consequently, the greater volume of food needed to fulfill their caloric requirements also furnishes, in proper balance, the additional vitamins, minerals and other elements needed in time of stress.[5]

Gaines advises waiting until the sixth week before increasing the amount of food given to a gestating bitch.[6] Purina counsels to wait until the seventh or eighth week.[7] Supplementation should be avoided. Excessive use of Vitamin A may result in dead or deformed

---

[1]Onstott states that a whelping on the 74th day is possible. *Op. cit.*, p. 48.

[2]I. W. Everett, "Hints on Rearing Irish Wolfhounds," The Irish Wolfhound Club (Britain), *Year Book* (1926), p. 23.

[3]See Index at Health Maintenance, Parasites, Worms.

[4]See Index at Health Maintenance, Ears.

[5]Gaines Nutrition Center, *Basic Guide to Canine Nutrition* (1965).

[6]Gaines Nutrition Center, *Care of the Brood Bitch and Puppies* (n.d.)

[7]Robert K. Mohrman, "Feeding of Dogs", *Purina Kennel News* (1975) I.

puppies.[1] Feed the bitch twice a day. Despite this increased feeding, a dam should not be more than 5% or 10% heavier after whelping than she was at the time of breeding.

During the last two weeks her interest in food may diminish. If so, give protein concentrates, e.g. fish (no bones), chicken (no bones), lean meat, cooked eggs, milk. Too much milk could give her indigestion. Small amounts of raw or lightly cooked liver are excellent.[2] Do not vary the basic diet too much. Of course, fresh water should be continuously available, as usual. If the bitch becomes constipated during the last two or three weeks, give her baby suppositories.

After the fifth week of pregnancy, do not allow her to take any violent or lengthy exercise, but do exercise her every day by walking her on a lead. After seven weeks, separate her from other dogs so that she will not be tempted to run and play. Have the veterinarian check for possible infection.

Signs of pregnancy may appear in some bitches and not in others. They may appear at varying times. Usually, about the fifth week, the nipples and the belly enlarge and swollen lines appear along both sides of the belly. She may start losing hair around the nipples at or before the seventh week. A week before the due date, cut the hair around the nipples and around the vulva. The belly will drop about the seventh week and the puppies may be felt about the eighth.

Extraneous environmental influences can prenatally affect the subsequent behavior of mammals. The practical implications of these findings can be drawn at this stage: avoid excessive handling or emotional disturbances to the bitch during pregnancy, especially if the bitch is repeatedly exposed to these traumatic stimuli over a long period of time; gentle handling and familiarization with whelping quarters at least 2 to 3 weeks before delivery would facilitate the animal's adaptation to changes in daily routine, and minimize such disturbing influences. It must be emphasized that some individuals may be, on the basis of "constitution" or genetic factors, more sensitive and reactive to environmental disturbances.[3]

As early as six months after conception, the heartbeat of a [human] fetus will increase in reaction to sounds. Small

---

[1]General Foods Corporation, *A Report on Soft-Moist Foods*, (1970), p. 2.
[2]Kirk, "Kennel Management," *op. cit.*
[3]Fox, *op. cit.*

malformations in its nervous system can develop as the result of loud noises.[1]

Construct a whelping pen that is long enough so the dam may lie down at full length and wide enough so that she may easily turn around. The sides should be high enough to keep out drafts. One side should be low enough to allow the dam to get in and out easily without endangering the lives of the puppies by being forced to jump in. The pen illustrated shows boards with stakes which engage the boards directly below, thus the sides can be raised as the puppies grow to prevent them from climbing out. The floor is 8' x 4' x 6". Some breeders place a 4-inch railing in the pen about 6 inches above its floor and covering the outer limits of the floor to minimize the possibility of the dam accidentally stepping or lying on a puppy. The personal attention which I give the puppies renders this unnecessary for me to do. See Index at Whelping, Care of dam.

A week before the whelping is due, I thoroughly clean and disinfect the whelping pen and assemble it in the whelping room. This is a room on the ground floor with a door leading to both a gravel and a lawn area, separated from that used by the other dogs. In the lower half of the door is a two-way swinging panel which allows the bitch to go in and out as she pleases. A large plastic sheet is placed on the bottom of the pen and is turned up at the sides of the pen to prevent the liquid discharged at whelping from flowing onto the floor beneath the pen. The floor itself is covered with linoleum. Many newspapers are then placed over the plastic so that the latter will not be torn by the bitch when she begins pawing as her hour draws near. The pen should be in a secluded area where she will later be able to have her puppies in isolation. Do not spray this room with insecticide within two weeks of the time for whelping. The dam will want to have her puppies in the place where she has been accustomed to staying. If she has been living in the house and, just prior to the time for whelping, she is placed in the garage, she will frantically try to get back into the house. The reverse is also true. The emotional upheaval could affect the time of delivery.[2] Encourage her to sleep in the whelping pen for at least one week prior to her due date.

---

[1]Theodore Berland, *Smithsonian* (July, 1972), p. 15.

[2]Marion John Freak, "Abnormal Behavior During Pregnancy and Parturition in the Bitch," a chapter in *Abnormal Behavior in Animals*, edited by Michael W. Fox. Quoted in *Gaines Dog Research Progress* (Spring, 1970).

It may be desirable to have the following articles at hand:

1. 2 rectal thermometers. To check on the dam's temperature so that the due hour can be more easily ascertained and to check her condition and that of the puppies after whelping.
2. Scissors for possible use in cutting umbilical cord.
3. Corn starch to stem bleeding of umbilical cord.
4. Alcohol to sterilize thermometer, scissors, hands.
5. Sterile thread, dental floss or heavy suture for possible use as ligature on umbilical cord.
6. Antiseptic in shallow dish in which to dip thread and also for application on end of umbilical cord.
7. Bucket for placenta and other material to be discarded.
8. Paper toweling, soft cloths, clean rags to dry the puppies, clean the dam and for general cleaning up.
9. Cotton swabs, gauze, bandage or rough wash cloth. To assist in a difficult whelping.
10. Rubber gloves to prevent infection of the bitch and puppies.
11. Cardboard box in which to place puppies when dam is about to have another puppy.
12. Weight scales capable of measuring in grams up to a kilogram (2.2 lb).
13. Electric heating pad or hot-water bottle to keep puppies warm when temporarily removed from the dam. Rough towels placed over these articles to avoid overheating.
14. Pad of paper to record whelping data. Two pencils.
15. Soap and water to wash hands.
16. Baby oil for use on puppies to assist in discharge of feces and urine.
17. Boric acid solution to keep dam's abdomen clean.
18. Brandy, aromatic ammonia, or smelling salts for puppies if needed.
19. Tweezers if needed to draw puppy's tongue. Can also be used as a hemostat on the umbilical cord prior to cutting.
20. Esbilac for emergency feeding of puppies. Liquid Esbilac facilitates the task. See Index at Puppies, Esbilac for equipment needed to hand raise puppies.

21. Eyedropper or rubber syringe to remove mucus from throat and nose.

22. Pail to hold warm water. To revive apparently dead puppies.

23. Flashlight to observe bitch when she goes outside in the dark. She may whelp there. Also the electricity in the home may fail.

24. Blue litmus paper to test dam's milk.

25. Camera. If you are experienced enough to do two jobs or if you have an assistant.

26. Infrared lamp or other means of maintaining the required high temperature. Since the dam's temperature at whelping is about 100°, it is necessary to have the whelping room warm (say 85°) and free of drafts.

27. Thermometer to check room temperature and, possibly, hygrometer to check humidity.

28. Incinerator to burn soiled papers.

You should have been collecting newspapers since the mating. The whelping process is quite messy. Papers will also be needed after the whelping. Unshredded newspapers used as footing are smooth and may result in abnormalities in puppies. Breeders use a variety of bedding, e.g., shredded newspapers, soft grass hay. Straw is a stiff and coarse material that will irritate a puppy's skin. Indoor-outdoor carpeting is excellent since if provides firm footing and is washable. It may be hung over a fence and thoroughly hosed down. However, it is slow drying, so have at least one spare available. Large quantities of newspapers should be placed under the carpeting as the urine penetrates it rapidly.

Ask your veterinarian to be available day or night should an emergency arise. It he is unwilling to make a commitment, alert some other veterinarian. Have your automobile ready in case it becomes necessary to transport the dam to the veterinarian. Have plenty of suitable material to use in your car to prevent if from being soiled.

During the 9th week of pregnancy, take the dam's temperature twice a day. When it drops to 99°, you may expect puppies within 12 hours. If there is much delay beyond this, call a veterinarian. Bathe the nipples and vulva with a boric acid solution or with a solution of salt and soda water (1 teaspoon to a cup of warm water). It is not an infallible rule that the temperature will drop to 99°.

Dams have varying characteristics at whelping time but they will usually exhibit these same characteristics each time they whelp. As her time draws near, the dam will often grab some article in the pen with her teeth and whip it around vigorously. It is suggested that some suitable article be left in the pen for this purpose—some discarded piece of carpeting, pillow, etc.

A few days before the due date, the vulva will start to enlarge and become soft and relaxed. There may be a slight discharge. A day or two before she is to whelp, the bitch will refuse food, drink often, urinate frequently, whimper, paw her nest, exhibit signs of restlessness, pant for long periods. She should not be confined to the pen but be allowed to walk off her restlessness. An air of calm should prevail. Children and visitors should be barred.

There is a condition called "false pregnancy" which occasionally occurs even though the bitch has not been bred. She shows some of or all of the signs of pregnancy: gain of appetite, loss of appetite, nipples enlarge and milk appears, breasts sag, restlessness, pawing of bed, shaking bedding with teeth, enlargement of vulva, discharge, whimpering, panting. But, alas, no puppies!

> Though false pregnancy is a sign of hormone unbalance, it would be wrong to regard it as indicating any form of sexual abnormality or as likely to affect a bitch adversely as a brood bitch ... On the contrary, it rather suggests that in the affected animal the sexual and maternal instincts are highly developed and if mated [and if she conceives] the bitch will probably prove a prolific and devoted brood bitch.[1]

G. WHELPING

The breeder should be present at the whelping. Those who maintain that this is a natural act and that, therefore, the bitch can manage for herself, either have been extremely fortunate in the past or have had little experience. It is true that animals in the wild have their young without human assistance but many mothers and progeny are also unnecessarily lost for this reason. There are many serious complications that can arise in whelping. I strongly recommend Captain R. Portman Graham's *The Mating and Whelping of Dogs* for a discussion on this point.

A four-year study of Beagles at the School of Veterinary Medicine, University of California, Davis, California, which involved 1,157 births, concluded that during the colder months whelping occurred

---

[1]Dr. E. Fitch Daglish. Article in *British Dog World.* Quoted in *Gaines Dog Research Progress* (Summer, 1962).

in late afternoon; in the warmer months, it took place in early morning.[1]

The room should be kept warm. See Index at Whelping, Temperature of whelping room. When it appears that the bitch is about due, do not leave her even for a few minutes. Your presence will serve to alleviate her anxiety if nothing else. While she may obtain comfort from your presence, this does not apply to other persons. She will be upset by any confusion and, besides, visitors may bring infections.

The bitch's abdominal muscles will contract and relax. She may cry out in pain, may vomit, and may glance apprehensively at her vulva. Sponge her belly, nipples, vulva and anus with a boric acid solution, and repeat this if she goes out and lies on the ground. Once labor pains have set in, puppies should be born within 2 hours or so. If not born within 3 hours, call a veterinarian.[2]

The first puppy may be whelped within minutes of the first labor straining. He will be preceded by a "water bag", a greenish-black fluid contained in a membrane. The puppy itself will shortly follow and will be in a somewhat transparent membrane sac filled with fluid. Occasionally the sac is ruptured during delivery. Normally, puppies are presented head first with the paws alongside the head but breech births (hind feet first) are not uncommon. The puppy will be followed by the placenta, or afterbirth. Pull gently on the cord leading to the placenta if it did not come with the puppy. Make sure you account for a placenta for each puppy. A placenta retained by the dam can cause serious complications. It can sometimes be observed by a greenish discharge from the vulva. A red discharge is usually evidence that no placentas have been retained.

The dam will tear away with her teeth the membrane covering the puppy, sever the umbilical cord, also with her teeth, and eat the placenta. Eating more than two placentae may nauseate the dam. Any over this number may be thrown into a waste bucket for later disposal.

I prefer to remove the membrane rather than to wait to see if the dam will do so as she may delay too long, may, through nervousness, cause a hernia, eviscerate the puppy or even eat it. One must start at once at the head of the puppy as the puppy separated from the womb of his dam may drown in the amniotic fluid that fills

-----

[1]A.C. Andersen, *op. cit.*, p. 153.

[2]Onstott says that labor "may last from three to twelve hours, or even longer, before the appearance of the first puppy." *Op. cit.*, pp. 48, 49.

the sac. I also prefer to cut the umbilical cord rather than to let the dam do it. Her teeth may be uneven. She may tug at the cord instead of biting it and cause a hernia, she may infect the puppy with her teeth or she may cause bleeding. Before cutting the cord, clear the mucus from the puppy's mouth and nose with an eye dropper or rubber syringe so he may breathe. If the puppy is alive, hold the placenta above the puppy, not the reverse, to avoid pressure on the umbilicus and a possible hernia. Stroke the cord toward the puppy to minimize blood loss. Crush the cord with a hemostat or fingers to stop seepage of blood. Then cut it an inch and a half or two from the puppy's body. The cord may be severed by pinching and then tearing with the fingernails, but the cord is slippery and tearing may be difficult to do. If you do tear, make sure you pull towards the puppy and not away from him. Otherwise, you may cause a hernia. I use blunt scissors. If the cord is cut too short, and blood starts to ooze from the cord, apply cornstarch and press with the fingers using a dry, clean towel. It is also possible to tie boiled thread which has been dipped in iodine (or Lysol solution, boiling water, etc.) around the cord a half inch from the puppy and then cut the cord an inch from his body with sterilized scissors.[1] However, the cord is slippery and it is easier to cause a hernia by using this method. Touch the navel with disinfectant such as mercurochrome or peroxide. The cord will shrink and fall off in a few days.

Encourage the dam to lick the puppy. Should she not do so, use a rough towel to dry the puppy. Weigh the puppy and record information regarding him. This is especially important if the litter is large as weight loss can portend a serious condition and this must be attributed to the correct puppy.

WHELPING RECORD
Date: 14 April 1976. Order of whelp: 1

Time	Sex	Weight	Comments	
11:45 P.M.	M	18 oz.	Breech birth. Burst sac.	
Markings				

Head	Back	Chest	Front feet		Hindfeet		Tail
Tan, Black mask	Rear darker than front	Blaze	Left Toes	Right Toes	Left Toes	Right Toes	
			1 2 3 4	1 2 3 4	1 2 3 4	1 2 3 4	
			w w		W W W W	W W W W	w

Note: W: all white.   w: a little white

---

[1]Onstott recommends tying the cord about three or four inches from the puppy. *Op. cit.*, p. 49.

Observe that toe nails are dark unless there is white hair over the toes, in which case the nails are light. You may find that the markings change as the dog grows older, e.g. the white on the tip of the tail may gradually disappear.

Test the dam's milk with a strip of blue litmus paper. The acid should turn it pink. Excessive acid will turn it red. If the latter is the case, do not allow the puppy to nurse. Call the veterinarian. It would then be logical to hand feed the puppies or to give them to a foster dam.[1] If there is nothing wrong with the dam's milk, give the puppy to her to suckle. If a puppy has too much difficulty in finding a nipple, open his mouth and hold it up to one of them. Squeeze out a drop of milk to get him started should he fail to suckle. Puppies should be nursed within 3 hours of whelping. Normally puppies are whelped at intervals of 10 to 30 minutes and, at times, one hour. Should the period between whelps last over an hour, the dam might be taken out on a lead to relieve herself and to drink water but only for a few minutes and only if she is agreeable to leaving her puppies. She may prefer to stay in the pen. Do not expose her to cold or rain. Watch her closely. She may drop a puppy outside. Wash her nipples with warm water several times during whelping. After each puppy, clean up the pen as much as possible without unduly disturbing the dam.

If there is a greenish discharge instead of a puppy, the sac has burst inside the dam and the fetus will shortly die. Call the veterinarian at once. The lives of all remaining puppies and that of the dam may be in danger. If a Caesarean section becomes necessary, the dam will have to be taken to the vet. On the next day, she will be ready to nurse her puppies. Bathe the puppy's anus and adjacent parts with cotton batting dipped in baby oil until the feces and urine are expelled.

When it appears that the dam is about to have another puppy, some persons remove those in the pen to a cardboard box which they have heated with a hot water bottle or electric heating pad; they have covered these articles with a towel so that the puppies will not get burned. The purpose of removing the puppies is to avoid the possibility of the dam stepping or lying on them accidentally. If the bitch appears too worried about the removal of the puppies, speak to her gently to reassure her and keep the box in her sight lest, in fear, she kill the other puppies. This is a risky maneuver. The dam may quickly kill any new born puppies before you can intervene or cessation of labor may occur. It is better to leave the puppies with her

---

[1]See Index at Feeding, Puppies, Dam, Foster.

Whelping pen.

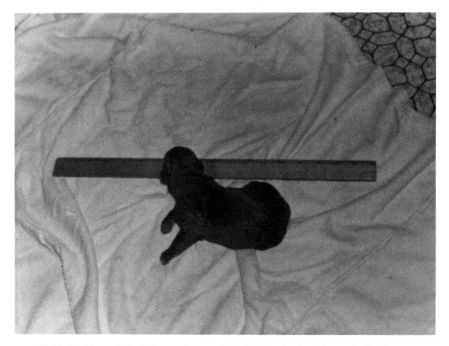

Keltic Siobhan, C.D. Fifteen minutes old (1971). Ruler is eighteen inches long.

Ch. Sulhamstead Marda, C.D., **Ch. Ballykelly Charlie Girl**, C.D., and four-week-old Keltic Siobhan, C.D. (1971).

Litter of five-week-old puppies by Mrs. **Charles Southey**'s Patrick of Brabyns out of Margot of Clonard (1925-England).

Ch. High and Mighty of Carrickmines and Ch. Ballykelly Powerscourt Tomas at three months (1968). Owned by Dr. and Mrs. Thomas Powers (Powerscourt Kennel).

Inisfail Kate, a nice three-months-old puppy, owned by Chuck Coomer. Note that she appears to "knuckle over" at the carpal joint. This will straighten out. Note also that, with the metatarsal bones perpendicular to the ground, the hind legs are not perpendicular to the ground. This too will become adjusted as the puppy grows.

and to be ready to move them out of harm's way, but within the whelping pen, should the dam start to move about too strenuously.

When the dam has settled down after a whelping, return all puppies to her. If she settles down with an air of complete relief and contentment, she may have had her last puppy. If she should give signs of uneasiness and should 3 hours elapse since the birth of the last puppy, call the veterinarian. He may administer pituitrin to stimulate contraction of the uterus so that any retained fetuses or placentae may be ejected. Dr. A. C. Andersen says: "Whelping should be completed within four hours from the onset of labor; any delay in delivery is critical to pup viability."[1]

An apparently dead puppy may oftentimes be revived. Do not cut the umbilical cord if the puppy appears to have been born dead. This means that you will have to prevent the dam from eating the placenta while you break the sac and see if the puppy is alive. The puppy should gasp for air when the sac is broken. If it does not and the dam does not stimulate his breathing and clear his nose by licking him, then you must get him to breathe, you must help his circulation and you must conserve his body heat. The following measures have been recommended. Keep his hindquarters at a higher level than his head, clear the fluid from his nose and mouth with an eye dropper, or rubber syringe, make sure his tongue is not lodged in his throat. Rub the puppy briskly with a rough towel to stimulate circulation. Hold his body in one hand and his head in the other. Swing him violently two or three times in an arc with his head downward and stop quickly to force mucus from his lungs. If he still does not breathe, put a drop or two of brandy on his tongue or use smelling salts or spirits of ammonia. If he does not emit a gurgling sound and therefore there is no fluid in his mouth, breathe into his mouth at the rate of twice a second as you alternately apply and relax pressure on his ribs (about 1/4 inch depression) for about 15 minutes. To prevent him from getting chilled, either immerse his body up to the neck in warm water for a couple of minutes at intervals or put him in a warm oven with the door open for a few hours — temperature about 90°. To test for life in a puppy, drop him from a height of 2 or 3 inches onto a hard surface. If he is alive, his legs will gradually extend.[2]

If a puppy should have such a serious defect that he should be destroyed, the most humane way is to have your veterinarian give

---

[1]A. C. Andersen, *op. cit.*, p. 158.
[2]G. W. Crighton. As reported in *Gaines Dog Research Progress* (Spring, 1969).

him an "overdose" of pentobarbital sodium which will instantly put him to sleep. Next to that, I suggest drowning in a bucket of warm water. Fortunately, I have never had to adopt either of these procedures.

The only mention of a difficult birth which I shall make is the one especially liable to occur if it is a breech delivery and the hind feet are tucked under the puppy's body. This will be kept brief. The dam can sometimes be assisted by gently moving the puppy's hind feet out and then grasping the partly-emerged puppy with some rough piece of material such as gauze or Turkish towel to furnish a grip and pulling gently downward and outward (45° angle) whenever she strains to expel him. As soon as the puppy is clear and there is no danger of his being withdrawn into the vagina, grasp the umbilical cord and gently pull out the placenta. Again be careful not to cause a hernia. There are so many possible complications, I prefer to recommend that you read Capt. R. Portman Graham's book. As an example of an unusual event, a dam whelped six puppies in an eight-hour period. About 48 hours later, she gave birth to another. All puppies were alive.[1]

H. POSTWHELPING CONSIDERATIONS

I.   Biological data at birth and the first few weeks of life.

A.   Respiratory rate
1.   First 24 hours of life 8-18/minute. 2. Twenty-four hours to five weeks 15-35/minute.

B.   Temperature
1.   First two weeks, 94-97°F. During the first six days most body heat comes from the bitch. If pups are out of the nest or away from bitch the body temperature may fall to 75°F. (This may predispose the puppy to fatal generalized infections). 2. Two to fourth week 97-99°F. 3. Fourth week on 100-101°F. (Shivering reflex in response to cold develops on 6th day of life.)

C.   Heart rate
1.   First 24 hours, 120-150/minute. 2. Twenty-four hours to five weeks, 220/minute.

D.   Eyes are closed at birth. Lids open 10-16 days of age. Pupillary reflex is slow until 3-5 weeks. Puppies may be cross-eyed until 25 days of age.

---

[1]The Irish Wolfhound Cub of America, *Harp and Hound* (1968) XIX, No. 1, pp. 6, 7.

    E.   Ear canals open at 15-17 days.

    F.   Umbilical cord falls off 2-3 days of age.

    G.   Toothless at birth: 3 to 6 weeks (baby teeth), (on each side of face); Upper: Incisors, 3; Canine, 1; Premolar, 3. Lower: Incisors, 3; Canine, 1; Premolar, 3. 4 to 6 months (permanent teeth): (on each side of face); Upper: Incisors, 3; Canine, 1; Premolar, 4; Molar 2, Lower: Incisors, 3; Canine, 1; Premolar, 4; Molar, 3.

    H.   Gag reflex develops at day 10. (Passage of stomach tube after day 10 is more difficult.)

II.   Appearance of puppies in health and disease. Dog owner should evaluate the general health and appearance of a litter of young puppies at least every 4 or 5 hours. The following are signs of health and signs of illness.

Healthy Puppy	Sick Puppy
Good muscle and skin tone	Loss of activity
Round firm, plump body	Scattered around in nest
Pink color to mucous membranes	Limp, wrinkled skin (dehydrated)
Straight back and legs	Poor muscle tone
Yawns frequently	Reddish-purple mucous membranes
Twitches frequently while asleep	Pot-bellied, weak back
	Crooked legs
	Splayed legs
	Flexed neck[1]

Puppies are born blind and deaf. Their eyes will usually open between the 10th and 16th day. If not open by the 17th day, bathe them twice daily with a warm boric acid solution on cotton batting. The eyes will have a blue cast until they are 6 to 8 weeks old. At about the third week, puppies progress from crawling to walking, and about the fourth they react to sounds and recognize people. Body twitching is normal in a puppy 1 to 3 weeks of age. This symptom disappears after 4 weeks. Testicles may descend by ten weeks; they could appear as late as eleven or twelve months. A puppy's ears are flat at birth. They begin to assume a rose appearance at about two months.

> Environmental disturbances, apart from the question of inhibition of labor at any stage, may adversely affect behavior [of the dam] toward pups already born. In some individuals, this type of behavior will include biting and actual killing; in many

---

[1]George W. Mather, D.V.M., Ph.D., "Canine Pediatrics," *Pure-Bred Dogs — AKC Gazette* (Nov., 1974), pp. 38, 39.

cases it amounts only to exceedingly rough grooming in which there is a tendency to nip with the incisors at the remains of the umbilical cord and to pick the puppy up by it. A Border Terrier, after an easy, apparently pain-free and unresented forceps delivery of a breech-presented puppy, killed her entire litter of three within two minutes after being left alone. This animal was in an open bed in a trailer situated in the yard of a noisy boarding kennel and had been subject to virtually continual disturbance.[1]

In addition to an unusual environment, some dams may kill their puppies because of pain from which they, the dams, are suffering due to mammary congestion or a Caesarean wound. To increase the probability of a dam accepting a Caesarean-born puppy, allow the latter to suck before narcosis or tranquillizers have completely worn off.

Because the puppies leaving the warmth of the dam's womb are apt to become chilled and chilling accounts for half of puppy losses from birth to weaning, authorities recommend keeping the temperature of the room at 85° the first four days, gradually reducing it to 80° by the 7th to 10th day and to 75° by the end of the 4th week.[2] One study concluded that a temperature of at least 70° should be maintained during the first week if the puppies stayed with the dam and that, if the dam had previously suffered losses of puppies, the temperature should be 80° to 85°, the puppies should be given oral glucose and treated with antibiotics. The reason for the high temperatures is that puppies do not have the ability to shiver during the first week and do not effectively develop fever (which destroys many microorganisms) until three weeks of age. Therefore, they cannot regulate their body heat.[2] The Ralston Purina Co. reports: "We try to maintain a temperature of 95° for the first week of life, 90° for the second week, and 85° for the third. This is one of the practices which have helped us maintain a weaning average of over 89% in the last 15 years.[3] A puppy's body temperature, measured with a rectal thermometer, should be 94° to 97° during the first two weeks, 97° to 99° during the next two, and 100° to 101° thereafter. If a puppy is taken from his dam, the environmental temperature should be about 87° to prevent his body temperature from dropping below 94°. If it should go under 94°, he becomes a chilled puppy and the dam will reject him. His esophagus is so relaxed that he cannot nurse and even if he can he will die of starvation since his digestive

---

[1]Freak, *op. cit.*
[2]Cornell, *op. cit.*
[3]*Purina Kennel News* (1976) IV.

tract is paralyzed. Should you have a chilled puppy, you must *gradually* warm him in an incubator or next to your body, turning him over every ten minutes to prevent congestion on the lower side of his body. Warming him too rapidly will kill him. *After* he is warmed, feed him glucose preferably, otherwise, in order of preference, honey, Karo syrup, table sugar. If fed before his temperature reaches 94°, he will die.[1] Avoid direct heat on the puppies such as having the rays of an infrared lamp pointed at them. Heating pads covered by a blanket or towel may be used to prevent chilling, but beware of burns. If a heating lamp is used, make sure it is affixed to an object which cannot be knocked over by puppies as the lamp could then ignite papers on the floor. Electric cords should be out of reach of the puppies.

After the litter has been whelped, offer the dam some warm milk. She may or may not wish to have some. For the next two days, feed her only milk, eggs, oatmeal, or broth, several times a day. Fresh water should always be available to her. If she refuses to leave the pen offer her a bowl of fresh water frequently. She will drink huge amounts.

The day after the whelping have a veterinarian examine the dam to make sure that no unborn whelps remain. He may give her an injection to clear her system. Take her out on a lead for a short walk. Some veterinarians routinely administer antibiotics to the dam after parturition. The prevailing expert opinion seems to be that this should be done only in the event of infection or prolonged dystocia. Moreover, high or prolonged doses of antibiotics, especially chloramphenicol, may harm the puppies causing diarrhea, bilateral overgrowth of the gut and mortality.[2] A German Shepherd breeder, in a 1975 article that was adjudged by The Dog Writer's Association of America to be the Best Magazine Article of the Year, cites a number of cases where the puppies of dams who had been given penicillin developed severe diarrhea because their intestinal flora had been destroyed and were slowly dying until given *Lactobacillus acidophilus*. This medication can be obtained from a veterinarian or from a drug store under the trade names of Lactonoc and Lactinex.[3] Veterinarians, at this writing, are not convinced that this drug is efficacious for the purpose intended.[2]

---

[1]Dr. Jacob Mosier, "Puppy Survival". Portion of lectures published in Bill Tarrant's "Gun Dogs" column, *Field and Stream* (May, 1976), p. 159.

[2]Dr. John Leonard in *Canine Practice,* quoted in *Gaines Dog Research Progress* (Fall, 1975).

[3]Dorothy Helm, *Midwestern Shepherd* (1976).

The dam will have a slight discharge for about ten days after whelping. A greenish discharge indicates that a placenta has been retained and is decomposing. If the discharge is bright red, there may be a hemorrhage. In either case, call your veterinarian. A dark red discharge usually means that all placentae have been expelled.

During the first week of lactation, the dam's intake will increase 50% to 75% over maintenance values. By the end of the second week, her requirements will be 250%, and by 5 weeks or so about 300%.[1] She should be fed two or three times a day. Her protein requirements may be double the maintenance value.

Observe if there is a reduction in the amount of milk from the dam. If so, it may be necessary to wean early. If the milk is not drained from the dam's breasts by the puppies due to early weaning or because she refuses to nurse them, the breasts will cake and swell and feel hot and hard. This is painful to her. Massage gently with camphorated oil twice a day or warm vinegar in the morning and warm camphorated oil at night to dry up her milk and shrink her breasts. Remove any traces of these liquids before allowing her to nurse. If the breasts become inflamed, call a veterinarian. Take the dam's temperature every day for two weeks. If it is high, call the veterinarian. See Index at Health, Maintenance, Thermometer.

Calcium deficiency in the dam will cause her to stagger, be short of breath, and become partially paralyzed. This is known as eclampsia. Get veterinarian help immediately.

The puppies' teeth and toe nails hurt the dam. Wash her nipples and breasts with warm boric acid solution to soothe them. Once the puppies have been weaned, reduce the flow of milk from the dam by giving her less food for a few days. This also reduces udder problems. Gradually return to the feeding method followed before breeding.

Puppies require a lot of sleep. Do not disturb them. Do not wake them up for visitors. Do not have visitors. They upset the dam and she may growl at them. She will certainly drive out any dogs even though they may be her kennelmates. Humans and animals may also be germ carriers and the means of infecting the puppies thus causing their deaths. Puppies need sleep as much as they need food. Keep them out of drafts. Keep them from cold, excess heat and sudden changes in temperature. Weigh them at birth, then every 8 hours for 4 days, weekly until 3 months of age, and then monthly until a year old. Puppies are more relaxed and less liable to jiggle the

---

[1]Dr. G. W. Mather, "Some Reasons Why Food Requirements Vary," *Gaines Dog Research Progress* (Spring, 1967).

scales when being weighed if this is done immediately after feeding. If they nevertheless wriggle too much, put them in a sling — possibly a small section of cloth — and lower them gently onto the scales. You may have to tape a small cardboard box onto the platform if the latter is too small to hold the puppy. When the puppy has been deposited, deduct the weight of the box. Should a puppy lose more than 10% of his birth weight in the 24 to 48 hour period after his birth, begin hand feeding as later described. This condition in a puppy is called "fading." Unless action is taken, he will begin to cry, stop nursing and die. It may be difficult to observe a 10% loss if a scale graduated in ounces is used. You may wish to purchase a scale graduated in grams from 0 to 1000.

Examine the puppies' navels each day. They should be healed within a day of the whelping. Any bleeding should be stopped with sterilized thread tied ½ inch from the belly. *Do not pull the cord in the direction away from the puppy or a hernia may develop.* Check the puppies' anuses periodically to make sure they are not caked. Normally the dam keeps them clean. If she has not, apply vaseline and stroke the abdomen in the direction of the anus.

At 3 days, have a veterinarian remove the dew claws. In Europe, the dew claws are allowed to remain. There is nothing in the Standard of Excellence on this subject. Dew claws, if not clipped, may curl back and cut into the skin. While nursing, the puppies will paw the dam and may injure her. Cut toenails at 5 days and every week thereafter with sharp scissors or a nail cutter so that the dam won't be injured, so that the puppies won't injure their eyes in play, and so that their toes won't become widespread. Cut only the tips so that you won't cut into the quick and cause pain and bleeding. As the puppies get older, nails can be cut every two weeks or possibly longer periods if they exercise much on hard surfaces. If the nails do bleed, apply styptic powder or corn starch. Cut the nails after the puppies have fed and are more relaxed. It is easier to do if someone else holds them while you do the cutting.

Puppies may be infected with worms prenatally; they may swallow the larvae on the dam; they may, like grown dogs, get them from the ground or other animals. In explanation of the fact that puppies are often born with worms even though the dam had previously been declared free of these parasites is the theory that round worm larvae are encysted in the dam's muscles and that these are activated about the sixth week of pregnancy. If untreated, worms will undermine the health of the puppies and possibly kill them. Pale gums may be an indication of hookworms which can cause a puppy to die at 10 to 12 days of age. Diarrhea may also be an indication of worms. Beware of patent worm medicines. While many of them are proper, you may not know which type of parasite is infesting your dog, there may be side effects such as vomiting, diarrhea; you might give him an overdose. Remember that worm medicines are poison. Worm the puppies and the bitch when the puppies are three to five weeks old and again a couple of weeks later to remove the mature worms that were larvae at the time of the first worming, but only if your veterinarian so advises after having made a fecal examination. Since the amount of medication is dependent on the puppy's weight, make sure you know what this is.

The first teeth, also called milk or temporary teeth, will appear between the 3rd and 6th week and the second teeth between the 4th and 6th month. Molars (not premolars) are always permanent.

When a puppy cries, he may be too hot, too cold, hungry, or sick. Press the dam's nipples to see if she is giving milk. The causes of sickness may be toxic milk, umbilical infection, septicemia, viremia, "puppy strangles", parasites or distemper. The symptoms of the first three are bloating and crying. If the milk is toxic, the puppy will have diarrhea and green stools; his anus will be raw and protruding. His reluctance to swallow even saliva will cause moisture to accumulate around his lips. If the dam has a pinkish or almost clear discharge at the vulva, her uterus may be infected. Have the veterinarian treat the dam. Hand feed the puppy for a day or two or until the veterinarian tells you breast feeding can be resumed. If the puppy has an umbilical infection, his abdomen will appear bluish or reddish and there will be pus on the navel. Unless immediately treated with antibiotics, he will die in 12 to 18 hours. Septicemia occurs from the third to the fortieth day. Twelve hours after the symptoms appear in the first puppy, another puppy is affected; 18 hours later the first puppy dies and a third is afffected, etc. Have a veterinarian treat the dam. Hand feed the puppies until weaned. A puppy with viremia cries continuously because he is hemorrhaging; pain killers do not seem to be effective. Keep him in 100° temperature for a couple of hours, gradually reducing the temperature over a two-day period to 85°; maintain the humidity. Even if the puppy survives, he may have incurred kidney damage. At about four or five weeks, a puppy with "strangles" develops a skin condition around the muzzle which expands until the puppy appears to have the mumps. Veterinarian care is indicated. A puppy off by itself has been rejected by the dam because of underdevelopment or, more likely, because his body temperature is below normal. It should be 94° to 97° during the first week. If it is from 78° to 83°, he is sick. Warm him slowly with a heating pad or other means, turning him often. With a dropper, give him a teaspoon of sugar to an ounce of water every 30 minutes for 2 to 4 hours.

Take the puppy to the veterinarian if he does not appear well, if he is limp, cold and clammy (in which case, the dam will most likely reject him), if he fails to suck vigorously when you place your finger in his mouth, if he has diarrhea. Keep the puppy warm on your trip to and from the veterinarian. One method of doing this is by having him rest next to your body while you wear a warm jacket.

My wife and I alternate in spending the first two weeks, day and night, with the dam and puppies in the whelping room to remove any hazards that may be created. For example, the dam, with her chest resting on the floor, may lie down completely on her side and thus land on a puppy. His yelps may cause her to rise and accidentally step on another puppy. Initially, one side of the pen is left open so that the dam may enter and leave with ease. As the puppies grow larger, the planks on the fourth side are emplaced to prevent them from crawling out. It would not do to leave the planks up when the dam wishes to nurse the puppies as she would jump in and might possibly land on some of the puppies. I therefore remove the boards on the fourth side, tell the dam "Stay!", hold the puppies to one side of the pen, tell the dam "Come!" and then "Down!" when she is in the pen, and finally release the puppies to nurse. When the dam indicates by her movements that she is ready to leave or when the puppies have had their meal, I again hold the puppies to one side and give the dam the command "Out!" The boards are then replaced. Thus for the first two weeks the possibility of the dam stepping on the puppies or rolling onto them is considerably minimized. Thereafter the dam is kept by herself and periodically allowed in to nurse the puppies with the same precautions being observed as during the first two weeks. These are extraordinary precautions but well worthwhile. Most breeders will allow the bitch to enter and leave the whelping pen by herself. They usually install on all four sides of the pen a guard rail that is about 6 inches above the floor and 4 inches wide. It reduces the probability of the dam accidentally injuring or killing the puppies by stepping or rolling onto them. Some breeders leave the bitch in with the puppies in a room or pen. The dam cannot thus escape the harassment of the puppies when they grow a little older.

Here are some details which may prove helpful. We are now at the stage where the dam is only brought into the whelping room periodically, say every four hours. It is time for feeding. Wash the dam's nipples. Go into the whelping room without her. The puppies are all asleep on the indoor-outdoor carpeting which was placed in the whelping pen after the whelping. Layers of newspapers are under the carpet. As soon as the puppies awake, they will mill around, yelp and urinate. To reduce the amount of urine on the carpeting, quickly put the puppies onto the floor of the whelping room which has first been covered with linoleum and then with newspapers. With paper toweling, remove any feces in the pen. If you have added boards to one side of the pen so as to prevent the puppies from leaving or entering it, remove them, call in the dam and replace the boards. The dam may stand until you put the puppies into the pen. With all the scurrying that then goes on she may step or lie down on one. Or she may lie down on her chest near one side of the pen so that the puppies will have difficulty in finding the nipples. Have the dam lie down in the center of the pen before putting the puppies into the pen. As the dam goes down push her gently so that she is completely on one side. The next time reverse the side. If she is facing the opening of the pen, she will be able to see what is going on and won't be concerned about anyone entering or leaving the room. This is one instance where obedience training proves of value. Tell the dam to "Stay" and put the puppies into the pen. Some of them may need guidance if they go towards the dam's head or to the wrong side of the pen. You may wish to feed in relays if the litter is large. Otherwise, much of the puppies' time will be spent in shoving for position and the weaker ones may not get their share of milk. It may be desirable to supplement the puppies' feeding if the litter is large as the dam may not be able to nurse all of them. If this is done, hand feed one group of puppies while the remainder are in the pen. After a certain length of time has expired, hand feed the puppies that were in the pen and place in the pen those previously hand fed. The length of time the puppies are allowed to nurse will depend on the amount of milk the dam can be expected to produce. If she indicates she wants to leave the pen after 30 minutes, then each relay should be of 15 minutes duration. If you have any spare time, clean up the wet and dirtied newspapers and either burn them or put them in a large plastic bag for later disposal. Replace the newspapers. When all the puppies have finished eating, put all of them onto the whelping room floor, let the dam out of the room, replace the wet newspapers that may be found under the indoor-outdoor carpeting. Put the puppies back into the pen. Wash the dam's nipples with boric acid solution. Feed her.

All of the above presupposes a gentle dam. What does one do if the dam growls menacingly when the owners try to adjust a puppy, replace one puppy with another, or have the dam leave the pen? This is a most unusual situation. It happened to us when Siobhan had a litter of eight and we decided to have them nurse in two groups. For three days after whelping, whenever one of us entered the pen she would put her head protectively over the puppies and growl. Two methods of countering this move proved effective. One was to offer her nourishment and remove the puppies as she drank or ate. The other was to let her sniff at a puppy from the group not in the pen while, with my other hand, I rapidly took the puppies from the pen and gave them to my wife. The reason for Siobhan's strange behavior lay in the fact that she had a temperature of 105° the day after the whelping and 103° on the two following days. Repeated veterinary care brought her temperature down to normal and she and the litter fared well thereafter.

There was actually a third method but this was only used when it was advisable to get her out of the pen so she could relieve herself or be treated by the veterinarian. A chain collar and a leash was put on her before she was allowed into the whelping room. After she had lain down, the leash was draped over the side of the pen. When I wanted her out of the pen I would take the leash, snap it lightly forward and say "Siobhan, come!" If she showed reluctance to leave the puppies and did not instantly obey, I would snap the lead repeatedly and harder as I urgently and strongly repeated "Siobhan, come! Good girl! Come!" The idea is to give the dog no time to think it over but to rely instead on the habit of instant obedience.

During the entire period of high temperature, Siobhan behaved normally when away from the puppies.

Occasionally, a puppy of about two weeks of age is unable to walk. He remains sprawled flat with his front legs at right angles to his body. He is called either a "flat puppy" or "swimmer", the latter describing his motions as he tries to walk. This occurs in some heavy-boned puppies, especially if they are fat. The condition can usually be corrected by providing him with firm footing such as grass or indoor-outdoor carpeting. Nursing puppies who are left on newspaper cannot obtain the secure grip needed by their hind feet to push against the dam.

For more serious problems, additional steps may have to be taken:

> The veterinarian may choose to administer injections of vitamin E and selenium, and calcium; excellent results have been seen from this treatment. He may consider that taping the puppy's front legs together under its body is sufficient therapy. This procedure molds the rib cage into a normal rounded shape and puts the legs into proper position. It can be effective in one or two weeks. Or, the owner may be sent home with an exercise regimen to follow with the puppy. This usually consists of gently massaging the rib cage and manipulating the legs. Several times a day the puppy is placed on its back, on a towel in the owner's lap. The rib cage is massaged from the spine forward or rolled in the palms of the hands to mold it into shape. It is not hard to shape a very young puppy's pliable bones — which is why they are so easily misshapen! The fore and hind paws are taken in the owner's fingers and the legs moved back and forth; the hind legs

flexed at the hock joints. Naturally, great care must be taken not to tire the puppy.

A further refinement to the exercise routines was devised by the owner of a severely afflicted swimmer who refused to accept a hopeless prognosis for her puppy. She floated the pup in the palms of her hands in a basin of warm water four or five times a day, for five minutes a session. The puppy was submerged to mid-chest, his rib cage cupped in her hands and legs dangling straight under his body. The owner "swam" him back and forth and soon the puppy voluntarily was using his legs. When he was dried after each swim, the legs were exercised again. Recovery was complete.[1]

The above article goes on to relate how one doctor suspended a "swimmer" in a sling for ten days removing him only to nurse while being held in the doctor's hands so that he would not lie flat. The puppy became completely normal.

All dogs should be vaccinated against distemper, hepatitis and leptospirosis. Puppies receive temporary immunity from their dam if she is immune and if they are nursing. The degree of immunity varies with the dam and decreases rapidly after weaning. It interferes somewhat with the efficacy of the vaccine. A nomograph can show when vaccine should be given. It takes three to seven days to build up immunity after being vaccinated, so do not expose your dog during this period to other dogs or to persons who have handled dogs. The immunity given by vaccine also decreases in effectiveness and some dogs have none a year after inoculation. It is therefore advisable to give your dog a booster shot each year. One speaks of "active" or "passive immunization", not of "permanent shots".

The vaccine may be either modified live virus or inactivated. The latter requires three injections at two weeks interval and, after three months, the immunity has considerably decreased. The former (of chicken embryo or tissue culture origin) requires only one injection if the dog is at least 12 weeks old; puppies younger than three months of age should receive two or more doses. A suitable program might be to give shots at the ages of 6, 9, and 16 weeks, with annual revaccination thereafter. Vaccination does not provide absolute protection to all dogs. Measles vaccine may be given as early as two weeks. This provides protection until the puppy can receive modified live vaccine at 16 weeks and is especially important if a foster dam is used.

---

[1]"Solving the 'Swimmer' Problem", *Gaines Dog Research Progress* (Spring, 1976).

Serum, also called anti-serum, is now believed to be of little value.[1]

Since there are constant improvements in the field of medicine and since certain hazards are known mainly by veterinarians, follow their advice. Dogs should not be introduced into a household where there has been a case of distemper until a month has elapsed since inoculation.

I. WEANING

Make sure that all puppies nurse and that some are not constantly bullied away by the more aggressive ones. Start weaning at three weeks and complete it by the end of the fifth week so that the dam may be sooner relieved of the puppies biting and clawing. This can be done by hand feeding the puppies before giving them to the dam to nurse and by gradually reducing the time they are left with the dam. When the puppy indicates that he is hungry, infant food, cottage cheese, cooked oatmeal, or finely ground raw beef may be placed with the finger onto the puppy's tongue. It may be placed in a shallow dish and the puppy's nose gently pushed into it. He will lap it off his face and then realize the source of the delicacy. Esbilac, manufactured by the Borden Company, is an excellent substitute for the dam's milk. It comes in both powdered and liquid form. Liquid Esbilac requires no preparation. Some breeders start weaning at 4 weeks and give the puppies warm milk for four days in addition to the bitch's milk. This may be canned milk diluted with equal parts of water. Other breeders offer canned baby foods or a thin mixture of Pablum which they thicken every couple of days until its consistency becomes medium. After a few days on Pablum, they give the puppy a teaspoon of very finely ground raw minced steak. At 5 weeks the daily meals consist of 2 meals of Pablum with milk. At this time, the puppies are left with their mother only at night and at 6 weeks they are completely weaned. Gaines recommends a gruel of water and soft-moist foods with ever-decreasing amounts of water. See Index at Feeding, Stand for a recommendation on the use of a stand. For a puppy, a sturdy box set in a corner may be used.

Water should be offered to puppies several times a day until they are a few weeks old when it should be continuously available to them. Use a heavy flat-bottomed glass or ceramic dish to minimize the possibility of its being tipped over. Initially, it should not be too deep. One breeder — of a different breed — had a pail of water so

---

[1]Priscilla Stockner, "Primary Preventative Medicine," The American Kennel Club, *Pure-Bred Dogs — AKC Gazette* (October, 1975), p. 55.

arranged that it could not be tipped over; his young puppy drowned in it. Eventually, the puppies will cease walking in the drinking water or tipping over the container and you can then use a dog bowl. I use the same type steel bowl as those from which the older dogs eat and drink.

You will find that puppies are extremely fast. Shuffle your feet along the whelping room floor to avoid stepping on a puppy. When you close the whelping room door reach down and push the puppies back into the room or you may catch a puppy's foot or tail.

There may be occasions when it is necessary to raise puppies by hand methods: death or illness of the dam, rejection of puppies by the dam, emotional instability of the dam, puppies too weak to nurse. Large litters may also be a reason, although there are other solutions to this last problem. One is to divide the litter and feed in shifts with a supplement being given between feedings. Another is to locate a foster dam through local veterinarians who may know of a false pregnancy or of a bitch (even though of another breed) with a small litter. Great care must be exercised in providing a warm environment and sanitary facilities.

It is very important that puppies get milk from the dam, at least for the first five days if possible, as the colostrum (dam's milk) provides immunity from distemper. Otherwise, their only immunization is that received *in utero* and their protection lasts only about one week. We have seen that the period from birth to weaning is the most hazardous of a puppy's life.

The first method of feeding to be described is called gavage or tube feeding. Equipment needed is a No. 10 French catheter and a 20 cubic centimeter plastic hypodermic syringe. The illustration shows how to determine the amount of tube to be inserted into the puppy. The tube should be marked with a ball point pen or with tape at a point ¾ of the distance from the puppy's last rib to his nose.[1] Don't forget to move this mark as the puppy grows. Do not prepare more formula than can be used in 24 hours. That which is not used should be refrigerated, then heated to about 100° and allowed to cool before feeding. After the tube is attached to the syringe, draw up the correct amount of previously-warmed formula through the tube and expel all the air. There is no need to lubricate the tube as the formula will serve this purpose. Place the puppy on a rough towel that has been spread out on a firm surface, open his mouth slightly without raising his head and insert the tube gently

---

[1]Ben E. Sheffy, "Meeting the Nutritional Needs of the Bitch and Puppies", *Gaines Dog Research Progress* (Summer, 1968).

over his tongue. If the puppy struggles, withdraw the tube. Don't force it into him. If the puppy is newly-born, make sure he is warm or the shock of warm food may kill him. The illustration shows how the marker on the tube is just short of the puppy's mouth.[2] It is not possible to damage the trachea or to cause damage to the walls of the esophagus or intestines. The catheter has to go into the stomach. An involuntary reaction will cause the puppy to close the opening leading to the lungs. Assurance that the tube is in the stomach may be obtained by inserting the other end into some water and observing that no bubbles are produced. If the tube is too long, it will curl up inside the stomach and greater force will be required to operate the plunger of the hypodermic. Hold the puppy with the left hand and, with the right hand, gently force the plunger down. The puppy's stomach cannot expand as rapidly as the plunger can be depressed. If the plunger is operated too rapidly, the stomach will become filled and then the formula will come up the esophagus into the pharynx and the puppy may inhale it. Inject 2 or 3 ccs., wait a little while, repeating the operation until you can tell from the slight distention and firmness of the puppy's stomach or the slight resistance of the plunger that he has had enough. There is no need to burp the puppy. He can be fed as seldom as three times a day. Liquid medication can also be given in this way. Either allow the dam to clean the puppy or else stimulate the external excretory orifices with cotton or a moistened wash cloth. Tube feeding can also be used to furnish nourishment to ailing adults. In their case, strained baby food may be forced through the tube, diluting if necessary. After use, the tube should be flushed and stored in a cold disinfectant. Rinse off before reusing.

There are several important advantages to gavage feeding over bottle feeding. There is no chance of producing accidental pneumonia by getting liquid into the lungs, or of causing colic by ingestion of air. It is simple and takes little time.

MEASUREMENTS
(Approximate Equivalents)

cc	Oz	Household measures
4	1/8	1 scant teaspoonful
5		1 teaspoonful
8	1/4	1 dessertspoonful
15 or 16	1/2	1 tablespoonful
30	1	2 tablespoonfuls
60	2	1 wineglassful
120	4	1 teacupful
240	8	1 tumblerful
		(drinking glassful)

---

[2]Borden, Inc., *The Borden Guide to the Care and Feeding of Orphan Pups* (n.d.).

Equivalents:

> 1 oz, 8 drams, 30 ccs or grams, 450 grains or drops.
> Usually what is meant by a cup of dry dog food is the
> amount contained in an 8 oz measuring cup.

Next we consider feeding by eyedropper and bottle. You will need an eyedropper, a doll or baby bottle, a cup graduated in ounces, Pyrex or plastic Squeeze nursing bottles, and anti-colic nipples (usually with three holes).

If a puppy is fed by eye dropper, place a drop on his tongue and feed him slowly so that he won't choke and possibly develop pneumonia.

For bottle feeding, shake out a few drops of milk so that the bottle will not contain air bubbles. Milk should slowly ooze out when the bottle is inverted. If it does not, enlarge the holes with a red hot needle. Puppies will not nurse if the milk comes too quickly. If the formula is overheated and the nipple thus becomes clogged, they will get discouraged and not drink.

Put the puppy on his stomach on a firm surface which has been covered by a rough towel or hold him in your left hand. Open his mouth and insert the nipple on top of his tongue as you withdraw the finger. Do not hold the bottle too high. Pull slightly on it to encourage sucking. If air bubbles rise during the feeding, the puppy is getting milk. Never squeeze milk out of the bottle while the nipple is in the puppy's mouth. After each feeding, hold the puppy upright against your shoulder, rub and pat his back to make him burp. Before feeding another puppy with the same nipple, place the hard rubber nipple in boiling water.

It is better to underfeed than to overfeed the first few days. Increases should be gradual. The puppy's health can be checked by observing whether his weight is increasing sufficiently and whether his stool is firm and yellowish. If fed three times a day, he should have three to five bowel movements a day; if fed four times a day, he should have four to six bowel movements. If diarrhea develops, cut the strength of the formula in half by adding boiled water. If the condition persists, consult a veterinarian. To stimulate his natural body functions, after each feeding rub his anal region towards the rear and also his abdominal areas with a cotton swab moistened with warm mineral oil, baby oil, or water. If this fails, fill a baby or ear syringe with warm water, insert into the rectum and gently squeeze the bulb. Try small amounts of water until successful.

If the puppies whine or cry, they may not be getting sufficient milk from the dam. She may start giving sufficient milk in a day, but meanwhile supplementation is necessary.

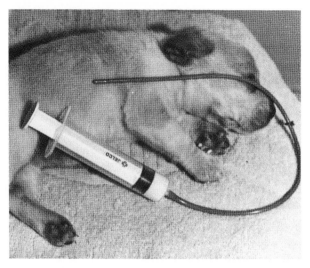

Gavage. Amount of tube to be inserted into puppy has been marked with tape.

Tube gently inserted into puppy as far as the tape on the tube.

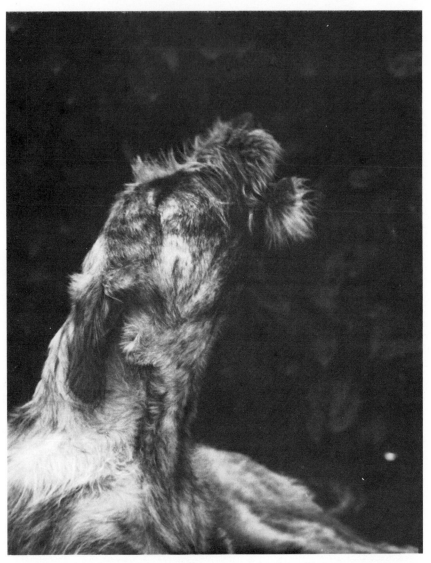

Major Acres Tancred O'Magnus, C.D., at six months. Owned by Boardman Moore.

Major Acres "S" of Engerth at eleven weeks. Owned by Mary Major and Coraline Engert.

Major Acres Rial Dhu, C.D., at eleven weeks. Owned by Boardman Moore.

One formula that is recommended by all authorities is Esbilac[1] for use by bitches both before and after whelping and as a replacement for bitches' milk if needed. The manufacturer advertises as follows:

Nutrient	Bitch's Milk (a)	Borden Liquid Esbilac (b)	Cow's Milk
Fat %	9.00	8.20	3.54
Lactose %	3.10	2.87	4.65
Protein %	8.00	7.63	3.20
Minerals %	0.90	1.16	0.70
Energy cals./gm. ..	1.28	1.29	0.68

(a) All values from "Canine Pediatrics."
(b) 21% solids.

If powder is used, one part of it should be mixed with four parts of warm sterile water. A quantity sufficient for four days may be prepared and stored in the refrigerator until needed when the amount needed should be warmed. Borden recommends three feedings a day at eight-hour intervals and says that the daily caloric intake per pound of body weight should be: 60-70 during the first week, 70 in the second week, 80-90 the third week and 100 the fourth week.[2]

Dr. Kirk notes that, in general, commercial powdered food has 1 calorie per cubic centimer. Therefore a newly-born 1¼ pound Irish Wolfhound would get 75-108 ccs. the first day. If fed three times that would be 25-36 ccs. per feeding.

One formula advocated in *Gaines Dog Research Progress*[3] is:

> 1 can evaporated milk
> ½ can water
> Egg yolk
> 2 tablespoonfuls of cream
> 1 teaspoon of Karo or honey (if puppy's bowels are loose, reduce
>   this amount).

Ralston Purina lists three formulas as replacements for a bitch's milk:

---

[1] Prepared by Borden Chemical, Borden, Inc., Animal Feed Supplements, P.O. Box 419, Norfolk, Virginia, 23501. Other address: Borden's Feed Supplements Division, 350 Madison Avenue, New York, New York, 10017.

[2] Borden, Inc., *op. cit.*

[3] Ben E. Sheffy, *Gaines Dog Research Progress* (Winter 1957-1958).

A.   Esbilac

B.   Emergency use. 1 cup of milk; 3 egg yolks (no albumen); 1 tablespoon corn oil; 1 drop Poly-Vi-Sol (baby vitamin-liquid, Mead Johnson); pinch of salt. Mix-blend uniformly and warm to 95-100°F. for puppies under 2 weeks. Use dropper, bottle, spoon or gavage.

C.   20 grams Puppy Chow and 80 grams water. Place in blender and mascerate into slurry that can be fed by bottle, spoon or gavage.

During lactation, a dam may consume much more food than normally. Let her eat all she wishes so that she may produce the required amount of milk.[1]

If a foster dam is employed, give her the least desirable puppies. To improve the possibilities of her accepting them, a number of methods have been employed: Rubbing the foster dam's puppies against the newcomers, rubbing some of the foster dam's vaginal fluid and milk on them. Watch the dam very carefully to make sure she does not turn on the new puppies or refuses to let them nurse. If she does either of these or appears to be emotionally unstable you will have to hand feed them. To reduce production of milk in a dam and thus spare her some stress, withhold food for 24 hours prior to the first day of weaning; on the next day, give her 1/4 of the normal amount, then on successive days, 1/2, 3/4 and the normal maintenance level.[1]

Captain Graham advised:

> Whelps, when once weaned, should never be shut up except at night, or in bad weather, as they must have exercise or they soon develop crooked legs.[2]

[1]Mohrman, *op. cit.*

[2]George A. Graham, "Irish Wolfhounds," *The Kennel Encyclopaedia, op. cit.,* p. 855.

V

The Puppy

A. SALES

We now assume that you wish to keep one puppy and to sell the others. You have advertised in dog magazines and possibly newspapers. You have informed the Secretary of the Irish Wolfhound Club of America and some of its other members. You receive telephone calls and letters from all kinds of people. For instance, they want an Irish Wolfhound "as a pet, not to show, therefore do you have a runt?", or "A fierce watchdog but one who is nice with children," or "A puppy who will be the tallest of all Wolfhounds."

How do you decide which puppy to keep? How can you meet the requirements of would-be purchasers?

Puppies are usually sold at 3 months. At that age, in my home, they have had their immunization shots, are less subject to disease, have been at least partially housetrained, have had the opportunity to develop with their littermates, have been accustomed to human companionship since all puppies are taken into the living quarters for short periods, do not object to a leash and collar.

Scientific studies have been made which have led to the conclusion that the period from 4 to 12 weeks is when puppies develop strong attachments to humans, dogs and to the physical environment.

> This period is critical, because the social experiences—types of species exposed to and whether the experiences were pleasant or traumatic—greatly affect behavior in later life. Recent studies have shown that if pups are taken away from their littermates at 3½ to 5 weeks of age and have only human contact, by 12 weeks they are asocial toward their own species. Thus if pups are taken as pets when they are very young and do not have the opportunity to develop social relationships with their own kind, they may become over-attached to their owners (or to a companion cat in the household), especially if over-indulged and if given no opportunity to meet their own kind subsequently. Such cases are often unsuccessful breeders and may show sexual responses toward their owners.

There is an optimum time to take a pup as a pet: any time between 6 and 10 weeks is generally within this optimum age span, for the pup will have had sufficient social interaction with its own kind and will not have reached the end of the critical period at which time it would be difficult to socialize it to a new environment and to strangers. Such pups are more easily housebroken, can be trained more easily and make successful breeders in later life.

One problem that has been frequently pointed out to me by several breeders of a variety of dogs is that, although the pups had plenty of human contact during the critical period of socialization, they were difficult to handle and often excessively timid by 6 months of age. What actually occurred was that the pups were played with when young and often allowed in the house. But as they matured, they were returned to the kennels and had less human contact. Dr. Benson Ginsburg, working with wolves at the University of Chicago, found a similar phenomenon. Thus, during the critical period, the capacity for a long-lasting social bond is established, but without subsequent reinforcement, it may deteriorate and the dog becomes de-socialized. Some dogs are more severely affected by short-term deprivation of human contact; innately timid dogs regress much more than more outgoing individuals, and their recovery is protracted.[1]

Because of the studies mentioned above, some persons have been of the opinion that puppies should be in the hands of owners before they were three months old. However, the scientific studies to which I have referred discovered that two twenty-minute periods of human contact per week were sufficient to create normal attachments by dogs to humans. In my home, the daily care, the weaning, and the deliberate inclusion of puppies in the household activities amount to two to four hours a day and have resulted in well-adjusted puppies.

At three months, one cannot be certain how puppies will develop although certain qualities and faults can be noted. To some extent, one can say that the heaviest will be the tallest provided one is not fatter than another, but bone size is also a factor in weight. One breeder kept a bitch out of a litter and sold another which later won the Irish Wolfhound Club of America Specialty (a show restricted to Irish Wolfhounds) for two consecutive years. There are many similar instances of breeders failing to select the best puppy. You will want to keep the best bitch, or possibly the best male, for

---

[1]Fox, *op. cit.*

yourself. By "the best", I mean the one that gives promise of being as close to the Standard as possible. One can usually distinguish between the best puppies and those of lesser quality at the age of three months. If the puppies are fairly even, it may be advisable to keep them for a few more months. One point deserves mention here. An undershot jaw in a puppy will become worse with age. A slightly overshot jaw will gradually improve.[1] Prospective purchasers may prefer the largest, the most aggressive, the cutest, etc. or they too may wish to have the best show prospect. Other breeders in your vicinity will be glad to offer their opinions. After you have made your selection, do not show him to persons who have come to buy. Some breeders will show one or two puppies, others will show all the available ones. Do not allow the puppies to be handled.

Some breeders assert that it is cruel to keep an Irish Wolfhound in an apartment. I do not agree that this is always the case. Under certain circumstances such a hound might be much better off than he would have been at the breeder's kennels. An Irish Wolfhound in an apartment or in a house with a small yard might spend his entire time with his owner who will see that he gets the required exercise, whereas the breeder might see the hound only at feeding time and might confine him to a kennel run 20 feet long and 4 feet wide. One must examine each individual situation.

There is another aspect to which attention should be paid. Are there any dogs or cats in the household? If the owner is experienced with animals and possesses good judgment, all may be well, but a grown cat can easily ruin a puppy's eyes—or a grown dog's for that matter. A grown dog of an aggressive breed might seriously injure an Irish Wolfhound puppy who, because of his size, may appear as a threat.

If the person inquiring about a puppy lives some distance from you, call an Irish Wolfhound owner in the area where he lives for references and information. Owners are glad to check on such matters.

A person who breeds Irish Wolfhounds for the first time should inquire of other breeders as to the prices generally charged for a puppy. If a much higher price is set and the puppies are sold, the purchasers may later feel that they have been defrauded. Too high a price may result in unsold puppies; the breeder might then panic and either sell at too low a price or try to give the older dogs away. Selling Irish Wolfhound puppies at too low a price proclaims, in

[1] R. H. Smythe. Quoted in "Lakeland Terriers," American Kennel Club, *Pure-Bred Dogs—American Kennel Gazette* (July, 1969) LXXXVI, pp. 70, 71.

effect, either that your puppies are not very good or that other breeders are charging exorbitant prices.

All puppies in a litter are not necessarily worth the same price. The one who gives promise of most closely living up to the Standard should command the highest price. The sex of a puppy has no effect on the prices at which I sell puppies. I do not know why it should. Many persons charge more for a male than a female. I base the sales price strictly on how well the puppy may meet the Standard for the breed. Many persons claim that it is better to have a bitch. Their arguments and my views are set forth:

1. *Argument*
    The bitch is more intelligent and more easily trained. She is more easily housetrained. She does less damage to furniture and furnishings.

    My View
    These are generalities and are not necessarily correct. I have found it as easy to train a male as I have a female. I had one male Irish Wolfhound who received his Companion Dog obedience degree at 6½ months. Some females are more aggressive than males. Some males are more affectionate than females. It all depends on the individual. According to some authorities, the bitch is a more aggressive hunter than the male. See the chapter on Hunting.

2. *Argument*
    The bitch does not roam so much as the male.

    My View
    Neither dog nor bitch should be allowed to roam.[1]

3. *Argument*
    She is gentler with children.

    My View
    All Irish Wolfhounds are gentle. Of course, the heavier the dog the easier it is for him to push over a child, but in view of the size of the Irish Wolfhound, it is immaterial whether a child is accidentally pushed by a 140 lb. bitch or a 180 lb. male.

Some persons may object to a male because of his propensity for frequent urination while on a walk and because he will thus ruin

---

[1] See Index at Exercise area, Restriction to.

plants and bushes. He will of course, also be attracted to bitches in season.

Don't sell a puppy "on approval". The new owner should be made to reflect seriously on his obligations to the puppy before he decides to buy. He is not buying a piece of property, he is buying an Irish Wolfhound. Therefore, the transaction is not to be taken lightly. It is not fair to the puppy to be shifted from household to household. He will be confused and distressed by the change of owners and environment and may become a shy and nervous dog. Moreover, it may be the occasion of his bringing back disease to your kennel thus endangering your other dogs. However, if you should ever believe that one of your hounds is not in the proper home, by all means try to get him back!

Don't sell on the installment plan. No matter how well-intentioned and upright the purchaser of a dog may be, he will be quick to conclude that any defect which he later observes in the dog, any injury or disease, was latent and really existed prior to the sale. Since he does not have a perfect dog, he may want to return the dog or he may refuse to pay some of the balance due on the purchase price. Should you, despite my admonition, sell on the installment plan, have a written agreement that title will not pass and the registration certificate will not be transferred until the full amount of the purchase price has been paid. In the event of a default you could sue to repossess the dog. In any case, he would not be allowed to show the dog or to obtain a registrable litter by breeding him.

At this point, I would like to relate a personal experience. I received a telephone call from a lady who was extremely interested in purchasing an Irish Wolfhound puppy. Although I had none for sale, I invited her and her husband, a professional man, over to see the hounds. She became wildly enamored of a four-months old puppy bitch and I reluctantly agreed to a sale. I explained to her that, as a precautionary measure, I had had a radiograph taken of the puppy, that the veterinarian had prescribed a high protein diet, no calcium and much rest, and that he had assured me the puppy would be all right. I advised her to get the radiograph from him and show it to her veterinarian. She frequently telephoned and wrote to me expressing great joy at her possession and saying that her veterinarian also liked the puppy very much. Her veterinarian had told her that my veterinarian was foremost in the field of the puppy's problem and that his advice should be followed. Some time later, she wrote that the puppy was deformed and would always be so. She sent me a copy of an article written by my veterinarian which had appeared in a professional journal. The article did not support her position. My veterinarian reaffirmed both to her and to me his previously-stated position. She wrote that she would not pay me the balance due—I had, for once, broken my own rule and made a sale on the installment plan—unless the dog developed into a show dog. She asserted that I had not told her that there was anything wrong with the puppy and that I had known at the time of the sale that the puppy had no chance for recovery. I promptly answered that I would repay her all she had paid me plus all her veterinary expenses if she would return the puppy to me and that, should she decide not to do so, title to the puppy would not pass to her until full payment was made, in accordance with the terms of our written agreement. She accepted my offer and her husband returned the puppy three and a half months after they had picked her up. He told me that the puppy had one bad habit. She would drink out of the toilet bowl at night and then drip water on his face as he lay in bed! I advanced the thought that he could have closed the toilet seat cover and provided her with a bowl of fresh water. I examined the puppy very carefully. She was in no way deformed, but was extremely thin; she was friendly but not playful and would not lap faces or hands as Irish Wolfhounds generally do; she did not wag her tail and was extremely reserved and sensitive. The veterinarian discovered whipworms and she was therefore treated and segregated from the other hounds for two weeks. Had she stayed in the household of the purchaser, she would have been a poor show specimen. As it is, she became the best Irish Wolfhound I had ever owned. What had gone wrong? There was no question that the lady purchaser loved the puppy. It is my opinion that the household, which included two young children, was a highly active and emotional one and proved to be a nerve-wracking experience for the puppy. From the telephone calls and letters which I received from the purchaser, I concluded that the puppy was constantly on exhibition and not given the rest prescribed by the veterinarian.

Some breeders will sell a puppy at less than the usual price in return for an agreement that the puppy sold will later be bred and a puppy from that mating will be given to them. This is not inherently a bad agreement. For example, a sale by one breeder to another is not the same as one to a person who is buying his first hound. The latter may be forced by the agreement into a breeding for which he is ill-equipped by reason of inexperience, lack of facilities, etc. He may find himself with a large litter and, in order to rid himself of a burden, may sell puppies to unsuitable homes. Should the buyer decide not to breed and should he live some distance from the seller, or should he move far away after acquiring a puppy, the seller may have a difficult time enforcing the agreement.

Many puppy mills offer contracts which appear to be good "business propositions", e.g. if a veterinarian declares that a purchased puppy has a disease or serious physical defect, the puppy will be replaced within six months of purchase. From six months to two years after purchase, 40% credit towards a new puppy will be allowed. From two years to ten years, 25%. Most people, however, become attached to their dogs and will not "turn them in for a new model". Also how long do most puppy mills stay in business? As moved as you may be by the pitiful sight of an Irish Wolfhound puppy in a pet shop, do not buy him. This would merely encourage the owner to buy more Irish Wolfhounds. However, do not hesitate to complain to the proper authorities if grounds for complaint exist.

Here are some of the complaints I have heard about purchases of Irish Wolfhounds from an American breeder:

1. "[She] was 3½ months old when we bought her from Mr. [X], and she had been in this country for less than 24 hours. She had examination papers from an Irish vet and someone at the P.O.E. [Port of Embarkation] here which attested to her health and listed the shots, etc. . . . She was thin when she got here and a month later, instead of eating 4 lbs. of food that [X] had said, she stopped eating entirely and was in the words of our second, very good, vet dangerously thin and near to malnutrition . . . She was diagnosed as suffering from an unidentified virus, brought on because she was run down. She also had a bad infestation of coccidia . . . She also had a bad case of round worms . . . Until she was 8-9 months old—that is, in recent weeks—she has seemed somewhat susceptible to stomach upsets, runny nose and general lack lustre . . . She is still thin but not gaunt and she doesn't eat a great deal. Her appetite has never been good . . . We are particularly upset about the lack of enthusiasm of other reputable owners about breeding to a [X's kennel] dog. We are interested, however, not just in [our hound] but in the breed and would like to (and intend to) learn much and become as involved as we can over the years."

2. "August: We gave Mr. [X] a deposit on . . ., who, Mr. [X] said, was a five month old female. We returned the beginning of Sept. to pick up the dog. I noticed that she was severely bitten from head to toe-nail, and that on her hind leg, one of the dew claws was growing in a circular manner back into the flesh creating an infection. I mentioned these two items to Mr. [X] and he remarked that puppies will be puppies and immediately had an attendant cut back the dew claw and check the other "puppies" for this infection. I looked at . . . teeth and remarked that the teeth were remarkably well developed for a dog that was only five months old. I said that she looked as if she were over a year old.

Mr. [X] said this was impossible and showed us a paper that was nailed on the kennel door which stated the name, color, and age of the dog (giving the month only) . . . we took her home. Her demeanor was that of extreme shock. We had to carry her from the car into our home, at which point she ran into a corner and crouched there, refusing to move.

"The next day, we took . . . to our vet. Upon examination he said that she was in extremely poor shape, over one year of age, weighed only 60 pounds, some of the open bites were infected, that she was anemic and infested with worms and hookworm.

"Mr. [X] told us that if we were not satisfied with . . . we could take her back at the end of the month. . . . showed no personality characteristics except fear, but we felt that if we returned her she would surely die. We noted that she seemed to relate to other dogs, so that we felt she might perhaps relate to a puppy. . . . papers arrived and we noted that she was whelped in April of '65 not '66.

"When we called Mr. [X] to convey our general displeasure at the state of affairs, he semed genuinely astonished when we told him of her age. He offered to pay for . . . worming and B12 shots or to take her back. When we mentioned that she might relate to another pup, he offered us first choice out of four litters that were arriving at the end of September.

"October: . . .completely wormed, fifteen pounds heavier, all sores healed. We returned to Mr. [X] to pick up a male pup, and saw pedigrees which were in no way aligned with [the bitch previously purchased] . . . Several weeks later when the pedigree arrived by mail, we noted that the only difference in the pedigrees of [the two wolfhounds purchased] was that the mothers of the two dogs were half sisters. Other than this, the pedigrees were exactly the same.

"April: [First puppy purchased] . . . now weighs 140 pounds, is still extremely shy and withdrawn, but recently exhibits "normal" canine traits such as chewing on a bone, guarding her bone, and playing with the pup.

"In conclusion: Although we noted that Mr. [X's] kennels were clean, his dogs were not well cared for, and the older ones were in extremely poor shape."

3. Another purchaser of a dog from the same kennel showed him to me at about 3 months of age. The puppy carried his hind legs completely under his body and weighed about half what he should have. After two years the new owner sent photographs of the dog to Mr. [X] and informed him that several judges and breeders had advised her not to show the dog in breed classes as it

was a very poor specimen. The lady asked for a partial reimbursement since Mr. [X] had advertised his dogs as of "Exceptional Size and Conformation". Mr. [X] offered to take the dog back and replace him with a puppy from a new litter. Naturally, the owner was too attached to her dog to agree to this.

4. One person bought a puppy from Mr. [X] and immediately took him to a nearby veterinarian. Upon being advised to return the puppy, he did so. Mr. [X] promised him a puppy of a certain age in the near future. When the purchaser was notified that the puppy was available, he went to Mr. [X's] kennel to pick him up only to discover that the puppy was somewhat older. Nevertheless, he took him home. For about a year, he treated the dog for a variety of problems, spending a total of $700 in the process. The dog was so weak in hindquarters and had so much difficulty in walking that, eventually, the owner had to return him to Mr. [X]. He asked for reimbursement and this was granted. Mr. [X] said he was going to give the dog to someone else.

5. Mr. X sold a male puppy to a man and told him that the puppy should weigh twenty-five pounds at three months. The mean weight of a three-month old male puppy is about fifty pounds.

The "puppy mill" operator and the pet shop dealer have one interest: making money. Their dogs are confined because it would cost money to provide them exercise. Here are some statements on the effects of this practice.

The results of a growth study to compare the effects of cage environment with outdoor pens [320 square feet] resulted in some interesting data. From five litters whelped and weaned in cage units, one male and one female from each litter were maintained in the cage unit and their siblings placed in outdoor pens. The growth plateau was reached at 12 months for the cage-reared dogs and at 10 months for the outside dogs. The Beagles in outdoor kennels attained better muscular stature than the comparatively "flabby" Beagles reared in the cage units.[1]

Dr. Wayne H. Riser, School of Veterinary Medicine, University of Pennsylvania, cautioned that confinement "seriously retards the development of intelligence and personality."[2] Dr. Michael Fox

---

[1]School of Veterinary Medicine, University of California, Davis, California. Studies quoted in "California U. Cage Has Unusual Features," *Gaines Dog Research Progress* (Fall, 1963).

[2]Wayne Riser. Interviewed by Dr. M. J. Deubler on Canine Hip Dysplasia, *Popular Dogs* (January, 1966), XXXIX, p. 34.

says that pet shops mark down puppies at 16 weeks to half price because damage to the dogs' behavior has then been done. "They commonly suffer a crippling nerve overload and withdraw into a dark corner—both psychically and physically."[1] The effect of confinement on human prisoners of war results in a much higher rate of suicide, murder and accidents among them after their release than among the average population.

I mentioned that the "puppy mill" operator often buys entire litters from breeders and usually at the age of six weeks to cut down transportation expenses. This is a barbarous practice and one that has been condemned by all reputable breeders and dog organizations and publications. The seller is not the slightest bit concerned as to whether the puppies are placed in good homes. I have both seen and heard of the illnesses, diseases, and poor physical and temperamental characteristics of some of these poor puppies. The purchasers, who loved the puppies despite their defects, were broken-hearted and spent large amounts of money in vain attempts to remedy the conditions. There is a greater danger in importing a puppy than in buying one locally, unless the foreign breeder is reputable, as in the former case one does not have the opportunity of seeing the parents of the puppy or the conditions under which the puppy is being raised.

Most individuals are unaware of the points mentioned in this chapter. They believe that all pure-bred dogs are good and that one advertiser is as good as the next one. They tend to place their faith in the printed word although some advertisements are misleading. Whether an advertisement is misleading is often a question of opinion. One should bear in mind that:

1. The fact that a puppy's ancestors were champions does not mean that he will be one or even that he is a fair specimen. It is better to say that he shows promise.

2. It is difficult to say whether a certain puppy will be outstandingly tall. Often they grow fast, slow down, and are surpassed by others in the litter.

3. "Five Generation Pedigree" is meaningless. All dogs have ancestors. A dog can have many serious faults even though many of his ancestors were Champions.

4. "AKC Registered" is not a guarantee of anything other than

---

[1] Michael Fox, "Neurosis in Dogs,"*Popular Dogs*.

that the puppy is purebred. It is not a guarantee that the hound advertised could become a champion or even that he is a fairly good specimen of the breed.

The American Kennel Club cannot stop puppy mills from operating or pet shops from callously treating puppies. Puppy mills and pet shops are legal enterprises. The American Kennel Club concerns itself, under its charter, with proper record keeping of purebred dogs, registration procedures, dog identification, and conduct of dog shows. It can prevent a person from registering or showing his dogs if he has made false claims regarding them, e.g. inaccurately stating their pedigrees.

The wise purchaser will select a reputable breeder, a person who has a reputation to maintain. A dog purchased from him has a much greater probability of having an Irish Wolfhound's physical, mental, and temperamental characteristics. The reputable breeder provides his puppies with the proper nutrition, exercise, veterinary care, environment, and close companionship. Often, people telephone or write to me inquiring where they can purchase Irish Wolfhound puppies. I always reply: "You realize that I cannot vouch for the quality or soundness of any puppies from litters other than my own. There is always the possibility that in any litter one or more puppies may be substandard or have some disease. Nor can I pass on the reasonableness of the price asked by other persons. I do know that so-and-so has had a litter." If I have no knowledge of the breeder's qualifications, I say no more. If I do have some knowledge, I will add either "The breeder is honorable" or "I suggest you look elsewhere." I then suggest to them that they consult the Irish Wolfhound Club of America[1] which will supply them with the names of some reputable breeders and that they buy only from someone on that list or from someone who is recommended by a person on the list.

Although there can be only one official club, i.e., one recognized by the American Kennel Club, there are many regional clubs which have been formed to help the breed. Write to the Secretary of the Irish Wolfhound Club of America for the names and addresses of the secretaries.

There are many persons who purchase Irish Wolfhounds bred in England or Ireland. The sale price is generally less than in the United States. However, transportation costs are quite high. It is because of transportation costs that some foreign breeders export

---

[1]Secretary's name and address available from the American Kennel Club, 51 Madison Avenue, New York, N.Y., 10010.

puppies as young as six weeks. If one knows that the foreign breeder is reputable, that he is qualified to breed good specimens, that he is not primarily concerned with financial profit, that his kennels are well maintained and that the hounds and puppies get the best of care, then it is perfectly proper to purchase a puppy from him. But, I must warn you, there are "puppy mills" in England and Ireland as well as in the United States. Most of the kennels which I have seen in foreign countries should be strongly condemned. They do not meet the standards established by good breeders. The hounds and puppies are regarded as merchandise and raised like chickens or cattle, whereas I believe that dogs should be treated as "man's best friend". If a breeder maintains a slovenly kennel, one may well wonder whether he maintains accurate breeding records. In the commercial enterprise of exporting puppies, many foreign breeders are not in the least concerned about the kind of homes in which puppies will be placed. They make no inquiries whatsoever. I recommend that hounds be purchased from overseas only if the purchaser has personally conversed with the breeder and has inspected his kennels. If this is not possible, then the prospective purchaser should discuss the matter with an American breeder who is acquainted with overseas operations. The person who cannot visit foreign kennels must weigh the advantages which exist in being able to see a puppy prior to purchasing him.

The purchase of a puppy should be evidenced by a written agreement. Here is one type of such a document. It is always well to consult an attorney should it be desired to incorporate unusual provisions in a contract.

SALES AGREEMENT

Agreement made this _____ day of _____,

19_____, in _____ between
(location)

_____ , hereinafter known as the seller, and

_____ , hereinafter known as the buyer,

whereby title to a male/female Irish Wolfhound, _____ ,
(Cross out one)   (Registration No.)

whelped on the _____ day of _____,

19_____ , by _____
(Sire)

out of _____
(Dam)

and now owned by the seller will vest in the buyer and the seller will deliver to the buyer the duly completed AKC registration certificate on this hound as well as a health certificate filled out by a veterinarian and a three-generation pedigree upon fulfillment of the following conditions:

1. Purchase price of $＿＿＿＿＿＿＿＿ paid by the buyer to the seller.

2. Transportation costs paid by the buyer.

The seller warrants that the hound is in excellent health but has not made and does not now make any further warranties as to the hound's condition or potential.

The seller urges the buyer to have the hound examined by a veterinarian of his own choice within forty-eight hours.

Witness our hands and seals this ＿＿＿＿＿ day of＿＿＿＿＿＿,

19＿＿＿＿＿.

＿＿＿＿＿＿＿＿＿＿＿＿＿＿＿＿＿＿＿
(Seller)

＿＿＿＿＿＿＿＿＿＿＿＿＿＿＿＿＿＿＿
(Buyer)

Should a puppy have a serious defect, you will have to make a decision whether to destroy him (also called "putting to sleep" or "putting down") or to find him a home as a pet. Should the latter be your decision, embody the terms of your agreement into a written document. Here is one specimen.

SALES AGREEMENT

Agreement made this ＿＿＿＿＿ day of ＿＿＿＿＿＿＿＿,

19＿＿＿＿, in ＿＿＿＿＿＿＿＿＿＿＿＿＿＿ between
(location)

＿＿＿＿＿＿＿＿＿＿＿＿＿＿＿ , hereinafter known as the seller, and

＿＿＿＿＿＿＿＿＿＿＿＿＿＿＿ , hereinafter known as the buyer,

whereby title to a male/female Irish Wolfhound whelped on the
(cross out one)

＿＿＿＿＿＿＿＿ of ＿＿＿＿＿ 19＿＿＿＿ , and now owned by

the seller will vest in the buyer upon payment by the buyer to the seller of the purchase price of _____ and of transportation costs.

It is agreed between the parties that:

1.   The animal being sold is not of sufficient quality to be shown in breed competition or to be used for breeding purposes.

2.   The buyer disclaims any right to American Kennel Club registration papers and pedigree information on the animal and agrees that none will be provided by the seller.

3.   The animal will not be exhibited in breed competition and will not be used for breeding.

4.   The buyer will have a veterinarian castrate[1] the animal within two months after the animal comes in season for the first time (if a bitch)[2] or within two months after the animal becomes one year of age (if a male). If these time periods have already occurred, then the buyer will have the operation performed within two months of acquisition of the animal. A veterinarian's certificate that the operation has been performed will be supplied the seller within one month of the operation.

5.   Title to the animal will not be transferred to any person or organization other than the seller, whether by sale, gift, loan, or otherwise, except in the following manner:

a.   The animal will first be offered by the buyer to the seller under the same terms and conditions as to the third party.

b.   Should the offer not be accepted by the seller, then the buyer and seller will enter into a written agreement whereby the animal will become a gift to the seller and the seller will in turn enter into a written agreement with the third party similar to this one except that the purchase price will be that agreed upon between the buyer and the third party. All proceeds from the transfer to the third party will be given to the buyer by the seller.

---

[1]The term "castration" is not restricted to males; it includes the spaying of females.

[2]One recommendation is that spaying be done when the bitch is 6 to 8 months old, but this refers to dogs generally and was possibly not intended to apply to Irish Wolfhounds, who come into season later than smaller breeds, although the reference, which I now cite, is in a book on Irish Wolfhounds: Elsworth S. Howell, Milo G. Denlinger, A.C. Merrick, D.V.M. "General Care and Training of Your Dog." in Alma Starbuck's *The Complete Irish Wolfhound* (1969), Part II, p. 53.

Two five-month-old puppies. Bred and owned by Alma Starbuck (1940).

Gweebarra of Eagle at seven and a half months of age adjudged Best Puppy in Show at 1971 Irish Wolfhound Club of America Specialty by the author. Gweebarra, as a Champion, was Best of Opposite Sex at the 1975 Specialty. Breeder-owner-handler Samuel Evans Ewing, III (Eagle Kennel).

6.   Failure on the part of the buyer to comply with clauses 3, 4, or 5 will render him liable to the seller for liquidated damages in the amount of $5000 plus reasonable attorney's fees, if incurred, because of the harm done to the name of the breeder, his kennel operations, and to the Irish Wolfhound breed generally.

A copy of an agreement not to provide registration papers, whether with or without conditions, should be given to the American Kennel Club. The Club will honor the agreement provided the buyer remains the owner. It will issue a registration certificate if a third party who has become the owner and who has not signed such an agreement requests it. The seller's sole remedy would be to sue the original buyer for damages. If the seller has prior knowledge of an intended sale, he could ask the court for an injunction.

An alternative is to agree that a registration certificate and other papers will be given when castration has been performed. A signed agreement by a buyer to do something or not to do something does not prevent him from doing whatever he pleases. Should you give him the registration before the hound is castrated and should he then show or breed the hound, your only remedy would be to seek redress in court, a time-consuming and expensive affair, especially if the owner and dog have moved to another State. Moreover, the owner could breed the hound and attribute parentage of the litter to some other hound owned by him.

The Canadian Kennel Club has approved a Non-Breeding Agreement which differs from the one above.

If you have had limited experience in the sale of puppies and a purchaser calls to complain about some alleged defect and to ask what you are going to do about it, it may be advisable to get all the details and tell him you will call him back. Then contact a long-established Irish Wolfhound kennel and ask for advice. This may assist you in doing whatever is honorable in settling the issue should the complaint be a valid one and prevent you from being defrauded if it is not.

Upon receipt of payment, give the new owner a copy of the bill of sale, the registration papers, a three-generation pedigree and a statement from your veterinarian certifying that the puppy is in good health. If you suspect that the new owner's check may not be good, tell him you will mail the registration certificate. Do so after the check has cleared. The veterinarian's statement should include the breed, sex, age and dates and type of worm medication and of serum or vaccine given the puppy. If he has been immunized against rabies, data should be provided. The inclusion in the agreement of the provision that the puppy be examined by a veterinarian within forty-eight hours may avoid much difficulty with people who mishandle a puppy or allow him, through carelessness, to contract a disease and then expect that you will take the puppy back, refund their money, and pay their veterinarian's bills.

There are several ways of listing pedigrees. I have designed the one shown here. Readers may use this format if they wish. Incidentally, when speaking of a puppy's parentage one says that he is "by" the sire "out of" the dam.

Only purebred dogs can be registered. A purebred dog is one that belongs to one particular breed. He is not a "thoroughbred", a term reserved for a distinct type of horse. Should someone ask why a purebred dog is preferable to a mongrel, a proper answer is that a purebred will generally have the appearance of his breed, its characteristics, its temperament whereas a mongrel's attributes may vary considerably. There is no truth to the generally-quoted statement that a mongrel is hardier than a purebred.

In order to be shown in the United States, a dog must be registered with either the American or the Canadian Kennel Club. The AKC has as its objective the protection and advancement of purebred dogs. It does not have individual members. Each breed club and other recognized dog associations elect a delegate who attends AKC meetings and votes on policies and other matters. The AKC is located at 51 Madison Avenue, New York City, N.Y., 10010. Its rules on registration are occasionally changed so no mention of present procedures will be made here. The AKC provides a free pamphlet "Rules applying to Registration and Dog Shows" which all owners should have.

Normally, it is the breeder who registers the individual puppies. His kennel name thus becomes a part of the puppies' names. Some breeders register the litter but not the individual puppies which they sell. Instead they authorize the new owner to do so. The only advantage to this course of action is that the breeder saves the cost of registration. The bad feature is that the new owner may give the dog a ridiculous name, one not befitting an Irish Wolfhound.

Registration data are invaluable to anyone who wishes to follow a breeding program or who wishes a continuous history of the breed. The late LeRoy E. Fess, former editor of the Irish Wolfhound Club of America's *Harp and Hound,* with the assistance of his wife, was able to obtain and publish all American Irish Wolfhound

Pedigree of Keltic Aluinn

Parents	Grand Parents	Great Grand Parents	Great Great Grand Parents
			8
		4	9
	2		10
		5	11
1			12
		6	13
	3		14
		7	15
			23
		19	24
	17		25
		20	26
16			27
		21	28
	18		29
		22	30

Keltic Aluinn

1. Ch. Wild Isle Warlock
2. Ch. Wild Isle Wizard of Id
3. Ch. Mistimourne Wild Isle Mirage
4. Ch. Edgecliff Piper of Cu
5. Ch. Fleetwind Clidna of Wild Isle
6. Ch. Eohey of Eagle
7. Ch. Sulhamstead Minita
8. Ch. Timothy of Edgecliff
9. Nell of Cu
10. Ch. Balbrigan of Balingary
11. Ch. Fleetwind Edain
12. Ch. Hillaway's Padraic of Eagle
13. Ch. Ambleside Edain of Eagle
14. Ch. Sanctuary Brave Knight
15. Ch. Sulhamstead Maria
16. Keltic Siobhan, C.D.
17. Ch. High and Mighty of Carrickmines
18. Ch. Ballykelly Charlie Girl, C.D.
19. Ch. Connel of Nendrum
20. Warren Queen
21. Ballykelly Cavin
22. Ballykelly Cead Mile Failte
23. Ch. Sulhamstead Max
24. Ch. Carol of Eaglescrag
25. Daheen of Fionn-Uisge
26. Noinin Na Sleibhte
27. Ch. Colin of Nendrum
28. Ballykelly Bawneen
29. Ch. McGilligan of Ballykelly
30. Kingsholme Jet

registrations to 1955 inclusive.[1] At the time of his death, the American Kennel Club, because of the tremendous increase in

[1]LeRoy E. Fess, *Fifty Years of Irish Wolfhound Registrations in America— 1897-1955* (1957). Published by the Irish Wolfhound Club of America.

C.K.C. FORM NO. 201

THE CANADIAN KENNEL CLUB COPY

THE CANADIAN KENNEL CLUB

NON-BREEDING AGREEMENT

I, _____

NAME IN FULL OF BUYER (PRINT IN BLOCK LETTERS)

OF, _____

ADDRESS

HEREBY CERTIFY AND AGREE THAT ON _____

DATE

I PURCHASED OR OTHERWISE ACQUIRED A DOG (SEE PARTICULARS BELOW) FROM

_____

NAME IN FULL OF PERSON SELLING OR OTHERWISE DISPOSING OF DOG

(HEREINAFTER REFERRED TO AS THE "SELLER")
ON THE DISTINCT UNDERSTANDING THAT:

(1) UPON COMPLETING PAYMENT FOR THE DOG I AM TO BE PROVIDED WITH A CERTIFICATE OF REGISTRATION ISSUED BY **THE CANADIAN KENNEL CLUB** SHOWING MYSELF AS THE RECORDED OWNER OF THE DOG.

(2) THE DOG SHALL NOT BE USED FOR BREEDING PURPOSES BY ME OR ANY OTHER PERSON AND I HEREBY UNDERTAKE TO ACT AS INSURER IN THIS RESPECT AND TO PAY TO THE SELLER THE SUM OF $ AS LIQUIDATED DAMAGES FOR EACH TIME THE DOG IS USED FOR BREEDING PURPOSES.

(3) NOTWITHSTANDING THE PAYMENT OF THE AFOREMENTIONED LIQUIDATED DAMAGES ANY PROGENY OF THE DOG SHALL NOT BE ELIGIBLE FOR REGISTRATION IN THE RECORDS OF **THE CANADIAN KENNEL CLUB,** NOR MAY SUCH PROGENY BE REPRESENTED AS PURE-BRED.

(4) SHOULD I SELL OR OTHERWISE DISPOSE OF THE DOG, IT SHALL BE A CONDITION OF SUCH SALE THAT THE NEW PURCHASER SHALL EXECUTE AN IDENTICAL AGREEMENT AS THIS ONE AND I SHALL FORTHWITH FILE A COPY OF THE SAME WITH **THE CANADIAN KENNEL CLUB.**

_____   _____
SIGNATURE OF WITNESS   SIGNATURE OF BUYER

_____   _____
DATE   ADDRESS

BREED _____ SEX _____

NAME OF DOG (IF REGISTERED) _____ REG. NO. (IF REGISTERED) _____

BORN _____ 19 _____ COLORS AND MARKINGS _____

SIRE _____ REG. NO. _____

DAM _____ REG. NO. _____

I, _____

FULL NAME OF SELLER (PRINT IN BLOCK LETTERS)

OF_____

ADDRESS

HEREBY CERTIFY THAT THE ABOVE MENTIONED DOG WAS SOLD, OR OTHERWISE DISPOSED OF UNDER THE CONDITIONS STATED IN THIS AGREEMENT

_____   _____
SIGNATURE OF WITNESS   SIGNATURE OF SELLER

_____   _____
DATE   ADDRESS

NOTE:

(1) This agreement must be completed in TRIPLICATE. One copy is to be retained by the seller, one is to be given to the buyer, and the other is to be forwarded with the application for registration (or certificate of registration if dog already registered) and application for transfer of ownership to the Registration Division, The Canadian Kennel Club, 2150 Bloor St. West, Toronto, Ontario M6S 4V7.

(2) This agreement may only be cancelled by the mutual consent of the parties hereto. Such consent must be on the "Consent to Cancellation" form (Canadian Kennel Club form #301). Any progeny born prior to the date of the cancellation of the non-breeding agreement shall not be eligible for registration in the records of The Canadian Kennel Club. The Consent to Cancellation form, together with the certificate of registration issued for the dog, and the cancellation fee of $10.00, must be forwarded to: Registration Division, The Canadian Kennel Club, 2150 Bloor St. West, Toronto, Ontario M6S 4V7.

registrations of dogs generally, was forced to abandon the publication of registration details. By writing to all known breeders and owners, I was able to gather the data from 1956 through 1964 and this also has been published.[1] Pat Huntley has managed to acquire registration data on many Irish Wolfhounds for the period 1965 through 1975. The Irish Wolfhound Club of America has published this as a book. Additional publications will not be possible unless breeders send to Pat Huntley or to me information on each litter: date of whelp, name of sire, name of dam, and, with regard to each puppy, name, sex, registration number and date, name and address of owner. It is important that the names of the owners be given, so that, each year, they may be contacted to see whether they have successfully bred their Irish Wolfhound or to give a lead regarding some other listing of which we may be unaware. Of course, if breeders gave additional particulars, such as the number of puppies by sex that were dead at birth, died within a week, etc., this would also be helpful in gaining knowledge of the breed.

Let us assume that the new owner has arrived in his car to pick up the puppy. On your advice he has brought along a leash, a collar, a bowl for water (and for feeding, if it is a long trip), a large spoon to mix the food, many clean cloths and newspapers to prevent the puppy from soiling the car. Give him a few days supply of dog food. Advise him on feeding and care of the puppy and suggest he apply for Associate Membership in the Irish Wolfhound Club of America.[2] As an Associate Member, he will receive the Club's official publication, *Harp and Hound*. I also subscribe to *Pure-Bred Dogs*, which is published monthly by the American Kennel Club, and to an excellent bimonthly *The Gazehound*, 16258 Lovett Place, Encino, CA 91436.

Shipment by air is fast but is fraught with danger. Since few holds are soundproofed, the high pitched sound of a jet could damage a dog's hearing. Baggage compartments may be pressurized but they are not air-conditioned. When the doors are closed, the compartments are practically airtight in order that lack of oxygen may extinguish any fire that occurs. This allows the build-up of lethal carbon dioxide. Avoid shipping a dog on Easter or Mother's Day weekends when huge quantities of flowers are being shipped. A minimum-maximum indicating thermometer in a suitcase located

---

[1] Alfred W. DeQuoy, *Irish Wolfhound Registrations in America—1956-1964* (1969). Published by the Irish Wolfhound Club of America.

[2] Name and address of the Irish Wolfhound Club of America Secretary may be obtained from the American Kennel Club, 51 Madison Ave., New York, N.Y. 10010.

in the baggage compartment of a United States-Europe flight recorded extremes of 0°F and 104°F. An airline trade association reported that temperatures in compartments can go as high as 130°F while the plane is on the ground.[1] Many dogs have suffocated on flights. Ryan Industries, Seattle, Washington, rents a cylinder which includes a thermometer, barometer and hygrometer. This can be placed in the shipping crate. After the flight, Ryan Industries will analyze the data, if requested. The airplane company cannot legally prohibit use of the instrument. Ryan Industries' findings would be admissible evidence in court proceedings.[2] In 1973, the Civil Aeronautics Board ruled that animals should be the last cargo to be loaded and should be nearest the doors and above floor level, that the crate should be secured, that cargo doors will remain open until the plane is ready to taxi for takeoff, that the animal will be quickly unloaded at destination and that the airline will throughout exercise the utmost care. The shipper can obtain additional services by paying extra charges, e.g. veterinary services if required. The Boeing 747 and Lockheed 10-11 have greater compartment space and are air-conditioned. Some airlines allow small animals to be taken into the passenger section. Reservations must be made long in advance and the animal must be small enough to fit into a specially-designed container.

Rail transportation also presents problems. The ideal solution is to have the owner take the puppy in his automobile or to charter a private plane where the hound will be in the passenger compartment. If you do ship by commercial airline, try to get a direct flight on a jet. At the airports in New York (Kennedy), Philadelphia, Boston and Washington, D.C. (National), humane societies will take care of animals being shipped. Insist on a passenger jet. The cost is the same, the airline more closely observes the schedule, and the ride is smoother since the plane flies above bad weather. Check with the airline to make sure that there will be no dry ice in the compartment and that the plane will not have been fumigated within four hours prior to flight time. If the days are warm, try to ship during the evening, night, or early morning. Avoid weekends and holidays unless the flight is non-stop since small airports may be closed during these periods and the dog will remain unattended until regular business hours are resumed. Inquire about Reserved Air Freight (RAF). If the carrier has this service and you call early enough, you will be guaranteed that your

---

[1] Consumers Union of United States, Inc., *Consumer Reports*, March, 1973.

[2] Roy Carlberg, Executive Secretary, The American Kennel Club. *Pure-Bred Dogs—American Kennel Gazette* (January, 1977) p. 169.

dog will not be left behind for other priority cargo and will not be removed at some intermediate stop. Otherwise, if he is removed, it is probable that you will not be notified.Consult with the Cargo Divisions of all airlines involved in the shipment as to the maximum size of crate permissible on the particular type of aircraft being used. At this writing, a Boeing 720 door requires that the maximum size of a crate be 44″ long, 33″ wide and 39″ high. The crate should be large enough for the dog to stand and to be able to turn around and lie down on his side.Strong protective ridges around the edges of the crate will serve to keep it at a distance from adjacent cargo and allow more ventilation. Two-inch flat spacers at the bottom will keep the bottom of the crate from contact with cold or wet ground. Plywood is a good material. Wire on three sides and a sliding door on the fourth side will give maximum ventilation, although the dog will be somewhat exposed to the elements if the crate is left outside. Openings in the wire should be small enough so that the dog cannot put his nose or a paw through them. Place a large sheet of aluminum foil with the edges turned up on the floor of the crate so that urine will not leak out. On this place a large quantity of paper either shredded or torn into one-inch wide strips. Mark the top of the crate: "Dog, Handle with Care." Staple or otherwise firmly attach two tags with the following information: Name, address, and telephone number of purchaser; name, address, and telephone number of seller. Attach the health certificate of the dog (Some States require that the health certificate be mailed to them in advance). If travel time will exceed 24 hours, there should be instructions for feeding, watering, and exercising. In this case, attached to the crate should be a lead, leather collar, food and a dish. A metal dish may be secured to the inside of the crate near the door and a funnel may be attached to the outside. An attendant, if instructed, may then pour water into the dish after the crate has been loaded and thus diminish the likelihood of the water being spilled. A puppy may chew a plastic dish. Insure the dog for the maximum allowable amount. The cost is low and it will assure your dog of special care even though, in the event of death, you could only recover his market value.

Notify the purchaser of the date and time the plane will arrive, the airline's name, flight number, air waybill number, and airport. Tell him to call or wire you when he has picked up the dog. Remind him that he must pay the transportation charges and return the crate if you are the owner of the crate. Give him an estimate of the cost. Check with the airlines regarding the time when the dog should be at the airport. Do not feed him for some time—about six hours— before the flight departure. Do not give him any water within two hours of the trip. Stay with him until the plane actually leaves or you may have the unfortunate experience of having the flight cancelled and your dog passing the night at the airport. Just before you must leave the crate to the airline, "exercise" your dog, i.e. allow him to relieve himself. Take him to an area where there is no excitement and allow him plenty of time. A baby suppository will help. You may wish to give him a tranquilizer. Consult your veterinarian. A tranquilizer shot will have a longer effect than a pill. If the hound is tranquilized, note this fact on the crate and on the air waybill. Place him in the crate at the last possible moment. After he is in the crate, do not put your fingers inside. A worried puppy may bite.

It is important that you keep yourself in communication with the purchaser and, if possible, that during the travel time you stay near the telephone whose number you have indicated on the crate. Many things can go wrong. The airline may call you for instructions.

Transportation charges are payable by the purchaser. Send the puppy and crate C.O.D. If the crate belongs to the seller, the purchaser should send it back transportation prepaid. If you make the trip with your dog, you will find that the cost of his transportation will be greatly reduced.

The importation of dogs presents not only transportation problems but also that of customs. After arranging for the fastest flight from overseas and making sure that the crate will be accepted by all airlines concerned, you may have to make special arrangements to have a customs officer present if the plane arrival time does not coincide with the U.S. Customs working hours. There will be an additional charge for this. If you do not make this arrangement and the customs office is closed, your puppy will have to remain at the airport until the customs office opens. The New York Office is always open. You may wish to have a broker handle the paper work with customs. There is no duty on dogs imported for breeding purposes.

B. CARE

The first item a new owner should get is a rectal thermometer. See Index at Health maintenance, Thermometer.

The new owner who picks up the puppy at your home and intends to drive back to his own home should be accompanied by another person who can devote his attention to the puppy. A fifty-pound puppy who crawls onto the driver's lap creates considerable difficulty for the driver. Several layers of newspaper should be placed on the seat and on the floor of the automobile in case the puppy relieves himself or vomits. Before beginning the trip, allow the puppy the opportunity to relieve himself. If the trip is to be a long one, it may be advisable to give him a motion sickness pill obtained from the veterinarian. Stop frequently to allow the dog to relieve himself and to overcome any imminent nausea. Exercise the greatest of precautions so he won't escape from you into automobile traffic. His collar should be of leather and should be inexpensive since he will soon outgrow it. Have the collar fit snugly so he won't wriggle out of it. Attach a leash to the collar and keep him under control at all times. After this initial ride, make automobile rides short until he becomes a seasoned traveler. Until he is somewhat older, do not leave him alone in the car: he may chew up the upholstery.

I suggest that when a puppy is picked up at the airport, the new owner remove the puppy and send the crate back to the breeder rather than take both puppy and crate home. Exercise care when the crate is opened. Irish Wolfhound puppies are very fast and, if one should escape, it would be quite difficult to regain possession. Bring along a glove, so that if the puppy is frightened and reluctant to leave the crate, you can remove him without getting your hand bitten. His coat may be soiled if he has had to relieve himself in the crate so rub him down with a towel and some corn meal. Of course, before going to the airport call the cargo supervisor to see if the plane will be on time.

When you arrive at your home, let him relieve himself outside, then put him in a room where it won't be a serious matter if he should relieve himself there. A room with tile or linoleum is a possibility, or a small room that has been covered with newspapers. Bear in mind that he may chew whatever is in the room, including the molding. Put up a folding gate at the door so he won't feel shut off from companionship. If he has a rug or other soft material as a bed and you take it with you when you and the puppy travel, he will always feel at home; don't get anything valuable until he is over his chewing habits. A rug will also minimize the possibility of calluses on elbows and hocks. Always bear in mind that it may be a long, long time before he stops chewing whatever is within reach: furniture, rugs, valuable papers, etc. If he does cause damage, you are at fault. Nevertheless, correct him properly. You may wish to put him in a baby playpen (which he will chew and which he will soon outgrow) with newspapers under it. If so, set it up where he can be with someone: in the kitchen with your wife during the day, in the bedroom at night. Do not isolate him in the basement. He is now a member of the family and should be treated as such. Remember that he has just been separated from his mother, brothers and sisters and his only home. He is now being exposed to strange sounds and sights. He is lonesome, frightened. Give him some warm milk. Handle him as little as possible. Speak softly to him. No squeals from the children. Don't let them grab at him like a new toy. Don't scold him if he does something wrong. Do not undertake to train him for a few days until he knows you and trusts you, until he has regained his self-confidence.

Let him get plenty of sleep, away from all the turmoil of the household. Don't wait for him to drop exhausted. Frequently take him to his "den". Give him a glove or other article to which he was accustomed in his former home. He will most likely cry piteously when you leave him. If possible, stay with him. That night you may decide to put him in the place you have assigned for him to sleep. If this should be in a place other than your bedroom, he will whine and possibly give forth long and loud mournful howls. You will end up either sleeping in his room or having him sleep in yours. This will make him a very happy puppy and, when he is older, he will protect you against intruders. Many owners allow their dogs to share their beds. I do not, although an occasional puppy has "conned" me into doing so. If he is to stay in your bedroom, take precautions. Spread newspapers quite thickly. After a few days, establish a regular routine. Some persons place a hot water bottle under his blanket and a loud ticking clock next to it (presumably to simulate the dam's heart beat).

If the hound is to sleep in the basement or some other ignominious place, provide him with a raised platform so he will escape drafts. An 8' x 4' masonite sheet nailed onto 2" x 4" boards is satisfactory for this purpose. Avoid tops of stairways, the areas in front of radiators or cooling vents. Chilling, dampness may cause respiratory diseases. Do not make him a bed of cedar shavings. One person who had "adopted" an apparently lost or abandoned pheasant chick observed paralysis developing in the bird. This was traced to the cedar bed. He consulted an instructor in chemistry and was told: "Cedar wood dust contains chemical irritants which can cause conjunctivitis, intense lachrymation, iridocyclitis, keratitis as well as dermatitis. Removal from exposure will cause symptoms to disappear."[1] If cedar could paralyze a bird, it might also have serious, although undiscovered, effects on dogs.

Irish Wolfhounds are happiest when they are with their owners. A few owners keep them in dog houses or kennel runs. In such cases, both the owners and the hounds lose the pleasure which

---

[1] Walter A. Wheeler, Jr., "Is There Danger in Dog Bedding?", The American Kennel Club, *Pure-Bred Dogs—American Kennel Gazette* (May, 1967) LXXXIV, p. 17.

companionship provides. But if you must exile your dog, make sure that his home is adequately large, dry, draft-free, cool when the weather is warm and not too cold when winter arrives. Plans for a dog-house are occasionally printed in the American Kennel Club's *Pure-Bred Dogs* and in publications of Gaines and Ralston Purina. Write to these organizations.

A puppy's capacity to absorb knowledge is quite limited. Even more limited is his capacity to retain what he has been taught and seemingly learned. Bear this constantly in mind. Do not let his great size deceive you. He is still a puppy.

Housetraining is no problem in my home. There are two doors leading into the back yard which have two-way swinging doors installed into them. These are 29½″ x 23½″ and one is shown in the illustration. I take the puppy at two or three months, say "Out!" and gently push him from inside the house against the door. Then I go to the outside, praise him and, and after a while, repeat the procedure (the command is still "Out!"), pushing him into the house. After a few of these exercises, I stand on one side of the swinging door while he is on the other side, open the door a little and encourage him to open it the balance of the way. Some dogs learn faster than others but soon all that has to be done is say "Out!" in a gentle but firm voice. Do not shout at the puppy. Do not leave a puppy in a room with a swinging door if he has not been trained in its use. Drive a small nail into the door on each side of the swinging door so that he won't accidentally get a foot caught in it and pull back in alarm thus causing him injury. Until you are satisfied that the puppy is *fully* trained in the use of the swinging door, block it somehow until you can again observe him in its use. There is one possible risk in leaving dogs alone with access to a swinging door. Some object carried by the dog might be dropped in such a way that the door cannot be opened in either direction. This has occurred twice in my experience of 19 years (1977), once with a shoe and once with a glove. The dog could be locked either in or out. The probability of this is, however, very slight. Over a period of 19 years, I would estimate that my dogs have gone through the swinging doors 500,000 times. Now even though the puppy is trained to go through the door, he is not necessarily housetrained. You and I still must accomplish this.

First, a few thoughts. The puppy is like a baby. He eliminates body waste naturally without any particular reflection. It is you who must teach him that he should not do it in the house. But he is still a baby! Therefore it takes some intelligence and patience on your part to teach him. And it takes a little aging on his part before he begins to understand, let's say at three months of age. Before that, evacuation is practically a reflex action and scolding him or punishing him is equivalent to treating a baby in diapers in the same fashion. He will be frightened and nervous but will not understand the reason for your actions.

Here is the housetraining procedure. Teach him good habits rather than punish him for bad ones. *As soon as you arise* in the morning, take him to the outside area you want him to use. Don't play with him. Give him time to relieve himself, then praise him lavishly. If he urinates, wait to see if he will also defecate (and vice versa). Then take him back into the house. Repeat the procedure after each meal, after playing with him, whenever he appears restless and sniffs about, before putting him to bed, and when he wakes from a nap. As you do this, keep saying "Out!" "Out!" so that, after a while, the word will mean something to him. When you take him outdoors, have him either in an enclosed yard or on a leash or he may run away—and he is very fast. Give him water after each meal but do not leave it with him at all times. Don't let him wander through the house unobserved. If you do and he relieves himself, he will have retrograded in his training. Remember that even after he is trained, accidents will happen, in moments of stress or great excitement. Don't scold him for this. When you observe an "accident", correct him first and then take care of the damage. Hold his head so he can see the result (but do not put his nose in it), shout "No!" and then take him rapidly to the area he should have used. As for urine, get a roll of towelling paper, use it to absorb as much of the liquid as possible, then pour on the spot a small amount of white vinegar—a 50% solution which, with foresight, you have previously prepared and are keeping in a bottle—and blot that up. Do not rub. Don't scold the puppy if you did not observe the "accident". You will only worry and confuse him. He won't connect the scolding with his prior performance. Follow the same cleaning procedure if the accident occurs on wood or linoleum but use Lysol in a soap and water solution. Otherwise he will be again attracted to this location.

Paper training an Irish Wolfhound is of dubious value. They excrete huge amounts and you will have to retrain him for outdoors.

A sudden shout when the puppy is about to relieve himself may frighten him and cause him to do exactly what you don't want him to do. Call his name, instead, and command "Come!". If you take your dog onto your front lawn to relieve himself, other dogs will be attracted to the same spot and will ruin your lawn or shrubbery. Take him to the street. This will be proper training so that when he is grown he won't sully the sidewalks. A messy sidewalk sometimes causes pedestrians to curse dogs; they should curse the owners instead. Remember that, until he is about 5 months old, he will not have the bladder control necessary to prevent excretion for an eight-hour period while you are away from home. He should not be punished for any involuntary action.

Be patient with your puppy. Uncontrolled shouting and punishment will make him forever shy. You will feel rather abashed if he later crouches when approached by your friends and tries to slink away. Indeed, if you have so affected him, you undoubtedly will scold him for his timidity, thereby more firmly establishing the undesirable characteristic.

The following method may be tried with a puppy three or more months of age. Walk towards the door, saying "Out?" in a questioning voice and urging him to accompany you. When he gets to the door, say "Good boy!" and let him out. After a while, he will go to the door by himself when he wishes to go out. You must be alert to interpret his actions. If he keeps walking up to you and then to the door and you ignore him, don't punish him if he relieves himself on the living room carpet. Of course, he may be going to the door just to go out and play. If you do not want this, bring him back in. He will learn that he is to go to the door only when he has to relieve himself and that you will take him out for a walk when you desire to do so, not when he wants it. Encourage your dog to make his wants known. If he nudges you, yelps, whines, or barks, ask him. "What is it, boy? O.K., boy, go ahead!" etc. Keep talking to him and urge him on so he will learn that he is to take you wherever it is he wishes to go. If it turns out, he wants to do something you don't want him to do, e.g. eat, then say "No! Good boy!" He will have learned that he can communicate his desires. No specific time can be set as that within which a puppy can be housetrained. One can always expect certain lapses in good conduct.

I did say that housetraining was no problem in my home because of the swinging doors but, despite this convenience, it took one three-month old purchased puppy five months before he could be fully trusted. This was most unusual. It points out that one should not generalize as dogs are individuals.

Don't allow puppies to jump up on you or they will do the same to your guests. Push them away and say "No!" in a harsh voice. Puppies have sharp teeth. They can be taught not to bite by use of the word "No!" If a puppy does seize your hand, don't pull it away sharply or your hand may be cut or scraped. Instead, use the other hand to open his mouth and then withdraw your hand.

Don't allow every member of the family to order the dog around without purpose: "Come!", "Sit!", "Down!", "Out!" etc. Such conduct will encourage him to disobey. When children in the neighborhood yell out commands to my dogs, I explain to them that since the commands cannot be enforced, they are in effect teaching my dogs to disobey. Moreover, the dogs will not mind them any more than the children would obey me if I issued a string of purposeless commands to them.

All animals should be approached slowly. There should be no sudden movements. A child who rushes towards a puppy or suddenly extends his arm towards him will frighten him and possibly cause him to become shy, nervous, and irritable toward children. A grown dog might bite the child in such a situation—although this is highly unlikely in the case of an Irish Wolfhound. Children are apt to thrust a hand at the dog's head and then, fearful, immediately and rapidly withdraw it. A dog could construe this as an assault. Should the child's hand have entered the dog's mouth, a sudden withdrawal may result in a cut from the dog's sharp teeth. The child would then most likely say that the dog had bitten him. The dog would be punished and, henceforth, would apprehensively shy away from all children or bark at them.

Puppies will chew anything. Some things may be only aggravating, such as the expensive slippers which your wife bought in Italy. Other things will be more serious, such as an electric light cord, a poison, or even a piece of string which could block his intestines, give him epilepsy, and result in death. An occasional knuckle bone is all I give to my dogs to chew on. Puppies can be given an old shoe, with all nails removed, a strip of hard leather, a tennis ball, etc., anything that cannot be swallowed, that does not have poisonous substances on it. There are various items for sale which are intended for the dog to chew. The only one I have found that lasts more than an hour is a Nylabone but the dogs have not cared for it. Some people claim that one should not give the dog an old shoe since he won't be able to discriminate between an old and a new one. However, he soon learns that his privileges are limited. Do not let him chew on rubber heels as he will swallow portions of these. Beware of nails in shoes. You will enjoy seeing your puppy dribble a tennis ball by dropping it, catching it on the rebound, hitting it with his feet, pouncing on it, bringing it to you and challenging you to take it away from him, retrieving it when you do throw it, etc. Puppies love to play and will harass other animals in the household. Use good judgment. If an older dog growls at the puppy, this is a sign that he has had enough annoyance. Separate the dogs. Do not leave them alone together until the older dog has grown tolerant of the incessant nibbles and paw strokes.

Keep a monthly record of your dog's weight as a check on his health until he is a year old and then weigh him annually. Initially, you may wish to pick him up, step on the bathroom scales, and then subtract your own weight. Lift him up in the proper way or you may injure him. Never pull on his legs. At 3 months, he weighs about 50 pounds. Put one arm behind his thighs bringing them under his body; the other arm may be either under his chest or it may be passed between his front legs so that the hand is under his chest. Three months later, he will weigh about 100 pounds and you may decide not to lift him. Junkyards or other business firms have large scales. Send the information on weights to me so that I may gather as much statistical data on Irish Wolfhounds as possible. When your dog dies, please let me know the dates of whelp and of death and the cause of death, if known. Autopsies on all Irish Wolfhounds would be of inestimable value to the breed. If you become a breeder, please give me the names of the sire and dam, date of whelping, the number of puppies born alive as well as the number born dead, sex of puppies, and, later, the names and addresses of the persons to whom sold, so that I can maintain my information and can later trace other owners, should these new owners breed their dogs. Your name will never be connected with any data that could be considered detrimental. Your data will be intermingled with others and presented in a statistical fashion only.

It is considerably easier in later life if you start cutting a dog's toe nails when he is still a puppy. Have him lie down, sit next to him, take one of his toes in your left hand and cut the nail with Resco clippers held in the right hand. Talk to him soothingly, but hold him down firmly with the left arm or with a leg. It may be necessary to have another person hold him initially. He may offer no objection or he may be frantic and try to bite. If you shout at him or abuse him, he will panic in later years every time you try to cut his nails. See Index at Grooming, Nails.

Don't worry about his ear carriage. He will often carry them up and out—what we call "airplane ears". Then again, one ear may flop over onto the top of his head. If you can manually adjust the ears so that they give the "rose ear" appearance, everything will most likely turn out all right. Some owners, observing that their puppy's ears lie flat alongside the head like a bloodhound's, will use adhesive tape or liquid to mold them into the proper shape. I cannot comment one way or the other on the efficacity of this method or on whether it seriously inconveniences the puppy.

Many homes now have swimming pools. The relation of an incident may interest you. One evening, I visited Mr. Henry Weaver accompanied by Ard Ri of Ballylyke whom I had purchased from him. It was a cold January evening. Ri, still a puppy, was left outside with the other hounds. An hour or more later, when I left the house, I could not see Ri although the other hounds were all there. Finally, I saw him in the swimming pool. He had broken through the icy surface and was paddling in the center of the pool I called to him and he swam to me. On my knees at the edge of the pool, I reached into the water and managed to pull him out. At that time he weighed about 100 pounds. We took him inside and rubbed him down with towels. He was shivering. His toe nails had been completely worn down evidently by his exertions to climb out. How painful this must have been! It was midnight and no veterinarian was available. I took him home, gave him three aspirin tablets, wrapped him in blankets and he and I spent the night on the kitchen floor. The next morning, he was given veterinary care. He fully recovered. How long had he been in the pool? How long could he have kept swimming? The solution for swimming pool owners with dogs may be to install a sloping side to the pool. Poor Ri later contracted chorea at a well-known veterinary clinic and had to be put to sleep. He had won his Companion Dog's degree in obedience at the age of 6½ months and was a lovely dog.

When the puppy has settled down in the household, gradually extend his horizons. Let him get acquainted with strangers and with strange surroundings. A new owner should be prepared to sustain the usual comments made by persons as they observe an Irish Wolfhound for the first time.

1. "He's as big as a pony."
2. "He's big enough to ride."
3. "Why don't you put a saddle on him?"

The impression made by an Irish Wolfhound is so great that the speaker has been led to speak spontaneously without thought that the same statement must have been uttered many times before.

Don't be too hasty about taking him on tours. Remember the danger of infections. Do not take him on an escalator. He may become seriously injured.

A puppy, when first subjected to a collar and leash, will shake his head, hop up and down, paw at the collar and try to pull away. Let him carry on for a while, as you talk soothingly to him. Then start giving a series of sharp tugs on the leash as you say "Come!" Praise him to the skies should he come to you. Walk in the direction he wants to go,—for example, home,—and you will find he has less objection to the leash. If, after he is accustomed to the leash, you should take him for a walk on lead and he suddenly sits down and refuses to budge, he is not being stubborn. He is tired. He is too heavy to carry, so either call from the nearest house for an automobile or wait until he is rested.

Here are three comments, taken in chronological order, on

Major Acres Rial Dhu, C.D., at eleven weeks (1977).

Ch. Keltic Findabair leaving the house by a two-way swinging door (1972).

Year-old Keltic Carragan and his litter sister, Keltic Aluinn, at play (1977).

exercise for puppies, made by Judges N.A. Loraine, Florence Nagle (Sulhamstead Kennels) and Ruth Jenkins (Eaglescrag Kennels).

> I rather gathered from some remarks that these big fellows were being asked too much before their great frame was equal to the strain. The bigger an animal the more time he takes to develop and what a greyhound puppy might be capable of, without injury, would pull a Wolfhound to pieces for good and all.[1]

> One of the greatest mistakes when the puppies are weaned and on their own is to make them exercise. They want freedom to play, and when they are tired to lie down and sleep, but no set or forced exercise. They are growing at an enormous rate between two and six months, and it is essential not to let them get too heavy on their legs or to carry too much fat. Take them to a lawn, field or paddock and let them run about loose, and when they tire take them back to their run . . . Never exercise behind a bicycle, or run after a car.[2]

> The question arises of how much exercise should be given to a young puppy. The answer is not much, mostly he needs freedom to romp and sleep at will. However, a twenty minute excursion once, and later twice, a day will help to develop the mind and keep limbs growing straight and strong. During these outings there should be time both on the lead and freely galloping. Later on, at 6 months or so, galloping will play an even greater part in the proper development of the puppy. This should therefore not be denied to a young dog. I must stress the word "free" in relation to this galloping; on no account should a young, very-rapidly growing Wolfhound be subjected to following a bicycle.[3]

Dr. Wayne Riser cautions:

> Large young dogs are often victims of over enthusiastic feeding practices with vitamin-mineral supplements and forced vigorous exercise. This predisposes the dogs to skeletal abnormalities and bio-mechanical imbalances.[4]

Irish Wolfhounds can easily be crippled when they are young. They are so large that people are apt to consider them as mature

---

[1] N.A. Loraine, The Kennel Club (Britain), *The Kennel Gazette* (October, 1924) XLV, p. 756.

[2] Nagle, *op. cit.*, p. 38.

[3] Ruth Jenkins, "Hints on Rearing Irish Wolfhounds," The Irish Wolfhound Club (Britain) *Year Book* (1964-1966), p. 72.

[4] Dr. Wayne H. Riser, *et al.*, "Genu Valgum: A Stifle Deformity of Giant Dogs," *Journal of the American Veterinary Radiological Society* (1969) X, p. 36.

despite the fact that they are gangly and awkward and have big feet and joints.

In a puppy, each of the long bones of the legs consists of a central shaft and two ends which are joined by cartilage. Gradually the cartilage develops into bone. Repeated jumping or other shock may put the ends out of line and result in permanent deformity. Do not encourage the puppy to stand on its hind legs at the kennel door, fence, or elsewhere. Do not hold his front paws as he stands on his hind legs. Do not let him jump over obstacles, down from retaining walls, etc. Play should be in moderation. No wild chasing after people or dogs with abrupt turns and halts. No running on hard surfaces.

> Sudden fore limb lameness in the juvenile dog of larger breeds may be a manifestation of osteochondritis dissecans, an increasingly diagnosed condition of the shoulder joint. The disease has been reported as occurring most frequently in large and giant breeds between the ages of five and twelve months, a time at which the skeletal system is most susceptible to injury. A typical history of lameness after strenuous exercise or sudden stops in front of fences, and in connection with training or jumping, is common . . . Most dogs afflicted with this will make a functional recovery with rest and restricted exercise.[1]

Two or more hounds will run and play together thus increasing the amount of exercise. Do not be concerned if the puppy "bunny hops," i.e. advances both hind feet at the same time as he runs. One breeder believes that a bigger puppy is more apt to do this than a smaller one and that the unusual movement usually ceases at about four months. He adds that in the majority of cases that continue beyond then there is evidence of improper growth in the region of the hips. Even grown dogs who possess good movement will occasionally move the hind feet simultaneously in play if the area in which they are confined is not large enough for them to run at full speed. Do not be too hasty in declaring a dog a cripple because he bunny hops. Let a qualified veterinarian decide. A puppy at play will occasionally yelp in pain and limp. Pick him up and apply light pressure at various points of the leg to determine the affected area. Gently massage it. Slowly extend the leg and bend it at the joints. If this causes the dog to cry out, stop at once and keep him isolated from other dogs until you can take him to a veterinarian. In most cases, there has only been a slight sprain and the puppy will be ready to play again in a couple of minutes. The same type of

---

[1]Orthopedic Foundation for Animals, Inc. *Letter to Miss Mari Thomas.*

treatment is applicable to adult hounds. As the dog grows older, he calms down. He will run only occasionally. Do not expect him to be constantly on the go like a poodle or terrier.

At six months, he should be inoculated against rabies and a dog license obtained from local authorities. He should be reinoculated each year unless he was given a three-year type of inoculation.

C. FEEDING

Here are suggestions from two sources on puppy feeding. They are presented so that you may know the practices of some prominent breeders.

1. Mr and Mrs. Gordon Graham (Cu Kennel)[1] (1969):

Period

Weaning   Supplement dam's milk with Esbilac.

7-10 days   Scraped fat-free raw beef. Initially once a day. Gradually increase to three times a day.

12-17 days   Primary Diet—a Lifespan product. Initially once a day.

            Gradually increase to three times a day. Gradually replace the Esbilac and Primary Diet with evaporated milk, well-soaked fine kibble and trimmed ground steak. Again gradually, change from the ground steak to ground chuck.

4-5 weeks   Puppies have been weaned.

3-6 months Early morning: Four cod liver oil tablets (1 tablespoonful) per puppy.

            Morning: 3 cups kibble, 1 can beef, moistened with warm water or broth. Two tablespoonfuls of steamed edible bone meal per puppy.

2. Ruth Jenkins (Eaglescrag Kennels, Wales)[2] (1966):

After the age of ten weeks a puppy's daily meals may be reduced from five to four, and the following routine is suggested:—

---

[1]Mr. and Mrs. Gordon Graham, "A Feeding Program for Irish Wolfhounds," In Alma Starbuck's *The Complete Irish Wolfhound* (1969), pp. 154, 155.

[2]Ruth Jenkins, *op. cit.*, pp. 70, 71.

9:00 a.m.   About ¼ lb. breakfast cereal, brown bread or puppy meal soaked in ¾ pint warm milk, one egg, raw or lightly cooked.

1:00 p.m.   ¾ lb. raw meat, i.e. tripe, beef, horsemeat, mutton, not too fatty and cut up fairly small. Lightly cooked meat may be given on occasion. (Tinned meat should be reserved for emergencies.) Add 1 teaspoonful cod liver oil.

5:30 p.m.   A repeat of the 9 a.m. feed.

9:30 p.m.   A repeat of the 1 p.m. feed, excluding the C.L.O. Add thereto a dessertspoonful of bone meal specially prepared for animal feeding. This may be obtained from W. & J. Dunlop Ltd., of Dumfries.

One should keep to this pattern, gradually increasing the amount of meat and milk until at about 3½ months of age the puppy will be taking one pint of milk, and one pound of meat at the appropriate meals. At about 4 months the daily intake of carbohydrate may be increased by adding a handful or so of puppy meal to the second meat feed. This should be soaked in boiling gravy first.

Between six and seven months, depending as always on the progress of the individual, the daily food may be divided into three meals, possibly as follows:—

9:00 a.m.   1-1½ pints milk, two raw eggs beaten up therein. This to be followed by dog biscuits, stale brown bread, dry hound meal, etc. He may eat about ½ lb. or so of this.

1:00 p.m.   1 lb. raw meat cut up with one teaspoonful cod liver oil added. More than 1 lb. meat may be needed depending on size, appetite and condition.

6:30 p.m.   1 lb. raw meat cut up, ½-1 lb. terrier meal soaked in boiling gravy, 1 dessertspoonful bonemeal as before.

Probably around twelve months of age it will be found that two meals will suffice under ordinary circumstances. This is brought about by giving 2 lb. of meat plus the ½-1 lb. soaked meal for the evening feed. The cod liver oil and bone meal will also still be required.

Cod liver oil, bone meal, brown bread all contain important vitamins and minerals in a natural form, the same may be said of liver and raw beef suet. Accustom the puppy to the two latter from about nine months.

My advice is to start him, after he is weaned, on commercial dry food moistened (not soaked) with hot water and not to supplement with meat, minerals, or vitamins. The reasons are fully stated in the next chapter but here is one brief comment by Dr. Corbin on the effects of an all-meat diet.

> If meat is the ONLY diet fed to 6-week-old puppies after weaning, death may result in the next six weeks. Rapidly growing puppies demonstrate the ill effects of meat much quicker than mature or nearly grown dogs. Individual dogs react at different rates to the deficiencies associated with meat, and a tremendous amount of damage may occur before the owner realizes a change has occurred in his dogs.[1]

Puppies have voracious appetites and, after a while, will eat more than adult dogs. From seven to nine weeks, puppies require three times as much food as grown dogs. This requirement then gradually diminishes.[2] Puppies should not be allowed to get roly poly. The unnecessary extra weight on their legs is detrimental and encourages the development of hip dysplasia.[3]

> The Purina Research Center has investigated the influence of nutrition on hip dysplasia. No specific nutrient level (excess or deficiency) has been associated with dysplasia up to this point; however, excess caloric intake resulting in fat puppies during the early growth stages appears to cause increased incidence of dysplasia.
>
> When puppies are born their bones are in an extremely fragile, immature state of development. As the puppies continue to grow and the bones lengthen, it is easy to see how excess fat in a puppy would produce a lot of stress in the hip socket and cause a malformation or distortion of the hip socket. The head of the femur under pressure, also becomes misformed. Limiting food intake to produce lean, healthy puppies helps prevent poor hip formation.[1]

Dr. Kirk expresses his concern:

> A not infrequent experience is seeing puppies of the large or giant breeds of about 16 weeks of age which are as fat as butter, with glossy coats and clear eyes. In fact, they are the picture of health except that they do not want to walk. The owners are, of

---

[1] James Corbin, Ralston Purina Company, *Purina Kennel News* (Winter, 1971).

[2] National Academy of Sciences, *Nutrient Requirements of Dogs,* (1972), p. 2.

[3] Dr. M. Josephine Deubler, "Ask Your Doctor," *Popular Dogs* (February, 1967), p. 26. See Index at Health Maintenance, Hip dysphasia.

course, greatly concerned. In these puppies there is usually swelling of the extremities and a lot of pain. They have a low ascorbic acid level, but it is believed that this is a result not a cause. The syndrome is well recognized. It was reported about 15 or 20 years ago and termed "osteodystrophy".

A common history in these dogs is that they are loaded with supplements. We have a case now of a St. Bernard puppy that was getting one cup of bone meal three times a day plus cod liver oil and various other vitamin-mineral supplements in the belief that the puppy needs this supplementation for bone. We find that these puppies usually are "shell shocked" with vitamins and minerals. In treating these cases we get the best results by putting the puppies on a standard, well-balanced diet, very slightly fortified with vitamin D.

Another facet of treatment is exercise. If these puppies are left in the kennel, they do not recover. With forced exercise, after the pain is gone, the puppies do quite well in many cases. At least they are not deformed, as when they are just left to sit.[1]

Usually, dog owners are advised that a proper feeding schedule is something like this:[2]

Age	Meals a Day
Until 6 weeks	4
6 weeks to 4 months	3
4 to 8 months	2
Thereafter	1

Dr. Ben E. Sheffy disagrees. Speaking of the post-weaning phase, he says:

The age-old philosophy of feeding every 2 to 3 hours is completely false. It is not only unnecessary but actually undesirable to feed more than 3 times a day, 8 hours apart. Common sense is the most important ingredient in any feeding schedule. Start the puppy on the minimum amount, increasing it gradually as he gains weight and responds favorably to feeding. A correlation between the pup's steady gain in weight and the condition of his feces is the best evidence of satisfactory progress.

---

[1]R. W. Kirk, "Feeding Practices—Especially Puppies," *Gaines Dog Research Progress* (Spring, 1967).

[2]Gaines has suggested the following feeding times. From weaning to 3 months: 7 a.m., noon, 5 and 10 p.m.; from 3 to 6 months: 7 a.m., noon, 5 p.m.: from 6 to 12 months: 7 a.m., 5 p.m., thereafter, 5 p.m.

If diarrhea develops, immediately reduce solids intake to one-half and then gradually increase it.[1]

Puppies, as well as grown dogs, should be fed in an area that is quiet so that they will not be distracted from the business at hand. They grow very rapidly, weighing about 1½ pounds at birth and about 100 pounds at 6 months. Weigh them each day at about the same hour for the first month, then weekly until 6 months old, then monthly until 18 months old, then annually. If a puppy does not gain at about the same rate as the others, supplement his food by gavage (tube feeding). All utensils should be thoroughly washed and scalded.

The accompanying table is intended to let both the breeder and the new owner gauge the progress of their puppies. Do not jump to erroneous conclusions. While it is true that of two puppies of similar bone size, health and appetites, the heavier will most likely be the taller, a puppy below the weight shown will not necessarily be small. Neither will one who is heavier necessarily turn out to be a huge dog. Occasionally, one will have a puppy—it may be a bitch— that is not only heavier at birth than the rest of the litter but that widens the gap between itself and its littermates as the months go by. Then suddenly the puppy's rate of growth is considerably slowed and it is passed by the others.

Immunization shots, worm medicine, illness may diminish a dog's appetite and cause him to gain less rapidly for a short while. Do not delude yourself into believing that by overfeeding a puppy, he will become taller. He will merely become fatter.

When the litter is small each individual tends to be heavier in the latter stages of gestation. Conversely, in large litters individual weights are often below average for their age class.[2]

---

[1]Ben E. Sheffy, *Gaines Dog Research Progress* (Winter, 1957-1958).

[2]Howard E. Evans, "Prenatal Development of the Dog." *Gaines Dog Research Progress* (Winter, 1975), p. 5.

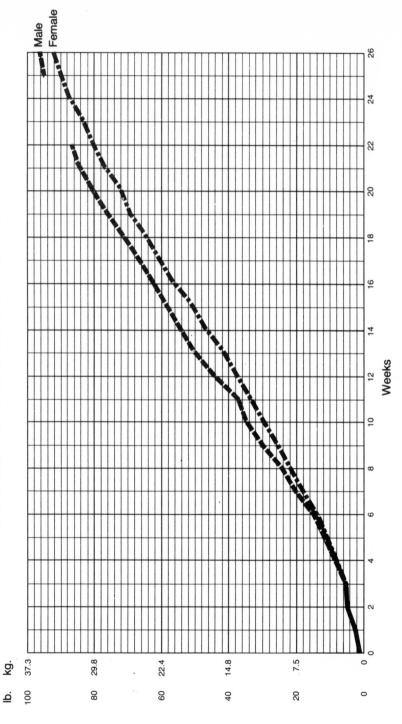

MEAN WEIGHT OF IRISH WOLFHOUND PUPPIES

Weight by Week

Age	Dogs No. Measured	Pound Mean	Pound Max.	Pound Min.	Kilogram Mean	Kilogram Max.	Kilogram Min.	Bitches No. Measured	Pound Mean	Pound Max.	Pound Min.	Kilogram Mean	Kilogram Max.	Kilogram Min.
Birth	3.5	1.2	1.8	0.6	0.5	0.8	0.3	27	1.2	1.9	0.6	0.5	0.9	0.3
1	27	2.5	3.5	1.6	1.1	1.6	0.7	18	2.5	3.8	1.2	1.1	1.7	0.5
2	29	4.0	6.5	2.1	1.8	2.9	1.0	17	4.2	6.8	2.9	1.9	3.1	1.3
3	31	5.7	8.5	3.3	2.6	3.9	1.5	24	5.5	8.5	3.3	2.5	3.9	1.5
4	34	8.5	11.8	5.3	3.9	5.4	2.4	27	8.8	11.3	5.8	4.0	5.1	2.6
5	18	11.9	15.5	9.1	5.4	7.0	4.1	24	11.4	18.0	7.4	5.2	8.2	3.4
6	18	15.3	18.5	11.8	6.9	8.4	5.4	21	14.5	17.5	11.3	6.6	7.9	5.1
7	19	20.0	24.0	17.0	9.1	10.9	7.7	23	18.1	22.0	14.0	8.2	10.0	6.4
8	23	24.5	30.0	19.0	11.1	13.6	8.6	25	22.1	28.0	17.0	10.0	12.7	7.7
9	22	30.0	37.0	23.0	13.6	16.8	10.4	28	25.0	37.0	18.5	11.3	16.8	8.4
10	14	35.0	40.0	28.0	15.9	18.1	12.7	19	30.0	37.0	21.0	13.6	16.8	9.5
11	11	37.3	44.0	32.0	16.9	20.0	14.5	18	33.5	43.0	26.0	15.2	19.5	11.8
12	18	44.5	51.0	37.0	20.2	23.1	16.8	19	38.0	48.0	32.0	17.2	21.8	14.5
13	24	50.0	56.0	35.0	22.7	25.4	15.9	29	41.0	58.0	34.0	18.6	26.3	15.4
14	8	54.1	64.0	45.0	24.5	29.0	20.4	11	46.8	58.0	37.0	21.2	26.3	16.8
15	7	58.1	68.0	50.0	26.4	30.8	22.7	10	50.7	65.0	47.0	23.0	29.5	21.3
16	10	62.3	74.0	55.0	28.3	33.6	24.9	10	56.3	67.0	48.0	25.5	30.4	21.8
17	13	66.8	80.0	53.0	30.3	36.3	24.0	12	60.8	69.0	52.0	27.6	31.3	23.6
18	13	71.4	82.0	45.0	32.4	37.2	20.4	12	64.2	69.0	52.0	29.1	31.3	23.6
19	6	76.0	87.0	62.0	34.5	39.5	28.1	5	69.6	75.0	62.0	31.6	34.0	28.1
20	7	80.0	91.0	64.0	36.3	41.3	29.0	9	71.5	77.0	63.0	32.4	34.9	28.6
21	10	84.4	95.0	67.0	38.3	43.1	30.4	3	77.0	83.0	70.0	34.9	37.6	31.8
22	8	85.4	96.0	75.0	38.7	43.5	34.0	11	80.1	88.0	61.0	36.3	39.9	27.7
23								3	83.7	90.0	75.0	38.0	40.8	34.0
24								3	87.8	92.0	67.0	39.8	41.7	30.4
25	1	95.0	95.0	95.0	43.1	44.9	44.9	2	90.0	98.0	82.0	40.8	44.5	37.2
26	16	96.0	110.0	80.0	43.5	49.9	36.3	16	92.0	107.0	79.0	41.7	48.5	35.8

VI

The Adult Hound

The Yearling[1]

By rules of fitness and of tense,
By all old canine precedents,
O Adult Dog, the time is up
When I may fondly call you Pup.
The years have sped since first you stood
In straddle-legged puppyhood —
A watch-pup, proud of your renown,
Who barked so hard you tumbled down.
In Age's gain and Youth's retreat
You've found more team-work for your feet.
You drool a soupçon less — and hark!
There's fuller meaning to your bark.
But answer fairly, whilom pup,
Are these full proof of growing up?

I heard an elephantine tread
That jarred the rafters overhead.
Who leaped in mad abandon there
And tossed my slippers in the air?
Who sitting gravely on the rug,
Espied a microscopic bug,
And stalked it, gaining bit by bit —
Then leaped in air and fell on it?
Who gallops madly down the breeze,
Pursuing specks that no one sees?
Then finds some ancient boot instead
And worries it till it is dead?
I have no adult friends who choose

---

[1]Anonymous untitled poem found among the papers of the late Canadian author Mazo de la Roche and published in The Irish Wolfhound Club of Canada's *Bulletin* (1974) III, No. 2, p. 28. Title is mine.

To gnaw the shoe-strings from my shoes,
Or eat up twine or paper scraps,
Or bark while they are taking naps.
O Dog, you offer every proof
That stately age yet holds aloof.
Grow up? There's meaning in the phrase
Of dignity as well as days.
Oh, why such size, beloved pup?
You've grown enough, but not grown up.

A. FEEDING

Dog owners have always disagreed on the subject of proper feeding. But then, there is no agreement as to the proper diet for humans. Some resort to the old argument that dogs are carnivorous and should only have meat. Others relate that their parents always fed Nero scraps from the table and he remained in good health. Many follow the diet prescribed by the breeder. A few allow the dog to select the food he likes, although they would not allow their own children similar latitude. The theory that dogs have an unerring instinct for proper foods is not sound. Dogs, like children, will eat whatever tastes good regardless of whether or not it is good for them. My own contention is that dog research groups have conducted scientific studies of this problem for many years, that their conclusions are based on extensive experimentation on thousands of dogs of various breeds and that their recommendations should therefore be adopted. Two of these nutrition organizations are Gaines Nutrition Center in Kankakee, Illinois, and Purina Dog Care Center, with a farm near Gray Summit, Missouri.

Both follow strict and properly scientific approaches to the subject of proper feeding. The nature of the tests, the controls, the analyses may be obtained by writing to these companies.[1] They follow the guidance established by the National Academy of Sciences—National Research Council.[2]

---

[1]Gaines Nutrition Center, 250 North St., White Plains, N.Y., 10025 also publishes a free periodical *Gaines Dog Progress Research*. Purina Dog Care Center, Checkerboard Square, St. Louis, Mo., issues at no cost *Purina Kennel News*.

[2]The Subcommittee on Canine Nutrition of the Committee on Animal Nutrition issues a publication, *Nutrient Requirements of Dogs* (1972). Copies may be purchased from National Research Council, National Academy of Sciences, 2101 Constitution Avenue, Washington, D.C.

They have availed themselves of the results of research performed by colleges, universities, and various other companies. It would not be possible for an individual breeder to study the subject as thoroughly as they unless, at an early age, he became an expert in biology, dietetics, veterinary medicine, and operations research, had extraordinary financial backing, and lived to a ripe old age.

In this chapter we shall consider the essential nutrients, the various kinds of commercial dog foods, and the different methods people follow in feeding Irish Wolfhounds.

The essential nutrients are: Water, carbohydrates, fat, proteins, vitamins and minerals. Unless these are properly balanced, decreased body size, structural deficiencies, ailments and even death will result. Throughout this chapter we shall give examples of the results when nutrition is imbalanced.

Let us start with the view which many people have that dogs should subsist on meat alone. Meat lacks carbohydrates and is deficient in vitamins A, D and E and in minerals such as calcium, phosphorus, iron potassium, magnesium, manganese, copper, sodium, cobalt and iodine.[1] When carbohydrates and fat are insufficient to meet energy requirements, the dog will use up more protein to supply the need. Moreover, the ratio between calcium and phosphorus is 1:16.9 in muscle meats as compared to the proper ratio of 1.2:1.[2] "It would be impossible for an Irish Wolfhound or any other growing dog to consume enough meat to supply its calcium requirements," says Doctor Corbin, former Director of the Purina Dog Care Center and Chairman of the Subcommittee on Dog Nutrition, Committee on Animal Nutrition, National Research Council, National Academy of Sciences. The National Research Council recommends that dry dog food fed to a growing puppy contain 1.0% calcium and 0.8% phosphorus. It should never exceed 3%. Tests at the Purina Dog Care Center resulted in markedly depressed rates of growth when 5% calcium and 4% phosphorus were fed to puppies, even though the 1.2 to 1.0 ratio was correct.[3] In an editorial in the Journal of the American Veterinary Medical Association, Dr. D. A. Price said:

> Veterinary practitioners say they are treating an increasing number of dogs for nutritional deficiencies resulting from the

---

[1]Corbin, *Letter to author* (June 7, 1971).

[2]Lennart Krook, Ph.D. "Overnutrition and Skeletal Diseases in Growing Dogs," *Gaines Dog Research Progress* (Winter, 1975), p. 8.

[3]Richard D. Kealy, "Bone Structure of the Dog," *Purina Kennel News* (1974).

consumption of so-called all-meat products. Why? Because so many dog owners have been led to believe that meat alone is suitable as a diet for dogs. . . . Such persons do not know or else choose to overlook that wild carnivores do not subsist on muscle meat alone. They consume not only some skeletal and glandular tissue but viscera likely to contain vegetable matter. . . .The "superiority" of meat as a protein for dogs is also questionable, for properly prepared plant proteins are suitable for normal, healthy dogs and are more economical.[1]

Dr. Krack reported:

Because it is cheaper, horse meat is frequently used but a few words have to be said about horse meat. First it must be fresh and must be taken from horses that have passed official inspection and have not died from disease, otherwise there is great danger of poisoning. And this cannot be avoided by cooking as some may think. But even the feeding of the best horse flesh is not always without undesirable results. Too much feeding of any kind of meat may lead to an over acidity of the cell juices. With horse meat this danger is especially great. Horse meat is very rich in substances that tend to give the blood an undesirable combination, it makes the blood "sharp". Over indulgence in horse meat is also responsible for the kidney complaints so often found in older dogs. The waste matter of the albumen burdens the kidneys too heavily; the resulting refuse must alway pass through the kidneys for there is no other way. And an organ that has been abused for many years finally takes its revenge by going on strike. Chronic skin disease, frequently with incurable itching, occur very frequently after an exclusive meat diet. Meat alone is not a balanced diet.[2]

We have already seen Dr. Corbin's warning about feeding meat as the sole diet for puppies.[3] He adds:

Since all-meat diets do not fulfill dogs' needs, dogs draw on their own body reserves until they are depleted. Then damage results in the form of poor growth, poor bone calcification, poor eyes, poor immunity and misformed bones. If females are raised on diets that are too high in meat, they will have pelvis malformations which may prevent normal delivery. Many otherwise healthy brood females require Caesarean sectioning, because they

---

[1]D. A. Price, "Dogs Need More Than Meat," *Journal of the American Veterinary Medical Association* (1970) CLVI, No. 6, pp. 681, 682.

[2]Krack, M.V.D., Lecture given before the Kynological Society of Koenigsberg, Prussia, *Dog News* (Apr. 1967).

[3]See Index at Feeding, Meat.

received a high meat level during their growing period.[1]

How can one tell if a dog food is nutritionally balanced? One Gaines article says:

> Looking at the guaranteed analysis on the bag of package means practically nothing. By this basis or this form of analysis, as the late Dr. Babcock used to say, soft coal, if analyzed and presented this way, would make a good cattle feed. Checking the ingredients listed? This gives some idea but is not adequate. A complete list of all ingredients and the amount of levels in each pound of the product will give some idea of what it contains. Check the features of the product against the National Research Council requirements.
>
> Another important thing to know is the total energy content of the food. How many calories per pound? Also, what is the digestibility and actual available energy of the food? And, of extreme importance, what is the biological value of the protein; that is, how much of that protein will the dog actually retain? Freshness is an important factor. The best balanced dog food, nutritionally speaking, is worthless if the dog will not eat it, so palatability is an extremely important consideration.[2]

A simple solution is to select a company which has done major research in the field of dog nutrition and use its product provided it is advertised as a "complete and balanced ration". There are three types of complete and balanced rations in the United States today:

1. *Dry products.* Called "biscuit" if of large size, "kibble" when broken up, and "meal" if in the shape of flakes or pellets. Examples are Gaines products: Meal and Gravy Train, and Purina products: Dog Chow, Dog Meal, Chuck Wagon, Puppy Chow.

2. *Soft-moist Products.* Because of its concentration, owners are apt to over-feed this type. This is a special type of food. It does not mean a dry product that has been moistened. Examples are Gaines products: Gainesburgers, Prime and Top Choice. They would seem especially suitable for weaning puppies or for older dogs with worn down teeth. Small dogs would prefer the small size of Gainesburger and Top Choice to Prime which comes in "chunk" form.

---

[1]Dr. James Corbin, *Purina Kennel News* (Winter, 1971).
[2]Ben E. Sheffy, "Meeting the Nutritional Needs of Normal Dogs," *op. cit.*

3. *Canned Products.* Meat combined with cereal-based foods. The high level of nitrogen in meat imposes a severe burden on the kidneys of dogs.

A dog eats primarily to satisfy his caloric needs.[1] His caloric requirement depends on his size, age, activity, and general metabolism. A large dog has a smaller caloric requirement per pound of body weight than a small dog. An older dog needs less calories than a younger one. More calories are required if the dog gets considerable exercise, is exposed to cold weather, is frequently used as a stud or is a lactating bitch.[2]

While calories are needed for energy, it is essential that the food contain the necessary nutrients and that they be in proper proportion.

> To give an example, if a pound of product supplying 1,600 calories per pound is fed to an adult dog requiring 1,600 calories per day for maintenance, the dog's nutritional requirements are satisfied for the day. By adding two ounces of fat to one pound of the same food, it now contains 1,891 calories per pound. If fed this way over an extended period of time, theoretically, the dog will consume only about 13.5 ounces of this food instead of the 16 ounces he would normally eat. The 13.5 ounces now supply 1595 calories, but many of these calories are from an excessive quantity of fat. The fat-supplemented ration supplies only about 84% of the other essential nutritional elements. The supplemental fat added to rations often becomes an unwanted nutritional "minus" instead of the hoped for "plus".[3]

This is an example of supplementation, that is, the nourishment which many persons feel dogs should have in addition to a scientifically balanced and sufficient diet. We shall now go into this subject in some detail.

The Purina Dog Care Center advertises:

> Purina Dog Chow is a careful blend of all 43 nutrients known to be needed by dogs for good growth, reproduction and lactation. You can feed Purina Dog Chow for weaning on without supplementation.

Gaines maintains the same position for its products. Dr. Kirk wrote:

---

[1] One Calorie is equivalent to one thousand small calories. It may be abbreviated to Kcal., i.e. Kilocalories.

[2] Gaines Nutrition Center, *Basic Guide to Canine Nutrition* (1965), p. 40.

[3] General Foods Corp., *A Report on Soft-Moist Dog Foods* (1967).

> Supplements in general are bad news. In most cases they are not
> needed. In an individual case a supplement may be indicated...
>
> We had a case of a very fine Vizsla bitch with a beautiful litter. On
> the advice of someone (not us) her owner had given her a half to
> one lb. of liver every day while she was in whelp. It is
> remarkable that she didn't have severe diarrhea with this
> tremendous amount. Her puppies were born reasonably well,
> but they gradually became crippled and deformed and several
> died when one or two months old. These pups had vitamin A
> levels about 1,200 times the normal requirement. This is an
> example of what excessive supplementation can do. . . . The stud
> dog does not need a special diet.[1]

Raw eggs can cause hair loss and dermatitis in dogs and can affect
the growth of puppies because they contain an enzyme which affects
a vitamin essential to growth and to good coat condition. Eggs
should be cooked, if fed at all. Excess Vitamin D will result in
abnormal bone development in growing dogs and in soft tissue
calcification. High levels of Vitamin A may result in death and will
result in a porous bone structure. Subluxation in dogs is due to a
lack of manganese which may be due to feeding excess vitamins A
and D and to feeding excess calcium.[2]

On August 27, 1965, the following article appeared on the first
page of the *Washington Post* (D.C.):

> A dark cloud of suspicion is moving over the sunshine vitamin.
> Recent Food and Drug Administration studies indicate that
> pregnant women who get too much Vitamin D may produce
> malformed or mentally retarded babies. In consequence the FDA
> proposed yesterday that addition of the vitamin to milk be
> limited to 400 USP units per quart, and that extra dosages be
> entirely eliminated from margarine, enriched flour, rice.
>
> Vitamin pills providing more than 400 USP units of the vitamin
> per day would require a prescription.
>
> Commissioner George D. Larrick said the FDA studies were
> prompted by a pediatrician's charge last November that too
> much Vitamin D could result in infantile hypercalcemia.
>
> The pediatrician, Dr. Robert E. Cooke, of the Johns Hopkins
> Hospital, described victims of the disease as "elfin or Pekingese-
> faced" infants with wide-spaced eyes and excess folds at the sides

---

[1] Robert W. Kirk, "Nutrition for the Dog in Stress," *Gaines Dog Research
Progress* (Summer, 1969).

[2] E. Gladstone, *Dog World* (Britain), Quoted in Gaines Nutrition Center's *Basic
Guide to Canine Nutrition* (1965), p. 24.

of the nose, with ears low set and pointed, and with a nose that in profile looks like a ski-jump.

Unseen effects are narrowed lung arteries and constriction of the aorta, he said.

In September, 1973, the Food and Drug Administration placed a limit on the potency and formulation of vitamin and mineral supplements. Having found that large dosages of Vitamins A and D retard children's mental and physical growth, it directed that a doctor's prescription be obtained for dosages of Vitamin A above 10,000 international units (the recommended daily allowance) and of Vitamin D above 400 international units (the recommended allowance for two days).

James Corbin, realizing that, despite all warnings, people will supplement, gives the following advice:

It is not necessary to have the secret formula of beef melts, chicken hearts, cottage cheese, calf liver, baby vitamins, baby cereals, cod liver oil, etc., for your dog; it isn't even recommended. If you must cook for your dog, there are a few important "dos" and "don'ts".

DO. . .
—Select good fresh ingredients, just like you'd use for yourself.
—Use a minimum amount of fresh liver because of possible vitamin A accumulation and toxicity.
—Boil or heat all meat products thoroughly to destroy bacteria.
—Keep cod liver oil or wheat germ oil in the refrigerator after it's been opened to prevent rapid oxidation and to prevent loss of Vitamins A, D and E.
—Chop meat particles finely enough so the dogs won't choke on them.

DON'T. . .
—Overcook protein products. This can destroy one of the needed amino acids, lysine, and it can produce an imbalance.
—Use an excess of cod liver oil or vitamin D. It can cause excess calcium deposits in the blood vessels and produce abnormal heart conditions.
—Use cod liver oil or wheat germ oil that is unrefrigerated since both will destroy vitamin E while they are going rancid.
—Feed excess quantities of fats to your dog.
—Feed bones that can splinter and puncture the esophagus.
—Satisfy your dog's energy requirements with excess fat before the requirements for other nutrients have been met.

If you must cook for your dog, it is recommended that not more than one-fourth of the dog's diet be homecooked foods with three-fourths (by weight) of commercial dog foods. Commercial diets are prepared with an approximate safety margin of 25% and the addition of excess tablescraps and vitamin and mineral supplements can produce problems. Excess feeding of such supplements can even result in reduced litter size, poor growth, and lowered resistance by the dog to bacterial infection. Supplementation should only be undertaken on the advice of your veterinarian.[1]

A veterinarian may recommend that a pregnant bitch, especially from 4 to 6 weeks of her pregnancy, have additional protein. He may recommend that a lactating bitch, i.e. one nursing her puppies, have extra calcium and phosphorus. These requirements could be satisfied without upsetting the balance of the nutrients by increasing the dry food ration. There may be two objections to this procedure. First, the bitch may be unwilling to eat greater quantities of food. This may be overcome by feeding her a more condensed type of food such as a soft-moist ration. The following is an example of this approach:

In *Current Veterinary Therapy* there is a chapter written by Lt. Col. James H. McNamara of the USAF V.C. on weight loss that occurs among dogs under physical or psychological stress. These include racing dogs, hunting dogs and sentry dogs. McNamara's work concerned army dogs under stress in high temperatures. Feeding is an important facet in keeping sentry dogs. It was found that a dog can lose as much as 10% of its body weight in a 6-hour tour of duty. A common problem with sentry dogs in hot weather areas was refusal of a portion of their daily ration of food and resultant weight loss, which directly affected their efficiency, as well as their state of health.

As the temperature increases above 80° F, the working dog's caloric requirements increase. During high temperature periods (80° to 120° F), the average weight loss may range from 12 to 20 lbs., just as similar problems may be experienced in areas of extreme cold. McNamara found that by increasing the caloric density of the ration and the density of protein in a balanced way, the total food volume needed was reduced. With the dense caloric ration, the dogs did not have to eat a great amount of food to get the calories they required for efficiency in their work. Dogs were similarly affected in high humidity.[2]

---

[1]Corbin, "Canine Nutrition," *Popular Dogs* (October, 1969) XLII, p. 54.
[2]Kirk, "Nutrition for the Dog in Stress," *op. cit.*

A second objection to an increase in the ration may be that weight will be added when it is considered undesirable to have this result. In this case, ask your veterinarian how to supplement the ration. Incidentally, fresh hamburger meat averages 18% protein, while the percentage of protein in commercial dog food varies from 20% to 27%.

Strangely enough, Alma Starbuck's book, *The Complete Irish Wolfhound* (1969), does not contain any of her own advice on feeding. She does, however, advise as daily supplementation for each hound a tablespoonful of bone meal and one of yeast, a vitamin pill almost every day, and wheat germ oil and liver.[1] Part II of the book, not written by Mrs. Starbuck, advises that puppies be "roly-poly fat" until they are at least five or six months old and then a little fat until mature. It also says that meals should include meat, liver, milk, cod liver oil and calcium phosphate. Great stress is laid on the provision of meat.[2] I do not agree with these recommendations.

Some breeders maintain dry dog food continuously before their dogs. This method is known as "self-feeding". I have been told that this helps control coprophagy, the habit of eating excrement. A number of food additives have been recommended as deterrents to coprophagy: a drop of anise, meat, hard-boiled eggs with the shells and with cottage cheese, pineapple, figs, squash, pumpkin. The anise gives the stool a bad odor, the other items may help because of a diet change. If they do not work, consult your veterinarian. As for self-feeding, a study of 24 Great Danes in which half were fed all they would eat, while the other half was restricted to 2/3 of this amount, resulted in a finding that the first group became lazy, clumsy, and skeletally deformed. Among the effects were hip dysplasia and osteochondrosis dissecans. The calcium content of the food was twice that recommended by the NRC and the vitamin D content was high. One dog in the second group was mildly affected by osteochondrosis dissecans.[3]

I will now relate my feeding method for adult Irish Wolfhounds. Feeding of puppies is covered in the preceding chapters; for references to pregnant bitches and dams see Index at Feeding, Supplementation. Food should be stored in a cool, dry place to prevent deterioration. I feed the adult dogs twice a day and give them all the kibble they will eat without getting overweight. This amounts to about 1½ to 2 lb a day, depending on the dog's weight.

---

[1]Alma J. Starbuck, *The Complete Irish Wolfhound* (1969), pp. 147, 148.
[2]E.S. Howell, Milo Denlinger, A.C. Merrick, *op. cit.*, pp. 21-23, 45.
[3]Krook, *op. cit.*, p. 8.

An increase in exercise would increase the caloric need. Food is served in 6-quart steel bowls sold by restaurant supply houses. The kibble is moistened, but not soaked, with warm water. I recommend setting the bowls on a stand of some type so that the hound may eat and drink comfortably. The stand should have a back and sides about 4 inches high to decrease the possibility of the bowls being pushed off by an avid eater.

Should a dog leave his food to lie down, or otherwise than momentarily, it is removed and either offered to the other dogs or placed in the refrigerator depending on the quantity remaining. Any dog food that has been placed in the refrigerator is warmed to room temperature at the next meal and again offered to the dog who has previously refused it. Should he again fail to eat, the food is thrown out. My first Irish Wolfhound went four days without eating and I found it difficult to agree with the veterinarian that "when she's hungry enough, she will eat". But he was right. Of course, I took her temperature every day to make sure she was well.

One Irish Wolfhound owner reported to me that his hound was not ill but would not eat. He forcefed him and in his own words, "this was a traumatic experience for both of us. Now when he sees the food dish, he begins to tremble. Nevertheless, he will not eat even if he is left alone with the food." I suggested he immediately desist from force feeding and that he pamper the dog for a while with the most appetizing food possible — whatever the dog would eat. After the dog had been spoiled, he could then gradually wean him back to his regular food. I do not know whether this approach was successful. Allow the dogs to eat in a quiet environment. If distracted, they may leave their food and you will incorrectly assume that they are not hungry.

After the dogs have eaten, the bowls are thoroughly washed. Water is continuously available to the dogs, even during meals, except after strenuous exercise. Twice a day the water remaining in the bowls is replaced by fresh water. Water in the commode is most likely contaminated. Do not let the dog drink from it. If he does and then he laps your hands or face, you may become ill. Keep the commode cover down.

Dogs do not need variety in their diet; desire for variety is a learned trait. Man eats different foods because no one food is nutritionally complete in itself. A sudden change in diet may cause diarrhea. About every two weeks, we cook fresh meat in a pressure cooker. The liquid is used to moisten the kibble and is not served at the same meal as the cooked meat. The following directions may be helpful. Brown meat in a tablespoonful of fat, season, add vegetables and one quart of water, cook for one hour in pressure cooker. Remove bones. Serve a small portion with regular food. Keep the balance refrigerated until the next meal at which time reheat another small portion. Some bones, e.g. chicken backs and necks, fish, are cooked so well in a pressure cooker that they can be pulverized and served with the meat. Fish is relished by dogs. Between-meal snacks are not advisable, although an occasional tidbit is permissible. A dog that has some ailment, e.g. renal disease, diabetes, may require a special diet. See your veterinarian.

A dog that is exhausted from the heat or from exercise should be allowed to rest before being fed. Water should be given to him in small quantities. To avoid digestive upset, do not feed him just before he is going to be extremely active or prior to an automobile or airplane trip.

Eating grass is a method used by some dogs in cleaning out the intestines. The grass is often vomited. This is nothing to be alarmed about.

Opinions differ on the advisability of giving bones to dogs. Marrow beef bones or knuckle bones are all right, but steak and pork bones may splinter and puncture or tear the stomach or intestines. Of course, bones from chicken, turkey, rabbit, or fish should not be fed. Bones are a source of contention among dogs. And so is food. If a new dog is introduced into the house and the dogs are fed together, make sure that the newcomer learns that he is to eat only from his dish. Otherwise, there is liable to be a fight.

> Water is necessary to regulate the temperature of the body. If the temperature rises and menaces because of too much heat, then water appears on the skin; the animal perspires and gains coolness through evaporation. This does not apply to the dog as much as to the human beings. The dog perspires through the skin very seldom, generally only through the balls of the sole. But he opens his mouth and lets the water evaporate from his tongue. The result is the same. Through water also the digestive materials of the stomach and intestines become effective. When there is great thirst, they do not function. Therefore there is no appetite when there is great thirst. Thirst is much harder to bear than hunger. Thirst rapidly leads to emaciation and death. The animal can stand hunger for weeks without being harmed, if it has a sufficient supply of water. But thirst it can bear only for a very short time. I tell you this to impress on you the importance of fresh clean water. . . .Food that only consists of soup and wet mash is not suitable for a dog.[1]

---

[1]Dr. Krack, *op. cit.*

Finally, you may wish to determine the costs of feeding various products to your dogs. This, of course, is by far the least important consideration. I will let you make the computations rather than doing them myself since prices vary from region to region and, indeed, from store to store, and since the more economical large size containers of some products may not be available in your locality. To determine feeding costs, divide the price of the largest size bag or case available by the number of pounds of food in a bag or case and multiply the quotient by the number of pounds required daily. The number of pounds required will vary with the size of the dog, his activity, whether he is a puppy or full grown, etc. Feed him as much as he will eat provided this does not result in excess weight.

Both Purina and Gaines have programs for professional breeders and kennel operators whereby cash refunds are made upon the receipt of that portion of the product which indicates the weight. Write to them for details.[1]

Comparison of Some Commercial Dog Foods
Amount Required

Product Name	Type	Largest Size Container	Calories Per lb.[2]	Daily lbs. Required[3]
Purina				
Dog Chow	Dry	50 lb. bag	1,980	2.08
Puppy Chow	Dry	25 lb. bag	2,010	2.05
Chuck Wagon	Dry	25 lb. bag	2,010	2.05
Gaines				
Meal	Dry	50 lb. bag	1,600	2.58
Gravy Train	Dry	50 lb. bag	1,600	2.58
Top Choice	Soft-Moist	27 lb. case	1,400	2.86
Gainesburgers	Soft-Moist	27 lb. case	1,440	2.86
Prime	Soft-Moist	27 lb. case	1,440	2.86
Quaker				
Ken-L-Ration	Canned	57 lb. case	525	6.95

[1]Dog Care Division, Ralston Purina Company, Checkerboard Square, St. Louis, Missouri, 63199. Gaines Professional Services, General Foods Corporation, White Plaines, New York, 10602.

[2]These will vary as the manufacturers make changes in the preparation of their products.

[3]Based on an assumed requirement of 3,300 calories per day for an adult 150 lb. Irish Wolfhound. 80% of calories assumed to be digestible, except for Ken-L-Ration which Quaker reports is 90% metabolizable.

NUTRIENT COMPARISONS

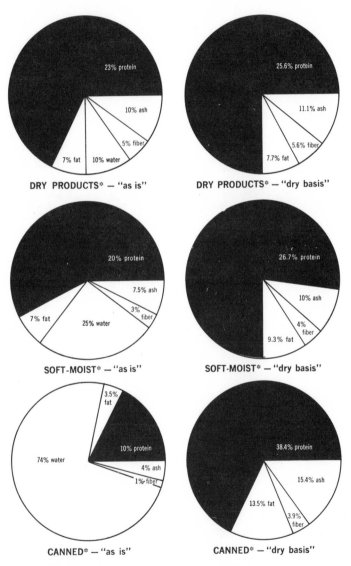

DRY PRODUCTS* — "as is"

23% protein
10% ash
5% fiber
7% fat   10% water

DRY PRODUCTS* — "dry basis"

25.6% protein
11.1% ash
5.6% fiber
7.7% fat

SOFT-MOIST* — "as is"

20% protein
7.5% ash
3% fiber
7% fat   25% water

SOFT-MOIST* — "dry basis"

26.7% protein
10% ash
4% fiber
9.3% fat

CANNED* — "as is"

3.5% fat
74% water
10% protein
4% ash
1% fiber

CANNED* — "dry basis"

38.4% protein
15.4% ash
3.9% fiber
13.5% fat

NOTE: In order to make accurate comparisons of the nutritional values of products
with different moisture levels, it is necessary to reduce all products to a dry basis.
The equation at the right may be used:

* Complete and Balanced Type

$$\frac{\text{Guaranteed \% of nutrient}}{\text{\% of dry solids (100\% minus \% of moisture)}} \times 100 = \text{\% of nutrient (dry basis)}$$

As an example, if the fat content of a soft-moist food (containing 25% moisture
and, therefore, 75% dry solids) is 7% on an "as is" basis, it is 9.3% on a dry basis. 3

Percentage of Nutrients in Some Commercial Dog Foods[1]

Product Name	"As is"				"Dry Basis"[2]		
	Protein	Fat	Fiber	Moisture	Protein	Fat	Fiber
Purina							
Dog Chow	21	8	4.5	12	23.9	9.1	5.1
High Protein Dog Meal	26	10	4	12	29.5	11.4	4.5
Puppy Chow	27	9	5	12	30.7	10.2	5.7
Chuck Wagon	23	8	5	12	26.1	9.1	5.7
Gaines							
Meal	21	6	5	11	23.6	6.7	5.6
Gravy Train	21	6	5	11،	23.6	6.7	5.6
Top Choice	19	7	3	33	28.4	10.4	4.5
Gainesburgers	19	7	3	32	27.9	10.3	4.4
Prime	19	7	3	32	27.9	10.3	4.4
Quaker							
Ken-L Ration	10	2.5	1	75	40.0	10.0	4.0
Recommendation of National Research Council					22.0	5.5	—

[1] These will vary as the manufacturer makes changes in the preparation
of his products. Symbols. ◁ = not less than; ▷ = not more than.
[2] Percentage of nutrients with moisture removed.

> The minimum carbohydrate requirement for dogs has not been
> determined . . . Diets containing as much as twice the minimum
> required amount of protein can have serious consequences,
> irrespective of vitamin and mineral supplementation of food, if
> fed over long periods.[1]

Note that Ken-L-Ration has 157% of the protein recommended by
the National Research Council.

B. CARE

Dogs may be kept inside or outside. If outside, they should have
shelter from cold, heat, dampness, drafts, rain and snow. There
should be adequate ventilation to provide air circulation during the

---

[1]National Academy of Sciences, *op. cit.,* pp. 3, 7.

summer. A dog house painted white will be 6 to 8 degrees cooler than one painted with a semi-gloss black paint if the outside temperature is between 25° and 30° F; it will be 15 to 20 degrees cooler if the outside temperature is about 90°.

Controlled tests have proved that "dogs do not tolerate heat nearly as well as humans and are further incapacitated when humidity enters into the picture. . .Rectal temperatures fluctuated from the normal 101 degrees to 107 in different animals undergoing the same experience".[1]

However, Irish Wolfhounds have been exported to and bred in Africa, India and South America with apparently no ill effects. My own home is air-conditioned during the summer and the dogs, during that season, spend less time out of doors than they do when the weather is cold.

Tieing an Irish Wolfhound should be an emergency and temporary measure only. Otherwise, it is closely akin to cruelty. The hound is unable to exercise. His temperament will gradually turn vicious. He could be attacked by other dogs, or by humans, in which cases he would be limited in his ability to defend himself. At all events, remember that he will rapidly chew through any restraining cord other than a metal one. Fresh water should be constantly available. It should be of the same quality as that drunk by humans. In the summer, dogs prefer water between 60° to 70°F. In the winter, water should be kept from freezing and the chill should be removed. More water will be consumed if the water is at a proper temperature.[2] It should not be placed where the sun will heat it. I use 6-quart steel bowls, available at restaurant supply houses. The bowls are also used for feeding. Irish Wolfhounds crave human companionship. Whenever possible, the hound should be with humans. In my home, the dogs have the run of the house except when it is muddy outside.

When people hear that I have several grown Irish Wolfhounds and that I occasionally have litters of puppies, they exclaim: "You must have a huge place." I do not. The lowest portion of the house, divided into three rooms, is always available to the dogs who may go outside and return whenever they wish, through either of two two-way swinging doors that have been set into the lower halves of regular doors. Immediately outside these swinging doors is a gravel area (No. 5 gravel) which is used when the grassy area is so wet that the dogs would turn it into a marsh if they were allowed on it. The gravel also serves to reduce the amount of dirt and mud brought into the house by the dogs. Beyond the gravel area, there are two grassy

---

[1] *Gaines Dog Research Progress* (Spring, 1970).
[2] National Academy of Sciences, *op. cit.,* p. 21.

areas. Each of these areas is divided by rustic fences (post and rail). This permits separation of puppies from grown dogs, injured or ill dogs from those who are well, etc., whenever necessary. Two smooth-surfaced boards about five feet by four set onto the gravel, one which will receive the sun's rays during a portion of the day and the other which will be in the shade, will give one dog a comfortable place to rest. The dogs prefer boards covered with indoor-outdoor carpeting.

The swinging doors are 29½″ inches high and 23½″ inches wide. They fit into an opening cut out of the lower half of a regular door. The swinging doors are not of greater size because, I have been told, the larger door would not hold its form unless the cutout portion was bounded by at least 2 inches of regular door at the bottom and 4 inches on each side. The opening is sufficient for dogs of any size. Unless sheltered in some way, you will find that high winds will open the swinging doors and allow snow and rain to be driven into the house. Pad the edge of the swinging door with foam rubber covered with Naugahide so that the dog's tail won't be irritated when the door closes on it. There are other possibilities; electronic eyes, weight-activated doors, etc. but the dog might decide to stay in such a position that the door will remain open!

Dogs can be trained not to leave an area whether enclosed or not. Nevertheless, if your home is next to a well-travelled highway, and does not have an enclosure, it would be dangerous to let your dog remain free. It is possible to enclose your property and still have it look well. I have rustic fences measuring 3′ 8″ in height subdividing the area. The dogs could easily jump over or go through the rustic fence. To discourage them, I once made use of an electric fence. This consisted of two strands of wire, one between the bottom rail and the ground, the other between the two bottom rails. I would turn the power on for a day or two and be quite observant to make sure that none of the neighbors' children came close. Actually, they would not have been harmed as only 4 to 6 volts were emitted, thus producing a light shock, but many local governments have ordinances against the use of electric fences and the neighborhood children were accustomed to patting the dogs. After the dogs had been shocked a couple of times they would run to the center of the enclosure. After a while, they would venture back but would not approach the fence closer than a couple of feet. Eventually they would overcome this fear and would even touch the wire but they made no attempt to jump the fence or to go through it. If there had been a strong reason for them to cross the barrier, such as my calling them, I feel certain they would have done so.

While the electric fence did keep my dogs within the enclosure, it did not keep other dogs from coming in, for the obvious reason that the electric current was very rarely on. So I replaced it with a green plastic-coated 3½′ fence which I stapled (heavy duty) and wired onto the wooden fence. It blends well with the background and is barely noticeable. I learned, however, that even small dogs can jump onto the top rail of a 3′8″ fence and then propel themselves onto the other side. In one area, I installed a 4′ wire fence which extends above the top rail and which will not allow dogs to jump onto the top wooden rail but dogs are quite ingenious and small ones have managed to squirm under the wire fence. My countermove in this battle of wits — which I hope to win — is to run a heavy wire under the bottom rail of the wooden fence, intertwining it with the wire fence and affixing it with heavy-duty staples onto each wooden post. Observe that the problem is not keeping the wolfhounds in, other than puppies, it is keeping the friendly native canine population out.

One company manufactures devices which purport to be effective in preventing a dog from wandering outside a specified area. One such device consists of a wire buried slightly underground on the perimeter of the area, a small powerplant and a special collar. The collar has a small receiver attached to it as well as two metal studs which project from the inside of the collar onto the dog's neck. When the dog approaches the buried wire, he receives a shock. The effective distance can be adjusted from 0 to 8 feet. Another device is similar but is operated manually by the owner as he observes the dog approaching the prescribed area. I recommend that these not be used. There are too many possibilities of mental and physical injury to the dog even when the devices are used in conjunction with proper obedience training methods. I also strongly urge that no one use electronic devices for the purpose of preventing a dog from barking. These are sound-activated and give the dog a shock when he barks. However, they also work when other sounds are made, e.g., certain radio signals, passing cars, thunder, other dogs barking, human voices. And a dog that gets shocked when he barks is apt to bark again out of surprise which will give him another shock, etc. The manufacturer warns that, when a shock is applied, the dog may consider the person or dog nearest him as an aggressor and may then attack. The Food and Drug Administration ordered one manufacturer to recall the collars it had sold when it was discovered that dogs had received 1800 volts of electricity causing holes in the skin and also burns.

It can be expected that a dog will dig. Evidently the earth below is cooler than the lawn above. Of course, a dog can be trained not to dig but this requires "eternal vigilance" and is not worth the effort. I prefer to allow him this liberty and to reseed one-half of the area each year. Thus, for one month, the dogs' grassy play area is reduced by half. Reseeding also takes care of the small areas burnt by the dogs' urine.

W. R. Koehler has a solution for the person whose dog digs holes:

> If your dog has dug a hole, fill the hole brimful of water. With the training collar and leash, bring the dog to the hole and shove his nose into the water; hold him there until he is sure he's drowning. He will struggle, of course, but stay with it. Fill the hole with water and repeat the experience the next day, whether the dog digs any more or not. On the third day let him watch you dig a hole and prepare it for dunking. You can bet he'll swear off hole digging.[1]

I have never tried this. If you do, you will get an idea of the Irish Wolfhound's strength and agility as you try to drag him to the hole!

Dogs should be trained so that they will not be a nuisance to the owner and to others. Too often people blame their dog, when they themselves are to blame. An Irish Wolfhound should not be allowed to roam on other people's property. His urine ruins shrubbery and lawns; his exuberant friendliness might possibly terrify children or other dogs; he might get run over by an automobile; he might eat some poisonous substance; he might get lost or be stolen. In the city, watch your dog carefully and get him into the street if he is about to relieve himself on the sidewalk, so that pedestrians will not be inconvenienced.

A chain collar should not be so loose-fitting that it might slide off when the dog's head is lowered. Otherwise, it could be lost when the dog is running free. Do not leave an Irish Wolfhound alone with a chain collar on. In the Irish Wolfhound column of the AKC *Gazette* for May, 1963, the following was reported:

> The young hound recently became tangled in the male's chain collar. His sister's back leg somehow had slipped through the collar as they were lying on a low couch. Then, they had twisted so that the foot was tightly held and the male was being choked. Happily, a family member arrived and, with considerable difficulty, achieved a release.

Miss Katherine O'Connell related the following incident:

---

[1]W. R. Koehler, *Koehler Method of Dog Training*, according to *Gaines Dog Research Progress* (Summer, 1962).

As is usual, I let the hounds out about 6:30 a.m. and watched them romp and play. . . I then went to put on the coffee, etc., and went back to the door with a handful of dog biscuits. Lying on the ground just outside the door was my beautiful Kilala—dead! Beside her crouched her mother, Marion (Ch. Sulhamstead Marion of Riverlawn). . . . In playing, somehow Marion's lower teeth had hooked onto Kilala's collar. Since the lower tusks curve up and backward, Marion couldn't shake the collar loose. Kilala must have panicked and Marion had to hold 175 pounds of frightened, choking dog with her lower jaw. Kilala choked herself to death and Marion was snubbed close to her neck.[1]

I have also heard of a case where a Basset had a canine tooth caught in the collar of a Beagle and the ensuing struggle resulted in the Beagle's death. Another occurrence involved an Irish Wolfhound whose collar became caught while he was in an automobile. After some difficulty, his owner succeeded in freeing the hound.

The moral is don't leave an Irish Wolfhound alone if he has a chain collar on. At a benched show, attach the bench chain to that collar ring which will not cause the collar to tighten when pull is exerted on it. Irish Wolfhound exhibitors usually have one of their number "baby sit" when they leave the area where their dogs are benched. See Index at Breed competition, Show types, Benched.

An Irish Wolfhound is careful around furniture and will not ordinarily knock over objects. However, his tail has a powerful whip effect and can clear a coffee table in an instant or give physical pain to a human. Exercise judgment. Don't take him into a china shop. Don't praise him or get him excited when fragile objects are within reach of his tail. If a situation becomes dangerous, place yourself near the danger spot and command "Come!", so that when he responds his tail will be in a safe zone.

For your own welfare, do not place your head above the lowered head of the Wolfhound. If he should raise it suddenly, you will understand how a boxer feels when he has been given a stiff uppercut.

There are a number of preparations that are sold for the purpose of keeping dogs away from furniture or other articles. One can supply his own—anything with a strong odor—e.g. Musterole. I do not know whether any are effective. The simplest way is to say "No!" when he behaves otherwise than you wish him to.

---

[1] The Irish Wolfhound Club of America, *Harp and Hound* (1961) XII, No. 1, p. 9.

Occasionally, the dog may sleep with his eyes open and the owner will be startled to observe that the opening is filled with red tissue. There is no cause for alarm. This is a membrane called the third eyelid or the nictitating membrane. It is used to wipe away foreign matter that reaches the surface of the eyeball.

If you have more than one hound, exercise care when you take one out with you and leave the others at home. Upon your return, the dogs that have remained will sniff at the hound who has been away. He may resent this attention and a fight could easily follow.

Irish Wolfhounds are not quarrelsome, but one should always exercise caution lest fights develop even when dogs have been brought up together. Each dog has a personality of his own. Reactions to situations will vary between dogs and even the same dog may react differently on a certain day. Always anticipate trouble or you may be too late to prevent serious injuries. As an example, my Ch. Sulhamstead Samando Patrick ("Sahib") had injured a hind leg. It became well again, but was always a little weak. One day, going down some steps in the house, he fell and could not immediately get up. He promptly issued a warning growl and I hurriedly had the other dogs leave the area. Sahib evidently realized that he was vulnerable to aggression and, bluffing, wanted all to know he was ready to fight. In a situation such as that, the growl could have provoked an attack, and an attack by one dog might induce others to join in by reason of "mob" or "pack psychology".

Owners of a single Irish Wolfhound have such love for their dogs that they only remember the first part of the breed's motto "Gentle when stroked". They look askance at a Wolfhound who growls. Irish Wolfhounds are canines not lambs. Owners of several hounds kept together have experienced occasional fights among them.

Important advice:

1. Always assume that a fight may develop between dogs who are strangers to each other and between dogs who have been separated for some time. Keep them on leash while introducing or reintroducing them.

2. A dog that is recovering from anesthesia or otherwise weak should not be put in with the other dogs. His weakness may cause him to threaten the others and his threat may be resented.

3. At the first indication of trouble, such as a growl (not the playful kind), a tense pose, separate the dogs.

4. If a fight appears imminent, do not reach for one of the dogs. If you do, the other will charge. Give loud commands. The type of command will depend on the situation. If you should order one dog

out of the room, the other may attack. You might yell "Down!" or "No!" But then you will somehow have to get them separated.

5. In the event of a fight, do not place any portion of your body where the distraught dog may bite it. Get behind the dogs' heads.

6. Use a chair against the dog who has the advantage at the moment. Do not hit him with it or you may cripple him. Press it against his throat. Push him against something solid or he will escape you and return to the attack. Have someone use a chair against the other dog to prevent him from resuming the combat. Put the dogs in separate rooms. Possibly leads slipped around the dogs' necks will work but there is danger of getting bitten while putting these on. A number of other ways have been suggested: throwing a blanket or heavy plastic cover over the dogs' heads, use of water (a fire hose, perhaps!), a lighted newspaper, etc. A chemical spray may result in blindness. I cannot vouch for the efficacy of any of these means. If a dog is really provoked, possibly nothing will deter him from continuing the fight. If the irritation is mild, he may be willing to desist at your command. At all events, don't take anyone's word that certain actions cannot harm the dog. Having read in a dog magazine that a carbon dioxide fire extinguisher was effective in stopping dog fights and that the combatants would not be injured through its use, I inquired of the Underwriters' Laboratories. Here is the reply.

It is true that when a carbon dioxide extinguisher is discharged the noise created is quite loud and would most likely scare most any dog. Much of the discharge is the solid form of carbon dioxide and has the appearance of snow. As a matter of fact, if the extinguisher is discharged at close range (less than 2 ft.) a buildup of solid carbon dioxide on the object being aimed at is quite normal. I would not recommend the use of an extinguisher for anything other than extinguishing a fire. These extinguishers are capable of intermittent operation, and hence it is quite possible that a small amount would be used to stop a dog fight, and then the extinguisher would be returned to its "ready" position. If a fire emergency were then to occur, the extinguisher would not be up to its full potential.

I believe it would be dangerous to discharge a carbon dioxide extinguisher in the direction of any living animal since the snow form of carbon dioxide extinguisher can exist only at a temperature of -110 F or lower. Therefore, if a dog were contacted on the skin, nose, eyes, mouth or any other exposed part of its body, a localized freezing condition would develop immediately. The initial appearance of such a contact is that of a burn, but unlike a burn the tissue is not immediately destroyed. It is true that if this condition is left untreated the eventual results may be as severe as a burn. Since there is generally a great amount of activity and violent action in a dog fight, it would be virtually impossible to discharge a carbon dioxide extinguisher in a manner to effect a stop to the fight without getting some of the solid carbon dioxide snow on the animals involved.[1]

Whatever method is used, bear in mind the possibility that an excited dog might consider you to be the enemy, so have a chair handy. I do not wish to alarm you, merely alert you. You will most likely never see an Irish Wolfhound involved in a fight.

Irish Wolfhounds should not be left in automobiles with insufficient ventilation. In the heat of summer, the windows should be left open. This may present a problem since the dog could escape, especially if not obedience-trained, but it is nevertheless of great importance. Even with the windows partially open, the heat and reduced ventilation may be sufficient to cause his death in a short period of time. If the outside temperature is 85° and your car windows are slightly opened, the temperature inside the car will reach 102° in 10 minutes and 120° in 30 minutes. On warmer days, the inside temperature will go even higher. A dog with a body temperature of approximately 107° will suffer irreparable brain damage or death in a short while. Shades inside the car are not of much value since heat will already have entered the car by the time the sun's rays strike the shades. One can apply Aluminized Mylar (Pittsburg Plate Glass Company) to the outside of the glass; this will create a reflective surface without greatly reducing visibility. Or one can, when ordering a car, specify vapor- deposited metallic-coated windows. Of course, a light-colored car reflects more heat than a dark-coated one. But these measures by themselves, are insufficient to eliminate the danger. Some persons leave their dogs alone in closed cars with the engine running, the hood raised, and the air-conditioning on. I did this at a dog show. When I returned to the car, I was told by another exhibitor that grinding sounds had started to issue from the air-conditioning unit. He had shut off the engine and opened the windows. Major damage was caused to the air-conditioner. Had the air-conditioner failed and the exhibitor been afraid to enter my car with an Irish Wolfhound in it, the dog might have been overcome by the heat. At a later date, I left a hound in the car with the air-conditioner on but did not raise the hood as I was going into a store for only a few minutes. Upon my return, no more

---

[1]S. E. Auck, Underwriters' Laboratories, Inc. *Letter to author* (Aug. 2, 1971).

than five minutes later, I found that the water hose had burst and the engine had stalled. The hound within the car was not affected by the heat, but had I been delayed. . .! Don't forget to give your dog fresh water and to keep him cool. Check on him frequently.

Information on shipping a dog by air or on taking a dog to Europe may be had from a booklet of the American Society for the Prevention of Cruelty to Animals, Humane Education Department, 441 East 92nd Street, New York, N.Y. The cost is 25 cents. Gaines annually issues a pamphlet called *Touring with Towser* which lists hotels and motels throughout the country which accept dogs. The pamphlet costs 25 cents.

There is no duty on dogs taken into Canada to compete in breed shows or obedience trials. The procedure is very simple but, since regulations are subject to change, check with the U.S. Customs well in advance. I say "well in advance" because at the present time, the United States requires a rabies certificate dated at least 30 days prior to the date of leaving Canada.

If it becomes necessary to board the dog, inspect the kennel accommodations to make sure your dog will have a large cage and access to a run. The premises should be clean, well-ventilated, and provide comfortable air temperatures. Let the kennel operator know where you can be reached at all times and arrange for emergency veterinarian care if needed. If possible, let your hound stay home and have someone come to take care of him. Boarding kennels may and veterinarians' offices do harbor dogs with infectious or contagious diseases. When at the veterinarian's office, wait outside until it is your turn. If the puppy is not too heavy, carry him in. Keep him as far away as possible from other patients.

If it is desired to delay the season of a bitch because you are showing her in obedience, hunting or travelling with her, or for any other reason, your veterinarian can administer a drug which will have this effect. One injection of Promone, for example, which is given two to three weeks before the bitch is due will postpone the season six or more months. I have a great aversion to any drugs unless absolutely required. Too many have had side effects which were not discovered until years later.

The average person who acquires an Irish Wolfhound would laugh if he were asked: "Is there any possibility of your hound getting lost?" He would consider it as improbable as losing a bass drum. But it isn't! Many Irish Wolfhounds become lost. This may occur while they are far from home or it may be from your own front door. When he is let out of the house, he may chase some animal and you may never see him again! To minimize this possibility teach your dog obedience so that he will come when called; keep up the training so that he will always come when called regardless of the situation; take him on familiarization walks on lead around your neighborhood, and don't let him be off lead when away from home or leave him alone in an automobile which has its windows completely lowered unless you have installed in your car a system of metal bars which will prevent his exit. While it is undoubtedly true that some dogs have traveled great distances to rejoin their master, this may be the exception rather than the rule.

Should your dog become lost or should you find an Irish Wolfhound, notify the police, the dog warden, the local Humane Society, the Secretary of the Irish Wolfhound Club of America, veterinarians and Irish Wolfhound owners in the vicinity, as well as the local radio stations. Place an advertisement in the local newspaper. If the dog has been found by you, do not describe him in the advertisement except by breed. Let the person who claims him prove ownership by stating sex, color, name of dog, whether he was wearing a collar, date, location and circumstances of his becoming lost, and finally presentation of registration or bill of sale. Ask the Post Office to alert their mailmen. If your dog has been lost, inquire everywhere if a big dog has been seen. Tell everyone he is gentle and that, if seen, efforts should be made to entice him into a house to prevent him from wandering further. Give your name, address, and telephone number. Have someone constantly at that telephone. Despite all these measures, you still may not see your dog again.

Here are some cases of lost hounds that were later found.

1. One of the most unusual incidents relating to lost Irish Wolfhounds is that of Ch. Fleetwind Tralaigh of Eagle owned by Samuel Ewing III, a former president of the Irish Wolfhound Club of America. The hound escaped when the vehicle in which he was riding overturned on the New Jersey Turnpike. Several days search failed to find him. It should be explained that in the center of the turnpike there is a barrier which separates Northbound from Southbound traffic, that wire fences are placed about 50 feet away on each side of the turnpike to prevent vehicles from entering or leaving except through toll booths, and that there is a continuous and furious stream of traffic on the turnpike. Ten days after the accident, Mr. and Mrs. Gordon Graham (Mr. Graham later succeeded Mr. Ewing as President) saw an Irish Wolfhound alongside the New Jersey Turnpike. The hound was on the other side of the center barrier and, therefore, the Grahams could not pick him up. Traffic was so heavy and fast that they could not stop and cross over on foot. They stopped at the next exit and called Mr. Ewing who drove madly to the scene and picked up Tralaigh. The

hound was within yards of the accident scene but in poor condition. A true but almost incredible story. How Tralaigh managed to live for 10 days in that area, I do not know.

2. Mr. and Mrs. David Bulk and their seven children moved to Freehold, New Jersey. About midnight on the first night, their seven-year old bitch asked to go out. Mr. Bulk took her out and stayed with her. She suddenly took off and failed to answer his whistles and calls. Police and humane societies were notified, advertisements were placed in the newspapers. All to no avail. Some time later Mr. Roy Truchon of Hightstown, New Jersey, who breeds and shows Alaskan Malamutes, was driving on the New Jersey Turnpike when he saw some police officers and children gathered around a large hound. He recognized her as an Irish Wolfhound. She was thin, in poor condition, and had a rope around her neck. Mr. Truchon took her to his home and began a search for the owner. By consulting show catalogs, he obtained the names of Irish Wolfhound owners and contacted them. He notified the Irish Wolfhound Club of America. He wrote to the Secretary:

> Thank you for offering to come and get the Duchess, but we don't mind keeping her a while. She is well behaved, completely housebroken and gets along fine with my cats. The dogs are a different story. . . .We tried her with the male we keep in the house. . . .He usually sleeps in our bedroom with our old female but the Duchess has dispossessed them both. . . .we are actually enjoying her company even to the extent we almost hope when, and if, we locate her owner they won't want her back. . . .

> We have had her a week today. . . .She is acting better now and eating better. She was in terrible condition when we picked her up and probably would not have lived much longer. We dosed her with penicillin. . . .She was running quite a fever, spoon fed her some beef extract and got her to eat some meat. Now she is gobbling. . .and I've added some extra vitamins. . . .She is still all bones but at least her tummy feels nice and full. If you wonder about my calling her The Duchess, I dubbed her that almost immediately. She either sprawls out on my couch or in the middle of our bed and my comment upon seeing this was, "Well, look at the Duchess."

Finally, Mrs. Evelyn Monte, who is an associate director of Gaines Dog Research Center and who writes a Sunday dog column in the Newark, New Jersey, *Star-Ledger*, was told the story and mentioned it in her column. Friends of the Bulks saw the column and notified them. The Bulks picked her up. She had been gone one month and was 15 miles from home.[1]

3. A hound owned by a Cincinnati, Ohio, man was being shown by another down South. While travelling from the Birmingham, Alabama, show to one in Columbus, Georgia, the handler stopped for a rest and observed that a bolt was broken on the door of the trailer in which the hound had been and that the trailer was empty. Three weeks later, after assistance from newspapers and radio stations, the hound was located in thick brush. He would not come out and it was necessary for the owner's son to fly down. At the familiar whistle, the hound bounded out.[2]

4. A man, who had used his Irish Wolfhound to hunt in Alaska as well as Central America, lost all his money and gave the hound, then 12 years old, to another man in Texas. The latter locked her in a shed when a storm came up as the bitch greatly feared storms. She escaped and was located a year later 100 miles away. She had been roped by a cowboy on the plains who mistook her at first for a wolf. Given to another home, she died at the age of 15 when hit by an automobile.[3]

5. A four-year old hound escaped from a shipping crate, was lost for six weeks in Long Island, New York, and then found, still free.[4]

Here is a case of a lost hound that was not found. One morning in January, 1971, Mr. and Mrs. Putnam Little, of Issaquah, Washington, let out of the house Champion Mavourneen of Glocca Morra, the Best of Opposite Sex winner of the 1970 West Coast Specialty, and a kennel-mate, Ardfert of Eagle. Shortly thereafter, Ardfert returned alone. The Littles searched the mountain trails and the brush of the area but without success.

> Much has been made of the domestic dog's ability to successfully find his way home over great distances. But critical tests show that dogs carried blindfolded or in closed containers from which they cannot see the route, and released at least ten miles away in totally unfamiliar country seldom found their way back. Robert M. Lockley, a British zoologist, describes a series of experiments in which a dog was released one, two, four, nine, twelve, and twenty miles away from home, but always in the same direction. It always came home, alone and unaided, and quite quickly, because it had learned that home was always along the some compass bearing. But when the dog was carried in a closed box

---

The Irish Wolfhound Club of America, *Harp and Hound* (1961) XII, NO. 1, pp. 2, 6.

[2]*Ibid.* (1950) I, No. 4, pp. 30, 31.

[3]*Ibid.*, p. 31.

[4]*Ibid.* (1949-1950), Vol. I, No. 3, p. 9.

and released twenty miles in the opposite direction in unfamiliar territory, it started out as it had learned to in the usual direction. In this case, it was the opposite direction and the dog quickly became lost. The dog's sense in direction appears to be no better than that of man.[1]

Irish Wolfhounds away from their owner have been shot or poisoned. Others who have been near their owners have been stolen. Three dogs were stolen from an automobile parked near a supermarket in Pennsylvania: a shy two-year-old Irish Wolfhound, a ten-months-old Golden Retriever, and a ten-months-old Dandie Dinmont. The thief smashed a car window to effect entrance.

Membership in the National Dog Registry (NDR)[2] could lead to the recovery of many lost or stolen dogs. The organization, established in 1966, is endorsed by the Humane Society of the United States, WARDS, Guiding Eyes for the Blind, Inc., and many other groups. For a one-time fee of $15, a person's nine-digit Social Security number is permanently listed with the Registry. All dogs now owned or later acquired by the registrant are tattooed with the Social Security number. A new owner can add letters or numbers and register this identification with NDR. Laboratories, medical schools, pounds, humane workers and many police departments have been alerted to look for numbered tattoos and to report them to the Registry. NDR is operational every minute of the year and will contact its registrants, located in any of the 50 States, the District of Columbia, Puerto Rico and the Virgin Islands, as soon as a number is reported to it.

Tattooing can be done painlessly and quickly by veterinarians, by kennel clubs, humane societies, or individuals. It should be done in the groin area; a tattoo in a dog's ear can be removed. NDR does not perform tattooing. It does advise on tattooing equipment and technique, on setting up a clinic, on the names and addresses of tattooing services nearest the registrant. Tattooing without registration in the NDR is of no value. Tattooing does not constitute a change in appearance by artificial means requiring disqualification of a show dog.

While not strictly pertaining to Irish Wolfhounds, the problem of lost or abandoned animals should be mentioned here.

---

[1] Samuel A. Gardner, "A Dog's Senses," The American Kennel Club, *Pure-Bred Dogs—American Kennel Gazette* (November, 1968) LXXXV, p. 11.

[2] National Dog Registry, 227 Stebbins Road, Carmel, N.Y., 10512.

There are about 80 million to 100 million cats and dogs in the United States today with another 2,000 to 3,500 born every hour, according to the Humane Society of the United States.

Of the 15-17 million cats and dogs turned into the nation's animal shelter in 1973, 13.5 million were put to death, mostly in decompression chambers (which some animal care groups call torture chambers). The rest were reclaimed or adopted.

Stray dogs not picked up live only about 2½ years before they die of starvation, disease, freezing or from being struck by a car, according to a study in Baltimore by sociologist Alan Beck.

Public and private animal-control programs in the United States cost about $500 million a year, mostly in feeding and other care costs. But death costs something too, and some private animal care groups want to use that part of the bill to help find homes for more pets.

With a growing public awareness of the immense slaughter of strays each year, dozens of private animal-care groups have sprung up across the country in the past several years.

The Humane Society says the new private groups help a little, but that large-scale reductions in the death of pets will come only through:

● Increased public assistance in neutering or spaying pets. The typical fee for such service in private veterinary clinics is $50 to $65 for dogs and $35 to $45 for cats. Much lower rates are offered through a handful of publicly funded programs such as those of Los Angeles City and County, Palo Alto and Berkeley, Calif.

● More public education on the need for curbing pet births.[2]

Unfortunately, there are people who have no sense of attachment to a dog even though he may have been with them for many years. Should circumstances force you to place your hound "in a good home", you might consider retaining the title to him, i.e. just lending him. In this way, you can get him back should he not be properly cared for. Should you transfer the title, incorporate in the written agreement a provision, with penalty for violation, that the dog may not be bred, sold, given or boarded without your personal concurrence and that he shall be returned to you if the custodian decides to abandon him. Otherwise, your old friend may end as a stray, in a dog pound, on a vivisectionist's table, or subject to a cruel master. Don't fail to check periodically on his welfare.

------

[2]Robert M. Press, "The Strays," *Christian Science Monitor,* In *The Washington Post* (21 November, 1976), p. F12.

There comes a time when a dog suffers pain from age, injury or illness. A decision must be made whether or not to put him to sleep. Some owners do so if the dog exhibits the slightest discomfort. They would possibly hold a different view if it were they who were arthritic and the dog were the master. On the other hand, it is inhumane to allow a dog to suffer great pain. Unless you have the utmost confidence in the integrity of your veterinarian, have the dog put to sleep in your presence. An unscrupulous person — and there are some in all walks of life — may perform painful experiments on him or sell him alive to some research organization. Make sure the dog is dead or he may awaken on some dump heap. In one experiment, a veterinarian kept reviving the "dead" dog and then putting him back to sleep. Don't let this happen to your dog. An "overdose" of pentobarbital sodium injected into the vein of a leg will instantly and painlessly cause the dog to die.

Provide in your will or otherwise for the disposition to be made of your dogs upon your death. Do not insert the dogs' names in your will as the provision would then not apply should those dogs have died and been replaced by others. If your wishes are not put in writing, inform more than one person what they are as a declaration to one's spouse would be ineffective should both persons die in a common accident.

C. HEALTH MAINTENANCE

1.*Veterinary care*

A veterinarian should be consulted whenever a dog gives indications of not being well:

(a) Abnormal behavior, sudden viciousness, or lethargy.

(b) Abnormal discharges from nose, eyes or other body openings.

(c) Abnormal lumps, limping, or difficulty getting up or lying down.

(d) Loss of appetite, marked weight losses or gains, or excessive water consumption. Difficult, abnormal, or uncontrolled waste elimination.

(e) Excessive head shaking, scratching, and licking or biting any part of the body.

(f) Dandruff, loss of hair, open sores, and a ragged or dull coat. Foul breath, or excessive tartar deposits on teeth.

(g) High temperature.

Very Important. If your veterinarian is inexperienced with large dogs, warn him that Irish Wolfhounds do not require much anesthetic. They may take from 24 to 48 hours to recover from a small dose. A large dose could be fatal. This may also apply to certain medicines. A dog which is to be immobile for 12 or more hours should be rolled over every 15 to 30 minutes and covered with a blanket to prevent pneumonia. If a dog is to be anesthetized in the morning, it is advisable not to feed him after 5 P.M. on the previous day and to withhold water from him after midnight.

Dr. Robert Brown's comments on overdoses of anesthesia used on Great Pyrenees is pertinent:[1]

> The use of anesthesia on healthy Pyrenees should present no problem if the *low basal metabolism* of this breed is kept in mind. Most of the problems that Pyrs have with anesthesia are from the use of the intravenous variety. . .the ultra-short and short acting kind are widely used. The ultra-short (i.e. Surital) gives surgical anesthesia for five to 15 minutes and is ideal for wound closures, X-ray techniques, like HD pictures, since the animal is back to an ambulatory state in 30 minutes normally. The short acting variety (i.e. pentobarbital) is useful for surgical procedures up to 45 minutes and for treatment of strychnine convulsions. Only in rare instances are the intermediate and long acting barbiturates used. The normal dosage of pentobarbital in dogs is one grain per five pounds of body weight. As a rule of thumb I figure *half* of this dosage for Great Pyrenees and then if the desired plane of anesthesia has not been achieved more anesthesia can be given to effect. I will give the calculated dosage (one-half normal) over several minutes and then to effect so that the administration of pentobarbital will take four or five minutes. With the ultra-short acting Surital for wound closure or radiography, I figure 10 cc of 5% solution per 100 lbs of Pyrenees. I give 5 cc immediately, wait 30 seconds and give the remaining 5 cc. It has been my experience that this will immobilize a hundred pounds Pyr for about five minutes and they will return to a conscious normal state in twenty minutes. If your Pyr is somewhat high strung the dosage will need to be increased accordingly. At any rate, this is *well under the normal calculated dosage of* 1 cc of Surital per lb of body weight that any other dogs take.

If your dog often shakes his head, rubs it against the floor, tilts it to one side, or scratches his ears, he may have an ear infection. Sometimes, a foul odor may be present. Take him to the veterinarian. If his eyes must be closely examined, he should be

---

[1]Robert Brown, "Anesthesia and Great Pyrenees," *The Pyriodical.*

suspended in a sling rather than be anesthetized. This discovery was made in 1975 by Dr. Waldo Keller, chairman of the Department of Small Animal Surgery and Medicine, Michigan State University. The dog becomes so immobile that a biomicroscope can easily be used with a camera attached. In the suspended position, a dog finds it difficult even to shake his head.

If the dog is continually lapping his anus, his anal sacs may be impacted. See your veterinarian. He will very quickly squeeze them and thus release the pus and trapped secretions. You may wish to do this yourself.

An older dog, like a puppy, needs special care and understanding. Observe him carefully for indications of pain or discomfort. He may have kidney problems, constipation, etc. If he should relieve himself in the house, remember that his distress will be greater than yours. Take care of the old boy or girl.

2. *Temperature*

A rectal thermometer *must* be purchased not later than the day a dog is acquired. It should be used whenever there is any indication that the dog may not be well. When not in use, store in a small bottle filled with alcohol. Have the dog lie down. Lubricate the thermometer, insert it in the dog's rectum, and let it stay there for at least 2 minutes. Keep the dog quiet. Morning and evening are the best times to take a dog's temperature. The normal temperature of a dog is from 101° to 101.5°. A temperature of 102.5° is slight, 104° is high, 105° is very high. Aspirin given 2 or 3 times a day will reduce the temperature and make the dog feel better. It will not cure his ailment. Normally a high fever will be accompanied by an increase in the pulse rate. The rate will decrease in cases of shock, anemia, or leukemia. The normal rate is regular and runs betwen 70 and 100 beats per minute. If the rate is 180 in a puppy or 120 in an adult, the dog may be quite ill. The pulse may be taken by rolling the femoral artery — located inside the upper thigh — gently under the fingers and counting the beat. If possible, treat a sick dog at home rather than leave him at a kennel. He will feel less anxious and will recover more rapidly. After use, a thermometer should be wiped clean with alcohol and stored in a small bottle filled with alcohol.

3. *Administering medicine*

When it is desired to give a dog a pill, place it in a small ball of food. An alternative method is to grasp his upper jaw with the left hand, insert the pill with the right hand *as far down the throat as possible. Immediately* clasp the jaws together, before he has a chance to bring the pill up. Rub his throat to cause him to swallow.

Should he fail to do so, briefly hold your hand over his nostrils. Observe him for a moment or so after you release him; he may regurgitate the pill. Giving the dog liquid medicine may prove to be difficult. If he will eat his food when the liquid is mixed with it, this may solve the problem. Or it may have a good flavor, in which case, he will lap it up. Otherwise, have someone hold his head, pull out the side of his lower lip and slowly pour the liquid into this pocket. Do not raise his head while doing this or he may choke or the liquid may enter his lungs. A turkey baster may work but expel the liquid slowly.

4. *Diarrhea*
Give milk of bismuth 3 times a day for 3 days. Very little water. Or feed two tablespoonfuls of Kaopectate in cooked rice 3 times a day. If diarrhea persists, consult your veterinarian.

5. *Constipation*
A dose of milk of magnesia or mineral oil in the food.

6. *Skin ailments*
Frequently a dog will scratch or bite himself until the hair is worn off and an open sore develops. This is usually on the rump near the base of the tail. The cause may be external parasites (fleas, ticks, lice, chiggers), worms, improper nutrition, an allergy, a hormone problem or an infection. A deficiency in fat may be corrected by the linoleic acid in lard, soybean, safflower, corn or peanut oil.

One should consult a veterinarian the moment one observes the dog biting the same location frequently. Often it is a matter of trial and error until some preparation is found that gives relief. Baking soda solution is good for dry itchy skin if the skin is not broken. Itchiness of "hot spots" may be relieved by applications of dry corn starch. Apply liberally several times a day for a few days. A first step is keeping the dog and the kennel free of fleas. It often happens that a certain treatment which is effective with one dog will not work on another, possibly because the ailments are different. One of my hounds developed, at the age of 5 years, an itching condition such that her skin would twitch if her spine were touched. She did some severe biting of her rump and hind legs. The following took care of the situation: Selenium disulfide (Trade name *Seleen* manufactured by Diamond Laboratory) applied as a shampoo. Allowed to stand for 20 minutes and then washed off. Repeat each day for 3 days, then weekly and finally at longer periods.

7. *Parasites*
a. *Fleas and ticks.* Fleas and other parasites will be observed when

grooming the dog or attention will be called by the dog's scratching. Fleas are disease carriers and are responsible for many skin disorders. Your veterinarian will advise which preparation to use to treat the condition. The Department of Agriculture recommends the use of insecticide powders or sprays containing no more than 5% malathion, 5% methoxychlor, 1% rotenone or 1% pyrethrum.[1] The chemical in flea collars can be harmful. It can cause dermatitis. It has a lingering effect on the dog's liver and can cause hepatitis. Veterinarians will not anesthetize a dog until two weeks have elapsed since a flea collar was used, otherwise the dog may die. Moreover, the strong, disagreeable odor which constantly emanates from the collar must decrease the palatability of food and must make the dog's life quite unpleasant.

Dr. Deubler advises:

> Read the directions supplied with collar and do not keep it on the animal for more than the recommended period. Check it at least once a week to be sure it is not too tight—three fingers should fit easily under the collar. If the dog is receiving any medication of the same type in the collar (especially worm medicines), remove the collar for a week.

> If the dog is bathed, remove the collar. If a medicated shampoo is used, keep the collar off for at least four days. If the dog is out in the rain, take the collar off and be sure skin and hair are dry before putting it back on. . . .

> If a dog loses its flea collar within the first two months of its use, it is best to wait a week before using a new collar.[2]

I have additional suggestions if you decide to use a flea collar. Do *not* use one on a puppy or a sick dog. Air it for a day prior to use on a grown dog so that the fumes will be less concentrated. Remove it at night so that the dog may have some respite from the ordeal of continuous chemical vapor inhalation. Observe the neck for signs of irritation. Don't use insecticides or pesticides on the dog or in a room occupied by the dog.

Not only must the dog be rid of fleas and ticks but so should the bedding and the surrounding areas, including all cracks and corners. Dogs should be examined for ticks particularly the ears and toes, whenever they have been in grass or brush. Soak the tick with denatured alcohol, chloroform, etherial or fatty oils, nail polish

---

[1] United States Department of Agriculture, *Home and Garden Bulletin No.* 121. Write to Office of Information, USDA, Washington, D.C. 20250.

[2] Deubler, *Popular Dogs* (November, 1971), p. 26.

remover, vaseline, turpentine, etc., to cause him to release his hold. Remove him gently with tweezers. Examine the tick to be certain that his head has not remained imbedded in the dog. Reapply the alcohol or use iodine to prevent infection. The ticks must then be squashed, burned up, killed in alcohol, or flushed away to prevent reinfestation. For 5 cents, one can obtain from the Superintendent of Documents, Washington, D.C., Department Circular 338, *Parasites and Parasitic Diseases of Dogs.*

b. *Worms.* Your dog may get worms from the ground or from other animals. Roundworms (ascarids), hookworms, and whipworms, may be discovered by your veterinarian when he makes a microscopic examination of the stool of your dog. Large number of roundworm larvae may lead to pneumonia. Severe cases of whipworms may cause death. Heavy hookworm infestation will usually kill puppies. The presence of heartworms, transmitted by mosquitoes and possibly fleas, can only be determined from a blood test. Sometimes, a radiograph of the heart and lungs is needed. Symptoms are lack of stamina, labored breathing, gasping cough, great nervousness, weight loss, temperature elevation. Heartworm, formerly a tropical parasite, can now be found throughout the United States, although its incidence in the North is less than in the South. Preventive medication is available as well as treatment for an already infected dog. Unless treated soon enough, an affected dog will die of the infestation.

The presence of tapeworms is not always evident in a stool sample. Segments may be seen in the dog's bedding, at the base of his tail, or in his fresh stool. They look like rice grains, are pinkish and wriggle when fresh, brown when dry. They are most commonly obtained from eating fleas or rodents.

Worming medicines are poisons. Get them from your veterinarian, not from a local store. Do not worm a sick or weak dog unless advised to do so by your veterinarian. The dog being wormed should not wear a flea or tick collar for at least three days preceding the worming and three days after. During this same six day minimum period, no other chemicals or disinfectants should be used in the kennel or on the dogs.

The frequency with which you should have your dog's stool examined will depend on his physical environment. Since the amount of medication depends on the dog's weight, make sure you know his correct weight. If you tell the veterinarian that the dog weighs more than he actually does, the dosage he receives may kill him. If you underestimate his weight, it is possible that all worms will not be eliminated.

c. *Coccidiosis.* When coccidia, one-celled organisms, get into the small intestines of dogs, they destroy considerable tissue and, if untreated, will cause the dog's death. Symptoms of coccidiosis are diarrhea in which the feces are mucoid and possibly streaked with blood, loss of appetite, general weakness. The infected dog, through his feces, can contaminate an entire kennel. See your veterinarian.

8. *Bursitis.* David Atwell, M.D., comments on this condition.

Olecranon bursitis, or elbow hygroma, is the soft to firm swelling that occurs just behind the elbow in IW's and other large breeds. The swelling is caused by the accumulation of fluid in the normally empty sac, or bursa, which in the adult Irish Wolfhound is about the size of a collapsed ping-pong ball. The bursa lies between the skin and prominent elbow bone (olecranon) and has a slippery lining on its inside. This bursa acts to reduce the friction of the skin passing over the olecranon during movement. By far the commonest cause of bursitis is the trauma to the bursa that results from lying on a hard surface. A small amount of non-tender swelling behind the elbow is the first sign. At this stage prevention of further trauma may alleviate the condition. Various types of bedding from foam rubber pads to old mattresses have been recommended. This can be combined with padded bandages to cover the elbow. Ace wraps, Elastikon and adhesive tape over gauze have been used with success. The important factor is NOT to apply the pad so tightly that it may stop circulation of the anterior radial vein.

From a practical standpoint, it is usually difficult to follow these measures, and the bursitis recurs and presents as a large firm swelling. It is at this stage that much confusion exists regarding treatment. The choices are:

1. Aspiration of the fluid and local injection of a steroid (20-40 mg Depo-Medrol or 1-2½ cc Aristocort), with or without penicillin or other antibiotics.

2. Surgical excision of the bursa sac.

3. Aspiration and local injection of from 2-5 ml. Furacin and an equal amount of 5% tincture of iodine combined with oral Tetracyclene (W. J. Ambrose, DVM, Phoenix, Arizona).

4. X-ray therapy to the region.

The placing of a drainage tube into the swollen bursa that is not infected is mentioned only to be condemned, as it invites infection that may lead to serious complications.

My personal and successful experiences have been similar to

those of D. R. Lemburg, DVM, Wichita, Kansas, M.E. Grimwood, DVM, Hobbs, New Mexico, and others who recommend treatment with local steroid. Briefly, the method I have used is to carefully scrub the area of swelling with sterile gauze pads and Phisohex soap for at least ten minutes. An 18- or 20-gauge needle attached to a 50 cc syringe is inserted through the scrubbed skin into the middle of the fluid filled sac, and all the fluid is withdrawn. *Leaving the needle tip in place,* the 50 cc syringe is removed from the needle and a syringe filled with 1½ cc of Aristocort is then attached to the needle which still lies in the now empty sac. The Aristocort is then injected into the sac and the needle removed. An elbow pad and soft bedding should be used for seven days.

L. G. Gayle, DMV, Dallas, Texas, and others have not been impresssed with the results from steroids and recommend excision of the bursa. When done by an experienced veterinarian, this appears to be a successful alternative treatment, as even when successful, the steroid treatment should not be repeated too frequently, because of the possible side effects of the drug.

In cases of long standing, the skin in this region may develop an open ulcerous sore which may bleed and become easily infected. Surgery would appear to be indicated here.

A few cases of bursitis may not be caused by trauma, but by bacterial infection. In these cases, the swelling may be warm, red, hard and tender. These cases require antibiotics and at times surgical drainage. *Steroids should NOT be used in these cases.*

Regardless of the treatment, there is general agreement that once the elbow becomes troublesome the condition will recur unless trauma to the region is prevented.[1]

Even though you may have carpeting throughout the house, a puppy could still develop a hygroma by dropping onto the ground outdoors. As soon as you observe a swelling, make a harness for him: a strap over the withers, one across his chest, and cloth-covered foam rubber pads to absorb the shock of the elbows.

9. *Hip dysplasia.* This condition has caused great concern among dog breeders. Some of Dr. Wayne Riser's comments[2] are included in this paragraph. Normally, the rounded head of the femur fits snugly into a cup-shaped portion of the pelvis called the acetabulum. All puppies are born with normal hip joints. Later in life, the acetabulum may become less concave and more shallow

---

[1]David Atwell, *Letter to author* (September 20, 1971).
[2]Dr. Wayne H. Riser interviewed. *Op. cit.,* pp. 34, 36.

and the femoral head will flatten. In the most serious cases, it will be entirely away from the acetabulum. The condition cannot accurately be determined until radiographs are taken when the dog is 2 to 6 years of age. Great skill and experience are needed for evaluation. The Orthopedic Foundation for Animals, Inc. (OFA)[1] is extremely well qualified to do this work. While it will evaluate radiographs of younger dogs, it will not issue a breed OFA number unless the dog is at least 2 years of age. There is no satisfactory treatment. Avoid overfeeding and overexercising puppies[2]. Mild hip dysplasia cannot be detected by mere observation of a dog's movement.

Dr. Gerry B. Schnelle who pioneered in the study of hip dysplasia among dogs has arrived at conclusions[3] which I consider eminently sound:

> In 1954, I introduced the term "hip dysplasia" (HD), versus congenital dislocation of the hip, and a radiographic classification of degrees of the disease, grades one through four, to the veterinary profession. The former was to conform to its new name in man and the latter to provide a basis for communication among veterinarians and breeders when speaking or writing about the disease. During the past decade it has become apparent that many veterinary radiologists and other veterinarians are still adhering fairly closely to the Schnelle classification, while I have gradually deviated from it. Several factors have influenced this drift. Documented studies cast considerable doubt upon the supposition that hip joint laxity is synonymous with femoral head or acetabular dysplasia in the sense that they both refer to the same disease, hip dysplasia. Of much importance are the known facts that anesthesia or tranquilization both increase joint laxity and to a great degree directly relate to the depth of the desired effect produced by the drug. The recently popular fulcrum technique also greatly increases joint space in the hip joint depending upon (1) inherent joint laxity of the individual, (2) the degree of anesthesia, and (3) the force applied to achieve the desired position. Some investigators believe that if hip joint laxity is used as a criterion for the diagnosis of hip dysplasia in the young dog, then no German Shepherd Dog, Saint Bernard, Golden Retriever or Beagle is free from the disease. Possibly joint laxity is

---

[1] University of Missouri, 817 Virginia Avenue, Columbia, Missouri, 65201.

[2] To the same effect, se the recommendations of Corbin and Deubler. Index at Exercise, Puppy and at Feeding, Puppies, Overfeeding.

[3] Gerry B. Schnelle, Letter in *American Veterinary Medical Association Journal* (August, 1972), 236-240.

due to either the type or the maturation of collagen in connective tissue, and acetabular or femoral head dysplasia is a multigenic inheritance. In view of these new understandings, I disavow my 1954 classification of degrees of hip dysplasia.

Apart from the question of X-ray diagnosis of HD there are important factors which should affect our attitude.

First, there is recognition of the acute phase which occurs during the period of rapid growth of the breed involved and from which most individuals "recover" without any interference by the veterinarian.

Second, there is the later life phase during which visible osseous changes may appear and these changes (1) cause no apparent discomfort or malfunction, (2) cause variable and intermittent symptoms influenced by "incidental" trauma, or (3) cause crippling and severe pain.

The third factor is that of deciding whether the radiographic deviation from perfection of the joint is a characteristic so undesirable to the breed involved that a real effort should be made to eliminate it. For example, an "open" acetabulum usually means little to a Pekingese but can be disastrous to a Retriever. All veterinarians should also know that the business of breeding and registering purebred animals depends upon confidence. Litters are neither conceived nor born in the office of the registering organization. Placing a dog or bitch upon an "approved list" of HD-free individuals does not really guarantee any more accuracy and truth than an identification of its sex when the judgment has been based upon a pelvic radiograph.

In 1954, and before that, those of us who were interested in and studying HD had little history of the canine disease to lean on and were leaning heavily upon its history in man. There seems to be little doubt that HD in man and in dogs is reasonably identical, although it has been described in cattle, horses, bears and other animals. From a clinical and subjective standpoint, however, HD in the dog and in man are quite different. Man lives an average of seventy years while dogs live about thirteen years. On this basis alone, hip imperfections have far greater importance in man. Another very important difference, subjectively, is that man walks solely upon his hips while dogs bear only fifty per cent of their weight on their hindlimbs, or even much less if there is pain.

I plead guilty to making dire predictions about the eventual outcome when HD was diagnosed in early life. Now I am sorely troubled by the frequency with which such predictions still are being made when the dogs go on for years to confound the predictor. I do not imply that HD cannot or does not at times severely cripple a dog, but evidence indicates that those who are so crippled are in the minority. It is not proper to include laboratory animals in such an analysis since caging or otherwise confining the HD-affected dog has a marked deleterious effect. Knowledgeable veterinary radiologists know that osseous changes around the hip joint do not bear any direct relationship to the clinical signs or lack of them. He also knows that these bony changes are more pronounced in some breeds, for example in the German Shepherd Dog or Clumber Spaniel, then in others. There is evidence that hip joint laxity in the Saint Bernard at one year of age was not followed by either lameness or osseous changes at three years.

A recent publication on maturation of bones in several breeds is the most revealing study on the etiology of HD in dogs to date, but it does not provide a complete understanding of this condition. Its etiology in man is still not well understood.

When HD is being diagnosed in ninety-eight per cent of Saint Bernards, eighty-eight per cent of Alaskan Malamutes, eighty-six per cent of Golden Retrievers, and eighty-four per cent of Mastiffs in "statistics" credited to Dr. John Bardens, and presumably X-ray diagnosed with the anesthesia-fulcrum technique, then the profession can surely be credited with being the great savior, or the great wrecker. . .of several breeds of dogs. President John Lafore of the AKC in a personal communication said, "A program of selective breeding may eliminate or greatly reduce the hereditary defect but it is also likely to change the breed in question." The profession has not only the right but the moral duty to interfere with the breeding of dogs with hereditary blindness, but hereditary laxity of the hip joint or even wide acetabular differences among various breeds of dogs are both far more widespread and far, far less serious to the dog. There is little doubt that some birth control measures are in order in many breeds of dogs, but hip joint laxity hardly seems to be the correct fulcrum for this sort of program. Many, many pitiful letters from dog owners state that they had their pup or juvenile dog put to sleep because they thought it would become a hopeless cripple. One or more instances in which HD dogs had intractable pain does not supply sufficient background to allow the passing of death sentences upon individuals which have been shown to have hip joint imperfections. Nor are there any published statistics proving that pectineal myotomy or tenotomy are in fact long-term either preventative or curative procedures.

It seems that now it is time to (1) avoid over diagnosis of HD, (2) avoid diagnosis of HD in pups as being an unproved procedure, (3) avoid dire predictions on the eventual outcome of dogs with

HD, and (4) pay attention, in advising on selection of breeding stock, to temperament and functional performance of the individual. One giant step in 1972 towards this goal would be for the HD Registry to declare a moratorium on "certification" and "approved lists of dogs."

In a later article,[1] Dr. Schnelle wrote:

Sufficient statistics have accumulated to establish beyond doubt that CHD is genetically influenced but a Swedish study on 11,036 German Shepherds showed that ten years of selective breeding not only failed to reduce the number of CHD offspring but also did not reduce the number of grade 2 or 3 (moderate to severe) cases. The Swedish authors concluded that CHD was not as greatly genetically influenced as they formerly had thought. They found that other characteristics of the pelvic slope and the shape of the pelvic inlet were suggestive indications and that the rate of bone maturation of the breed or individual also were important.

11. *Hypertrophic osteodystrophy.*

This is a term used to describe an error in bone growth seen in young dogs of the large and giant breeds. The condition is usually observed between 3 and 8 months of age. Affected puppies have an obvious reluctance to move and may have painful swellings of the long bones usually just above the carpal (wrist) or hock joints. The swellings may be warm or hot to the touch and are firm and non-movable. The rectal temperature of the puppy may be elevated to 104-106°F. Confirmation of the diagnosis is generally made by radiographic examination. Severe cases may show a "cuff" of boney tissue around distal radius and ulna.

The cause of this condition is unknown. It is most frequently seen in rapidly growing puppies being fed excessive amounts of Vitamin D and mineral supplement, usually calcium diphosphate. Excesses of Vitamin D and a "mineral overload" of calcium diphosphate have been associated with this condition.

The duration of the condition can last several months with improvement generally noted at skeletal maturity. Adequate nutrition should be maintained, however excessive supplementation should be discontinued. Mineral supplementation should be replaced by calcium carbonate, calcium gluconate or calcium lactate. The severity of the case determines whether there will be a residual deformity of the legs such as bowing of the radius at maturity.[2]

---

[1]Gerry B. Schnelle, "The Present Status and Outlook on Canine Hip Dysplasia," *Gaines Dog Research Progress* (Spring, 1973).

[2]Orthopedic Foundation of America, Inc. *Hypertrophic Osteodystrophy* (Release Sept., 1974).

12. *Osteochondrosis.* Primarily degeneration of the cartilage. If the dead cartilage gets into the joint fluid and into the joint cavity, the joint becomes inflamed. The lesion is then called osteochondritis dissecans. The condition usually appears in fast growing dogs, especially males, between the ages of 4 to 7 months. The first indications are lameness, which becomes worse after exercise, and stiffness after rest. Some veterinarians recommend that exercise be restricted. Others advocate additional movement. If the condition does not improve after 4 to 6 weeks, surgery may be advisable. A radiograph will reveal the course to be taken. "Trauma is given as the most likely etiological factor."[1]

13. *Canine Brucellosis.* A contagious bacterial disease caused by the consumption of unpasteurized milk, its products or unaged cheese. A plate agglutination test should be used.

It is recommended that dogs be tested under the following circumstances:

1. Females with a history of abortion.

2. Males with scrotal irritation, enlarged and painful testes, or other reproductive problems.

3. Females that fail to conceive repeatedly.

4. Whenever a new dog is obtained, especially when it is to be introduced into a breeding kennel.

5. In dogs to be shown, or used in field trials.

6. As part of the routine physical examination, or prebreeding examination, especially in kenneled dogs.

7. In kennels with proved B. canis infection, to identify actively infected animals and hasten their removal.[2]

Treatment is very difficult and possibly the best solution is to have the infected animal put to sleep.

14. *Insecticides.* Shell Corporation sells "No-Pest Strips" (Vapona). These are very effective in keeping flies and other insects from an area. They have been found to have harmful effects on children and old persons confined to the same room where the strips

---

[1]Merck Veterinary Manual (1969), p. 619.

[2]Leland E. Carmichael, and John M. Olin, "A New Rapid Blood Test for the Detection of Canine Brucellosis," American Kennel Club, *Pure-Bred Dogs — American Kennel Gazette* (March, 1975) XCII, p. 420.

were hung and where ventilation was insufficient. Do not keep hounds in the same room where this product is used or where food or food dishes are located. A litter of eleven Mastiff puppies was stillborn; the probable cause of death was excessive use of a spray insecticide.[1] Experiments on rats indicate that DDT may cause infertility.[2]

Beware of all chemicals! There are so many preparations now on the market and others being developed that it would be of little use were I to name some. Beware of weed killers, tree sprays and flea collars.

15.   *Care of grounds.* If you have a garden, consult a lengthy article by Deborah Harper on poisonous plants which lists those dangerous to dogs.[3]

The yard should be cleaned of excrement at least twice a day to reduce the possibility of your dog being infected with worms or becoming coprophagous. Disposition of the excrement may prove a problem depending on your location. Plastic bags may be used and then turned over to the trash man. Burning or use of a septic tank are other methods. Some large kennels use a 55-gallon capacity oil drum with holes in the bottom. It is placed on stones so that it is just a little above ground level. Lime or some other decomposing product is spread over the contents once or twice a week. For odor removal, gravel or concrete areas can be treated by applying a strong salt solution (2¾ lbs. table salt/1 gallon of water/10 square feet) or a sodium borate solution (2 lbs. table salt/1 gallon of water/50 square feet). Lime can be spread over grass or dirt areas. Spade it in, leave for a few days, level and sow to grass.

16.   *Exercise.* In answer to the question: "Do they need a lot of exercise?" I reply: "Obviously, an Irish Wolfhound would be in better physical condition if he were exercised regularly and reasonably than if he were cooped up in a kennel. He would also be more pleased if he were allowed to roam at will. But he can remain in good health in restricted surroundings just as a tiger can in a zoo." Breeders usually say that an Irish Wolfhound should have a large area in which to live. Yet, some of these same persons will keep their dogs in a kennel where the indoor space is about 12 feet square

---

[1]Sharon Eronemo, "Mastiffs," The American Kennel Club, *Pure-Bred Dogs—American Kennel Gazette* (January, 1971) LXXXVIII, p. 57.

[2]"Female Infertility Linked to DDT." A report rendered to an American Cancer Society seminar, *Washington Post* (April 5, 1971), p. A14.

[3]Deborah S. Harper, "Plants Toxic to Dogs," The American Kennel Club, *Pure-Bred Dogs—American Kennel Gazette* (June 1968), LXXXV, p. 37ff.

and the outdoor run about 20 x 4 feet. One breeder turns her dogs loose in a small field for 10 minutes each day.

In placing puppies which have been offered for sale, I try to find a person with a fair amount of acreage, or who loves the dog so much that he will exercise him. How much exercise should a dog get and of what type? I have heard good judges say that he should be taken on a fast walk on a lead, not trotted. Others have claimed that it was better to make him trot than walk. Some owners let their dogs run free while they ride horseback; they contend that the Irish Wolfhound is a galloping hound, not a walker or trotter. Some keep the dog on a lead and have him follow a bicycle or an automobile. I know of one who throws a stick up a hill and has the dog retrieve it; I imagine that a sedate Irish Wolfhound would soon be bored with this game.

> I was told recently of a rare tip, or that was what he called it. Having some few hounds to exercise and being anxious to carry as little kennel labour as possible, he devised the plan of getting them so handy on the lead that he took out three or four at a time on a cycle. As distance appeared to be the main object he was able to get it over so much quicker on cycle than on foot, and so get many more exercised in the day in this manner. But when I pointed out to him how much less benefit the poor brutes gained in this way, he simply said, "Anyway, they get a good shake up." This they could get by being dropped to the ground from some high building, but it would not be helping them in the same way as a nice six or seven mile walk in the country with an interesting kennelman who will talk to and interest them while "padding the hoof". A very great difference can be made in a dog if his exercise is made a really pleasant event instead of just a dull monotonous slouching along for the whole distance. A dog made to enjoy his walk gets a bright, corky carriage about him, and carries a much more happy expression than the poor brute which has not such an advantage.[1]

We have seen, in the section on Puppy Care, that both Mrs. Nagle and Mrs. Jenkins objected to the use of a bicycle in training hounds and that Mrs. Nagle also found automobiles objectionable for this purpose.

> To get the hounds really fit and muscular, road work and not long tiring gallops, is the most important form of training. A quarter of an hour or twenty minutes' galloping a day, or even

---

[1] I. W. Everett, "Hints on Rearing Irish Wolfhounds," *op. cit.,* pp. 41, 42.

every other day, is sufficient. Over-training is as disastrous as the opposite.[1]

May I present my own experience. I frequently take the dogs out on foot without a lead and allow them to travel at any gait they choose. They initially run ahead but continually check back to make sure I am still with them. After a while they tire a little, then they walk near me taking off at a trot or run as something excites their interest. Thus they have used all their gaits. They have run at moderate and at full speed, they have trotted at a moderate rate, they have walked fairly fast to keep up with me. When I have been on horseback, I have set a pace which allows them to follow the same routine. This not only reduces boredom but, more importantly, it allows proper development of muscles. The use of an automobile or a bicycle in exercising an Irish Wolfhound on a lead may lead to muscle binding and improper muscle development since there will be forced exercise at times when the muscles should be allowed to relax. Motion will also be only in a forward direction with practically none laterally as would be the case if the hound were free. Moreover, this type of exercise forces a dog to run when he may be sick, lame, tired, or just too old. If the dog is well, the use of a bicycle over a short distance would not be harmful.

Running on a hard surface will not harm a dog unless it is done regularly or for long distances, in which cases the pasterns might break down. If hounds are taken onto surfaces that have been treated with chemicals to melt ice, make sure that their feet are thoroughly washed. Turning to another aspect of exercise, dogs do not breathe through their mouths. However, under great stress, they may exhale air through the mouth.[2] Dogs do not perspire through the skin although somewhat through the soles of their pads. Evaporation takes place from the tongue.

What is usually overlooked in discussions on exercise is the fact that conditioning involves more than gait. One must know the individual dog's daily health condition, his powers, his limitations. One must take into account the weather and terrain. In brief, one must have knowledge similar to that of a physical health expert. Dogs, like humans, should be warmed up before strong exercise. They should also be allowed to cool down gradually after exercise. Walk them the first mile, trot them a little, walk the last mile. Two

---

[1]Phyllis Hudson, "The Irish Wolfhound as a Sporting Hound." The Irish Wolfhound Club (Britain), *Year Book* (1933-1935), p. 70.

[2]Smythe, *The Conformation of the Dog, op. cit.,* p. 106.

or more dogs will play together and thus get additional exercise as well as canine companionship.

Irish Wolfhounds suffer from excessive heat and humidity. They could easily die if overworked under such conditions. It is better to confine the exercise periods to cool weather and to evenings during the warm season. Water should be withheld after exercise until the dogs have had a chance to cool off. Older dogs and puppies should not be subjected to the same degree of exercise as a dog in its prime. In the U.S., a 6-year-old Irish Wolfhound is called a "veteran". If possible, he should be separated from younger dogs as he will find it difficult to resist the temptation to play at length and this may prove too much for him. As for "jumping", see Index at Jumping.

17. *Grooming.* Grooming not only is good for the health of the dog, but it also keeps him looking neat and enables you to observe any cuts, bruises, presence of ticks, etc., so that prompt treatment may be given. Brushing removes a dog's dead coat and stimulates the skin. Use a stiff bristle brush or a not too stiff nylon brush. Combing should be done with a steel-toothed comb which has widely spaced teeth rounded on the ends. An Irish Wolfhound, properly groomed, sheds very little. If the hair is matted or snarled, do not pull on it. Attack small portions of it with the fingers and a wide-toothed comb until it is again smooth. If it must be cut, do so along the grain of the hair until it can be straightened out. The Oliver Mat and Tangle Splitter, obtainable from pet shops, is reputed to be an excellent device. Exercise care that the teeth of the comb, especially teeth bent out of line, do not scratch the dog's skin. Combing a wet coat will pull out an exessive amount of hair.

Fecal material under the tail may be removed with blunt-edged scissors. Exercise great care not to cut the skin. Foul-smelling particles may attach themselves to the hair between dogs' toes, when the dogs wander through the countryside. Use blunt-edged scissors. Pluck out with the fingers hair that is inside the ears.

Use "Q-tips" (also called "swab sticks", cotton wrapped around a thin stick of wood) moistened in water, alcohol or mineral oil to clean the ears. Do not attempt to clean any area not visible to the eye. Be gentle. Remove excess oil with dry cotton. The only liquid which should be put in a dog's ear is that prescribed by a veterinarian for medication.

The tartar that occasionally forms on the teeth can be removed with a scraper specially made for the purpose. It is quite sharp and if you attempt to do it yourself, you may injure the gums, so I recommend that a veterinarian do this for you. The dog may first be anesthetized. Unless tartar is removed, the dog will have bad breath and receding gums. He may also lose many teeth while quite young. Wild animals keep their teeth clean by chewing tough meat, gristle and skin. Dental caries in dogs is practically non-existent.

> It is very doubtful whether the practice of giving a dog a bone to gnaw is as good as is generally assumed. The theory is that the hardness of the bone keeps the teeth clean and free from tartar. As a matter of fact, no amount of bones will remove tartar from the neck of a tooth, and the practice does far more harm than good. The constant gnawing of bones not only wears the teeth down, but, consisting as they do, chiefly of indigestible lime salts, gives rise also to chronic constipation. Then there is a grave risk of large fragments or splinters being swallowed, the result of which may well be fatal.[1]

A dog's eyes may be bathed with warm water, a mild saline solution or a mild boracic solution using soft cloth or cotton. Work from the eye corner out, *not* across the eye. Do not let your dog ride with his head outside the automobile. He may suffer eye injury.

Irish Wolfhounds should not be bathed unless they have contrived to get themselves covered with some objectionable matter. They do not have what is commonly termed "doggy odor" if regularly groomed, allowed to go out in the open, and if their quarters are kept clean. Bathing removes oil, tends to dry the skin and soften the hounds' hard coats. Dry skin leads to irritation, scratching and open wounds. The dogs may be rubbed down with cornmeal. Should you dog's coat be stained by grease or grass, sprinkle baking soda on a damp sponge and rub onto the coat. If unusual circumstances dictate a bath, dry the dog well and keep him out of drafts. It is often convenient to have the dog lying down while he is being groomed. See Index at Obedience, Exercises, Lying down. When one side of the dog has been groomed, call him to make him stand, then give the command "Down!" As he sits just prior to lying down, gently push his shoulder in the direction you want him to go. Apply the pressure *before* he swings his hind legs to one side, otherwise he may lie down on the same side as before.

If toenails are allowed to get too long, they may cause the dog's toes to spread and affect the bone structure of the feet. The "quick" or sensitive portion of the nail will grow and make it more difficult to cut the nails without causing bleeding and pain. If the nails are very long, your veterinarian will anesthetize the dog and cut his

---

[1]R. Brookes-Simmonds, "A Dog's Teeth," The Irish Wolfhound Association (Britain), *The Irish Wolfhound* (1925), p. 34.

nails. Cutting of toenails is often a traumatic experience for dog and owner. I recommend the RESCO Nail Trimmer (large size) obtainable from pet shops or at dog shows. The nail is inserted into an opening in the trimmer, the handles are squeezed and a blade cuts off the portion of the nail that extends beyond the opening. The portion of the nail that is taken off is that which lies below the point where a definite indentation can be felt. Dogs usually object to having their nails cut but it can be done quite efficiently if the person cutting the nails remains calm but persistent. The puppy should not be scolded or hit. I usually get down on the floor with the dog and in the case of a puppy, hold him in my lap. He will squirm constantly but by talking soothingly to him and repeatedly turning him on his side when he tries to get up, eventually the nails can be cut. Stypic powder or cornstarch will stop the bleeding. A styptic pencil is too hard and will hurt the dog. Bleeding, of course, happens when the nail is cut too short and the quick is exposed. Nails can also be filed, with less probability of bleeding, but this would have to be done weekly. If you have never previously cut a dog's nails, I recommend that you initially observe an experienced person do so and then practice under his supervision.

See the section on Grooming in the chapter on Breed Competition.

18. *Safety Precautions.* One should exercise the same precautions with dogs as with children. Keep poisons, pins, tacks, marbles, other small objects, cleaning supplies, paint, insecticides out of reach. Do not leave a puppy alone in a room where there is an electric cord plugged into a socket. Don't leave a flat iron on an ironing table; if the puppy should knock over the table, the iron might fall on him. It is not possible to mention all the home hazards. Just remember: *The dog depends on you for his safety.*

D.   FIRST AID

1.   *Burns.* Wet packs of strong tea solution or ice. If a large area is involved, immerse the dog in a bath tub of cold water containing ice cubes. I imagine that his legs would have to be tied so as to keep him immobile and that he would have to be muzzled.

2.   *Choking.* Reach into mouth. Remove obstruction.

3.   *Drowning.* Same procedure as for humans.

4.   *Electric shock.* If the electric cord is still in the dog's mouth, pull the cord from the socket before touching the dog to avoid shock

to yourself. Pull out his tongue and keep his mouth open. Call the veterinarian for instructions. Apply artificial respiration by compressing and releasing his chest about twenty times a minute or by breathing into his mouth. One to two hours may be needed to revive him.

5. *Fits and Convulsions.* In a pamphlet issued by the Carnation Company, Los Angeles 36, California, it is stated:

> Fits and convulsions are not uncommon in puppies. These conditions may be caused by acute indigestion, internal parasites, a high fever or by certain poisons like strychnine. A deficiency of Vitamin D in addition to causing rickets may cause convulsions. Fits or convulsions are often caused, too, by inflammation of the brain or spinal cord, by such diseases as infectious hepatitis and distemper, and by various bacterial diseases.

> Be sure to protect the affected puppy from doing bodily injury to himself by confining him under a box or basket. And be sure to protect yourself against unintentional injury by the pup. Confine the puppy in a quiet dark area until recovery. Then find out what is causing the trouble by presenting the pup for a veterinary examination.

6. *Fractures.* Muzzle. Immobilize, but do not tie too tightly. Keep dog warm. Take him quickly to a veterinarian. See Index at Muzzle, Use of.

7. *Heat stroke.* Remove to cool place, sponge with cold water, give cold water enema. Take him quickly to a veterinarian.

8. *Paint and tar.* Do not use kerosene or gasoline. Rub mineral oil or Mazola into the hair or use a hand paint remover. Bathe in lukewarm water using a mild soap.

9. *Poison ivy.* Put on rubber gloves. Bathe dog in hot water, using strong soap. This precaution is for the sake of humans since dogs do not get poison ivy.

10. *Frostbite.* Apply tepid water, then gradually apply warmer water.

11. *Poisoning.* Evidenced by crying, vomiting, trembling, panting, coma. Antidotes are the same as for humans. If poison is unknown, force the dog to drink large amounts of beaten egg whites, milk or salt solution. Find out the nature of the poison. Get

the dog to a veterinarian. If a dog has swallowed solid objects, feed him boiled cereal or soft bread. A dog may be made to vomit by putting several tablespoonfuls of salt far back on his tongue and then holding his mouth closed until he swallows.

12. *Porcupine.* Muzzle the dog. Twist the quills and pull out individually. Wash with antiseptic. Keep dog warm. See Index at Muzzle, Use of.

13. *Shock.* Evidenced by weakness, panting, coma. A dog involved in an accident may suffer from shock. Treatment is the same as for humans. Keep him quiet and warm. Call a veterinarian. If necessary to take him to the veterinarian's office, carry him on a door, tightly held blanket or other fairly level surface to immobilize broken bones. Since a dog in pain may bite even his owner, muzzle him with a tie, belt, etc. Apply artificial respiration if breathing stops. See Index at Muzzle, Use of.

14. *Skunk.* Scrub with soap and water, followed with a rinse of 10% ammonia or tomato juice. Use boric acid solution on eyes.

15. *Snake bite.* Same procedure as for humans. Apply a tourniquet above the wound. After 45 minutes, release for 2 minutes, then reapply for 15. Continue with the 2 minute release and 15 minute application. Take the dog to a veterinarian. If you must walk him, do so slowly. In an extreme emergency, enlarge the wound and suck out the venom, provided your mouth does not have any breaks in the skin.

16. *Stings (Bee, hornet, or wasp).* Extract stinger. Apply boric acid powder. Ice packs will reduce swelling. If sting is near eye, apply vinegar, call the veterinarian.

17. *Wounds.* Wash surface wounds with an antiseptic or soap and water. Apply zinc ointment, an antibiotic ointment, or BFI powder. Cover with sterile gauze and bandage. If the wound is deep, cut off surrounding hair to reduce the possibility of infection. Clean thoroughly with soap and water. Apply a wet dressing of a mild antiseptic. If the bleeding has not stopped in 15 minutes, apply a tourniquet and release the pressure every 10 minutes or so. Get the dog to a veterinarian. A dog may be less apt to pull off a bandage and lap a foot wound if a sock is put on the foot. Adhesive tape sould be loosely applied to the upper portion of the sock then pressed against the leg.

The whip of an Irish Wolfhound's tail is powerful. Do not keep delicate objects within reach of it, e.g. on a coffee table. Should you personally be hit by it, you will become convinced of its power. By experience, you will learn not to praise the dog if his tail is near someone or something. You will learn to place yourself so that when the dog faces you his tail will be in the open. If the situation calls for rapid action, command "Down!" or hold onto his tail.

Not only can a wagging tail hurt people and break objects, it can also develop into a long and painful experience for you should its skin be broken, therefore do not allow a dog to get excited when his tail is near a solid object, e.g. in a kennel run or near a door or wall. Face him toward the solid surface, or command "Down!", or seize his tail, or walk away in the hope he will resume his calm demeanor. Do not let him place his front feet on a fence if the stand is hard, such as concrete, as he will injure his tail by wagging it.

You will immediately be made aware of the fact that the skin on his tail has been broken: blood will be splattered on walls, ceilings, and furnishings. Treatment may be very simple. Possibly adhesive tape a few inches above the injured portion, application of Furacin, a cloth bandage to cushion shock, and adhesive tape covering both the cloth and a portion of the adhesive tape already applied. Every three days remove the lower portion of adhesive tape and bandage. Reapply Furacin, a new bandage and tape. Leaving the upper tape in place will reduce the amount of hair torn out. In most cases, the tail will heal, with proper care, and your problems will be minor. But if the dog keeps lapping the tail or reopens the wound by striking it against some solid object, your problems will continue.

Dogs react differently. Some will pull bandages off and will lap the tail regardless of how disagreeable the taste of the medication is. One owner was quite successful by applying Methoform frequently. I have tried 4-inch plastic and metal tubes with holes drilled in them to allow circulation of air. The plastic tube (used to hold clubs in golf bags) was chewed up by one dog. The aluminum tube was bitten and bent by the same dog and it caused a number of dents in walls and furniture. The same dog would lap the tail through the tube openings. On another dog, the tubes worked very well. If they are used, don't forget to smoothe out the interior of the tubes after drilling the holes. Adhesive tape can irritate the skin. Use paper tape as much as possible. If the hound is caught lapping the tip of his tail, hold it near his mouth and say "No!" in a sharp voice.

The system which I shall now describe has worked very well, even on my problem dog. Have the dog lie down. Apply liberal portions of Morumide onto the open wound or soft tissue. Wrap cotton or gauze around the tail from the tip for about 8 inches. Secure the upper portion of the bandage with adhesive tape so the bandage won't slip. Do not put the tape onto the tail, only onto the bandage. Put a small amount of cotton batting around the extremity of the tail as a cushion against blows. A small strip of adhesive tape will hold it there temporarily. High on the tail, apply adhesive tape for about three inches. Apply adhesive tape onto this tape, run it straight down the side of the tail, around the end, and up the other side to the tape high on the tail. Wrap cotton or gauze around that portion of the tail that has not been covered with this material, i.e. from 8 inches above the tip to the tape at the top of the tail. Wrap the tail with adhesive tape from the tape high on the tail to the tip. *Do not apply the tape tightly.* Apply it loosely and then press it against the tail. When the tail has healed, the ointment may be omitted but leave the padding on for a long time until the skin becomes hardened and is covered with hair. This procedure causes sufficient adhesive tape to adhere to the tail so as to secure the bandage and minimizes the amount of tail surface that must be covered by adhesive tape thereby minimizing loss of hair when the tape is removed. Expose damaged portion of tail to air every five days for at least a few hours while dog is under your observation. Reapply medication and covering.

18.   *Foxtail.* A grass with spines. If your dog has been in an area where foxtail occurs, carefully examine his paws, ears and nose. If foxtail is implanted in the nose, the dog will sneeze. A few drops of castor oil will dampen the foxtail and may enable you to remove it with tweezers at once before the foxtail begins its path of infection and causes death. If the foxtail cannot be removed, call a veterinarian.

19.   *Gastric Dilatation — Torsion.* A number of Irish Wolfhounds have died from this condition. The cause may be mineral imbalance.[1] Hereditary predisposition may be a factor.[2] Where the condition develops over a long period of time it may be caused by parasitism, inadequate diet or pancreatic insufficiency. The acute form may be due to large feeding of dog food followed by rigorous exercise and the drinking of much water.[3] One cause may

---

[1]Charlotte Woodruff, "Acute Gastric Dilatation." The American Kennel Club, *Pure-Bred Dogs — American Kennel Gazette* (January, 1967) LXXXIV, p. 9.

[2]B. Funkquist and L. Garmer, *Journal of Small Animal Practice* (September, 1967).

[3]*Merck Veterinary Manual* (1955), pp. 181, 182.

be bacterial contaminants in the kennel and feeding equipment.[1] An inadequately exercised dog may thereby be prevented from excreting a sufficient amount of phosphates. Some possible causes are listed in a Gaines Dog Research Progress article. Speaking of rapid changes in blood chemicals, it is said:

> Foremost among these is alkalosis, when the base of the blood (also called alkalia) becomes greater than the amounts of acids present, through loss of acids from the blood. Acid is always withdrawn into the stomach during meals to aid digestion. But an exceptionally heavy meal or one rich in protein uses more than the normal amount of acid. . . .Alkalosis also is brought on by loss of water and salt through excesssive panting and drooling, heavy breathing. . . . Miscellaneous events can lead up to drops in blood calcium in roundabout ways, among them infections, or dogs refusing food and water at shows, or while boarded.

> Mild gastric distention may relieve itself when the dog is confined, and food withheld or offered as liquids, then feeding a bland diet for as long as seems indicated. Gas pressure may be eased by use of a stomach tube.[2]

Severe bloat, however, allows very little time for action. It has been reported that 90% or more of its victims die as a result. The dog must be removed to the veterinarian's office immediately. The latitude of time may be from one to four hours. The fortunate owner may be able to observe some of the early signals: restlessness, distended abdomen, inordinate thirst followed by vomiting of the water drunk, reluctance to lie down, difficulty in breathing, unsuccessful attempts to vomit. The dog is in intense pain. The stomach may have twisted clockwise along a head-to-tail axis. It has been suggested that gastric torsion is present when the degree of rotation at the gastro-esophageal junction is less than 180° and obstruction is not complete and that volvulus occurs when the rotation is greater than 180° and obstruction occurs at each end of the twisted segment.[3] The expansion of gas prevents blood from reaching the heart. When the dog does lie down, death is imminent.

---

[1]T.B. Follis, D.V.M., Ph.D., Manager Veterinary Services, Ralston Purina Company, *Letter to author* (9 September 1974).

[2]"By Any Name, 'BLOAT' Signals Danger," *Gaines Dog Research Progress* (Summer, 1969).

[3]I.B. Kirsner: "The Stomach" in Sodeman, W.A., Jr. and Sodeman, W.A. (ed.) *Pathologic Physiology, Mechanisms of Disease* (1974), p. 710.

If the bloat has progressed to the point where the stomach is tightly against the abdominal wall and a veterinarian is not available, the following procedure may be used.

> We should each have a 12 or 14 gauge needle, which is about 1 and 1½ inches long. . .It would be best if the needle were sterile, but if the situation does arise we would not have time to worry about that. If, then, the situation arises, we should roll the dog over on his back, cleanse the abdomen with cotton and alcohol in the midline beneath the navel. The needle should be pushed quickly and strongly through the skin into the abdomen in the midline about two inches below the navel. If you push it far enough the air [i.e. gas] will rush out like that of a punctured inner tube. The needle should be left there until the air [i.e. gas] ceases to escape and until you gently push on the abdomen to push out as much gas as possible. No anesthetic is needed and your dog not only will not feel it but will be grateful to you because he will be a lot more comfortable. You must then remove the needle and rush, I said rush, your dog to a competent vet who can and will perform immediate surgery.[1]

Many doctors consider that the above procedure may be dangerous, because of the changed anatomical relationship of the organs, and that the spleen may thus be damaged. The veterinarian may pass a stomach tube. If the stomach is not twisted, immediate relief will be obtained. Otherwise, he will immediately perform surgery. He may give a transfusion for shock. He may suture the stomach with wire to the abdominal wall to prevent recurrence.

Bearing in mind that no one has been able to reproduce the malady under controlled conditions and that no one can state with assurance what causes it, nevertheless, the following suggestions have been offered for the prevention of bloat and gastric torsion.

1. Have your dog routinely checked for kidney and parathyroid disorders and for internal parasites.

2. Give him sufficient exercise to prevent kidney degeneration.

3. Don't overexercise him.

4. Feed him a balanced diet.

5. Feed him more than once a day. If he gulps his food, serve him small quantities at each meal. If fed only once a day, do so in the

---

[1]Dr. Donald Potts, "The Bloat and What To Do About It." The American Kennel Club, *Pure-Bred Dogs — American Kennel Gazette* (November, 1969), LXXXVI, p. 19.

morning (assuming someone will be at home during the day). This will make it more likely that any change in his condition will be observed and that a veterinarian with assistants will be available. Avoid group feeding where the dog believes he is competing for food.

6.   Do not allow him to exercise or to become excited by the presence of visitors, etc., for two hours before and for two hours after a meal or after drinking a large quantity of water.

7.   Allow him continuous access to fresh water, except for the two hours after vigorous exercise when he should be given water in small quantities.

8.   Ask your veterinarian whether he is prepared to treat an emergency case of this nature and whether he is continually available to do so. Ask him whether there are any drugs which may be helpful when a crisis arises.

Some people have reasoned that commercial dry or semi-moist dog food should not be fed, or should be fed only in limited quantities, on the ground that it provides the environment for gas-forming bacteria. Gas formation may also be caused from fermentation of vegetable material or putrefaction of meat. As of September, 1974, Ralston Purina Company and Gaines Dog Research Center each had had only one case of acute gastric dilation. Purina and Gaines feed only once a day. Although there are no Irish Wolfhounds in these kennels, there are other large breeds.[1]

There remains one point worthy of discussion. If the consumption of dog food followed by the drinking of water can lead to bloat, should the dog food be first soaked in water or should water be withheld for an hour after meals? We have seen, in the chapter on Feeding, that it is undesirable to serve soaked dog food. If water is not constantly available to the dog, then withhold it for an hour after feeding. Otherwise, he should have maintained a certain amount of fluid in his system and he will not drink excessively after eating. Dogs that have had bloat may suffer a recurrence.

[1]T. B. Follis, *op. cit.*
Patricia Davis, *Letter to author* (September 19, 1974).

VII

Obedience

A. TRAINING

There is no question that all dogs should be trained to obey if they are to become trusted companions. A person who objects to training a dog in obedience is really objecting to the type or degree of training. I shall discuss some of his objections later. In actual practice, this objector most likely has trained his dog to come when called, to lie down, and to perform other elementary actions. An unmanageable dog is a reflection on the master.

Hundreds of examples of the value of training can be given. I shall relate a few pertaining to my hounds.

All dogs, males and females, are housed together and are free to go out of doors or to come indoors through two-way swinging doors. At meal time, I have them lie down while I prepare their food to avoid any commotion. I then deposit each bowl on stands. Each dog goes to his proper place without command and eats his food. No dog goes to another's dish even if another dog has left food in it. If there is food left over, I may call one dog's name and point to the bowl. If he is still hungry, he will eat. No other dog interferes.

If I have meat scraps left over from our meal, I will cut them up and distribute them evenly to the dogs, one morsel at a time. The dogs will stand before me and will take their portion only when I call their names.

If I am eating in the front of the automobile and the dogs are in the rear, they will not beg for food.

If it is a warm day and I do not wish to have the dogs leave the car, I can open all doors to allow a draft to be created and tell the dogs "Stay!" They will not leave the car.

I have had as many as four Irish Wolfhounds in New York City at one time for the Westminster Kennel Club Show. We stayed at a hotel, took the elevator and walked to and from the show without any difficulty. Arriving at the hotel room, I commanded "Stay!", opened the door, removed the collar and lead from one dog, called his name and said "Out!". He entered the room. The others did not move. Each dog responded in turn. It can be imagined how difficult

243

it would have been had the dogs not been trained.

An obedience-trained dog is more easily examined and treated by a veterinarian than one who is not.

I take the dogs out for walks, usually in the evening when it is cool. Normally, they are allowed to run free. The area is suburban to Washington, D.C., is built-up and, therefore, has some traffic, although there is less in the evening than during the day. The dogs will run ahead, explore an occasional field and return to me every few minutes. They are never beyond sound of my voice or dog whistle. If a car appears in the distance and the dogs are not in the street, I will cry out "Stay!" The dogs do not move until I say "Okay!" If one dog should happen to be in the street, I cry out "Stay!", to keep the other dogs in place and then tell the individual dog "Come!" When I call one dog's name, the others do not respond. Of course, common sense has to be exercised. If the dog is on the opposite side of the street at some distance from me, I cross the street as I call the dog so that he won't have to come diagonally across the street. At intersections, we cross as a group. If I see a cat or dog before the dogs do, I say "No!" and the dogs leave it alone. Even when the dogs are in full pursuit, a call or a whistle will make them return instantly. There are risks in the above situations. A dog could take off suddenly and run into an automobile. However, I exercise great precautions, giving the dogs suitable commands whenever an auto does appear in the distance. I do not recommend the above procedures unless a dog has been well trained for some period of time, has been tested repeatedly and unless obedience training has been maintained. A dog which responded immediately six months ago and whose training has not been maintained, may not answer readily or may not answer at all.

People out walking in the evening are apt to be shocked by the sudden appearance of a galloping pack of Irish Wolfhounds. Upon this occurrence, I call the dogs to heel. I calm people's fears by telling them about Irish Wolfhounds and giving a little obedience demonstration with all dogs participating.

When I say that all Irish Wolfhounds should be trained, I do not mean that they should receive the same training as would be needed to obtain degrees in obedience trials. It is not absolutely necessary, for example, that they should be taught to jump obstacles on command, or to select out of many articles one bearing your scent. I will discuss the essential training accomplishments later. It is below the Irish Wolfhound's dignity to do "tricks" such as "play dead", "roll over". Teach him something useful. May I add that, properly done, obedience training will not curb an Irish Wolfhound's spirit.

Any person of average intelligence and ability can train an Irish Wolfhound.

There are three steps in training:

1. Command.

2. Enforcement of command.

3. Praise.

The command should preferably consist of a one-syllable word. The words should not sound somewhat alike. Examples of commands are: Come, Stay, Sit, Down, Jump, Fetch, Find it, Out, No, Heel.

The command should be given in a firm but not a threatening or loud voice and should be preceded by the dog's name to draw his attention, e.g. "Tara! Come!" There should be a slight interval between the two words. Don't say: "Taracome!" The dog is not capable of saying, "I beg your pardon! I was not paying attention. Were you speaking to me?"

Do not submit your dog to an extensive monologue, e.g. "I have told you time and time again that I don't want you getting onto the bed. Now get off and stay off. If I see you on that bed again, I'll punish you". You will get better results by saying "No! Out!"

The dog should not be given commands unnecessarily. A human would not like to be told: "Come! Down! Sit! Heel!" etc. and be forced to obey for no reason other than to demonstrate his obedience. Neither should an Irish Wolfhound. Don't be a "nagging wife". Children (or other persons) who issue commands and cannot enforce them or enforce them improperly will only confuse the dog.

In very early training, it is permissible to repeat a command several times as you enforce its execution, e.g. "Down!—down!—down!" as you force him to lie down. This is to connect the command with the act. Soon, give only one command. The dog should be taught to obey instantly, not on the second, third or fourth command. Otherwise, he will wait until you give a succession of commands.

Commands should be reasonable and understandable. You should be consistent. You cannot expect obedience if you allow exceptions. It is difficult for a dog to understand that he can jump up on you when you have old clothes on but not otherwise, that he can rest his head on your lap but not on those of your friends, that he can only come in the kitchen on Sundays, etc. In brief, it is desirable that the trainer be more intelligent and exercise better judgment than his canine pupil.

"No!" is a command with a variety of usages. It means "whatever you're doing or thinking of doing, don't." It means "don't sniff at the meat on the table", "don't chase that cat across the street," etc. If you have more than one dog, precede the command "No!" with the name of the dog you are addressing. Otherwise you will confuse the others.

All commands should be enforced, otherwise the dog will not consistently obey you. Therefore, except in an emergency, a command should not be given unless it can be enforced. A collar and a leash are almost a necessity in training as they assist you in enforcing your command. Running after an Irish Wolfhound to enforce a command is undignified as well as ineffectual.

For a puppy under three months, I recommend a leather collar fastened so that the puppy cannot wriggle out of it when he decides he's had enough. If possible, conduct your training in an enclosure to eliminate the possibility of your hound running away from you into automobile traffic. When he is three months old, get a chain collar consisting of large rounded links. These do not readily twist or catch. Avoid jewel-cut links as they will catch in his hair. If the collar is too large, it will take too much time to tighten it when you want to enforce a command; it may slip off his head when he lowers it. On the other hand, one should be able to slip it on quite easily. The leash should be 6 feet long. A metal chain is unnecessary and inadvisable for use as a leash. Flat leather is all right. I use braided nylon. The clasp on the leash which I prefer is the bolt type. Other kinds are illustrated here.

The chain collar has a ring at each end. Hold a ring in each hand. Raise the right hand and allow the chain to run through the ring in the left hand. You now have a circle of chain. You will observe that upon pulling the right hand ring, the circle decreases. The collar should be placed on the dog so that when he is on your left, the moving portion of the chain lies on top of his neck and towards you. Thus when you pull on the right hand ring, the collar will tighten; when you release it, pressure will be reduced. Pulling on the other ring will exert pressure on the dog's neck but will not change the size of the circle. Attach the lead to the right hand ring which should come over the top of the dog's neck, not under it. Keep the dog on your left as you move with him. Pulling on the lead tightens the collar to enforce obedience. If the dog is performing properly, the lead is kept loose and the collar is likewise loose.

Properly used, a chain collar does not hurt the dog despite the fact that it is often called a "choke" collar. Do not confuse this with a "spike" or "prong" collar. These are cruel and unnecessary. They are barred by the American Kennel Club for use in obedience showing.

The exact manner of enforcing commands will be discussed in the section dealing with particular exercises. At this point, I will merely discuss certain general principles in training Irish Wolfhounds.

The Irish Wolfhound is extremely sensitive to reprimand. Normally, this is sufficient to correct the dog, provided he understands that he has done something wrong. If an owner were to find out that, in his absence, the dog had chewed the rungs of a chair, it would be senseless for him to fly into a rage and immediately start berating or beating the dog. A connection must be established between the evil act and the correction. One method of doing this may be to show the dog the chewed rung and to say "No!" several times in a severe tone of voice. However, it is questionable whether the dog will know what you mean. Do you mean not to crawl under the chair, not to sleep in it, etc? If one can catch him in the act, so much the better. Then, one cries out angrily "No! No! You bad dog!" A blow with a rolled newspaper can be used. It should be borne in mind that the cure will be effected by the sound of the voice and of the blow, not by the force of the blow itself. It should never be necessary to hurt the dog. It is quite easy to injure a dog permanently, even a grown Irish Wolfhound. A blow on the ears could deafen him, one between the shoulder blades could cripple him, a stick or stone thrown at him could damage an eye or cause him to turn suddenly and either tear a ligament or cause the patella to move out of position. Do not hit him with a leash. This should be a harbinger of pleasure, not of pain. The Irish Wolfhound is most anxious to please. If he fails to do what you wish, it is because you have not made it clear to him what it is you want, he has temporarily forgotten what you have taught him, or he is deterred by some fear of the act to be performed, e.g. passing an area where loud and sudden noises are occurring, or it may be fear that he will be punished if he does not do exactly what you want—a most regrettable state of affairs. A cringing Irish Wolfhound is not a well-trained dog; it is an indication that he has been forced to obey commands, not that he is willingly doing it to please his master. Shouting at an Irish Wolfhound or beating him is also a waste of time and effort. The dog will become so upset that he will "freeze" and do nothing, or he will try to escape from his nerve-wracking experience. It is the tone of voice, not its volume, which acts as a corrective. If, in training your dog, you become angry with him, the best thing to do is quit for the day; it will be better for your nerves as well as the dog's and you will not undo the work you have already accomplished with him.

If, as is likely, the dog having been reprimanded comes to you with wagging tail and licks your hand, don't pat him. But don't keep reprimanding him either or he will think he is being reprimanded for being friendly. Don't continue being angry for more than a few minutes. Forget your grievance. Your dog will have done so. The fact that he cringes does not mean that he remembers his misdeed. He merely remembers that you are angry with him. Occasionally one has an Irish Wolfhound that is extremely sensitive, one that becomes completely unnerved by a harsh "No!" In such a case, one uses a gentle "No!" and otherwise modifies the training. In teaching such a dog to heel, for example, the leash is not snapped sharply to force the dog to conform; instead, one coaxes the dog repeatedly while slapping one's left thigh: "Come on boy! Good boy! Come on! Heel!" etc.

If your dog does something wrong, don't call him to you and then punish him when he does so. He will be reluctant to come to you in the future. If you run at him, he will probably run away from you. Call him. When he comes to you, reprimand him only if he can be made to understand what he has done wrong. For example, if he was chewing the bark off one of your trees, cry out "No!" to stop him. Walk up to him calmly. If he runs away, call him. Take him to the tree, hold his head near the damaged portion and, in a cross tone of voice, say "No! Bad dog!" Should the act be repeated, calmly put a collar on him, walk him to the tree, hold his head close to the chewed bark, hit him on the haunches with a newspaper to create noise and say "No! Bad dog!"

A dog should not be punished, he should be corrected. Correction should be connected with the evil deed. For instance, you call your dog, he ignores you. You go into the house, get a collar and lead and put them on the dog. Yelling at him or striking him will serve no useful purpose. He won't know the cause of your anger. Instead, start teaching him again to come while on lead. Praise him when he does. An untrained dog will often come to his owner if the latter calls him as he runs away from the dog.

Now that we have discussed general principles in the issuance and enforcement of commands, let us start our training with a puppy. He can be trained as early as 3 months. Undoubtedly, it could be earlier but the puppy's spirit might be affected were he constantly being ordered about and being corrected at an age when his period of concentration is quite small. Let him play, let him develop confidence in your friendship.

The following suggestions are the minimum for training. More details, including preparation for showing in obedience trials and actual showing, may be obtained from a book which I highly recommend: *Dog Obedience Training* (1958), by Milo Pearsall and

Charles G. Leedham. It is published by Charles Scribner's Sons, New York.

It is desirable that Irish Wolfhound owners attend dog training courses. There are many held throughout the country. Your veterinarian should be able to advise you where one is located. For a small fee, you are taught how to train your dog. You receive advice, you obtain experience in handling your dog in class, you observe other students' mistakes or proper handling, your dog becomes accustomed to the close presence of humans and dogs. Classes may be held for one hour once a week. The excitement generated by the presence of other dogs may be sufficient to sustain your Irish Wolfhound's interest for this length of time but remember that Irish Wolfhounds are easily bored. At home, about ten minutes of training a day is ample.

The following consists of simplified instructions. It is not my intention to write a book on obedience training.

Calling the dog

With a leash on the dog, say the dog's name and cry out "Come!" in a happy voice. Clap your hands lightly to attract his attention. If he comes, praise him extravagantly and pat him. Giving him tidbits as a reward is bad practice. It will lead him to expect it and it may interfere with proper nutrition. The dog expects nothing more than your expressed satisfaction. Praise the dog lavishly when he does something right, even though your private opinion may be that the dog is stupid. Call the dog's name whenever you are going to do something that he will enjoy: play, eat, go for a walk, etc.

If he does not come, give a series of slight tugs on the lead and when he arrives at your feet, praise him. It is of the greatest importance throughout your dog training that you learn to give sharp tugs on the lead. A steady pull will force the puppy to obey but you will not be able to hold a full grown Irish Wolfhound this way. If the dog is pulling away from you thus keeping the lead taut, it will be necessary to step towards the dog and then jerk the lead.

Heeling

The puppy will soon learn that no pressure is exerted on his neck when he responds to your call. Take him for a short walk on your property, not where there will be distractions such as children, other dogs, etc. Hold the lead in both hands. Say the dog's name and "Heel!" Move forward. If he forges ahead, lags behind or wanders away, give a series of jerks on the lead until he gets in position close to your left side. Praise him when he does. Initially, it is permissible to repeat a command several times, since the puppy is apt to forget quickly. Enforce each command. After the puppy learns what is expected of him, give the command only once. If it is not immediately obeyed, jerk the lead as you repeat the command and enforce obedience. A tug on the lead will not hurt the dog if common sense is exercised. Pulling the puppy off his feet by jerking the lead is evidence of poor judgment. Not only is it unnecessary, it is strongly inadvisable. The dog is not being obedient when he is forced into position. He is being obedient if he moves into position when the lead is slack. When the dog is heeling properly, the lead should be slack and the collar should be loose on his neck. After a while, try turning to the right, the left, the rear, jogging, then walking. The dog should remain at your side. Do not make such abrupt changes in direction or speed that the dog is caught unawares. The object of the exercise is to make him heel not to fool him.

After the dog has learned to heel *perfectly* on a lead, it may be taken off and "heeling free" attempted. Do not try this near automobile traffic. Do so in an enclosure to eliminate danger in the event of disobedience and to facilitate correction. If the dog does not heel properly off lead, immediately go back to training him with a leash. A silent dog whistle, if well made, is a useful item to have. For one thing, it obviates the necessity of yelling your dog's name throughout the neighborhood at night when you have had your dog out for a walk (off lead in this case) and have lost sight of him. Of course, you will have first taught him in your own yard the meaning of whistle calls.

Sitting

In obedience classes, dogs must sit whenever the handler comes to a halt unless they are otherwise directed. The purpose of this is to assure greater control. A sitting dog requires a little more time to dash off than does a standing dog. You need not worry about your dog sitting in the breed ring if you exercise judgment. When showing your dog in breed classes, you can either command "Stay!" to stop him from sitting, or, instead of stopping while facing to the front, as you do in the Obedience Ring, turn towards the dog and place your left hand under his belly.

To make a dog sit, give him the command, pull up on the lead with the right hand and push down on his rump with the left. When he sits, praise him. Repeat a few times then discontinue until the next day. When you praise him, you can expect that he will get up. Say "No! Sit!" and make him sit. He should change from the sitting position only when you tell him to do so. I use the word "Okay!" as a release signal from any command. Irish Wolfhounds are usually

Correct way of putting a chain collar on a dog. Keltic Dathchaoin with Mrs. Alfred (Miriam) DeQuoy.

COLLARS

Spike   Chain

CLASPS

Snap

Seeing Eye

French

Bolt

Ch. Feasgar Bruadar of Ballylyke, U.D., clearing a three-foot single bar jump (1957).

Marhaba of Berryfield, W.D. Ex., U.D. Ex., T.D. Ex., scaling a six-foot wall (1977). Owned, trained and handled by Joan N. Milnes, M.R.C.V.S., England.

Marhaba of Berryfield at the top of the six-foot wall (1977).

R. Montagu Scott exercising his hounds (1925). (Ifold Kennel — England).

Breaking cover. Hounds of R. Montagu Scott (1925).

Dan O'Malley of **Ambleside** with his owner, Desmond Slattery (1953).

Kevin Kilkelly of Skyline and **Palomino Kelly of Skyline** with owner, James G. Haizlip (1955).

Growing Pains

A shoemaker?

A gardener?

A literary critic?

Or perhaps he has a calling
for the religious life.

I wonder what he will be when he grows up!
Gael Pendragon of Eagle at one year of age.
Owned by Mrs. Thomas (Teddie) Hanophy.

"Sharks?"

Boardman Moore's Major Acres Tancred O'Magnus and Major Acres Rial Dhu, C.D.

H.M. The Queen and Shaun (1966).

not comfortable in a sitting position. In the ring, they will shift from one side to the other thereby causing you to lose points and also causing you to worry that they are about to stand or lie down. Don't make them sit too long in practice sessions.

Lying Down

When the dog has learned to sit, command "Down!" In the case of a puppy, the command may be enforced by pulling down on the lead so that he is drawn to the floor or ground. Praise immediately. A large dog must be treated differently. Have him sit. Take hold of his front legs above the carpal joint and extend them forward from his body. Do so quickly or he will stand up. Hold him down and praise him.

Staying

This command may be given whether the dog is standing still, sitting, lying down, or in motion. Have the lead in your left hand. Give him the command "Stay!" as you put the palm of your right hand near his face, and move out to the end of the lead. Should he attempt to follow, say "No!" and put him back in his original position. To prevent him from sitting when you are walking and you have given the command, "Stay!", place your left hand under his belly and exert pressure upward. If he stays for a few seconds when you walk away, praise him and let him relax. Repeat, gradually extending the time. Don't tempt fate by making the dog stay untied on the sidewalk while you do some shopping.

Jumping

Irish Wolfhounds, of course, can jump without any instruction and will jump if there is a sufficient incentive. Obedience training is given for the purpose of making him jump when you want him to do so. Training in jumping will facilitate a dog's decision to do so since he will have tested his capabilities. For the reasons advanced in the next section, I no longer teach my hounds to jump. However, I believe there should be some discussion on the Irish Wolfhound's capabilities in this field.

I have been asked whether teaching a dog to jump will not make it more likely that he will try to jump out of any enclosure in which he may be. I have had only two such occurrences. Upon returning from a three-week overseas military assignment, my wife informed me that my first hound, Gamine, had got in the habit of jumping over a 4 foot fence[1] sometime during the night and returning the following

---

[1] A chain link fence later replaced by a post-and-rail fence.

morning. The next day I got up early to observe whether the offense would be repeated and, sure enough, there was Gamine outside the enclosure and walking up to it. I rushed outside before she could jump back in. She ran to me. I repeatedly said "Bad girl!" and opened the gate for her. The incident was never repeated.

Ch. Keltic Phantom II C.D.X. was a nice, pleasant, easy-going dog. When I would crossly say "Bad dog!" he would lie down momentarily in shame and them jump up quickly, lap my face and wag his tail. A very difficult situation for me! One day, upon returning from work, I was told by my neighbor that Phantom had seen a cat and had gone in pursuit by first jumping a 5-foot snow fence, then crawling through the post-and-rail fence. When the cat escaped down a storm drain, Phantom crawled back through the post-and-rail fence and jumped back over the snow fence. Under the conditions, there was no sense in reprimanding him. He would have had no idea what I was talking about.

I do not know how high an Irish Wolfhound can jump, nor do I consider it advisable to try to find out. The possibility of injury is too great. But let me relate one incident. I was crossing a street in Williamsburg, Virginia, when I observed an automobile some distance away heading in my direction. Gamine and her daughter, Banshee, were at my side, off lead. I cried out "Heel!" and ran across the street. Banshee evidently thought I was going to jump over the brick wall which stood between the sidewalk and the William and Mary College grounds because she sailed over it without hesitation. My heart was in my mouth! I would estimate that the wall was 5 feet high and 2 feet wide.

Proper behavior

A properly behaved dog does not jump up on people. Teach him not to do so by pushing him away and saying "No!".

Don't feed the dog in the kitchen or he will expect that whatever is within reach may be eaten. The best solution is not to allow the dog in the kitchen. The commands "No!" and "Out!" will solve the situation.

The dog can be trained not to accept food from strangers or any that is lying about unless specific approval is granted by the owner. This takes care of possible intentional or accidental poisoning. Training is simple. The occasion is presented by leaving food on the ground or by having another person offer food to the dog. If he tries to take it, the lead is pulled back sharply and he is told "No!" Occasionally, he may be told "Okay!" but not always or he will assume that, in your absence, he can eat any food after a reasonable wait, say 5 seconds.

Irish Wolfhounds can be trained to growl and to attack on command. Certain circumstances may justify this, e.g. if one lives alone in some deserted area, but it could be risky. Remember the motto "Fierce when provoked". At law, one can only use reasonable force to prevent the commission of a crime or to apprehend a criminal. The killing or maiming of a harmless trespasser by a dog would most likely result in criminal action against the dog's owner.

In my training I do not try for perfection. As long as the dog executes the command I am satisfied. For instance, most owners train their dogs to sit straight either at their side or in front of them. Failure to do so causes the loss of points in competition. I am happy if the dog sits. The time that would be required to achieve perfection in such details does not seem warranted. But especially am I fearful that constant repetition would dull the dog's spirit. There are people who claim that obedience training results in a listless show dog. This is not true if the training has been properly conducted and not overdone. The degree of vivacity that a dog shows in the ring is dependent on his age, temperament, health, and relationship with the handler. If he has been frequently shown, he may become bored. If he has been confined to a kennel for some time, he may be active because of his release from confinement, but if I had only one choice of two alternatives I would rather have a dog who is happy at home than one who is alert on the few occasions when he is shown.

Once you have trained your dog well, you must often give him refresher training. Even though, long after he has been taught, he will remember what he should do, nevertheless he may either not obey or not do the work properly. Don't try to show off your dog's accomplishments if you haven't been working with him lately; you will be embarassed and may be tempted to vent your anger on the dog. It is really your fault. No coach sends his men into competition after a long layoff without getting them back into condition.

While much of the above discussion has involved the training of a puppy, I can assure you that older Irish Wolfhounds can also be trained easily. One dog whom I had sold as a puppy was reacquired by me when the owner felt that he could no longer keep her because of changed conditions in his life. At the time she was almost 6 years old. Training was conducted at irregular intervals but there was no problem in teaching her the basic exercises which I have previously described. She won her Companion Dog degree when she was almost 7.

I repeat. The above is a bare outline of obedience training. Buy the Pearsall book and join an obedience training class. I still periodically attend classes of the Northern Virginia Dog Training Association with whose director, John S. Ward, I started in 1957. It serves as a refresher for me and it gets my dogs accustomed to the distractions and temptations created by people and dogs.

B. SHOWING

Obedience trials are held either separately or in conjunction with breed shows. The rules and regulations may be obtained without charge from the American Kennel Club, 51 Madison Avenue, New York, N.Y. Some dog food manufacturers issue free booklets on this subject.

The following constitutes merely an outline of the procedures. After a dog has learned certain basic exercises, such as Heel, Come, Stay, he may be entered in a Novice Class. Generally, should he obey all commands the first time they are given, should he get a score of over 50% in each exercise and should he get a minimum of 170 out of 200 points, he will get a "leg" on his degree. Three legs under three different judges entitle him to a Companion Dog degree and the initials C.D. may be placed after his name.

He then may compete for a Companion Dog Excellent (C.D.X.) degree in the Open Class under the same conditions except that the exercises are more advanced, e.g. he must jump over a high hurdle to retrieve a dumbbell and must then return with it over the jump to his handler. This exercise is done on command of the handler; the dog does not retrieve at the moment the dumbbell is thrown.

Successful completion of still more advanced exercises entitles the dog to a Utility Dog (U.D.) degree. Among other exercises, the dog must pick out by scent an article placed among articles of similar appearance, he must respond to hand signals, jump over high hurdles in the order pointed out by the handler.

Beginning 1 July, 1977, a dog that has a U.D. may earn the title of Obedience Trial Champion (O.T.Ch.) by winning two first places in a Utility class and one in Open, or two in Open and one in Utility. These three first places must be awarded by three different judges. There must be at least 3 dogs in competition in the Utility competition and at least 6 in Open. Moreover, the dog must acquire 100 points according to a schedule which allocates points for first or second place based on the number of competitors.

All dogs shown by me in obedience classes have qualified for the degrees they have been attempting to earn. In only one case did a dog fail to qualify in three straight shows for the C.D. degree. And this was due to the fault of the handler. I had entered two dogs in the same show expecting that, because of the large number of dogs entered, there would be two sessions of the Long Sit and Long

Down. Unfortunately, all dogs were called to perform this exercise at the same time. I called on another person to handle one of the dogs. The dogs were placed in a sitting position. The judge said "Leave your dogs!" The handler said "Stay!" and immediately moved out. The command did not immediately register with the dog and she stood up in the belief that she was expected to heel. Realizing the error, she stood in place but was, of course, disqualified. The handler should have hesitated a fraction of a second after saying "Stay!" and before moving out. At the date of writing, my Irish Wolfhounds have earned two U.D.s, four C.D.X.s and ten C.D.s. The total number of degrees won by Irish Wolfhounds in the U.S. through 1975 have been 3 U.D.s, 17 C.D.X.s and 149 C.D.s. My first Irish Wolfhound got her U.D. at 20 months and 10 days, having won all her degrees in less than 11 months, a noteworthy accomplishment. She was also the first Irish Wolfhound to earn an obedience degree in Canada. Another of my hounds won his C.D. at 6 months and 16 days. Dogs cannot be shown until they are 6 months old, therefore the earliest a dog could earn his C.D. degree would be at 6 months, 2 days. This would not only require three consecutive qualifications (a simple matter) but also it would be necessary to have three shows on consecutive days with the first show date being on the dog's 6-month birthday. Since shows are usually held only on weekends, this would be rather fortuitous. Once I expected that I could improve on the record of 6 months and 16 days. Keltic Charlemagne got his first two legs on a Saturday and Sunday, the two days succeeding his birthday of 6 months. Unfortunately the shows on the following weekend were cancelled because anti-Vietnam War demonstrations were expected on the college grounds where the shows were scheduled to be held.

Earning a C.D. degree is quite easily accomplished. The others are more difficult. In the show ring, the Irish Wolfhound performs the exercises with great deliberation. Generally, he does not show any alacrity as do some other breeds. A common complaint of dog owners who exhibit in obedience trials is: "This is the first time he ever failed to do that exercise. He does it all the time at home." One can expect a series of varied disappointments. At one trial, the dog will look away as you give your hand signal and will thus fail to qualify. At another, he will be distracted by noise in another ring as he is about to pick up the dumbbell and he will return to you without it. In one competition, my Irish Wolfhound had done everything very well and all that remained was the "Long Down" where the dog lies down with all the other entries and stays there for 5 minutes with the handlers out of sight. When the handlers return to the ring, they walk up to their dogs, go behind them and stand to the dog's right. The judge then says "Exercise finished." As I returned to the dog's head, he stood up and thus failed. There are many such heartbreaking experiences.

There are also suspenseful situations which turn out well. Here are two of them. With Gamine at my side, in the Obedience Ring, I threw the dumbbell over the three-foot solid jump. At the direction of the judge, I said "Take it!" Gamine went over the jump, picked up the dumbbell walked back to the jump, dropped the dumbbell at the foot of the jump on the side away from me, placed her chin on the top of the jump, and looked at me. A command from me at that time would have disqualified her so I just stood there helplessly. The situation appeared hopeless. But then, she picked up the dumbbell and, from a standstill, jumped, walked over and sat down in front of me, allowing me to take the dumbbell from her. She repeated this performance on two other occasions. The most excruciating experience occurred in a Scent Discrimination test where the judge proffers to the handler 5 wooden, 5 leather and 5 metal objects, the handler rubs his hands over one object of each type in turn, and the dog picks out the scented articles. The first article to which I imparted my scent was the wooden one. The judge placed it among the 14 other articles in the center of the ring and directed: "Send your dog." I commanded: "Find it!" Gamine sedately walked to the articles, calmly surveyed the audience, slowly sniffed at all the articles, raised her head to observe the audience again, picked up the correct article and started her walk back to me. Halfway back, she stopped, dropped the article, looked at me, turned back to the center of the ring, again sniffed at all the articles, walked back very deliberately to where she had dropped the scented article, looked at me, picked up the article and brought it in. With my perspiring hands, I took the article from her. She qualified because she had been "continually working", but at what a pace! The rules have since been changed and the 5 wooden articles are no longer included in the test.

I do not believe that I shall again attempt to qualify any Irish Wolfhound for a C.D.X. or U.D. degree. I have always been fearful of an injury to the dogs, especially when jumping 3 feet high indoors. My decision not to show in these classes is due to the following three convictions: I know that the dogs can easily be trained to jump; any injury would cause pain to the dog; a condition might be created which would cause the dog to limp and thus prevent him from being shown in breed. I will, however, continue to train them to obey hand signals. These accomplishments can be of value.

The value of showing your dog in the Obedience Ring is that it repeatedly emphasizes the fact that your dog is not obedient unless he always obeys regardless of the circumstances.

In Britain, Obedience Trials are called Working Trials. They are much more severe than in the United States. The least difficult leads to the title of Companion Dog (CD). It corresponds somewhat to the American obedience degree of Companion Dog Excellent (CDX). In the order of increasing difficulty, the degrees are: Companion Dog (CD), Utility Dog (UD), Working Dog (WD) and Tracking Dog (TD). One does not have to qualify as Companion Dog before competing for the title of Utility Dog, but the last three degrees, all of which require tracking, can only be won in turn. There are two kinds of trials: Open and Championship. Degrees can only be won in Championship trials after qualification in Open trials. A minimum score of 70% is required in each exercise. If, in addition, one gets a minimum score of 80% overall, the designation Ex[1] (Excellent) is added to the title. An Irish Wolfhound with a TD title can become a Working Trial Champion by winning two firsts under different judges in Championship TD trials.

To my knowledge, the only Irish Wolfhound to have won any of these degrees was Marhaba of Berryfield owned, trained and shown by Joan N. Milnes, Member of the Royal College of Veterinary Surgeons. Marhaba, whose call name was Tara, qualified as UD Ex, WD Ex, and TD Ex, a most amazing accomplishment far greater than that of any other Irish Wolfhound shown in this type of work. She had never been entered in a CD trial, a much easier test. In her six qualifying trials, she was out of the ribbons only once (UD Ex); she was first twice (UD, TD Ex) and second on the three other occasions (WD, WD Ex, TD) — and all this in competition with other breeds, especially German Shepherds (called Alsatians in Britain) who had received rigorous training by the police. Unfortunately, Tara died before she could compete for the title of Working Trial Champion. She was whelped on June 16, 1971 and died on 9 March, 1977. Dr. Milnes had even taught her hound to speak on command and to cease her barking on command. This is one of the requirements for the TD degree. She explains her method: "The basis of this is

---

[1]British abbreviation.

'REQUIREMENTS TO WIN TITLES IN BRITAIN

Title Sought	Prior Title Needed	First Step: In an Open Trial, obtain a minimum score of 70% in each test and 80% overall	Second Step: Compete in a Championship Trial	Minimum Score 70% in each test and	
				Less than 80% overall	80% or more overall
CD or CD Ex	None	X	X	CD	CD Ex
UD or UD Ex	None	X	X	UD	UD Ex
WD or WD Ex	UD	X	X	WD	WD Ex
TD or TD Ex	WD	X	X	TD	TD Ex
Working Trial Ch	TD	Win two first places in Championship TD Trials under different judges.			

British Working Trial Requirements

Control	CD	UD	WD	TD
Heel on leash	X			
Recall	X			
2 min. sit. Handler out of sight	X			
10 min. down. Handler out of sight	X	X	X	X
Heel free.	X	X	X	X
Sending and dropping dog. (50 yds. minimum for TD, otherwise 20)	X	X	X	X
Retrieve dumbbell	X	X	X	
Steadiness to gunshot		X	X	X
Speak and cease on command				X

Agility	CD	UD	WD	TD
Scale 6 ft.	X	X	X	X
High jump 3 ft.	X	X	X	X
Long jump 9 ft.	X	X	X	X

Searching	CD	UD	WD	TD
Off leash				
Area (sq. yds.)	12	25	25	25
Time (mins.)	2	5	5	5
Articles to be found	1 ex 1	2 ex 4	2 x 4	2 ex 4

Tracking	CD	UD	WD	TD
On leash				
Distance (mile)		1/2	1/2	1/2
Minimum age of track (hr.)		1/2	1-1/2	3
Articles to be found		1 ex 1	1 ex 2	2 ex 3

frustration, not aggressiveness. For example, one can hold food out of the hound's reach until she barks. Tara was very difficult to frustrate. Finally I left her in the car when she wanted to go for a walk and, in her sight, played with my German Shepherd. At the first whine, I let her out of the car. This gradually progressed to a deep bark on command. If one teaches the bark on aggression, the dog is puzzled if it has to bark and there is nothing to be aggressive about."

VIII

Breed Competition

A. GENERAL

Persons show dogs in breed competition for various reasons. The breeder, of course, is interested in improving the breed. He seeks the opinion of the judge on the merits of his dogs as compared to other dogs. He is also interested in winning so that the value of his breeding program may be accredited and publicized. Success in the ring should result in more sales and at higher prices as well as higher stud fees. However, this does not necessarily follow since many purchasers are unaware of show records, unconcerned about them, or incapable of evaluating them properly.

An owner who is not the breeder and who does not intend to breed may show for one or more of the following reasons: pride in his dog, enjoyment of competition, the objective opinion of others.

A person intending to show in the United States should write to The American Kennel Club, 51 Madison Avenue, New York City, New York 10010, for a free copy of the *Rules Applying to Registration and Dog Shows.* These are occasionally changed and, therefore, strict reliance should not be placed on the notes in this chapter.

Dog shows are sponsored by local groups of dog fanciers with the approval of the American Kennel Club and are usually held on Saturdays or Sundays. Normally, active management is turned over to a dog show superintendent who has been licensed by the American Kennel Club. Write to the American Kennel Club for a list of show superintendents in your area. A calendar of shows is published in the American Kennel Club's *Pure-Bred Dogs— American Kennel Gazette* and in a number of magazines which concern themselves exclusively with dogs. The names and addresses of superintendents are also listed.

Upon request, a superintendent will send you a "premium list" for the show in which you are interested or will place you on a mailing list for all shows held within a radius of the number of miles you specify. The premium list provides details regarding the show:

location and date of the show, names of judges, prizes, rules and regulations, entry blanks, cost of entry, and date by which entries must be filed (usually about 3 weeks prior to the show date). The premium list contains entry blanks for only one particular show. It may be used for another show by substituting the name of the new show, date, etc. If a facsimile is made by you, make sure you include both sides of the entry blank.

An Irish Wolfhould that is at least 6 months old may be entered in a show if it is registered or eligible for registration with the American Kennel Club and if it has no disqualifying faults. It cannot be shown if it is blind, deaf, castrated, spayed or, if a male, it does not have two normal testicles in proper position. Also barred are dogs who have had their appearance changed by artificial means, unless authorized by the Standard. The ban on cryptorchids has been in effect in the United States since 1957. England followed the same rule from 1958 to 1971 but now, in that country, cryptorchids are allowed to be shown and the judge decides the seriousness of the fault.

Dogs six months of age or over which have not yet won their championships may be entered in one or more Regular Classes. The Puppy Class is for dogs from 6 to 12 months of age; occasionally the class is divided into two groups: 6 to 9 months and 9 to 12 months. The Novice Class is for dogs whose wins have been limited in certain ways specified in the AKC rules. The Bred-by-Exhibitor Class and the American-Bred Class are self-explanatory. Any dog may enter the Open Class. Each of the Regular Classes is divided by sex—one for Dogs and another for Bitches. In addition to the Regular Classes, there is a class for "Specials", i.e. champions. A champion may be entered either in the Specials Only class or in Open Dogs or Open Bitches. Even though authorized, it is not considered sporting in the United States to enter a champion in an Open Class as it may deprive another dog of championship points. There may be other classes, e.g. brace (two dogs), team (four dogs).

A decision on which class to enter must be made. In the United States, exhibitors usually do not enter more than one class. Generally, a puppy should be shown in the Puppy Class as it is unusual for one to defeat older dogs. If you have a mature and excellent Irish Wolfhound, entering him in an Open Class shows that you have confidence in him. Dogs whelped out of the country (other than Canada) must be shown in Open. When the competition is apt to be quite stiff, you may prefer to enter him in American-bred. You may thus have a better chance to win a blue ribbon and then compete for Winners Dogs or Winners Bitch. Bred-by-Exhibitor is a good class for a young dog who qualifies, especially if the show is the Specialty where competition is severe. The Novice Class is available to those with a beginner. Read the AKC rules to make sure you are eligible for the class in which you wish to enter.

After receipt of your entry and check, the superintendent will send you a judging program, an identification card, and an admission ticket. The program will inform you what number has been assigned your dog, in which ring he will be judged, and at what time. You will most likely receive it a few days before the show.

B. GROOMING

A beginner often wonders why it is necessary to groom a dog or to pose him. He believes that a judge should select an unkempt, unmanageable dog over one who is well-groomed and who stands and gaits well if the former is a better specimen of the breed. The judge does actually try to determine which is the better dog but he may have difficulty in judging a dog properly if the animal cringes, bounds up at his master or weaves from side to side when he is being gaited, refuses to stand still when being posed, or who is groomed so poorly that at first glance he appears to have some structural defect.

The handler of a dog in the ring is in the same position as a lawyer. He tries to present his client at his best. This means that he emphasizes the qualities and minimizes the faults.

The grooming described in this chapter serves two purposes. It not only keeps the dog clean and healthful but it also enhances his appearance. Owners are not in agreement on how the second objective should be achieved. Some prefer to leave their dogs *au naturel* and do practically no trimming, others "sculpt" the dog to give him a sleek outline. And then there are those who work within these extremes. There is no requirement that anyone groom his dogs in any particular way. It is a matter for his own judgment— possibly influenced by what the judges may like. The methods which I shall describe are those which, in my opinion, show the hound off best.

It is advisable to groom your dog thoroughly three weeks prior to the show so that he won't appear too newly shorn and to allow time to rectify any overzealous trimming you may have done. Any experienced Irish Wolfhound exhibitor will be pleased to help you in your initial efforts. The equipment needed may be purchased at dog show exhibits or from pet supply shops.

The ears should be "small and Greyhound-like in carriage". If an Irish Wolfhound is shown with long strands of hair hanging from his ears and if the hair on the ears should be thick, the judge may receive the impression that the dog exhibited does not have as ideal ears as another Irish Wolfhound. Most Irish Wolfhound owners pluck out long, ragged hair from both the inside and outside of the ears, in small bunches, with the fingers. This method, it is claimed, will result in the new hair remaining soft. Yet the same people pluck a puppy's soft, fluffy coat in the belief that it will cause replacement hair to grow out harsh. Medical opinion, I believe, is that neither theory is correct. The hair on the ears is normally soft and will grow out soft. As for the coat, it is softer on a puppy than on an adult dog, just as a human baby's hair is softer than that of a grown person. The outline of the ear should be smooth. The Kennel Club in Britain has a rule that this method is the only one to be used on any portion of the dog's body. Plucking hair from the ears does not hurt the dog if only a few strands are taken at a time. There may be an accumulation of wax in the dog's ears. See Index at Grooming, Ears.

The Irish Wolfhound should have long hair over the eyes and under the jaw. These are called "furnishings". The hair over the eyes should be combed forward; the hair under the jaw should be combed downward.

Since the muzzle should be "long and moderately pointed", it may help to trim a little hair from the face in the area from the mouth to the neck. The little tufts of hair which rise from the muzzle in front of the eyes should not be cut as they comprise part of the furnishings. They should be combed up towards the eyes. The neck itself develops a thick growth of hair, almost like a ruff, which is useful in a fight but which makes the neck look short and heavy. The Standard calls for the neck to be "Rather long, very strong and muscular, well arched, without dewlap or loose skin about the throat." I therefore apply thinning shears to the neck and then use a trimming blade. One should never use clippers as they create an artificial look. What the final appearance should be may be determined from photographs or by attending dog shows in which Irish Wolfhounds are exhibited. An abundance of hair should remain on the neck.

A hound's beard may become stained from food or from clay soil such as exists in the southern part of the United States. I have heard that a fast bleaching job can be done by first cleansing the beard with a boric acid solution and then by a daily application of a thick paste consisting of one-half boric acid powder, one-half fuller's earth (purchased at a drug store) and water. Brush out the dried powder before renewing the paste the following day. I have not tried this. Dr. Deubler says:

Any bleaching agent used will tend to make their hair brittle and break off, with resultant loss of whiskers and leg furnishings.

My only suggestion is to keep the mouth and feet as clean as possible. You may find that some shampoos, particularly detergents, have a whitening effect. If they are used often, it may be necessary to rinse with one of the products available for restoring natural oils.

Many dog people recommend giving large doses of Thiamine (Brewer's Yeast) to prevent tear stains. This is another "treatment" for which I can find no scientific basis. I mention it because so many readers report that it is effective.[1]

Some exhibitors spray white portions lightly with water and sprinkle on corn starch or white powder. When dry, the powder is brushed out. Other exhibitors use French chalk. The judge may order you to leave the ring if he detects any preparation by which the dog "has been changed in appearance by artificial means".

The hair that projects from the elbow should not be allowed to stick out. Round it off. Pluck with your fingers excess hair at the leg joints so that the hound does not appear to be afflicted with rickets. Comb the "feathering"—the long hairs on the back of the front legs—so that it flows away from the leg. Excess hair on the belly should be removed to show that the belly is "well-drawn" up. The hair around the sheath of the male dog should be cut with blunt-edged scissors. The root of the tail should be contoured so that it does not present a straggly appearance. Make sure there is no fecal matter under the tail. It the hair is abundant in that region, it may be advisable to thin it out.

Excessive hair extending beyond the toes should be cut so that the judge may observe that your hound has feet that are "moderately large and round . . . Toes well arched and closed." Cut stray hairs that project to the rear.

Hair between the toes should be trimmed with curved blunt-edged scissors to prevent mud from accumulating and to reduce the possibility of a splay foot, i.e. one where the toes are held far apart. The blunt-edged scissors are necessary to prevent injury should the dog make any sudden movement. Touching the bottom of the hind feet will cause the dog to kick out in a reflex action.

The length of toenails will vary with the amount of exercise the dog gets and on the type of terrain he travels over. They should not

---

[1]Dr. M. Josephine Deubler, "Ask Your Doctor," *Popular Dogs* (January, 1971), XLIV, p. 28.

touch the ground when the dog is standing squarely on a level surface. Over-long toenails spread the toes apart and change the appearance of the feet by pushing the toes upward. This can be painful to the dog. Such nails may also snag on fabrics and rugs and are susceptible of being accidentally torn off. Nail cutting is usually a traumatic experience for both hound and master. There is a vein called the "quick", which runs about three quarters of the way through the nail and which , when cut, causes the dog pain. It grows with the nail; therefore nails should be kept at the proper length. This vein can be seen through white, but not through black, nails. In the case of the latter, find the notch behind the nail which is formed by the bend of the nail and cut at that location. In case the nail is cut too short and bleeding is caused, apply alum, corn starch or some form of styptic powder. If the hound struggles, do not yell at him or strike him. This will not improve the situation. Try to calm him and use your strength on him. I suggest hooking a leg around the dog's hind leg above the hock thus limiting his movement, when you are working on his hind feet. The dog, of course, should be lying down.

C. PREPARATIONS

Each year your dog should be given a "booster" shot for distemper, hepatitis and leptospirosis. Avoid taking a puppy to an indoor show. Long before they are shown, dogs should be trained to "pose" and "gait" as described in the section on Showing in this chapter. They should be accustomed to having someone examine them just as the judge will do. Ask a friend to do the examination a few times.

You may wish to bring the following equipment to a dog show:

1. A 6-foot lead for use outside the breed ring and in the obedience ring. I prefer a nylon one.

2. A 1 or 2-foot leather show lead for use in the breed ring. A short lead does not interfere with the handler when he is setting up the dog.

3. A chain collar which the dog will keep on at all times when at the show.

4. A bench chain is used at benched shows to keep the dog in his stall. The number on the stall corresponds to the dog's number in the catalogue and on the identification card.

5.   A blanket, carpeting, or similar article for use in the stall.

6.   Grooming articles, including cloth and paper towels to be used in the event of rain, or if the dog should become mud-splattered.

7.   A steel bowl for food and water. Occasionally dog food companies provide cardboard bowls at the shows for this purpose.

8.   Dog food. Can opener if needed. Spoon. Dog food companies occasionally provide food at dog shows but it may not be what your dog is accustomed to or you may wish to feed after the show. If you are staying at a hotel or motel, feed him in the bathroom as spilled water or food can be more easily cleaned up when on a tile floor. Leave the rooms as clean as when you first entered. Take the dog some distance away from the hotel or motel to allow him to relieve himself.

9.   A 5-gallon can of water if you feel that the water at the show location might adversely affect your dog.

10.   Liver, dog biscuit. For possible use in the ring, to attract the dog's attention.

11.   Rosin or some other preparation to apply to the dog's feet at an indoor show to reduce the risk of slipping.

12.   Disinfectant to wash dog's feet.

13.   Dog's identification ticket.

14.   Your exhibitor's pass.

15.   Judging program.

16.   A thermometer, and some medication, e.g. Aspirin, Furacin.

Leads, collars, bench chains, and grooming articles may be purchased at the dog show. The sellers usually have a better knowledge of your needs than sales people at pet supply shops.

The judging program mailed to you will have told you how late you may arrive and how soon you may leave. At an unbenched show, one can arrive at any time before the dog is to be judged and leave immediately after if the dog's presence is no longer required. The dog need not be kept in any certain area, that is, he may be kept in a car, under a tree, etc. The premium list will have stated whether the show is "benched" or "unbenched".

Upon entering the show area, proceed to the section where Irish Wolfhounds are benched (assuming this is a benched show). Hounds are benched in the same general area. Placards on the benches identify the location for each breed. Lay his blanket or rug down on the bench corresponding to the number on the identification card mailed to you by the superintendent. Attach the snap at one end of the bench chain to the ring on the bench and the snap at the other end to the ring on the dog's collar. The ring on the dog's collar should be the one that, when pulled, will not cause the collar to tighten. If the bench chain is too long, the dog will be tempted to get partially off the bench thus interfering with persons walking by and possibly causing dogs to growl and fight. The bench chain can be shortened by sliding the snap through the bench stall ring and attaching it to the chain itself. The dog is not allowed to leave his stall except to be groomed and shown or to relieve himself in an area designated "Exercise pen". Take your dog to the pen about 15 minutes to a half hour before judging time so that he may relieve himself. If this is his first show, he may be a little slow in deciding what he is supposed to do. Let him sniff at the ground. Don't let him fraternize with other dogs in the pen.

Some handlers use rosin, either powdered or liquid spray, on a dog's feet if the show is being held indoors to minimize the chances of the dog slipping as he is gaited on a wooden floor.

The Regular Classes are judged in the order: Puppy, Novice, Bred-by-Exhibitor, American-Bred, and Open. Dogs are judged first. The winners of each class are then judged to determine Winners Dog, i.e., best male. The dog that was second in the Regular Class to the dog that has gone Winners Dog now competes against the winners of the other classes for Reserve Winners Dog (jocularly called "Best of Losers"). Bitches are judged in the same manner as Dogs. Winners Dog and Winners Bitch then enter the ring with the champions and the judge selects a Best of Breed, a Best of Opposite Sex to Best of Breed, and a Best of Winners. The last is awarded to either the Winners Dog or the Winner's Bitch who may also be either Best of Breed or Best of Opposite Sex. If a male is chosen Best of Breed, then the Best of Opposite Sex would be a bitch, and vice versa. There are over one hundred breeds of dogs recognized by the American Kennel Club. In the United States, these are divided into six groups: Sporting, Hounds, Non-Sporting, Working, Toy and Terrier. The Irish Wolfhound who is declared Best of Breed can now compete in the Hound Group against other hound breed winners. He is not required to compete for the Group title. If he wins the Hound Group, he goes into competition for Best in Show with the winners of the other Groups. Ribbons or rosettes are given to the first four dogs in each Regular Class (Blue, Red, Yellow, White), to Winners Dog and Bitch (Purple), Reserve Winners Dog and Bitch (Purple and White), Best of Winners (Blue and White), Best of Breed (Purple and Gold), Best of Opposite Sex (Red and White), the first four dogs in each Group (Blue, Red, Yellow, White) and to Best Dog in Show (Red, White, and Blue or other colors designated by the show sponsor).

Points toward a championship are won at licensed shows by the Winners Dog and the Winners Bitch and are based on the number of dogs of the same sex that are defeated. In some areas of the country where there are few dogs of a certain breed, the number of points is based on the number of dogs of both sexes that are defeated. The number of points to be awarded for defeating various numbers of dogs is established by the AKC and is based on the number of dogs of each breed which were shown the previous year in each section of the country. At the present time, the AKC attempts to arrange the requirements so that not more than 20% of the shows in any zone (of which there are 5 in the U.S.) will result in a dog getting three or more points (called a "major win.") The Best of Winners is awarded the same number of points as won by the other Winner should this number be greater. The defeated Winner, however, retains his points. Similarly, a Group winner may replace the points he has won in breed competition by those won by any single dog competing in that Group should the latter have more points. A Best in Show winner's points naturally would not be less than those won by any of the Group Winners.

Fifteen points, awarded by a minimum of three judges are needed to become a champion. Two of the wins must be "majors," (i.e., carrying at least three points) and must be under two different judges. Maximum allowable number of points in a show is five. Only a club or association which is a member of the AKC may hold a show at which championship points are awarded. One cannot gain points at "Sanctioned Matches"; these are conducted solely for experience. A "Specialty" show is a championship show where entries are restricted to one breed, in our case Irish Wolfhounds; the highest award in this case is Best of Breed. In Europe, the term "Irish Wolfhound Club Show" or "Irish Wolfhound Championship Show" is used instead of "Specialty".

The majority of Irish Wolfhound owners believe that a dog should not be shown in a regular class after he has completed his championship requirements but before this has officially been noted by the AKC. The dog does not need any more points and, by competing, he is lessening the probability of some other dog gaining points. There are considerations which may outweigh the arguments against allowing the unofficial champion to compete, but these I leave to the reader's judgment:

1.　One dog in the Open Class needs a major to finish his championship. If the unofficial champion does not show, there will not be sufficient dogs to constitute a major. The owner of the dog needing a major requests the owner of the unofficial champion to show his dog.

2.　The unofficial champion finishes on a Saturday. He is entered in obedience competition as well as breed on Sunday and needs one more leg to qualify as Utility Dog. He has traveled a great distance to attend the show. If he goes on the show grounds, he must compete in breed and obedience according to AKC rules.

3.　The unofficial champion is professionally handled and the owner is not present. If the handler scratches his entry without permission of the owner, he may be subject to criticism by the owner who would be hoping for a Group placement.

4.　The owner of the unofficial champion is not sure how many points his dog has won. Or he may be sure that he has exactly 15 points but will be surprised to see in the AKC *Gazette* that one of the Irish Wolfhounds he beat last month has been declared ineligible for the class and therefore he really has only 14 points. I suggest a letter to the American Kennel Club if there is any doubt as to the number of points earned. Note that, in its reports on shows, the number of points won by each dog is listed in the *American Kennel Gazette—Pure Bred Dogs.*

If your dog has 12 or more points but lacks one major, you may decide not to show him, even though you have entered, at a show that has insufficient entries for a major. The points will do you no good, should you win, and you are depriving someone else of points. Of course, abstaining from entering would deprive you of a chance of placing in the Group.

While a Champion may be shown in Open, this is never done in the U.S. as it deprives some other hound of championship points. The champion is entered in a class called "Specials Only". Mrs. Norwood B. Smith, one of the founders of The Irish Wolfhound Club of America, was strongly opposed to this practice and favored the English practice of entering champions in the Open Class.[1]

It cannot be said arbitrarily that a champion Irish Wolfhound is better than a non-champion. There have been many excellent Irish Wolfhounds who have not become champions for a number of reasons, e.g. a leg injury, an owner who does not wish or who is unable to show.

The fact that a dog becomes a champion only means that he has defeated a number of other dogs in competition. Generally, a champion is worthy of the title, but—at least in North America—it is possible to win a "cheap" championship by defeating only poorer specimens of the breed, puppies or old dogs. This could either be by arrangement or could be accomplished by competing for many years.

Some American champions are "campaigned" i.e., they are shown just about every weekend (usually two shows per weekend) throughout the country. They may win one of the four places in the Hound Group and may occasionally win a Best in Show. These are good dogs and they deserve their wins, but one should not conclude that the more high honors won by an Irish Wolfhound, the better he is as compared with others infrequently shown.

In brief, to make a just comparison between Irish Wolfhounds one should have observed them.

The dog whose picture appears on the cover of a national dog magazine is not necessarily the outstanding representative of the breed. I, and others, have received solicitations for this type of advertisement. Similarly, the great majority of pictures of dogs in dog magazines are paid advertisements.

D. SHOWING

Most Irish Wolfhound owners show their own dogs. A few employ professional handlers—persons licensed by the AKC— usually because they do not have the time, do not feel that they are qualified, or are getting along in age. Others do so because they feel that unless their hounds win their championships, they stand disgraced. As a result, they often spend large sums of money to gain their goals. This view should not be held. Many excellent Irish Wolfhounds have never become champions.

The show catalogue sold on the show grounds, and the judging program, mailed to you, both provide information on the time when the Irish Wolfhounds will be judged and specify the ring

---

[1]Mrs. Norwood B. Smith, "President's Message," The Irish Wolfhound Club of America, *Annual Reports* (March 1930-January 1932), pp. 35, 36.

where this will be done. The class will not be judged prior to that time. You are responsible for being at ringside when your class is called even though judging may be running late. Immediately prior to the judging, ask the steward who assists the judge to give you an armband with the identification number assigned your dog. This is worn on the left upper arm.

When your class is called, enter the ring and wait for the judge's instructions. He will most likely ask all exhibitors in the class to "gait" their dogs. The hounds are taken on a trot around the ring in a counter-clockwise direction. They should be on a loose lead to facilitate easy movement and should be on the left side of the handler. The judge observes the movement as an indication of proper bòdy structure and of spirit. If the dog shuffles along dispiritedly or if he lunges towards other dogs in play or in an attempt to leave the ring, the judge will find it difficult to evaluate him. Do not get too close to the dog ahead of you. This will affect the smoothness of your dog's gait and may upset the dog ahead, if not the handler. Do not pass the dog ahead, as is commonly done in horse show rings, unless he is refusing to move. This appears to be common practice although I see no reason for it. If the handler ahead of you is not moving fast enough as you circle the ring, slow down, let him get a good lead and then, *as you pass before the judge,* speed up so that the judge can observe the smoothness of your dog's gait, his power, his balance, his reach and recovery, the lack of bounce at the withers, the picking up of feet instead of their being swung. The handler should move with long, smooth strides.

There is no requirement as to the number of handlers when a brace (two hounds) or a team (four hounds) are shown. I prefer to be the sole handler in both cases, but one can have as many as two handlers in a brace class and four in a team class. Have your best moving hound on the outside (your far left) since this will be the one that will be mostly observed by the judge as the hounds are gaited around the ring. If you have a "problem child", e.g. one who refuses to pose very long, place him next to you so you can make corrections more rapidly and less noticeably.

The judge may then have all entries lined up in a column. Don't move your dog too close to the one ahead of you. It may annoy the other dog if you do so and it will make it difficult for the judge to observe the rear of this dog and the front of yours. You then "set up" or "pose" your dog. Look at his front feet. If they are not on line, perpendicular to the ground, and the correct distance apart, move one or both front feet to accomplish this. This is done from the right side of the dog by grasping the back of the front leg just below the elbow—with the right hand in the case of the right leg, with the left hand in the case of the left leg—and setting the leg down in the desired location. When the front legs are parallel, they are the correct distance apart. The dog's hind feet are then placed on line with each other and back sufficiently to show off the dog's angulation. To do this, from the right side of the dog grasp a hind leg just below and in back of the hock or just below and in front of the stifle. The leg below the hock (metatarsal bones) should be perpendicular to the ground. This accentuates the angulation and also gives the feet more of a "round" appearance than if the feet are advanced under the dog. When a young puppy's legs below the hocks are perpendicular to the ground, his front feet are often ahead of his shoulders and not perpendicular to the ground as is the case with an adult hound. Many handlers set the hind feet quite far apart. I suppose the purpose is to get the hocks as far away from each other as possible in an attempt to convince the judge that the dog is not cowhocked. If this is overdone, the hind feet turn out and the hocks turn in. If the hind feet are placed too much to the rear or if the dog's head is held too high, a dip may be created in his back. Some handlers place a hand under the dog and push upwards to straighten the top line. Judges are aware of this and will usually ask the handler to allow the dog to stand naturally.

Ideally, the hound being judged should stand by himself without the handler holding up his head, belly, steadying him, etc. However, inexperienced or untrained dogs often require this assistance. Even old campaigners require attention so that they do not turn their heads towards the judge, thus turning a hind foot in the same direction and also depriving the judge of the side view of the head which he is seeking. The judge can see whether the outline of the dog is being truly represented or whether it is being somewhat fabricated. Some handlers use boiled liver or dog biscuits to "bait" the dog so that he will hold his head high. I see nothing objectionable in this. Irish Wolfhounds may be bored with ring proceedings and not present an alert appearance. They should be shown in their best light.

There are a number of other ways in which the dog may be made to hold his head high: by use of the lead and chain collar, by placing a hand under his chin, by a slight movement of your hands in front of him at your chest level, etc. If the hound's ears should temporarily lie flat to his head, make them into rose ears by pressing with the thumb against the outside of the ears and then flipping the ears back. The judge may separate the dog's lips to look at his teeth or he may ask you to show him the teeth. If the latter, raise the dog's upper lip with your left hand and lower the lower lip with your right hand. The judge will lower his body slightly to examine the bite and soundness of teeth; when he raises his body, release the lips. He will then most likely take the dog's head in his hands to examine the eyes, ears, and general configuration. Stand by while this is being done. Some judges make odd vocal sounds or throw some small object on the ground; the purpose of this may be to test the dog's alertness or to see if they will carry their ears semipricked as Graham said they should do "when looking at objects in the distance".[1] There are Irish Wolfhounds (usually puppies) who will raise their ears at this performance, but most disdainfully ignore the procedure. The judge will then stand back and look at the dog's front. He may raise a front leg and let it drop to see the position which the feet will naturally adopt.

Now he will examine bone placement, length, and width of body, back-line, tuck-up of loins, rear angulation, texture of coat, firmness of muscle, etc. As he does this, you may want to hold the dog's head to keep him steady, especially if the dog is not accustomed to the show ring. If the dog turns his head far to one side, the hind foot on that side may also turn outward and the hock will turn in. The judge will move to the rear and study the dog from that position. Normally, an Irish Wolfhound tucks his tail between his legs while posing. The judge may extend it to its full length to see if it reaches below the dog's hocks, a desirable feature. He will check to see if males have both testicles descended.

He may now examine each dog in the ring, or he may stand in one corner of the square "ring" and ask you to gait your dog. He will tell you how he wants this done. Many judges have you take your dog to the farthest corner and return once or twice while they observe his movement. Others will ask you to go to a far corner, turn right or left to the next corner, and return either along the same route or directly back to them. If you start off too quickly, the dog's movements will be disconnected and awkward or he may start to canter and it will be difficult for the judge to evaluate his movement in comparison with the other dogs. Moreover, since dogs place their feet more or less in the center of their body when they move fast, inexperienced judges are apt to believe that these dogs do not have as good movement as slower moving dogs. The judge will be watching for the position of the feet, evidence of cow hocks, of crabbing, paddling, roll, and being out at the elbow. Start with a slow trot. If the dog breaks into a canter, pull the lead up sharply to get him back to the trot. Keep a loose lead but do not let the dog wander. He should move in a straight line away from the judge and back, and should move at an

---

[1]G. A. Graham. Quoted by I.W. Everett, "The Typical Irish Wolfhound," *op. cit.*, p. 63.

An ungroomed hound. All pictures in this series are of 6½-year-old Ch. Malachi McCourt of Dundrum (1977), owned by Nanse L. Cipri.

A groomed hound.

Ungroomed head. Note long, fine hair growth on ear and heavy mane.

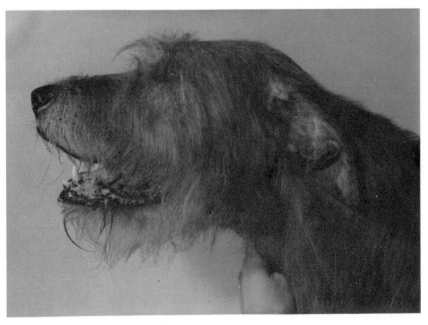

Groomed head.

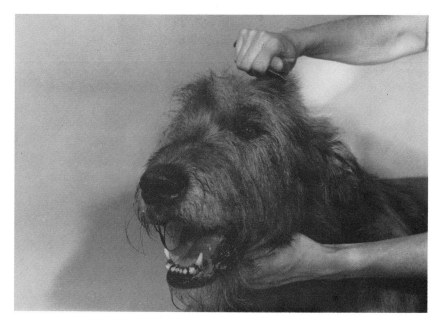

Stripping knife and fingers remove excess hair to emphasize length and balance of head.

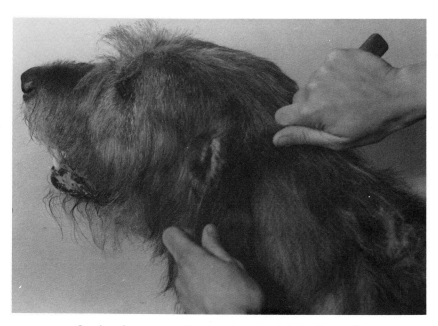

Continued onto nape of neck to show that it is "well-arched".

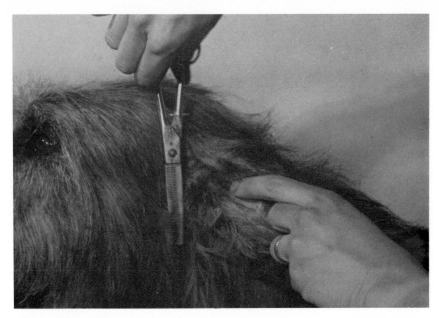

Bushy growth around the ears is thinned with fingers and, if necessary, with thinning shears.

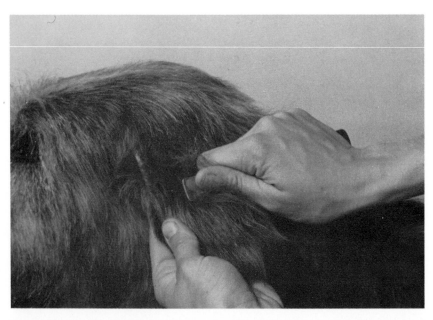

Excess hair on ear is plucked with fingers to show clearly that ears are small, correctly placed and "Greyhound-like" in carriage. Here stripping knife is being used. Do not remove all hair from ear.

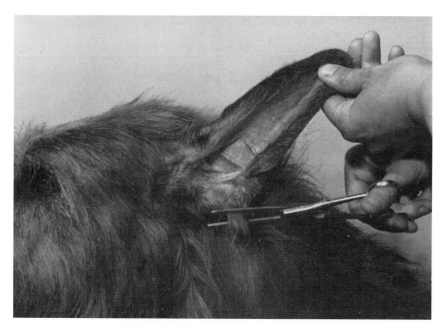

With thinning shears, trim projecting tufts of hair at base of ear. Do not allow hair to fall into ear.

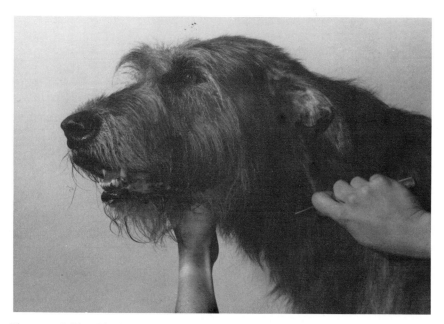

Fingers and either thinning shears or stripping knife thin out the mane on the sides of the neck to show that it is "rather long, very strong and muscular."

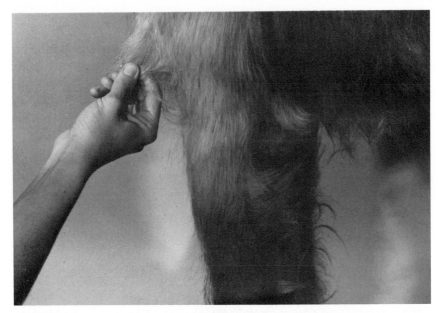

Excess hair above and in front of the forelegs is plucked and shaped to draw attention to shoulder angulation and foreleg placement.

Thinning shears and fingers remove hair tufts on elbows so as not to detract from a long and straight leg.

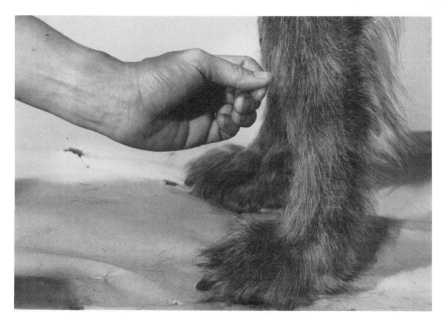

Pluck out long hairs over the carpal joint to prevent the impression being gained that the hound "kunckles over."

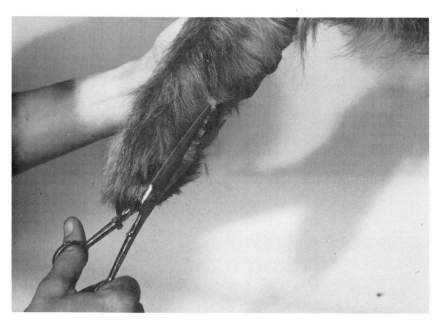

Trim neatly around the edges of the pads. Pluck any long tufts around the foot. Remove excess hair between the toes and pads with scissors having rounded tips.

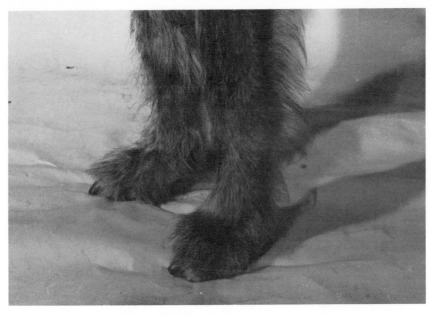

Note that the groomed foot, unlike the ungroomed one, appears "moderately large and round." The groomed leg presents a neater appearance.

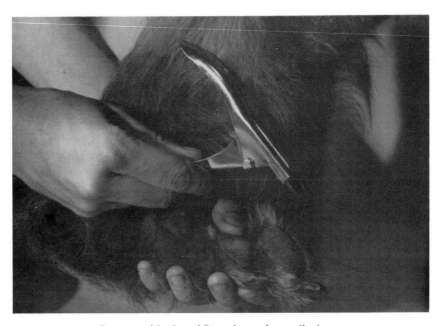

Proper positioning of Resco heavy duty nail trimmer.

Nail being cut at indentation.

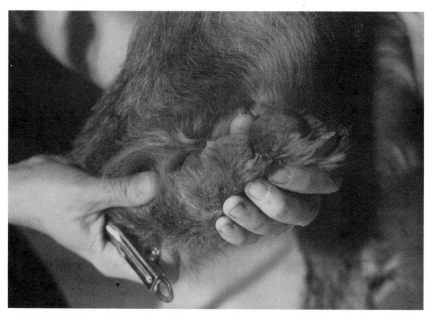

Trimmed nail showing the quick which supplies blood to the nail. Do not cut into the quick.

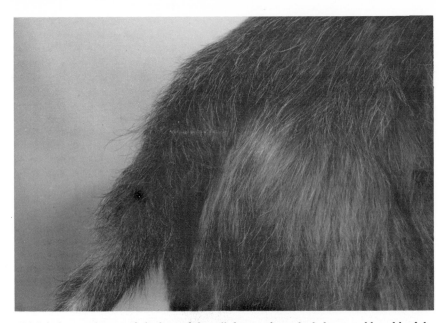

Thick hair growth around the base of the tail detracts from the balance and breadth of the hindquarters. Use a stripping knife, thinning shears or fingers on and around the base of the tail.

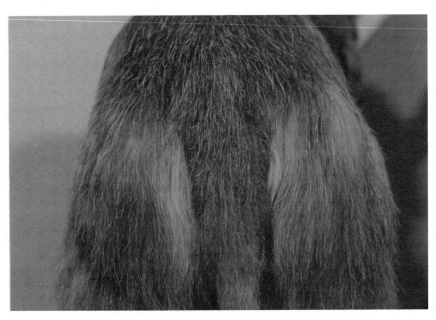

Base of tail after trimming.

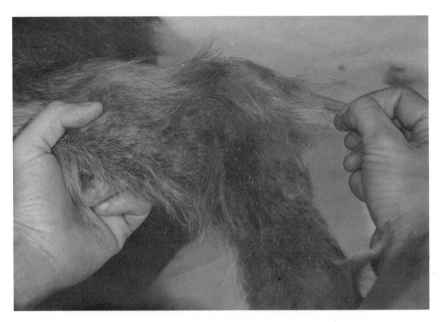

Remove long tufts of hair from hocks.

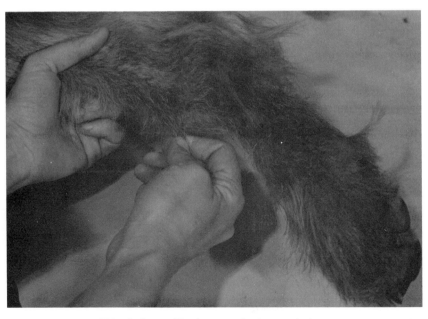

Trim in front of hocks to emphasize angulation.

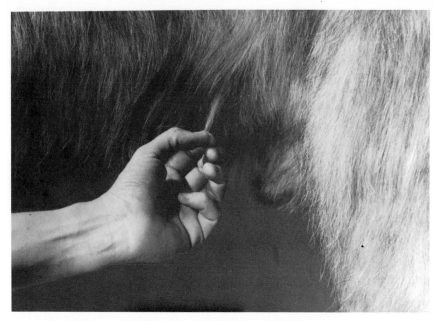

Set up the hound in a show stance. Shape the flank and underline with thinning shears and fingers to emphasize tuck-up. Trim the long hair aound a male's sheath.

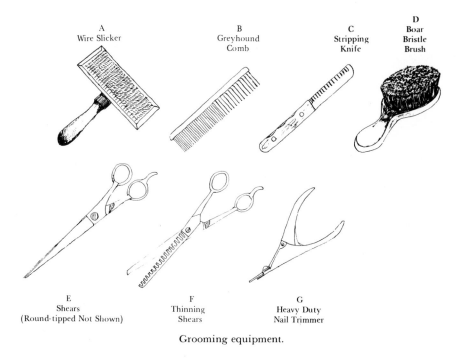

A	B	C	D
Wire Slicker	Greyhound Comb	Stripping Knife	Boar Bristle Brush

E	F	G
Shears (Round-tipped Not Shown)	Thinning Shears	Heavy Duty Nail Trimmer

Grooming equipment.

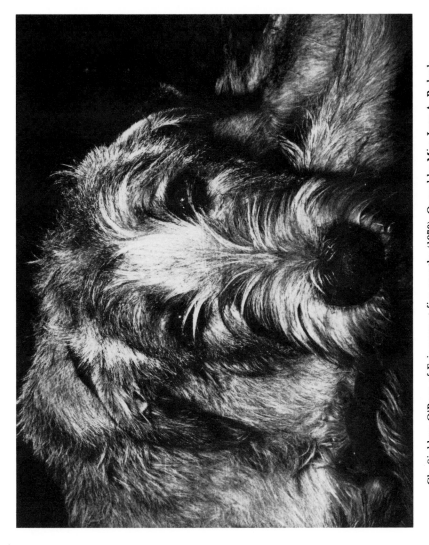

Ch. Siobhan O'Born of Erinmore at five months (1970). Owned by Miss Jane A. Rubeck.

Roddy of Killybracken **with Mary Jane Ellis** (1976) (Killybracken Kennel—USA and co-owner of Sulhamstead Kennel—England).

Winner of team class at 1966 and 1967 Irish Wolfhound Club of America Specialty Shows. Judge Winifred Heckmann. Out of two litters bred by owner-handler Alfred W. DeQuoy.

IWCA Specialty

1963 Best 9-12 months old
1961 Winners Bitch

1963 Best of Opposite Sex
1965 Reserve Winners Bitch

Westminster Kennel Club

1962 Best of Breed
1963, 1964, 1965 Best of Opposite Sex

1966, 1967 Best of Opposite Sex

Ch. Keltic Phantom II C.D.X.
Ch. Keltic Banshee U.D.

Ch. Keltic Ghost of Ballylyke C.D.
Ch. Keltic Tara C.D.X.

Effect of posing a hound with the hind feet too far apart. This might give some persons the impression that the leg bones are not straight and that the hound is "cowhocked." This hound is Keltic Siobhan, C.D., winner of the Best Hindquarters Class at the 1975 Irish Wolfhound Club of America Specialty. See her picture on the fifth page of photographs preceding page 49.

Effect of posing a hound with the hind feet too close together. Keltic Siobhan, C.D.

even pace. If his head is to the left of his hindquarters, give a slight jerk on the lead to straighten him out; if, instead, he heads towards you, press the back of your left hand on the side of his head to straighten him out. The judge may ask you to stop in place on your return so that he can examine the dog while he stands naturally, i.e. without being posed. If the dog ends up in an unnatural position, give a little tug on the leash to straighten him out, but do not pose him. The judge will then have you go to the tail of the column and he will proceed with the examination of the next dog.

Occasionally, one hears the objection that, in hunting, the Irish Wolfhound's normal gait is the gallop and therefore judgment of movement should be when he is moving at this gait.

Smythe said:

> The slow walk . . .affords insufficient evidence as to the soundness or otherwise of the exhibit.[1]

An English judge, Percy Shewell, is quoted in the *Kennel Gazette* (Britain) for January, 1904, as saying:

> The showing as "Sporting" dogs of hounds that are not only incapable of running true but even walking true is lamentable, and we should like to see them galloped before being judged instead of being handled painfully round a 30-foot ring, at a walk, as at present. [2]

The adoption of this suggestion would present a number of problems such as the ability of the handler to move rapidly enough, the physical space required, etc. It is possible to judge a dog for movement by observing him at a walk and trot, although it would be desirable to see him gallop since he may move more widely in the rear while galloping efficiently at a good rate of speed than while trotting. It should not be said that the gallop is the only "natural" gait of the Irish Wolfhound. In exercising my dogs I have found that they vary their gaits from walk, trot and canter to gallop.

Graham made this comment:

> The writer knows by experience how hard it is to judge freedom of action in the show ring, as he has seen hounds which he knows, from having watched them gallop over a country, to be perfect in this respect, taken direct from their cramped benches,

---

[1]Smythe, *op. cit.*, p. 89.
[2]Percy Shewell, The Kennel Club (Britain), *The Kennel Gazette* (January, 1904), p. 9.

where perhaps they have been for 16 hours and possibly a long railway journey as well, and brought into a show ring some 20 feet square and their necessarily stiff action adversely commented upon.[1]

At this point, the judge may look at all the dogs as they stand in column and make his decision, or he may follow a number of different routines: having the dogs posed in line and facing him, having some or all of the dogs go through the same steps as previously, etc.

My procedure in judging is to examine each dog in turn, first in place and then as he moves away and back. After all dogs have been examined, I ask the handlers to gait them around the ring.

During all of this, remember not to keep your dog posed if it is apparent that the judge is not going to look at him. Allow the dog to relax. On the other hand, if your observation of the judge has revealed that he is liable to check your dog at intervals, keep him posed. Always keep the dog between the judge and yourself.

Answer any of the judge's questions but do not attempt to sway him in your favor by volunteering information regarding the dog's recent wins, etc. The judge will tell you how your dog placed, if it did. Go to the numbered marker in the ring corresponding to the placement and wait for the judge to give you a ribbon. Be courteous towards the judge and other exhibitors. Do not object to any decision; the judge is entitled to his opinion. Reserve any questions you may have for the judge until the breed has been completely judged. Since the judge may have other classes to judge according to an established schedule, he may ask you to see him after his judging assignment has been completely fulfilled.

In the United States, judges are licensed by the AKC to judge one or more breeds according to a Standard of Excellence adopted by the breed clubs and approved by the AKC. Owners are usually partial to their own dogs and often feel that a judge who does not place their dogs above others is incompetent or is favoring the owner or handler of the winning dog. As justification, they may say that on the following day, Judge X, who is an expert on the breed, reversed the order of placement.

It should be borne in mind that judging is not a precise mathematical exercise. Capable judges may very well disagree on whether Dog A is better than Dog B; they may interpret the Standard differently; they may have differing views on the respective weights

---

[1]George Graham, in *The Kennel Encyclopaedia, op. cit.,* p. 860.

to be given certain features of the dog. It also happens that a dog performs better on some days than others or even at different periods of the same day. The same is true of the handler. Here is an example from my own experience. At the 1964 Specialty, one of my hounds placed third in the Open Class and another hound which had a previous Best-in-Show to his credit, went Best of Opposite Sex. The next day, a different judge gave my hound Best of Breed and gave the other dog third place in the Open Class. This judge commented that the rear movement of my dog was the best he had seen in years. Yet the same judge, later in the day, did not place my hound in the Group because, as he said, he did not move as he had previously done. Another example: P.M.C. Toepoel of Holland, judging at Crufts, in London, placed two dogs first and third in one class, and later in the day, in another class, reversed the order, placing the same dogs third and fourth. The change was intentional.[1]

In 1971, I judged the Irish Wolfhound Club of America Specialty Show. There were 150 hounds actually present. On the following day, at another show, 67 of these hounds were exhibited in twelve classes. On the day after that, only 43 were shown in nine classes. Obviously, many of the Specialty ribbon winners were absent at either one or both of the other shows. However, the first place winners on the second day had also been judged by me to be superior to the others in nine out of the twelve cases. The first place winners in the nine classes on the third day had been judged by me to be better in seven of the nine cases. In view of the difference in opinions of judges and of the possibility that hounds may not have shown up as well on each day, a high degree of consistency in the judging was thus demonstrated.

Exhibitors should closely observe dogs in the ring and make up their minds *before the judge places the dogs* as to how they would rate them. The object is not to see whether you and the judge are in agreement. It is to force you to evaluate dogs in a short period of time. You will not have the advantage which the judge has of placing his hands on the dog and possibly of observing as many details as he. You may not be as good a judge as he. He most likely has examined many more Irish Wolfhounds than you and has observed points which may have escaped you. Yet the procedure is good practice.

If your dog limps in the ring, the judge may excuse him from

---

[1] P.M.C. Toepoel, "Irish Wolfhounds," The Kennel Club (Britain), *The Kennel Gazette* (1937) LVIII, p. 222.

further judging. The judge is bound to disqualify any dog which has a fault which the Standard of that breed or AKC rules call "disqualifying". Lack of height or weight in an Irish Wolfhound is not a reason for disqualification. Both the American Kennel Club and The Kennel Club in Britain have stated that the minimum heights and weights specified in the Standard of Excellence are advisory only. In his discretion, a judge might penalize a hound for height or weight below that prescribed by the Standard by giving it a lower ranking or even by withholding a ribbon,[1] just as he might for any other serious defect.

Before leaving for home, apply a disinfectant to the feet and nose of your dog to reduce the possibility of transmitting disease from the other dogs to your kennels. Repeat the application upon arrival at home. If possible, keep the dog away from other dogs in your kennel, especially puppies, for two days.

E.   FOREIGN SHOWS

International

The Fédération Cynologique Internationale (F.C.I.)[2] authorizes the award, at a limited number of Championship Shows, of a Certificat d'Aptitude au Championat International de Beauté (CACIB) to the best dog and to the best bitch of each breed if they are considered to be of championship caliber and are at least fifteen months old. Reserve CACIBs may be awarded to the second best dog and bitch. To become an International Champion, four CACIBs must be won while competing in Open Classes—once in the country of registration or, in the case of Irish Wolfhounds, in England,[3] and three times in at least two other countries; at least three different judges must award these certificates and at least twelve months must elapse between the first and the last qualifying awards.

As in the United States regular classes, males and females are judged separately. However, instead of selecting the four best

-----

[1] John Brownell, The American Kennel Club, *Letter to author* (December 28, 1966).

C.A. Binney, The Kennel Club (Britain). *Letter to author* (January 23, 1967).

[2] See Index at Organizations, Kennel Club, F.C.I.

[3] Because England has been designated the "country of origin" of Irish Wolfhounds. England has a six-month quarantine law.

hounds in each class, the first order of business is evaluation of quality. The judge determines whether the entries are excellent, very good, good, unqualified, or incapable of being judged. Unqualified would involve serious faults. Incapable of being judged are uncontrollable hounds, or those that are too fat, ungroomed, or with a poor coat. The hounds that are excellent then compete for first, second, third, fourth and Reserve. Only those hounds judged to be excellent compete for what we call Winners Dog, Winners Bitch, Reserve Winners Dog, Reserve Winners Bitch, Best of Breed, and Best of Opposite Sex. The judge must comment on the qualities and faults of every hound shown.

If one agrees that only a dog qualified under F.C.I. rules can be called an International Champion, then dogs who do not so qualify but win championships in several countries can only be designated as Champions of individual countries, e.g. American, British and Canadian Champion. In Great Britain and Ireland, the title "International Champion" is commonly applied to dogs that hold championships in both of these countries.

Continental Europe

It is possible for a dog to be an F.C.I. International Champion and yet not be a national Champion. National championships are obtained by winning CACs. Requirements vary. For example, to become a German champion, a dog must be rated Excellent and earn four CACs under at least three different judges, two of them in different West German States and one at a CACIB show over a period of at least one year. In Holland, a dog can become a Champion by winning four CACs under at least two different judges on at least three different dates. A CAC awarded at the Amsterdam "Winner Show" or at a Championship Club Match (Specialty) counts for double. While an Irish Wolfhound as young as nine months may compete for a CAC in Holland, he must be at least twenty-seven months old to win the CAC that qualifies him as a Champion. Luxembourg is the only country where only one CAC is needed to become a national Champion.

Britain

The largest show in the world is Crufts, which is run by the Kennel Club. Other shows in that country are operated by Breed and Canine Societies. There are many classes: Puppy, Junior, Maiden, Novice, Tyro, Debutant, Undergraduate, Graduate, Post Graduate, Minor Limit, Mid-Limit, Limit, Open, and others. Dogs and bitches are frequently judged separately.

Dogs are often entered in several classes. In the United States this is the exception. Colored cards are awarded to the four best dogs in each class: red (1st), blue (2nd), yellow (3rd), green (reserve). A fifth card, V.H.C. (Very highly commended), or a sixth card, H.C. (Highly commended), both white, may be awarded at the discretion of the Show Committee. There are six groups: Hounds, Gundogs, Terriers, Utility, Working and Toys. Some groups and Best-in-Show are judged by more than one but never by more than three judges.

There are several types of dog shows but at only one, "Championship Shows", can a dog make his way to a championship and only if his breed has been specified. In addition to Specialty Shows, championship shows include 24 all-breed shows and a championship show for each group designated in advance by the Kennel Club. Three challenge certificates (CC) awarded by 3 different judges at Championship Shows are needed to become a Champion but one Challenge Certificate must be gained after the dog has reached the age of 12 months. A CC may be won even though there is no competition, although this has never happened. A judge can withhold a certificate for want of merit. The number of CCs to be awarded in any year is dependent on the number of registrations over the previous three years, up to a maximum at present of 40 sets, i.e. 40 for males and 40 for females.

Dogs contending for CCs can compete against Champions, the latter being entered only in the Open Class in competition with non-champions. The judge awards a Challenge Certificate to the Best of Sex exhibit entered in the classification for the breed provided he is clearly of the opinion that the dog is worthy of the title of Champion. After awarding CCs to a dog and a bitch, the judge selects one for Best of Breed and the other for Reserve Best of Sex.

Ireland

To become a Champion, a dog must win Green Stars totaling at least sixteen points in value. Within this total, there must be at least one 4-point Green Star or at least two 3-point Green Stars. The same judge can only award one 4-point or one 3-point Green Star to the same dog; thereafter, his award counts for only one point. The number of dogs or bitches that must be defeated to gain points is dependent on the show popularity of the breed in the preceding year. A Green Star may be withheld for lack of merit. If Green Stars are offered, the judge must select a Best of Breed and Reserve Best of

Breed. Champions compete against non-Champions in the Open Class. The five Groups are Sporting (which includes Hounds), Gundog, Terrier, Non-Sporting and Toy.

Canada

To become a champion, an Irish Wolfhound must earn at least ten points under at least three different judges. The number of points earned is based on the number of Irish Wolfhounds of the same sex in competition. If there is none, the sole entry gains one point. An additional requirement for a championship is that at least one other Irish Wolfhound must be defeated or there must be a group placement with at least five breeds competing in the group.

Mexico

An award of a pale blue ribbon is made to a dog that is considered worthy. Competition is not required. Four awards by different judges result in the title of champion.

IX

Coursing

Game and dogs are the invention of gods.
Xenophon (c. 430-c. 354 B.C.)
Cynegetica i. l.

Coursing is a very ancient sport.

> In its earliest stages it apparently comprised the hunting of
> various animals with dogs bearing a strong resemblance to the
> modern greyhound, which confines its hunting to the hare . . .
> The dogs are run in couples which are drawn by lot. The winner
> of the first course meets the winner of the second, and so on until
> the last two dogs left in compete for victory . . . The hare must be
> given a clear run of not less than from 60 to 80 yards before the
> dogs are released. The slipper releases them simultaneously by
> means of specially devised slip collars attached to a single lead.[1]

In some types of modern competition a lure is used instead of a
hare.

The use of Irish Wolfhounds to hunt hare is mentioned only three
times in Irish literature.[2]

The first modern field trial or "meeting" ("meet" in the United
States) was held by The Irish Wolfhound Association on November
6, 1924, at Pippingford Park, Nutley, Sussex, England. Events
consisted of hound trailing, a forest trial, and coursing. Please
observe in the account that follows that these Wolfhounds are
hunting by scent during the first two events.

> The first trail had been laid from Pippingford Park out into the
> forest, finishing again on the boundary of the park. Mr.
> Hamilton-Adams, who acted as starter and judge, got the hounds
> well away, and they disappeared amidst the gorse and bracken.

---

[1]"Coursing," *Encyclopaedia Britannica* (1955), VI, p. 602.
[2]Alfred W. DeQuoy, *op. cit.*, p. 83.

About a quarter of a mile out the first fault occurred; which was, possibly, due to the trail being laid too near to a crossroad, where several cars happened to be passing, but the hounds were able to make a recovery and were soon off again on the line down into the valley. There was a very strong wind, and this caused the hounds to scatter somewhat, and it spread the scent over rather a large area. At the bottom of the valley where the trail turned at right angles on the home run there was again a fault, and Mr. Wade's Kathleen-na-Houlhan, which had made excellent way up to this point and had been the first to own the line, was here passed by Mrs. Massy's Maureen of Ifold and Desmond of Ifold. The last portion of the trail was uphill. Maureen, closely followed by Desmond, appeared over the brow, with Colleen next. These three hounds finished in this order, and Maureen was declared the winner. The second trail was laid entirely within the boundary of the park in full view of the field. A bad fault was made near to the start where the trail passed through bracken. This was caused through the hounds putting up a squatting rabbit. Mr. Wade's Kathleen, however, held true to trail, despite the circumstances which drew all other hounds off, and, following true to the finish, was adjudged the winner. She was followed home by Mrs. Massy's hounds again, which were the first to break away from the line of the rabbit.[1]

Nine Irish Wolfhounds competed in the coursing, seven being bitches. One male was eliminated in the first round, the other in the second. The final round, between Captain Hudson's Colleen of Brabyns and Nora of Brabyns, was won by the former.

There is a reference in the 1925 Year Book of The Irish Wolfhound Club (Britain) to meetings on Salisbury Plain[2] and in the 1926 Year Book to an Irish Wolfhound Coursing Club Meeting at Amesbury Flats.[3]

Ten other meetings were held in England by The Irish Wolfhound Coursing Club from 1934 to 1939.[4] In the first eight, dogs and bitches competed against one another five times in Novice Classes and twice in Open Classes. A male won once in Novice, females the other four times. The same male, Mrs. Nagle's Sulhamstead Finn, won both of the Open Classes. He also won three Open Dog matches.[5]

[1]"Field Trials," The Irish Wolfhound Association, *The Irish Wolfhound* (September, 1925), p. 31.

[2]I. W. Everett, "Impressions at Bath Show," *op. cit.*, p. 27.

[3]Harding Cox, "Irish Wolfhounds at Ranelagh and Amesbury," The Irish Wolfhound Club (Britain), *Year Book* (1926), pp. 40, 41.

[4]Marion Clark, *Letter to the author* (16 December, 1969).

[5]The Irish Wolfhound Club (Britain), *Year Book* (1935-1937), pp. 95, 98, 101.

Irish Wolfhound owners began competing in coursing meets in California in 1968 under the auspices of the Open Field Coursing Association. These were Mixed Meets, i.e. competition was among gazehounds: Afghan Hound, Borzoi, Greyhound, Irish Wolfhound, Saluki, Scottish Deerhound and Whippet. The Ibizan Hound has since been added to this list. Italian Greyhounds compete only among themselves. On 19 January, 1969, Jerry Greenwood's Love Lioness of Mordor and Paul Pilat's Ch. Sable Kathy of Shanid took first and fourth place respectively in a Mixed Open Stake which had about 33 entries consisting of all sighthound breeds except the Scottish Deerhound. In the following year, "Love" killed a jack rabbit during a course and accumulated enough points to become Pacific Coursing Champion. She died of a broken neck in a later competition.

The Open Field Coursing Association went out of existence and with it went the title "Pacific Coursing Champion." In 1974, the National Open Coursing Association (NOFCA) was incorporated. It employs live game. While the quarry could be any animal, jackrabbits are coursed because they are more easily found. The term "open field" refers to the fact that the jackrabbit is coursed in the region he inhabits and without any enclosures. "Park coursing" would occur if barriers were constructed to prevent the prey from escaping or to limit him to a few avenues of escape. In open field coursing, hounds are judged on desire, speed, agility, endurance and "touch and/or take". A "take" results in the capture or death of the quarry. A "touch" occurs when the prey is touched but not "taken". To qualify as a "Coursing Champion," a hound must earn 100 points with a minimum of 10 mixed and 10 breed points; in addition, he must have at least one first or two second placements; finally, he must have had either one unassisted take or two assisted takes. To become "Coursers of Merit," Irish Wolfhounds and Scottish Deerhounds have to earn 100 points in breed competition and have at least one first or two second placements; takes are not required. There have been a number of Irish Wolfhound Coursers of Merit — but no Coursing Champions.

A number of lure coursing clubs have been formed in the United States. Many have been members of the American Sighthound Field Association (ASFA) which was established on 21 May, 1972. This organization is seeking American Kennel Club recognition. Since the office of secretary may change hands over the years, the name and address of the present incumbent will not be given here. The American Kennel Club or the Irish Wolfhound Club of America can provide you with at least the name and address of an active participant in lure coursing. The ASFA publishes a booklet of rules and procedures, including the requirements for becoming a "Field Champion." An Irish Wolfhound must be at least one year old to enter competition. A Canadian Sighthound Field Association was formed in 1976.

In lure coursing, the lure is usually a rabbit skin or fox tail. A mechanical device keeps the lure just ahead of the leading hound. Hounds are judged on enthusiasm, follow, speed, agility and endurance over a course at least 375 yards in length and preferably not less than 440 yards. The Coursing Plans given as suggestions in the Running Rules and Field Procedures (May ,1, 1976) show courses from 440 to 880 yards with 9 to 12 turns. To become a Field Champion, a hound must earn 100 points in Open Stakes and must have finished first at least once or second at least twice. A fourth place gives a hound points equivalent to the number of entries in the Open Stake; third place is worth twice the number of entries, second place three times, and first place four times. The maximum number obtainable in an Open Stake is 40 points. While Field Champions can compete in Open Stakes, they usually do not. The winners of the Open Stakes and Field Champion Stakes compete to determine Best of Breed and the Best of Breed winners run against one another for the title Best in Field. In the 1976 Grand National Lure Course held in Colorado, Best in Field was Michael John Bowen's Irish Wolfhound Ch. Sanctuary Fair Erin, F. Ch. A Whippet finished second and a Saluki third. All gazehound breeds (except the Italian Greyhound) competed — a total of 104 hounds. On the first day of the competition, Erin ran two 660-yard courses; on the following day, over a period of seven hours, she ran two 440-yard courses, one of 880 yards and finally one a mile long. The interval between the half mile and mile run was only an hour and a half.

Michael John Bowen comments: "As a rule, bitches run better and longer than dogs, but big bitches run as well or better than middle-sized ones, depending on the amount of 'heart' they have . . . Irish Wolfhounds do better at longer distances — 880 yards or better."[1]

One is often asked questions about the relative speed, agility and stamina of various breeds. A number of comments on these points is included in this chapter. Miss Anastasia Noble, editor of the British Deerhound Club *Newsletter,* rendered her opinion of this breed:

Deerhounds were originally for hunting deer. We use them for

---

[1]Michael John Bowen, "On Coursing the Irish Wolfhound," *The Gazehound* (March/April, 1977), pp. 80, 83.

hare coursing because we want to keep the working ability and to give them something they really enjoy, and because we who do it, love seeing them run and enjoying themselves. Being a sight hound, and as chasing is a basic thing in dogs, the working ability is not lost as easily as some types of work, therefore most hounds will run, though naturally some better than others . . .

We used to think when we started that a small hound would be best, but now I am not so sure. Other things being equal, a big hound with its big stride gets there quicker and so scores that way.

The keener your hound is the older it should be before it does much running as it will run too much and perhaps damage itself. It also depends on how they are developed, some doing so quicker than others.[1]

That the instinct for the chase must be developed is borne out by two quotations:

As a rule, Whippets inherit a strong desire for chasing and pursuing a lure or live game, but in a few cases, there are individuals that seem to lack the inherited instinct for racing.[2]

The article goes on to describe the schooling that is necessary. The following quotation indicates that this is applicable to other breeds:

Many people are under the impression that a Bloodhound is born with the fully developed ability to trail. Though it is true that through centuries of selective breeding he has developed this instinct to trail, with every single dog it must be brought out by training.[3]

Coursing by Greyhounds is so well established that little mention will be made of it in this book except for comparison of their speeds with those of other gazehounds. These notes do not represent complete coverage of the subject, merely such pertinent items as have come to my attention.

Mrs. Starbuck observes:

We had two Greyhounds that ran with the Wolfhounds for a time, and as to the dogs' speed I can speak with assurance: the

---

[1]Anastasia Noble. Quoted in "Scottish Deerhounds," American Kennel Club, *American Kennel Gazette—Pure Bred Dogs* (February, 1970), p. 70.

[2]Eugene Jacobs, "Whippets," American Kennel Club, *American Kennel Gazette—Pure Bred Dogs* (May, 1962) LXXIX, p. 65.

[3]Robert Noerr, "Bloodhounds," *ibid.* (July, 1962) LXXIX, p. 66.

Greyhounds were quicker to get started and had the edge on the Hounds the first three miles, then they were finished; but the Wolfhounds, at that point, were just getting started and would hold up all day.[1]

At my request, Mrs. Jo-Ann Van Arsdale, who has both coursed Irish Wolfhounds in California and judged coursing gazehounds, answered a number of my questions.

The Greyhounds are by far the fastest dogs in a sprint. Very few of them last longer than one minute. Many of them cannot last out the walk as the search for the game proceeds. They are especially vulnerable on warm or hot days. We find that if the average Greyhound does not catch the hare in the first 60-90 seconds that he will very often not catch it at all. He is extremely fast on the get away and almost always turns the hare in the first 30 seconds. This is an enviable feat. The Whippet is also a good sprint dog but seems to possess more stamina than the Greyhound. We have many long courses (2 minutes or more) with Whippets. He is extremely agile and an exciting dog to watch. I would say that the Whippet picks up the game with ease and usually dispatches it authoritatively. Picking up the hare is not easy, it takes a great deal of skill and experience for a dog to become a good "taker". The best one I have ever seen was a Whippet. The Saluki combines all the best in a strikingly beautiful running machine. He is fast. Some as fast as the Greyhound, and he possesses unbelievable stamina. We have many, many long (3 minutes or over) courses with Salukis. The weather does not seem to affect them the way it does the Greyhound. In a mixed course with a Greyhound the Saluki may trail for 30 to 45 seconds but he will come on after that time and leave the Greyhound behind. There are of course many exceptions but I am now speaking in generalities. He is adroit at turning and taking the game. This skill usually comes after much practice, but I feel this is true with all the breeds. In my opinion, the Saluki is the finest breed of coursing hound. He combines all the qualities in a beautiful package.[2]

In 1933, the Saluki Club Members' Show conducted 440 yard flat and 300 yard hurdle racing at the Dartford Greyhound Stadium, in England. It was reported:

All the dogs ran well and keenly and took their hurdles in good style. Though times were not as fast as first-class greyhounds,

---

[1] Alma Starbuck, *The Complete Irish Wolfhound* (1965), pp. 133, 134.
[2] Jo-Ann Van Arsdale. *Letter to the author* (November 4, 1969).

this was hardly to be expected as the Saluki is a stayer with a good turn of speed rather than a sprinter over a short course. The time for the 440 yards was 28.30 secs., and a satisfactory feature was the fact that both the winner and runner-up are champions on the bench.[1]

Dog racing appears to be well established in Sweden. There are two main organizations: Swedish Sight Hound Club and Swedish Sight Hound Racing Society. The former is open to all sight hounds; the latter is restricted to Greyhounds. Racing is a sporting event among dog owners; it is not a commercial venture. The fastest times for Salukis on a 450 metres (492 yards) grass track in pursuit of a mechanical hare was 29.7 seconds for a male, Zorro, and 29.9 and 30.0 for his sisters, Ditte and Dolly. The number of hounds in the Swedish Sight Hound Club are 30 Whippets, 20 Greyhounds, 14 Salukis, 2 Afghans and 1 Italian Greyhound.[2]

Racing Times in Seconds (Miles per Hour)

Distance		Flat Greyhounds		Flat Horses	Hurdles Greyhounds	
Yards	(Meters)	World Record[1]	Irish[3]	World Record[2]	World Record[1]	Irish[3]
300	(274)		16.35 (37.5)			
440	(402)			20.8 (43.3)		
500	(457)	26.13 (39.1)[4]	27.73 (36.9)			29.26 (35.0)
525	(480)	28.17 (38.1)[4,5]	28.44 (37.8)		29.10 (36.9)[6]	29.43 (36.5)
550	(503)		30.09 (37.4)			32.04 (35.1)
600	(549)		33.04 (37.1)			
660	(604)	37.60 (35.9)		33.5 (40.3)		
700	(640)	38.72 (37.0)[7]	39.66 (36.1)			
800	(732)		44.73 (36.6)			
900	(823)		51.94 (35.4)			

[1]"Sporting Record," Encyclopaedia Britannica (1976), p. 452.

[2]*Ibid.*, p. 463.

[3]Records established in Ireland prior to 1975 or by Irish-bred Greyhounds in Britain in 1974, whichever were faster. *Bord na gCon* (The Irish Greyhound Board) *Annual Report-1974*, pp. 18, 23.

[4]Straightaway track.

[5]499 yard (456 meter) circuit.

[6]Four flights of hurdles.

[7]562 yard (514 meter) circuit.

---

[1]"Saluki Racing," The Kennel Club (Britain), *The Kennel Gazette* (July, 1933) LIV, p. 576.

[2]Erik Lundholm. Quoted by Esther Bliss Knapp, "Salukis," *Popular Dogs* (March, 1971), p. 64. 450 metres is equivalent to 492 yards.

Now we have comments on how the Afghan Hound behaves in the field.

> The late Alex Scott, manager for Amelia White's Kandahar Kennels in Santa Fe, N. Mex., wrote as follows: "Afghans are wonderful when run on the chase. They will turn in their own length. On rough, sloping ground, nothing can out-distance them. We used to have two packs of Irish Wolfhounds which I took out with the horse each morning. The first Afghan I took with them was Ch. Tufan of Ainsdart (Peter). He would turn the coyote or hold it until the Wolfhounds closed in."[1]

Mrs. Van Arsdale is of a different opinion.

> The Afghan Hound in the field is a sorry sight. I love Afghans and owned one of the best Afghan Hounds to course in 10 years. They are slow, sadly slow, but they possess a marvelous persistence, they will not give up as long as they can see the game or follow the other hounds. They possess stamina on the order of the Saluki, and will run all out for more than 3 minutes if they are properly conditioned. I have not seen a number of Afghan Hounds kill so I cannot fill you in on their skill in that department. My dog I feel was exceptional. He earned the most difficult requirements for his coursing championship which are an official kill and a first place finish in a sanctioned hunt. I feel that the breeders of the Afghan have altered the breed to the extent that about the only thing they have left is desire. They have been bred for so many generations with coat and head as the main criterion that they have lost most running ability. They are very weak in the hindquarters, at least on this coast, and structurally have been deteriorating for some time. There are of course exceptions, such as Mrs. Tracy Hegy's black bitch, Kashi, who has placed NBQ [Next best qualified] in a mixed stake with very tough competition.[2]

I now quote an instance of a 13½ month old Scottish Deerhound, Rocky, in competition against an undefeated coursing Afghan in Australia in 1965. One should not conclude from this single incident that Scottish Deerhounds are faster than Afghans anymore than one would say persons of one nationality are faster than those of another because one individual of the first group defeated one of the second in a foot race.

---

[1] Marion Florsheim, "The Magnificent Afghan Hound," *Popular Dogs* (June, 1965), XXXVIII, p. 49.

[2] Van Arsdale, *op. cit.*

My wife and I decided we would visit by invitation the Afghan Club's coursing meeting which it conducts once a month on a Greyhound track . . . The champion Afghan is a bitch which is undefeated this year; a nice type with exceptionally good hindquarters; is trained to chase the lure. I took Rocky (Atlas's call name) along for the ride, not thinking of running him. Indeed that morning he had been wormed, not fed 'til 11:45. He was admired and it was suggested he should run against the champion bitch.

Naturally in view of his condition I was not too happy to run him, but eventually gave in, partly in the interest of good relations and partly because I did not want to appear to be apologizing for a Deerhound, although young Rocky is very fast, has hunted a little and has a really beautiful running action and is very intelligent.

I showed him (over the fence) a few races, each time giving him a signal I gave only in the bush when hunting. It was thought that "to encourage him to run" the bitch would start first so that Rocky would follow her. So that is how it was.

The track is 660 yards. The bitch went and I set Rocky after her, he went past her like the wind and nearly caught the "hare" until the man responsible for it stepped up the pace. It really was beautiful to watch him reaching out with his tremendous stride, folding and unfolding over the ground in the poetry of motion.

None of the crowd noticed the bitch — 12 lengths behind at the back straight and more than 20 lengths behind at the finish. He ran the fastest time of the afternoon, by some 10 or 20 seconds and did not negotiate the turns very well.

They closed a five-bar gate at the finish which the "hare" gets through, but Rocky flew over this, raced to the "hare", now stopped, and pulled part of it off and chased back to me, tail wagging and very pleased with himself.[1]

In a subsequent letter, the author of this letter, Mr. Gorman, wrote about Rocky:

Over a straight 790 yards he beats a top class Greyhound by four lengths, and regularly beats the Afghans by 50-70 yards over 500 yards.[1]

---

[1]John Gorman. Quoted in "Scottish Deerhounds," American Kennel Club, *American Kennel Gazette—Pure-Bred Dogs* (June, 1967) LXXXIV. p. 83.

Other comments by Mrs. Van Arsdale:

The Scottish Deerhounds do not come out often but have shown remarkable speed and agility. The few that I have seen have impressed me. For a large dog they are very speedy. The Borzoi is a breed that runs from very talented to very bad. The Gillettes of course have done extensive work with the breed and they have many good coursing hounds. There are many Borzoi who have finished their coursing championship. The good runners are fast, not as fast as the Whippet, Saluki, or Greyhound, as a rule. They are very agile, and are able to kill with skill. Mr. Art McConnell's Dante easily finished his coursing championship and was one of the topdogs of the season. Many times he performed go-byes on N.C.A. Greyhounds [i.e. from a position a clear length behind National Coursing Association Greyhounds he went a clear length ahead]. I have been much impressed this last year with the speed the Borzoi are exhibiting. A number of fine specimens have been out, Lois Cooper's Nadya, Wayne Thornton's Corona, the McConnells' Dante. They are very well conditioned and have many times left the "faster" breeds eating their dust.[1]

The Irish Wolfhound has only been in the coursing field with any kind of conditioning or skill in the last year. It has been my observation that the dogs are not affected by the weather to any extreme degree. They can outwalk the Greyhounds. They are not a sprint dog. They do not possess extreme speed, but they are deceiving in observation because we must remember that they have an enormous stride and they seem to get a long way away in a short amount of time. Their legs do not move as fast but they cover twice as much ground. I would say however that the Borzoi and the Deerhound are faster.[2]

A correspondent who calls himself "Borzoi" wrote to the editor of a Dublin weekly[3] in 1892:

I was present at a trial which took place in the jumping enclosure of the Royal Dublin Society's premises, Ballsbridge, during their last show between a Borzoi and an Irish Wolfhound, and in several spins of about 200 yards the Borzoi was unable to get more than a length clear. I may mention that the Borzoi has been used for coursing hares, and is quite fast enough to run into one, as are

---

[1]Van Arsdale, *op cit.*

[2]Van Arsdale, *op cit.* and *Letter to the author* (July, 1, 1971).

[3]*The Kennel, the Farm, the Poultry Yard,* Dublin, Ireland. (February 20, 1892), p. 74.

the Irish Wolfhounds, as I have been told by those who tried them. According to the Stock-Keeper, an Irish Wolfhound bred by Mr. Townsend, and exported by him to the Rocky Mountains, killed forty wolves single handed during one winter.

Hogan, commenting on this newspaper article, conjectures, without assignment of any basis:

"The writer in *The Kennel* by Borzoi means, I presume, the Siberian wolfdog, not the Russian one."[1]

In view of the fact that the correspondent, earlier in his letter, referred to Captain Graham judging the recognized breeds of Borzois, Irish Wolfhounds, and Deerhounds, and that The Kennel Club (Britain) has never listed a "Siberian wolfdog," I do not see how Father Hogan can conclude that the reference was to anything but a Borzoi.

I asked many questions of Mrs. Van Arsdale regarding head carriage, barking and fighting during coursing, and the relative speeds of dogs and bitches. Here are her comments:[2]

All experienced sighthound breeds carry their heads high when searching for the quarry. They are alert and aware of every movement in the area. When in pursuit of the quarry all of the breeds run the same. The head and neck are extended as far as possible when the dog is trying his best. When the dog is about to give up and is going to stop or is not trying his best, maybe due to lameness, etc., he starts running "high", with head and neck held up. This is our best guide as to the "desire" of each dog. In the early chase the pups and younger dogs should never run "high", if they do they don't care. When they are really trying they always run with head and neck low to the ground and fully extended.

I have never seen an Irish Wolfhound run alongside the quarry, so I couldn't elaborate on this. The other breeds are still running with head and neck low at this time, usually reaching for the game at periodic intervals. This is when the hare will start to turn and dodge so you will not see an extended run that remains parallel.

We course on very flat level ground in the main. We do have a dike that runs through the field, and in Southern California we did have one course go up the side of a very steep hill. These hills

---

[1]Edmund Hogan, *The Irish Wolfdog* (1897), p. 106 and (1939), p. 93.
[2]Van Arsdale, *op. cit.*

were not rocky or broken terrain where the dogs were running. On the way up they would still be in the extended position, at the top of the dike head and neck would come up in order to sight the game (Split Second); on the other side of the dike most dogs would land about halfway down the side from the momentum gained on the long run and uphill pull. Many would fall and roll a couple of times, the others would land at a full running pace. If a dog falls, he always comes up looking for the game, unless injured of course.

It is my conclusion as far as head position goes that when searching and at full attention, i.e. dogs in the gallery who are not slipped, the head is held very high with neck very arched and tense, ears even come forward. When in full pursuit, the head and neck are carried low and extended.

Unfortunately good pictures of coursing are rare and very hard to come by. Most of the action takes place about a mile away so without a very elaborate setup, good photos cannot be taken. Many people are willing to bring a very elaborate setup until they find out that in the course of one hunt the gallery usually walks an average of twelve miles. This is a long way to haul that much equipment.

The only breed I have observed to bark while in pursuit is the Whippet, I presume this trait comes from the terrier blood. The Afghans, Salukis, and Greyhounds are often very vocal when they are forced to remain in the gallery and are not slipped. I have not noticed much commotion from the larger breeds, Borzoi, Irish Wolfhound and Deerhound, but have seen all of them bark at one time or another, but only after the game has been flushed and they have not been slipped.

Fights are very, very rare even between dogs who are normally aggressive off the field. In the past three years of judging I have only disqualified one dog for fighting. Even at our practice lure chases we have no problems with fighting. As far as I am concerned it is not known that one sex is faster than the other. It seems to be a matter of individual talent rather than one sex dominating. Looking over the list of Coursing Champions you will see that in breeds where there are several champions that both bitches and dogs have obtained their titles. From the experience of my litter of Wolfhounds I am firmly convinced that a great deal of ability has to do with mental attitude and mostly desire. I am still in very close contact with three of the pups from my bitch. Kirsty (the mother) was an excellent courser, for an Irish Wolfhound. She had great desire, speed and a certain amount of stamina. I kept two of the puppies which I thought had the best conformation, especially for running dogs. The third pup I mention was the second pick of the litter and was raised in an environment where he was not exposed at an early age to coursing as my two pups were. My pups even had the opportunity to learn from their mother, which I feel is important. In any case neither of them turned into talented coursers. The third pup, Chubasco Macho owned by Dean Kaplan, however, has shown an amazing amount of talent. Dean just started him the middle of last season. Macho won the Irish Wolfhound Stakes at his first hunt and went on to run in the Grand Course which is an invitational hunt with only the top running dogs of the season competing. At the Grand Course there were 40 entries. Macho made it through two days of hard coursing to the finals and scored a kill towards his Coursing Championship. He was outstanding, and received many compliments from the participants. He showed a great deal of speed, stamina, desire and most of all courage. Dean has done a great job of conditioning the dog but no amount of conditioning will put that desire in a hound. I had the top dogs from my kennel at this hunt[1] and both were eliminated in the first day's competition. One of these dogs is a Coursing Champion, the other has 80 points and only needs a third placing to finish her title. A great majority of the entries at the Grand Course are Coursing Champions so you can see that Macho was competing against the best. He has proved his worth as a coursing hound and along with Love Lioness of Mordor, Coursing Champion, earned new respect and admiration for the Irish Wolfhound in the field.

The purpose of my inquiry on head carriage was to check the validity of the Standard of Excellence requirement: "Head and neck carried high." Mrs. Van Arsdale's remarks bore out my belief that Irish Wolfhounds, like tigers and other carnivores, raise their heads when it is necessary for them to survey an area, lower and extend it when the game is in sight and they are at a full run, and lower it even more if necessary to bite the quarry. I conclude that the Irish Wolfhound should not be expected to keep his head higher than at a 45° angle, at the most, as he is gaited around the ring. The puppy may do so, out of excitement. The veteran has seen it all before. Normally the Irish Wolfhound, on a loose lead, will carry his head at the same level as his back or a little higher, in motion around the show ring.

My request for motion pictures of the Irish Wolfound in action was for study purposes of his movement. I wanted to know about his

---

[1]Not Irish Wolfhounds.

barking as many such references have been made in Irish literature.[1] This may well have been caused by his being restrained when the quarry first became visible.

Because of his great size, an Irish Wolfhound is under a handicap in turning with a hare and in reaching down, while at a run, to kill him. Some owners of present-day Irish Wolfhounds take violent objection to his use in coursing claiming either that it is beneath his dignity or that rapid turning to get the hare may cripple him. This point of view has existed for some time. For example King Cormac mac Art (A.D. 254-277) hunted hare during the siege of Druim Damhghaire. Bairshinn Blaith, daughter of King Sidh Buirdh of Leinster, scolded him saying that this was a decadent practice for a King, that he should use his hounds on boar or stag.[2]

In 1925, Mr. Beddoes expressed his concern in the same publication as that in which an Irish Wolfhound coursing meeting was reported:

> Coursing may be useful for exercising hounds, but as a specific sport it can hardly hope to succeed, for the simple reason that the Irish Wolfhound *is not built for it*. We are breeding for size, combined, of course, with proportion and substance. If therefore we use our hounds for coursing, we must—if we wish to be successful—reduce the size and weight.
>
> No one would, I think, care to play polo on a heavyweight hunter, neither would a well matured M.F.H.[3] care to follow his pack in full cry, over rough country on a light polo pony.
>
> The height and build of the Irish Wolfhound prevents him coursing small ground game; his weight, another all-important factor, prevents him, when going at full speed, turning with the rapidity that is an essential. One can imagine the terrific strain on the shoulder muscles of a heavy hound going at full speed in an endeavour to suddenly turn at right angles.
>
> Again, what is the natural attack of an Irish Wolfhound? Surely it is an upward slash, an in and out attack, a slash straight for the jugular vein of his prey, and not a downward grab. Nowhere in history have I read of this breed being used for coursing as a specific sport. There is therefore no record of their success or failure in this particular kind of sport, and my remarks are made

---

[1]DeQuoy, *op. cit.*, pp. 39, 42, 72-74.

[2]M. L. Sjoestedt, "Le Siège de Druim Damhghaire," *Revue Celtique* (1926), XLIII, p. 23.

[3]Master of the Fox Hounds.

solely from the little knowledge I possess of the work or sport to which, from their build, the various types of dogs are adapted.

Mr. Beddoes suggested as suitable sports for the Irish Wolfhound: high and long jumping, tracking, and "has anyone ever throught of a dog 'Grand National'? It is not impossible—where fitness, strength, courage and perseverance—all attributes of the Irish Wolfhound—would win today."[1]

The above is a very interesting suggestion. But how would one get the dogs to run a sufficient distance to test their stamina as well as their speed? One method would be to have the owner or trainer mounted on a horse and following the same course. The horse would have to be in the lead at all times. It seems likely that this would be the case judging from the racing times given a little earlier, especially since the Irish Wolfhound is said to be a slower starter than the Greyhound. For the longer distances, one can use times made in steeplechasing. Mr. J. E. Cooper, the Executive Secretary of the National Steeplechase and Hunt Association, Belmont Park, Long Island, New York, has been kind enough to generalize for my benefit. He says that there are basically three types of jumps: hurdles, brush, and timber. The hurdle is made of cedar and is approximately four feet four inches in height. The brush is about eight inches higher and twice as thick from front to back. Hurdle races are generally run at distances from a mile and a half to two miles and a half. Races over brush are usually between two and three miles long and timber races between three and four miles. A two-mile hurdle race would be run in approximately three minutes and forty seconds (32.7 miles per hour), a two-mile brush race in about three minutes and forty-eight seconds (31.6 miles per hour) and a timber race at about 20 to 25 miles per hour.[2] The Grand National Steeplechase is run twice around a course for a total of four miles, 856 yards, including thirty jumps. The record time is 9 minutes, 20.4 seconds, for an average speed of 28.9 miles per hour.

Major Harding Cox commented as follows on the coursing which he judged at Amesbury Flats in 1925:

> What surprised me more than anything was the way these Wolfhounds, most of whom were but half-trained whilst some were obviously not trained at all, managed to "stick it out" in vain pursuit in long courses, over very heavy going! It left me

---

[1]C. E. W. Beddoes, "The Necessity of Training." The Irish Wolfhound Association (Britain), *The Irish Wolfhound* (Sept., 1925), p. 28.

[2]J. E. Cooper, National Steeplechase and Hunt Association, *Letter to the author* (August 6, 1971).

wondering what their stamina would be if intensively trained for such ordeals.

As to the real use of Wolfhounds for *coursing hares* I am more than doubtful. But this demonstration was deemed necessary by their admirers in order to prove that these great, gentle creatures are well endowed with the sporting afflatus and are equipped with speed and stamina. This was amply demonstrated at Amesbury. The way the Wolfhounds comported themselves showed that they would surely prove of immense value in tackling big game, coursing wolves, jackals, antelopes, etc. This fact should make them in great demand in various parts of the globe, so that British breeders are likely to find a ready market for their superfluous stock.

I retract everything I said as to Irish Wolfhounds not being pukka sporting dogs.[1]

In 1935, Mrs. Hudson, owner, with her husband, of the famous Brabyns Kennels, wrote an article which is reprinted here in its entirety.

THE IRISH WOLFHOUND AS A SPORTING HOUND[2]

By PHYLLIS E. A. HUDSON

During the last two years, breeders and owners of Irish Wolfhounds have been given the opportunity to test their hounds' stamina, speed and sporting capabilities by the formation of a Coursing Club for the breed. This venture has been a marked success, and thanks are due to those who put such a lot of time and hard work into making the necessary arrangements. Accounts of these two meetings in 1933-1934 have already appeared in detail in the cannine press.

One of the chief things we all learned was that, contrary to some prophecies, it was not a triumph for the smaller, deerhound type of hound, as in some cases was anticipated. But it definitely was a triumph for the Club Standard of Excellence. Apart from colour of eyes, or coat, and minor details of this description, the two finalists, in any case in dogs, conformed very accurately with the Club Standard in outline and conformation. The winning bitch was possibly rather more masculine in appearance than some of her opponents, but she was certainly one of the biggest, if not the biggest, there. A big, well-balanced, properly-shaped hound

---

[1]Harding Cox, *op. cit.*, pp. 40, 41.
[2]Phyllis Hudson, *op. cit.*, pp. 69, 70.

must of necessity be faster, as he will have the bigger stride, and it is the stride in the run-up that is half the battle.

Training these hounds is a comparatively simple matter, if the hound is properly fed. To breed a successful coursing hound, any shyness or timidity must be avoided at all costs in the pedigree. It is these shy dogs in the slips that cause the most trouble. Gun-shyness does not matter. I know several gun-shy dogs that go well out of slips. The owner of one hound should, if possible, try and get his or her hound into slips, or even led coupled with another hound, before entering for coursing, as a hound which has always been by himself sometimes dislikes a strange hound so close to him. Those who own several hounds are not so often faced with this difficulty. Another important point about training, and possibly the first step in training, is to teach your hound obedience; to come back to the whistle or some special call. Personally, I have never found any difficulty in achieving this. Though it is best to start from puppyhood, I have seen older hounds trained to do this in quite a short time. There are some whom no one nor nothing seems to make obedient, but this can often be accounted for by the pedigree. Dispositions are just as hereditary as other faults or failings, and in-breeding is to blame for a great many.

To get the hound really fit and muscular, road work and not long tiring gallops, is the most important form of training. A quarter of an hour or twenty minutes' galloping a day, or even every other day, is sufficient. Over-training is as disastrous as the opposite. These hounds are natural hunters, or should be, and any hound that can chase a rabbit and has a little experience of getting away from slips, even if only slipped in couples from an ordinary handkerchief, will, if he or she be the right make and shape, give every satisfaction in the coursing field. I have had the honour to take part in the training of the winner of the first coursing meeting ever held of the breed, in 1925,[1] and the runner-up in 1933 and 1934, when the coursing was revived, so possibly can be excused for laying down the law. Also in a friendly trial privately arranged, I also, with my husband, was responsible for the finalists. Of these four hounds, not one had ever coursed a hare or been in official slips. They had only been hunted in couples and, just occasionally, had a slip with a handkerchief through both collars—that was all. The temperament, conformation and stamina did the rest. I might also add that all these hounds have been brought up as domestic pets, and coursing has made no difference to their behaviour towards other

---

[1]See the first page of this chapter where the first meeting is stated to have been held on November 6, 1924.

Note the crouching position and low head carriage of the leading Irish Wolfhound as he prepares to reach for his prey. This serves to slow him down and thus handicaps him as compared to a smaller dog.

Ch. Sulhamstead Match in motion. Bred and owned by Mrs. Florence Nagle and Miss Marion Clark.

Mixed field in pursuit of a hare. From left: Whippet, two Greyhounds, Ch. Keystone's Garda Siocana Doc, Ch. Keystone's Lace Curtain Irish, Saluki, Ch. Keystone's Gretchen and Keystone's Sage of Kingarrow. All Irish Wolfhounds owned and coursed by Mrs. Robert (Donna) Elzer (Keystone Kennel). Note that the hounds are single-tracking.

Marhaba of Berryfield, W.D. Ex., U.D. Ex., T.D. Ex., tracking a three-hour-old scent. Owned, trained and handled by Dr. Joan N. Milnes, England, (1977).

The three finalists in Irish Wolfhound competition at the 1977 Grand National Lure Course in Colorado. Michael John Bowen with his Ch. Sanctuary Fair Erin, F. Ch.; Janet McEwan with her Ch. Dannybrook Jason, F. Ch., Dr. Jack England with Mr. Bowen's Ch. Kilchrohane Sandra, F. Ch.

Ch. Sanctuary Fair Erin, F. Ch., released by her owner, Michael John Bowen (1977).

domestic animals; in fact, if anything, they are gentler and more tractable than those without their experience.

Mrs. Florence Nagle, who has had a long and successful career in breeding and showing Irish Wolfhounds (Sulhamstead Kennels— now associated with Killybracken Kennels) and horses, who has judged the Specialty Show of the Irish Wolfhound Club of America and whose hounds have been outstanding in coursing, has written:

> Soundness and activity have been greatly helped and encouraged by the meetings of the Irish Wolfhounds Coursing Club . . . There is no better cure for a nervous hound than a spell of coursing—I have known it to work wonders.[1]

> It takes a Wolfhound longer to get up to a hare and the hare gains a lot at turns but the Wolfhound stays on well and can sometimes run him down with his extra stamina. A Wolfhound to course hares must be fit and muscled up. Of course, the ability to go and the requisite courage come into importance in breeding for performance and a well-made hound may not have these two essential qualities and the one with faults may have them and so win on the field of battle. However, both in my hounds and setters, I inbred for certain qualities in make and shape and, most important, performance and found that my best and high-class winners all tended to have the same important physical qualities. I only bred from a few bitches that had proved they were tough and would gallop till they dropped in both breeds and, as you may know, I had world-famous winners in both breeds.[2]

Irish Wolfhounds on the run have always reminded me of lions because of their grace, power and long bounds. One gets the impression that he is watching a film in slow motion. Others evidently have had the same reaction:

> It was extremely interesting to see the different styles of running. The Whippets and Borzois ran like Greyhounds, the Wolfhounds rather like lions (maybe that is a personal feeling because the first one I saw running was red) and the Deerhounds and Salukis were entirely individual and could not be compared with either.[3]

---

[1]Florence Nagle, "A Résumé on Irish Wolfhounds," The Irish Wolfhound Club (Britain), *Year Book* (1935-1937), p. 87.

[2]*Id., Letter to the author* (March 16, 1970).

[3]Vera H. Watkins, *Our Dogs* (England). Reported in Irish Wolfhound Club of America's *Harp and Hound* (1960) XI, No. 3, p. 5.

Esther Croucher, commenting in *Dog World* on the statement that the Irish Wolfhounds reminded one of lions, described it this way, "It is a little bounding, almost doubling-up action of a sound, well-muscled wolfhound in full gallop, so often seen when we held those unforgettable meetings at Sulhamstead in between war years."[1]

I was once asked the question: "Why don't good coursing hounds do well in the breed ring?" The query carried two implications. One is that good coursing hounds have not become breed champions. The facts are that a number of breed Champions have also won coursing titles in either open field or lure coursing. For example, the first Irish Wolfhound Field Champion and the first two Coursers of Merit were Breed Champions. In the 1976 Grand National Lure Course, the three best Irish Wolfhounds were Breed Champions and one of these declared Best in Field. The second implication is that a dog that courses well is the ultimate in the breed and that any failure on his part to excel in the breed ring should be attributed to poor judging.

For the sake of argument, let us assume that an outstanding coursing Irish Wolfhound—a fictitious one, for our purpose—has been in breed competition but has not won any breed championship points. The reasons for this state of affairs could be many. The hound may have been improperly shown, not shown enough, or shown only in shows where the competition was severe, e.g. the Specialty. He may have been too young when shown, or ill or injured. There are many reasons for non-accomplishment. Possibly, however, the real reason is that some other hound, or hounds, in the breed ring more closely approached the Standard of Excellence than the courser. The owner of the courser might counter that statement by saying: "If that is the case, the Standard is wrong because my dog has proven himself in the field and this is the ultimate test." I would disagree with this rejoinder. While it is true that the Irish Wolfhound can course and catch hares, his original purpose was quite different. Irish literature gives ample proof that one of his roles was to attack men and horses in combat. I would judge that this required great strength, agility, courage and stamina rather than speed—unless the enemy was in retreat and either mounted on horseback or in a chariot. Another important aspect of the Irish Wolfhound's history is his use in the chase. Again, Irish literature teaches us that his usual quarry was deer and boar for the

---

[1]Esther Croucher, *Dog World*. As reported in The Irish Wolfhound Club of America, *Harp and Hound* (1960) XI, Nos. 3, & 4, p. 5.

reason that his owners needed food and clothing. The hunting of wolves usually occurred, not for sport, but because depredations by wolves were depleting the number of livestock. The method of hunting with Irish Wolfhounds was this. Smaller dogs, hunting by scent and accompanied by men, flushed out the prey from the forests into the open. The Irish Wolfhounds were then unleashed. Speed was needed to overtake the quarry before it reached some other woods and was lost to sight but stamina was also required.

It does not seem to me that the ideal hunting Irish Wolfhound is necessarily one that can overtake a hare on a straight run, turn rapidly when the hare does, catch up to him, reach down about three feet and pick him up while on the run. Such a hound *could be* light of bone, of small size, with hare feet, lack courage, be shy or vicious, be undershot, and have a Scottish Deerhound head. The hound would not be typical: he would be well below the Standard of Excellence and a breed judge might even well refuse to give him a ribbon. I believe that an Irish Wolfhound breed champion should be able to do well in combat against deer, boar and wolves but not necessarily in the pursuit of hares.

The Standard of Excellence calls for "great size", "power" i.e. strength and stamina, "activity" i.e. agility, and "courage."

Strength means not only powerful jaws, but also a large muscular body so as to overpower the enemy quickly or to tire him into submission. This means size. This means weight. Not fat, but muscles. The old saying is still true, "A good big man is better than a good small man."

Stamina enters into the picture if pursuit of the quarry is over a great distance. It is also essential when one prey has been killed and pursuit of another is initiated. If the hunt lasts all day and game is abundant, great endurance is required. Stamina does not involve merely ability to run for long periods. It is essential in the actual combat if the quarry is large or a fierce, agile fighter.

Agility in attacking a stag, stopping short as the animal lowers its antlers, feinting, wheeling and withdrawing if there is a counterattack. Agility in feinting towards a wolf's throat and legs, slashing and jumping away, evading the wolf's fangs which are directed at his throat and legs. Agility if there is more than one adversary.

Courage. A tired, possibly injured, hound needs courage to continue the pursuit and to maintain constant pressure on the quarry once overtaken. Courage is needed if the enemy are numerous.

It is not possible for a judge in the breed ring to be certain that he is correctly evaluating these characteristics in a hound. If this were possible, one would be able to examine visually and superficially a number of human athletes and correctly decide which one would be the fastest in a sprint, have most endurance in a distance run, and then be the strongest and most agile so as to be able to kill an opponent. If this could be done, there would not be any need of foot races, wrestling, boxing, weight lifting, etc. We are certainly not going to revert to animal combats to test certain characteristics of our hounds. The judge in the breed ring does the best he can. The hound he selects as Best of Breed may have all the desirable characteristics to the highest degree but still may lack the interest to pursue a hare or lure.

There is, in the United States, a tracking test which the American Kennel Club includes under the general title "Obedience." Strictly speaking, tracking tests should be considered a separate entity for, while they involve some degree of obedience, as does breed showing, only one command, at most, is issued. The command is "Find it!" or something of this import. A summary of the procedure follows. A strar.ger to the dog places a dark glove or wallet on the ground after having walked 440 to 500 yards and making at least two 90° turns. One half-hour to two hours later, the handler indicates to the dog the beginning of the track and orders him to find the article. The dog is on a 20 to 40 foot leash. The handler cannot approach closer to the dog than 20 feet and cannot guide him. On May 20, 1973, the first Irish Wolfhound to win a tracking degree did so at the remarkably young age of one year and two days. He was Imperial Irish Sweepstakes, owned and handled by Cathy S. Bricker. Since then other Irish Wolfhounds have qualified and are thus entitled to add the letter "T" — for "Tracking" — after their names. Miss Bricker says that her hound does not pick up the article after finding it. "He simply stands over it and looks at me as if irritated that he must stop tracking before he has found who he is looking for. He would like to bring in one of the tracklayers."

As I observed in the chapter on Obedience, it is much more difficult to win a Tracking Degree in Great Britain than it is in the United States. In this country, a dog needs to qualify only once. In Great Britain, he must qualify in both obedience and tracking in three Open Trials and in three Championship Trials. Many of the obedience tests are more difficult than the American tests. In the TD Open and Championship Trials, he must track for one-half mile (one-quarter mile or a little more in the United States); the track must be at least three hours old (one-half to two hours old in the U.S.); the dog must find two out of three articles (In the United

States, only one article must be located). Dr. Joan N. Milnes and her Marhaba of Berryfield worked together in achieving the ultimate honor: TD Ex.

Hunting

Irish literature abounds in tales of the hunting done by Irish Wolfhounds—hunting of deer primarily, then boars and wolves[1]. Deer and boar served to provide food as well as sport, whereas wolves were hunted to protect domestic animals and also for sport.

Other stories relating to Irish Wolfhound prowess in the hunting field will be told in books which I plan for future publication. Here, I shall confine myself to 20th century occurrences.

There is an idea among some owners that Irish Wolfhounds hunt by sight. This has been chiefly done by the fact that they have *wonderful* sight, but they have a *wonderful* nose also. Some time ago, while in Kenya, about six months after the puppies, Tiger II (Simba), Terry and Buller, had had distemper, and it was a hot day, we shut Tiger II (Simba) into Col. Durand's room, as he was going out into some very dense bush to cut a new road through it, a part of the country none of the hounds had ever been to before. Tiger escaped an hour later (about noon). When the sun was really hot, this hound found Colonel Durand (whom he is devoted to) about two miles away in dense bush. Colonel Durand heard some animals coming at a gallop, and got his rifle ready, expecting to be charged by a furious rhino, at least, as we have several about that part of our property, and in consequence had never before taken the dogs, and then he saw Tiger following his line. Grim (Faugh-a-Ballagh), picked up the line of a wounded impala in a ploughed field, and took the line at a gallop over the open. I was on my horse; and followed the old hound, at a good pace, too; he put the buck up in some thick bush, and Col. Durand was able to shoot the poor beast. Buller, Grim and Tiger have scores of times picked up the line of a duiker[2] in the garden, and even after the sun had been up for some time they have taken the line at a gallop into thick bush and put the animal up again, and in some cases have got him.

---

[1] Alfred W. DeQuoy, *op. cit.*, p. 83.
[2] Small African antelope.

When they are in hard condition they are very hardy. Tiger (No. 1) accompanied Col. Durand during the war and did two marches of twenty-five miles and twenty-three miles on two successive days in pelting rain, slept in snow and rain, but even so, the dog was none the worse.

During the time we were in Kenya Colony the hounds sometimes used to get on to some very thrilling line and disappear for days together. Once they (Grim, Buller and Terry) were gone for four days and four nights; right away in the lonely wild bush of Africa, and came home not a penny the worse.[1]

Colonel Durand wrote:

Though, as I said before, too much exercise with a horse is not good for Wolfhounds, I must admit I used to take two or three of them from time to time with a pony and a rifle and wander for hours over the plains—a very fine sight it is to see these hounds pick up the line of a buck, take it at a gallop for half a mile or more, and run into it in the open. There are few hounds or dogs of any breed that I know of that can hunt a line and are also fast enough to catch a buck.[2]

All dogs have some scenting capability. We have read, in the preceding chapter, how Irish Wolfhounds have followed the trail of both men and hare and in the chapter on Obedience how they have qualified for the Utility Degree which requires discernment of scent.

Mrs. Beynon gives a very interesting account of some incidents that have occurred while she and her hounds were together.

I enclose a photo of the three puppies that saved my life from lions while in Kenya Colony—where I took Bournstream Faugh-a-Ballagh and Bournstream Biddy in 1920. I walked almost into a lion, lioness and two cubs on a newly killed stag, and they were *not* pleased. I called out "Tally-Ho" to the hounds—a cry I only used when I viewed game, and they knew it well, and Bournstream Buller, Bournstream Simba (called Tiger by us), and Terry (sold to a lady in Holland), were away hunting in some bushes. Tiger heard me first, came into view, and hesitated for a moment, when up went the lion's tail, and I thought I was to be the dessert. I called Tally-Ho again, and out came Buller—he in a flash gave one roar of fury and galloped at the lion and Terry and Tiger then joined in—the lion never waited. The hounds followed the lion across the bit of open into

[1]Mary Beynon, *op. cit.*, pp. 25, 26.
[2]Durand, *op. cit.*, p. 48.

some bushes, the lioness crouched down, evidently in doubt, and I walked on. This was Xmas, 1923, 8 a.m.

I would like to have one thing especially noted by all who care to read my notes. That Buller has *light* eyes, and several old breeders who, alas, are gone from us, would agree with me. Light eyes are always the bravest, and present day shows are making a big mistake in penalising light eyes, and so helping to breed out courage. If your life depends upon the quick responding to your call for help—even to attacking a lion—if the lion won't run—I would always pick a light-eyed hound if it was to be my life which was to be so tested.

On another occasion, about fifteen years ago, I was walking across a field with a white West Highlander bitch and some Irish wolfhounds, and a bull came charging across. My old bitch (light eyes again) was the first. In a flash she sprang right up at the bull's nose, slashed and tore some part of his face, and turned him, and then, of course, the *next* second the others joined in.

It is very important to understand the *method* of an Irish Wolfhound's fighting. It is jump in, slash, and jump out. Instance Buller, Tiger and Grim (Faugh-a-Ballagh), were out riding (while in Kenya) with me, when we met a wart hog—this was the one enemy I had always dreaded during our lonely rides or walks over the Kenya plains. The hounds showed the most wonderful agility as the hog charged. They waited till he was almost into them, then they jumped, and as he passed, they were round, slash, slash, and away. The pig turned in a flash and charged again and again and each time he never even touched one of the three hounds. They tore him absolutely to pieces. The Irish Wolfhound does not by nature hold on, and he is not good at catching small things, though after a thing is killed he likes to eat it and not give it up.[1]

One should not conclude from this story, as some people have, that the Irish Wolfhound has been used to hunt lions. While one must admire the courage and intrepidity of Mrs. Beynon's hounds, I would consider it foolhardy to risk the lives of Irish Wolfhounds in the pursuit of, as opposed to defense against, lions. I know of no scientific basis for Mrs. Beynon's assertion that light-eyed Irish Wolfhounds are braver than dark-eyed ones and, empirically, Mrs. Beynon's experiences have been entirely too limited to come justifiably to this conclusion. I must say, however, that the only hound which I have owned that was fury incarnate, fast and fearless

---

[1]Mary Beynon, *op. cit.*, pp. 26, 27.

Ch. Feasgar Bruadar of Ballylyke, U.D., with a stuffed Wyoming wolf (1957). Note three-inch spikes in wolf's feet.

Fraud!

when provoked, was Ballykelly Charlie Girl ("Rebel"), a light-eyed bitch.

Now let us go to another continent.

IRISH WOLFHOUNDS IN AUSTRALIA[1]

by

Ronald K. Monro

To overtake, pull down and hold at bay a huge Sambhur stag in rough mountainous country without the aid of any other dogs, is truly a wonderful feat of speed, strength and endurance. This is only one of the many notable achievements of "Thunder of Killara" an Australia born Irish Wolfhound, bred by Miss Bruce Reid at her kennels at Bundoora, Victoria, Australia.

Four and a half years ago I was undecided as to which breed of dog to purchase to accompany me on my hunting trips and that would also be a real pal for a bachelor who spent a great deal of leisure time away off the beaten tracks. It was not so much a gun dog that I needed as a hunter, and one that would be heavy enough to negotiate rough country. After much reading of doggy books, and talking with breeders and dog lovers generally, I finally decided on the Irish Wolfhound as being the most suitable for my particular requirements. I have never regretted the choice as Thunder has more than fulfilled my wildest expectations. Now rising five years he is a perfectly developed upstanding dog with a kindly quiet nature, wonderfully intelligent and obedient, and above all a dashing hunter and a real killer.

When I brought him home he was just four months old, a loose-limbed straw colored pup, very shy and just his kennel manners. I started right in to train him very gently and rewarded his efforts with a biscuit or two. He quickly became a well educated dog, obeying my every wish conveyed by word, whistle or sign, every command just being spoken loud enough for him to hear. He was still rather shy in the presence of strangers so I used to take him out on a lead and walk him among as many as convenient, and in this way he got used to them when in public places, but was still a very good watch-dog at home.

I started him off hunting rabbits and he took naturally to the job. He made his first catch at night by the aid of my car headlights. Now, as he drives along the country roads at night, taking up the

---

[1]Ronald K. Monro, *op. cit.*, pp. 90-92.

whole of the back seat, he keeps a sharp lookout for game of all kinds, and when let out seldom fails to catch it. He is a splendid jumper and even at night will take five foot wire fences in his stride. His sight at night seems particulary good. In the day time when I shoot rabbits or hares from the car, I just let him out and he jumps over the fences and brings them back to me.

From rabbits I took him out after wallabies with a pack of other mixed dogs. I can well remember the first one that he saw caught. He just peeped into the sprawling dogs and watched from a safe distance, he was just seven months old then. Now he just picks up the biggest wallaby and kills it as easily as a terrier does a rat. He soon learned the idea of wallaby and kangaroo hunting together with dingoes and foxes. He not only runs by sight but has a wonderful nose and will run a kangaroo for miles on scent until he catches sight of it and then he soon has it thrown to earth.

Early in his career he was ripped by a 'roo, now he is very careful and never rushes into an old man kangaroo that is bailed up and ready to fight for his life. He quickly circles him, then rushing in from behind, grabs him by the butt of the tail and after breaking it kills by either throat or heart grip, continually pulling away from the terrible and death-dealing blows from the powerful hind legs. When Thunder was three and half years old I took him into the hills deer hunting. After he had seen one caught and pulled down by a pack of fox hounds, he soon learnt that the big deer were even better game than the old men kangaroos. The country in which the big Sambhur deer live in Australia, is very mountainous and is covered with a dense undergrowth which is almost impossible to penetrate. Foxhounds are used for trailing the deer in this class of country, then when a moderately clear section is reached such as a river flat, Thunder then joins in the chase and soon has the huge stag at bay in the river bed or pulled down in some thicket. Once last year when being led to a likely spot by my brother (he will not leave me to follow anyone else) a big stag broke cover and Thunder pulled away with six feet of rope tied to his collar. Notwithstanding the handicap this rope must have been in the timber and undergrowth, he pulled him down three times and brought him to bay (where he was shot) within five hundred yards of the starting point.

The stag was found to have broken off one of its huge antlers when either charging at Thunder, or when striking the earth when pulled down by him. So thick was some of the country through which they had run that the antler could not be found, and so a fine trophy was spoilt. Thunder is a very good natured dog and never starts any fights, but when he catches any game, or is with me when I shoot any he will not allow another dog near his property. He will not let a stranger near me if I am in the bush either sitting or lying down, but as soon as I get on my feet will then let them approach.

I can honestly say that he is a really wonderful pal always by my side (he is at my feet as I write this) ready for a game or serious hunting or a quiet rest, and understanding all I say to him. He is a thorough gentleman both at home and abroad, and above all a brilliant and natural hunter.

Speaking of Irish Wolfhounds in Australia, Miss Phyllis Gardner wrote:

I have a letter from Mr. Corfield, who tells of one who was the only dog, out of a mixed or "bobbery" pack, that dared stand up to the Old Man Kangaroo, and, though badly slashed, held on till Mr. Corfield ended the matter with a bullet through the Old Man's head.[1]

Señor Agustin Nores Martinez, the ambassador from Argentina to Canada, implies that he used a ten-year old hound to hunt boar. This would be quite unfair to the hound.

In my country, Argentina, I had one of those beautiful, useful and faithful dogs. After ten years in my possession, I lost it while on a wild boar hunting trip and now I wish to get another for hunting and as a companion to my children, the best friend I think I could get for them.

I am very fond of dogs, and for many years and even now, am a member of the Commission of the Kennel Club Argentine of Buenos Aires. I have acted as judge in many shows held in Argentina and other South American countries, exhibiting hounds and working dogs.[2]

Here is one brief account of the Irish Wolfhound's hunting activities in Canada.

A good many years later, when farming in Western Canada, I saw the Irish Wolfhound at his best. Hunting the fast and wily Prairie Wolf (or coyote) on the open prairies is great sport, but one must have the right type of hound to deal with these animals. He must be fast to get on terms with the wolf—and strong to make a quick kill, otherwise he will get badly cut up, as it is nothing unusual to bag four or five wolves in a day, and they are all scrappers.

---

[1]Phyllis Gardner, "The True Successor," The Irish Wolfhound Club (Britain), *Year Book* (1930-1932), p. 95.

[2]Agustin Nores Martinez, *Harp and Hound* (1950) I, No. 3, pp. 9, 10.

I am not advocating the deerhound type, as they are too light, particularly when it comes to a scrap with a timber wolf, which happens every now and then, and the heavy, thickset hound, so much in favor by some judges, I found to be much too slow. If the Irish Wolfhound grabs on the run the hold is usually behind the shoulder, then hound and wolf roll over and over. If the coyote turns at bay, as they often do, the hound charges right in and bowls him over. In either case the struggle doesn't last very long when a couple of big rangy hounds are used.[1]

The reference to the "wolf" being seized by the Irish Wolfhound "behind the shoulder", I believe must be to the "Prairie Wolf (or coyote)." This is a much smaller animal than the timber wolf who would be seized by the neck. The weight of the coyote varies from 18 to 30 pounds, his height from 18 to 22 inches; his length is about 36 inches exclusive of a 12 to 15 inch tail. He ranges from Alaska to Guatemala.[2] Lyon says:

> Size for size, the coyote is perhaps the greatest trotter among wild animals even though the fox is a skillful performer. The coyote has been known to cruise between 15 and 20 miles within an hour, using the trot exclusively.[3]

In North America, wolves may be found from the Arctic to Mexico. They do not exist in South America.[4] The name Timber Wolf is applied to the wolves of eastern and northern North America. They are larger than those from other regions, reaching a length of 54 inches, exclusive of a 12 inch tail, and a weight of 100 pounds.[5] Young and Goldman say that the height and weight of wolves, even in fully matured animals, vary considerably. They give the range in measurements of gray wolves as from 25 to 38 inches in height and from 60 to 175 pounds in weight. The latter weight would be that of the largest wolves in Alaska and the McKenzie River district of Canada. Weights of other fully matured wolves reported to Young and Goldman are given on the following page.[6]

---

[1]M. J. Hogan, "I Wonder . . .," Irish Wolfhound Club of America, *Annual Reports* (March 1930-Jan. 1932), p. 48.

[2]"Coyote," *Encyclopaedia Britannica* (1955), VI, p. 626.

[3]Lyon, *The Dog in Action* (1963), p. 47.

[4]"Wolf," *Encyclopaedia Britannica* (1955), XXIII, p. 695.

[5]"Timber Wolf," *ibid.*, XXII, p. 222.

[6]Stanley P. Young and Edward A. Goldman, *The Wolves of North America* (1944), pp. 69-72.

Height and Weight of Wolves
Reported to Young and Goldman

Habitat	Description	Height (in.)	Weight (lb.)	Length[1]	Tail length
Alaska	Black male	38	135	5' 9"	
	Gray male	37	125	5' 9"	
	Female	29¾	64	5' 6½"	18"
	Other Grays	From 25	157, 175, 60 and up		
Northwest Canada	Male		101	5' 7½"	20½"
Colorado			125		
Wisconsin	Male	33	100	5' 10"	
Minnesota	Male		96	5' ½"	12½"
	Male		85	5' 1"	17"
	Male		80	5' ½"	17½"
	Male		77	5' 2"	17"
	Male		76	5' 6"	17"
	Male		75	5' ½"	16½"
	Male		74	5' ½"	16½"
	Male		58	4' 11½"	17"
	Female		68	4' 11"	17"
Washington			86		
Vermont			90-100[2]		
Arizona			98		
Arkansas	Black male			4' 10½"	
	Black female			3' 6¾"	
	Others		45-64		
Texas	Red male	21¼	50	4' 4¼"	14½"
Greenland			45-64		

Note that in the preceding table, the measurements reported to Young and Goldman exceed in many cases those which the *Encyclopaedia Britannica* attributes to the largest of wolves, the Timber Wolf: 100 pounds, 66 inches long, including 12 inch tail. Weights are easily ascertained and, therefore, can generally be accepted as correct. There are two possibilities which might militate against exactness: The wolf may have eaten a huge meal prior to his measurement after death or the hunter may have exaggerated the weight to emphasize the importance of his kill. As for the height

---

[1]Includes tail.
[2]Middle of 19th Century.

measurements, I question them. *Rigor mortis* sets in from about four to six hours after death. Once it does, accurate height measurements cannot be taken from the body. Before it does, measurements may vary considerably depending on the methods used. I think it is fair to expect that height measurements given by hunters who are not scientists will err on the high side. This conjecture is corroborated by comparing heights and weights of Irish Wolfhounds with the reported measurements of wolves.

	Wolf			Irish Wolfhound
Habitat	Description	Weight (lb.)	Height (in.)	Mean Height (in.) Corresponding to Wolf's Weight
Alaska	Black male	135	38	33¼ at 1 to 2 years of age (35¾ max.)
	Gray male	125	37	32½ at 9 months of age (33½ max.)
	Female	64	29¾	24¼ at 4½ months of age (27 max.)
Wisconsin	Male	100	33	29¾ at 6½ months of age (31¼ max.)
Texas	Red male	50	21¼	21½ at 3 months of age (22 max.)

It may be that the weight of wolves is indeed much less than that of Irish Wolfhounds in proportion to height. This is a subject deserving of much study and it will be analysed—with much more data—in a forthcoming book.

Young and Goldman say that a wolf has been clocked at 28 miles per hour for 200 yards, that the wolf can run about 22 to 24 miles per hour for a mile or two and that his speed would then be reduced to about 12 miles per hour. "The hunting technique of wolves is based on the exhaustion of their prey. Their greater endurance over that of most, if not all, of the big game animals, is one of their main assets in overcoming prey."[1]

I have had no experience in hunting with Irish Wolfhounds and therefore the following observations are strictly conjectural. I should think that if it were desired to hunt wolves with Irish Wolfhounds, one would have to start training them on less dangerous game or put them in with an experienced pack of dogs. Too much should not be expected of a young dog. Because of his great size, people are apt to overlook his youth and inexperience. To test the reactions of my first Irish Wolfhound, I arranged with the United States National Museum (commonly known as the Smithsonian Institution) for a stuffed Wyoming wolf to be set up near its building as I approached around the corner with Gamine

---

[1]Young and Goldman, *op. cit.*, pp. 74, 75.

(Ch. Feasgar Bruadar of Ballylyke, U.D.) on leash. Gamine was exactly one year old, stood 32½ inches at the shoulder and weighed 123 pounds. At sight of the wolf, she stopped, then advanced gingerly. Without being led, she cautiously circled the wolf, sniffed tentatively, and then relaxed completely. Please note from the pictures that the wolf stands on three-inch spikes, so that the difference in height is greater that at first apparent.

Another of my hounds, Rebel (Ch. Ballykelly Charlie Girl, C.D.) had an entirely different temperament than Gamine. The latter was imperial, gentle. The former bold, even in her affection. One evening, my wife had her on leash in Washington, D.C. As they arrived near the Alaska Air Lines office, Rebel saw in the window a huge Polar Bear standing about ten feet tall on its hind legs. She let out a roar and bared her teeth as she stood braced for the expected encounter. It was with some difficulty that my wife pulled her away.

Mr. William Mahood, Prince George, British Columbia, Canada, gives a very interesting account of his dogs' experiences and reactions in hunting coyote and jack rabbits. His letter was in reply to my numerous questions.

> At the time of these incidents, I had four Irish Wolfhounds: Canadian Champion Fenton of Eaglescrag (2 years old and known as "Simon"), Champion Sabre of Norwolf (over 1 year of age), and two yearling bitches, Ardess of Eagle whom I call "Tara", and Molly, Simon's daughter. At the very beginning of the hunt Fenton was challenged by Sabre. Fenton dumped Sabre by the neck. Sabre showed submissiveness so Fenton let it stop. We were hunting in Northern Saskatchewan. There were some fences and these proved to be a problem. The fences were 3 strand wire and were run through patches of brush. There were 3 men and the dogs. The method was we asked all over the area for sightings of jacks and of coyote. We would then go to this area far out about 100 yds. apart and walk hoping to jump jacks or coyotes from the small bluffs or patches of brush. This took place in December. The first jack we jumped was a dandy. Incidentally Sabre and Tara were wondering what the hell was going on. Fenton walked with his head high very alert. Sabre varied from worrying about Tara to wondering what was happening. The first jack was after literally walking miles. We were as startled as the rabbit. Before we had the dogs loosed the rabbit had a 30 yd. start and was leaving the country. Simon saw him and was after him. Sabre and Tara saw Simon and were gone after him. Can't say if Sabre or Tara ever did see that jack. The chase was straight away for 1½ miles (a guess). We were running but were still far behind the dogs. Simon had closed on the jack and was holding about 10 yds. behind when they hit a fence. Simon stopped and

went along it. Sabre plowed into it. The jack disappeared. The hounds quit the chase relatively easily after they lost sight. A red bone[1] running with them messed around for an hour before he quit. *None* of the Irish used their noses very much. Simon was faster but not that much faster considering he was a two year old. He carried himself with surety and poise which the young dogs did not have. After the first challenge of Sabre's there was no question which dog was the boss.

The next day we were driving and spotted a fox in the middle of a huge field. The fox was a mile or so from the nearest bush. We stopped and all four dogs were loosed. Simon and Red spotted him and left. Tara and Sabre followed but I don't know if they saw the fox or not. The fox opened up for the bush but the dogs had him very quickly. Simon was first there and overshot him. Then all you could see was dogs. Each dog had a hold and the fox was dead. The trail hound Red was difficult to make let go. The IWs weren't. They lose interest quickly when the prey is dead. I would say in this and in all subsequent kills I have seen that a bitch is a more aggressive natural killer than a dog in IWs. Last year in February I hunted Sabre, Tara and a white Malamute. We put up one coyote in a large plains area west of Williams Lake. The country was quite flat and no fence. We jumped a coyote out of a small brush in a dip in the landscape. All the dogs saw him at the same time. He had perhaps a 100 yd. start. They caught him in the bottom of the next dip perhaps 500 yds. away. Sabre grabbed him across the shoulders as he swung alongside of him. He drove the coyote into the ground and then threw him sidewise. At that point all the dogs had a hold. The coyote's back was broken and every rib was broken. This was about a 27 lb. bitch coyote. The fox referred to earlier weighed perhaps 20 lbs. The kills I have seen were by breaking the back by grabbing and thrusting the back down. Molly weighs about 125 lbs. She plays with a shepherd male 88 lbs., one year old. He runs from her. She catches him, forces his throat to the ground so fast and hard that his rear end goes over his head and he is stretched right out flat on the ground. At this point if he were a coyote all the dogs would have a piece of him.

I have never hunted a single dog except once and that was with Simon in fairly thick timber. We jumped either a moose or a deer. Simon got a glimpse of it and I didn't. He chased and of course almost immediately lost sight. He would run four or five paces and then leap straight up to look about, come down and repeat this. His leaps without exaggeration would put his feet 5 feet off

---

[1] A hound.

the ground. A really astounding thing to observe. The man I was with who has bred Newfoundlands all his life remarked the sight staggered him.

A point perhaps worthy of mention on the negative side. These dogs that I have observed have little peripheral vision and not very well developed ears or nose. I have had Simon in a river boat at the bow with two trail hounds. The trail hounds had body-scented a moose and were excited and trying to pin point it with their eyes. We were drifting without motor. In a hundred feet or so the trail hounds had the moose located and were raising hell. Simon never did figure out what all the commotion was about.

I would say young Irish Wolfhounds have to get the idea they are watching for something. The chasing is natural. The killing happens after they get nipped. The watching is where they must learn. There is a large hill behind the kennels at my farm. Both my bitches when free go up to almost the top of the hill and sit there by the hour watching. They both bring back muskrats and brush rabbits. The dogs don't do this.

Coyotes are very vicious animals when cornered. If they stopped running and turned to fight they would certainly get a few good licks in before they died. Especially with inexperienced dogs. Usually they are caught in full stride and as a result die quickly. A 35 lb. dog coyote could give an 80 lb. German shepherd a licking. They will fight in packs or pairs so against a single dog would be a most formidable foe. Coyotes have relatively small teeth. They slash. They could easily lay open ears and noses and eyes. Never measured the height of a coyote. Would guess between 18″ and 22″.

Our brush rabbits are very small compared to a jack who can weigh 15-16 lbs. and run 40 m.p.h. or better. The wolves in this area would range males 30″-36″, 90-130 lbs.—bitches 24″-28″, 75 lbs.-105 lbs. Have heard of the exceptional wolf weighing 150 lbs. All of the recorded measurements taken show only one or two over 150 lbs. and they would have 20 lbs of fresh kill in them. The largest I have ever read of being recorded was 175 lbs. Don't know how high but probably 3′ or better. They have long legs, tremendously large feet and heads. An average size wolf, say 105 lbs., leaves a track in snow far larger than my largest Irish Wolfhound. The average wolf head mount would make you feel they were much larger than they are. I'm speaking of our Canadian timber wolf. Prairie brush wolves are a much smaller sub species.

In bad snow conditions, a wolf must rest every 100 yards. I know Irish Wolfhounds trained and conditioned can run 8-10 miles at up to 15 m.p.h. because I have run mine at this distance. I also know that a full grown male and female wolf running on lake ice at full speed for 2 miles is almost at the collapse state from having chased them by plane.

I'm reasonably certain if Sabre chased a male wolf for 2 miles and on lake ice and then caught him he might get some lumps but he would kill him. If however the wolf did not run to near exhaustion but fought almost immediately I would be very worried about losing a dog even though the dog outweighs the wolf by 40-50 lbs. Wolves fight to survive from the moment they are born. Our dogs by comparison even when conditioned well are quite pampered. An Irish Wolfhound running at full speed? I don't know. Not very far at over 30 m.p.h. At 20-25 m.p.h. chasing something 3-4 miles. The youngest Irish Wolfhound I've hunted with is Molly at 1 year, only on rabbit though. She has never seen coyote or fox. I run my hounds behind a truck. Sabre will stay with the truck regardless of the speed I drive if he can. Barney and Tara run about 12-15 m.p.h. and if I burst up to 25 they just carry on at their own speed. They know where I am. Same thing behind a Skidoo.[1] Sabre will stay with me. Tara and Barney only expend themselves when they are actually chasing something so it is very difficult to judge their speeds. The dogs are run for around an hour each day at speeds varying from 8 m.p.h. to a maximum of 35 m.p.h.

I've never chased more than one coyote so don't know what the dogs would do if the coyotes split up. All the wolves I have observed in February and March are usually in groups of 2 or more up to 5 or 6. I really don't know what to expect if the 4 dogs set up after 3 wolves that go in three different directions. I *hope* they will stay together on a single wolf.[2]

In February, 1971, Mr. Mahood took five Irish Wolfhounds into the Great Beaver Lake area. He and two friends traveled by Skidoo. The hounds followed and "covered thirty-five miles in hock-deep snow and on a shale type of crust which cut all the dogs badly."[3]

In the 20th century, Irish Wolfhounds have been used in the United States on wolves, coyotes, bears, wild cats and hare. Here is one account of the experiences of two Irish Wolfhounds without hunting experience, who were brought into Montana to destroy predators.

We tried practically every known method to keep this pirate

---

[1]A snowmobile.

[2]William Mahood, *Letter to author* (January 28, 1971).

[3]*Id., Letter to author* (August 16, 1971).

[coyote] under control, including poison, traps, high-powered rifles, and hounds of nearly all kinds. Yet he continued to more than hold his own.

Then someone suggested the Irish Wolfhound. It was just an idea, and having tried so many other reputedly fast, clever, courageous, and strong hounds, we did not really expect that the Irish variety could do much better. . . .

Turning the dogs loose we broke cover and started down the mountain on a high lope. The coyotes knew danger was near and started across the flat the instant we were in sight. But the ever-alert wolfdogs had spotted their quarry at the same moment and were off at a mad pace. Their long hind legs reached out far ahead of their front ones in frantic efforts to push still more ground behind them, their backs bowing like barrel hoops. And turning into gray streaks, those coyotes fairly flew in hectic retreat.

Having followed some kind of hounds most of their lives, our horses joined in the fun and the race was on in earnest. We tore down that steep mountainside and each time these ponies struck ground they raised a cloud of loose gravel, and bits of bunch grass flew through the air. . . .

The coyotes split up, one going around a small knoll while the other kept straight ahead. The pack, consisting of one Irish Wolfhound and our various other hounds, continued on the straight line, but Silver Tip climbed right over the knoll. . . .

The chase was nearing its end now, the long legs of the hounds having proved too much for the coyote. Right here it might be mentioned that the Irish Wolfhound had been setting a fast pace in this scramble, and the Russian, the staghound, the greyhound, and one of half mixture of grey and Irish, were tagging right along.

Before that coyote knew what was happening, a pair of gaping jaws were flashing at his side. But as the prairie wolf is much smaller and quicker than a wolfhound, he easily dodged and left the dog a dozen feet to one side. Doing this, however, took a little precious time, and our Russian ran right over the top of him. Too slow in regaining his feet, the coyote was surrounded by four big dogs. Each one got a mouthful of coyote and they stretched him out. Two had fastened into his throat. The fight looked like a tangle of heads and tails and feet, all flying around a circle at once. . . .

Silver had not turned up, so we set out over the hills to locate the trouble. Finally we discovered that the big dog had run the coyote up a dry creek bed until they came to a cut bank on three sides. Here the wolfhound cornered him and they fought it out.

Knowing he was done for, the coyote had locked jaws with the hound. There they were when we found them, the fangs of each locked in the other's jaw. And the big dog, not being able to shake loose this 65-pound coyote, had tussled around until exhausted.

Many pools of blood lay in the snow, and at first glance it looked as if both the dog and the coyote had done for each other. Then the other wolfhound dashed in, clamped his teeth over the entire head of the coyote and exerted such great pressure that the jaws fell apart and the now lifeless coyote dropped limp in the snow. Although cut up pretty badly, Silver was soon on his feet and by taking it slowly, finally managed to get back to the ranch.

Since that time we have added to our collection of Irish Wolfhounds and do not take them out on a big hunt until they are trained. It takes several years and a hundred chases to develop the eyesight of a hound so that he can spot his game instantly. In general, to be a good hunter a dog should be raised on the range. Then all his faculties develop together. He gets sound, tough feet, better wind and keen eyesight. Usually we use an older dog to train the puppies, for otherwise it takes a much longer time, and a puppy which is whipped is sometimes ruined. Really, training a good wolfhound is an art in itself.

We have discovered that the Irish Wolfhound excels in three ways —grit, ambition and intelligence. He is not a fighting fool. He is not as lazy as most hounds, and he tries to "savvy" things so that naturally he learns more. The gameness and willingness of the Irish Wolfhound was demonstrated very well in an exciting bear hunt we had here some little time ago.

Several years ago a large brown bear developed a dining-car appetite for fat lambs. Each spring, when the sheep were camped in a certain canyon on Pine Mountains, fresh lamb chops were the mainstay of mother-bear's table.

The late May snow storm furnished an excellent tracking snow, and in a few minutes the Irish Wolfhounds were hard after mamma bear and her two cubs. As the big dogs closed in, the bear family took to a fir tree. Getting a glimpse of me as I came through the timber, the old bear jumped out of the tree and ran for the mountain top.

Like great gray flashes the wolfhounds tore after her and soon forced her up another tree. Five times as I approached, she would leap far out over the circle of baying hounds and gallop through the timber. Just as she was about to reach another climbable fir tree, Blue Boy, the leader and fleetest dog of the pack, made one vicious leap and fastened his teeth in her hind leg.

She wheeled to cuff him loose, but Spottie, a powerful hound weighing well over 100 pounds, hurtled through the air and secured a hold on the scruff of her neck. The weight and momentum of the big dog overbalanced the brown bear.

Over and over they went, down the steep hillside, enveloped in a cloud of snow. As she reared up, turning to bite Spottie, Blue Boy fastened on to one of her big ears. The other dogs all tried to get a mouthful of bear at the same time, joining the mass of heads and tails and snarls and growls, tumbling down into the canyon floor while dog hair and bear fur floated in the air above the bloody, snowy trail.

Breaking away from the dogs, the bear made her last stand on top of a fallen log while, though torn and bleeding, the circle of dogs darted in and out. Claws and fangs flashed and tore. A bullet ended the fight. . . .

Perhaps I may seem a bit too enthusiastic about the Irish Wolfhound, but it would be impossible to live with these dogs and see what they can do without becoming almost rabid upon the subject of their excellence. They have speed and fighting ability and sense in unstinted degree, but aside from all that they are sturdy, companionable creatures that can stand upon their own feet and do more than their share of any work necessary and which is within the ability of an animal. Their value in our business is inestimable.

Something of this was discovered when we trapped pine marten or sable—America's rarest and most beautiful fur animal—alive for foundation purposes on our fur farm. This animal usually lives high, very high, in the mountains. Naturally their habitat is some distance from the ranch and that makes it necessary to take with us anything needed on the trip. So we packed our Irish Wolfhounds over the high Rockies and these big dogs scrambled around the slide rock cliffs and boulders with an agility second only to that of a wildcat.

We reached a height of more than 13,000 feet at the summit, traversing Sky-Top Creek and over the granite peaks. Yet this climb was a weightcarrying feat, especially for the dogs. Each hound was loaded with two box traps and some bait, which often totalled 40 pounds. Yet I saw Silver jump a 12-foot span across a roaring mountain stream. The heavy pack came down so hard that it completely overbalanced the dog when he landed. But he did not let out a whimper, for these big dogs are game. We have not tried the Irish Wolfhounds as a sled dog, but we have packed the breed everywhere. Also the breed does not mind the cold, as was demonstrated one day last winter, when, with the thermometer standing at 60 below zero, we hauled hay to the stock. The Irish Wolfhounds were with us and they romped and played tag in the snow. Some day it is my intention to mush into the sacred circle of huskies and malamutes, my sled trailing behind six long-geared [sic], gaunt, hardened, galloping dogs of the Range Land, each standing nearly three feet high at the shoulder. And we will pit our muscles, our grit, and our endurance against those trail eaters of the North Land.

If the gods of fortune give us an even break, I will miss my guess if those fighting Irishmen do not flash past their opponents and on to the trail end, far, far in the lead. For truly the Irish Wolfhound is a he-dog and the best of pals.[1]

It has been claimed that an Irish Wolfhound killed a grizzly bear![2] Was it a month-old cub? Lacking any details on this exploit, I would entirely disregard it.

Alex Scott, manager of Amelia White's kennels in Santa Fe, New Mexico, relates how an 18-months old hound was attacked by seven dogs of mixed breed which had been running wild and killing cattle and horses. The hound killed four of the dogs and routed the remainder.[3] The Irish Wolfhounds in this kennel were used on coyotes.[4]

Frank A. Kelley III's Rathrahilly McGilligan killed many coyotes in Kansas.[5]

Mr. Peter Parnall wrote me[6] that his Ballykelly Ballyfinan was hunted at least twice a month and that in the previous couple of months this hound "killed three 'coy-dogs', the smallest of which was 79 pounds. Once the animals were tracked and sighted he caught and killed them quite handily." Two weeks later, Finnigan killed a fifty-pound animal near Woodstock, New York, which "could've been a coyote."[7]

Helenette Silver, Game Biologist, Fish and Game Department, New Hampshire, who has also written *History of New Hampshire Game,* informed me[8] that there are no coydogs in that State but that there are some in New York. "While dog x coyote breeding is

---

[1]Warren A. Depuy, "Where Dogs Still Guard the Herds," The Irish Wolfhound Club (Britain), *Year Book* (1930-1932), pp. 75-84.

[2]Alma Starbuck, *The Complete Irish Wolfhound* (1965), p. 133.

[3]L. O. Starbuck, "Retrospection," The Irish Wolfhound Club of America, *Annual Reports* (1932-1934), p. 56.

[4]Florsheim, *op. cit.*, p. 49.

[5]The Irish Wolfhound Club of America, *Harp and Hound* (1960) Vol. XI, No. 1, p. 3.

[6]Peter Parnall, *Letter to author* (January 14, 1962).

[7]*Id.* (January 28, 1962).

[8]Helenette Silver. *Letter to author* (February 24, 1962).

possible, we feel that the chances of its occurring in the wild are remote. Our animals may be coydogs, but there is not one iota of proof. Physically there is no resemblance to the domestic dog except for very general canine characteristics, and the pattern of sexual maturity does not appear to be right. . . Superficially, these beasts resemble the Canadian brush wolf more than anything, but skulls are wrong."

Some time ago I received a letter from a gentleman who wanted to buy a Wolfhound for the purpose of hunting wolves in the North. In my response, I said:

> I can appreciate why you would want to have an Irish Wolfhound for protection against wolves but I personally would not want to risk injury to him, or his possible death, to say nothing of the financial investment, by urging him to seek out and destroy wolves. It is unlikely that he would be able to avoid being bitten. He would, at least, suffer pain. To what purpose? Amusement for the hunter. I am also personally opposed to the destruction of wild life unless such a drastic measure is required. I regret that I cannot sell you an Irish Wolfhound.

Here is one authenticated account given by Mr. Robert E. Francis of a wolf being killed by an Irish Wolfhound.

> We were in a forest located in the western foothills of the Pacific Coast Range. No camping, hunting, etc., is allowed there and we were hunting fossils in an old rock quarry with no thought of contact with any wildlife although it is abundant there.

> The confrontation occurred on March 28, 1971, at about 1:30 p.m. There were two dogs with us that came along for the ride rather than for chasing game. My male Irish Wolfhound, Clancy (Aran of Killeen) who was almost four years old, and his best buddy, a small mongrel that also belongs to me, were doing a pretty thorough job of canvassing the countryside. We spotted a large animal about 200 yds. ahead that I thought to be a German Shepherd. Clancy began to act strangely and was very excited. The little mongrel did not react at all and never showed any interest in anything that followed, even though he has keen senses. Clancy has been a terrific coyote hunter and though he has killed them on sight, has never fought with or even threatened another dog, so I let him go and he was off and after the large Shepherd to play, I assumed. The wolf could not retreat due to the cliffs and had to come out or be trapped by Clancy. It appeared to us as if the two were running to meet each other. Then the wolf retreated and at the instant he turned to come at bay, Clancy hit him and they both rolled over. The wolf was up in an instant and instead of coming to bay again, took off in another direction. This was the moment

that it occurred to us that we weren't watching two dogs at play. The first contact could have been mistaken as such, but we had a good view of the chase since they cut directly in front of us. I would say that it took only about 100 yds. for Clancy to catch him and it all ended with Clancy grabbing him right behind the ears, and another roll with only Clancy getting up. I was ready to stop the chase for a moment but was so fascinated that I refrained, but I doubt that I could have stopped it in time. Fortunately, I got a good look at the victim before I punished my dog for fighting and decided that he deserved praise rather than punishment for the feat. Clancy seemed to know that he had done something to be proud of and, believe me, it showed all over him. I was not sure at the time that it was a true wolf, but knew that whatever it was, it was obviously wild. Clancy was unmarked and not really tired. He has a slight limp in his right front leg, but not enough of a strain to hamper any activity. The amazing thing about it was that the wolf, who was very much dead, was unmarked with the exception of a few teeth marks on the back of his neck. It was interesting to note how more agile Clancy was over the rough terrain than the wolf, and much faster. A wolf is not as fast as he is maneuverable, and Clancy began his hunting career chasing jack-rabbits and knows how to move. I would say that a coyote is much harder to catch than a wolf and much quicker at close quarters. Clancy has always grabbed coyotes by the back and this is the first time to my knowledge that he has gone for the neck of an opponent. Maybe it was good judgment or maybe luck, but I know that he would have been in serious trouble had he grabbed this wolf by the back. Whether it was accident, instinct, or judgment, the grab was quick and effective. I had the taxidermist give me an autopsy report on how the wolf died and if in fact it was a wolf at all. It was verified by the taxidermist that it was a mature Timber Wolf, about five years old, wild not a pet, male, and died from a broken neck. He was at least 28" high at the withers and weighed 118 to 125 lbs. The exact weight was not possible due to the dehydration of the carcass when I brought it in the next day. I didn't exactly make any points by bringing in a whole carcass, but have never skinned an animal in my life and I don't care to learn now. Anyway, I had it made into a rug and it is a very impressive trophy if you like that sort of thing.

I have been asked by the Oregon State Fish and Game Commission not to reveal the exact location since the Timber Wolf is a protected species and I suspect that we may possibly have wandered into the result of some state predator stocking program, but they won't admit it. They don't want armies of gun-happy hunters going in there. The state asked me to refer to the locale as merely Northwest Oregon and no more. I would appreciate your confidence also, but on the return I plan to be

Aran of Kileen (Clancy), the wolf he killed, and Doria Francis, ten-year old daughter of Robert E. Francis (1972).

Ch. Sabre of Norwolf, owned by William Mahood (1970) (Norwolf Kennel — Canada).

equipped with camera equipment so that if it happens again I can record it.

Clancy is 34 1/16 inches tall and weighs 164 pounds. He is a great jumper and has tremendous spring in his rear legs. Without the previous experience and conditioning he has had, he would never have been able to destroy the wolf in the mere 30 or so seconds it all lasted. He now has 12 points towards the 15 needed for his championship and needs one major win to finish. Here are a few notes which may be of interest to you:

1. Clancy will only attack an opponent to his right. He may make a pass to his left, but all physical contact is from his right side.

2. He will run a female coyote, but will only actually attack a male.

3. He will not chase anything without permission except cats, but he has never harmed one.

4. After he has made a kill, he is quite oblivious to the victim. There are no signs of possessiveness and he is very calm. He will not play with the carcass, maul it, or even try to chase other dogs from it.

5. He is easy to control and will halt pursuit if called off.

6. He has spent many hours running rabbits and will not kill one.

7. There has never been any training for hunting, and he killed the first coyote he ever had seen with as much ease as the last one he killed.

8. He does not waste any moves at all and is very serious and aggressive while on the attack. It all appears as if he is doing something he has to do. If he finds coursing fun, I have seen no evidence of it, but then again he willingly chases anything or everything in sight without being forced to do so, but it's serious business and not fun.

9. He is fearless on the attack and will not give any ground. He is always on offense and has yet to make a defensive move. He is very confident.

10. The speed and agility of a dog the size of an Irish Wolfhound is unbelievable, and can only really be truly seen when he is in relentless pursuit of something that he is going to kill. I have seen what one can do in his ancient role and the modern Irish Wolfhound is no slouch. I couldn't believe that the fast animal that I was watching

was my dog, the first time I watched him do some serious running.

11. My hound will tend to overexert if he is not in top shape. There is a lot of speed even when he is not in the best of shape, but lacks the power and drive. If a coyote isn't killed instantly he can do considerable damage to a dog. The coyote's fangs are impressive.

12. Clancy does not make a sound when attacking. There is no growling, barking, or anything else. His encounter with the Timber Wolf was soundless, except for running sounds.

13. He will come back from a kill with his jaws bloody and still be his normal self. He isn't affected by the "taste of blood".

14. Clancy has more than proved himself as a hunter and though he appears fierce on a hunt, is still gentle and affectionate. He won't fight with other dogs and even has been abused by a few, but his killing seems directed only toward something wild and, for some reason, male.[1]

Here is a touching story about a small Irish Wolfhound (27 inches) that came to the Reches in the fall of 1937.[2]

THE GHOST HOUND OF YUCCA VALLEY

By KIT RECHE

The refreshing sound of water gurgling from a pipe attracted the strange dog. Step by step he drew closer to the watering trough, which was set deep in the ground to keep it cool. Indoors, Walt and I stood quietly watching through a window. We had never seen this massive, shaggy creature before.

By his markings and general appearance, we identified him as an Irish Wolfhound, though he was small for the breed. We waited as he drank his fill. Then, cautiously, he sniffed around the yard, picking up our dog's scents. Conscious we were watching him, he moved so his back was never turned towards us. Finally satisfied with his investigations, he lay down under a tree and waited.

---

[1]Robert E. Francis, *Letter to author* (5 August, 1971).

[2]Kit Reche, "The Ghost Hound of Yucca Valley," The Irish Wolfhound Club of America, *Harp and Hound* (1953) IV, No. 2, pp. 53-57.

Walt went outdoors alone. The hound arose, growled, stood his ground. Walt ignored him, walked over to the corral. There he talked in his naturally low voice to the various horses as they came up to him. The hound listened. Soon he lay down again.

At meal time I fixed him a dish of food. Walt placed it near the water trough. When he raised his hand to get his cigarette makings from his shirt pocket, the hound crouched and emitted a low growl. This told Walt the dog probably had run away from a cruel and abusive master.

The fact he wasn't footsore indicated he had not traveled far. In a sparsely-settled country like ours, everybody knows the other's dog. This one was new to us. Perhaps he had jumped out of a passing car. Walt came back indoors. After a few minutes, the hound ate the food.

At chore time, we let our own dog, Feller, out. He sized up the new dog. Both being males, we wondered. The hound gave evidence by by his actions that he was only a pup. Feller treated him as such. Much canine conversation went on. The hound then trailed Feller on his rounds of fence posts. Here again he proved his age. The posts meant nothing at all to him.

It was two weeks before Walt could touch the dog. By this time we had named him Butch. That he intended to stay with us we felt sure, but on his own terms. He and Feller spent hours chasing rabbits and jumping coyotes. Soon, Butch's clumsy puppy actions gave way to co-ordinated grace of muscle. He left Feller far behind. Walt began taking him along when he rode the range, looking after the cattle.

Ten, 20, even 30 miles a day they traveled. Butch became hardened and lithe. Feller wasn't able to take it on those trips. He felt left out of things and resented the bond between Walt and the new dog. A jealousy was born.

We make a mistake one day. We tied Butch in the saddle shed. He didn't like it. Feller aggravated the situation by prancing just beyond Butch's reach, taunting him. Then it happened.

Butch backed up, giving himself some slack. Feller closed in— too close. Why Butch didn't kill him in that single lightning-like thrust, we'll never know. Those things happen so quickly. Feller's injuries took weeks to heal. As soon as he recovered, he left home. Search as we did, we never found him.

For the next few years, Butch ruled the place alone. He became a house dog—to a degree. Though he never entirely lost his distrust of humans, his actions clearly showed his love for us. Yet, whenever he received an injury, slight or serious, he staunchly refused help.

When Morgan, our son, was nearing four years old, he and the hound were playing one day near a large table. The boy did something that hurt the dog. I heard Butch's deep growl, then an ear-splitting shriek from Morgan. The three steps around the table seemed miles to me. Morgan was on the floor. Butch was standing back, trembling. Walt came dashing in from outdoors. The boy had a fang mark on his forehead near the hair line, another one under his chin, indicating the dog had had the child's whole head in his mouth. But unlike his chastisement of Feller, he had merely pushed, not bit. The rest had been sound effects. There wasn't a single break in the skin where his teeth had been in contact with Morgan's face.

Walt punished both boy and dog for the part each had played in the fracas. From that day on, Morgan could not pet Butch. Yet, whenever I wanted to spank Morgan, Butch intercepted, standing between us, as if to say "Hands off!"

After the table incident, Butch transferred his love to Donna, our daughter two years younger than Morgan. She learned to walk by clinging to his shaggy coat. But he would drop her in a heap when Walt rode up to the door. He was definitely Walt's dog.

The years passed pleasantly at the line-camp, but we longed for a ranch of our own. So we moved back to the district where Walt used to live. There on 320 acres we set up shop of ranching. Walt's stallion spent more days in his corral than under saddle. Butch began taking his outings with Morgan and his .22 hunting rabbits.

Then came the bobcats. The crop of kids from our herd of 45 goats attracted them. Butch took early morning and late evening runs by himself in the open desert. While on one such trip, we heard his deep baying across the still sand. Walt rode out to see what was the matter. There, in a big Yucca tree, sat a bobcat. Walt shot it, the bullet hitting a front leg.

Thrown off balance by the sudden pain, the cat tumbled to the ground. Before it landed, Butch had it. Walt then witnessed the cleverest display of fighting instinct he had ever seen. Butch had seized the bobcat across its chest, his massive jaws forcing the air from its lungs. Lying on his own chest, his front legs folded back out of the way of the ugly claws, Butch never released his hold. Each time the cat tried to scratch, he tightened his death grip. Finally, the cat gave up. Butch made a very thorough job of breaking every bone in its body, though not once drawing blood or breaking the skin.

Butch strutted home, proudly bearing his quarry. Walt weighed the cat—35 pounds. Butch wouldn't let us take it away from him for disposal. He stood guard over it for three days. As time went on, he got four or five more bobcats, mostly running them down afoot. Only once did one draw blood on him, nicking the tip of one ear. It bled profusely. We thought the wound was serious until we washed away the blood.

A great deal of company visited us at the ranch, some friends, others strangers. We soon learned to go along with Butch's okay on people. It was uncanny. A few he wouldn't even allow to get out of their cars. All had to stand inspection as they passed through the gate. We began to wonder about Butch's surly disposition as he got older. The children were still his wards, but by now he wouldn't let anybody pet him.

One night as we came home with a truckload of feed, hay and groceries, Butch came up the road to greet us, as was his custom. Just as he approached us, a rabbit scurried across the road, and Butch dashed after it. The front bumper caught him amidships, threw him under the truck. We could feel the sickening jolt as a back wheel went over him.

Walt stopped as quick as he could and ran back. There was no dog to be seen. But in the gravel of the road was the imprint of his whole body—mute evidence he had taken the brunt of the load. Walt hunted for him with the car for over an hour, stopping frequently and calling his name over and over. He took his gun along—just in case.

When he returned home after a fuitless search, the headlights reflected the dog's eyes by the back fence. Walt went to him. A slight limp showed, but no surface bruises or bleeding. Internal injuries, we thought. We tried to make a closer check. But Butch arched his neck, growled. He wanted no help from us. He would take care of himself.

We had a rabbit on the truck. Walt skinned it. The dog ate it. Couldn't be in too much pain to eat. We stayed with him through the night. He remained standing all the time. And hour after hour he kept picking up one hind foot, then the other. He urinated, had a bowel movement. At least those organs were not not injured. But something HAD to be from all that weight.

Butch kept up the constant motion of his hind legs all that night and until 4 the next afternoon. Then, seeming to know the danger of paralysis had passed, he lay down under his tree and slept for more than 12 hours.

He still had the limp when he awakened, but otherwise seemed all right. But he could no longer jump fences and had to slow down on his coursing. Strangely enough, his disposition mellowed after the accident. He became more tolerant, wanted to be petted, and he developed a warm friendship with his two canine pals.

Incidentally, by this time our dog family numbered three. We had a shepherd dog, Su Lin, for herding and a toy spaniel, Ginger, for no reason at all.

Because we never allowed any of the dogs to yap just for the fun of it, we came to know their different barks—when a car was approaching, an unseen coyote in the bush, and the snake bark. If it was a snake, Butch would call us. Here again, he used the same down-on-chest tactics as with the cats—but not seizing it, just holding it at bay until we arrived on the scene.

Only if the children got too close did he loyally charge in. He never got bit by a snake defending us. But on one occasion later, when his sense of scent and hearing began to fail, he got it in a front leg. The snake bite was not fatal, but Butch was a very sick dog. This time he allowed me to treat him. I applied hot brine and salt poultices every half hour. On the third day as I came to him, he raised his head, smiled—and growled gently, as much as to say he was ready to take over. Which he did.

Butch came out of it with flying colors, but soon after met with another accident. One of the burros got loose and charged him. In whirling to take the animal, he lost his footing and wrenched his shoulder. A large blood clot formed. We had the vet look at it. Because of his advanced age—he was shading 15—the advice was sleeping pills.

We held a family council. Butch did not seem to be suffering. His nightly romps with Ginger and Su Lin, the other two dogs, continued. He even went on a few hikes by himself. We decided to wait for evidence of pain before we did anything. Then one evening in June when he was with me as I was watering the garden, he did something that told me he was ready to go.

He repeatedly came over and leaned against me. Apparently, he wanted to tell me something. When I paid no attention other than constantly talking to him, as I do with any dog I'm with, he went over and lay down in the freshly watered tomato patch— which he knew was strickly out of bounds.

I was just on the point of scolding him when a sense came over me. I went over and sat beside him. I asked him if his leg hurt. He looked deeply into my eyes. Then, in a flash, he reached down and tore the skin from the old injury. Blood spurted out. It was what the vet had feared—an ugly sore that would not heal. I called Walt. He went to the vet's office and got the sleeping pills.

After Walt had gone, Butch came down to the house with me. He walked about, slowly, took long looks at everything. The children and I choked up. Ginger and Su Lin sensed something, too. They invited him out to romp in the cool evening. He went, and though they tried to be very gentle with him, he plunged into the game with his usual gusto. When Walt drove into the yard, he cavorted gaily alongside the car.

The next morning I gave him the pills. He seemed to smile, as though he knew—and approved. We laid him to rest at our new house site, in what was to be the center of a circular driveway. We planted a young tree at the head of his grave. For three days Ginger and Su Lin lay beside the mound. On the fourth day they resumed their romping. As we walked back to the house that day, they made wide circles each time they neared his heeling position. We felt Butch's spirit released and walking with us.

A day soon after that I was typing a letter in the house. Ginger lay near me on the floor. I heard a scratching at the door and, thinking it was Su Lin, I arose to let her in. But before I got to the door, I could see her asleep near the couch.

I felt strangely weak. I opened the door. "Come in, Old Fellow." I said. And I think he did just that.

A few minutes later, Su Lin woke up whining. In running to me, she made a wide detour around the spot on the floor where Butch always used to lie.

One morning we all were sleeping late. I was partially awakened by a wet nose. Instinctively, I reached out my arm and felt shaggy hair. Not realizing the full significance, I just rumpled the hair sleepily. Then, in that unspoken language common between man and dog when there is complete understanding, he said to me: "I will always guard you in spirit until another Wolfhound comes to relieve me. If danger ever threatens any of you, I will BARK!" That brought me up with a start. Su Lin lay asleep 20 feet from us. Ginger was at the foot of Donna's bed.

We held another family council. We all agreed that Butch must be released to go to his well-earned rest. Afford it or not, we had to get another dog of his kind. We couldn't consider anything else. Today we have The Boyne of Edgecliff, a beautiful golden dog with his soul glowing from his deep brown eyes.

This wide open rugged life was a shock to him at first, kennel-bred as he was. We had to work with him slowly during his period of readjustment. Su Lin and Ginger helped. They talked to him, really did more than we could. After he had been with us a few weeks, the time came to inform him of his purpose with us.

At sunset, when desert folk come to life and wander around in God's loveliest hour of the day, I took the three dogs and went to see the grave.

I said nothing to The Boyne, merely opened the gate of the fence that protects the tree. While I lingered back, Su Lin and Ginger ran over to the mound. The Boyne followed them. He sniffed at great lengths. He looked at Su Lin, who was making small sounds. He looked at me, sniffed some more. Then I called them all out of the enclosure.

As I bent down to fasten the lower catch of the gate, The Boyne came over to me. He looked solemnly into my eyes, he glanced back towards the grave. Then he licked my face, gently, thoroughly. We walked home in silence.

The Boyne grew up that day. From that time onward, he sought out and took each sleeping spot Old Butch had favored. In the house, at night, he slept on a pallet—on THE spot.

Again one early morning (known to the occult as the hour of spiritual contact), I was dreaming of Butch. I asked him if he liked The Boyne. He said he did, but that we must be tolerant and teach him slowly. I begged Butch to go now to his rest. He did not answer. But he smiled his warm smile; his brown eyes were soft.

As the other time, I reached out and rumpled his shaggy neck. When I felt his wet nose on my face my eyes opened wide.

There stood The Boyne! It was as if the two dogs had melted into one.

Time shall tell.

Now grown still with age,

And many a painful chase, the wise old hound,
Regardless of the frolic pack, attends
His master's side, or slumbers at his ease
Beneath the bending shade.

William Somerville (1675-1742)
The Chace

I have never heard the voice of a hound a-hunting on plain, on
bog, or spreading slope, since I parted with my bold hound, but
that woe would come upon my heart.

Bran's Departure from the Fian
Irish text dates c.1250
Trans. by Gerard Murphy.

APPENDIX A

REPORT OF THE WORLD SMALL ANIMAL VETERINARY ASSOCIATION COMMITTEE APPOINTED TO CONSIDER BREED STANDARDS IN RELATION TO THE HEALTH AND WELFARE OF DOGS[1]

Introduction

At the XVIIIth World Veterinary Congress held in Paris 17th-22nd July 1967 a symposium took place entitled "Factors influencing the official control of inherited defects in dogs". The following resolutions were accepted by the meeting and ratified by the Permanent Committee of the World Veterinary Association at its 12th meeting held on July 22, 1967.

(a) The meeting unanimously declares that concern for the health and welfare of dogs demands that breed standards should not include requirements and recommendations that hinder physiological function of organs and parts of the body.

(b) That the W.S.A.V.A. establish a Committee to study the standards of every registered breed and report upon those which hinder physiological function of organs or parts of the body.

General comments on breed standards

For reference the Committee used the Kennel Club (Britain) Standards of the breeds Z 1-6.

These standards contain a variety of prescriptions and recommendations concerning the conformation and appearance of the dog and even some mental characteristics. Starting with the anatomical appearance, prescriptions on details relevant to the function of dogs are mingled with prescriptions on colour and other "beauty-details". From a physiological point of view this is very unfortunate since the judges, who are usually laymen, often do not

---

[1]The Kennel Club (Britain), *The Kennel Gazette* (May, 1969) XC, pp. 207-209.

realise the relative importance of these points. This matter is most unfortunate in connection with "Faults", listed with many standards. One flagrant example: Weimaraner, Z (2), page 21. Here the faults are even graded and more importance has been attached to eye colour than conditions of the limbs and skull.

Of course it would be impossible to prevent standards from paying attention to coat colour, eye colour, ear size and performance etc. But the recommendations on mental condition, sound anatomical structure and movement should be separated from the beauty details and appropriately emphasized.

It is appreciated that a very large proportion of the recommended standards is compatible with soundness, health and physiological normality and indeed many standards are intended to establish and maintain these points. The danger lies on the one hand from the variations of interpretation which inevitably exist between one judge and another, and on the other hand the development of certain standards to an extreme degree. For example, in the Pekingese the head should be massive, skull broad . . . nose very short . . . muzzle wide, well wrinkled, profile should look quite flat with nose well up between the eyes. An animal which meets these requirements to an extreme degree is highly vulnerable to nasal and facial fold dermatitis, defective function of the nasolachrymal ducts, keratitis and corneal ulceration.

There is undoubtedly considerable danger if in the search for "beauty" breeders disregard normal physiological requirements and produce a state of affairs which is a direct cause of disease and physical discomfort.

The Committee considers that every standard should have a *recommendation to the judges of the breed,* where attention is drawn to such anatomical details which are important for normal physiological functions of the dog, mental condition and movement. These recommendations should be included in the standard or they could be written as an addendum.

Frequent reference to these points by judges in their report and even open discussion between judges and breeders could highlight unfortunate trends and perhaps influence the selection and future breeding within each breed.

Breed standards in relation to anatomical features

Head Large heads are recommended in some breeds and can be expected to give rise to complications at parturition. Large heads (in the case of Boston terrier square skull) are recommended in: Z (2): Spaniel (Clumber). Z (4): Boston Terrier, Bulldog, French Bulldog.

Z (6): Griffon, Japanese, Pekingese, Pug. In the Committee's view large heads should be excluded in all standards.

Eyes In many breeds large or small eyes are demanded. Large eyes increase the vulnerability of the bulb to be injured.

Large eyes are recommended in the following standards: Z (3): Dandie Dinmont Terrier. Z (4): Boston Terrier, Shi Tzu, Tibetan Terrier. Z (6): Griffon Bruxellois, Japanese, Cavalier King Charles Spaniel, King Charles Spaniel, Pekingese, Pug. These recommendations should be excluded.

On the contrary small and/or sunken eyes predispose to entropion and exaggerate the consequences of trichiasis. Small and/or sunken eyes are recommended in the following standards: Z (1): Bloodhound. Z (2): Spaniel (Irish Water). Z (3): Airedale Terrier, Australian Terrier, Bedlington Terrier, Bull Terrier, Cairn Terrier, Fox Terrier, Irish Terrier, Manchester Terrier, Welsh Terrier. Z (4): Chow Chow, Schipperke. Z (5): Mastiff, Newfoundland, St. Bernard. Z (6): English Toy Terrier. The recommendations should be excluded.

In addition three breeds: Z (1): Basset and Bloodhound and Z (5): St. Bernard state prescriptions for ectropion as a breed characteristic which is unfortunate and should be excluded.

Hindquarters Perhaps the most curious detail concerning anatomical construction (demanded by the standard) in any breed could be found here. In Z (4): Chow Chow, the hind legs should be "perfectly straight" and also in the characteristics of the breed is spoken about its "unique stilted gait". It should not be necessary to keep the breed at this extreme status. On the contrary the standard should state: "The straight construction of the hind leg should not be too pronounced."

In Rottweiler the Swedish standard and also the German, which is the model of the Swedish one, speak about a short and broad thigh (the German standard: "Oberschenkel kurz, breit . . ."), which will produce straight hind legs. This detail is fortunately not included in the English standard. Recommendation on short thigh should be excluded in the German standard (the home country of the breed) and in any standards which have used the German as a model.

Concerning several spitz breeds there are recommendations on straight hind legs. English standards hold such instructions for (in addition to Chow Chow) Z (1): Elkhound and Finnish Spitz. Z (4): Keeshond. Breeds not in the British list but which nevertheless demand straight hind legs are as follows:—

Alaskan Malamute   Probably U.S.A.

Karelian Bear dog   Finland

Norwegian "Buhund"   Norway

Swedish "Lapphund"   Sweden

The recommendation should be excluded.

Tail   In Z (4): Boston Terrier and French Bulldog screwed and kinked tails respectively are permitted. Referring to what was said about the Bulldog, too screwed and short tails are to be avoided. Probably standards cannot forbid screwed or kinked tails in the breeds in question today because they are too common, but it should be clearly stated that the tails must not be too short or too screwed as this predisposes the animals to frictional dermatitis.

Standards requiring special consideration by breed societies

In the opinion of the Committee the following points should be studied by breed societies with special reference to the possibility of anatomical or physiological features developing within the particular breeds which are or would be detrimental to the health of individual animals particularly if the features referred to are developed to an extreme degree. The Committee appreciates that many points highlighted below are subjects for discussion and professional advice may be required before changes in wording or emphasis can be made. Furthermore, the Committee appreciates that certain points not mentioned below may ameliorate the significance of the points listed.

BASSET HOUND
    Eyes: ". . .and the red of the lower lid appears, though not excessively."
    Comment: Such conformation leads to ectropion and in some cases interference with the function of the nasolachrymal duct.
    Forequarters: "The knees at least slightly crooked inwards but not to so great an extent as to prevent free action or to result in legs touching each other when standing or in action."
    Comment: This feature, which can lead to abnormal angulation at the carpus, is common and greatly handicaps the animal. The word "knee" is used incorrectly in this context.

BEAGLE
    There are no faults listed under this breed but poor temperament is increasing and the Committee considers this feature to be of importance for the future of this dog.

BLOODHOUND

Eyes: "The eyes are deeply sunk in the orbits, the lids assuming a lozenge or diamond shape, in consequence of the lower lids being dragged down and everted by the heavy flews."

Comment: This characteristic leads to ectropion with increased susceptibility to conjunctivitis and interference in the function of the nasolachrymal duct.

ELKHOUND

Hindquarters: "Legs straight at the hock . . ."

FINNISH SPITZ

Hindquarters: "Strong, hocks comparatively straight."

Comment: The latter standard is too vague and in both breeds a straight hock is often linked with a straight stifle which is an unsoundness.

LONG-HAIRED DACHSHUND

No faults are listed under this breed, and in consequence no reference is made to unfortunate trends in temperament.

RHODESIAN RIDGEBACK

No faults are listed under this breed, and in consequence no reference is made to unfortunate trends in temperament.

COCKER SPANIEL

Faults: No reference is made to excessively long ears which predispose to otitis externa. There is no reference to unfortunate trends in temperament in this breed.

WEIMARANER

Comment: Priorities seem to be wrong. Coat and eye colour are considered to be of more importance than poor gait, poor feet, cow hocks, overshot and undershot jaws. It is suggested that faults affecting the skeleton should take precedence over points of "beauty".

BULLDOG

Comment: There is no reference to ease of breathing at rest or following exercise. The facial conformation of this breed makes the animal particularly vulnerable to stress of any type, and dyspnoea occurs in this breed following even light exercise or an increase in environmental temperature.

"From its formation the dog has a peculiar heavy and constrained gait, appearing to walk with short, quick steps on the tips of its toes, its hind-feet not being lifted high, but appearing to skim the ground, and running with the right shoulder rather advanced, similar to the manner of a horse in cantering."

Comment: This paragraph should be omitted since it creates confusion about the sound movement of a dog.

Head and Skull: "The skull should be very large—the larger the better . . ."

Comment: This feature is responsible for the high incidence of dystokia in this breed.

Eyes: "The eyes and 'stops' should be in the same straight line . . ."

Comment: This feature, which has resulted in considerable fore-shortening of the skull, is basically responsible for the following conditions: nasal fold dermatitis, corneal irritation frequently due to the direct contact of facial hairs upon the cornea, entropion and prolonged soft palate which is a condition that is generally relative to the length of skull.

Faults: No faults are listed in this breed, and in particular there is no reference to cork screw tails being a fault. This condition leads to an irritating and painful dermatitis.

CHOW CHOW

Hindquarters: ". . .and hocks well let down and perfectly straight which are essential in order to produce the Chow's characteristic stilted gait."

Comment: Why should a Chow have a stilted gait which is basically unsound movement?

Faults: No mention is made of unfortunate trends in temperament.

FRENCH BULLDOG

Head and Skull: "Head massive, square and broad . . . the loose skin forming wrinkles." "Nose extremely short."

Comment: Collectively, these features lead to the following: nasal fold dermatitis, corneal irritation with melanotic deposit sometimes leading to blindness, direct irritation of the cornea by facial hair, entropion, and indirectly to prolonged soft palate which as in the Bulldog is relative to the foreshortening of the skull.

ALSATIAN

Characteristics: ". . . the most outstanding traits are incorruptibility, discernment and ability to reason."

Comment: How often are these traits tested in the show ring?

Hindquarters: "The hindquarters should show breadth and strength."

Comment: Whilst strength is important, it is impossible to test this adequately in the show ring and many Alsatians show breadth of hindquarters not because of good conformation, but rather due to the existence of hip dysplasia. Whilst it is perhaps unfair to single out this particular breed, there is little doubt that the high incidence of hip dysplasia should require the production of a certificate of normality based upon the radiographical examination of the pelvis before an Alsatian be awarded prizes in the show ring.

DOBERMANN

Characteristcs: "Shyness or viciousness must be heavily penalised."

Comment: This is one of the few breed standards to highlight this extremely important feature, and many other breeds should include specific reference to temperament.

ROTTWEILER

Faults: "6. Nervousness and viciousness are highly undesirable."

Comment: It is pleasing to note this unfortunate trait is highlighted in this breed.

ST. BERNARD

Eyes: ". . . the lower eyelid drooping so as to show a fair amount of haw at the inner corner, the upper eyelid falling well over the eye."

Comment: These features in excess lead to conjunctivitis and disfunction of the naso-lachrymal duct.

WELSH CORGIS

Faults: No mention is made of unfortunate trends in temperament.

CHIHUAHUA

Head and Skull: "A well rounded 'Apple Dome' skull with or without Molero . . ."

Comment: This conformation frequently leads to a permanent fontonella which makes the individual highly vulnerable to blows or accidents involving the skull.

GRIFFON BRUXELLOIS

Head and Skull: "Nose always black, as short as possible . . ."

Eyes: "Large . . ."

Comment: The combination of these features leads to excessive nasal folds frequently causing direct irritation to the cornea with subsequent melanotic keratitis.

KING CHARLES SPANIEL

Head and Skull: "Nose . . . very short . . ."

"The cheeks should not fall away under the eyes, but be well cushioned up."

Eyes: "Very large . . ."

Comment: The combination of these features leads to excessive nasal folds frequently causing direct irritation to the cornea with subsequent melanotic keratitis.

PEKINGESE

Head and Skull: "Head massive . . . Nose very short . . . Profile should look quite flat with nose well up between the eyes."

Eyes: "Large . . . Prominent but not bolting."

Comment: The combination of these features leads to deep nasal folds resulting in nasal fold dermatitis, entropion, direct irritation of the cornea by the hair on the nasal folds leading to corneal ulceration, keratitis and melanotic pigmentation frequently resulting in blindness. In addition, the overshortening of the skull predisposes to a relatively prolonged soft palate resulting in dyspnoea to varying degrees.

PUG

Head and Skull: "Head large, massive, round . . ." "Wrinkles large and deep."

Eyes: ". . . very large . . ."

Comment: The combination of these features leads to deep nasal folds resulting in nasal fold dermatitis, entropion, direct irritation of the cornea by the hair on the nasal folds leading to corneal ulceration, keratitis and melanotic pigmentation frequently resulting in blindness. In addition the overshortening of the skull predisposes to a relatively prolonged soft palate resulting in dyspnoea to varying degrees.

Conclusion

The Committee hopes that the comments made in general terms and also those specifically relating to the various breeds will prove helpful, and that those carrying responsibility will review the breed standards as a matter of urgency. Whilst the Committee has specifically mentioned undesirable temperament in some breeds it is considered that this is a feature which should be carefully studied in every breed and listed as an important fault.

Whilst most of the criticisms relate to physical features which can be recognised by experienced breeders and judges, there are others which are of equal if not greater importance which can only be recognised by a veterinary surgeon using sophisticated diagnostic aids. It is appreciated that reference to these cannot be made in breed standards but, nevertheless, the increasing incidence of progressive retinal atrophy and hip dysplasia needs urgent investigation in all breeds in which the conditions have been reported. In addition, there are certain unfortunate conditions which are highly specific, for instance encephalitis in Keeshonds, and lipodystrophy in English Setters, to quote but two examples.

In 1964, the British Veterinary Association and The Kennel Club (Britain) mentioned additional breeds as subject to disabling physical conditions.

Dislocation of the knee-cap, or patella luxation is the name given to a condition of the stifle or knee-joint. . . This condition is particularly common in small breeds of dogs, Miniature and Toy Poodles, small Terriers and Pekingese. It is most often congenital but may be acquired as the result of injury . . .

Entropion . . . is the name given to a condition in which the eyelids are turned inwards towards the eyeball. It is met with in many breeds but appears to be most prevalent in Spaniels (Cocker), Golden and Labrador Retrievers, Chows, Miniature Poodles, the Bull breeds including Boxers, Wire-Haired Fox Terriers, Dalmatians, St. Bernards and Airedales. . .A comparatively mild condition can progress into one causing constant pain and discomfort and eventual blindness.

Progressive Retinal Atrophy is known to be hereditary . . . in various breeds of dogs [It leads to eventual total blindness] . . . Commonly affected today are Miniature and Toy Poodles, Cocker Spaniels, Rough Collies, Border Collies, Labrador Retrievers, and English Springer Spaniels. The first breed to be seriously affected was the Irish Setter and prompt action by the Kennel Club and dog breeders eradicated P.R.A. from this breed.[1]

---

[1] "Joint Memorandum from the British Veterinary Assoc. and the Kennel Club on Hereditary Defects in Dogs," *The Kennel Gazette* (August 1964), LXXXV, pp. 342-345.

Extracts from a different article on another disease:

Posterior ectasia syndrome, an eye condition in Collies leading to retinal detachment and blindness, is now believed to affect 50% or more of this breed in the U.S., according to Dr. Seymour R. Roberts, a veterinarian specializing in ophthalmology, who has been investigating the disorder for the past six years.

"Unless effective measures are taken, this very serious disease, which is both congenital and hereditary, may ultimately doom the Collie breed in this country," Dr. Roberts told *Veterinary Dispatch* in an exclusive interview here during the 31st Annual Convention of the American Animal Hospital Association.[1]

---

[1]*Veterinary Dispatch*, June, 1964.

APPENDIX B

Registrations

Figures are approximate only. They have not been checked against individual registrations and therefore may include erroneous entries, re-registrations, etc. Irish registrations were included in Great Britain's until 1922. The first hound registered in Canada is mentioned in the 1889-1891 Stud Book Register; the exact year is unknown as the records have been stored and have been declared unavailable. However, his registration number was 1510 and, since there were 1704 registrations during the period, I am assuming he was registered in 1891.

Year	Britain	United States	Canada	Ireland
1886	24			
1887	30			
1888	23			
1889	18			
1890	9			
1891	21		1	
1892	16			
1893	21			
1894	21			
1895	17			
1896	38			
1897	39	2		
1898	46			
1899	46			
1900	60			
1901	25			
1902	63			
1903	52	2		
1904	44			
1905	52			
1906	41	2		
1907	44	12		
1908	53	15	3	
1909	42	18	1	
1910	40	27	1	

Year	Britain	United States	Canada	Ireland
1911	42	9		
1912	53	8		
1913	51	8		
1914	36	16		
1915	24	26		
1916	21	25		
1917	23	19		
1918	3	6		
1919	16	14	1	
1920	28	7	3	
1921	49	49	4	
1922	58	20	3	10
1923	78	60	1	
1924	115	54	9	4
1925	127	74	11	10
1926	176	42	3	8
1927	176	58	3	20
1928	202	56	8	27
1929	200	88	3	18
1930	199	99		35
1931	123	87	3	33
1932	130	51	3	25
1933	103	54	8	19
1934	112	61	7	35
1935	148	74	9	6
1936	134	60	6	2
1937	83	52	6	15
1938	141	77	5	15
1939	90	69	4	10
1940	40	60		6
1941	14	74		1
1942	28	16	7	4
1943	28	24		
1944	40	20		1
1945	27	43		11
1946	60	61	1	14
1947	40	21	5	8
1948	48	56	8	29
1949	26	56	4	40
1950	53	52		20

Year	Britain	United States	Canada	Ireland
1951	40	74	4	28
1952	33	99	3	23
1953	50	69	1	41
1954	13	68	2	49
1955	79	78		42
1956	74	66	2	20
1957	53	75		35
1958	48	81	4	22
1959	64	65	6	35
1960	63	82	5	50
1961	82	77	1	48
1962	129	117	3	55
1963	115	121	3	62
1964	183	132	3	139
1965	122	225	4	185
1966	169	231	9	259
1967	191	400	15	218
1968	157	527	7	237
1969	303	580	24	276
1970	258	769	28	364
1971	431	992	122	409
1972	511	1,251	109	365
1973	654	1,309	133	492
1974	695	1,347	150	390
1975	643	1,411	138	323

Summary

Period	Britain	United States	Canada	Ireland
1886-1895	200		1	
1896-1905	465	4		
1906-1915	426	141	5	
1916-1925	518	328	28	
1926-1935	1,569	662	47	226
1936-1945	625	495	28	65
1946-1955	442	634	28	294
1956-1965	933	1,041	31	651
1966-1975	4,012	8,817	735	3,333
Total	9,190	12,122	903	4,509

IRISH WOLFHOUND REGISTRATIONS

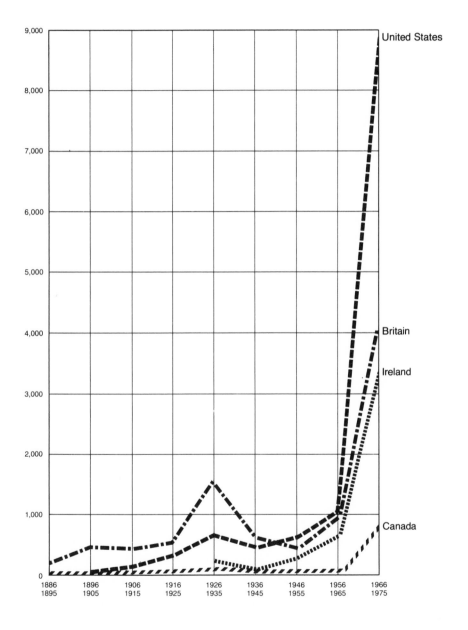

APPENDIX C

IRISH WOLFHOUND LITERATURE

I. Non-Fiction
Current

DeQuoy, Alfred W. *The Irish Wolfhound Guide* (1977). Second edition, xvi, 405 pages. Illustrated. Privately printed. First published in 1973. 6800 Broyhill St., McLean, Va., 22101.

————— *Irish Wolfhound Registrations in America*—1956-1964 (1969). Illustrated. 46 pages. Publisher: The Irish Wolfhound Club of America.

Donovan, John A. *You and Your Irish Wolfhound* (1976). 96 pages. Illustrated. Denlinger's, Fairfax, Va.

Fess, LeRoy E. *Fifty Years of Irish Wolfhound Registrations in America*—1897-1955 (1957). 111 pages. Illustrated. Irish Wolfhound Club of America.

Gordon, John. *The Irish Wolfhound* (1973). 104 pages. Illustrated. John Bartholomew and Son, Ltd. Edinburgh.

Graham, George Augustus. *The Irish Wolfhound* (1973). 80 pages. Illustrated. Reprint. Combined with Edmund Hogan's *The Irish Wolfdog*. The Irish Wolfhound Club of America and The Irish Wolfhound Club of Ireland.

————— *Irish Wolfhound Pedigrees*—1859-1906 (1959). 44 pages. Illustrated. Compiled from Graham's *Working Stud Book*. Edited by Miss Delphis Gardner. Irish Wolfhound Club (Ireland).

Hogan, The Rev. Edmund, S.J. *The History of the Irish Wolfdog* (1973). 174 pages. Illustrated. Reprint. Combined with G.A. Graham's *The Irish Wolfhound*. The Irish Wolfhound Club of America and The Irish Wolfhound Club of Ireland.

Huntley, Patricia K. *Registrations*—*1965-1975* (1978). 200 pages. Illustrated. Irish Wolfhound Club of America.

Irish Wolfhound Club of America. *Harp and Hound*. Recent and out of print issues are listed under *Out of Print*.

Irish Wolfhound Club of Canada. *The Bulletin*. Quarterly. First issued in 1971.

Irish Wolfhound Club (Britain) *Year Book*. Recent and out of print issues are listed under *Out of Print*.

Irish Wolfhound Club (Britain) members. Not a Club publication. *The Irish Wolfhound*. Quarterly. First issued in April, 1972.

Irish Wolfhound Club of Ireland. *The Irish Hound*. Semi-annual. First issued in July, 1972.

Irish Wolfhound Club of New South Wales (Australia). *Newsletter*. Quarterly. First issued in September, 1976.

Irländska Varghundsklubben (Sweden). *Varghunden*. First issued in 1976 as a triannual.

Murphy, Elizabeth C. *The Irish Wolfhound* (1976). 305 pages including 137 on Irish Champions. Illustrated. Available from the author at Ballyhagen House, Carbury, Co. Kildare, Ireland.

Nederlandse Vereningvoor de Ierse Wolfshond en Deerhound (Netherlands). *Ierdie* Bi-monthly beginning with 1976. First issued in 1974 as a quarterly.

Rassemblement des Amateurs de Lévriers d'Irlande et d'Ecosse (France). *Bulletin*. Quarterly. First issued in fourth quarter, 1974.

Starbuck, Alma. *The Complete Irish Wolfhound* (1969). 320 pages. Illustrated. Howell Book House, Inc., New York.

Suomen Irlanninsusikoira r.y. (Finland). *Irlanninsusikoira*. Quarterly. First issued in 1969.

Sutton, Catherine G. *The Irish Wolfhound* (1975). 93 pages. Illustrated. K&R Books, Queniborough, Leics., England.

Westover, Fredric and Margaret. *How to Raise and Train an Irish Wolfhound* (1964). 64 pages. Illustrated. Crown Publishers, Inc., New York.

The Gazehound. An excellent bimonthly magazine on sighthound breeds. Contains articles of value and is well illustrated. First issued in 1970. Subscriptions: 16258 Lovett Place, Encino, CA. 91316.

Note: Kennel clubs of various countries publish books and magazines which include articles on all breeds. Numerous ancient Irish and Scandinavian manuscripts refer to the Irish Wolfhound. Some of these have been translated into modern languages.

Out of Print

DeQuoy, Alfred W. *The Irish Wolfhound in Irish Literature and Law* (1971), xvi, 405 pages. Illustrated. Privately printed. 6800 Broyhill Street, McLean, Virginia 22101.

Fess, LeRoy E. *Irish Wolfhounds—AKC Registrations—1897-1917* (n.d.). 32 pages. Not illustrated. Typewritten.

———— *Irish Wolfhound Review Supplement* (1950). 13 pages. Not illustrated. (1951). 10 pages. Not illustrated. Typewritten reports on show results for those two years.

Gardner, Phyllis. *The Irish Wolfhound* (1931). 253 pages. A short historical sketch with over 100 wood engraving specially cut by the author and her sister. The Dundalgan Press, Dundalk, Ireland.

Graham, George Augustus. *The Irish Wolfhound* (1885). 47 pages. Illustrated. Originally compiled in 1879. Revised and completed in 1885. Whitmore and Son, Steam Printers, Dursley, England. Reprinted in 1939. 80 pages. Illustrated. Combined with Edmund Hogan's *The Irish Wolfdog.* The Irish Wolfhound Club of Ireland. Dublin, Ireland.

Hogan, The Rev. Edmund, S.J. *The History of the Irish Wolfdog* (1897). 167 pages. Illustrated. Sealy, Bryers & Walker. M.H. Gill & Son. Dublin, Ireland. Reprinted in 1917. 169 pages. Illustrated. 200 copies privately printed by Joseph A. McAleenan, New York. Reprinted in 1939. 174 pages. Illustrated. Combined with G.A. Graham's *The Irish Wolfhound.* The Irish Wolfhound Club of Ireland, Dublin, Ireland.

Irish Wolfhound Association (Britain). *The Irish Wolfhound* (1925). 64 pages. Illustrated.

Irish Wolfhound Club of America.

Annual Report (10 vols.; 1927-1947). Illustrated. The first four volumes have brown covers. The first, marked *Annual Report—1927-1928,* is for the period March 1927-March 1928; the second is marked *Biennial Reports—March 1928-March 1930;* the third is marked *Annual Reports—March 1930-1931, March 1931 to January 1932;* the fourth is marked *Annual Reports—January 1932-1933, January 1933-34.* The next six volumes have green covers. The first volume is marked *1934-1935* and has a title page which erroneously shows 1933-1934; the second is marked *1936-1937* and has a title page which erroneously shows 1935-1936; the third is erroneously marked *1939-1940* but the title page correctly shows 1938-1939; the fourth is marked *1940-1941;* the fifth consists of two issues and is marked *1942-1943, 1944-1945;* the sixth is marked 1946-1947.

News Bulletin (1947-1949). Illustrated. A green bound volume marked *Vols. 1 & 2—1947-1949,* consisting of six mimeographed bulletins originally issued unbound. The first news Bulletin, consisting of four 8½″ x 11″ pages, went out in October, 1947. It was reprinted to conform to the size of the other bulletins. The bulletins are marked *Vol. 1, No. 1—*

Autumn 1947, Vol. 1, No. 2—August 1948, Vol. 2, No. 1—Autumn 1948, Vol. 2, No. 2—Winter 1949, Vol. 2, No. 3—Spring 1949, Vol. 2, No. 4— Summer, 1949.

Harp and Hound (1949 to date). Illustrated. Issued in paperback form quarterly and periodically bound in green covers. In 1960 and 1964, there were only three issues, Number 3 and 4 being combined. For the next six years (1965-1970), *Harp and Hound* was issued only three times a year. It resumed its quarterly appearance in 1971. Examining the bound volumes, we see that Vol. 1 is marked *1949-1950* and follows the pattern of the News Bulletin in that its issues are numbered *1, Autumn 1949—2, Winter 1950—3, Spring 1950—4, Summer 1950,* Vol. 2 is marked *1951* and its four issues mark the beginning of a new alignment with the calendar year; they are marked 1, *Winter 1951—2, Spring 1951—3, Summer 1951—4, Fall 1951.* After 1958, each bound volume comprises more than one year. The succeeding bound books are *Vol. 10-11—1959-1960, Vol. 12-13—1961-1962, Vol. 14-19—1963-1968, Vol 20-22—1969-1971, Vol 23-27—1972-1976. Harp and Hound* became a semi-annual publication in 1973.

Irish Wolfhound Club (Britain) *Year Book* (1925 to date). Illustrated. Green bound volumes marked as follows: 1925, 1926, 1927, 1928-1929, 1930-1932, 1933-1935, 1935-1937, 1938-1954, 1955-1957, 1958-1960, 1961-1963, 1964-1966, 1967-1969, 1970-1972, 1973-1975. Until the 1935-1937 issue, volumes covered the year prior to the dates on the cover. Then, the dates on the cover and the period covered were the same.

Irish Wolfhound Society (Britain) *Year Book,* Illustrated booklet. Vol. I (1937) 44 pages, Vol. II (1938) 49 pages.

2. Fiction
(with the Irish Wolfhound as the principal character)

Byrne, Brian Oswald Donn. *The Hound of Ireland* and other stories (1934), 250 pages. Sampson Low & Co., London.

Chipperfield, Joseph E. *Boru Dog of the O'Malley* (1965). 190 pages. Canine with Irish Wolfhound sire and wolf dam. David McKay Co., New York.

Dawson, Alec John. *Finn, The Wolfhound* (1909). 487 pages. A few woodcuts. Grant Richards, London.

———— *Jan, Son of Finn* (1917). 310 pages. Illustrated. Constable & Co., London.

Dunn, Joseph Allan. *Boru* (1926). 195 pages. Not illustrated. Grosset & Dunlap, New York.

———— *Gone Wild* (1926). 191 pages. Illustrations by Edwin Megargee. Duckworth, London.

Finn, Reginald Arthur Weldon. *The Pups I Bought* (1933). 165 pages. Country Life, London.

Hall, Lynn. *Nobody's Dog* (Original title: *To Catch a Tartar)* (1973) 80 pages. Illustrated. Scholastic Book Services, New York.

Hinkle, Thomas Clark. *Barry* (1938). 242 pages. Not illustrated. William Morrow & Co., New York.

———— *Wolf, A Range Dog* (1948). 192 pages. Not illustrated. William Morrow & Co., New York.

Howe, Janet Rogers. *Star—an Irish Wolfhound* (1959). 158 pages. Illustrated. The Westminster Press, Philadelphia.

Johnson, Margaret S. and Johnson, Helen Lossing. *Derry the Wolfhound* (1943). 75 pages. Illustrated. Harcourt, Brace and Company, New York.

Linehan, Patricia and Landreth. *Tarlach—Wolfhound of Eire* (1977). 60 pages. Illustrated, Van Loan Studios, Greeley, CO.

APPENDIX D

IRISH NAMES

1. Pronunciation Guide

Phonetic spellings used in this Appendix are shown in the left hand column. They should be pronounced as in the words of the right hand column emphasizing the letters in italics. For example, in the next section read:

Ailbhe	*Al*-iv-e

From the table below we see that "a" is pronounced as in "ah", "i" as in "din" and "e" as in "let", with the accent being on the first syllable:

Phonetic Spelling	*Pronounce as in the English word*
a	*ah*
ai	h*ai*l
ame	*tame*
ane	m*ane*
ar	f*ar*
arr	*carry*
aw	l*aw*n
awin	*law-in*
awr	*hour*
ay	d*ay*
e	l*et*
ee	sh*ee*n
eo	*yeo*man
etch	f*etch*
eye	*eye*
i	d*i*n
idge	m*idge*
idth	w*idth*
ie	t*i*re
j	*l*iege
o	bl*o*ck
oe	*foe*man
oi	l*et*
on	d*on*
ong	*song*
oo	r*oo*t
orr	s*orr*ow
ou	sh*ou*t
ow	sh*ou*t
u	f*u*ll
y	*y*acht
d	brea*the*
dy	fin*d y*ear
kh	lo*ch* (Scottish)
	i*ch* (German)
kn	*kn*aben (German
koll	*coll*ar
sh	*sh*out
t	*th*ank[1]
tao	*th*ane
thr	*thr*all
ty	brigh*t y*ear

---

[1]Except pronounced Pawrch in "Pairt".

2. Names of Men

Aedh	Ay	A flame of fire. Hugh. Egan.
Aenghus	*Ee*-nus	The chosen one. Angus.
Ailbhe	*Al*-iv-e	The gentle one. Albert.
Ailín	*Al*-een	Of gentle birth. Alan. Allen.
Amhlaoibh	*Owl*-ee	Ancestral relic. Olaf. Humphrey.
Angus	*An*-guss	Anglicised form of Aenghus.
Aralt	*Orr*-ollth	Harold.
Art	Art	A stone, Arthur.
Artagnán	*Art*-ag-nawn	Little Art.
Bóroimhe	*Boer*-iv-e	Boru.
Brénainn, or Brénann	*Bray*-nunn	Brendan.
Brian	*Bree*-un	Brian. Bryan. Bernard.
Buadhach	*Boo*-okh	Conqueror. Victor.
Caoimhín	*Kueev*-een	Sweet offspring. Kevin.
Cathal	*Ka*-hul	Strong in battle. Charles.
Cian	*Kee*-un	Ancient. Kean. Cain.
Cionaodh	*Kyunn*-ee	Fire-sprung. Kenny. Kinney. Kenneth.
Cionáoth	*Kyun*-e or *Kyun*-aw	See Cionaodh.
Colm	*Kull*-um	Dove. Colum. Comlan. Columba.
Colmán	*Kull*-um-awn	Dove. Colum. Colman. Columba.
Conaire	*Kun*-er-e	Connor.
Conchobar	*Kun*-a-hoor	High desire. (Also interpreted as "Lover of *cu*".) Connor. Cornelius.
Conchur	*Kun*-a-hoor	See Conchobar.
Conn	Konn	Intelligence. Reason. Constantine.
Cormac	*Kur*-mok	Charioteer. Charles.
Críostóir	*Kreest*-ore	Christ-bearing. Christopher.
Deasún	*Jass*-oon	Of South Munster. Desmond.
Díarmad	*Dee*-ar-muid	A freeman. Dermot. Jeremiah.
Domhnall	*Doe*-null	Power of the deep. Donald. Daniel.
Donnchad	*Dunn*-ukh-a	Brown warrior. Donough. Denis. Duncan
Donnghal	*Donn*-ull	The brown one. Donald. Dongal.
Dubhghal	*Doo*-oll	The black one. Dugald. Dougall.
Éamonn	*Ame*-unn	Blessed protection. Edmund.
Éanna	*Ane*-a	Enda.
Eoghan	*Owe*-un	Well-born. Owen. Eugene.
Eoin	Owen	Gift of God. John.
Fear	Far	A man.
Fearghal	*Farr*-ull	Bravest of the brave. Fergal. Virgil.
Feargus	*Farr*-ees	Manly strength. The choicest one. Fergus. Ferdinand.

Fergarbh	Far-*gor*-uv	Rough man.
Finn	Fyunn	Fair haired. Bright. Finn.
Flann	Flonn	Blood-red.
Giolla Chríost	*Gil*-la-*kreest*	Servant of Christ. Gilchrist.
Laighneach	*Line*-akh	A Leinsterman. Spears. Javelins.
Liam	*Lee*-um	Strong protector. William.
Lorcán	*Lurk*-awn	Fierce. Lawrence.
Maghnus	*Mon*-uss	Great. Manus.
Niall	*Nee*-all	Champion. Neil.
Oisein, or Oisín, Ossian	*Ush*-een	Ossian.
Oscar or Osgar	*Uss*-kur	Spear of God. Oscar.
Pádraig	*Pawd*-rig	Noble. Patrick.
Peader	*Pad*-er	Rock. Peter.
Phadraig	*Faw*-drig	See Pádraig.
Piaras	*Peer*-uss	Peter. Piers. Pierce. Pearse.
Pól	Pole	Paul.
Ruaidhri	*Roo*-e-ree	Famous ruler. Rory. Roger. Roderick.
Seoirse	*Shor*-shah	George.
Séamus	*Schay*-muss	Supplanter. James.
Seán	Shawn	Gift of God. John.
Tadhgh	Th-eye-g	A poet. Teague. Timothy. Thady.
Tarlach	*Tor*-lokh	Incarnation of the thunder. Turlogh. Terence.
Teigue	Th-eye-g-	See Tarlach.
Traolach	*Trail*-ukh	Tarlach.
Turlogh	*Tur*-lokh	Anglicised form of Tarlach.
Uilliam	Ill-*ee*-um	William.

3. Names of Women

Aibhilín	*Av*-leen	See Eibhlín.
Aife	*Ee*-fe	Eva. Eve.
Áilne	*Awl*-ne	Beauty. Joy. Anne.
Aisling	*Ash*-ling	An epiphany. A manifestation of the divine. Esther.
Áluinn	*Awl*-in	Beautiful.
Aoibheann	*Ee*-vunn	Lovely shape. Eavan.
Aoife	*Ee*-fe	See Aife.
Becfola	Byug-ulla	Dowerless, or small-dowered.
Blathnaid	*Blaw*-ned	Smooth, or flower-like Florence.
Brighid	Breej	Strength. Bright. Brigid. Bridie.
Cáit	Kawtch	Pure. Kate. Kathleen. Katherine.
Caitilín	*Kotch*-ill-een	See Cait.
Caitrín	*Kotch*-reen	See Cait.
Caomhóg	*Kay*-of-ogue	Beautiful girl.
Chinn Óir	*Kinn*-ore	Of the golden hair.
Ciara	*Kee*-ar-a	The dark one. Keary.
Ciarnait	*Keer*-net	Dark lady.
Cruith-gheal	*Kri*-gyal	Feminine name.

Damhnait	*Dow*-net	Little poetess. Devnet. Damhnait. Dymphna.
Dearbhfhorgaill	*Jar*-iv-urr-gal	Feminine name.
Duinseach	*Din*-shock	Brown-haired girl.
Eádoin	*Aid*-een	Edwina.
Eibhlín	*Eye*-leen	Sunlight. Eileen. Evelyn. Helen.
Eilís	*Ell*-eesh	Word of God, Elizabeth.
Eitche	*Etch*-e	Etta.
Eithlin	*E*-hlin	See Eibhlín.
Eithne	*E*-hinny	Kernel, Ethna, Edna.
Etáin	*Aid*-een	See Éadaoin.
Fionnchaomh	Fyunn*kheev*	Fair-headed beautiful girl.
Fionnuala	Fyunn-*oola*	Fair shoulder. Finola. Nuala.
Folt-léabhar	Fullt-*low*-er	Long-haired.
Gobnait	*Gub*-net	Small mouth. Abigail. Deborah.
Gormfhlaith	*Gur*-um-hla	The lady stranger. Barbara. Gormley.
Gráinne	*Grawn*-ye	Perfect. Virginal. Grania. Grace. Gertrude.
Íde	*Ee*-de	Thirst. Ida. Ita.
Liadain	*Lee*-a-dan	Grey lady. Ninth century Irish heroine.
Máire	*Moir*-e	Of the sea. Bitterness. Mary (Other than the mother of Jesus). Maria, Miriam, Maura, Moya. May.
Mairéad	*Morr*-ayd	A pearl. Margaret. Marjorie.
Meave, or Medb	*Mav*	Meave.
Moing-fhionn	*Mwing*-yoon	Fair-haired.
Muire	*Mwirr*-e	Mary (Mother of Jesus).
Niamh	*Nee*-av	Radiant.
Nóra	*Noe*-ra	Honorable. Norah.
Nuala	*Noo*-ulla	Nuala.
Orfhlaith	*Ore*-le	The golden lady. Orla.
Proinnséas	*Prinsh*-ace	French. Frank. Frances. Fanny.
Sadhbh	S-eye-v	Goodness. Sive. Sophia.
Síle[1]	*Shee*-le	Blind. Sheila. Cecily. Julia.
Siobhán	Shiv-*awn*	Joan. Johanna. Jeanne. Hannah.
Siún	Shoon	See Siobhan.
Sorcha	*Surr*-ukh-e	Bright. Sarah.
Úna	*Oo*-ne	The white one. Agnes. Winifred. Freda. Inez.

4. Family Names

Cobhthach	*Kuv*-okh	Coffy.
Conall	*Kun*-ull	Tall and strong. Brave as a *cu*. Connell.
Donn	Dun	Brown-haired. Dunnigan.
Donnchad	*Dun*-ukh-a	Brown warrior. Donahg. Donoghue, Donough. Duncan.

---

[1] Also Seila, Seilagh, Shela, Shelagh, Sheela, Sheelagh, Sheila, Sheilagh, Shiela, Shielagh, Shila, Shilagh, Siela, Sielagh, Sila, Silagh.

Donnghal	*Donn*-ull	The brown one. Donnelly.
Dubhceann	*Doo*-kyonn	Black head. Deighan. Deegan. Duigan.
Dubhthach	*Duff*-akh	Black-haired. Duffy.
Eochaidh	*Yoe*-khee	A horseman. Keogh. Haughey.
Giolla Brighde	*Gill*-a- *Breej*-e	Gilbride.
Giolla na Naomh	*Gilla*-a-na-neev	Servant of the saints. Nehemiah.
Giolla Peadraig	*Gill*-a-*paw*-drig	Servant of St. Patrick. Gilpatrick.
Giolla Phoil	*Gill*-a- *Foe*-il	Gilfoyle.
Gorman	*Gurr*-mawn	A blue person. Gorman.
Mac an Ghabhann	*Mok*-a *Gow*-an	Mac Gowan.
Mac Conmara	*Mok*-*kun*-mara	Son of the Irish Wolfhound of the sea. MacNamara.
Mac Conmidhe	*Mok*-kun-*mee*	Mac Namee.
Mac Con Uladh	*Mok kun*-ull-a	Son of the Irish Wolfhound of Ulidia. Mac Anulla. MacNully.
Mac Criomhthain	*Mok*-*Criff*-an	Mac Griffin.
Mac Fhlannchadha	*Mok*-*lonn*-ukh-a	M'Clanaghy. M'Clancy.
Maol Chiarain	Mweel-*keer*-awn	Devotee of St. Kieran. Mulkerne.
Mathghamhain	Mah-*gow*-na	A bear. Mahony. MacMahon.
Mórdha	*Moor*-uh	Moore.
Muireadach	*Mwirr*-a-dukh	Murray.
Ó Cathail	Oe *Ka*-hel	O'Cahill.
Ó Chonain	Oe *Khun*-awin	O'Conan.
Ó Cléirigh	Oe *Klay*-re	Cleric. O'Clery.
Ó Cobhthaigh	Oe *Kuv*-ee	O'Coffy.
Ó Coileáin	Oe *Kill*-yawin	Irish Wolfhound puppy. O'Cullane. O'Collin.
Ó Conáill	Oe *Kunn*-ull	High. Mighty. Brave as a *cu*. Connell. Conall.
Ó Cuinn	Oe *Kuin*	O'Quinn.
Ó Donnghaile	Oe *Dunn*-al-e	Brown valor. Donnelly.
Ó Dubhagáin	Oe *Doo*-a-gawn	O'Dugan.
Ó Dubhain	Oe *Doo*-awn	Diminutive of *Dubh*, black. Dwayne. Doon.
Ó Dubhthaigh	Oe *Duff*-ee	Black-haired. O'Duffy. O'Dowey. O'Dooey. O'Duhig.
Ó Faeláin	Oe *Fwayl*-awn	O'Phelan.
Ó Flahertaigh	Oe *Flo*-har-tee	O'Flaherty.
Ó Flannagáin	Oe *Flon*-ugg-awin	Little Flan. O'Flanagan.
Ó Floinn	Oe *Flinn*	O'Flynn.
Ó Hartagain	Oe *Hart*-ag-awin	O'Hartigan.
Ó Labhraid	Oe *Low*-ree	O'Lawry. O'Lowry. O'Laverty.
Ó Láidir	Oe *Lawd*-er	Strong. O'Lauder.
Ó Laoghaire	Oe *Lay*-er-e	O'Leary
Ó Loegaire	Oe Lee-er-e	O'Leary.
Ó Loingseacháin	Oe *Linn*-shukh-awin	O'Lynch.
Ó Maelsheachlann	Oe *Mwael*-okh-lunn	O'Melaghlen.
Ó Maoil Bhrighde	Oe Mweel *Vreej*-e	O'Mulready.
Ó Maol Chonaire	Oe *Mwael Kun*-er-e	O'Mulconry.
Ó Muireadhaigh	Oe *Mwirr*-e	O'Murray.
Ó Raghallaigh	Oe *Rie*-ell-ye	O'Reilly.
Ó Riain	Oe *Ree*-inn	O'Ryan.
Ó Ruaire	Oe *Roo*-irk	O'Rourke.

Ó Sirideáin	Oe *Shir*-e-dawn	O'Sheridan.
Ó Suilleabháin	Oe *Sool*-a-wain	The dark-eyed. O'Sullivan.
Rudraigi	*Roo*-ree	Rury.
Sláine	Slawn	Sound. Healthy. Slaney.
Suibhne	*Siv*-ne	Sweeney.
Tír Eoghain	*Teer*-oan	Tyrone.
Tuathal	*Too*-hull	Toole.

5. *Irish Wolfhound Names Mentioned in Irish Literature*

Abhlach	*Owl*-akh	
Adhnuall	*Eye*-noo-ull	A great cry.
Ailbe	*Al*-iv-e	
Aindeoin	*An*-yeon	
Ainmhear	*An*-var	Very quick.
Airc	Ark	
Aire	*Ar*-e	
Airrchis	*Ar*-ick-ish	A snare.
An-uaill	*On*-ool	
Aolan	Ail-awn	
Arann	Awr-onn	
Ard na seagha	*Awrd*-na-shaw-a	
Ard na Sealga	*Awrd*-na-*shal*-iga	High one of the hunts.
Ard-léim	*Awrd*-lame	A splendid leap.
Baeth	Bway	
Báire	*Boy*-re	
Banduir	*Bonn*-ir	
Barcán	*Bork*-awn	
Beart	Barth	
Bioga	Bee-ug-a	
Bolg	*Bull*-ug	
Bonn	Bonn	
Bran	Bron	
Breac	Brak	
Brioghmhar	*Bree*-u-wor	Strong.
Brod	Brud	A goad.
Buadhach	*Boo*-akh	Victorious.
Buidhe	Bwee	Yellow.
Bunsach	*Bun*-sakh	
Callaire	*Koll*-ar-e	Bellman.
Caol	Kuale	
Caolan	*Kuale*-awn	Slender.
Carragán	*Korr*-agawn	
Casluath	Koss-*loo*-a	
Cathbhuadh	Ka-*woo*-a	Victorious in battle.
Ceann Doscuthach	Kyon-du-*skuh*-ukh	
Cian	*Kee*-an	Ancient.
Ciarchuill	*Kee*-ar-*khuill*	Which outstripped every hound.
Cluain	*Kloo*-in	
Cluasán	*Kloo*-asawn	
Cluid	*Kloo*-idge	
Cnagaire	*Knog*-ir-e	
Cnámhach	*Knaw*-vukh	
Cóisir	*Koe*-ishir	

Comrith	Kum-ri	
Conbeg	Kun *-byug*	Little hound.
Conbel	Kun-*bail*	
Conuall	Kun-ool	
Cor	Kur	
Cor Dhubh	Kur Goo	Straight black one.
Corrbheann	*Korr*av-yon	Straight one of the peaks.
Crithire	*Kri*-hir-e	
Crom	Krum	
Cuach	*Koo*-akh	
Cuaird	*Koo*-erd	To go on an errand.
Cuan-choimead	*Koon*-kum-*awd*	Harbor guard.
Cuill-sgeach	Kuill-sgokh	
Cuirtheach	*Kir*-hokh	
Cumán	*Kum*-awn	
Créacht	*Kray*-akht	
Daithlend	*Da*-lun	
Daoil	Deel	
Daol	Dale	
Dáol	Dawl	
Daolán	*Dale*-awn	
Dathchaoin	Da-*kheen*	Bright-complexioned.
Derg	*Dyar*-rig	Red.
Dian-rás	Dee-an-rawss	Swift in the chase.
Díbhearg	*Dee*-varg	
Dobhrán	*Dow*-rawn or *Duv*-rawn	
Dochar	Dukhur	
Doelchú	Dale-khoo	
Dóilin	Doe-*leen*	
Dordán	Durdawn	
Dorr	Dorr	
Drithleann	*Drill*-un	
Drothladh	*Drull*-a	
Duanán	*Doon*-awn	
Dúil	*Doo*-il	
Duilleog	*Dill*-yoeg	
Duthach	*Du*-fakh	
Éachtach	*Aikh*-tukh	Of the tricks, or feats.
Éadrom	*Aid*-rum	
Éaga	*Ai*-ga	
Eile	*Ail*-e	
Eirleach	*Air*-lukh	
Eisdeacht	*Aish*-dukht	
Éisteacht	*Aish*-tukht	Act of listening.
Eitill, or Eiteall	*Et*-chill	
Eloir Derg	*Ell-er Dyarrig*	
Én-Fuath	Ain-*Foo*-a	
Eolach	*Owe*-lukh	
Failinis	*Fal*-in-ish	
Faire	*Farr*-a	
Faobhar	Fwayr	
Faoidh	Fwee	A cry.
Faraire	*Farr*-ar-e	
Fead	Fad	
Feall	Fyowl	
Feam	Fam	
Feamaire	*Fam*-er-e	
Fear Baoth	Far Bway	

Fear Glinne	Far Glinn-e	
Fear Gloun	Far Glonn	
Fearán	*Farr*-awn	
Feargach	*Farr*-ig-ikh	Angry.
Feas	Fass	
Fearb	Farrb	
Féirín	*Fare*-een	
Feruaine	Fer-oona	
Fiadhman	*Fee*-a-mawn	
Faill	*Fee*-oll	
Fiamhach	*Fee*-uv-ukh	
Fíor	*Fee*-ur	
Foghar	*Fow*-ar	A sound.
Fostadh	*Fuss*-too	
Fostaigh	*Fuss*-tee	
Fostuigh	*Fuss*-tee	
Fothram	*Fu*-hrum	
Fuadach	*Foo*-a-dukh	
Fuaim	*Foo*-em	
Fuarán	*Foor*-awn	
Fuarma	*Foor*ma	
Fuilteach	*Fwil*-tukh	
Fuinneamh	*Fwin*-yuv	
Fulang	*Ful*-ang	
Futhlamh	*Fu*-lov	
Gaill-fhéith	Gal-ay	
Gaillinn	Gal-in	
Gáir	Gawr	A shout.
Gaoithe	*Gueeh*-e	
Gaoth	Gu*ay*	
Gar	Gor	
Garbhán	Gorr-a-vawn	
Garraidh	Gorry	
Geall	Gyowl	
Géar-léana	Gare-lain-a	
Géibheann	*Gyave*-unn	
Giodan	*Gyud*-awn	
Gluaire	*Gloo*-a-re	
Got	Gut	
Grianán	*Gree*-a-nawn	Bright as the sun.
Gruaim	*Groo*-em	Gloom.
Iarratach	*Ear*-a-takh	
Imchian	*Im-khee*-an	
Ladruin	*Lad*-rin	
Láinbhinn	Lawn-vin	
Laoidh	Luee	
Laom	Lame	
Larbharán	*Lar*-var-awn	
Leagaire	*Log*-ar-e	
Leigean	*Lig*-an	
Léim	Lame	A leap.
Léim-ar-Luth	Lame-er-Loo	
Léim-fhada	Lame-ada	A long leap.
Lérbhuaidh	Lair- *boo*-ee	Ler of victory.
Liasán	*Lee*-as-awn	
Loinn	Linn	
Lomaire	*Lum*-ar-e	
Lom-bhall	Lum-wall	Bare-limbed.

Lom-luth	Lum-loo	
Lonn	Lonn	
Lorgán	*Lurg*-awn	
Luabán	Loo-a-bawn	
Luadhas	*Loo*-uss	Swiftness, speed.
Luadrán	*Loo*-ad-rawn	
Luas	*Loo*-uss	See Luadhas.
Luath	*Loo*-a	See Luadhas.
Luingeach	*Ling*-akh	
Lúth na Lon	*Loo*-na-*lun*	
Mac a Truim	Mok-a-*Thrim*	
Mac-an-coill	Mok-a-*Kyle*	
Mac-an-Smóil	Mok-a-*Smole*	
Machaire	*Makh*-er-e	
Máigh	Maw	
Mallaire	*Moll*-ar-e	
Manaire	*Mon*-ar-e	
Maoin	Mween	Wealth
Marbhadh na gCat	*Mor*-roona-*Gat*	
Meadhair	Mar	
Meanmhuin	Man-vin	
Mearán	Mar-awn	
Mire	Mir-e	Frenzy.
Monarán	*Mon*-ar-awn	Turf-ranger.
Mor-dhail	More-awl	
Morthan	*More*-han	
Néall	Nail	
Néimh	Nave	
Niamhrach	*Nee*-uv-rukh	
Nóin	*Noe*-in	
Nóinin	*Noe*-n-een	A daisy.
Páirt	Pawrch	Affection.
Radaire	*Rod*-ar-e	A ranter.
Radharc	*Rye*-urk	
Rás	Rawss	
Reachtaire	*Rokh*-ter-e	
Rian	*Ree*-un	
Rinn	Rinn	
Rinn-bhar	Rinn-var	
Rin-ruith	Rin-ri	Star of running.
Rith Fhada	Ri-ada	
Rith re hÁrd	Ri-re-*hAwrd*	
Rith Rod	Ri-Rud	Rith the ruddy.
Ritheann	*Ri*-hunn	
Saimhear	Sa-ver	
Saothar	*Say*-har	Toil.
Sár-ruith	Sawr-ri	
Sceólang	Shg-*yeo*-long	
Seabhac	*Shou*-akh	
Seangaire	*Shong*-er-e	Slender.
Searc	Shark	Affection.
Seasg	Shasg	
Sgainnear	*Sganner*	
Sgal	Sgoll	
Sgáth Úr	Sgaw-oor	
Sgeolang	Shg-*yeo*-long	See Sceólong.
Sgiamh	Shg-*eev*	Loveliness.
Sgiarlóg	Shgeer-loe-g	

Sgread Ghábhaidh	*Shgrad-Gaw*-ee	
Sguaba	*Sgooba*	
Sliomhan	Schliv-an	
Soirbh	*Serr*-ev	
Steallaire	*Schtal*-ar-e	Spatterer
Stiallaire	*Schtee*-l-ar-e	
Suan	Soon	
Suanán	*Soon*-awn	
Taom	Thame	
Teanán	Tyann-awn	
Trachtan	*Thrawkh*-tawn	
Traost	Thraist	
Treabhaire	*Throw*-ar-e	
Tréan	Thrain	Strong.
Tréan-lúth	*Thrain-loo*	
Treoir	Troe-r	
Triall	*Tree*-ull	
Tuairt	Thoort	
Uaill	Oo-ull	
Uaill-bheo	Oo-ull-vyoe	Lively howl.
Uaithninn	*Oo*-a-ninn	
Uacht Árd	Ukht-*Awrd*	
Urlach	*Ur*-lakh	

6. *Miscellaneous*

Abhainn	*Ow*-onn	A river.
Achadh	*Okh*-u	A field.
Aireachchluais	*Ar*-ukh-*loosh*	Heedful ear.
Alainn	*Awl*-inn	Handsome. Beautiful.
Aonchú	*An*-khoo	Chief hound.
Archu	*Ar*-khoo	Dog of slaughter. Genitive: archon.
Árd	Awrd	High.
Árd Macha	Awrd-*mok*-a	Armagh.
Áth	Aw	A ford.
Áthluain	Aw-*loo*-in	Athlone.
Baile	*Boll*-ye or *Bal*-ye	A homestead. A town.
Bán	Bawn	White.
Bandia	*Bon-jee*-a	A goddess.
Beag	Byug	Small
Béal	Bail	A mouth. An approach.
Bealach	*Bal*-okh	A pass. A highway.
Bean	Ban	A woman.
Beann	Byonn	A peak.
Bearna	*Bar*-ne	A gap.
Beltaine	*Byal*-tin-e	Beltaine.
Boand	*Boe*-onn	Cow-white. A goddess. Boyne.
Boinn	*Boe*-inn	See Boand.
Borb	*Burb*	Proud. Fierce.
Bóthar	*Boe*-hur	A road.
Bráthair	*Braw*-her	Brother.
Brehon	Bre-hon	Brehon (a judge). Anglicised form.

Brislech	*Brish*-lakh	A rout. Genitive: Brislighe (pronounced *Brish*-lee).
Cailín	*Koll*-een	A maiden.
Caiseal	*Kash*-al	A castle. A circular stone fort.
Caisleán	*Kask*-lyawn	A castle.
Caoine	*Keen*-e	Death song. A keening.
Carn	*Korr*-n	A heap or pile.
Carraig	*Korr*-ig	A rock.
Cathair	*Ka*-har	A circular stone fort.
Céad	Kayd	A hundred
Ceann	*Kyon*	A head.
Ceol	Kyole	Music.
Conairt	*Kun*-art	A pack of hounds. A rout of wolves.
Coill	Kyle or Kill	A wood.
Cill	Kill	A church.
Ciúin	*Kyoo*-in	Calm. Quiet.
Cloch	Klukh	A stone. A stone castle.
Cluain	*Kloo*-in	A meadow.
Cnoc	Knuk	A hill.
Cos	*Kuss*	A foot.
Cosluath	*Kuss-loo*-a	Swift of foot.
Crothach Geal	*Kro*-akh-*gyowl*	Triumphant.
Cruach	*Kroo*-ukh	A pointed hill.
Cu	Koo	An Irish Woflhound.
Cu allaid	*Koo-oll*-ee	The Wild Irish Wolfhound, i.e. the Wolf.
Cúil	*Koo*-il	A nook.
Cuilen	*Kill*-yawn	An Irish Wolfhound puppy. Collins.
Currach	*Kur*rakh	A marsh.
Dairbhre	*Darv*-re	Oak. Genitive: Dairbhreach, pronounced Darv-rukh.
Dearg	*Dyarr*-ig	Red.
Diseart	*Dee*-shert	A hermitage.
Doire	*Derr*-e	Derry.
Domhnach Broc	*Dow*-nukh *Bruk*	Donnybrook (Broc's church).
Dreoilin	*Droe*-leen	A wren.
Droichead	*Dre*-hidth	A bridge.
Droim	Drim	A ridge.
Dúbhchosach	Do-*kuss*-okh	Blackfoot.
Dún	Doon	A fort.
Eaglais	*Agg*-lish	A church.
Éire	*Air*-e	Ireland.
Fada	*Fod*-e	Long.
Fáilte	*Fawl*-te	Welcome.
Fearadhach	*Farr*-ukh	Manly.
Fenagh	*Fee*-na	See Fiodhnach.
Fiadh	*Fee*-e	A deer.
Finghín	*Fin*-een	Fair offspring.
Finnchosach	Fin-*kuss*-okh	White foot.
Fiodhnach	*Fee*-nukh	Woody. Anglicised form: Fenagh.
Fógartach	*Foe*-gurt-akh	Warning.
Fuath	*Foo*-ah	Victorious. A figure. A phantom. Hate. (Masculine noun).
Gáirech	*Gawr*-akh	Merry.

Gall	Goll	A foreigner. A stone.
Gaodhal	Gael	Gael.
Garbh	*Gorr*-uv	Rough.
Garrán	*Gorr*-awn	A grove.
Geasa	*Gass*-e	A prohibition.
Gilla	*Gill*-a	A servant.
Giolla	*Gvoll*-a	See Gilla.
Glaim	Glim	A bark. A roar. A growl.
Glanluadh	Glon-*loo*-a	Pure-spoken.
Glas	Gloss	Green.
Gleann	Gly-ann	A glen.
Gloir	*Gloe*-ir	Voice.
Gníomhach	Gin-*eev*-akh	Busy. Nimble.
Go brath	Gu *Braw*	Forever (literally "until judgment").
Gort	Gurt	A tilled field.
Gruaim		Gloom. Surliness. (Feminine noun.)
Inis	In-ish	An island.
Inisfail	*In*-ish-Fawl	Ireland.
Laoi	Lee	A bay. A poem.
Leitir	*Lett*er	A slope.
Laith	*Lee*-e	Gray.
Lios	Liss	An earthern fort.
Loch	Lokh	A lake. A sea inlet.
Lugh	Loo	The god of light in Celtic mythology.
Magh	Maw	A plain.
Machaire	*Mokh*-er-e	A plain.
Maine	*Man*-ye or *Mon*-ye	Maine.
Mainistir	*Mon*-ish-tir	A monastery.
Maol	Mwael	A bare hill.
Mear	Mar	Quick.
Mílchu or míolchu	Meel-*khoo*	Irish Wolfhound.
Míle	*Meel*-e	A thousand.
Mór	Moar	Big.
Muain	*Moo*-in	Munster.
Muileann	*Mwill*-inn	A mill.
Mumha	*Moo*-a	See Muain.
Óg	Oeg	The younger.
Oileán	*Ill*-yawn	An island.
Poll	Powl	A hole. A pool.
Port	Purt	A bank.
Ráith or Ráth	Raw	An earthen fort.
Riabhach	*Ree*-e-vukh	Striped.
Rinn	Rinn	A point of land.
Ros	Rus	A wood. A peninsula.
Rua	*Roo*-a	Red.
Ruaid	*Roo*-ee	See Rua.
Scathach	*Sko*-hukh	A shadow.
Sciath	*Shkee*-a	A shield.
Scolaidhe	*Skul*-ly	A scholar.
Seamróg	*Sham*-roag	A shamrock.
Sean	Shan	Old.
Siansán	Shee-an-sawn	Pleasant noise of hunting.
Sídhe, or síodh	Shee	A fairy hill.
Sionann	*Shin*-inn	Old one.
Sliabh	*Shlee*-uv	A mountain. An upland moor.

Sláinte	*Slawn*-te	Health
Teamhair, or Temuir	Tawer	Tara. Genitive: Teamrach.
Tír	Teer	Country.
Tor	Turr	Thunder. Roar.
Torann	*Tur*-in	Masculine noun.
Tuinn	Tinn	Waves.
Tulach	*Tul*-okh	A hill.
Ua	*Oa*-a	O'(Grandson of).
Uan	*Oo*-an	A lamb.
Uisce	*Ish*-ke	Water.

Three thousand, nine hundred Irish names, without pronunciation indications or English equivalents may be found in the index of *Corpus Genealogiarum Hiberniae* (1962) I. Edited by Michael A. O'Brien. Only one volume published.

BIBLIOGRAPHY

DOCUMENTS CITED

Aelianus, Claudius. On the Characteristics of Animals. Trans. by A.F. Scholfield (3 vols.; 1958-1959) I.
American Kennel Club. Brownell, John. *Letters to the author* (Dec. 28, 1966; May 20, 1971).
———— *The Complete Dog Book* (1968).
———— *Pure-Bred Dogs—American Kennel Gazette.*
    Angel, G.M., Mrs. "Salukis." (May, 1971) LXXXVIII.
    Carmichael, Leland E. and Olin, John M. "A New Rapid Blood Test for the Detection of Canine Brucellosis." (Mar., 1975).
    Corbin, James. "Collies." (Nov., 1970) LXXXVII.
    Eronemo, Sharon, "Mastiffs." (Jan., 1971) LXXXVIII.
    Gardner, Samuel A. "A Dog's Senses." (Nov., 1968) LXXXV.
    Gorman, John. "Scottish Deerhounds." (June, 1967) LXXXIV.
    Harper, Deborah S. "Plants Toxic to Dogs." (June, 1968) LXXXV.
    Jacobs, Eugene. "Whippets." (May, 1962) LXXIX.
    Jones, Arthur Frederick. "How Science is the Ruler of Halcyon's Famous Dogs." (Dec., 1935) LII.
    Lloyd, Freeman. "Many Dogs in Many Lands." (Feb., 1924) XXXVI.
    Mather, George W. "Canine Pediatrics." (Nov., 1974) XCI.
    Noble, Anastasia. "Scottish Deerhounds." (Feb., 1970) LXXXVII.
    Noerr, Robert. "Bloodhounds." (July, 1962) LXXIX.
    Potts, Donald. "The Bloat and What To Do About It." (Nov., 1969) LXXXVI.
    Smith, Donald A. "Afghan Hounds." (Nov., 1957) LXXIV.
    Smythe, R.H. "Lakeland Terriers." (July, 1969) LXXXVI.
    Stockner. Priscilla. "Primary Preventative Medicine." (Oct., 1975) XCII.
    Wheeler, Walter A., Jr. "Is There Danger in Dog Bedding?" (May, 1967) LXXXIV.
    Woodruff, Charlotte, "Acute Gastric Dilatation." (Jan., 1967) LXXXIV.
    "A Word from the Veterinarian." (Oct., 1960) LXXVII.
    "AKC Tops a Registration Mark." (Feb., 1959) LXXVI.
Andersen, A.C. "Puppy Production to the Weaning Age." *Journal of the American Veterinary Medical Association* (Feb., 15, 1957) CXXX.
Angel, G.M., Mrs. See American Kennel Club.
Arrian, *The Cynegeticus* (1831). Trans. from the Greek by William Dansey.
———— "De Venatione Libellus." *Arrianus* (1846). In Greek and Latin. Ed. by Charles Müller.
Atwell, David. *Letter to the author* (20 Sept., 1971).
Baily, John F. See Irish Wolfhound Club (Britain).
———— See Kennel Club (Britain).
Beddoes, C.E.W. See Irish Wolfhound Association.
Berland, Theodore. *The Fight for Quiet* (1970).
Beynon, Mary. See Irish Wolfhound Association.
Binney, C.A. See The Kennel Club (Britain) *Letters to the author.*
Borden, Inc. *The Borden Guide to the Care and Feeding of Orphan Pups* (n.d.).
Bowen, Michael. "On Coursing the Irish Wolfhound." *The Gazehound* March/April, 1977, pp. 80, 83.
British Veterinary Association. "Cryptorchidism in the Dog." *Veterinary Records* (1955) LXVII.
———— See Kennel Club (Britain)
Brookes-Simmonds, R.See Irish Wolfhound Association.
Brown, Robert. "Anesthesia and Great Pyrenees." *The Pyriodical.*

California, University of. School of Veterinary Medicine. See Andersen, A.C.
———— See Gaines Nutrition Center.
Carmichael, Leland E. See American Kennel Club.
Carnation Company. Pamphlet (n.d.)
Chimel, Walter N. See Gaines Nutrition Center.
Chiverton, D. *Letter to the author* (Aug., 15, 1963).
Clark, Marion. *Letter to the author* (Dec. 16, 1969).
Comfort, Alex. "Longevity and Mortality in Dogs of Four Breeds." *Journal of Gerontology* (April, 1960) XV, No. 2.
———— "Longevity and Mortality of Irish Wolfhounds," *Proceedings of the Zoological Society of London* (Sept., 1956) CXXVII, Part 1.
Compton, Herbert. *The Twentieth Century Dog.* (2 vols.; 1904).
Consumers' Union of United States, Inc. *Consumer Reports* (Mar., 1973).
Corbin, James. See American Kennel Club. See *Popular Dogs.* See Ralston Purina Company.
Cornell Research Laboratory for Diseases of Dogs. Cornell University. *Laboratory Report,* Series 2, No. 4 (May 1, 1974).
Corpus Genealogiarum Hiberniae (1962) I. Edited by Michael A. O'Brien. Only one volume published.
Cox, Harding. *Dogs* (2 vols.; 1906).
———— See Irish Wolfhound Club (Britain)
Crighton, G.W. See Gaines Nutrition Center.
Croucher, Esther M. See Irish Wolfhound Club (Britain)
———— See Irish Wolfhound Club of America.
Daglish, E. Fitch. See Gaines Nutrition Center.
Dalziel, Hugh. See Hutchinson, Walter Victor.
Dana, William D. See Irish Wolfhound Club of America.
Dansey, William. See Arrian.
Davis, Patricia. See Gaines Nutrition Center.
Denlinger, Milo G. See Howell, Elsworth S.
Depuy, Warren A. See Irish Wolfhound Club (Britain).
DeQuoy, Alfred W. *The Irish Wolfhound in Irish Literature and Law* (1971). Privately printed.
———— *Irish Wolfhound Registrations in America—1956-1964* (1969). Published by Irish Wolfhound Club of America.
Deubler, M. Josephine. See *Popular Dogs.*
Drury, W.D. *British Dogs* (2 vols.; 1903).
Durand, H.M. See Irish Wolfhound Club (Britain).
Elliott, Rachel Page. *Dog Steps* (1973).
Encyclopaedia Britannica (1955). "Coursing." VI; "Coyote." VI; "Timber Wolf." XXII; "Wolf." XXIII. (1971). "Sporting Record." XXI.
Eronemo, Sharon. See American Kennel Club.
Evans, Howard E. See Gaines Nutrition Center.
Everett, I.W. See Irish Wolfhound Club (Britain)
———— See Graham, George.
Fess, Le Roy. See Gaines Nutrition Center.
———— *Fifty Years of Irish Wolfhound Registrations in America—1897-1955* (1957). Published by Irish Wolfhound Club of America.
Field, Stephen J. See Gaines Nutrition Center.
Flower, Stanley S. "Contributions to Our Knowledge of the Duration of Life in Vertebrate Animals." *Proceedings of the Zoological Society of London* (1931).
Follis, T.B. See Ralston Purina Company.
Fox, Michael W. See Gaines Nutrition Center.
Francis, Robert L. *Letter to the author* (5 Aug., 1971).
Freak, Marion John. See Gaines Nutrition Center.
Frisch, Karl von. *You and Life.* Trans. from the German by Dr. Ernst Fellner and Betty Inskip (1940).
Fuller, John L. See Gaines Nutrition Center.

Funkquist, B. and Garmer L. *Journal of Small Animal Practice* (Sept., 1967).
Gaines Nutrition Center (Walter N. Chimel, Director), *Basic Guide to Canine Nutrition* (1965).
———— *Care of the Brood Bitch and Puppies.* Pamphlet. (n.d.).
———— *Gaines Dog Research Progress.* (Patricia Davis, ed.)
    California Correspondent. (Spring, 1957).
    California, University of. School of Veterinary Medicine. Studies quoted in "California U. Cage Has Unusual Features." (Fall, 1963).
    Crighton, G.W. (Spring, 1969).
    Daglish, E. Fitch. Article quoted from *British Dog World.* (Summer, 1962).
    Evans, Howard E. "Prenatal Development of the Dog." (Winter, 1975).
    Field, Stephen J. "The Stud Dog, Too, Needs Management." (Fall, 1958).
    Fox, Michael W. "Guidelines to Behavior in Dogs." (Spring, 1968).
    Freak, Marion John. "Abnormal Behavior During Pregnancy and Parturition in the Bitch," a chapter in *Abnormal Behavior in Animals,* edited by Michael W. Fox. Quoted in (Spring, 1970).
    Fuller, John L. "Dog Genetics," (Summer, 1961).
    Harrop, A.E. Article in *Journal of Small Animal Practice.* Quoted in "Infertility of the Male Dog." (Spring, 1967).
    Kingma, Fred J. "Factors in Canine Sterility and Fertility." (Winter, 1952-1953).
    Kirk, Robert W. "Feeding Practices—Especially Puppies." (Spring, 1967).
———— "Kennel Management." (Summer, 1961).
———— "Nutrition for the Dog in Stress." (Summer, 1969).
    Krook, Lennart. "Overnutrition and Skeletal Disease in Growing Dogs." (Winter, 1975).
    Leonard, Harmon C. "Flat Puppy Syndrome." (Spring, 1968).
    Leonard, John. Quotation from *Canine Practice.*
    Mather, G.W. "Some Reasons Why Food Requirements Vary." (Spring, (1967).
    McCuistion, W.R. Article in *Veterinary Medicine/Small Animal Clinician.* Quoted in "Dog's Tail." (Summer, 1966).
    Mosier, J.E. "Puppy Diseases Involving Litter Problems." (Summer, 1970).
    Schnelle, Gerry B. "The Present Status and Outlook on Canine Hip Dysplasia" (Spring, 1973).
    Sheffy, Ben E. "Meeting the Nutritional Needs of the Bitch and Puppies." (Summer, 1968).
———— (Winter, 1957-1958).
    Society for the Advancement of Canine Genetics. *Journal of Canine Genetics* (August, 1947). Quoted in "The 4 Systems of Breeding Defined." (Fall, 1947).
    Wallach, Joel. "Exotic Diets Are Not For Pets." (Spring, 1971).
    "By Any Name, 'BLOAT' Signals Danger." (Summer, 1969).
    "Heredity Influences Behavior." (Spring, 1966).
    "Inherited Defects Study." (Summer, 1963).
    "More Puppy Mortality Statistics." (Spring, 1965).
    "Scoring System Helps Reach Breeding Goals." (Summer, 1968).
    "Solving the 'Swimmer' Problem" (Spring, 1976).
    Editor: (Winter, 1963-1964; Spring, 1965; Spring, 1970). *Letter to author* (Sept. 19, 1974).
Gardner, Delphis. See Graham, George Augustus.
Gardner, Phyllis. The Irish Wolfhound (1931).
———— See Irish Wolfhound Club (Britain).
Gardner, Samuel A. See American Kennel Club.
Garmer, L. See Funkquist, B.
General Foods Corp. *A Report on Soft-Moist Foods* (1970).

Gladstone, E. In *Dog World*. Quoted in Gaines Nutrition Center's *Basic Guide to Canine Nutrition* (1965).

Glassner, Amy. *Letter to the author* (Feb. 25, 1971).

Goldman, Edward A. See Young, Stanley P.

Gorman, John. See American Kennel Club.

Graham, George Augustus, *Irish Wolfhound Pedigrees—1859-1906*. From his Working Stud Book. Edited for the Irish Wolfhound Club of Ireland by Delphis Gardner (1959).

———— *The Irish Wolfhound*. Compiled in August, 1879. Revised in May, 1885. Combined with Edmund Hogan's *The History of the Irish Wolfdog* and published by the Irish Wolfhound Club of Ireland (1939). The combined books were republished by the Irish Wolfhound Clubs of America and Ireland (1972).

———— "Irish Wolfhounds." In *The Kennel Encyclopaedia*. Edited by J. Sidney Turner (2 vols.; 1907-1908) II. p. 840.

———— Quoted by Everett, I.W. "The Typical Irish Wolfhound," See Irish Wolfhound Club (Britain).

Graham, Gordon, Mr. and Mrs. "A Feeding Program for Irish Wolfhounds." In Alma Starbuck's *The Complete Irish Wolfhound* (1969).

Graham, R. Portman, *The Mating and Whelping of Dogs* (1954).

Guillery, R. W. See *Science*.

Handbook of Biological Data. Ed. by William S. Spector (1956).

Harper, Deborah S. See American Kennel Club.

Harrop, A.E. See Gaines Nutrition Center.

Heckmann, Winifred. See Irish Wolfhound Club of America.

Helm, Dorothy. In *Midwestern Shepherd*.

Hogan, Edmund. *The History of the Irish Wolfdog* (1897). Combined with George Augustus Graham's *The Irish Wolfhound* and published by the Irish Wolfhound Club of Ireland (1939). The combined books were republished by The Irish Wolfhound Clubs of America and Ireland (1972).

Hogan, M. J. See Irish Wolfhound Club of America.

Howell, Elsworth S., Milo G. Denlinger, A.C. Merrick. "General Care and Training of Your Dog." In Alma Starbuck's *The Complete Irish Wolfhound* (1965).

Hudson, Phyllis. See Irish Wolfhound Club (Britain).

Huntley, Patricia. *Letters to the author*. (July 9, 1971; Aug. 5, 1971).

Hutchinson, Walter Victor. *Hutchinson's Encyclopaedia* (3 vols.; 1934) II.

Hutt, Frederick B. *Animal Genetics*. Copyright © 1964. The Ronald Press Company, New York.

Irish Kennel Club. *Letter to the author*. (May 24, 1971).

Irish Wolfhound Association (Britain). *The Irish Wolfhound* (1925).

   Beddoes, C. E. W. "The Necessity of Training."
   Beynon, Mary. "An Adventure in Africa."
   Brookes-Simmonds, R. "A Dog's Teeth."
   Reprint from *The Field:* "Field Trials."

Irish Wolfhound Club (Britain). *Year Book*.

   Baily, John F. "My Interpretation of Irish Wolfhound Type." (1927).
   Cox, Harding. "Irish Wolfhounds at Ranelagh and Amesbury." (1926).
   Croucher, Esther M. "Irish Wolfhounds in America." ((1961-1963).
   Depuy, Warren A. "Where Dogs Still Guard the Herds." (1930-1932).
   Durand, H.M. "A Short Chat on the Breed." (1926).
   Everett, I.W. "Hints on Rearing Irish Wolfhounds." (1926).
   ———— "Impressions at Bath Show." (1925).
   ———— "The Typical Irish Wolfhound." (1933-1935).
   Gardner, Phyllis. "The True Successor." (1930-1932).
   Hudson, Phyllis. "The Irish Wolfhound as a Sporting Hound." (1933-1935).
   Jenkins, Ruth. "Hints on Rearing Irish Wolfhounds." (1964-1966).

Krook, Lennart. See Gaines Nutrition Center.
Leedham, Charles. See Pearsall, Milo.
Leonard, Harmon C. See Gaines Nutrition Center.
Leonard, John. See Gaines Nutrition Center.
Lloyd, Freeman. See American Kennel Club.
Loraine, N.A. See Kennel Club (Britain).
Lundholm, Erik. See *Popular Dogs.*
Lyon, McDowell. *The Dog in Action* (1963).
───── See *Popular Dogs.*
Mahood, William. *Letters to the author* (Jan. 28, 1971; Aug. 16, 1971).
Martinez, Agustin Nores. See Irish Wolfhound Club of America.
Mason, William A. See *Science.*
Mather, George W. See American Kennel Club.
───── See Gaines Nutrition Center.
McCuistion, W.R. See Gaines Nutrition Center.
Merck Veterinary Manual (1955).
Merrick, A. C. See Howell, Elsworth S.
Mohrman, Robert K. See Ralston Purina Company.
Monro, Ronald K. See Irish Wolfhound Club (Britain).
Morris Animal Foundation. *Newsletter* (May, 1968).
Mosier, Jacob. "Puppy Survival." In *Field and Stream* (May, 1976).
───── See Gaines Nutrition Center.
Murphy, Gerard, Trans. "Bran's Departure from the Fian." *Duanaire Finn.* Irish
    Texts Society (1933), XXVIII.
Muybridge, Eadweard. *Animals in Motion* (1957).
Nagle, Florence. See Irish Wolfhound Club (Britain).
───── *Letter to author* (March 16, 1970).
National Academy of Sciences. National Research Council. *Nutrient
    Requirements of Dogs* (1972).
National Steeplechase and Hunt Association. *Letter to the author* (Aug. 6, 1971).
Noble, Anastasia. See American Kennel Club.
Noerr, Robert. See American Kennel Club.
Olin, John M. See American Kennel Club.
Onstott, Kyle. *The New Art of Breeding Better Dogs.* Revised by Philip Onstott
    (1967).
Orthopedic Foundation for Animals, Inc. "Hypertrophic Osteodystrophy." (Sept.,
    1974). *Letter to Miss Mari Thomas.*
Parnall, Peter. *Letter to the author* (Jan. 14, 1962).
Pearsall, Milo and Leedham, Charles G. *Dog Obedience Training* (1958).
Pegram, Louis. See *Popular Dogs.*
Plinius Secundus, Caius. "Naturalis Historiae." *Pliny.* Trans. by H. Rackham (10
    vols.; 1940) III.
Popular Dogs
        Corbin, James. "Canine Nutrition." (Oct., 1969) XLII.
        Deubler, M. Josephine. "Ask Your Doctor." (Feb., 1967) XL; (Jan., 1971)
        XLIV; (Nov., 1971) XLIV.
        Lundholm, Eric. Quoted in "Salukis." (March, 1971) XLIV.
        Lyon, McDowell. "The Dog in Action." (May, 1962) XXXV.
        Pegram, Louis. "Flat Feet in Purebred Dogs." (Dec., 1972) XLV.
        Riser, Wayne. Interviewed by Dr. M. J. Deubler on Canine Hip Dysplasia.
        (Jan., 1966) XXXIX.
Potts, Donald. See American Kennel Club.
Press, Robert M. See *Washington Post* (November 21, 1976).
Price, D.A. "Dogs Need More Than Meat." *Journal of the American Veterinary
    Medical Association* (1970) CLVI, No. 6.
Purchase, F.H. See Kennel Club (Britain).

Ralston Purina Company
    Corbin, James. *Letters to author* (Nov. 5, 1965; June 9, 1966; Nov. 25, 1966; June 7, 1971).
    Follis, T.B. *Letter to author* (Sept. 9, 1974).
———— *Purina Kennel News*
    Corbin, James (Winter, 1971)
    Kealy, Richard D. "Bone Structure of the Dog." (1974).
    Mohrman, Robert K. "Feeding of Dogs." (1975) I.
Reche, Kit. See Irish Wolfhound Club of America.
Riser, Wayne. *Letter to the author.* (Jan. 14, 1971).
———— Interviewed by Dr. M. J. Deubler. See *Popular Dogs.*
———— et al. "Genu Valgum: A Stifle Deformity of Giant Dogs." *Journal of the American Veterinary Radiological Society* (1969) X.
Salter, Edwin G. See Kennel Club (Britain).
Schnelle, Gerry B. Letter in *American Veterinary Medical Association Journal* (Aug., 1972).
———— See Gaines Nutrition Center.
Science. Guillery, R.W. and Kaas, J.H. "Genetic Abnormality of the Visual Pathways in a 'White' Tiger." (June 22, 1973).
    Mason, William A. and Kenney, M.D. "Redirection of Filial Attachments in Rhesus Monkeys" (Mar. 22, 1974).
Sheffy, Ben E. See Gaines Nutrition Center.
Shewell, Percy. See Kennel Club (Britain).
Silver, Helenette. *Letter to the author.* (Feb. 24, 1962).
Sjoestedt. M.L., "Le Siège de Druim Damhghaire," *Revue Celtique* (1926) XLIII.
Smith, Donald A. See American Kennel Club.
Smith, Norwood B., Mrs. See Irish Wolfhound Club of America.
Smythe, R. H. *The Conformation of the Dog.* (n.d. First published in 1957).
———— See American Kennel Club.
Society for the Advancement of Canine Genetics. *Journal of Canine Genetics* (August, 1947).
Somerville, William. "The Chace." *The Garland of British Poetry* (1832).
Spector, William S. See *Handbook of Biological Data.*
Starbuck, Alma. *The Complete Irish Wolfhound* (1965), (1969).
Starbuck, L.O. See Irish Wolfhound Club of America.
Stockner, Priscilla. See American Kennel Club.
"Stonehenge." See Walsh, John Henry.
Thomas, Mari. See Orthopedic Foundation for Animals, Inc.
Toepoel, P.M.C. See The Kennel Club (Britain).
Underwriters' Laboratories, Inc. *Letter to the author* (Aug. 2, 1971).
United States Department of Agriculture. *Home and Garden Bulletin No. 121.*
Van Arsdale, Jo-Ann. *Letters to the author.* (Nov. 4, 1969; July 1, 1971).
Veterinary Dispatch (June, 1964).
Wallach, Joel. See *Gaines Dog Research Progress.*
Walsh, John Henry ("Stonehenge"). *The Dog in Health and Disease* (1887).
————*The Dogs of the British Islands* (1886).
Washington Post (D.C.) (August 27, 1965); (April 5, 1971), (November 21, 1976).
Watkins. Vera H. See Irish Wolfhound Club of America.
Wheeler, Walter A., Jr. See American Kennel Club.
Williams, J.S. See Kennel Club (Britain) *Letters to author.*
Woodruff, Charlotte. See American Kennel Club.
Wright, Sewall. "Mendelian Analysis of the Pure Breeds of Livestock." *Journal of Heredity* (Nov., 1923).
Xenophon, *Cynegetica, Scripta Minora.* Trans. by E. C. Marchant (1925).
Young, Stanley P. and Goldman, Edward A. *The Wolves of North America* (1944).

OTHER DOCUMENTS CONSULTED

American Kennel Club. *Pure-Bred Dogs—American Kennel Gazette* (1889-1976).

Canadian Kennel Club. *Stud Book* (1889-1976).

Gering, Robert L. *Introduction to Pet Genetics* (1955).

The Kennel Club (Britain). *The Kennel Gazette* (1880-1976).

———— *Calendar and Stud Book* (1859-1968).

Mech, David L. *The Wolf* (1970).

———— *The Wolves of Isle Royale* (1966).

Murie, Adolph. *The Wolves of Mount McKinley* (1944).

Popular Dogs (1928-1976).

United States Department of Agriculture. *Beef Cattle Breeding* (n.d.).

Watmough, W. *Practical Inbreeding* (1955).

Young, Stanley Paul. *The Wolf in North American History* (1946).

Index